Third Edition

Malcolm Rider

Rider-French

Martin Kennedy

Independent Petroleum Engineering Consultant

RIDER-FRENCH

Published by Rider-French Consulting Ltd.
Scotland
Email: rider.french@gmail.com
www.riderfrench.co.uk
(for feedback)

Reprinted 2013
Reprinted 2014

ISBN 978-0-9541906-8-2

Designed by Melissa Alaverdy
www.thedesignwhisperer.com

Indexing and references by Whittles Publishing, Caithness
www.whittlespublishing.com

Illustrations digitised by Robin Farrow
www.robinfarrow.co.uk

Printed in Glasgow by
Bell and Bain

PREFACE

The success of the previous, widely sold, editions of *'The Geological Interpretation of Well Logs'* has been a surprise: it indicates that there is a need for a basic, practical book on logs and logging tools in which geological uses are featured. Like the previous editions, this new edition describes each of the common tools in terms of physical principles, basic tool design, log characteristics, quantitative and then qualitative, mainly geological uses. This order is maintained as far as possible and the log responses are illustrated with many *real* examples. As before, petrophysics, that is, the use of logs for quantifying hydrocarbons is considered, but only briefly. Following the chapters on individual tools, the information that all the logs provide is drawn together in chapters on lithology, facies, sequence analysis and sequence stratigraphy in which geological applications are the main subject, again illustrated with real examples.

This edition contains much new material which reflects the changes that have occurred since the second edition was published. In particular, many tools and techniques have either appeared since the second edition or have matured from specialist services to 'mainstream'. These include Logging While Drilling (LWD) tools for all the conventional measurements, Modular Formation Testers and Nuclear Magnetic Resonance (NMR) tools, which are all included for the first time. There is also a much expanded chapter on the modern image logs, both wireline and LWD. The volume of information from logs is now very large, and increasing exponentially. One trend especially is towards 'virtual' logs: raw measurements that need to be software manipulated and processed before they become meaningful. This is especially true of the resistivity tools, which now generate multiple curves that must be subjected to software manipulation before they can be used. The days of one or two raw resistivity curves that could be understood and interpreted are gone. Consequently, the subject of processing is covered when it is useful to do so. One more change: this third edition is in full colour throughout, as demanded by the modern log set and modern presentations. It is unthinkable that it would be otherwise.

Previously, *'The Geological Interpretation of Well Logs'* has been used as a course manual, the course having been designed around the book. This seems to have been successful, and it is hoped that such use will continue. Indeed, the design of the book has been influenced by the career experiences of both authors who, besides actively using the logs as tools, have given courses over a number of years around the world (www.nautilusworld.com). Judging from the past, the book is helpful to those who are just beginning to acquaint themselves with logs in either industry or academia. Those who are not involved with logs all the time use the book as an occasional reference and, for this reason, the text is as practical as possible, with mnemonics and acronyms kept to a minimum, or titles written in full to avoid annoying searches to find out what a particular set of three capital letters means.

Grateful thanks are due to a number of people. Jenny Garnham is thanked for technical input and reviewing several of the chapters. Melissa Alaverdy, whose tenacity and hard work have created an excellent and pleasing layout (www.thedesignwhisperer.com). Robin Farrow worked equally hard on the many diagrams (www.robinfarrow.co.uk). Dilys Brown significantly improved the manuscript with her concise editing. As ever, excellent guidance, professional advice and help in layout have been given by Whittles Publishing of Caithness, Scotland (www.whittlespublishing.com). Software and help were provided by: TerraSciences, especially Nigel Collins (www.terrasciences.com); Interactive Petrophysics by Frank Whitehead (www.senergyworld.com); and CycloLog by Djin Nio (www.enresinternational.com). All have helped to make this edition a reality. Edinburgh University GeoSciences are thanked for providing the right academic environment for the senior author to complete his work.

In an industry in charge of a diminishing resource, finding new reserves, developing them better, getting more from mature reserves and exploiting unconventional reserves, are all going to require geophysical tools to provide as much information as possible. New tools, new methods and new ideas will help. But logging seems to suffer from long lead-in times for new technology. The service companies develop new designs and new tools but users, especially geologists, are reluctant to take them up. The Nuclear Magnetic Resonance (NMR) technique is a case in point. The tool has been available since 1992 but is still considered as 'new', only for specialists, and not of interest to geologists. This is a shame. Technology needs to be understood first; it will then be used. This book is only a start.

If this edition is dedicated to anybody, it should be the late Highlander, Bill Grant of Rogart, who ran the Rider-French company finances for many years. He never saw the financial sense in writing a book, and considered that there were much better ways of using company time. He was right of course. So the only fitting quote for this edition, as for the previous one, is from Groucho Marx: *"From the moment I picked up your book until I laid it down, I was convulsed with laughter. Someday I intend reading it."*

FEEDBACK (www.riderfrench.co.uk)
To make a comment about the book, share an observation or point something out,
please visit the Rider-French website and click on FEEDBACK. We will respond as far as possible.

ACKOWLEDGEMENTS

The following organisations are thanked for their permission to use previously published figures:

especially the Society of Petrophysicists and Well Log Analysts (**SPWLA**);
the American Association of Petroleum Geologists (**AAPG**);
the European Association of Geoscientists and Engineers (**EAEG**);
the Geological Society of London (**GSL**);
the International Association of Sedimentologists (**IAS**);
the Society of Petroleum Engineers (**SPE**);
the Society for Sedimentary Geology (**SEPM**);

Baker Hughes™;
Halliburton;
Schlumberger;

Blackwells;
Elsevier;
Serralog

CONTENTS

CHAPTER 7 Resistivity logs 75

CHAPTER 8 The gamma ray and spectral gamma ray 117

CHAPTER 9 Sonic or acoustic logs 147

CHAPTER 10 The density and photoelectric factor logs 187

CHAPTER 11 The neutron log 211

CHAPTER 12 Lithology reconstruction from logs 239

KEY

LITHOLOGICAL SYMBOLS

 Shale

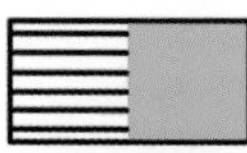 Shale (alt.)

 Organic shale

 Silt

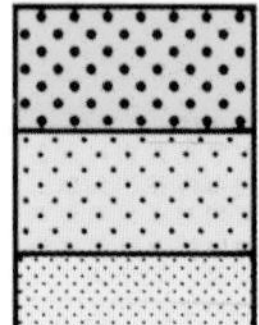
cse
med. } Sandstone
fine

 coal

 coal debris

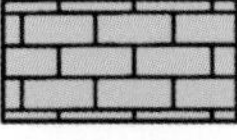 Limestone

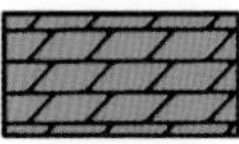 Dolomite

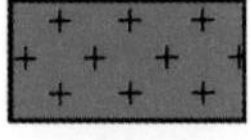 Salt (halite)

 Anhydrite

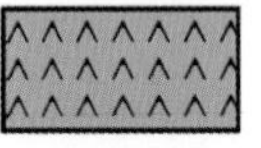 Gypsum

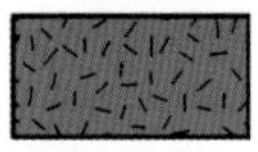 Volcanic

carbonate cement

SEDIMENTOLOGICAL FORMAT

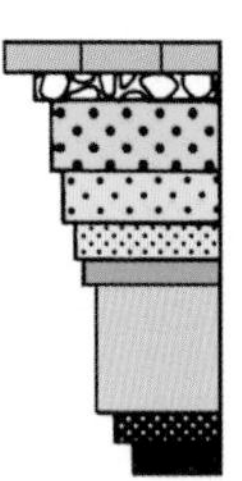

Carbonate
cgl
cse
me } Sandstones
fi
Silt
Shale
Organic shale
Coal

SEDIMENTARY STRUCTURES

cross-beds
current } ripples
wave
horizontal laminae
irregular laminae
concretion
horizontal burrows
vertical burrows
roots
shells
oolites

1
INTRODUCTION

1.1 Well logs – a definition and some history

The continuous recording of a geophysical parameter along a borehole produces a geophysical well log. The value of the measurement is plotted continuously against depth in the well (**Figure 1.1**). For example, the resistivity log is a continuous plot of a formation's resistivity from the bottom of the well to the top and may represent over 4 kilometres (2½ miles) of readings.

The most appropriate name for this continuous depth -related record is a 'geophysical well log', conveniently shortened to 'well log' or simply 'log'. It has often been called an 'electrical log' because historically the first logs were electrical measurements of electrical properties. However, the measurements are no longer simply of electrical properties and more than electrical signals are used, so the name above is recommended.

In France, where well logging was first developed by Conrad Schlumberger and Henri Doll, its original name was '*Carottage Electrique*' (electrical coring) as opposed to mechanical coring. 'Electrical coring' was achieved by lowering a measuring tool into the borehole on a wire line, the line acting as both a support for the tool itself and as an electrical conduit for the measured signal. This was the only system used for almost half a century and these were called 'wireline logs': which they still are and wireline logging continues to be used. Wireline logs can only be measured after the borehole has been emptied of drilling equipment.

As will be explained below, geophysical measurements can now be acquired as drilling is actually taking place. No wireline is used and the geophysical measurements are conveyed to the surface by pressure pulses through the mud used in drilling. These are Logging While Drilling, or LWD logs and they are available in 'real time', that is, as the bit drills. The measurements now acquired using the LWD technique are, for the most part, the same as those acquired using the older wireline method.

This book concerns wireline and LWD geophysical well logs.

1.2 Well logs – the necessity

Many different modern geophysical well logs exist. They are records of sophisticated geophysical measurements along a borehole. These may be measurements of spontaneous phenomena, such as natural radioactivity (the gamma ray log), which requires a tool consisting simply of a very sensitive radiation detector. Or they may be induced, as with the first log, which was an electrical experiment (**Figure 1.1**), or the formation velocity log (sonic log) in which a tool emits sound into the formation and measures the time it takes to reach a receiver at a set distance along the tool (**Table 1.1**).

Geophysical well logging is necessary because geological sampling during drilling (cuttings samples) leaves a very imprecise record of the formations encoun-

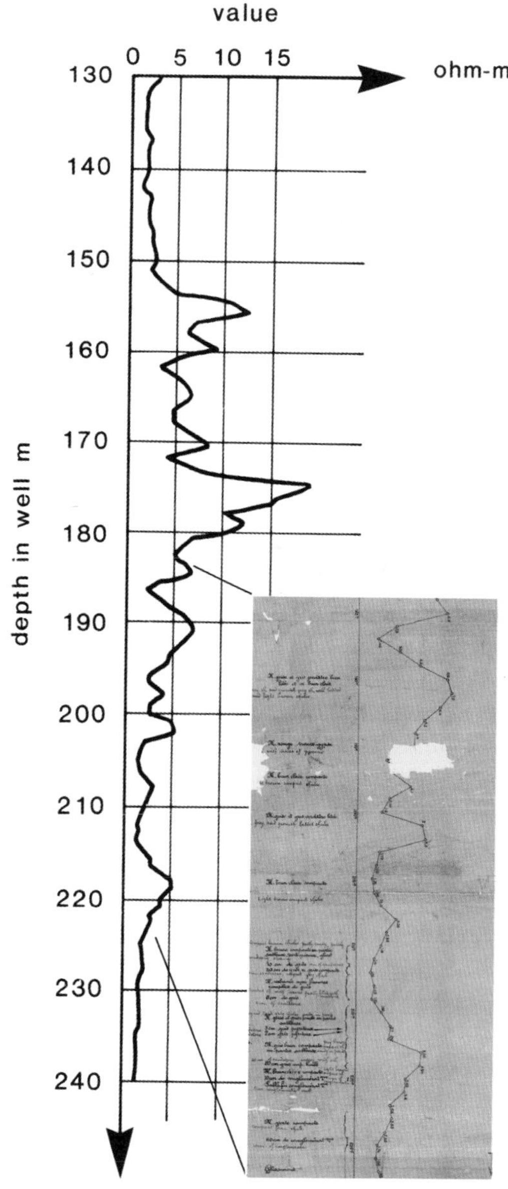

Figure 1.1 A well log. Representation of the first 'log' made at Pechelbronn, Alsace, France, in 1927 by H. Doll with a section of the actual log inset (modified from Allaud and Martin 1976).

Table 1.1 Classification of the common geophysical well log measurements (in 'open-hole')

	Log Type	Formation parameter measured
Mechanical measurements	Caliper	Hole diameter
Spontaneous measurements	Temperature	Borehole temperature
	Pressure	Formation fluid pressure
	SP (self potential)	Spontaneous electrical currents
	Gamma Ray	Natural radioactivity
Induced measurements	Resistivity	Electrical resistivity (direct measurement)
	Induction	Electrical resistivity (induced measurement)
	Sonic	Velocity of compressional, shear and Stoneley waves
	Density	Response to higher energy gamma ray bombardment
	Photoelectric	Response to lower energy gamma ray bombardment
	Neutron	Response to neutron bombardment
	Nuclear Magnetic Resonance	Induced proton electromagnetic field

tered. Actual physical formation can be brought to the surface by mechanical coring, but this is both slow and expensive. The results of coring, of course, are unequivocal. Logging is precise, but equivocal, in that it needs interpretation to bring a log to the level of geological or petrophysical experience. However, logs fill the gap between 'cuttings' and 'cores', and with experience, calibration and computers, they can almost replace cores, and they certainly contain enough information to put outcrop reality into the subsurface.

1.3 Wireline logs – the making

Wireline geophysical well logs are recorded when the drilling tools are no longer in the hole. 'Open-hole' logs, the subject of this book (open-hole indicates that the formation forms the wall of a well, as opposed to 'cased-hole', in which a tube of metal casing lines the well), are recorded immediately *after* drilling.

Wireline logs are made using highly specialised equipment entirely separate from that used for drilling. Onshore, a motorised logging truck is used to bring its array of surface recorders, computers and a logging drum and cable to the drill site. Offshore, the same equipment is installed in a small cabin left permanently on the rig. Both truck and cabin use a variety of interchangeable logging tools, which are lowered into the well on the logging cable (**Figure 1.2**).

To run wireline logs, the hole is cleaned and stabilised and the drilling equipment extracted The first logging tool is then attached to the logging cable (wireline) and lowered into the hole to its maximum drilled depth. Most logs are run while pulling the tool up from the bottom of the hole (although just to be sure of having a record, measurements are recorded, as far as possible, on the way down as well). The cable attached to the tool, as described, is both a support for the tool and a canal for data transmission. The outside consists of galvanized steel, while the 7 electrical conductors are insulated in the interior (**Figure 1.3**). The cable is wound around a motorized drum on to which it is guided manually during logging. The drum will pull the cable at speeds of between 300 m/h (1000 ft/h) and 1800 m/h (6000 ft/h), i.e. 0.3 to 1.8 km/h, depending on the tool used. As the cable is pulled in, the depth of the working tool is measured by specialised equipment, an odometer. This depth is adjusted for cable stretch and other physical factors (*see* Section 2.7).

Modern logs are recorded digitally. The sampling rate will normally be once every 15 cm (6"), although for some specialised logs it will be as low as once every 2.5 mm (0.1"). An average well of say 3000 m (10.000 ft) will therefore be sampled 20,000 times for each individual log, and for a suite of 8 or so basic logs, it will be sampled over 160,000 times (although for some specialised tools, this can be the sampling rate every two metres!). At typical logging speeds, data transmission rates will vary from 0.05 kilobits per second for simpler logs to over 100 kilobits per second for the more complex logs. This huge amount of data representing each logging run is fed into the computer of the surface unit. There is an instantaneous display as a log is acquired both on the rig and, if requested, by satellite link at the client's or operator's office. Colour hard-copy is immediately available if required. Data are stored electronically for future processing and editing.

Because rig time is expensive and holes must be logged immediately, modern logging tools are multi-function and multi-modular (**Figure 1.4**). They may be up to 33 m (100 ft) or more in length, but still have an overall diameter of only 15 cm (6 inches), although much shorter tools exist. For example, the Schlumberger wireline Platform Express (PEX), an integrated tool and widely used, is only 11.6 m (38 ft) long and can provide gamma ray, neutron porosity, bulk density, photoelectric cross-section, caliper, micro-resistivity and either a deep resistivity or an induction conductivity. The maximum diameter of the tool can be 11.76 cm (4.63").

The complexity of such tools requires the surface computer not only to record but also to memorise and to depth-match the various readings. The gamma-ray

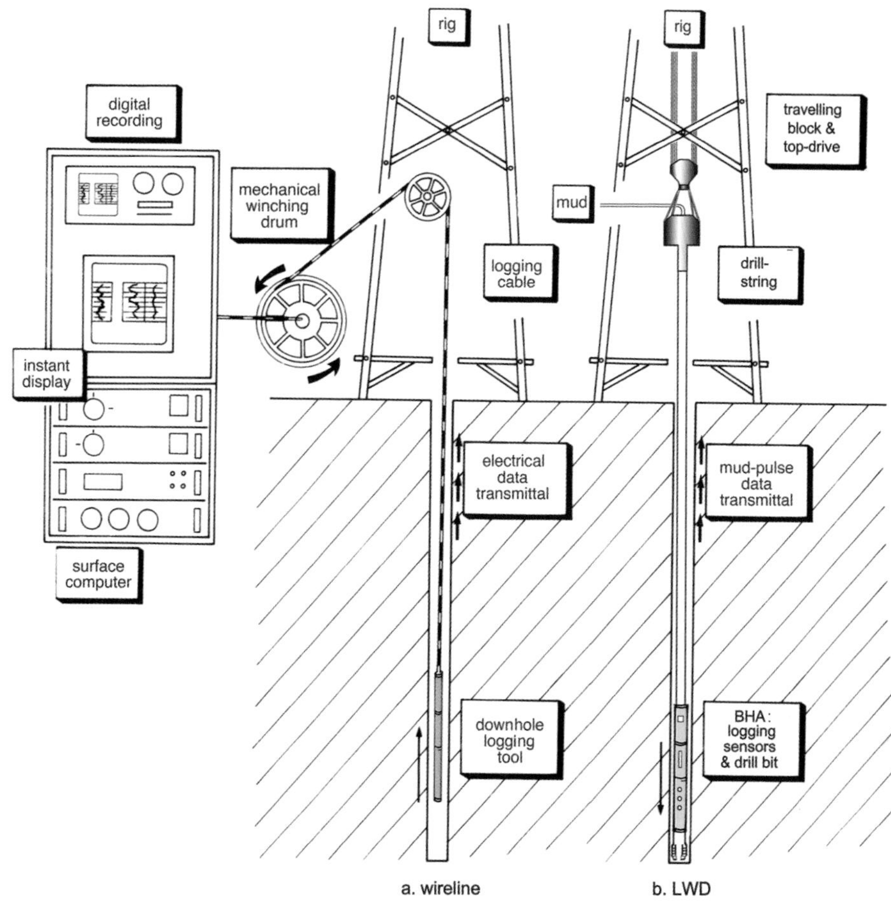

Figure 1.2 Schematic diagram of a modern a. wireline and b. LWD logging set-up. The surface computer and electronic equipment are housed in a logging truck (on land) or cabin (offshore). The wireline logging tool is winched up the hole by the logging cable which also transmits the tool readings. The LWD sensors are in the drill collars behind the bit during drilling and readings are sent uphole by mud-pulses. BHA = Bottom Hole Assembly.

sensor, for example, is not at the same depth as the conductivity sensors so at any one instant, different formations are being sampled along the tool. The surface computer therefore memorises the readings, compensates for depth or time lag and gives a depth-matched output. For more and more measurements there is also downhole processing. Some tools, such as the resistivity, produce many signals which can be processed downhole without deteriorating the final measurement, and this reduces the data volume sent up the logging cable.

Despite the use of the combined tools, the recording of a full set of wireline logs still requires several different tool descents. While a quick, shallow logging job may only take 3–4 hours, a deep-hole, full set may take 2–3 days or longer, each tool taking perhaps 4–5 hours to complete.

1.4 LWD logs – the making (MWD and definitions)

Logging While Drilling (LWD) has been available for the last 25 years and was introduced in the 1980s. LWD logging is different from wireline logging in that, as its name implies, the logs are made during drilling, the logging sensors being sent downhole with the drilling equipment (**Figure 1.2**). The LWD sensors are contained within purpose-built drill-collars (the heavy steel section just above the bit) and are thus part of the Bottom Hole Assembly (BHA) (**Figure 1.5**). The measurements from the BHA are transmitted back to the surface using pressure pulses transmitted through the drilling mud. There

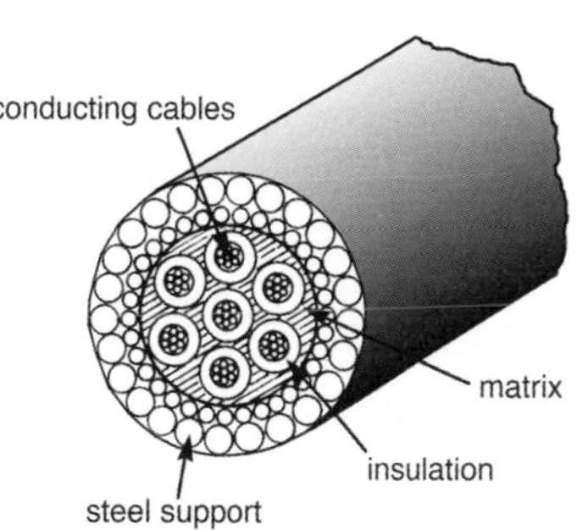

Figure 1.3 Schematic diagram of a 7 core logging cable (modified from Moran and Attali 1971).

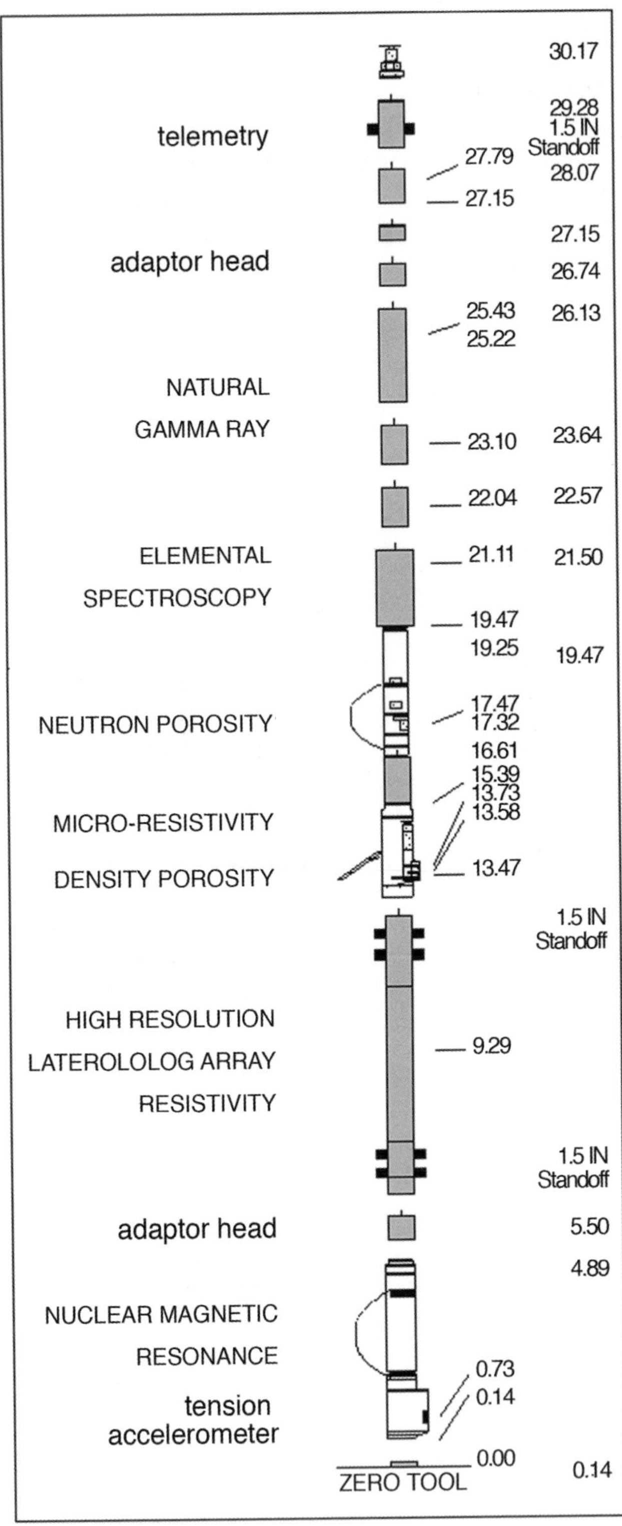

Figure 1.4 Map of a modern, integrated, combination wireline logging tool, a Platform Express (PEX) tool with combinable magnetic resonance (CMR) from Schlumberger. The tool illustrated provides; natural gamma ray, elemental spectroscopy, neutron porosity, density porosity, shallow micro-resistivity, array laterolog resistivity, nuclear magnetic resonance, head tension and accelerometer measurements and is 30.17 m (98.98 ft) long. The numbers on the right of the tool are module measurements from tool zero. Maximum tool diameter is 16.84 cm (6.63").

is no electrical connection. The basic measurement principles are generally the same for both the LWD and the wireline measurements and increasingly the two types of tool use a lot of the same components. Initially only gamma ray and resistivity measurements were available but during the 1990s density, neutron and sonic logs were developed and more recently Nuclear Magnetic Resonance (NMR) and formation pressure tools have become available. This means that all the basic geophysical logs can now be obtained using LWD tools.

It is also possible to record physical drilling parameters at, or just behind, the bit and these are transmitted using the same mud-pulse equipment as employed for the geophysical data. Examples of these measurements include downhole torque, weight-on-bit, vibration, pressure and directional data. These types of measurement are often referred to as 'Measurements While Drilling' (MWD) to distinguish them from the geophysical measurements (LWD) described in this book. Having said that, the term MWD has historically been used to refer to both types of data and the terms are still used interchangeably. Furthermore, at some point the term Formation Evaluation While Drilling, FEWD, was added to the list of acronyms as an alternative to LWD. This has created confusion. LWD is used throughout this book to indicate geophysical measurements made while drilling, and no other term.

Although the measurement physics is mostly the same for wireline and LWD logs, there are important practical differences between the two types. These variously affect the quality of the measurement, the cost, and what precisely is being measured. Such considerations ultimately determine whether to use LWD, wireline or both. The most important difference between the two systems, clearly, is that the LWD tool produces data as the well is being drilled. This allows earlier, and better informed decisions to be made, for example in geosteering and well deviation. Wireline logs, only acquired when drilling has finished (normally before each casing is set), obviously do not allow this. The many advantages of LWD and some disadvantages are given in the table (**Table 1.2**).

Wireline logging is still widely used and shows no sign of being completely replaced, indicating that LWD has some disadvantages. Depth reliability is one of those (**Table 1.2**). But most originate with the considerable engineering challenge of fitting delicate instruments within a drill-collar that must be as strong as any other part of the drill-string. As will be seen in the chapters dedicated to specific tools, this means that some measurements, such as the mechanical caliper, simply cannot be made in the LWD environment and others, such as the gamma

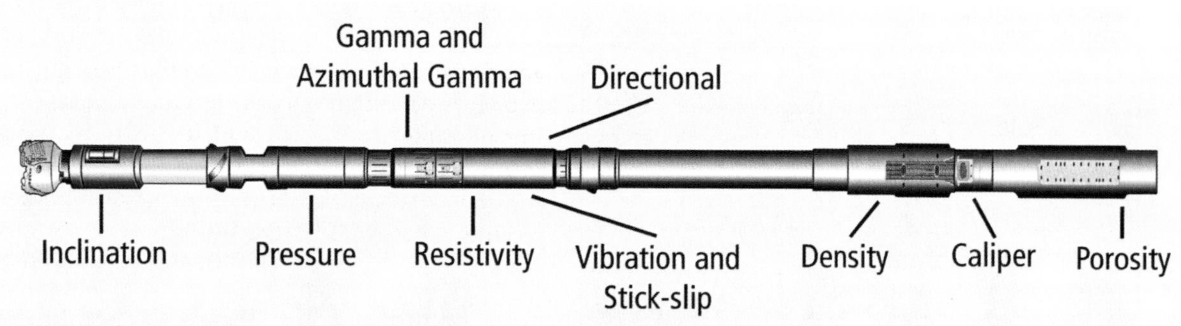

Figure 1.5 A Baker Hughes™ LWD Bottom Hole Assembly (BHA) showing the bit, MWD and LWD sensors. The assemblage provides the gamma ray, azimuthal gamma ray, 2 MHz and 400 kHz resistivity, caliper, density and neutron porosity as well as drilling information: it is 20 m (65 ft) long (from Ruszka 2003 with permission).

Table 1.2 Advantages and disadvantages of Logging While Drilling (LWD)

Advantages of Logging While Drilling (LWD) measurements
They provide the ability to steer the bit accurately and target precise volumes.
They allow decisions to change parameters and targets to be taken while drilling.
The time between drilling and acquiring the log is much shorter when using LWD, so formation alteration and damage are less.
Use of LWD tools saves the rig-time needed to run wireline tools.
For some tools, an image of the borehole wall can be generated because sensors rotate with the bit (i.e. gamma ray, resistivity, density, *Pe*)
It is much easier to run LWD tools in high angle and horizontal wells.
They provide insurance against being unable to acquire logs on wireline because of hole collapse.
Disadvantages
The physical environment of the LWD sensors is very harsh. It can cause breakdowns and tools wear is fast.
LWD tools are built to be used in only one hole diameter size, so the BHA is frequently changed.
The depth control on LWD logs, the driller's depth, is still poorly constrained. When depth mis-matches are encountered between wells it is often unclear whether they are the result of real differences or an artifact of driller's depth.

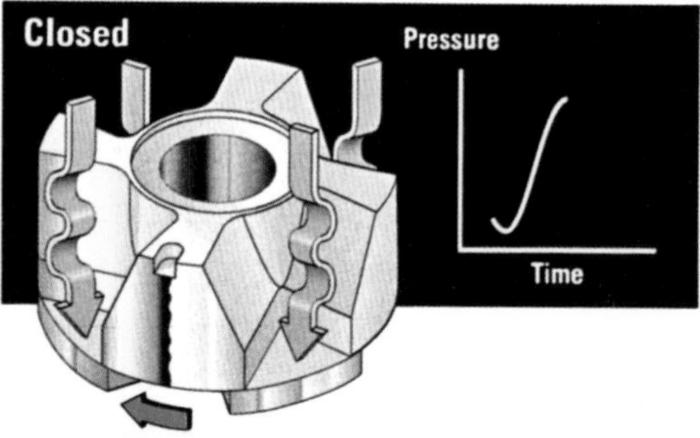

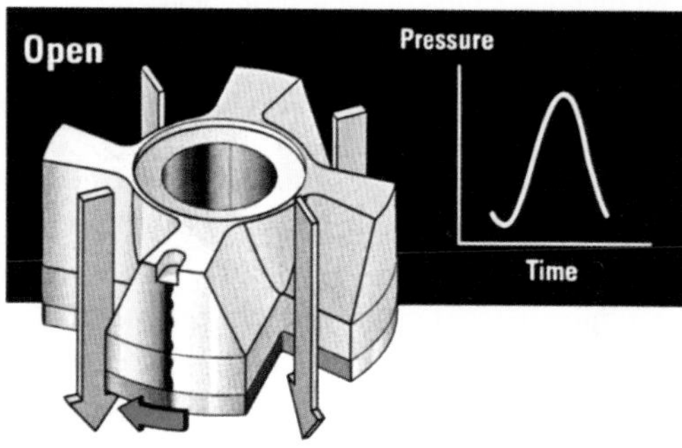

Figure 1.6 Illustration of one method of creating mud pulse pressure signals for data transmission. The Schlumberger PressurePulse motor. *Courtesy of Schlumberger.*

ray, have slightly different responses. Furthermore, each different hole size needs a different tool. By contrast, wireline tools can go from well to well and hole size to hole size, and will work for example in gauges between 6" to 17½" (common sizes).

It should also be realised that the transmission system currently used by LWD tools is slow and limited and has to be shared with the MWD information. LWD/MWD data is transmitted from downhole by mud pulses. These are produced by a system that interrupts or modifies the downward mud flow to produce pressure pulses that are transmitted up the mud inside the drillpipe to be recovered at the surface and turned into electrical signals (Arps and Arps 1964) (**Figure 1.6**). This method imposes a practical limit of about 10–12 bits/second on the rate at which data can be transferred. By contrast, seven conductor wireline cable can easily transmit 100,000 bits/second. This means that the 'real-time' time of LWD/MWD data is restricted to a small number of curves sampled at a low rate. The tools generate far more data than can be transmitted, so it is

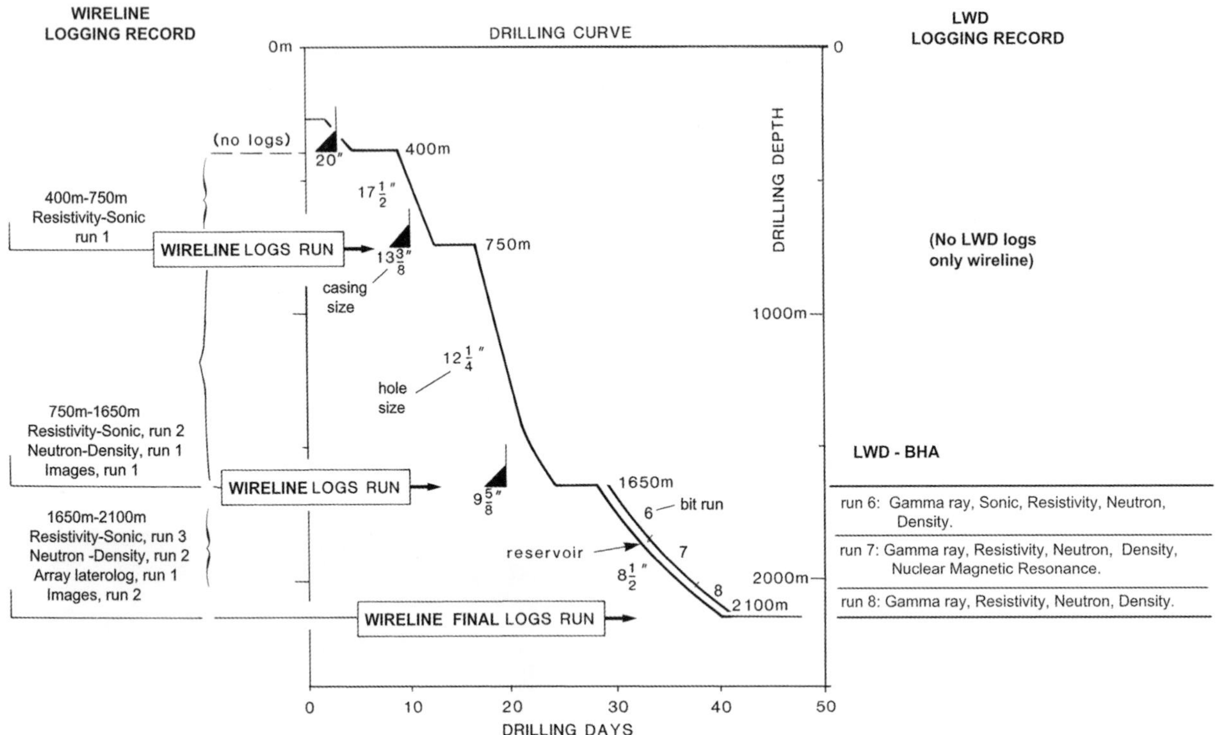

Figure 1.7 Logging record. Log runs are indicated on a typical offshore drilling curve. Horizontal lines indicate no drilling, when wireline logs are run. LWD logs, only run in this well over the 8½" phase, are run during drilling and are identified by the bit runs. Casing follows wireline logging.

stored in downhole memory and recovered when the tool-string is brought back to the surface. The memory data includes far more curves sampled at a high rate and is of comparable quality to wireline data: even better under some circumstances. The limitation imposed by slow mud-pulse transmission may be overcome soon by the availability of 'wired-pipe' (Hernandez *et al.* 2008), which allows data to be transmitted up the drill-string as electrical pulses, and therefore at much higher rates. Memory quality data will then be able to be transmitted in real-time (at the time of writing this technology is at an advanced field-test stage).

1.5 Log runs

When a log is made it is said to be 'run'. A wireline log run is typically made at the end of each drilling phase, i.e. at the end of the drilling and before casing is put in the hole (**Figure I.7**). Each specific log run is numbered, being counted from the first time that the particular log is recorded. Run 2 of the wireline Sonic, for example, may cover the same depth interval as a wireline Formation Density Log Run 1. In this case it means that over the first interval of the Sonic, (i.e. Run 1) there was no Formation Density log recorded (**Figure 1.7**).

LWD log runs are generally numbered with bit runs, as, each time a bit is changed, the Bottom Hole Assembly (BHA) of the LWD tool can be changed (**Figure 1.7**).

In any well, more logs are typically run over intervals containing reservoirs or with shows, than over apparently uninteresting zones. The choice of logs or logging method depends on what it is hoped to find and the physical conditions, such as deviation or horizontal drilling. Logging, costing 5–10% or more of total well costs, is expensive, so that exploration and appraisal wells (E&A) tend to have a more comprehensive logging suite than production wells in known fields. Cutting down on well logs is probably a false economy, but it can be forgiven when prices are considered.

1.6 Log grid presentations

Historically, when logs were produced only as a paper or photographic film record, a standard API (American Petroleum Institute) log format was developed (**Figure 1.8**). Some elements from it are still evident in modern electronic log displays. It had the following dimensions and characteristics. The overall log width was 8.25 inches (21 cm), with three tracks of 2.5 inches (6.4 cm), tracks 1 and 2 being separated by a column of 0.75 inches (1.9 cm) in which the depths were printed. Various combinations of grid were used. Track 1 was always linear, with ten standard divisions of 0.25 inches (0.64 cm). Tracks 2 and 3 could have a 4-cycle logarithmic scale, a linear scale of 20 standard divisions, or a hybrid of logarithmic scale in track 2 and linear scale

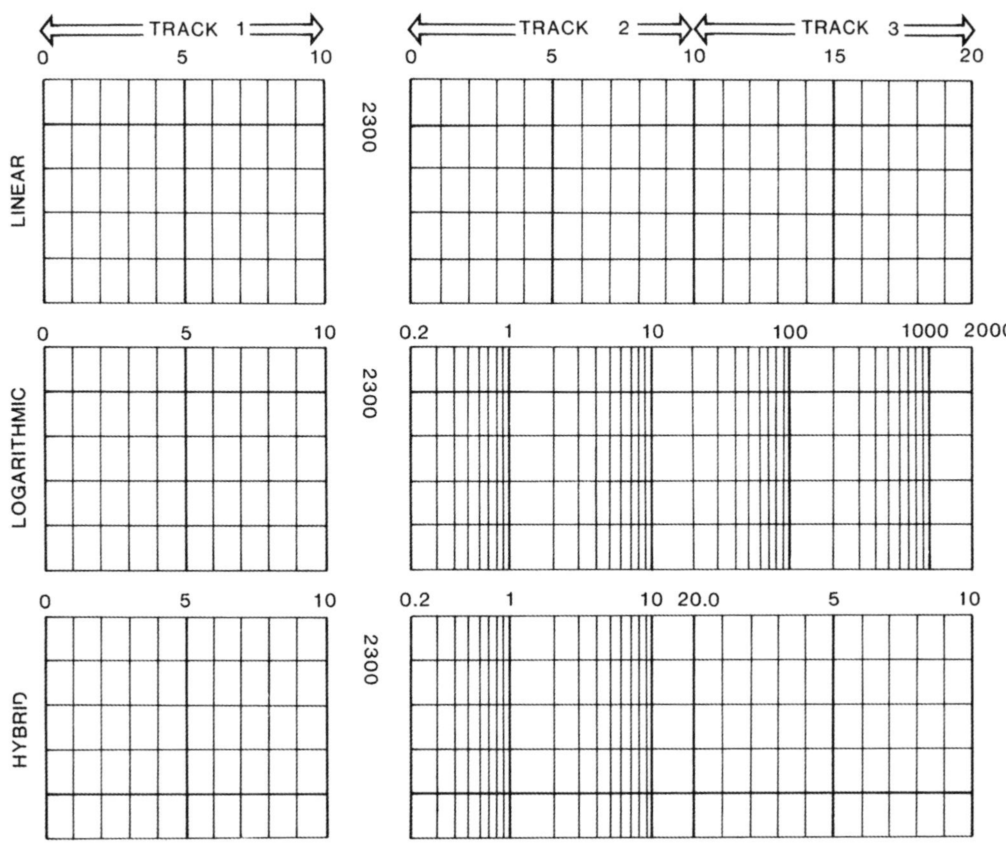

Figure 1.8 The three typical API log formats. Tracks are 2.5 inches wide with a central 0.75 inch depth column. Overall width is 8.25 inches. Vertical scales are variable (*see* text).

in track 3 (**Figure 1.8**). These classic dimensions are found in all the older logs.

The old analog logging systems were constrained to a limited number of vertical or depth scales. It was only possible to choose two of the following: 1:1000, 1:500, 1:200, 1:100, 1:40 and 1:20. From these, the most frequent scale combinations were 1:500 (1cm = 5m) for resumé or correlation logs and 1:200 (1cm = 2m) for detailed reservoir presentations. The American area was an exception where the available scales were 1:1200, 1:600, 1:240 and 1:48. From these the commonly-chosen scales were 1:600 (2″ = 100 feet) for resumé and correlation logs, and 1:240 (5″ =100 feet) for detail. These scales can still be found in occasional industry documents, but fixed scales are no longer an issue since any convenient scale can be produced. In the past, scale changes could only be made by unsatisfactory photographic methods.

One final aspect of the log grid to note are markers which indicate real time during wireline logging. Wireline logs are presented on a regular depth basis but on older Schlumberger logs, for example, time was indicated by dashed grid margins, each dash representing one minute, regardless of log scale (**Figure 1.9**).

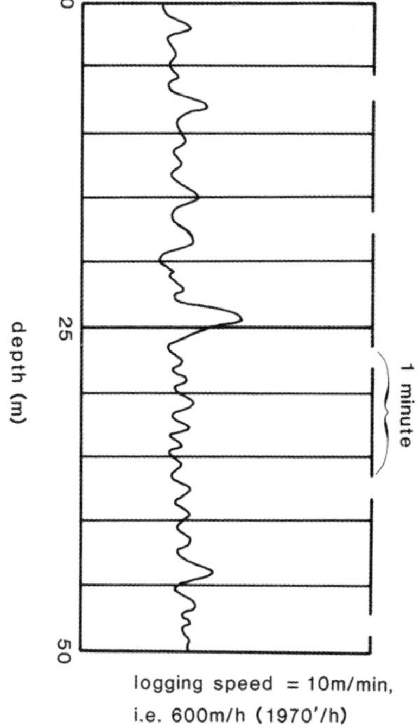

Figure 1.9 Dashed log margin representing minute intervals (Schlumberger). The wireline logging speed can be checked from these dashes.

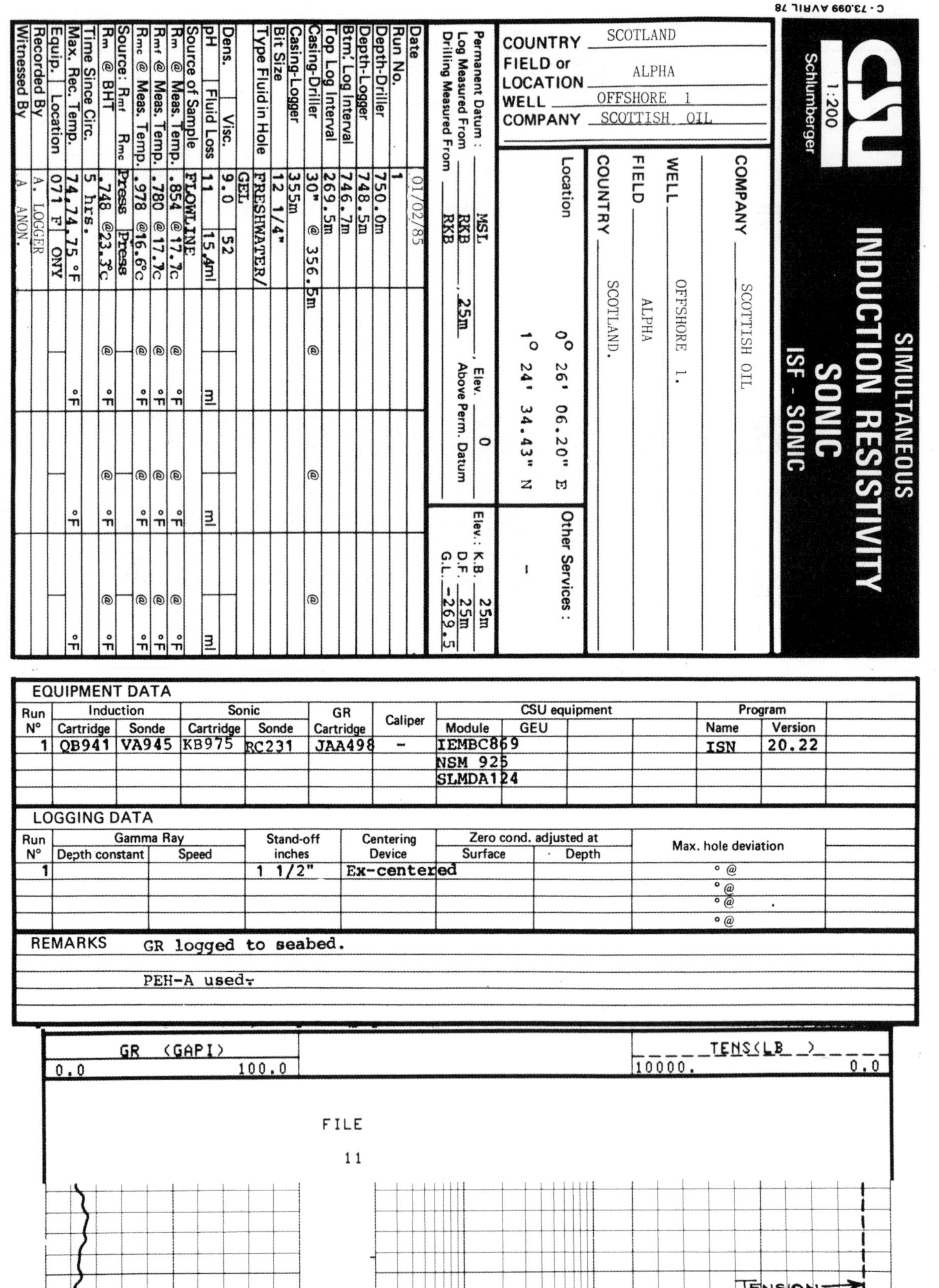
C - 73.099 AVRIL 78

CSU 1:200 Schlumberger

SIMULTANEOUS INDUCTION RESISTIVITY SONIC ISF - SONIC

COUNTRY SCOTLAND
FIELD or LOCATION ALPHA
WELL OFFSHORE 1
COMPANY SCOTTISH OIL

COMPANY SCOTTISH OIL
WELL OFFSHORE 1.
FIELD ALPHA
COUNTRY SCOTLAND.
Location 0° 26' 06.20" E 1° 24' 34.43" N
Other Services: -

Permanent Datum: MSL, Elev. 0
Log Measured From RKB, 25m Above Perm. Datum
Drilling Measured From RKB
Elev.: K.B. 25m D.F. 25m G.L. -269.5

Date	01/02/85		
Run No.	1		
Depth-Driller	750.0m		
Depth-Logger	748.5m		
Btm. Log Interval	746.7m		
Top Log Interval	269.5m		
Casing-Driller	30" @ 356.5m	@	@
Casing-Logger	355m		
Bit Size	12 1/4"		
Type Fluid in Hole	FRESHWATER/GEL		
Dens. / Visc.	9.0 / 52		
pH / Fluid Loss	11 / 15.4ml	ml	ml
Source of Sample	FLOWLINE		
Rm @ Meas. Temp.	.854 @17.7c	@ °F	@ °F
Rmf @ Meas. Temp.	.780 @17.7c	@ °F	@ °F
Rmc @ Meas. Temp.	.978 @16.6c	@ °F	@ °F
Source: Rmf Rmc	Press Press		
Rm @ BHT	.748 @23.3c	@ °F	@ °F
Time Since Circ.	5 hrs.		
Max. Rec. Temp.	74,74,75 °F	°F	°F
Equip. Location	071 F ONY		
Recorded By	A. LOGGER		
Witnessed By	A. ANON.		

EQUIPMENT DATA

Run N°	Induction Cartridge	Induction Sonde	Sonic Cartridge	Sonic Sonde	GR Cartridge	Caliper	CSU equipment Module	GEU			Program Name	Version
1	QB941	VA945	KB975	RC231	JAA498	-	IEMBC869				ISN	20.22
							NSM 925					
							SLMDA124					

LOGGING DATA

Run N°	Gamma Ray Depth constant	Gamma Ray Speed	Stand-off inches	Centering Device	Zero cond. adjusted at Surface	Zero cond. adjusted at Depth	Max. hole deviation
1			1 1/2"	Ex-centered			° @
							° @
							° @
							° @

REMARKS GR logged to seabed.
PEH-A used.

Figure 1.10 A typical log heading. This is an older Schlumberger heading but they are still very similar.

Master:12- Jan-2007 12:40								
EcoScope Integrated Logging-While-Drilling Tool - 6.75 inch Calibration								
Resistivity: Air								
Phase	Attenuation T1	Value	Phase	Attenuation T2	Value	Phase	Attenuation T3	Value
Master		8.904	Master		5.522	Master		5.513
7.000 (Minimum)	9.000 (Nominal)	11.00 (Maximum)	4.000 (Minimum)	6.000 (Nominal)	8.000 (Maximum)	3.500 (Minimum)	5.500 (Nominal)	7.500 (Maximum)
Phase	Attenuation T4	Value	Phase	Attenuation T5	Value	Phase	Attenuation T1 at 400KHz	Value
Master		3.925	Master		4.077	Master		8.735
2.500 (Minimum)	4.500 (Nominal)	6.500 (Maximum)	2.000 (Minimum)	4.000 (Nominal)	6.000 (Maximum)	7.000 (Minimum)	9.000 (Nominal)	11.00 (Maximum)
Phase	Attenuation T2 at 400KHz	Value	Phase	Attenuation T3 at 400KHz	Value	Phase	Attenuation T4 at 400KHz	Value
Master		5.707	Master		5.336	Master		4.103
4.000 (Minimum)	6.000 (Nominal)	8.000 (Maximum)	3.500 (Minimum)	5.500 (Nominal)	7.500 (Maximum)	2.500 (Minimum)	4.500 (Nominal)	6.500 (Maximum)
Phase	Attenuation T5 at 400KHz	Value						
Master		3.898						
2.000 (Minimum)	4.000 (Nominal)	6.000 (Maximum)						

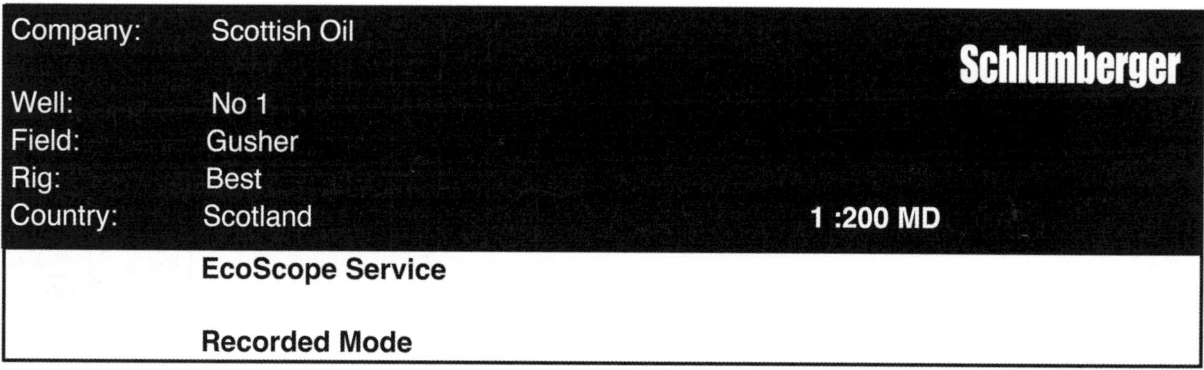

Figure 1.11 A typical log tail with graphical calibration checks. This tail is a modern Schlumberger format. During checks, whenever a calibration is not within the required limits, a graphical flag is raised. There are no flags on these checks, all are within requirements.

Other companies used ticks or spikes on the log grid for the same purpose. Since wireline logs are sampled on a depth basis, the longer the dash, the shorter the time for the sample. At a logging speed of 9 m/min (1800 ft/hr), a 15 cm (6") sample is taken each second. At 18 m/min (3600 ft/min) a sample is taken every ½ second. LWD logs are different in that they are acquired on a regular time basis and then converted to a regular depth increment for use, normally the same 15 cm (6"). Faster drilling implies a greater depth between samples. The quality of both wireline and LWD logs is a function of sampling time.

The API log format defined a comprehensive log heading and log tail. The content of this heading still influences the data given about a particular log run and covers all aspects which allow the proper interpretation of the log and, in addition, identification of the well, rig, location, logger and logging unit. The log heading illustrated (**Figure 1.10**) is an example of an older log, but modern headings are still very similar and show similar information.

Traditionally, the log tail gives a repetition, for convenience, of some of the log-head data but also, importantly, all the calibration data with the results of sensor tests at the surface (**Figure 1.11**). Added to the log tail, in addition, there may be short repeat sections, that is short lengths of log run before or after a main run, to ensure a tool works properly and which also may be used for empirical quality control.

1.7 Digital log data formats

The simplest form of digital log record is the ASCII format (American Standard Code for Information Interchange) (**Table 1.3**). The various log measurements are simply listed in space or tab separated columns and the format can be read by non-specialised text programmes such as Notepad or WordPad. The format is effective but columns can become mis-labeled and, for example, what should be a column of resistivity measurements becomes labeled as a column of gamma ray measurements.

To avoid this problem the LAS format exists (**Table 1.3**), the Log ASCII Standard, in which there are a set number of header lines and a standardised header format that was established by the Canadian Well

Table 1.3 Digital log formats

Acronym	long name
Number and information formats	
ASCII	American Standard Code for Information Interchange
LAS	Log ASCII Standard
LIS	Log Interpretation Standard
DLIS	Digital Log Information Standard
Picture Formats	
PDF	Portable Document Format (Adobe)
PDS	Picture Description System (Schlumberger)
Meta files	Picture files (Baker Hughes™)

Logging Society (CWLS). It is still, however, an ASCII type format. LAS has been revised several times and information on the LAS 2.0 format can be found at the Canadian Well Logging Society website (cwls.org).

The LIS format (Log Interpretation Standard) is more complex and was used by Schlumberger between the 1980s and 2000s. (Baker Hughes™ (Western Atlas then) used BIT and EBIT and Halliburton (Gearhart then) used DDL). LIS required specialist software to be read, but was extensively used for databases and allowed the storage of more complex measurements than could be managed by the simple ASCII format. However, with the development of yet more complex logging tools and data types, even LIS proved inadequate and the DLIS format was developed (Theys 1991).

DLIS (Digital Log Information Standard), an API standard, is used by most logging companies today (2010) and, at a minimum, can cope with variable sampling rates, data arrays and large dynamic ranges, none of which was possible with LIS.

Some log databases store logs simply as pictures, TIFF (Tagged Image File Format) being one favourite. These obviously do not allow manipulations of the measurements, but at least a record of the log exists and curves can be digitised from the pictures. Modern image logs (and others) are often converted to pdf (Portable Document Format), or by Schlumberger to pds (Picture Description System) and Baker Hughes™ to their meta files. The pdf reader is free from Adobe. Schlumberger and Baker Hughes™ provide pds and meta file readers, respectively, free from their websites.

1.8 Log acronyms (mnemonics)

Most logging tools, individual logging sensor measurements and log curves are known by their acronyms. The number is huge and many are registered as trade names. The publicly available mnemonic (acronym) dictionary available on the Schlumberger website (SLB.com/services) says that there are 50,000 entries! As an example, a formation density measurement is made by a density tool variously called, in wireline form, the Litho-Density tool (LDT) by Schlumberger, Compensated Densilog™ (CDL) by Baker Hughes™ and the Spectral Density Log (HSDL) by Halliburton and in LWD form, the Azimuthal Density (Ecoscope) by Schlumberger, the LithoTrak by Baker Hughes™ and the Stabilized Litho-Density (SLD) by Halliburton. All are trade names.

To look beyond simply the tool names. A porosity is the output from the Schlumberger Array Porosity Sonde (APS) and processed from a near detector count rate (ANEC), a far detector count rate (AFEC), a computed standoff (STOF) and a formation capture cross-section (SIGF) to provide a near/array limestone corrected porosity (APLC), the value required for log interpretation. Other neutron porosity tools, even from Schlumberger, have different acronyms.

The only way to cope with this ever increasing list is to use online look-up lists from the service companies (Schlumberger, Baker Hughes™ and Halliburton), the Society of Petrophysicists and Well Log Analysts (SPWLA), the International Ocean Drilling Project (ODP & IODP), various government agencies and even the familiar search engines and online encyclopedias, by searching under well log mnemonics or well log acronyms (**Table 1.4**). In this book, when acronyms need to be used, they are written long-hand on first appearance and kept to a minimum thereafter. Their page of definition is indicated in the index.

1.9 The logging companies

The wireline well-logging world is dominated by one, extremely successful, global company – Schlumberger. In many parts of the world, Schlumberger has a quasi-monopoly. The reasons for this domination are partly historical: it was the *frères* Schlumberger, Conrad and Marcel, who created the original SPE (Société de Prospection Électrique) in 1926, the precursor of the modern Schlumberger and it was the brothers, along with Henri Doll, who were the creators of the well-logging technique (Allaud and Martin 1976; Schlumberger 1982; Dorozynski and Oristaglio 2007). By business practices and good research, Schlumberger has maintained a leading position for more than 80 years.

Two other companies are major players in well-logging, Baker Hughes™ and Halliburton. Baker Hughes™ is generally Schlumberger's main competitor, but in some parts of the world it is Halliburton. There are also differences in the provision of wireline and LWD services, Schlumberger being less dominant in the LWD field. Baker Hughes™, as a single company, was formed in 1987 from Baker International and the Hughes Tool Company, both formed individually in the early 1900s. Baker Hughes™ incorporates many smaller companies that have been absorbed, notably Dresser-Atlas in the

Table 1.4 Acronym (mnemonic) sources

Organisation	web address
Schlumberger	www.SLB.com/resources
Baker Hughes™	www.bakerhughes.com/products-and-services
Halliburton	www.halliburton.com/ps (search log mnemonics)
SPWLA	www.spwla.org (technical resources menu)
IODP	iodp.ldeo.columbia.edu/TOOLS_LABS/tools.html
ODP	www-odp.tamu.edu/search.html (search acronyms)

Use also Google and Wikipedia with: 'well log acronyms', 'well log mnemonics'

logging field, and Teleco and INTEQ in the MWD/LWD field. Halliburton, equally a company from the early days, has also absorbed logging companies, for example, Gearhart, Welex, Sperry-Sun and Numar (nuclear magnetic resonance). Weatherford, another oilfield services company, offers wireline services, having acquired Computalog and Precision Drilling (who acquired BPB-Reeves). Some of the older company names still seem to crop up in marketing even though they are now part of greater conglomerates. A number of other smaller companies, mainly offering more specialised services, exist in North America.

(Nota: throughout this book, where it seems helpful, the company name given to a tool will be the name in use at the time. Modern company names are used where indicative, but it is sometimes difficult to know if the correct marketing term has been applied. Company takeovers are frequent. Names may be trademarks™.)

1.10 Well log interpretation and uses

The traditional, accepted user of the well log is the petrophysicist, also called a log analyst. His or her interest is quantitative. From the logs, a petrophysicist will calculate porosity, water saturation, moveable hydrocarbons, hydrocarbon density and so on, all the factors related to quantifying reserves and the volume of hydrocarbons in a reservoir, although their expertise also goes well beyond these aspects. The Society of Petrophysicists and Well Log Analysts (SPWLA), the principal society of log interpreters, is mainly composed of petrophysicists and reservoirs are their target.

Reservoir rocks, however, comprise perhaps only 15% of a typical well, and of this 15% only a small percentage actually contains hydrocarbons. The petrophysicist is therefore not so interested in 85% or more of the well logs recorded. The exploration geologist, by contrast, should be interested in 100% of well logs, as the amount of geological information they contain is enormous.

Because well logs are available during drilling, logs can now be used for geosteering, such as keeping the bit inside a thin reservoir section or avoiding a water contact, for a better assessment of hole conditions during drilling, and for identifying hole changes during and after drilling. They can also be used to pick pressure measuring points, better pick coring and rock sampling points and recognise known seismic reflectors. These while drilling tasks may involve geologists and others, as much as the petrophysicist.

The measurements made during logging provide a massive, sensitive, accurate and characteristic digital geophysical response of the formations logged. However, to those familiar with the aspect of rocks as seen at outcrop, the geophysical signatures of this selfsame rock in the subsurface are impossible to imagine. To an experienced geological analyst of well logs, the reverse is true. A formation that can be instantly identified on the logs, down to the nearest metre, can be very hard to find, even tentatively, at outcrop and even in core.

In the following pages it is intended to try to close this gap, to help understand geophysical well log responses in terms of the geology familiar at outcrop. Logs can and should be interpreted in terms meaningful to outcrop. They contain as much information, even sometimes more than the outcrop, but can be studied conveniently on a computer screen in the office, in the core store, on the rig, or at the outcrop itself.

1.11 This book – content and aims

Table 1.5 (*over page*) shows the logs considered in this book and their principal applications, both geological and geophysical. The applications have been divided into qualitative, semi-quantitative and essentially quantitative. Petrophysical, geomechanical and seismic applications are generally, by necessity, quantitative or semi-quantitative; geological applications are, by default, most often qualitative. This should not be. A log sample set of between 200,000 and 20,000,000 or more values for a typical well of 3000 m (10,000 ft) with some image log, represents an enormous *quantitative* database. Statistical, quasi-quantitative and of course purely quantitative methods applied to this digital log database can bring precision to *geological* interpretation.

It is hoped that in the following chapters information for making use of the logs will be adequately explained. Each type of open-hole log is described individually: first in terms of the theory behind the measurement; then the corresponding tool's capabilities in both wireline and LWD; then the characteristics of the logs produced; and finally their significance in terms of real formations and interpretation in common geological terms. In short, the *geological interpretation of well logs*.

Table 1.5 Principal uses of open-hole geophysical well logs

		General geology						Reservoir geology		Geomechanics	Geochemistry		Petrophysics						Drilling	Seismic		
Chapter	Measurement \ Uses	Lithology, general	Volcanics	Evaporites	Mineral identification	Correlation, stratigraphic	Facies, depositional environment	Fracture identification	Pressure/over-pressure identification	Borehole stability	Source rock identification	Maturity of source	Porosity	Permeability	Shale volume (V_{sh})	Formation water salinity	Hydrocarbon saturation (S_w)	Gas identification	*Geosteering	Interval velocity	Acoustic impedance	Bulk rock properties
3	Temperature								–			+						–				
4	Pressure								**@**					+		**@**	+	+				
5	Caliper									+				–								
6	SP					–	–							–	+	+						
7	Resistivity	–		–		–	–	–	+		–	**+**	+	–		+	**@**	–	–			
8	Gamma Ray	–	–	+	–	**–**	**–**				–				+				–			
8	Spectral gamma	–	–	+	+	–	–	–			+				**+**							
9	Sonic	+		–		–		+	+	+	+		@					–		**@**	**@**	**@**
10	Density	+	–	–	+		–	–	+	+	**+**		**@**					–	–		**@**	**@**
10	Photoelectric	+	–	–	+														–			
11	Neutron	+	–	–	–		–				–		@		–			–				
11	Neutron+Density	**+**	**–**	**–**	–	–	–						@		**@**			**–**				
13	NMR						–						**@**	**@**			+	–				
14	Dipmeter						–			+										dip	dip	
15	Images	–	–		–	–	**+**	**+**		**+**				+			–		**–**			

@ quantitative (within the limits of the method of application)
+ semi-quantitative and statistical, as well as qualitative
– essentially qualitative
Colour = best
* logs displayed as images

2
THE LOGGING ENVIRONMENT

2.1 Introduction

Logging tools are designed to measure the physical properties of a formation in the subsurface: the properties of the rock matrix, the fluids, the stress state, and more. However, the very act of drilling changes this formation severely: breaks the matrix, pollutes the original fluids, modifies the in-place stresses and changes the physical and chemical state of the target of logging. The damage is severest at the borehole wall, lessening with distance: least when the hole is first drilled, increasing with time. This is the logging environment.

It is tempting to think of a logging tool as making a series of precise measurements at discrete points, equally spaced along the borehole. But, to achieve this, the tool would have to be motionless at each point. In reality, tools move, measurements require a finite time to complete and sensors have dimensions, which can even be of the order of cubic meters. Tool design acknowledges this, and a compromise is made between a perfect measurement and one that is practical and practicable.

Ideally, then, a logging measurement should be two things: perfectly accurate, and refer to the undisturbed formation. As suggested, both objectives are effectively impossible to achieve. Accuracy is limited by the practical problems of making measurements in a small borehole with a moving sensor, which places considerable limitations on instrumentation. And, even if we do design a tool that is perfectly accurate, the measurement will be modified by the logging environment and be of the formation inevitably disturbed by the drilling process.

This chapter will examine these aspects of the logging environment in general terms: how drilling disturbs the subsurface environment, especially in terms of invasion; how logging tools cope with this; the effects of the logging method on the measurements; and what these measurements mean in terms of real beds. The notions of depth of investigation and minimum bed resolution will be examined, as well as ideas of size, volume and orientation of investigation.

To complete the chapter, depth measurement will be considered in the wireline domain, in the LWD domain and in the real world. And, finally, conveyancing methods are described, that is, how tools are placed in the subsurface.

2.2 Invasion and the pressure environment of boreholes

The pressure environment during drilling and, inevitably, during logging is made up of an interplay between two elements: formation pressure and drilling-mud column pressure.

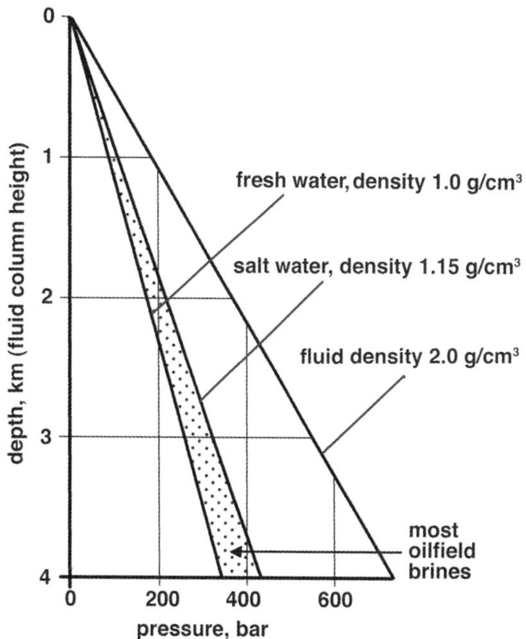

Figure 2.1 Fluid pressure and pressure gradients related to depth, or height of fluid column, and fluid density.

Formation pressure is the pressure under which the subsurface formation fluids and gases are confined. The pressure of the drilling mud column is hydrostatic and depends only on the depth of a well, that is, the height of the mud column and the mud density (**Figure 2.1**). Maintaining the pressure exerted by the column of drilling mud at just a little above the pressure of the subsurface formations encountered is one of the necessities for equilibrium drilling: it is a delicate balance. (Although under-balanced drilling exists, it is a very specialised technique.)

To give an idea of the pressures encountered during drilling it is useful to know that logging tools are designed to withstand pressures of 140 MPa (20,000 psi) in normal wells and 240 MPa (35,000 psi) in specialist, high pressure wells. (Pressure is dealt with in more detail in Chapter 3).

Invasion, drilling pressures

Under ideal conditions, the pressure exerted by the column of drilling mud will be such that, when a porous and permeable formation is encountered, as the drill enters the formation, mud will flow into it (**Figure 2.2**). The porous rock will then begin to act as a filter, separating the mud into its liquid and solid constituents. The

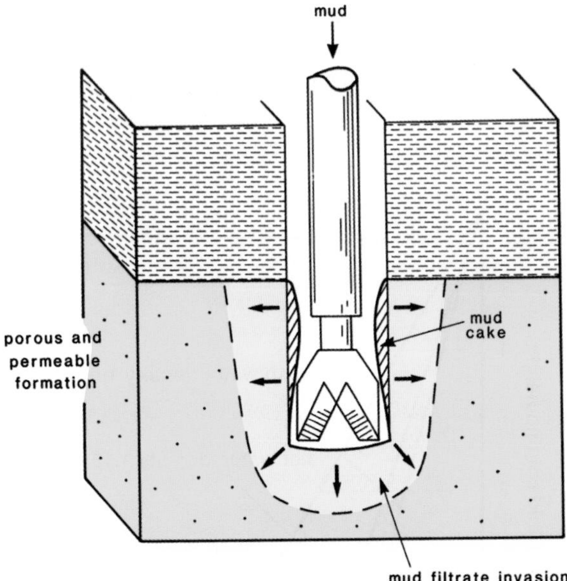

Figure 2.2 Schematic representation of dynamic filtration as a bit enters a porous formation. Note the progressive mudcake build-up.

mud filtrate (water, with any additional chemicals, used to mix the mud) will flow into the formation, while the solids (the mud) will block pore throats and form a deposit on the borehole wall as the bit passes. In the hole just drilled, the solid deposit around the borehole wall, the *mudcake*, will gradually build up and thicken to form a near impermeable skin over the porous and permeable interval.

Initially, as the bit enters the porous formation, there is complete disequilibrium and *spurt loss* takes place (**Figure 2.3**). That is, below and around the bit there is a continuous rapid flow of filtrate into the formation. LWD tools take their measurements during this phase or just after. Gradually, as a mudcake builds up, it creates an increasingly impermeable barrier, the flow of filtrate diminishing. This is the phase of *dynamic filtration* (Bonner *et al.* 1991). Finally, when the drill bit has passed, the mudcake becomes almost impermeable and filtration practically ceases: this is now the phase of *static filtration* (**Figure 2.3**). A cross-section through the borehole at this stage would show mud in the hole, mudcake on the borehole wall and the porous formation surrounding the borehole now filled almost entirely by mud filtrate. The original formation fluids have been pushed away from the hole (**Figure 2.4**). This is usually the situation when the open-hole wireline logs are run.

The phenomenon of the replacement of formation fluids by drilling mud filtrate is called *invasion*. Invasion affects porous and permeable formations in the immediate vicinity of a borehole. It is described by 'diameter' or 'depth' of invasion, that is, the distance from the borehole reached by the invading filtrate (**Figure 2.4**). Generally this depth is very small, a matter of centimetres, but deep invasion can reach 2 metres (6.5 feet) or more (**Table 2.1**) (*see* invasion, time effect below).

Since excessive invasion is the worst situation for logging, and takes the real formation fluids too far away from the borehole to be detected, chemicals are added to the drilling mud to reduce water loss and create a protective mudcake as quickly as possible. Products such as ligno-sulphonates and starch are used.

Invasion, the time effect

When certain LWD log measurements are compared to wireline measurements, it is obvious that invasion is a very dynamic process and that, when any type of logging takes place, it is simply measuring a 'snap-shot' of a constantly changing environment (**Figure 2.3**). As suggested, just behind the bit invasion has hardly begun and the mudcake is still thin and permeable. As drilling progresses, the mudcake builds up to eventually become almost impermeable and no more invasion takes place. However, this behaviour varies with both time and the permeability of the formation.

In general, counter intuitively, invasion is small in very porous and permeable formations but can be very deep in poorly permeable zones, vuggy carbonates and fractured formations (El-Wazeer *et al.* 1999). High formation permeability allows mud filtrate to penetrate more rapidly than low formation permeability (**Figure 2.5**). This is to be expected, as more permeable formations have larger pore throats. However, the quicker the flow, the greater the volume of filtrate invading the formation and the quicker the mudcake builds up. The quicker the mudcake forms, the sooner it becomes impermeable, seals off the formation and invasion ceases. When per-

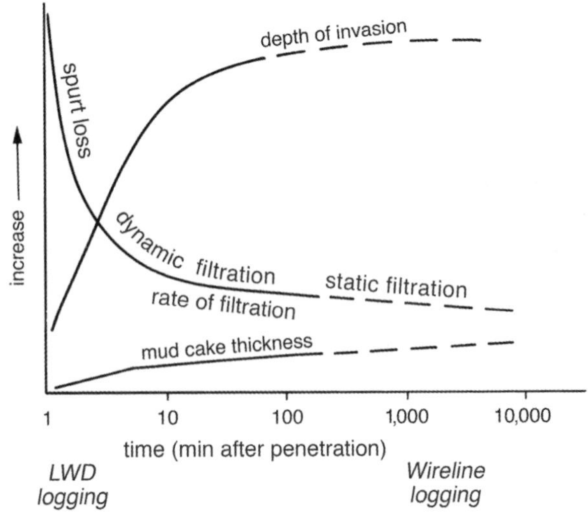

Figure 2.3 Graphic representation (schematic) of invasion and mudcake build-up as a porous formation is penetrated. LWD logging precedes the full mudcake build-up: wireline logs are run during the phase of stability (modified from Dewan 1983).

Table 2.1 Depth of invasion (distance from borehole wall) vs. porosity (approximate). (from Miesch and Albright, 1967).

Hole size (in)	**17 ½**	**12 ¼**	**8 ½**	**Ratio: Invasion diameter/ hole diameter**
Porosity	**Depth of invasion**			
1–8	200 cm (80″)	140 cm (55″)	97 cm (38″)	10
8–20	90 cm (35″)	62 cm (25″)	43 cm (17″)	5
20–30	22.5 cm (9″)	15.5 cm (6″)	11 cm (4″)	2
30+	≈3 cm (1.2″)	≈2 cm (0.8″)	≈1.7 cm (0.7″)	<2

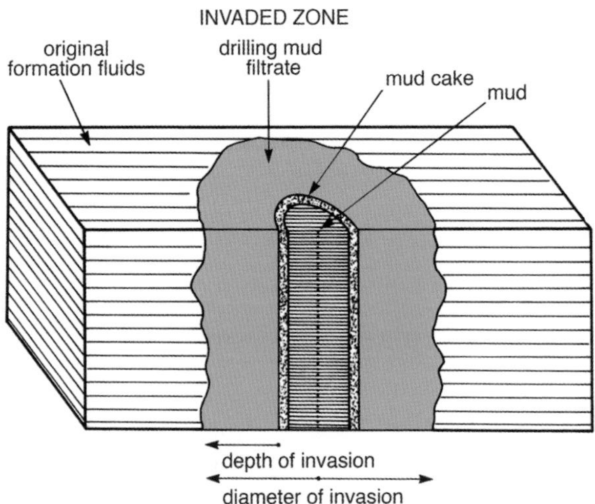

Figure 2.4 Invasion: simple representation of the effect of drilling on fluids in a porous and permeable formation.

meability is poor, filtrate takes longer to penetrate the formation, mudcake build up is slow and it takes longer to form a seal. In this situation, filtrate will have time to move further away from the borehole.

This means that invasion does not take a fixed time. For example, one suite of timed resistivity logs shows that it can take over 4 days (100 hrs) before the mudcake is nearly impermeable and equilibrium is reached (**Figure 7.10**), so that even wireline logs may not be run at maximum invasion. On the contrary, some LWD logs demonstrate that invasion can be extremely rapid and even the LWD measurements are affected (Bonner *et al.* 1991; Oberkircher *et al.* 1993).

So, high permeability formations tend to be quickly invaded but to a shallower depth, low permeability formations slowly invaded but to a greater depth. It seems that to build up a mudcake to its impermeable thickness requires a certain, critical volume of filtrate to flow into the formation and this takes longer the lower the permeability. Consequently, invasion distance tends to increase as permeability decreases.

However, in the final analysis, rate of filtrate loss depends on mud to mudcake interactions and not just on formation permeability or porosity (Allen *et al.* 1991). These aspects are complicated by the fact that circulating mud erodes previously deposited mudcake, thereby changing its permeability. Also, circulating mud exerts a higher pressure than static mud, equally changing the boundary conditions across the mudcake.

Invasion, the gravity effect

Even while drilling, heavier liquids in a reservoir will migrate downwards under gravity (and of course *vice versa*). Water based mud filtrate is generally more dense than reservoir fluids, certainly when hydrocarbons are involved, but also with water because of temperature and dissolved solids. In vertical wells the gravity effect on invasion is difficult to identify as any changes are symmetrical about the borehole. With deviated and horizontal wells the effect is not symmetrical and it is clear that the gravity effect is both common and significant (**Figure 2.6**).

When a vertical well drilled with water based mud (WBM) encounters an oil reservoir, a vertical interface between filtrate (water) and oil is created in the pore space between the invaded zone and the reservoir. This interface is clearly unstable. If the reservoir is quite permeable, the filtrate (water) will move downwards under gravity and the oil will re-migrate back towards the bore-

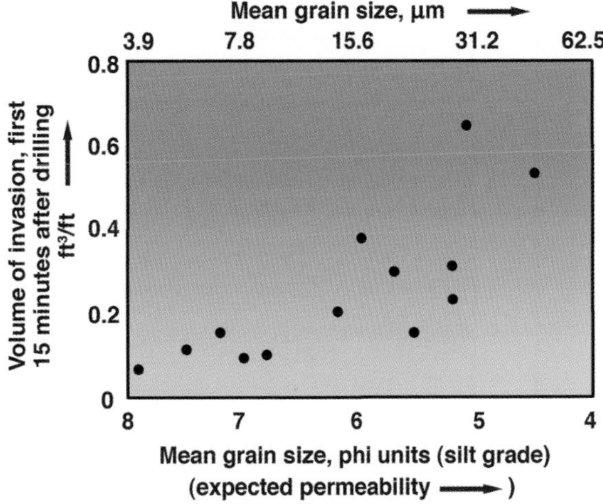

Figure 2.5 The effects of grain size on invasion. As the grain size increases, so the invading volume increases for the same period of time. Volume of flow during the first 15 minutes after drilling. Silt grade grain size (modified from Allen *et al.* 1991). *Copyright Schlumberger Ltd. Used with permission.*

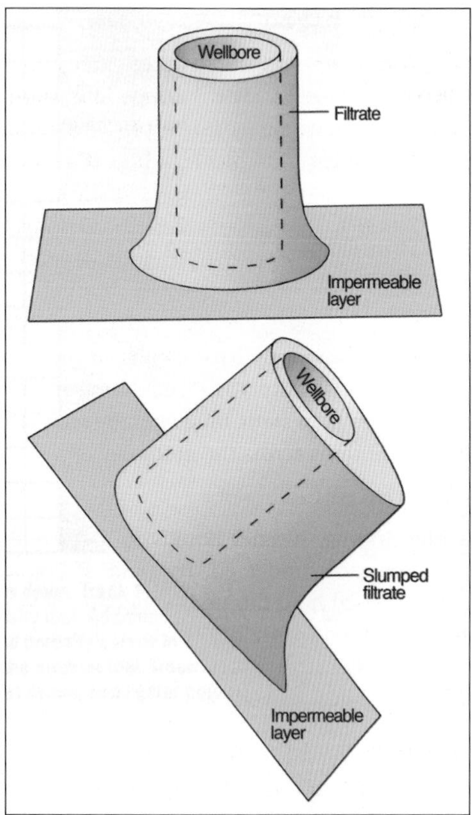

Figure 2.6 Gravity effects on mud filtrate behaviour in a vertical and a deviated borehole (from Bourgeois *et al.* 1998). *Copyright Schlumberger Ltd. Used with permission.*

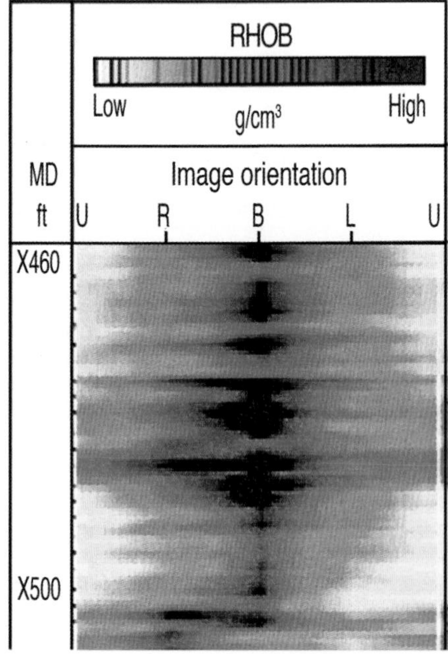

Figure 2.7 LWD Density image showing that the highest (and best) density is along the bottom of this horizontal well. U = up, R = right, B = bottom, L = left (Bargach *et al.* 2000). *Copyright Schlumberger Ltd. Used with permission.*

hole, even as drilling progresses or before wireline logging takes place. Such conditions are more evident when gas or light oil are involved, as in the case described in the chapter on resistivity logs (Chapter 7, **Figure 7.13**).

As stated, gravity effects are more easily observed in deviated and horizontal wells. Since water based filtrate is generally heavier than reservoir fluids, it sinks from the upside of the borehole to the downside, forming a pear-shaped invaded zone with the borehole at the top of the pear (**Figure 2.6**). Such a situation is clearly significant for well logs since an upward facing sensor will measure a quite different situation to a down-facing sensor. The solution in horizontal wells has been to control or know the orientation of the sensors. For example, density logs in a horizontal well can be acquired in four quadrants (as a minimum): top, left, bottom and right. Bottom is usually (but not always) best. A more modern solution is to construct an oriented image of the log measurements so that the image shows the spatial differences, as future chapters will describe (**Figure 2.7**).

2.3 Temperature environment of boreholes

Formation temperatures

Normal sedimentary basins show a more or less regular increase in temperature with depth (**Figure 2.8**). The increase is not linear, as frequently depicted, but varies according to lithology and depends principally on the latter's thermal conductivity (**Figure 4.1**). However, despite the irregularities, there is an overall, persistent increase in temperature with depth (**Figure 2.8**). This increase is often expressed as a gradient, the geothermal gradient, the increase in temperature per unit depth. The metric values are usually °C per km: Imperial units °F per 100 ft. Typical gradients for sedimentary basins are between 20–35°C per km (1.10–1.92°F per 100 ft) (**Table 4.2**).

Temperatures in boreholes

Just as the geopressure regime is disturbed by drilling, so is subsurface temperature. A well drilled into a subsurface formation introduces relatively cold mud and mud filtrate into a hot formation. While drilling continues and mud is circulating, the formation is cooled slightly and the mud heated. However, when circulation ceases, the mud remains undisturbed in the borehole and gradually heats up to reach, or at least approach, the temperature of the surrounding formation. The two, though, are rarely in equilibrium. The temperature regime of LWD tools is definitely that of the mud and not the formation. Wireline logging temperatures taken in the mud are often measured after 5–10 hours of mud immobility; equilibrium is probably approached only after 5–10 days!

Typical borehole tools are generally designed to withstand temperatures up to around 200°C (400°F) al-

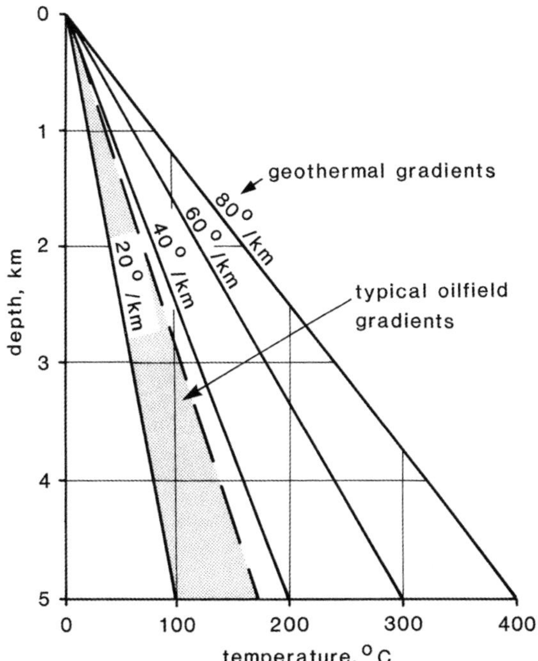

Figure 2.8 Geothermal gradients showing formation temperature increase with depth. The zone of typical oilfield gradients is indicated.

though for high temperature wells this can rise to 260°C (500°F): these figures give a guide to maxima expected during drilling. (To note, in certain cold or deep seas, drilling mud is warmer than the shallow formations. In areas where methane hydrate is found this can be a difficulty.)

(Temperature is considered at greater length in Chapter 4.)

2.4 Damage around the borehole

Two types of drilling-induced damage can occur in the formation immediately around the borehole: chemical and physical. They are briefly considered here but frequently referred to in subsequent chapters.

Chemical damage

Chemical damage occurs when the fluids and chemicals in the mud react with the minerals or fluids of the formation. A very common example of this is the behaviour of smectite (montmorillonite) rich clay or 'gumbo', as it is called in the U.S. Gulf Coast. The clay mineral smectite absorbs water easily, which happens when the formation is drilled. As is described in Chapter 5 (caliper), when such clays absorb water, they increase in volume, swell and cause hole problems. Another example is when fresh water mud is used to drill salt: obviously solution takes place. Not only does chemical damage cause hole problems but can also significantly disturb log measurements, as shown by the sonic (Chapter 9).

Mechanical damage

It is only with the advent of downhole image logs that it has become evident that the immediate formation about the borehole is subjected to physical formation damage. The simple fact of having a hole (the borehole) in a rock formation changes the stress field significantly. Oriented borehole enlargement (breakout) may form, and fractures may develop in the immediate borehole vicinity. The mechanical vibrations of drilling amplify these effects. With LWD images available at the time of drilling, and wireline images from much later, the effects of this damage can be observed over time. In addition, images can be acquired from different distances around the borehole, from the borehole wall to deeper within the formation. The orientation of the damage effects can also be studied.

This subject is dealt with in more detail in Chapters 5 (caliper), 9 (sonic) and 15 (image logs).

2.5 Logging tool capabilities: beds

At the beginning of this Chapter it was suggested that logging tools should be able to characterise the undisturbed formation. However, it has been shown that drilling disturbs the original formation and, importantly, that the original reservoir fluids are displaced and replaced by invading mud filtrate. But detecting the original fluids is a principal task of geophysical measurements. As a result, logging tools are in fact designed either to 'bypass' the invaded zone to reach the undisturbed formation fluids, or to deliberately measure the invaded zone itself. That is, they are designed with various depths of investigation, as will be explained. Inevitably, such demands on tool design create secondary effects. Logging is comparable to photography with its close-up lenses and long-distance lenses. Close-up logging tools give great resolution but little depth of investigation; long-distance logging tools give great depth of investigation but blurred resolution.

Three inter-related effects on logging tools are examined below: depth of investigation, minimum bed resolution and bed boundary definition. Computer characterisation of beds is also considered.

Depth of investigation

Most geophysical logs have an extremely shallow *depth of investigation* (DOI), where 'depth' means the distance away from the borehole to which the formation is having an effect on the tool reading. So-called 'deep' investigation is only a matter of 2 m (6.5 ft) into the formation and away from the borehole (rarely up to 5 m–16 ft). The environment of logging tools is therefore from the borehole itself (shallow investigation) to a distance of 2 m from the borehole wall (deep investigation).

With tools that subject the formation to a bombarding signal (**Table 1.1**), very generally, the depth of investigation depends on the separation distance between the emitter and receiver. In resistivity tools, for example (Chapter 7), when the emitting and receiving electrodes are very close, the depth of investigation is very small (**Figure 2.9**). Micro-Inverse resistivity tools, with electrodes 2.54 cm (1") apart, have such a shallow depth of investigation that they read only the resistivity of the mudcake (when present). Conversely, Induction conductivity tools with emitter and receiver up to 1 m (40") apart, have a depth of investigation of 2.3 m (90") and may even reach about 5 m (200"). The Deep Induction tool is most likely to investigate the real, in-place formation fluids (Chapter 7).

The emitter-receiver separation is not the only factor affecting a tool's depth of investigation. Necessarily, it varies with the geophysical signal being measured. Thus, for the sonic tools which measure the speed of compressional sound waves in the formation, the waves take the quickest path from emitter to receiver and this

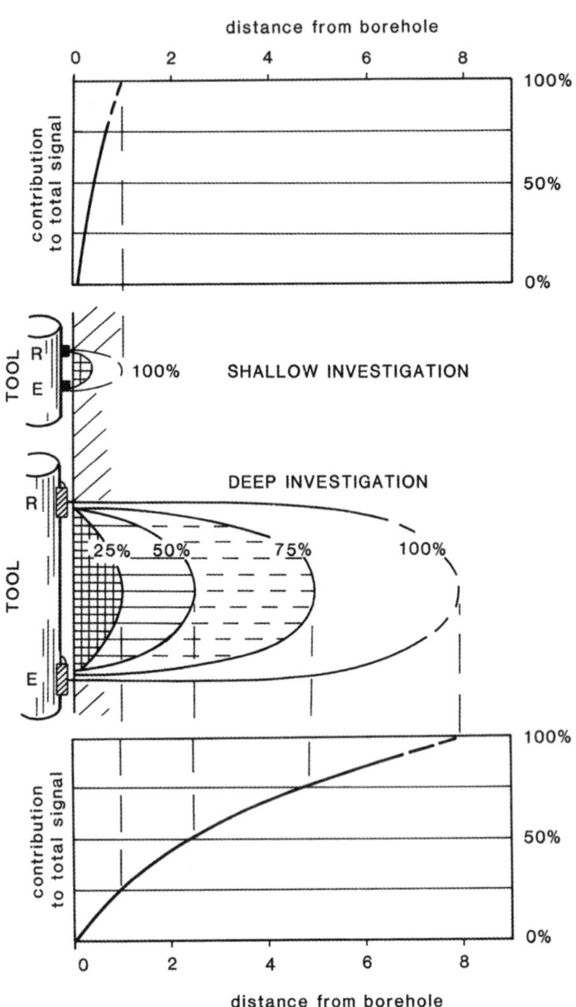

Figure 2.9 Illustration of the notion of depth of investigation. Two tools are shown schematically along with a graphic representation of formation contribution to their overall signal. E, emitter; R, receiver.

Table 2.2 Porosity dependent depth of investigation of the neutron tool. (modified from Serra, 1979, after Schlumberger)

Neutron porosity %	Depth* of investigation
0	60 cm (24")
10	34 cm (13.5")
20	23 cm (9")
30	16.5 cm (6.5")

*90% of the signal

is generally not far from the borehole wall (Chapter 9). For the density tools that use gamma rays to measure a formation's density, the depth of investigation will depend on the penetrating power of gamma rays. These characteristics are considered in more detail when each tool is described.

Finally, depth of investigation also depends on the formation, whether it is susceptible to penetration or not. In the case of the neutron tools, for example, a non-porous bed is 'seen' to a far greater depth than a porous bed. Neutrons are absorbed by the hydrogen nuclei in porous, water rich formations (**Table 2.2**).

In reality, depth of investigation is a very difficult term to fully understand. It is not precise: a bed is not investigated to a particular point and no further. It is a progressive character, like the radiant heat from a fire. We feel the heat near to the fire, but not at some distance away. Can we say exactly at what distance the fire has no more effect? With logging tools, the depth of investigation is more realistically defined as the zone from which *x*% of the tool reading is derived (**Figure 2.9**). For instance, the investigation of the neutron tool mentioned above (**Table 2.2**) is defined on 90% of the tool signal. Resistivity log depth of investigation is usually defined as the detection depth of 50% of the signal (cf. Theys 1991). These responses are represented by the experimentally defined *geometrical factor,* which will be described in the subsequent chapters.

Minimum bed resolution (and deconvolution)

The thinnest bed for which a logging tool is able to make a true measurement defines its *minimum bed resolution.* A tool is only capable of making a true measurement of a bed if the bed is at least thicker than the emitter-to-receiver distance of that tool (**Figure 2.10**). Thus, a resistivity tool with an emitter-to-receiver distance of 2.54 cm (1") can resolve beds down to 5–10 cm (2–4") to give their true resistivity. An induction log with an emitter to receiver distance of 1 m (40") can resolve beds to give their true resistivities only down to 1.5 m (5 ft), and that must be under ideal conditions. Some common tools are shown with their minimum bed resolution for true values under the best conditions (**Table 2.3**). Minimum bed resolution and depth of investigation are related: tools capable of measuring quite thin beds generally have a shallow depth of investigation (**Figure 2.11**).

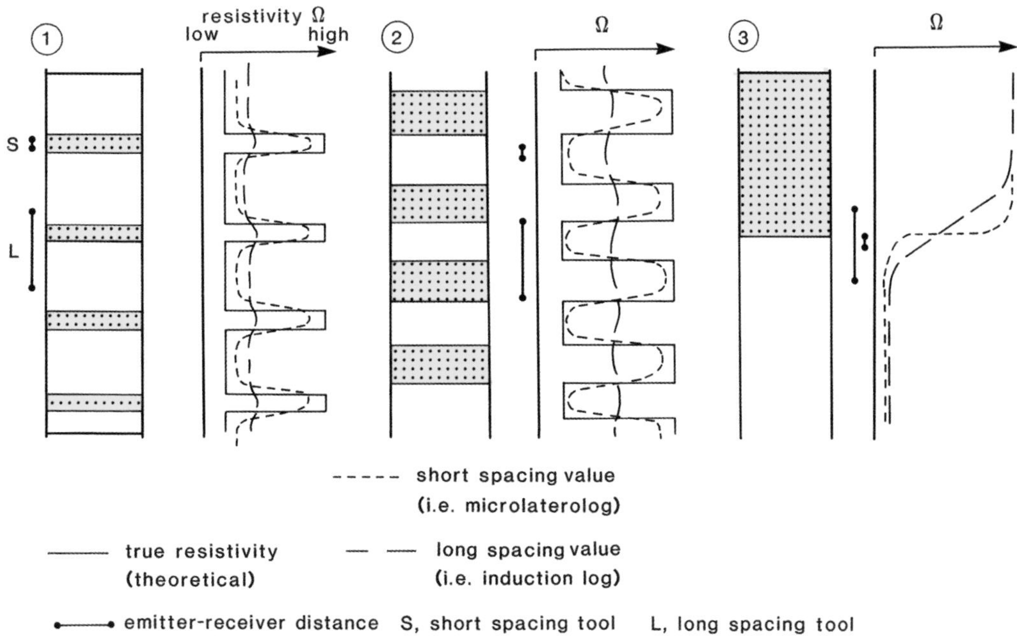

Figure 2.10 The effect of minimum bed resolution on logging-tool responses from various scales of inter-bedding. (1) Fine inter-beds; (2) coarse inter-bedding; (3) single bed boundary (schematic).

Table 2.3 Values for 'intrinsic vertical resolution' and actual bed resolution (refer to Figures 2.12 & 2.13) and sampling rate for some wireline tools (principally from Theys 1991; Serra 2000).

Measurement		Vertical Resolution (intrinsic)	Vertical Resolution for 'true' value (approx.)	Sample rate (wireline)
Electrical Imaging:	FMS/FMI	0.5 cm (0.2")	0.5 cm (0.2")	0.254 cm (0.1")
Dipmeters:	SHDT	1.1 cm (0.4")	1.1 cm (0.4")	0.254 cm (0.1")
	HDT	1.3 cm (0.5")	1.3 cm (0.5")	1.27 cm (2")
Microlog:	MicroInverse	5–10 cm (2-4")		1.27 cm (2")
	MicroNormal	10 cm (4")		
MicroSperically Focused (MSFL)		5–7.5 cm (2-3")		
Photoelectric (Pe)		5 cm (2")	10–15 cm (4-6")	
Nuclear Magnetic Resonance (NMR)		15 cm (6")	15 cm (6")	15 cm (6")
Array Laterolog (ARI)		20 cm (8")		1.27 cm (0.5")
High Resolution Laterolog (HALS)		20-41 cm (8-16")		
Gamma ray:	simple gamma ray	20–30 cm (8-12")	30-41 cm (12–16")	15 cm (6")
	Spectral (NGT)	20–30 cm (8-12")		
Litho-Density:	normal (RHOB)	41 cm (16")	51 cm (20")	15 or 5 cm (6" or 2")
	alpha processing	10 cm (4")	10–20 cm (4–8")	
Neutron:	normal (CNL)	51 cm (20")	61 cm (24")	15 cm (6")
	Resolution matched	61 cm (24")		
	alpha processing	25 cm (10")	25–36 cm (10–14")	5 cm (2")
Array Induction (AIT)		46 cm (18")	0.3, 0.60 or 1.2 m (1,2 or 4')	15 cm (6")
Laterolog:	Dual Laterolog (DLL)	71 cm (28")		15 cm (6")
Spherically Focused Log (SFL)		76 cm (30")		15 cm (6")
Sonic:	standard	1.22 m (48")	1.22 cm (48")	15 cm (6")
	Compensated	61 cm (24")	61 cm (24")	
	6" mode	15 cm (6")	15 cm (6")	3 cm (1.2")
Phasor Induction:	medium (ILM)	1.5–1.8 m (5-6')		15 cm (6")
	Deep (ILD)	2.1–2.4 m (7-8')		
	improved	90 cm (3')		
Spontaneous Potential (SP)		1.8–3 m (6-10')	1.8–3 m (6–10')	15 cm (6")

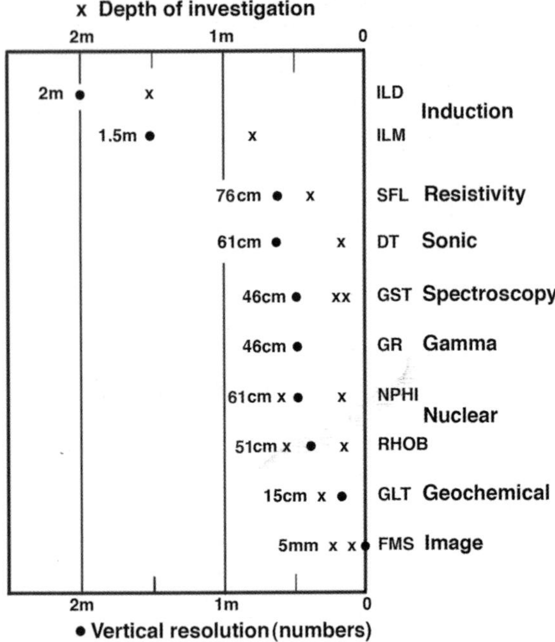

Figure 2.11 Depth of investigation compared to vertical resolution for some common tools. X = depth of investigation, • = vertical resolution (modified from ODP documentation).

A bed which is much thinner than a tool's minimum resolution may still be identifiable. However, the reading indicated on the log for this bed will only be a percentage of its true value. That is, the bed is *detected* (able to be identified) but not *resolved* (a true measurement made) (**Figure 2.12**). The tool takes a global measurement of the formation between the emitter and the receiver, the thin bed forming only a small percentage of this (**Figure 2.10,1**). The value on the log will depend on the percentage contribution

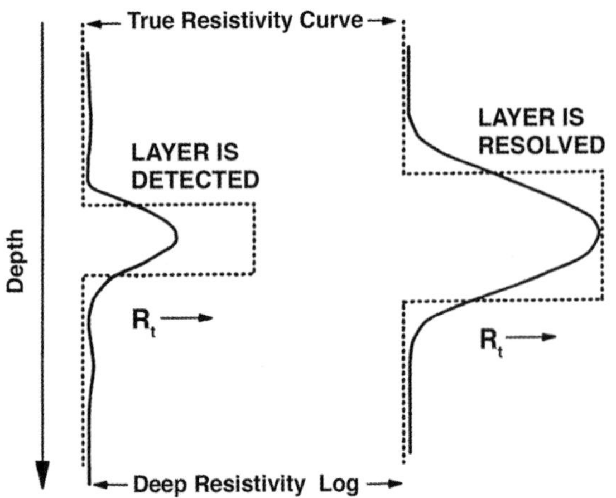

Figure 2.12 The difference between detection and resolution shown graphically (from Worthington 2000).

that this thin bed makes to the global measurement. An induction log opposite a thin, resistive, limestone bed in a shale sequence will show a subdued 'blip'. On a micrlog this becomes a fully developed peak (**Figure 2.10,1**). In reality, where lithologies vary rapidly, and individual beds are thin, it is only an average value that appears on the log, especially the logs derived from long spacing tools. This averaged value will tend to approach that of the dominant lithology. When the mixture is 50/50 the logs will give an 'invented' value somewhere between the two 'real' values (**Figure 2.10, 2**).

This type of resolution problem is very real and often encountered in today's deep-water turbidite plays. There are many parts of the world where hydrocarbons are produced from apparently shale rich horizons. It is simply that there are thin, clean, turbidite sands in clean, deep-water shales and the sand beds are below the resolution capabilities of the standard logs. They nonetheless contain hydrocarbons but, because of the resolution problem, the saturation in hydrocarbons cannot be calculated with any accuracy. This is the origin of the so called 'thin bed problem' (for an excellent summary of thin beds *see* Passey *et al.* 2006). Specialised tools exist to overcome the problem (Chapter 15, Image Logs).

Equating bed resolution to emitter-to-receiver spacing, as in the previous paragraphs, is not always correct. For the resistivity tools it may be reasonable, but for the nuclear tools it can be misleading. Rather than use this concept, an alternative is to use a tool's performance under laboratory conditions. In this context, a tool's *vertical (intrinsic) resolution* may be examined. This vertical resolution is defined as: *the full width, at half maximum, of the response to the measurement of an infinitesimally short event* (Theys 1991). This definition is shown graphically (**Figure 2.13**) and some values based on it for some common tools are shown in the table (**Table 2.3**).

The raw vertical resolution of a tool can be enhanced by processing. Thus, the response of a tool is a function of the real formation signal and the way that a particular sensor modifies or distorts it. This response is called the *vertical response function* of the sensor and is known from physics. A log therefore *convolves,* that is, mixes together the formation signal and the sensor modification of it (**Figure 2.14**). If this is expressed mathematically, the inverse of the sensor modification can be used to extract it from the overall signal and leave only the formation signal. This is *deconvolution* and it can improve bed resolution.

The differences between theoretical and actual bed resolution values (**Table 2.3**) show how difficult it is to define consistently what a tool is capable of resolving. A single tool, in fact, has variable resolution. A thin, very dense bed in a low density formation will be better resolved by a density tool than a similar thin,

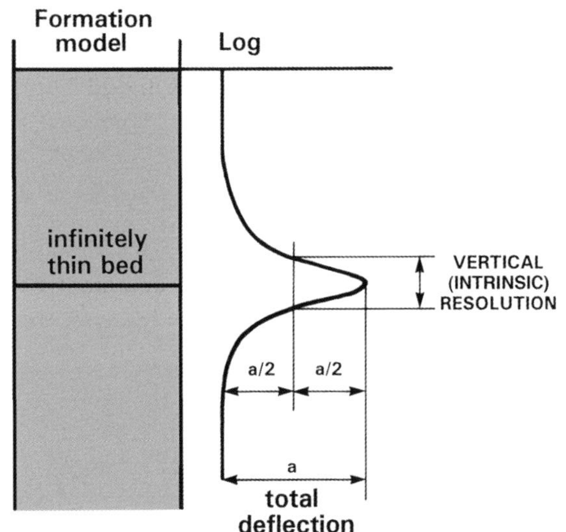

Figure 2.13 Graphical representation of the theoretical definition of tool vertical resolution (re-drawn, modified, from Theys 1991).

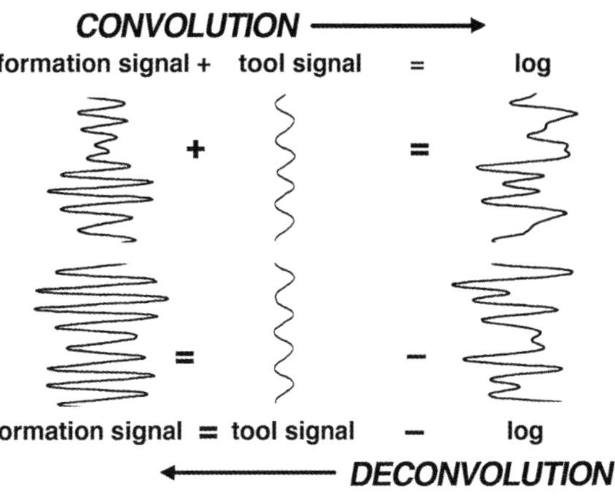

Figure 2.14 Logging convolves the tool and formation signals (top). Extracting the tool signal from the log is deconvolution (bottom).

low density bed in a dense formation. A resistivity tool can resolve thin beds in the salt water leg of a reservoir that it cannot detect effectively at high background resistivities in the hydrocarbon leg of the reservoir.

From a geological point of view, rather than be precise, it is probably more useful to indicate qualitatively the expected capabilities of the tools in relation to typical sedimentary and structural features (**Figure 2.15**). This enables the correct tool to be selected for identifying particular features. It is the qualitative indications that become clear, for example, when logs and cores are compared. For the petrophysicist, however, thin bed values have to be quantified.

Bed boundary definition

A bed, in geology, is generally thought of as a distinctive, planar unit (lithology, composition, facies etc.), limited by significant differences (in lithology, composition, facies etc.). The limits tend to be abrupt. On well logs, all boundaries are inevitably seen as gradations,

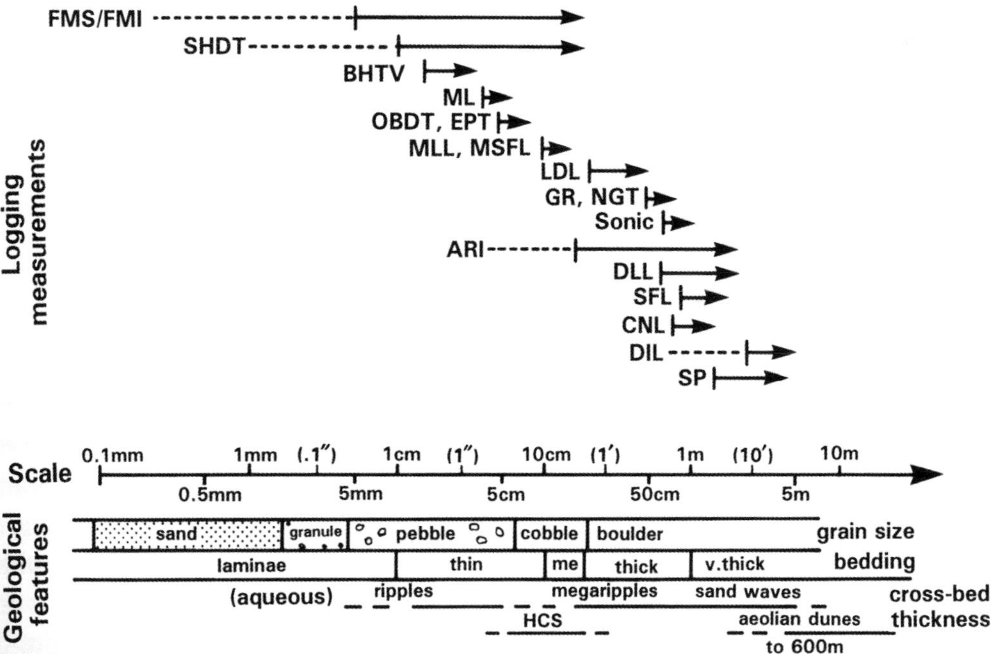

Figure 2.15 Qualitative indications of (Schlumberger) logging tool resolutions compared to the geological features of grain size, bedding thickness and typical cross-bed (sedimentary structure) thickness. Dashed line = higher sensitivity than resolution. SHDT = dipmeter, BHTV = acoustic images, OBDT = oil-based dipmeter, GR = gamma ray, ARI = array induction, SP = self potential. For other acronyms see Figures 2.11 and 2.18 (tool resolution from Serra *et al.* 1993).

even if in reality they are sharp. The way in which a boundary is seen on the logs, termed *bed boundary definition,* is influenced by several effects, the principal being the tool's vertical resolution (as defined above).

Vertical resolution, has been discussed previously in terms of depth of investigation and bed resolution. However, vertical resolution is also the principal influence behind tool response at a single bed boundary. A tool with a large vertical resolution will show a very gradual response, even at a sharp boundary, while a tool with a small vertical resolution will show a much more rapid response (**Figure 2.10, 3**). If, for example, a tool has a vertical resolution of 2 m (6.5 ft), then over approximately this thickness the signals from the bed above and from the bed below will be totally mixed (**Figure 2.10, 3**). This will produce a progressive response typically called a *shoulder effect,* a name which covers the special, often predictable tool effects at sharp interfaces between different beds (i.e. lithologies). In the present wireline example (**Figure 2.10, 3**), over the length of log which shows shoulder effects, the contributions of the two lithologies are being mixed in constantly varying proportions, the actual log values being more indicative of the tool position relative to the bed boundary, than to the values of the beds themselves. These shoulder effects are obviously much reduced in vertical thickness in tools with small vertical resolution: in these, bed boundary definition is good.

A different influence on bed boundary definition in the LWD environment is that of logging speed. LWD logs sample in time and not in depth **(Figure 2.27),** and bed boundary resolution becomes a function of the rate of drilling during which the logging is taking place. For example, the LWD gamma ray sensors need to collect radiations over a set time period in order to make a measurement, so that the limiting factor on resolution is now the distance travelled by the bit, that is, the rate of penetration (ROP), during this set time. Drilling rate may need to be restricted in order to make reliable LWD measurements. (In practice this is seldom the case with the gamma ray log).

Software 'beds'

Geological log interpretation often requires bed boundaries to be drawn. From the discussions above it is clear that placing a precise boundary involves interpretation: here are a number of possible positions. There is a general tendency to assume that the boundary is at the point of maximum change of value or maximum slope. This may not represent the reality but is a good guide and can be applied consistently (this is discussed further in Chapter 12, Section 12.5). However, in an effort to deal scientifically with the bed boundary problem, logs may be squared or blocked by computer. That is, an algorithm is used which eliminates all shoulder effects so that the log curves are resolved into zones of constant value, separated by horizontal 'boundaries'. They become more 'bed-like' in appearance (**Figure 2.16**).

In an older method, the squared log was simply a geometrical reflection of the raw log but with transition zones or ramps eliminated. The exercise was one of reassignment of the transition zone values to pre-designated blocks of real, non-transition values (Griffiths 1982). The algorithm applied assumed that the original log values were adequate. The method can be applied to several logs simultaneously so that they all become perfectly comparable (Serra and Abott 1980) and the problems of comparing logs with different bed resolution capabilities are eliminated.

A more modern approach is to either 'forward model' a log and apply some sort of earth model (with beds) to interpret its response, or to use a software 'focusing' on the raw data, presenting it as if it had a higher resolu-

Table 2.4 Software 'improvements' to vertical resolution and reliability. Density and PEF resolution as a function of acquisition and processing. (Schlumberger document).

Measurement	Output resolution	Stand-off	Confidence
ROMZ, RHOZ, PEMZ, PEFZ, DSOZ	(18″)	up to (1.2″)	good
ROM8, RHO8, PEM8, PEF8, DSO8	(8″)	less than (0.5″)	not so good
RHOI, PEFI, DSOI	(2″)	minimal	least

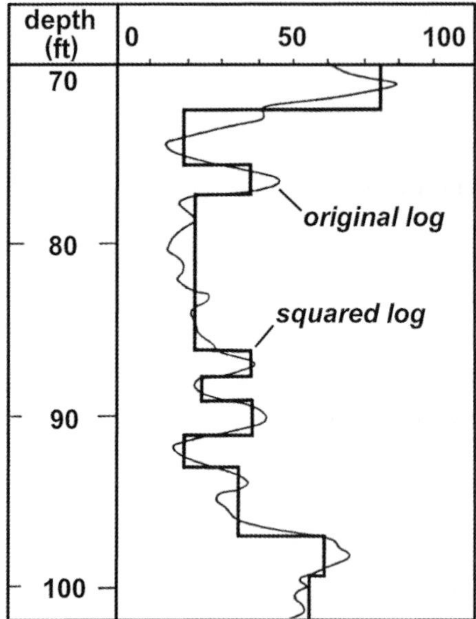

Figure 2.16 Blocking of log data. The response of this tool has been deconvolved to create a better (60 cm or 2 ft) resolution than shown by the original log.

tion than the raw logs (**Figure 2.16**,**Table 2.4**). Both methods use the tool's vertical response function. In other words, calculating the real formation values by taking out sensor distortion by signal deconvolution as discussed previously (*see* minimum bed resolution). The table (**Table 2.4**) shows that wireline density and photoelectric factor logs may be presented with apparent resolutions of 20 cm (8″) and 5 cm (2″) even though the actual tool resolution is 45 cm (18″). The 'robustness' (i.e. reliability) of the value, however, deteriorates as the apparent resolution increases. The approach may be applied using 2D algorithms or 3D in the case of dipping beds (*see* Chapter 7, signal processing). However, regardless of what method is used to improve vertical resolution, there are always implicit assumptions and approximations (e.g. sharp beds normal to the borehole axis). If these assumptions are wrong, the computed log will be a worse representation of reality than the original measurement.

2.6 Logging tool capabilities: spatial considerations

Volume and geometry of investigation

Because of the range of geophysical signals used in logging and the necessarily different tool designs, tools investigate a large range of formation volumes and volume shapes. For example, a deep induction signal investigates a volume in the order of 40 m³ (2,500,000 inch³), the size of a small van. A density signal, however, will only investigate 0.0040 m³ (250 inch³), the size of a desktop. A whole core volume is approximately 7000 cm³ per meter of depth (400 inch³ per 3 feet), while a core plug has a volume of 25 cm³ (1.5 inch³) (**Figure 2.17**, **Table 2.5**).

Volume shape is also variable (**Figure 2.18**). The resistivity tools can be designed to focus an electrical current in the formation so that, for example, the laterologs are considered to have a sheet-like field of investigation. Sonic waves generally stay very close to the borehole wall and so investigate a shallow, cylindrical volume (**Figure 2.18**). In the nuclear tools which depend on gamma ray penetration, the size of the volume investigated depends on source and sensor position, the investigation shape itself is spherical.

Finally, the formation can have an effect on the volume investigated. In other words, formation response is dynamic rather than passive. The volume of investigation of gamma rays is greater in low density formations. In an electrical test, when a resistive bed and a conductive bed are in contact, the conductive bed tends to act

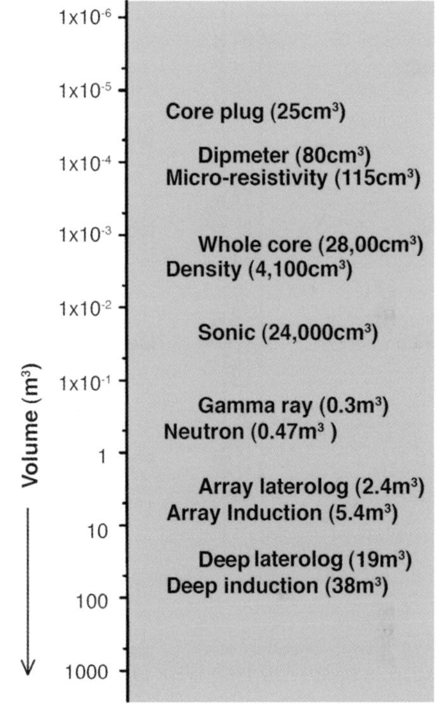

Figure 2.17 A comparison of the approximate volumes investigated by some of the common logging tools.

Table 2.5 Formation volumes investigated by some of the logging tools, cores, core plugs and side-wall cores (*see* Figure 2.18).

Measurement	Volume		Equivalent
Deep Induction	38 m³	(1342 cu.ft.)	
Deep Laterolog	19 m³	(670.9 cu.ft.)	small van, 10 m³
Array Induction	5.4 m³	(190.7 cu.ft.)	
Array Laterolog	2.4 m³	(84.75 cu.ft.)	small fridge, 1 m³
Neutron	0.476 m³	(16.8 cu.ft.)	
Gamma Ray	0.344 m³	(12.15 cu.ft.)	
Long Spaced Sonic	0.197 m³	(6.96 cu.ft.)	2 filing cabinet draws, 0.1 m³
Sonic	0.0246 m³	(0.87 cu.ft.)	
Dipole sonic			
Density	0.0041 m³	(250 cu.in.)	desktop computer
Whole Core	0.0028 m³	(170 cu.in.)	drink carton, 0.001 m³ (= 1 litre =1000 cc)
Microresistivity	1.15×10^{-4} m³	(7 cu.in.)	
Dipmeter	0.82×10^{-4} m³	(5 cu.in.)	
Core Plug, Side-Wall-Core	2.5×10^{-5} m³ = 25 cc (1.6 cu.in)		1×10^{-6} m³ = 1 cc.

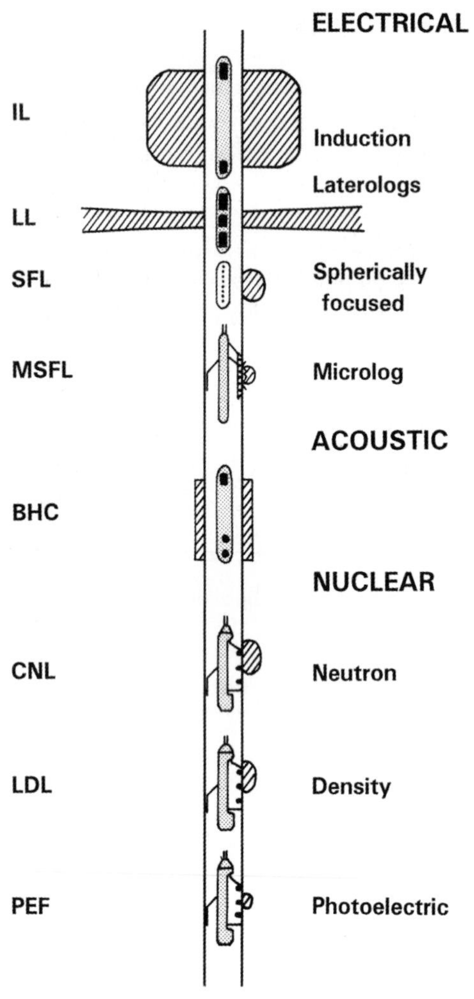

Figure 2.18 Investigation geometry of various logging tools (modified from Desbrandes1968; Serra 1979).

as a sink and the electrical current flows preferentially into it. Volume of investigation will be addressed more fully in the chapters describing the individual tools.

Deviated wells (dipping beds)

The previous discussion of logging tool capabilities and bed resolution implicitly considered only vertical wells. Responses in highly deviated and horizontal wells are different, each tool responding in its own way to the geometrical effects.

As the angle between a bed and the borehole increases, so the apparent thickness of that bed along the borehole increases. A 1 m (3 ft) thick bed in a well deviated at 20° has an apparent thickness of 1.06 m along the wellbore, at 40° deviation it is 1.3 m (4.3 ft), at 60°, 2 m (6.6 ft) and at 80°, 5.75 m (18.9 ft). These effects are seen especially on logs which investigate all sides of the borehole, such as a standard induction log. The figure (**Figure 2.19**) shows that, on the induction log, a 1.5 m (5 ft) bed broadens as the dip increases, while peak values diminish (Anderson *et al.* 1990; Clavier 1991). At high angles, distortion is extreme.

The differences between log responses in a vertical and a horizontal well are excellently illustrated by a set of modelled density tool logs (**Figure 2.20**). The tool used for the modelling has a near and a far receiver sensing only a strip along the borehole wall, as in a typical density tool (Chapter 10). The formation used consists of alternations of 2.0 g/cm³ (light colour) and 2.6 g/cm³ density (dark colour) rocks in various bed thicknesses (**Figure 2.20**). The first set of logs are from a vertical well, the second from a horizontal well (Radtke *et al.* 2006).

In the vertical well, the tool's vertical resolution, about 10″ (25 cm), is what affects responses; it is an *axial* response. True density is read in the 16″ (40 cm) thick bed but not in thinner beds. In beds thinner than 8″ (20 cm), density variations have no link to the reality, the log in the 4″ (10 cm) beds being more likely, in fact, to show a density increase when it should be a decrease (**Figure 2.20, a**). In the horizontal well, the log actually provides better detail, although there is a displacement of beds relative to their real depth (**Figure 2.20, b**). This is because the detail in the horizontal well depends on the *radial* investigation, which is smaller than the *axial*, source to receiver investigation. In a vertical well, the log slices the bed, while in a horizontal well, it effectively peels it away.

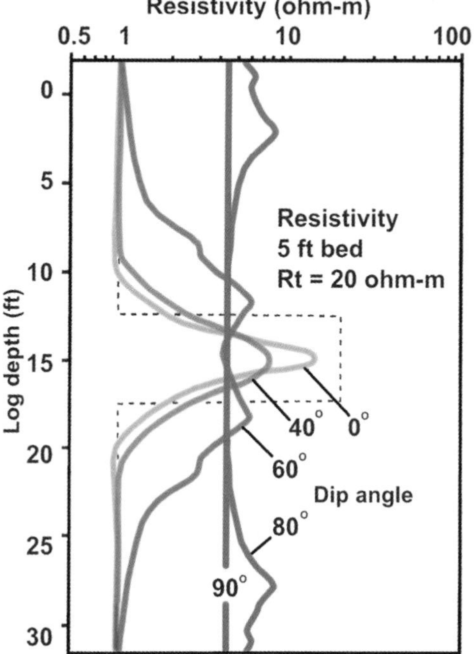

Figure 2.19 The effect of bed dip (or hole deviation) on the Induction Resistivity response. The greater the dip, the broader the signal. The example uses a bed with a true thickness of 1.5 m (5 ft) and resistivity Rt of 20 ohm.m. (modified from Clavier SPWLA 1991).

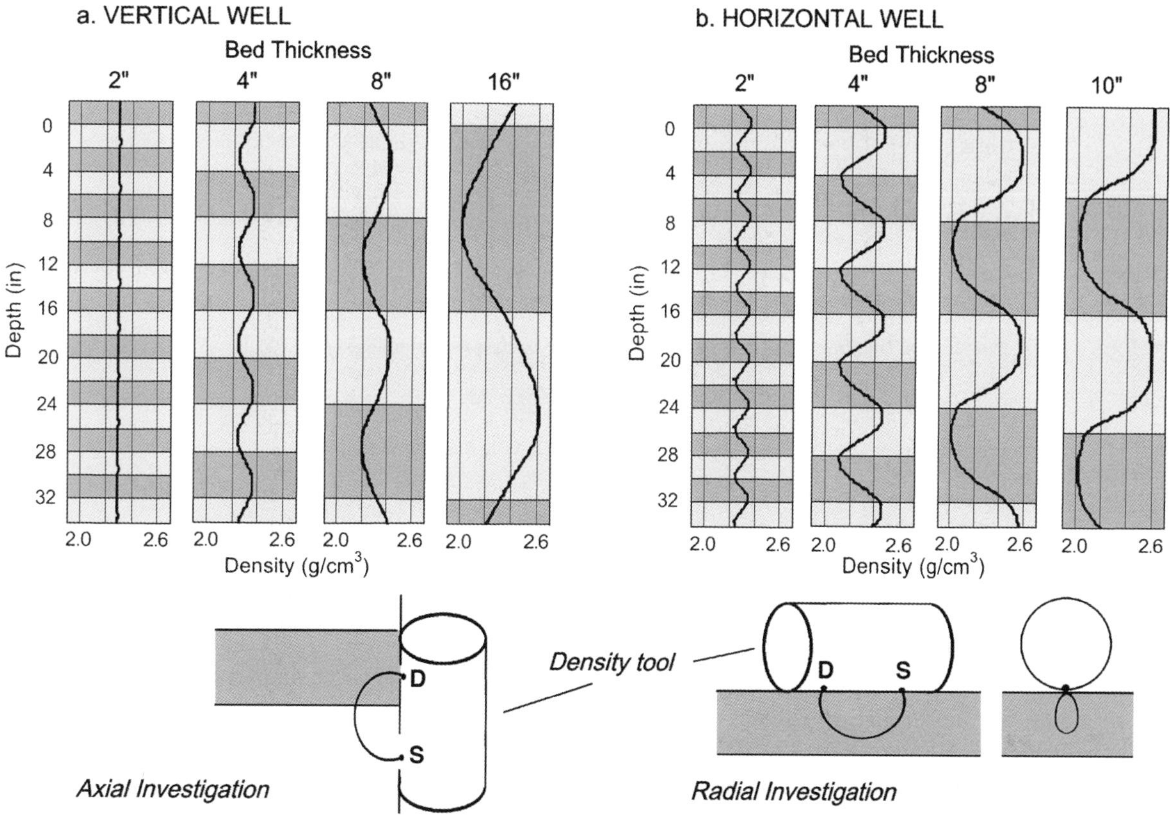

Figure 2.20 Modelled density tool responses in a vertical and a horizontal well compared. The responses are modelled for beds from 2" to 16" (5–40.6 cm) in thickness. Dark colour dense, light colour less dense. A vertical well (a) uses a tool's axial investigation while a horizontal well (b) uses the radial investigation as explained in the text. S = source, D = detector (modified after Radke *et al.* SPWLA 2006).

Azimuthal investigation

The advent of horizontal wells provided the stimulus for the development of LWD azimuthal tools, that is, the tool responses come from defined and oriented sectors around the well. The need for oriented log responses in horizontal wells has been discussed previously. Only some geophysical signals are suitable for this, the common ones being resistivity, gamma ray, density and photoelectric effect. An image can be made from these measurements.

The LWD density tool, for example, can be programmed to take measurements from only a limited sector of the borehole while rotating and storing these measurements in a discrete 'bin' (**Figure 2.21**). As the tool rotates, measurements are allocated to successive bins (sectors) and then, after several rotations, the bins are emptied before a new measurement sequence starts again. With a rotation rate of 60 RPM (rotations per minute, a typical value), during a 10 second period (10 rotations), enough counts are collected in the individual sectors to make a valid log for each one. The example shows 8 density logs from 45° sectors (**Figure 2.21**) but as many as 16, 22.5° sectors can be used, the number varying by log and by company. Azimuthal LWD logs are usually presented as an image and in real time, as is the

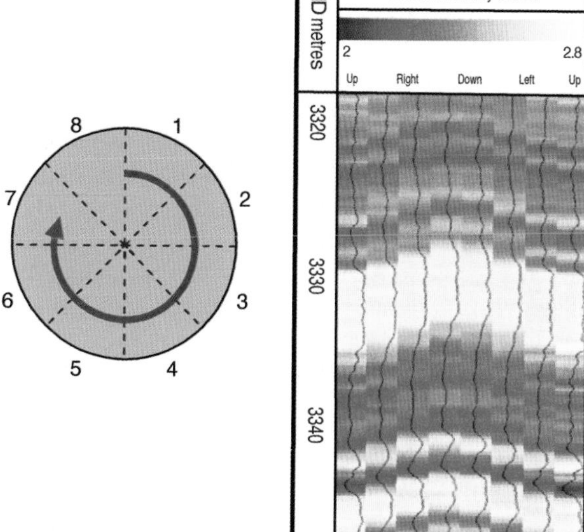

Figure 2.21 LWD azimuthal density image. Eight separate density logs in 8 sectors around the borehole are acquired. In this example, the 8 logs are shown as curves as well as colour bands, lighter colours representing higher density. In the final image the bands will be smoothed and merged (Meyer *et al.* SPWLA 2005).

Table 2.6 Some depth terms and their corresponding reference levels (*see* Figure 2.22).

Depth Term Acronym	Full Name	Reference Datum, notes
	Driller's Depth	DF, RT or KB. Measured during drilling
	Logger's Depth	DF, RT or KB. Measured during wireline logging
MD	Measured Depth	Drill Floor (DF), Rotary Table (RT)(about 20cm above DF), Kelly Bushing (KB) (about 50 cm above RT)
MDRT	Measure Depth Rotary Table	Rotary Table (RT)
DFE	Drill Floor Elevation	
TVD	True Vertical Depth	Sea Level (MSL), Lowest Astronomical Tide (LAT)
TVDSS	True Vertical Depth	Sea Level (SL)
TVDLAT	True Vertical Depth	Lowest Astronomical Tide (LAT)
TD	Total Depth	Rotary Table (RT), Kelly Bushing (KB)
SL	Sea Level	Sea Level (mean)
LAT	Lowest Astronomical Tide	Sea Level (lowest tide)
SB	Sea Bottom	Sea Floor (may be called ground level)
GL	Ground Level	Ground Elevation
	Mudline	Sea Floor (ocean bottom sediment surface)

case with the example. The log values are colour coded and contiguous values interpolated to produce the final, smoothed image which can be used for geosteering (Meyer *et al.* 2005).

2.7 Depth measurement in boreholes

All log measurements are eventually referenced to depth: it is the fundamental measurement. During the drilling of a well, two sets of independent depth measurement exist: *driller's depth* and *logger's depth*. Drill-string conveyed LWD logs (and core) use driller's depth and cable deployed wireline logs provide the logger's depth. Both these depth sets are *measured depths*, being referenced to the rig floor (indicated as DF = drill floor, RT = rotary table or KB = Kelly bushing) and recording depths or distance along the borehole trajectory (**Table 2.6**, **Figure 2.22**). Subsequent to drilling, depths may be modified and quoted as *true vertical depth* (TVD) and referenced to a common datum, typically mean sea level (MSL) offshore (best called TVDSS, TVD sub-sea) and ground level (GL) onshore. A common, absolute datum like MSL allows wells to be structurally correlated, fluid contacts compared between wells and the logs correlated to seismic sections (also normally referenced to MSL offshore). To make use of the common datum, elevation (GL) is noted onshore, sea depth and height of drilling datum (DF., RT. or KB.) above sea level offshore (**Figure 2.22**). Mudline is also used as a reference, generally in the deep ocean, that is depth below the sediment surface (in other words the water/sediment interface).

LWD (driller's) depth

Driller's depth is simply a record or tally of the length of drill pipe, drill collars, LWD tools and drill bit, present in the borehole. It is recorded and compiled by the driller measuring, with a tape measure, the single lengths (usually 9.6 m or 30 feet) or stands (usually 3 singles, 29 m or 90 feet) of drill pipe and other equipment as it is laid out on the deck, and then adding all the measurements up. This is the depth on the LWD logs and on core. Corrections are seldom applied and human error is not unusual. Lengths of drill-pipe can be 'forgotten' or new bottom hole assemblies (BHA) are not accounted for. Depth differences are reported between LWD and wireline logs of 24 m (80 ft) in a 7000 m (23,000 ft) vertical well (www.feswa.org) and up to 20 m (65 ft) in a 5000 m (16,400 ft) deviated well (**Figure 2.23**) (Pedersen and Constable 2006).

There is an effort today to correct driller's depth since it is so important in wells with LWD logs, and may, in fact, provide the only depth-set if wireline logs are not run, a situation becoming more and more common. The most important corrections to be applied to a drill string are for elastic pipe stretch and thermal expansion (Pedersen and Constable 2006 *op.cit*). These physical effects will act through the drilling parameters of torque and weight-on-bit (WOB). Pipe stretch, for example, in a 7000 m (23,000 ft) drill-string, varies between 7.98 m (26.2 ft) during drilling and 8.95 m (29.4 ft) when off bottom (Dashevskiy *et al.* 2006). A 7–8 m (23–26 ft) absolute depth correction can be expected but also a different correction depending on whether the drill-string is logging while drilling (usual) or logging while pulling out (common).

Wireline (logger's) depth

Logger's depth is measured with the cable when the wireline logs are run. It therefore post-dates the driller's depth and, for wells without wireline logs, it will not exist. There are two systems of wireline depth measurement, one using magnetic markers on the cable, the other using a direct measurement from

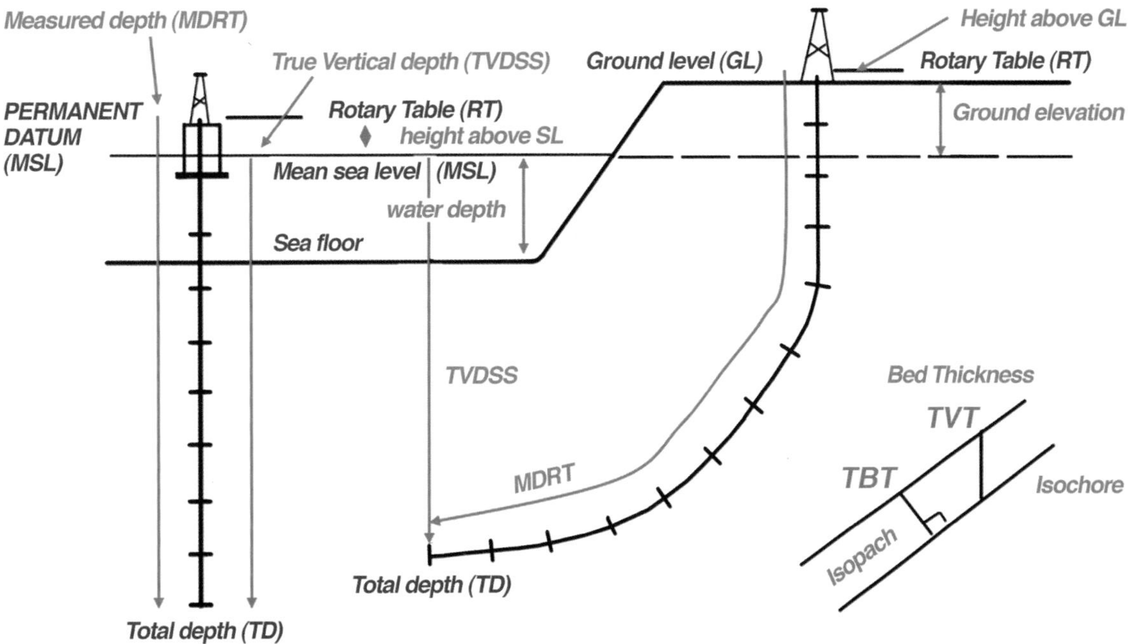

Figure 2.22 The common depth measurement conventions and the datum references. RT = rotary table, GL = ground, SL = sea-level, MSL = mean sea level, MD = measured depth, TVD = true vertical depth, TVDSS = true vertical depth sub-sea, MDRT = measured depth (below) rotary table, TD = total depth, SS = sub-sea, TBT = true bed thickness, TVT = true vertical thickness. MSL = mean sea level, GL = ground level.

an odometer. The direct measurement generally supplies the primary depth. The two measurement methods are briefly described.

Magnetic markers are placed on the cable by the logging company every 100 feet or 25 m under a standard tension of 1000 lbs. During logging, the marks are detected at surface as the cable is spooled (in or out) but, because of tension, the real depth between the marks will change (usually increase) and must be corrected. The system is reasonably accurate (error 1 part in 5000; Søllie and Rodgers 1994). Today, magnetic marks generally act only as a backup.

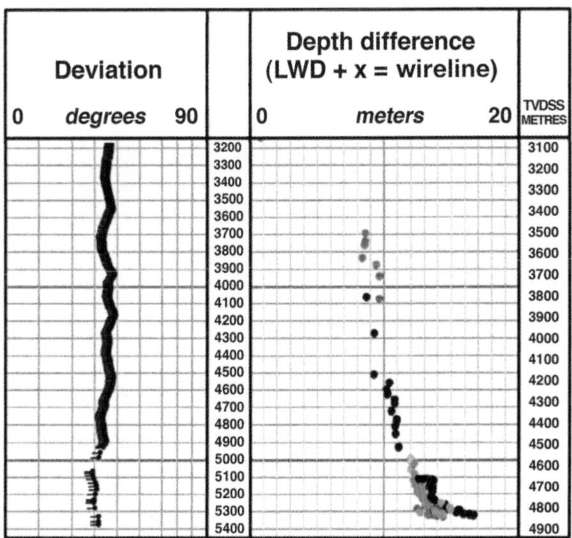

Figure 2.23 The depth difference between LWD and wireline logs in the Kristin field, offshore Norway. Wireline depths are deeper than the LWD depths and the difference increases with the depth and deviation of the well. The difference reaches up to 17 m (56 ft) at 5000 m (16,400 ft), that is, LWD depths are 17 m less than the wireline depths (from Pedersen and Constable SPWLA 2006).

The primary, direct measurement is made by wheels over which the cable is spooled into and out of the hole (the odometer). The equipment consists of two small wheels, tangential to the cable, which turn in opposite directions, each wheel supplying separate depth measurements which are combined for the final result. The measurement is considered very accurate. For Schlumberger, the primary depth measurement is from their Integrated Dual Wheel spooler (IDW) and, according to their website, is accurate to 30 cm (12″) over 1500 m (5000 ft) on parallel runs and to 75 cm (29.5″) over 1500 m (5000 ft) between different runs

This primary measurement, though, has been corrected. Pulling-out depths are compared to the running-in depths and then corrected for stretch (due to the friction induced tension difference between going in and coming out), temperature changes, mud pressure variations and so on (**Table 2.7**). Effects may work in opposing directions and, for example, tension extends the cable while temperature and mud pressure cause it to contract (Søllie and Rodgers 1994). The software derived corrections are applied automatically and usually produce reliable and repeatable results. Influences

Table 2.7a *Factors affecting wireline depth measurements. (from Theys 1991; Sollie and Rodgers 1994).

Factor	Potential error (m)	Remarks
Elastic stretch	3.0 m (10′)	includes cable twisting
Inelastic stretch	3.0 m (10′)	first runs only
Temperature	−1.5 m (−5′)	temperature change from reference
Mud radial pressure	−0.75 (−2.5′)	
Measuring wheels (a)	1-3 m (3−10′)	more recent wheels
(b)	1.5−3 m (5−10′)	old wheels
Surface set-up changes	1.0 m (3′)	cable sag, sheave movement
Tidal effects	±1.5 m (±5′)	offshore North Sea
Zeroing	−0.25 m (−0.8′)	not if zero in mud
Tool sticking	up to 12 m (40′)	
Yoyo	0.6 m (2′)	

*figures for heptacable at 3000 m (9840 ft) (from Theys 1991; Søllie and Rodgers 1994).

Table 2.7b Factors affecting drillpipe (i.e LWD) depth measurements. (from Theys 1991; Pederson and Constable, 2006).

Factor	Potential error (m)	Remarks
Incorrectly recorded talley	1−10 m (3−33′)	primary cause of depth differences
Drillpipe stretch	5−10 m (16-33′)	primary cause of depth differences
Thermal expansion	3−4 m (10−13′)	primary cause of depth differences
Pressure (mud density)	1−2 m (3−6′)	
Ballooning	2 m (6′)	
Others	1 m (3′)	

on the accuracy of the direct measurement method are shown in the table (**Table 2.7**).

A depth solution

With two independent depth sets, which is the more accurate, LWD or wireline? There is a conception in the industry that driller's depth is less accurate than the logger's depth and, for this reason, in the past, the supposed less accurate LWD depths have been 'corrected' to wireline depths. In practice, it is almost impossible to know what the 'real depth' is and hence which is the most accurate set.

In older wells (even without LWD), depth was tied to a particular wireline data set and the density often used as the 'master' log. In cases of a depth mismatch, other logs would be shifted to the 'master'. Modern software allows for a constant shift, a variable shift (stretching or squeezing) or an on-screen manual, point-by-point shift (**Figure 2.24**). Such 'corrections' are straightforward when only one depth data-set, for example just wireline, is being used.

To be scientific about depth (which almost nobody is), the theoretical error range of the two measurement methods should be known (Dashevskiy *et al.* 2006). This then allows the depth differences to be scientifically resolved (**Figure 2.25**). As the figure shows, if the error bars of the two methods overlap, then the depth used should be in the zone of overlap. There is therefore a tendency to treat neither dataset, wireline nor LWD, as the more accurate but to combine the two in as scientific a manner as possible (Dashevskiy *et al.* 2006 *op.cit.*; Pedersen and Constable 2006).

Even when the depth scale has been resolved, the log curves may still not match. For instance, differences in logging speed and tool stick cause mismatches on multi-sensor tools and depth matching at a very detailed, centimetre scale, such as between digital core photos and an image log, show differences. A master curve or set still needs to be chosen.

Absolute depth

Depths in a single well are *relative depths*; but they will eventually be tied to an external, common datum and will then become *absolute depths*. A common absolute datum is mean sea level (MSL).

Absolute depths are important when correlating wells or comparing well depths to absolute depth sensitive measurements such as fluid pressures or hydrocarbon contacts. Differences of up to 6 m (20 ft) are seen when fluid contacts

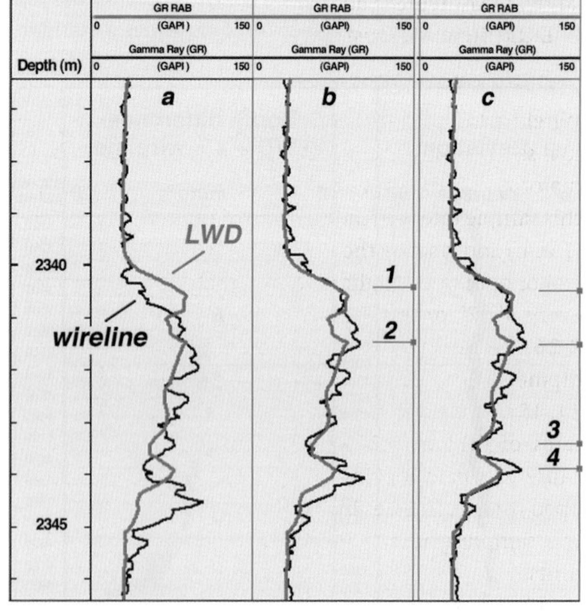

Figure 2.24 Manual, on-screen depth shift to rectify depth differences (track *a*) between two gamma ray logs. The shift is variable and done point by point. When depth points 1 and 2 (track *b*) are on-depth, points 3 and 4 are not. On track *c* all 4 tie points are used. In this example, the LWD gamma log is presumed to be at the correct depth (TerraStation routine).

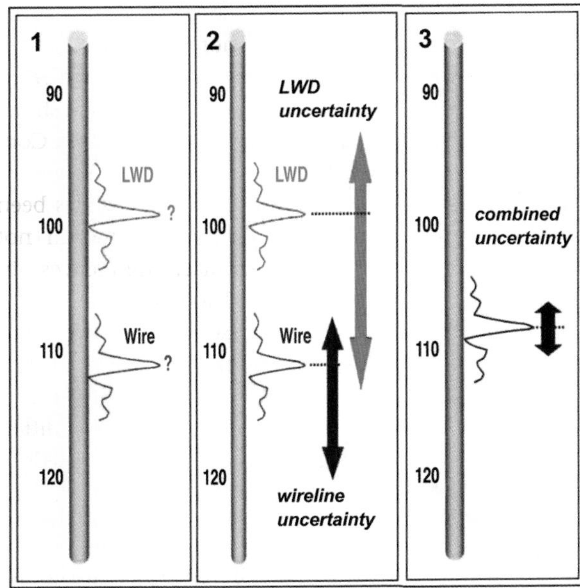

Figure 2.25 Graphical representation of a way of using both LWD and wireline depths to achieve a more scientific combination with a known uncertainty (*see* text) (modified from Lofts *et al.* SPWLA 2005).

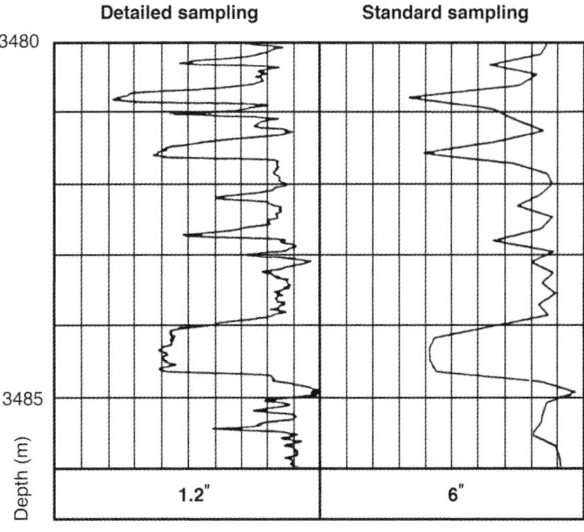

Figure 2.26 The difference in curve behaviour between the standard wireline 6" (15 cm) sampling and a more detailed 1.2" (3 cm) sampling.

are used as an absolute, horizontal marker (Søllie and Rodgers 1994). Accurate, absolute depths are needed when geosteering, referencing a horizontal well's measured depths to a datum or comparing well data to seismic. As deviation increases and the X –Y stepout gets larger, measurement accuracy decreases.

Little literature exists on the subject.

Sample depth frequency

Wireline logs, being digital, are constructed from punctual samples (measurements) at a set depth rate. For the majority of the standard wireline logs, this sample rate is a reading every 6 inches (15 cm) and is set by the surface depth control or odometer. Higher sampling rates of every 3", 2" or less are available (**Figure 2.26**). Some specialised logs such as the dipmeter and electrical images (Chapters 14, 15) are even sampled at the very high rates of 0.1" or 0.2" (2.5 – 5.0 mm). Because the main logging companies developed their businesses in the United States, the sampling rate is mostly in imperial units. This is of little consequence for the standard logs but important for the high resolution logs which must be processed in their native units, there being no precise conversion to metric units. The sampling rates discussed here do not indicate the functioning rate of a tool but that a log is constructed from that particular set of depth samples (**Figure 2.26**).

For the LWD logs, the initial, raw sampling rate is time based, although eventually converted to a depth based set for use. This means that in depth terms, sampling rate depends on the drilling rate. For example, when LWD measure points are acquired during fast drilling and are converted to depth, they are wider apart (in depth) than points from slow drilling. That is, there are fewer points per metre during fast drilling than during slow drilling (**Figure 2.27**). Sampling of LWD tools can be between 10–30 seconds, and a rule seems to be that around 1 ft (30 cm) can be drilled during one sampling period. So, for a general drilling rate (ROP) of 100 ft/hr (30 m/hr), 1 ft is drilled in 36 sec (30 cm in 36 sec), allowable considering the sampling rate.

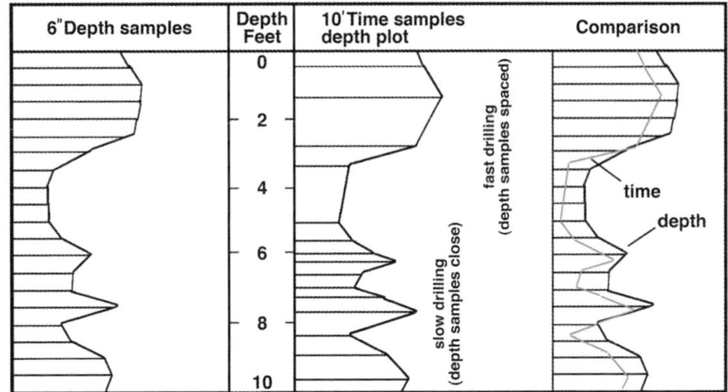

Figure 2.27 The difference between depth based samples and time based samples (allocated to a depth scale). Depth based (wireline) samples are regularly spaced usually at 6" (15 cm). LWD tools give a regular time sample (every 10 seconds in this example) which are irregular in depth terms. During fast drilling, samples will be widely spaced in depth: during slow drilling they will be closely spaced. LWD readings are converted to regular depth samples for archiving and use.

Software allocates and redistributes the time based measure points. The edited records that are used and put on the database, have an equal depth spacing of 6″ (15 cm) similar to the wireline logs. Other sample rates will be used for imaging and specialist tools. (LWD sampling rate is actually more complex than this as there are memory records which hold the full downhole data set and a subset, which is used in real time and sent up-hole during drilling, but the LWD record in the database will be the full set.)

2.8 Logging tool conveyancing methods

As modern drilling becomes more complex and the logging environment more extreme, conveying geophysical logging tools to the subsurface has become much more difficult. The simple traditional spooled wireline system is often inadequate and new methods have to be used. LWD conveyancing methods are becoming more common. Various methods are briefly described.

Wireline

Wireline, drill pipe, coiled tubing and the downhole tractor, are all equipment types used to take wireline logging tools into the subsurface. A simple, gravity driven wireline can be used in vertical wells and deviated wells up to about 65° (Alden *et al.* 2004). In horizontal and very steeply deviated wells, wireline tool-strings are usually conveyed by pipe, which requires special techniques. The logging tools are combined and attached to the end of the drillpipe with a male wet connector on top. The tool-string is then run on the drill pipe into the hole until it reaches the bottom of the casing (the casing shoe). The wireline cable, with a female connector on the end, is then pumped down the inside of the pipe to connect with the tool string and male connector waiting at the bottom of the casing. A cross-over sub is added to the top of the pipe, which allows the cable to pass from the inside of the pipe to the outside. Pipe is now added to the top of the drill-string and the tools logged downwards. The cable is on the outside of these added pipes. This system is slow but successful.

Coiled tubing that is wound on a large surface drum is another type of equipment that can convey tools, although it is mostly used for cased holes. Downhole 'tractors' are also being used. The tractor is usually conveyed on a wireline to a critical depth and then activated to pull or push the logging tool-string and wireline cable to places gravity will not take them. Tractors work by pulling their load as they are locked onto the casing or borehole wall, then moving forward freely to a new position before pulling again. They are also generally used in cased holes but can function in open-hole in consolidated formations.

An additional difficulty now faced in wireline conveyance, is the huge depth of some modern wells. Cables today are required to extend vertically up to 12,200 m (40,000 ft). This requires the ability to pull at surface up to 80 kN (18,000 lbs) while conventional cables generally only pull 69 kN (15,500 lbs). Such extremes need stronger cables and additional capstans on the rig floor (Alden *et al.* 2004 *op. cit.*). For these depths, tools have to be rated at higher temperatures and pressures, 260°C (500°F) and 240 MPa (35,000 psi) respectively. Even higher numbers may be required in the future.

LWD

Conveying LWD geophysical sensors in the drill-string, just behind the bit, is now common, especially in deviated and horizontal wells, as has been explained (Section 1.4). LWD sensors are housed in drill-collars, the heavy steel sections with more or less the diameter of the borehole, and placed close behind the bit. These are specially manufactured collars with ruggedised emitters, sensors and electronics all housed within the steel, and able to withstand the physically severe drilling environment. They are added to the bottom section of the drill string as part of the Bottom Hole Assembly (BHA). At the head of the BHA is the directional drilling section and the physical drilling sensors which provide the MWD measurements as explained (Section 1.4).

The drill bit and the LWD sensors are therefore conveyed by the same means: the drill string. LWD measurements require specialised drill collars and mud pulse equipment for conveying real time data, but otherwise are simply part of the drilling process. Indeed, LWD logging has now become very much a part of drilling, influencing drilling decisions, and modifying, or even locating new targets, as the bit advances. This is geosteering, logs directing the bit real time, a clear advantage of LWD conveyed logging.

2.9 Conclusion

It was suggested in this chapter that, for a proper interpretation, a logging tool is required to make a true, repeatable, geophysical measurement of an undisturbed, representative sample of the formation. This was shown, in fact, to be impossible because of drill-created disturbances (invasion, damage) and because of the logging method itself (moving tool). However, it was suggested that, with a knowledge of tool capabilities and log characteristics, it is possible to reconstruct reliable geophysical measurements which provide a high quality data set for qualitative and especially quantitative interpretation, adequately representative of the real formation. The remainder of the book attempts to justify this suggestion.

3 SUBSURFACE PRESSURE MEASUREMENT

3.1 Introduction

A knowledge of subsurface pressure is a prerequisite to understanding the behaviour of fluids during drilling and their subsequent behaviour in reservoirs during production. The first wireline pressure measuring tools, introduced in the 1950s, were principally for sampling downhole. These tools could only make one or two pressure measurements per trip in the hole and normally required an experienced operator to run them. Consequently they were never considered a routine measurement. This changed in the mid-1970s when Schlumberger introduced the Repeat Formation Tester (RFT). In principle this tool allowed an unlimited number of pressure measurements to be made, although in practice it was difficult to make more than fifty before some or other part failed (and in hostile environments packers failed after as few as ten measurements). The tool could also take two fluid samples (Ireland *et al.* 1992). Nevertheless, the ability to make more than one or two pressure measurements revolutionised reservoir engineering and soon all the logging contractors introduced their own versions of the RFT. The emphasis shifted from sampling to measuring formation pressure. ('RFT' is still often used as a generic acronym for formation testers but Wireline Formation Tester, WFT, is a better one).

The current generation of tools which appeared in the early 1990s, is essentially a kit of parts that can be assembled to carry out a huge range of measurements. A tool can effectively be custom built for a particular well. Modern tools can be configured to:

1. Measure formation pressures at multiple depths (arguably the original purpose and still the most common application).
2. Estimate permeability at a scale of about 10 cm (or strictly speaking mobility).
3. Estimate vertical transmissibility over an interval of the order of a metre.
4. Determine the fluid type at a particular location.
5. Determine the flowing phase (hydrocarbon or water).
6. Acquire samples of formation fluids (at reservoir pressure).
7. Inject fluid into the formation.
8. Measure fracture pressures for the formation at a particular depth.

New applications are developed every year and it is probably safe to say the only limitation on what can be achieved is the weight of the modules on the cable and the imagination of the operator. All these possibilities mean that expensive and often dangerous drill stem tests (DSTs) are performed less and less.

Pressure measurement is now possible while drilling, and LWD pressure measurement tools are being used more frequently, especially in deviated wells and the deep offshore. At the time of writing, LWD tools can be configured for downhole fluid identification and actual LWD fluid sampling is just beginning to be introduced.

Units

Because this book uses SI units (Système Internationale), pressure should be given in Pascals (1 Newton per square metre). However, in the oilfield, pressure is more often given in bars or psi. 1 bar is 100,000 Pa (Pascals) and is the notional atmospheric pressure at sea level (where pressure is due only to the weight of air column above). Using bars as units avoids having to take technical atmospheric pressure into account since 1 bar is very close to the technical atmospheric pressure of 1.01325 bar, the supposed pressure at sea level in Paris. The bar is an accepted alternative SI unit. Typical pressures encountered in a borehole are of the order of millions of Pa so that the unit normally quoted is the MPa (MegaPascals, = 10 bar, **Table 3.1**).

Pressures can be quoted as 'gauge' or 'absolute' depending on whether the reference is a vacuum with zero pressure or atmospheric pressure at sea level. The difference is 0.101 MPa (14.7 psi) which, for a typical reservoir pressure of 30 MPa (4351.14 psi), seems too small to worry about. But, in fact, pressure can be measured to this degree of accuracy and precision, and it can be important to know whether a difference in reservoir pressure between wells of 0.1 MPa is real or not. It is therefore necessary to know which of the two pressures is being used.

As noted, pounds per square inch (psi) is a very commonly used oilfield unit and although it has no SI component to it, it is unlikely to disappear any time soon. Many petroleum engineers are more comfortable working in psi than Pa and so logs are often still acquired in these units. Even if the log is acquired in MPa, it is highly likely that at some point it will be converted to psi. The pressure of the atmosphere at sea level is 14.7 psi and typical pressures encountered in the borehole are thousands of psi. When working in psi, gauge and absolute pressures are often distinguished by adding the

Table 3.1,a SI pressure units and some equivalents

SI	Other units
1 Pa	0.00001 bar (10^{-5})
100,000 Pa	1 bar
1 MPa (10^6 Pa)	10 bar
1 MPa	145.038 psi (pound per square inch)
1 MPa	10.1972 kg/cm^2
1 MPa	10.1972 atm (technical)
1 MPa	9.86923 atm (physical)
1.0 Bar	14.504 psi
1.0 Bar	1.01972 kg/cm^2

Table 3.1,b psi pressure unit equivalents.

1.0 psi	6894.76 Pa
1.0 psi	0.068948 bar
1.0 psi	0.070307 kg/cm^2
1.0 psi	0.070307 atm (technical)
1.0 psi	0.068046 atm (physical)
145.038 psi	1 MPa

Table 3.1,c Atmosphere equivalent pressure units.

1 .0 atm (technical)	0.0980665 MPa
1 .0 atm (")	0.980665 bar
1 .0 atm (")	1 kg/cm^2
1 .0 atm (")	14.2233 psi
1 .0 atm (")	0.967841 atm (physical)
1 .0 atm (physical)	0.101325 MPa
1 .0 atm (")	1.01325 bar
1 .0 atm (")	1.03323 kg/cm^2
1 .0 atm (")	14.6959 psi
1 .0 atm (")	1.03323 atm (technical)

SI = *Système Internationale*
MPa = mega Pascal
psi = pounds per square inch
atm = atmosphere (technical)
atm = atmosphere (physical)
Pa = Pascale

letter 'g' or 'a' respectively (e.g. 3412.2 psia tells us the pressure is an absolute value).

Another pressure unit occasionally encountered is kg/cm^2 (or possibly g/cm^2). Strictly speaking, these are not pressures as their dimensions are actually mass per unit area, but it is understood that the equivalent force is the weight of a 1 kg mass at the Earth's surface. The correspondences are given **(Table 3.1,a)** with the conversion values for psi units (**Table 3.1,b**) and atmospheres **(Table 3.1,c).**

3.2. Subsurface fluid pressures

Hydrostatic pressure

Fluids transmit pressure perfectly, so that the pressure exerted by a column of fluid is dependent simply on the height of the fluid column and the density of the fluid. The term 'fluid column' can be replaced by water depth in an ocean to understand the column concept. The pressure in kg/cm^2 in a column of water (or depth in an ocean) can be calculated thus:

$$\text{height of water column} \times \text{density} = \text{pressure (kg/cm}^2) \quad (1)$$

This relationship needs to be given standard units. Bar, as indicated above, is the accepted oilfield SI alternative unit. Thus, for a column of pure water of 2500 m (density of pure water = 1.00 g/cm^3), the relationship in bar will be:

$$\frac{2500\,\text{m} \times 1.0\,\text{g/cm}^3 \times 0.980665}{10} = 245.17\,\text{bar (3555.89 psi)} \quad (2)$$

(1 kg/cm^2 = 0.980665 bar, **Table 3.1,c**)

The pressure in a column of fluid is called *'hydrostatic pressure'*, which is therefore the pressure calculated in the example above (2) and shown previously as a graph (**Figure 2.1**). Hydrostatic pressure is otherwise called *'normal pressure'* and depends only on fluid density and fluid column height (best thought of as depth for the subsurface). Normal pressure can continue in the subsurface so long as there is permeability and a connection between the pore spaces of the formation and the surface. With no pressure barriers, as a formation is buried, compacted and looses pore space, the fluids can escape. Shales are dewatered, sands compressed and carbonates suffer diagenesis, but fluid pressure remains normal.

Since normal formation pressure depends only on fluid column and density, it means that a formation fluid at a subsurface depth of 1000 m will be at the same pressure as the sea floor below 1000 m of sea water, provided that the formation has a pore water density the same as sea water (1.025 g/cm^3 at 35,000 ppm). As water becomes more saline its density increases (**Figure 3.1**) so that, if it has a salinity of 140,000 ppm (parts per million) of solids (mainly NaCl), it will have a density of 1.09 g/cm^3 (at 15.5°C) and a column of water with this salinity at 2500 m will exert a pressure of:

$$\frac{2500 \times 1.09 \times 0.980665}{10} = 267.23\,\text{bar (3875.84 psi)} \quad (3)$$

Pressure gradients

It is useful to express subsurface pressures in terms of a *'pressure gradient'*, in other words, the rate of pressure increase with depth. The slope of a pressure gradient is related to the density of the fluid concerned and the acceleration due to gravity '*g*'. Fortunately *g* varies very little over the surface of the earth and over the depth range that boreholes cover. Because of this we can safely assume that pure water (density 1.00 g/cm^3) always has a gradient of 0.0980665 bar/m (0.4336 psi/ft). That is, a column of pure water will show a pressure increase of 0.0980665 bar per metre of column, which is equivalent to 0.4336 psi/ft or 1.421 psi/m (**Table 3.1**). The term 'column of water' is used when discuss-

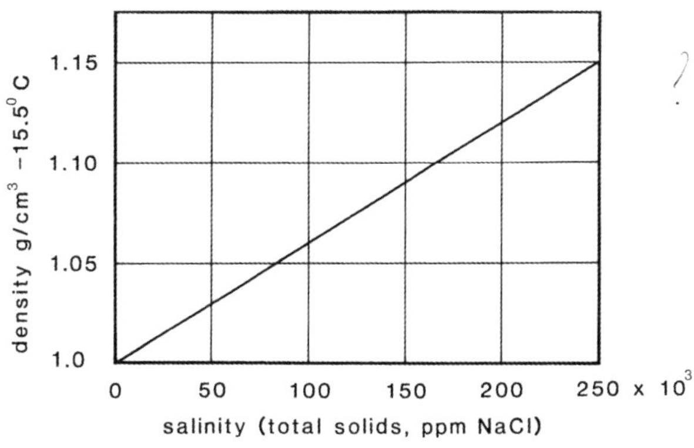

Figure 3.1 Graph showing the increase in water density with increase in salinity (NaCl) (from Pirson 1963).

ing pressure theory, but depth is more understandable when considering the subsurface.

Subsurface water pressure gradients vary from 0.098 bar/m or 0.433 psi/ft (density 1.00 g/cm³) in fresh water to 0.118 bar/m or 0.52 psi/ft (density 1.20 g/cm³) in salt saturated brine (**Table 3.2**). The gradient is directly proportional to the in place fluid density. Because oil and gas have markedly different densities to each other and to water, all have different gradients (**Table 3.2**). This is important because modern pressure measurements are sufficiently accurate to be able to identify gradients resulting from different fluid densities and, for instance, a gas gradient, oil gradient and water gradient can each be differentiated (**Figure 3.2**). Where the slope of a gradient is constant, the fluid (density) is constant, and where the gradient changes, the fluid changes.

The example (**Figure 3.2**) shows three different gradients: a water gradient of 0.099 bar/m (density 1.01 g/cm³); an oil gradient of 0.0813 bar/m (density 0.83 g/cm³); and a gas gradient of 0.0133 bar/m (density 0.136 g/cm³). Where the different gradients meet identifies the fluid contact, so that a pressure gradient plot through a reservoir can be used to identify hydrocarbon–water contacts. In cases where this is difficult using other means, for example, when there are strong capillary effects, the free water level (FWL) can be determined from where the water and hydrocarbon gradients meet. In addition, identifying a pressure gradient is a good way of finding fluid density under reservoir conditions. The density is simply fluid gradient in bar/m divided by 0.0980665 (psi/m divided by 1.421) (**Table 3.2**).

Gradients will be linear so long as there is pressure communication (density being constant) and, of course, so is the opposite: a linear gradient indicates pressure communication. Several reservoirs may be seen to have a common gradient, which indicates that they are in pressure communication, or a single reservoir may show different gradients, in which case pressure barriers are indicated (**Figure 3.3**).

Overpressure

In most geological basins, the pressure at which pore fluids actually occur increases from the normal to moderately overpressured (**Figure 3.4**). Overpressure is simply defined as any pressure above the normal (or hy-

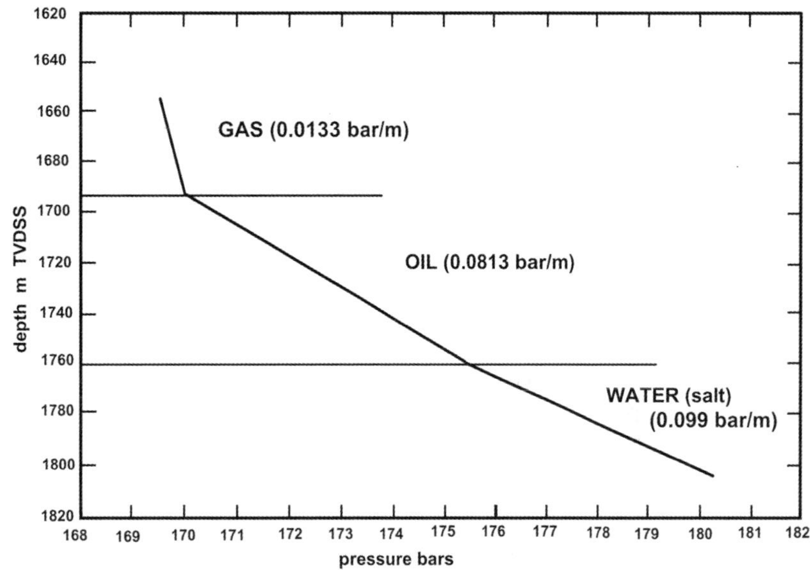

Figure 3.2 Changes of pressure gradient with fluid type (or gas) and delineation of the fluid (or gas) contacts. Gradients vary from water = 0.097 (density 1.01 gcm³), to oil = 0.0813 (density 0.83 gcm³) and gas = 0.0133 (density 0.136 gcm³). TVDSS = true vertical depth sub-sea (re-drawn, modified from Haynes *et al.* SPWLA 2000).

Table 3.2 Some typical pressure gradients and fluid densities

Fluid	Gradient bar/m	Gradient psi/ft	*Density g/cm³
Dry gas	0.022 bar/m	0.100 psi/ft	0.230 g/cm³
Wet gas	0.032 bar/m	0.140 psi/ft	0.320 g/cm³
Oil limit	0.069 bar/m	0.300 psi/ft	0.698 g/cm³
Oil 60°	0.087 bar/m	0.387 psi/ft	0.780 g/cm³
Oil 20° (heavy)	0.091 bar/m	0.404 psi/ft	0.934 g/cm³
Fresh water	**0.098 bar/m**	**0.433 psi/ft**	**1.00 g/cm³**
Sea water	0.101 bar/m	0.444 psi/ft	1.025 g/cm³
Salt sat. water	0.118 bar/m	0.520 psi/ft	1.20 g/cm³

*Figures from Moss *et al.* 2003, sea water from World Ocean Atlas 2001.
Fluid density = bar/m divided by 0.0980665 (psi/m divided by 1.421)
1 psi/ft = 0.2265 bar/m

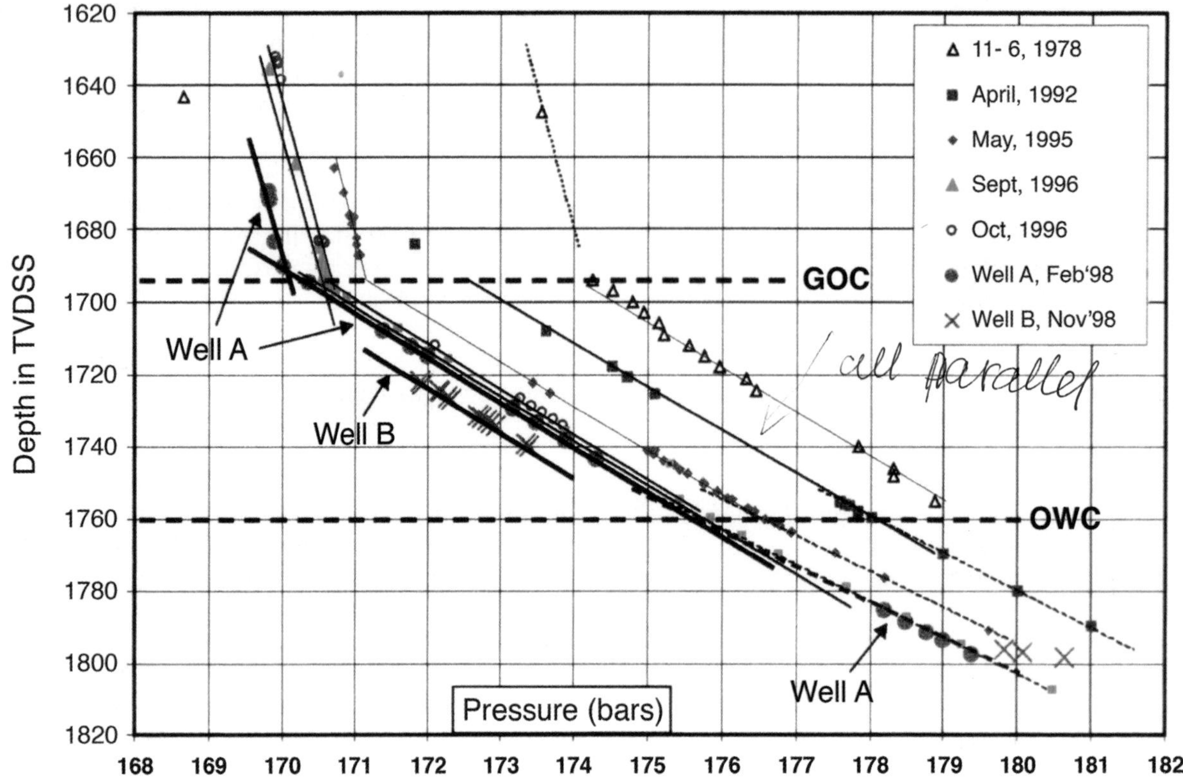

Figure 3.3 Constant pressure gradients despite the changes in absolute pressure. The pressure decline (in the Balder Field) from 1978 to 1998 is interpreted as a regional change in the aquifer pressure caused by the production from nearby fields (Haynes *et al.* SPWLA 2000).

drostatic) for that particular depth. Overpressure exists for a number of reasons, mainly lack of fluid release during subsidence (Lubanzadio *et al.* 2006). In all cases it means that the formation fluids are being squeezed by the surrounding rocks: fluids are supporting part of the overburden. It is similar to the pressure regime in car brakes. When the brakes are at rest, the brake fluid is at normal pressure. Putting on the brake puts the fluid under overpressure: it is being squeezed by the extra pressure of the foot.

If the measured formation pressure is 300 bar at 2500 m and the formation fluids are salty with a density of 1.09 g/cm^3, there is an overpressure calculated as follows:

Measured pressure at 2500 m = 300 bar

Normal pressure at 2500 m = 267.23 bar from (3)

Overpressure = 300 − 267.23 = 32.77 bar

Most wells show a typical subsurface pressure development. Shallow formations have normal or hydrostatic formation pressures and there is pressure communication with the surface. Deeper into the subsurface, slight overpressures are encountered which indicate that a pressure barrier is present. As the depths increase, so the overpressure increases and more pressure barriers exist (**Figure 3.4**). When drilled, overpressured fluids will flow up the borehole to the surface; hydrostatically (i.e. normal) pressured fluids will not.

An interval containing overpressured fluids is necessarily isolated from intervals of normal or differently pressured fluids. However, within that pressured unit, pressure gradients will be linear and still depend on fluid density. A water gradient in a normally pressured reservoir will have the same gradient as water in an overpressured reservoir, although the absolute (over) pressures will be higher (**Figure 3.3**). This means that the technique of using changes in pressure gradients to identify fluid contacts is valid whatever the pressure regime.

Overpressures can increase up to an empirical maximum called the lithostatic gradient. This gradient is also called the geostatic or overburden gradient and is taken as a convenient value representing the probable maximum pressure likely to be encountered in a well. This maximum actually depends on rock density. The average gradient frequently used of 1 psi/ft in American oilfield units (0.2262 bar/m), comes from the Gulf Coast of North America, and is a gradient that corresponds to an average rock density of 2.3 g/cm^3 (**Figure 3.4**) (cf. Levorsen 1967). The true lithostatic gradient will vary from well to well and will depend on the densities of the formations encountered. In the example given (**Figure 3.5**), which

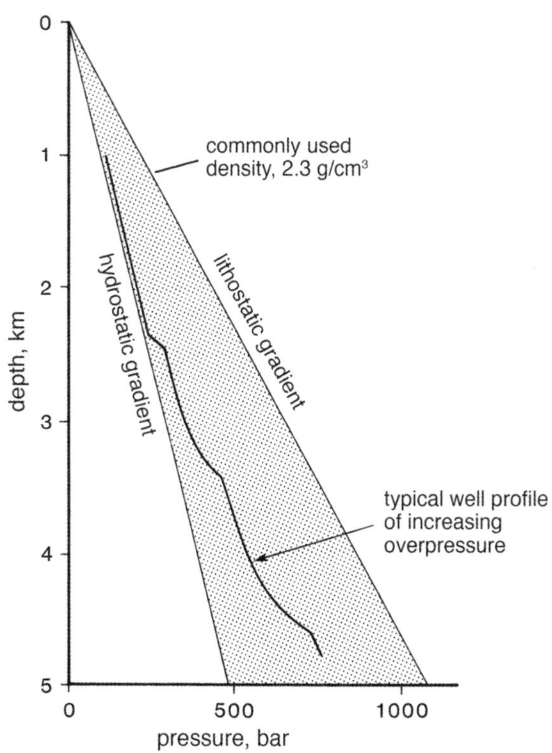

Figure 3.4 Formation fluid pressure increases with depth in a typical oilfield well. The pressure varies between the hydrostatic (fluid) and lithostatic (rock) gradients.

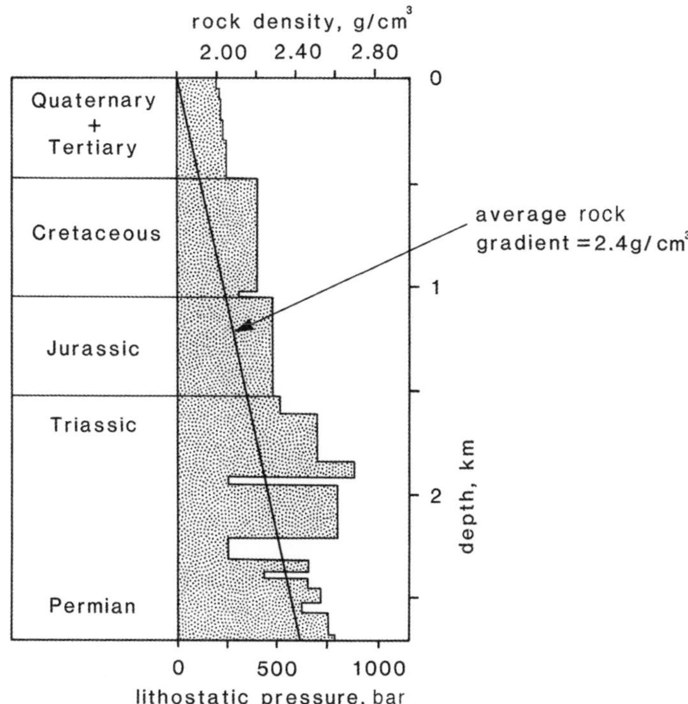

Figure 3.5 True rock density profile and average lithostatic gradient from a North German well (re-drawn from Meyer-Gürr 1976).

is from a well in Germany, the average formation density is 2.4 g/cm³ (Meyer-Gürr 1976). The lithostatic gradient is sometimes referred to as the overburden pressure (OBP).

Most wells, therefore, encounter formation pressures somewhere between the normal hydrostatic gradient and the lithostatic gradient (**Figure 3.4**). In absolute terms this will give usual logging pressures of between about 150 bar and 1000 bar (approx. 2000 psi–15,000 psi). Most oilfield logging tools are designed to withstand pressures up to a maximum of 1020–1350 bar (15,000–20,000 psi), that is, above the highest pressures usually encountered. However, as wells drill deeper, pressure ratings increase, and a tool rating of 1700 bar (25,000 psi) is not uncommon.

Pore pressure and fracture pressure

Pore pressure is another name for fluid pressure and, even before LWD tools were available, attempts were made to measure it during drilling. It affects drilling performance and the choice of drilling parameters such as mud weight. There were also, and still are, attempts to measure the fracture pressure or the pressure needed to fracture the formation and release the fluids. Pore pressure, as indicated, varies between the hydrostatic and the lithostatic but, in reality, can rise only as far as the fracture pressure. When pore pressure becomes higher than facture pressure, the pressured fluid can hydraulically fracture the formation and flow away as the pressure is released. Fracture pressure gradients may be slightly higher or lower than lithostatic pressure gradients, depending on rock strength.

Pore pressure can now be measured accurately by the borehole tools described below. Fracture pressure is measured by the fracture or leak-off test which is performed at the bottom of a casing string just after it has been set. To do this, the mud column is pressured up from the rig floor until it leaks into the formation at the casing shoe (bottom of the casing): leaking implies that the formation has been hydraulically fractured. The accuracy of this measurement is variable.

Using logs to estimate pore pressure is discussed in Chapter 9 (sonic) and very briefly in Chapters 7 (resistivity) and 10 (density).

3.3 Subsurface Pressure Tools

Tools that measure pore pressure are normally referred to as 'Formation Testers' (admittedly the term is not very informative) or wireline formation testers (WFT). As mentioned, these tools are also still informally referred to as RFTs although strictly that was the name of a Schlumberger tool that is now obsolete. (The RFT had such a profound effect on petroleum engineering that it is still informally used as a generic name for all formation testers regard-

Table 3.3 Wireline Formation Testing Tools (WFT).

Company	Older tools	Acronym
Schlumberger	Repeat Formation Tester (older)	*RFT
Baker Atlas	Formation Multitester (older)	*FMT
Halliburton	Sequential Formation Tester (older)	*SFT
	Modern tools	
Schlumberger	Modular Formation Dynamics Tester	MDT
	PressureXpress	
	Quicksilver	
Baker Hughes™	Reservoir Characterization Instrument	RCI™
Halliburton	Reservoir Dynamics Tester	RDT
	Compensated Quartz Pressure Tool	CQPT

* = older tools no longer used

less of the contractor). Formation testers are available as wireline tools and, since about 2003, as LWD tools. As is normally the case, both types of tool use the same principles and actually share components. The purpose of the tool is to place a pressure gauge at an accurately defined depth and then allow it to communicate with the free fluids within the formation. A pressure gauge is the heart of the tool but physically only represents a very small part of it. The bulk of the tool consists of a large number of electrical and hydraulic components whose purpose is to connect the pressure gauge to the formation.

Since both wireline and LWD pressure tools use the same basic principles to measure pressure, there are many tool design similarities. However, some routines are only possible with wireline tools while others are only used in the LWD environment. For this reason, the two types of tool are described separately, wireline first and in more detail.

Wireline pressure tools (Formation Testers)

Pressure measurement and fluid sampling are both integral to the modern wireline tools. As suggested, they are modular so that tools with sampling capabilities can be configured to take as many test measurements as required as well as several fluid samples (usually 6) on each run. The standard tools from the major logging companies are listed **(Table 3.3)**. The older tools, used prior to the early 1990s, are indicated in the table even though they are no longer used. They were less accurate and took fewer, less representative fluid samples and will not be described.

Measuring pressure

To measure formation pressure, a pad, called a packer, is extended from the tool to the borehole wall (**Figure 3.6**). The packer has a central, hollow probe which is further extended to form a conduit, which connects the tool's own internal fluid circuit to that of the formation, and isolates it from the borehole's mud pressure system (**Figure 3.7**). The packer must be tight against the mudcake to ensure a seal, so backup arms extend from opposite the packer section and press it tightly against the borehole wall (**Figure 3.6**). To make the pressure measurement, the tool first pumps (sucks) fluid out of the formation and creates a small flow, via the probe, into the tool. This is known as a *pre-test* (or pretest) and its volume and speed can be controlled. A volume of 10 cm^3 is usually enough but much less may be used

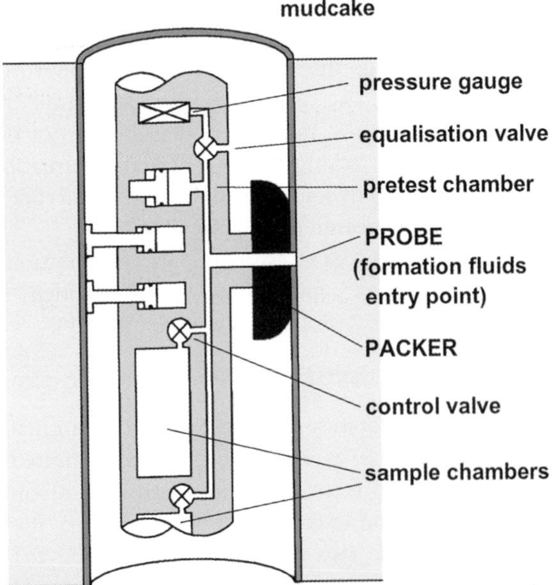

Figure 3.6 Schematic representation of a typical subsurface wireline testing tool that measures pressures and takes samples (re-drawn from Proett *et al.* SPWLA 1994).

Figure 3.7 The sealing packer from the while drilling pressure testing tool TesTrak™ from Baker Hughes™ INTEQ (from Baker Hughes™ 2004).

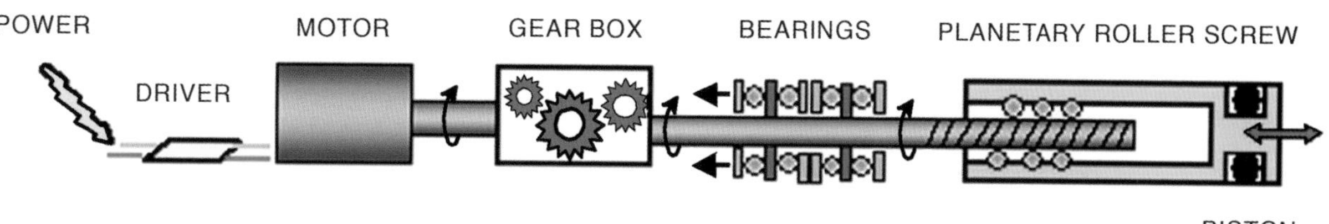

Figure 3.8 Diagram of the electro-mechanical pump which controls the pretest pump-out in the Schlumberger wireline pressure tool (from Manin *et al.* SPWLA 2005).

(Davenport *et al.* 2004). One of the Schlumberger tools, for example, has pretest volumes between 0.1 and 37 cm³, with the rate varying from 0.05 to 2.00 cm³/sec (Manin *et al.* 2005). The pretest pump may be hydraulic or, more often now, mechanical (**Figure 3.8**).

During the pretest pumping, fluid is being taken out of the formation and flows into the tool. The pressure in the tool is dropping as the fluid flows. When the pretest pumping is stopped, since the tool fluid circuit is open to the formation, flow into the tool continues and will do so until an equilibrium pressure is reached. This is the formation pressure and the object of the measurement. The probe is then retracted, the packer pulled back in to its recess, and the tool moved on to the next station.

The figure shows the pressure record of a typical pretest (**Figure 3.9**). The initial pressure seen in the flowline of the tool is that of the mud column (IHP, initial hydrostatic pressure, **Figure 3.9**). As the probe enters the formation, there may be a slight rise in pressure due to fluid compression. The pretest pump-out commences and the pressure in the flowline drops as fluid flows (is sucked) from the formation. A minimum pressure is reached, called the final flowing pressure (FFP, **Figure 3.9**). This is the *drawdown pressure*, being the difference between the reservoir pressure and the final flowing pressure (FFP). When the desired pretest volume has been extracted, or the pretest chamber is full, pump-out is stopped. However, fluid continues to flow from the formation but now the pressure rises as the tool reaches pressure equilibrium with the formation (FBU final build up pressure, **Figure 3.9**). The FBU is the formation pressure and is the measurement normally required. Finally, the probe is retracted and the final pressure is measured (FHP, final hydrostatic pressure). It should be identical to the IHP and is simply the (hydrostatic) pressure of the mud column.

The time for a pressure measurement is quite variable, mainly depending on permeability. 1 hour is a long test, 5 minutes is short, while around 15 to 20 minutes would be a reasonable time (Schrooten *et al.* 2007) (**Figure 3.9**). Normally, at each station, the pump-out is repeated two or three times. The first pretest assures that the seal is good. The tool is then activated one or two more times with brief opening and closing periods (also pretests) to measure the stabilised formation pressure. The initial pretest pressure is usually too high since the formation has not been cleaned of mud filtrate. It is only after the second and third pretest that a reliable formation pressure is measured (**Figure 3.9**).

During pump-out, drawdown pressure (or flowing pressure), is usually controlled. Firstly, because the final flowing pressure (FFP) must be lower than the formation pressure to provoke a flow from the formation into the tool and, secondly, because in a single phase hydrocarbon reservoir, if the drawdown pressure is too quick or too large, phase separation may be caused (**Figure 3.10**). For example, in a hydrocarbon with dissolved

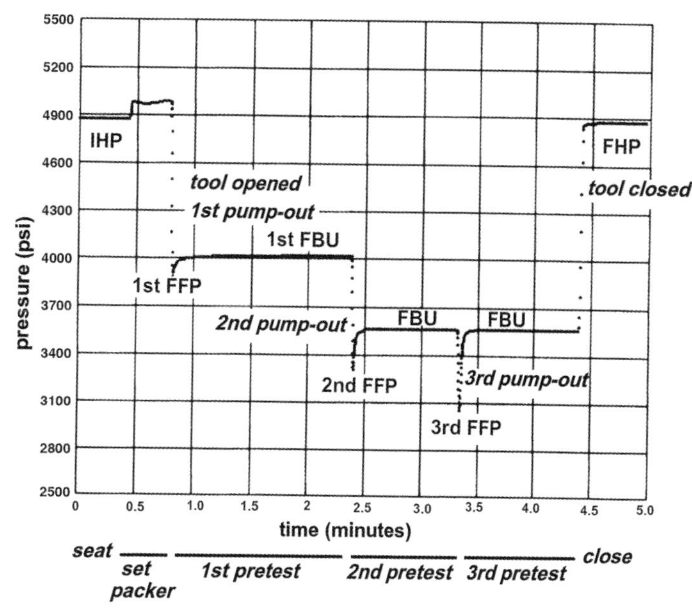

Figure 3.9 Pressure time plot of a surface controlled, wireline pressure test with 3 pretests, from a Baker Hughes™ Reservoir Characterisation Instrument (RCI™). The last 2 pretests have a similar formation pressure and so confirm a reliable measurement. IHP = initial hydrostatic pressure; FFP = final flowing pressure; FBU = final build-up pressure; FHP = final hydrostatic pressure (from Michaels *et al.* SPWLA 1995).

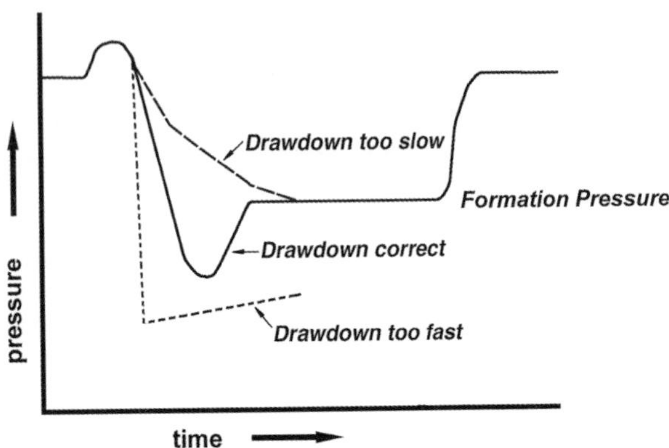

Figure 3.10 Sketch of a pressure plot illustrating the effect of drawdown speed. Care must be taken to preserve reservoir conditions as much as possible.

gas, the bubble point may be crossed if the drawdown pressure is too low (i.e. pump-out too fast) and gas will be released from solution. The attendant gas expansion will distort the formation pressure measured.

Supercharging and other measurement problems

A number of problems are often encountered during pressure testing. The most obvious is seal failure (**Figure 3.11**). When this occurs, the pressure measured is the borehole hydrostatic and from the mud column, not from the formation. Re-seating the packer is necessary. Seal failure will be recognised when the final buildup pressure (FBU) is the same as the mud hydrostatic value. Plugging of the flowline by filtrate or friable formation is also common (**Figure 3.11**).

A more difficult problem to solve is so called 'supercharging'. This occurs when, for some reason, the pressure in the near wellbore region is higher than the true formation pressure (**Figure 3.12**). It indicates that the formation permeability is less than the mudcake permeability, and that filtrate is flowing into the formation faster than it is able to disperse (Schrooten *et al.* 2007).

In a normal overbalance condition, the pressure in the mud column will be higher than the pore pressure in the formation. The pressure drop takes place through the mudcake. In a supercharged formation, at least some of the pressure drop occurs in the near wellbore region as well. This suggests that the invading filtrate is not dispersing rapidly enough to come to equilibrium with the formation fluids. Regardless of why the near wellbore region is over-pressured, this is where the formation tester measures pressure and so will measure a pressure intermediate between the hydrostatic and the formation value. Supercharging is normally associated with low permeability formations, mud filtrate that is immiscible with the formation fluids (e.g. OBM filtrate) invading a water sand, and/or high over-balance conditions. Symptoms can be very difficult to identify, but may include:

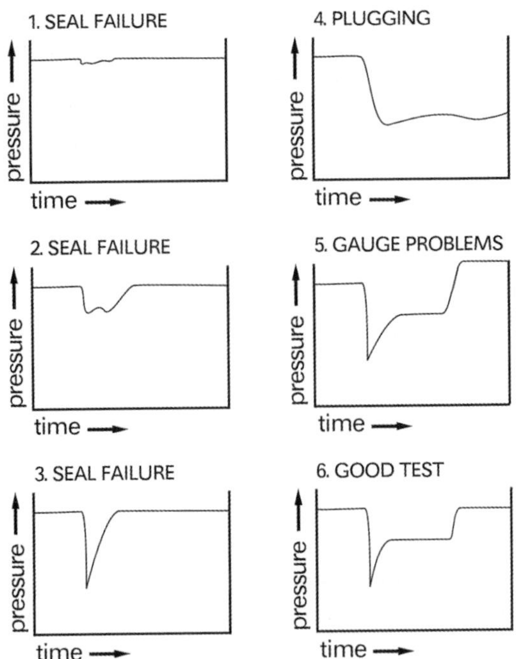

Figure 3.11 Illustration of some of the more common problems encountered when measuring subsurface pressure.

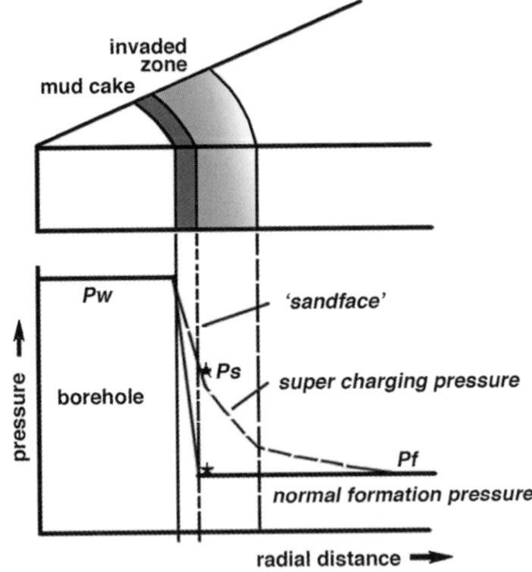

Figure 3.12 The origin of supercharging, when mudcake shows permeability. Pw = hydrostatic (mud) pressure; Ps = 'sandface' pressure (supercharged); Pf = formation pressure (re-drawn, modified after Lee *et al.* SPWLA 2003).

1. Repeated measurements at the same depth giving different pressures, the pressure normally dropping each time a measurement is made.
2. Scatter in pressure-depth plots where several measurements are made in the same sand.
3. Correlation between over-pressure and mobility or permeability.
4. Inconsistency with other data (e.g. inferred contacts not agreeing with logs).

The example (**Figure 3.13**) shows wireline formation pressure data from an exploration well drilled in the Atlantic margins off the UK (UKCS). Although a gas/water contact (GWC) could be clearly identified on conventional logs, the raw pressure-depth data showed too much scatter to define gradients and identify the free water level (**Figure 3.13**). The scatter is due to supercharging, since measurements repeated at the same depth showed a reduction in the measured formation pressure of a few psi. By selecting points showing stable pressure readings, gradients were constructed which corresponded to the gas and water legs indicated by the log data. Gas and water gradients were fitted to these points (**Figure 3.13**). Average core permeability is 4 mD.

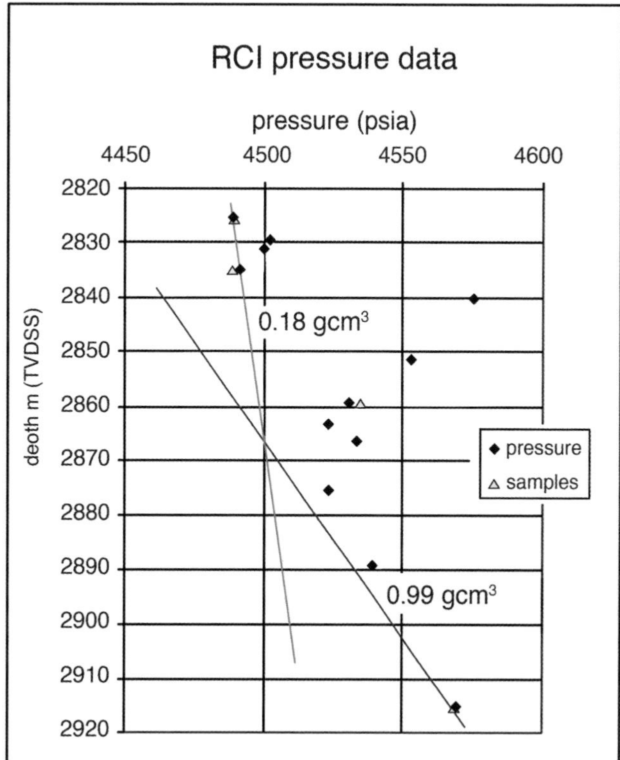

Figure 3.13 Example of the effect of supercharging on pressure measurements. The pressure-depth data show too much scatter to be able to define gradients and identify the free water level. However, by selecting points which show a stabilised pressure, gradients can be constructed which correspond to gas and water legs which are seen on the conventional logs. The free water level (FWL), between the gas (density 0.18 gcm³) and water (density 0.99 gcm³), is at 2866 m (TVDSS) (see text for explanation). Average core permeability is 4 mD.

Pressure gauges

A critical feature of downhole pressure measurements is the accuracy of the pressure gauges. Two basic types are in common use: the strain gauge and the quartz gauge. The strain gauge is small, fast acting and relatively cheap. If properly calibrated it is accurate to 1 psi and can resolve differences of 0.1 psi. Quartz gauges (the older type) were larger, more expensive and less robust than they are now, but were accurate to at least 0.1 psi and could resolve differences of less than 0.01 psi. The two types of gauge complement each other, and downhole tools often carry both kinds. The original, older quartz gauges were manufactured by third parties and were not specifically designed for petroleum applications. Consequently, through the 1990s most of the larger contractors spent a lot of time and money developing smaller quartz gauges. These new gauges combine the accuracy and precision of the traditional quartz gauge with the speed and robustness of the strain gauge. Most modern downhole tools use these new, purpose-designed quartz gauges (CQG = crystal quartz guage), which have a good accuracy (0.5–0.1 psi). After a few precautions, pressure tool measurement accuracy is now excellent.

Quartz is piezoelectric so that an applied pressure creates a positive and negative charge at opposite ends of the crystal. This gives quartz its pressure measuring capabilities (Barriol *et al.* 2005). However, it is also pyroelectric, meaning that it is sensitive to changes in temperature. Running in an offshore hole, the tool may pass through a cold, deep water section before being subjected to hot borehole mud, and then even hotter formation fluids during a measurement. To account for such large changes, acclimatisation or temperature stabilisation is needed, and is achieved by keeping the tool stationary for a period of time at the casing shoe (bottom of the casing). One example of the temperature effects on a modern gauge suggests that a change of 0.5 degree Farenheit/minute can be tolerated as it only causes a change of 0.1 psi/min in pressure (Davenport *et. al.* 2004).

Pressure gauges may be placed at several locations in a pressure tool: in the up-stream flowline, in the downstream flowline and as a permanent reference in the mud column. A strain gauge can be used in the latter location and a mixture of gauges in the former (Manin *et al.* 2005).

Log presentation and depth control

The log of the pressure tests is not, strictly speaking, a log. Each pressure point is plotted as a discrete depth record and the log plot shows time, not depth (**Figure 3.14,a**). The tracks typically represent different scales of sensitivity, the first representing 0.1 psi, the second 0.01 psi and the third 0.001 psi (**Figure 3.14,b**).

Depth control for pressure points is important, and from two points of view. The first is that a point is chosen because of lithology: for example, a permeable sand, a carbonate or a thin-bed facies. To locate this lithology, the depth must be correct. Secondly, depth

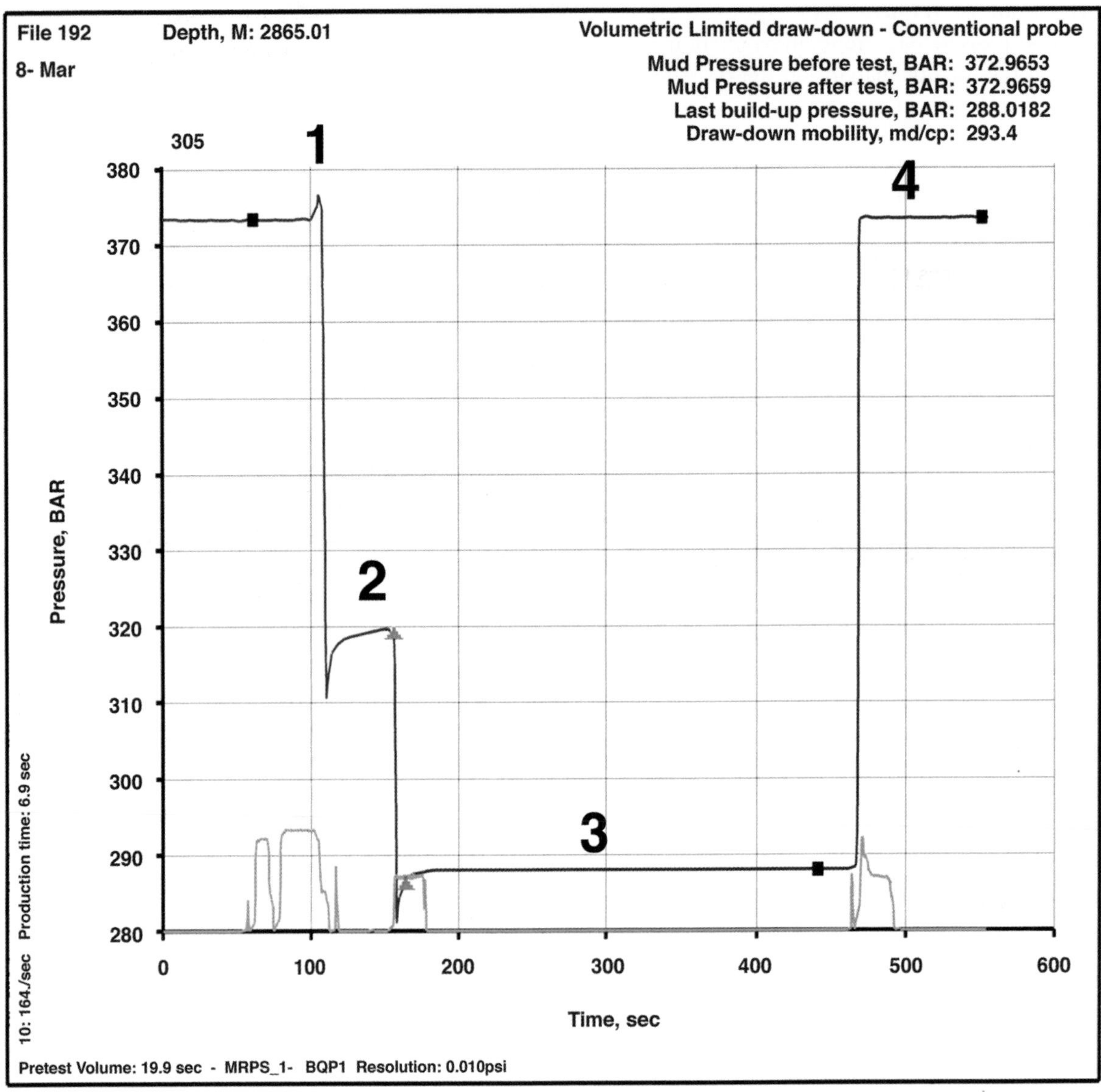

Figure 3.14,a Pressure plot summary of a measurement at 2865 m, from a Schlumberger MDT tool. Pretest volume 19.9 cm³. 1. Packer set and initial mud column hydrostatic pressure. 2. Probe filter retraction (allowing communication between the formation and the tool). 3. Pretest with stabilised build-up pressure (= formation pressure). 4. Final shut-in and hydrostatic mud column pressure. Green curve at bottom = motor speeds (hydraulic for setting, electromechanical for pretest). Black squares = pressure stabilised, red triangles = pressure drawdown.

is even more critical when pressure-depth gradients are plotted: inaccurate depths will distort the gradient. The wireline depth location is generally assured by a gamma ray sonde, which is run along with the pressure device. The required depth is identified on a lithological interpretation of the open hole logs, which includes the gamma ray (wireline). It is then re-identified on the gamma ray log run with the pressure device. To ensure the accuracy of the comparisons, cable tension for both logs and pressure tool should be similar, which means that pressures should be taken pulling up the hole (Lee *et al.* 2003).

While Drilling Pressure Tools

LWD pressure measurement tools became available from 2003-2004. They are being used more and more. The principle of the measurement is exactly the same as for the wireline measurement, except that all the equipment is housed in a drill collar and part of the bottom hole assembly (BHA). Also, because of data transmission restrictions, the pressure tool cannot be fully commanded in real time from the surface and only limited pressure data points may be available at the time of measurement, although Schlumberger do provide a pressure plot in real time (Bariol *et al.* 2005). Full data information is stored

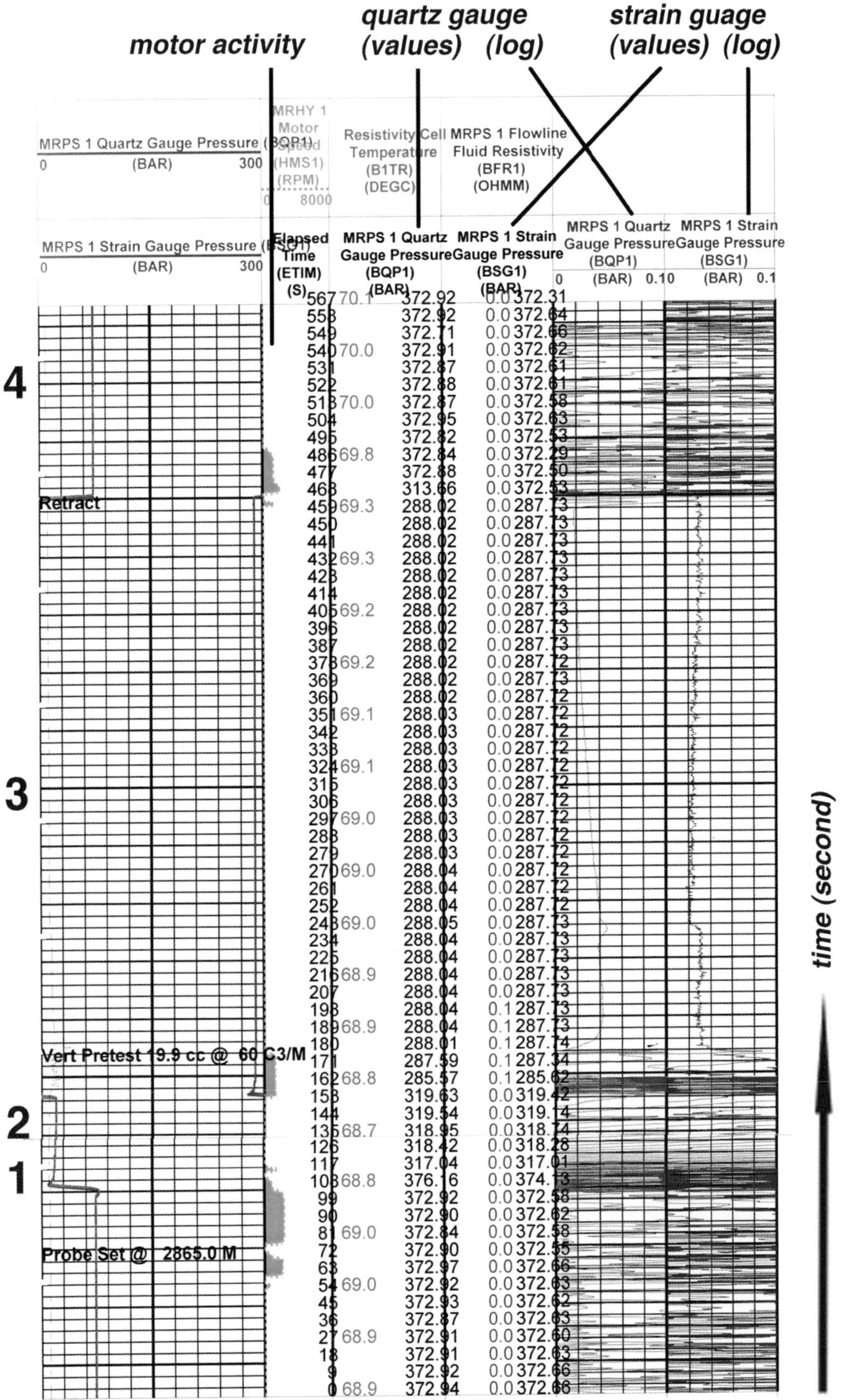

Figure 3.14,b Log of the events of the same pressure test as Figure 3.14,a showing quartz and strain pressure gauge logs, the corresponding pressure values and motor activity, all with a vertical axis in time (seconds) increasing from the base upwards. Points 1–4 as in Figure 3.14,a. The probe was open for 6 minutes (360 seconds).

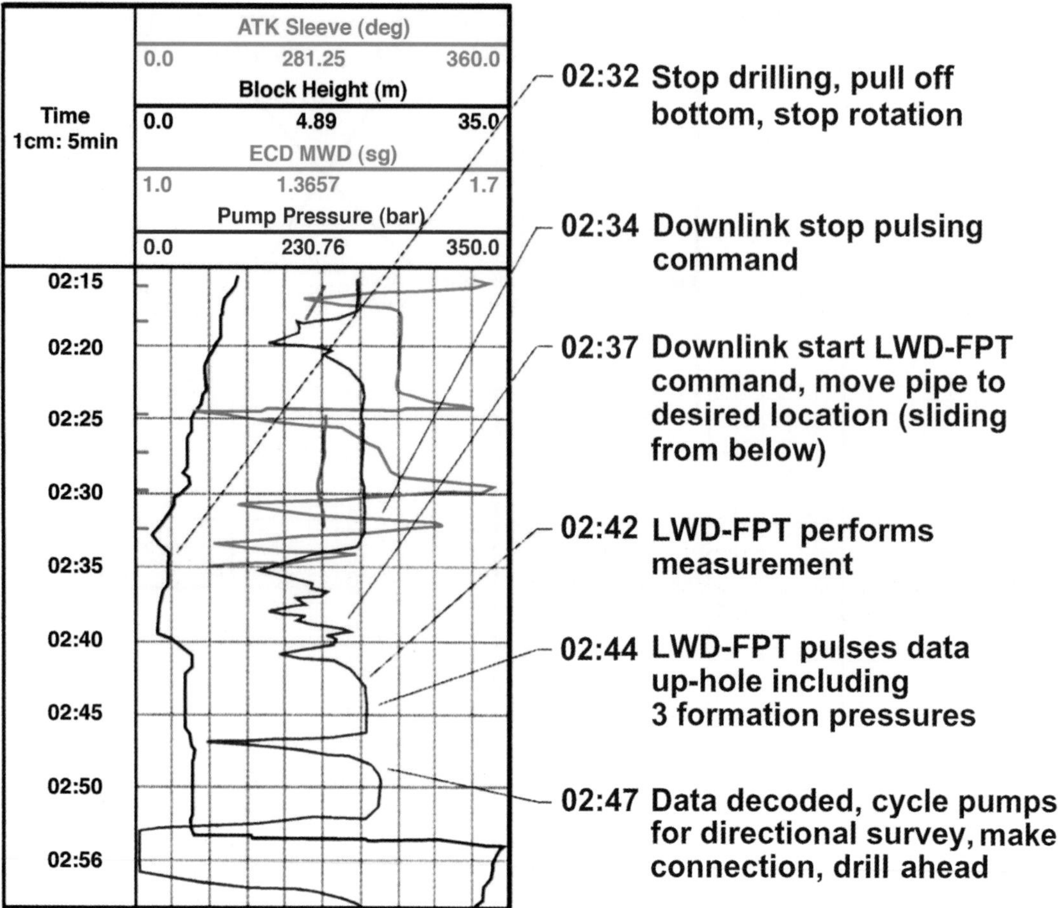
ATK Sleeve (deg)
0.0 281.25 360.0
Block Height (m)
Time
1cm: 5min
0.0 4.89 35.0
ECD MWD (sg)
1.0 1.3657 1.7
Pump Pressure (bar)
0.0 230.76 350.0
02:15
02:20
02:25
02:30
02:35
02:40
02:45
02:50
02:56
02:32 Stop drilling, pull off bottom, stop rotation
02:34 Downlink stop pulsing command
02:37 Downlink start LWD-FPT command, move pipe to desired location (sliding from below)
02:42 LWD-FPT performs measurement
02:44 LWD-FPT pulses data up-hole including 3 formation pressures
02:47 Data decoded, cycle pumps for directional survey, make connection, drill ahead

Figure 3.15 LWD pressure measurement diary from INTEQ. The entire measurement sequence took 15 minutes. FPT = Formation Pressure Tool, ECD = equivalent circulating density (from Meister *et al.* SPWLA 2004).

in memory but can only be downloaded when the tool is brought to the surface.

In an example bottom hole assembly (BHA), the LWD pressure tool (LWD-FPT) was placed 16ft from the bit, above the steering unit and the LWD logging tools (Meister *et al.* 2004). Generally, a section will be drilled but then, before a new stand (30m, 100ft) is added, the string will be moved to the pressure points required from the newly drilled section. This means that the pressure points can be measured a matter of tens of minutes after drilling, the tool being set by a single command from the surface using the downlink mud-pulse system (**Figure 3.15**). The tests can be repeated later for verification, either while pulling out of the hole or running in on subsequent trips (*see below*). The present LWD tools from the main logging companies are shown in the table **(Table 3.4)**

Because the LWD test tools are used during a time when the mud cake is building and invasion is progressing, two problems arise. The first is that supercharging during measurement is much more common than for wireline tools. During the period of mudcake build-up, the cake is thin and permeable and this allows filtrate to pass through while it builds. However, it also allows pressure communication and hence supercharging. If this is suspected, the pressure measurement can be repeated on subsequent runs. The tests are best performed with the mud pumps off and pulling out of the hole (Bariol *et al.* 2005 *op. cit.*). The second problem, already mentioned, is that surface control of an LWD test is not possible. Consequently, logging companies have designed automatic downhole systems that control and optimise a test. That is, several pretests are used, the second (and possibly third) being automatically configured based on the results of the first (or previous) test. Typically, one pressure test consisting of several pretests can take about 5 minutes or less, with the tool remaining on station for about 10 minutes.

To be sure that depth points are controlled properly, pipe stretch should be known. That is, pressure points are generally chosen from a real-time porosity and gamma ray plot, which are acquired while drilling ahead. By comparing the hook load when the BHA is fully supported with the hook load off and the BHA on-bottom, pipe stretch can be evaluated. As much as 1–2m (3–7ft) is reported (Meister *et al. 2004*) but it will depend espe-

Table 3.4 LWD Formation Testing Tools (LWD-FT)

Company	Tool, *notes
Schlumberger	StethoScope pressure, fluid identification
Baker Hughes™ INTEQ	TestTrak™ (MWD) Formation Pressure Tester™ (FMT) pressure, fluid identification
Halliburton	GeoTap pressure, fluid identification, sampling
Pathfinder	Dual Packer Tool

*= tool functionality at time of writing

cially on well depth and amount of deviation.

Initial comparisons between while drilling pressure measurements and subsequent wireline measurements suggest that they are comparable in formations with mobilities above about 5 mD/cP (Meister *et al.* 2004; Bariol *et al.* 2005). However, LWD pressures should be verified by repeat measurements because of supercharging, and measurement conditions should be controlled as suggested above. As more experience is gained with the LWD pressure tools, it is certain that more peculiarities of early pressure readings will come to light.

3.4. Sampling

Taking samples

The same wireline equipment that is used to acquire pressure data is used for downhole, formation fluid sampling. In the past, such samples were acquired by a drill-stem test (DST), that is, a test in which formation fluids are allowed to flow to the surface to be collected. This technique requires special equipment, a lot of rig time, and is generally very expensive and often dangerous. Many of the deep offshore wells drilled today cannot be tested like this. For this reason, wireline sampling is important. Most downhole pressure tools can be equipped with a number of sample bottles so that multiple samples can be taken during each run. The MDT from Schlumberger, for example, can be equipped with standard chambers of 3.8, 10.4 and 22.7 litres (1, 2.75 and 6 gallons) or 6 small 0.45 litre (0.12 gallon) chambers (Ireland *et al.* 1992). 6 samples can be taken in just one trip.

The objective of the wireline tool is to obtain samples which are not contaminated with filtrate and have the same PVT (pressure, volume, temperature) conditions as the formation. The two requirements will be considered separately. Sample purity first.

To take a formation fluid sample, the pressure tool is set and activated in the same way as for pressure measurement, the probe making connection with the formation. With pressure measurements, the time of this connection is short, with sampling, the connection is much longer, and the formation is allowed to flow into the tool until filtrate is cleared and representative formation fluids enter the tool's sample chambers. Only then is a sample taken. The liquid from the contaminated flow is dumped. To judge when the flow into the tool is no longer contaminated, a flowline can be equipped with sensors which allow the flowing fluid to be identified. These may be either electrical (resistivity) or, more commonly today, optical sensors (Ireland *et al.* 1992, Betancourt *et al.* 2003). Thus, in one example, the fluid flowing could be identified after 2 hours of flowing, but a further 2 to 3 hours were needed before samples were judged pure enough to recover (Betancourt *et al. op. cit.*). These same monitoring systems can also be used to recognise the type of hydrocarbon (*see* below).

The second objective is to take a sample preserving reservoir pressure and temperature (PVT) conditions. This problem has already been mentioned as influencing pressure measurement. If single phase fluids in the reservoir reach bubble point and begin to separate during sampling, the ratio of fluids entering the sample chamber will not be the same as in the reservoir. Flowing pressure and drawdown effects must be kept to a minimum. For example, a chamber may be filled by directing a sample into a chamber at atmospheric pressure and continuing until the pressure is in equilibrium with the formation. The method, however, risks causing excessive drawdown. Alternatively, a sample chamber may be filled through a water cushion, which avoids too low a drawdown pressure. Similar control can be achieved by using a valve to restrict the drawdown pressure. Collected samples are sealed into the cylindrical sample pressure bottles in the tool and shipped out for eventual laboratory analysis. With care, they will have been taken under formation PVT conditions (for temperature effects, *see* Section 4.4).

Downhole fluid typing

There are two reasons for wanting to recognise the type of fluid entering the testing tool. The first is to recognise filtrate contamination so that an uncontaminated reservoir fluid sample can be taken, as discussed, and the second is to type the reservoir fluid itself under reservoir conditions so as to predict behaviour under eventual production. Visible to near-infrared light absorption spectrometry, fluorescence, resistivity, dielectric effects, nuclear magnetic resonance and vibration properties are all used by different companies in various modules for these measurements.

Absorption spectroscopy at visible and near infra-red wavelengths is probably the most widely used technique for identifying and characterising hydrocarbons (including oil base mud filtrate). The method exploits the fact that hydrocarbon functional groups absorb light in this region quite strongly (laboratory instruments have exploited this for decades). The first downhole tools to

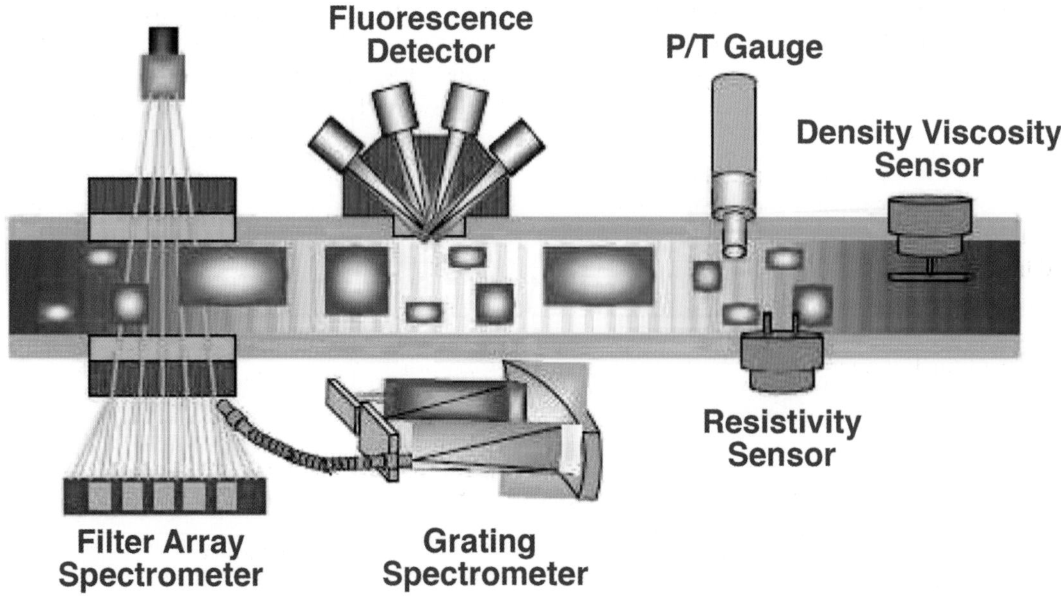

Figure 3.16 Schematic diagram of the downhole fluid sensors in the InSitu Fluid Analyser (*IFA) of Schlumberger (from Fujisawa *et al.* SPWLA 2008) *Mark of Schlumberger. *Used with permission.*

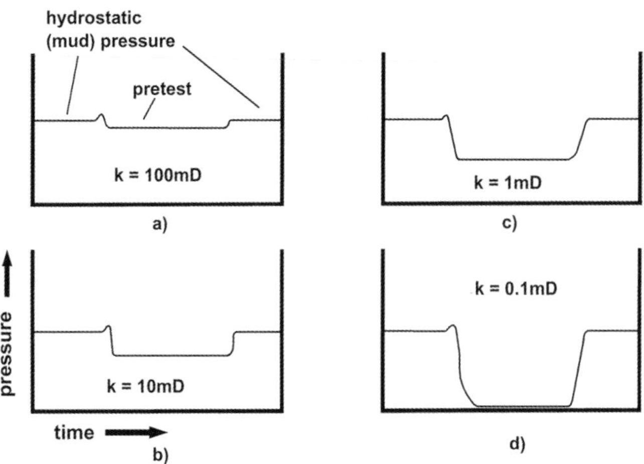

Figure 3.17 Schematic pressure plots illustrating the effects of different permeabilities. At low permeabilities a greater drawdown is required to make the formation flow.

use absorption spectroscopy appeared in the 1990s and were quite crude, simply measuring absorption in two or three broad bands. Since then, the number of bands has increased and the band width decreased, to the point now where absorption sensors measure a crude spectrum (**Figure 3.16**).

In the Schlumberger MDT, filtrate contamination is recognised by passing the fluid flowing into the tool past two optical sensors, one assessing light absorption, the other light transmission and scattering (Crombie *et al.* 1998). Filtrate causes high scattering, while water and oil can be identified by their different absorption. Different oils show different ranges of transmissibility. Recognising water based mud filtrate (WBM) is reasonably straightforward but, when oil based mud (OBM) or synthetic mud (SBM) are used, recognition is much more difficult. However, Schlumberger consider it is possible (Andrews *et al.* 2001). Gas can be reasonably well recognised passing the absorption window, which allows GOR to be estimated as well as filtrate contamination.

Recognising and quantifying hydrocarbon types downhole is even more complex. Schlumberger again use two optical detectors, one for fluorescence and one measuring transmission spectra (Betancourt *et al.* 2003). The fluorescence detector allows single or multiple phase fluid to be identified. The spectrometer is used to measure opacity (optical density) at several wavelengths and this allows the composition of a hydrocarbon to be estimated (Betancourt *et al.* 2003 *op. cit.*). If hydrocarbon composition changes progressively through a reservoir, for example becomes lighter upwards (higher API), no stable pressure gradient exists: it is 'bendy'. Fluid typing at regular points through the reservoir, as is now possible with the downhole tool, can identify this effect.

Estimating mobility and permeability

The flow capacity of a formation can be estimated from pretest characteristics. Pretests are basically miniature well tests and can be interpreted using the same principles. In simple terms, in a highly permeable formation, the fluid extracted during a pressure tool pretest will be almost immediately replaced, even as it is being sucked out and there is only a small pressure drop (small drawdown) (**Figure 3.17,a**). In a low permeability formation, the fluid cannot replace the extracted fluid fast enough, and a pressure drop is seen in the tool (drawdown) (**Figure 3.17,b**). Permeability can therefore be estimated in two ways:

1. The magnitude of the drawdown. (the higher the drawdown the lower the permeability)
2. The rate of the build-up once fluid extraction stops. (the faster the build-up the higher the permeability)

That is, the quicker formation fluid flows to replace the fluid extracted during a pretest, the greater the permeability. The difference between the final flowing pressure (FFP) and the final build-up pressure (FBU or reservoir pressure) (cf. **Figure 3.9**) is related to the permeability in the following relationship.

$$K = 1842 \times C \times \frac{(q\mu)}{(d\ \Delta P)} \qquad (4)$$

K = permeability
C = flow model factor = 0.75
q = flow rate = volume/time
μ = viscosity
d = probe diameter
ΔP = drawdown pressure (psi)

There are complications, however, due to the fact that pretests investigate very small volumes, and only extract a few cm^3 of fluid corresponding to formation volumes of 50–100 cm^3 (depending on porosity). Much, if not all, of this volume will have been altered by drilling. So a permeability taken from pretest characteristics will most likely not be representative of the formation, only the immediate vicinity of the borehole (the so called '*sandface*') and mainly the flushed zone. The fluid in this zone will almost always comprise some filtrate with an unknown fraction of formation fluids (in a gas well drilled with oil based mud three different fluids may be present). The permeability, therefore, refers to a fluid whose composition and properties vary as the test continues. Worse, it may actually consist of two or three immiscible components so that relative permeability effects come into play (two fluids in a formation each show a lower permeability, their mutual, effective permeability, than if they were the only fluid). Pretest characteristics are normally presented in terms of mobility, the ratio of permeability to viscosity, rather than just the permeability (with units of mD/cP another non-SI unit). The analyst then has to make the decision on the average viscosity of the fluid if they wish to convert mobility to permeability. Indeed, when flowing, the invaded zone fluids may form some sort of emulsion (Hashem and Ugueto 2002). Mobility is calculated in a similar way to the permeability shown above. Thus:

$$M\ (\text{mobility}) = \frac{(K)}{(\mu)} \qquad (5)$$

K = permeability, μ = viscosity

From a pretest:

$$(K/\mu)d = \frac{Cpf \times q}{\Delta Pss} \qquad (6)$$

ΔPss = steady state drawdown from pressure drop
q = pretest flow rate
Cpf = drawdown proportionality factor
ΔPss is 5660 for a conventional tool
M is typically 0.5 cP for filtrate
$K = M \times \mu$ (M is often taken as 1)
cP = centipoise

Some typical mobilities are given in the table (**Table 3.5**). If pretests are made after sampling, the viscosity of the sample can be measured in the laboratory and the value used to resolve the permeability from the mobility relationship (equation 5) (Hashem and Ugueto 2002 *op. cit.*). However, by luck, reservoir fluids at *in situ* conditions often have viscosities of the order of 1 cP, so that, despite what has just been written above, mobility can be a reasonable indication of the magnitude of permeability (in mD).

In addition to the fluid mixing complexities, calculated pretest permeabilities will be influenced by formation damage, that is, changes in the immediate borehole area, often called the 'skin', which modify real formation values. Pretest permeabilities are generally less than the true permeability. Mobilities from wireline testing tools are therefore only an approximate guide unless rigorous techniques are used (Hashem and Ugueto 2002 *op. cit.*).

Table 3.5 Fluid mobility ranges (from Meister *et al.* 2004).

Range	[1]Mobility mD/cP	Notes
Very low	<1	supercharging frequent
Low	1–5	supercharging frequent
Medium	5–20	Supercharging unlikely
High	20–500	
Very high	>500	mudcake build-up very rapid

[1]units, millidarcies/centipoises i.e. permeability/viscosity

3.5 Comment

The routine use of modern downhole pressure tools means that large datasets of accurate pressure measurements are now available over fields and basins. This is leading to a much better understanding of subsurface fluid behaviour, both in newly discovered reservoirs, entire basins and reservoirs during production. For example, regional pressure data over the North Sea area has allowed not only the overpressured areas to be mapped, but the associated fluid dynamics identified (Moss *et al.* 2003). Fluids leaking from the overpressured areas have sufficient flow to influence individual oil and gas fields and to tilt hydrocarbon contacts (Dennis *et al.* 2005; O'Connor *et al.* 2008). This is just one example in a growing field.

4 TEMPERATURE LOGGING

4.1 Generalities

A knowledge of borehole temperatures is important. It is required for accurate log evaluation and is effective in the detection of fluid movement and geochemical modeling. Quantitative geochemistry requires a knowledge of geotemperatures and it is a pre-requisite for geothermal and source maturity studies.

4.2 Subsurface temperatures and geothermal gradients

The temperature of the Earth normally increases with depth, indicating that thermal energy flows from the earth's interior to the surface: the Earth is cooling down. A well drilled into the subsurface, therefore, shows a persistent rise in temperature with depth which is usually expressed in terms of a temperature gradient, that is, in °C increase per kilometre of depth (or °F/100 ft) as has been discussed previously (Section 2.3, **Figure 2.8**).

$$\text{Geothermal gradient, } G = \frac{T^{\circ}_{\text{formation}} - T^{\circ}_{\text{surface}}}{\text{Depth}}$$

$T^{\circ}_{\text{formation}}$ = formation temperature;
$T^{\circ}_{\text{surface}}$ = average, mean, surface (or sea bottom) temperature (i.e. −5°C permafrost; +5°C cold zones; 15°C temperate zones; 25°C tropical zones)
(°F = 1.8°C + 32)

Thus, for a well in a temperate zone ($T^{\circ}_{\text{surface}}$ = 15°C) which has a maximum bottom hole temperature (BHT) of 80°C at 3000 m, the geothermal gradient is

$$G = \frac{80 - 15}{3} = 21.6\text{°C/km}$$
(1.2°F/100 ft. 1°C/km = 0.0549°F/100 ft)

This is an average gradient and assumes a linear increase in temperature with depth. In a homogeneous medium this is true. However, in detail, the geothermal gradient depends on a formation's thermal conductivity (the efficiency with which that formation transmits heat or, in the case of the earth, permits heat loss). Thermal conductivity is denoted as k and is measured in units of Watts/metre/degree Kelvin (W/m/K). Shale, like a blanket, is inefficient; it keeps heat in and has a low thermal conductivity. Salt, conversely, is very efficient, lets heat escape rapidly and therefore has a high thermal conductivity. **Table 4.1** gives some ranges of thermal conductivities for typical lithologies.

Table 4.1 Ranges of thermal conductivity values for some typical lithologies (from Serra 1979; Gearhart 1983; Norden and Förster 2006; www.engineeringtoolbox.com).

Rock type	Thermal conductivity k W/m/K	
Coal, lignite	0.14–0.42	low
Shale	*0.42–4.0 (2.85)	
Chalk	0.42–1.26 (.09)	
Water	0.58 (25°C)	
Porous limestone	1.0–2.09	
Compact limestone	2.09–3.4 (2.6)	
Siltstone	*1.7–5.5 (3.0)	
Sandstone	*1.26–5.11	
Salt	1.26–6.29 (6.0)	high
Basalt	1.67–2.93 (2.2)	
Granite	1.7–4.0 (3.1)	

W = Watts m = metres; K = degrees Kelvin (= °C−273);
*Large variation; typical figure = ( )

When a rock with high thermal conductivity is encountered, it will show a low thermal gradient. That is, the rate of temperature increase will be low (or rather, decrease upwards will be low if we think in terms of cooling). In shales, where the passage of heat is slow, the gradient will be higher. In other words a blanket of shale would keep us warm at night while a blanket of salt would not! Thus, the real temperature gradient in a well is not a straight line but a series of gradients related to the thermal conductivities of the various strata, the gradient varying inversely to the thermal conductivity (**Figure 4.1**). However, other factors are also involved since rapidly deposited, young sediments in the U.S. Gulf Coast have low geothermal gradients despite the high shale content (Nagihara and Smith 2008). Circulating fluids may be involved.

In oilfields, temperature gradients vary from the extremes of 0.5°C/km (0.03°F/100 ft) to 85°C/km (4.7°F/100 ft) although typical figures are 20°–35°C/km (**Table 4.2**, **Figure 4.2**).

Variations in thermal gradient are not just a result of different thermal conductivities, they are also a result of differences in heat flow, or the amount of heat that enters the strata from the earth's interior, and also the heat produced by the strata themselves. Typically, heat flow from basement areas is higher than from sedimentary areas. Equally, the heat produced by radioactivity in the rocks themselves is low in sediments, especially those recently deposited but high in granitic igneous or basement rocks (**Table 4.3**). The actual temperature in a well, therefore, depends on thermal conductivity, the heat-flow value for the area and the heat produced in the formations themselves.

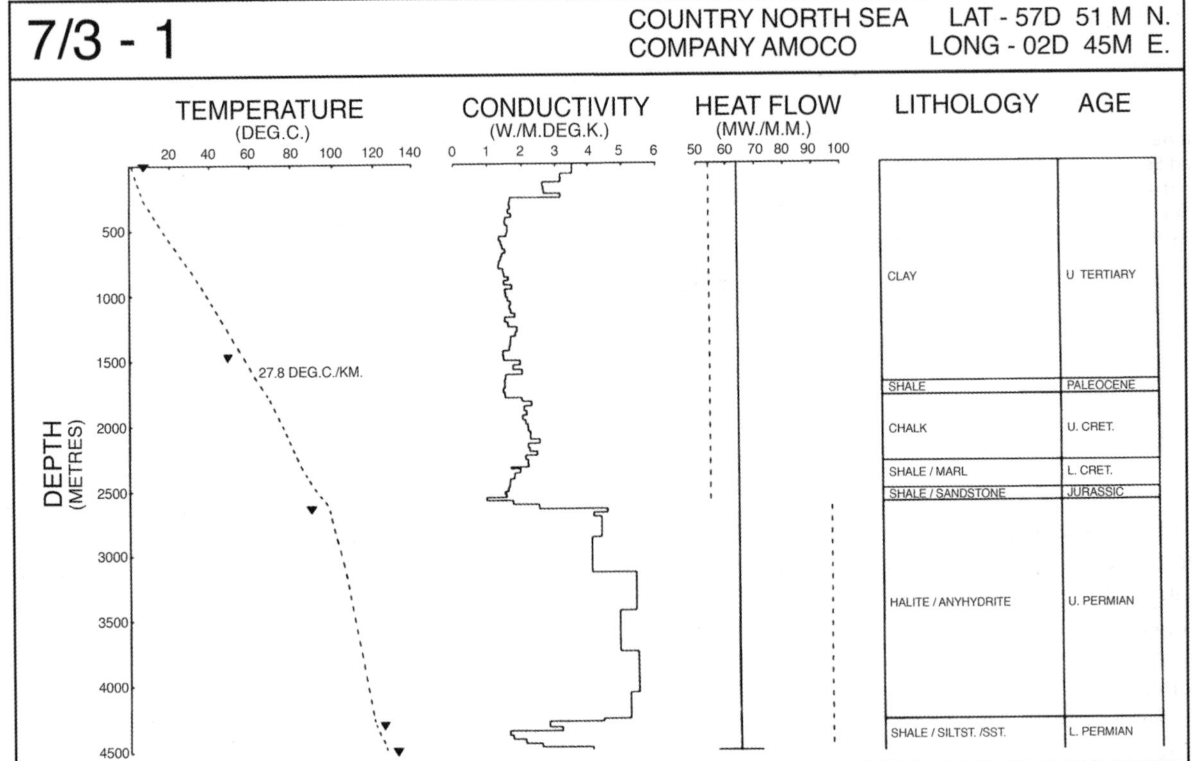

Figure 4.1 Temperature gradient, thermal conductivity and heat flow in North Sea well 7/3-1. Lithology and age are indicated (from Evans 1977).

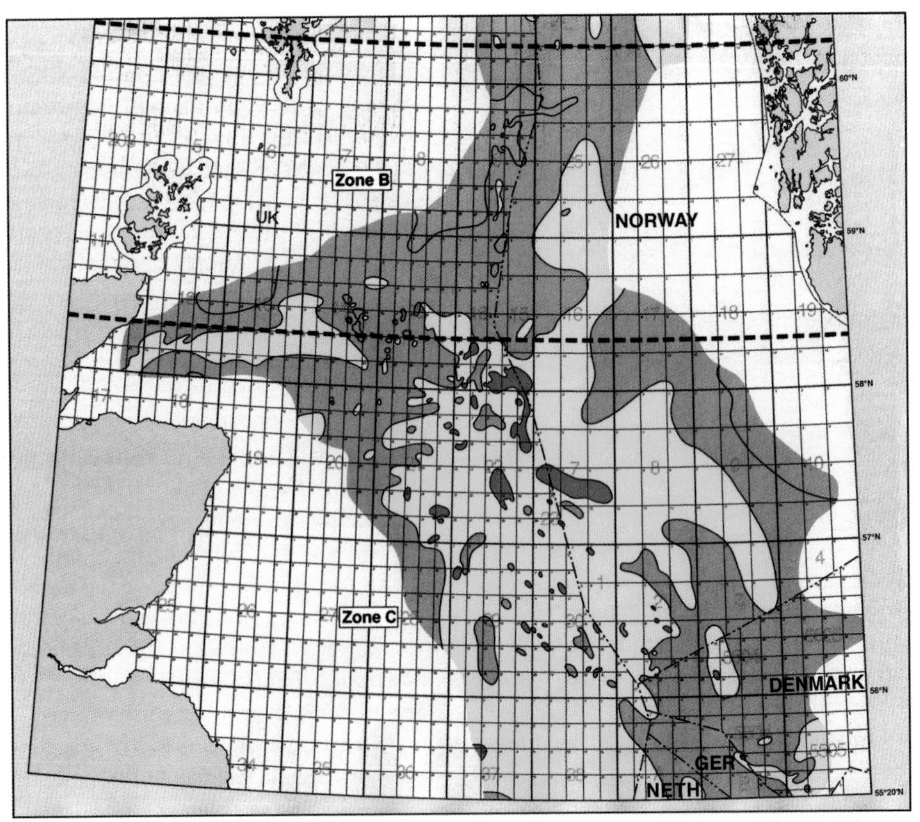

Figure 4.2 Present-day North Sea geothermal gradients in °C/km. Blue = <29, Green = 29–34.9, Yellow = 35-41, Red = >41 (from Kubala *et al.* 2003).

Table 4.2 Some typical geothermal gradients in sedimentary basins (Nagihara and Smith 2008 and various sources).

	Gradient °C/km	°F/100 ft	
Rhine Valley	66	3.6	High
Red Sea	45	2.5	
Central Ruhr Basin	40	2.2	
Madagascar	38	2.1	
North Sea*	34.6	1.9	
Western Canada, Alberta*	31.8	1.8	
Alabama*	25–30	1.4–1.6	
W. Louisiana-Texas*	30–60	1.6–3.3	
E. Louisiana*	15–25	0.8–1.4	
Eastern Canada*	22	1.2	Low

*Typical oil regions
1 °C/km = 0.0549°F/100 ft

Table 4.3 Heat production from some sedimentary rocks (from Norden and Förster 2006).

Age	Heat production μW/m³
Tertiary & Quaternary	1.07
Triassic to Cretaceous	1.39
Permian	1.36
Devonian to Carboniferous	1.41

μW = micro Watt

Spatial indications of temperature variations with depth and position in a basin may be expressed in map form using contours of equal geothermal gradients (**Figure 4.2**). Temperature differences may also be expressed by isotherms (lines of constant temperature) plotted for a certain depth or stratigraphic horizon. Isotherms may equally be used on geological sections (**Figure 4.3**). Maps are also made of surface heat loss.

4.3 Borehole temperature measurement

Every individual logging run should be accompanied by a reading of at least the maximum temperature in the borehole. Up until the mid 1980s, bottom hole temperature (BHT) was most commonly measured by strapping to the tool, usually three, pressure resistant, maximum thermometers. The three temperatures (maxima) were noted on the log-head and an average or the most reliable temperature used as the actual bottom-hole temperature (BHT). Tool strings now generally contain a special sonde (such as the Environmental Measuring Sonde [EMS] of Schlumberger) which measures temperature continuously along with mud resistivity and cable tension (**Table 4.4**). With this sonde a continuous temperature may be read either going into the hole (which is best as the mud is undisturbed) or coming out. The temperature range of the tool is 0–200°C (0–392°F) with a quoted accuracy of ± 1°C (1.8°F) and resolution of 0.1°C (0.18°F) (EMS Tool brochure, Schlumberger). This is a modern tool; older tools were not as accurate (Hill 1990).

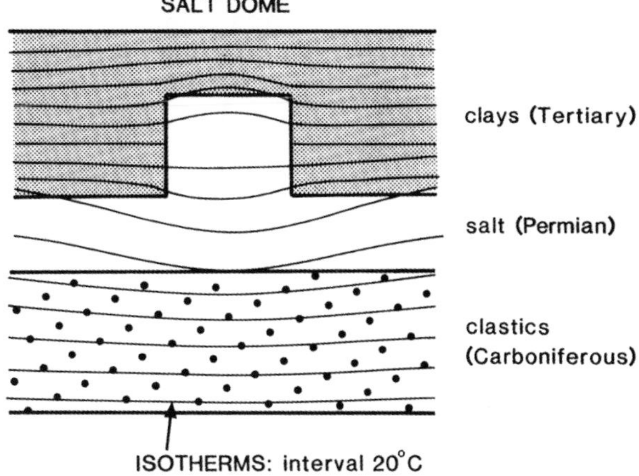

Figure 4.3 The theoretical distribution of isotherms around a salt dome indicated on a geological section: change in gradient is shown by isotherm spacing (re-drawn from Evans 1977).

When more detail is needed, a special thermometer tool may be used, such as the High Resolution Temperature/Acceleration/Pressure Tool (TAP) used by the Ocean Drilling Project (ODP). The tool uses two thermistors (a metal whose resistance is sensitive to temperature changes) fitted into the circuits of a Wheatstone bridge. The tool makes two measurements, one using the thinner, faster response thermistor, which records small abrupt changes and the other using the thicker, slower thermistor, which gives a more accurate thermal gradient (**Figure 4.4**). The temperature range of this tool is from −4°C to 85°C (25–185°F) with a quoted accuracy of 0.005°C (ODP documents).

A number of logging tool sensors, such as nuclear detectors and pressure detectors, are temperature sensitive. Also, the effects being measured may themselves be temperature dependent, as is the case with magnetisation in the NMR experiment (Chapter 13) and with resistivity (Chapter 7). Temperature log measurements are used, for example, to calibrate resistivity logs to standard temperature conditions, typically 24°C (75°F). Such effects are discussed in the individual tool chapters.

Most logging tools have a stated temperature rating, that is, a maximum temperature up to which they can function. This is typically either 177°C (350°F) or possi-

Table 4.4 Temperature measuring tools

Acronym	Name	Company
ERS	Environmental Measurement Sonde	Schlumberger
TTRM	Temp. Tension Resistivity Mud	Baker Hughes™
BHPT	Borehole Properties Tool	Halliburton
TAP	Temperature Acceleration Pressure	Ocean Drilling

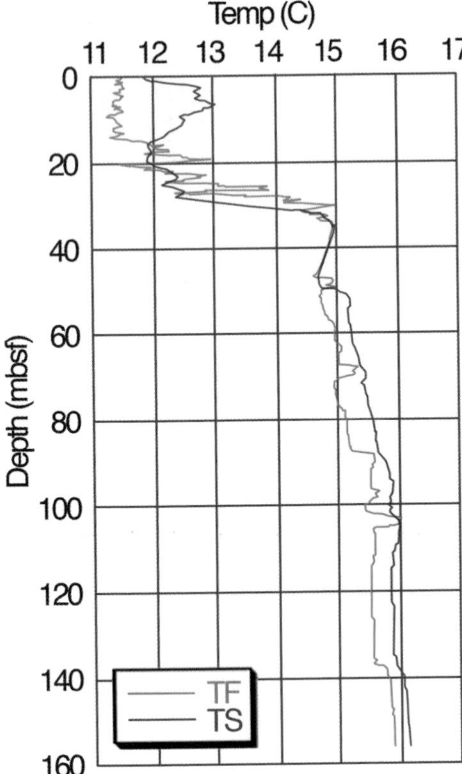

Figure 4.4 Detailed temperature measurements from the TAP tool. The smoother temperature is from the slow thermistor (TS, blue line). The fast thermistor (TF, red line) records local detail. The log should be recorded going into the hole (ODP document, http://iodp.ldeo.columbia.edu/) mbsf = meters below sea floor

bly for very hostile regions 260°C (500°F). High temperature is usually considered as above 150°C (300°F). Tool sensitivities to temperature will be mentioned under the tool chapters and will not be considered further here.

4.4 True formation temperatures and borehole corrections

Logging tool measurement corrections

The temperature measured in boreholes is not the formation temperature, it is the temperature of the mud in the borehole. Borehole mud is normally cooler than the formation being drilled (apart from the immediate surface strata). Thus, the invasion of mud filtrate into a formation near the borehole will cool it down immediately by convection. However, because of the infinite mass of the formation, the eventual equilibrium temperature of the filtrate, and even the borehole mud itself, will be that of the true formation temperature. Mud and filtrate will be heated up. But this process can only begin when mud circulation stops and, moreover, occurs through conduction and is very slow. Examination of the temperature from several wireline logging runs made at increasing time after drilling shows that equilibrium may be established only after months (**Figure 4.5**). Temperatures taken in boreholes during drilling or wireline logging are therefore consistently well below the true formation temperature.

To correct bottom-hole temperature (BHT) values numerous methods have been devised (cf. Hermanrud and Shen 1989). The modern tendency is to model the thermal recovery of a well from the available data but a generally accepted way of doing this does not exist and the results from presently available methods show considerable variation (Hermanrud and Shen 1989 *op. cit.*). One of the older and still frequently applied methods uses a Horner plot (Fertl and Timko 1972).

The Horner plot method, as applied to wireline logs, relies on the concept of a consistent and regular relationship between BHT and the log of $\Delta t/\Delta t + t$, where Δt = time in hours since circulation stopped, and t = time of circulation at TD before logging (**Figure 4.6**). Δt then represents the time available for an equilibrium temperature to be reached, while t represents the time that the formation is exposed to cooling mud. In practice, it is best to take t as the time needed to drill the last metre of hole plus the circulating time at TD (Serra 1979). Since a BHT is taken on each wireline tool descent, several temperature readings are available at different times after circulation stopped (Δt). The true formation temperature is on the line through these points where it crosses the abscissa at 1 (**Figure 4.6**). This form of correction

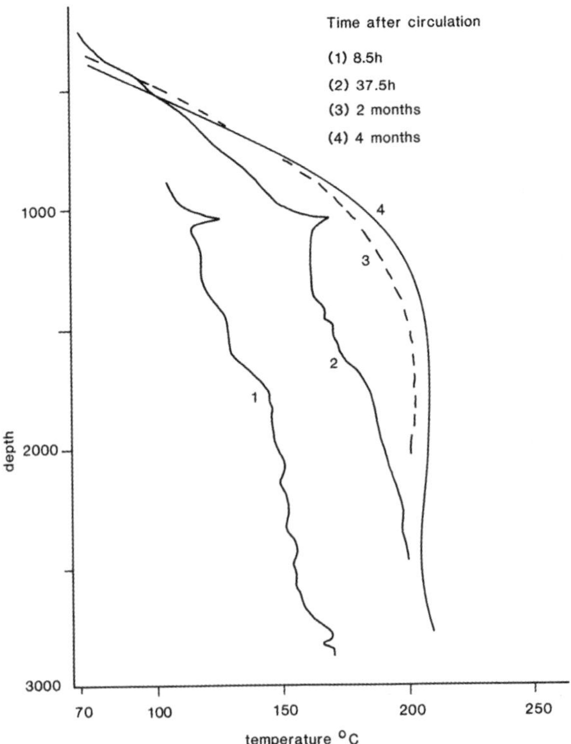

Figure 4.5 Change in borehole temperature with time (in a geothermal well). Equilibrium is only being re-established 4 months after circulation (i.e. drilling) stopped (re-drawn from Benoit *et al.* 1980).

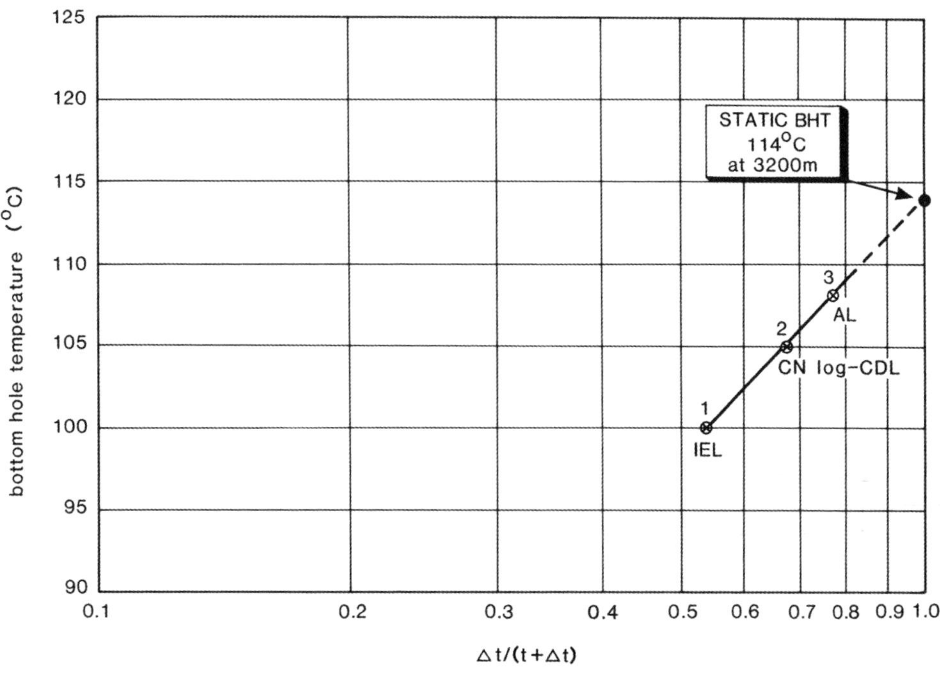

Log	Δt	Temperature recorded	Δt(t + Δt)
IEL	7	100°C	7/(6 + 7) = 0.538
CN-CDL	11.5	105°C	11.5/(6 + 11.5) = 0.671
AL	19.5	108°C	19.5/(6 + 19.5) = 0.765

Figure 4.6 Bottom hole temperature correction example. Δ*t*, time since circulation stopped (hours); *t*, circulation time (6 hours) (from Fertl and Wichmann 1977).

has a significant effect on measured temperatures and appears to make them more meaningful (**Figure 4.7**). It is a useful method for the multiple wireline logging runs of the pre-1990s.

Wireline Formation Tester measurements (WFT)

It is suggested that temperatures measured by wireline testing tools (Chapter 3), if taken correctly during sampling, can give the formation true static temperature (FTST) (Hashem and Ugueto 2003). When cool filtrate invades a formation, the invasion of fluid penetrates further into the formation than the change in temperature caused by the filtrate: the saturation front penetrates further than the temperature front (Hashem and Ugueto 2003 *op. cit.*). When the pressure tool takes a sample, the formation fluid is allowed to flow into the tool until an uncontaminated sample is obtained. That is, the fluid sample contains no filtrate. This fluid, by definition, is taken from beyond the saturation front and therefore from beyond the temperature front. If the temperature of the uncontaminated sample is measured, it will be the formation true static temperature (FTST).

The caveat to this being a true formation temperature is that it must be taken in a single phase, stabilised flow. In addition, the technique works better with synthetic oil-based mud (SOBM) than with water-based mud (WBM). It is nonetheless a source of true formation temperature (*see* Chapter 3).

4.5 Temperature log uses

Maturation of organic matter

Perhaps the best known use of borehole temperature measurements, using corrected BHT values, is for assessing a source rock's potential to produce. Organic matter maturity (the degree of conversion into hydrocarbons) is regulated by time, temperature and pressure. Temperature is considered the most important element but time is essential (Waples 1980).

A method for the quantification of hydrocarbon generation using the combined influence of temperature and time was proposed by the Russian, Lopatin (Waples 1980 *op. cit*). The method is based essentially on the time a source rock spends in a certain temperature range. For simple calculations, present day temperature gradients

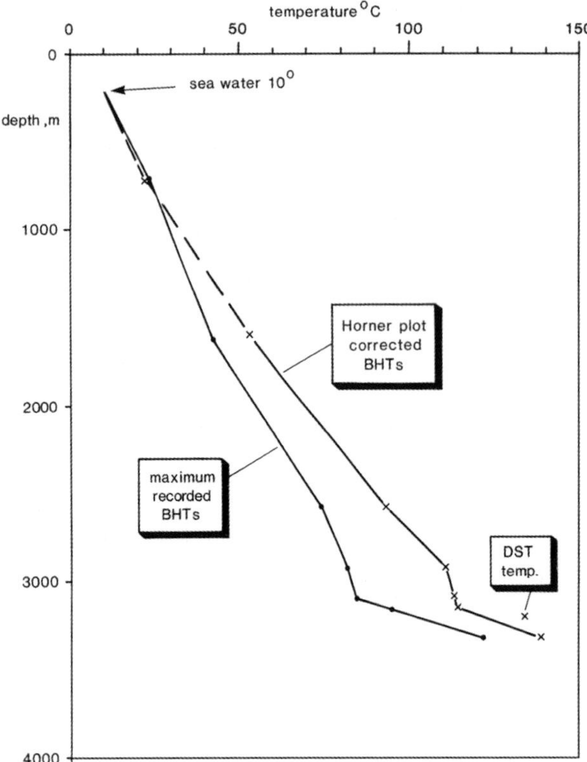

Figure 4.7 Effect of correcting recorded temperature by the Homer plot method. The correction is negative at surface (cold surface temperature) but requires up to 30°C increase at 3000 m. The Drill Stem Test (DST) temperature at 3200 m is considered to be a good measure of formation temperature (from stabilised build-up).

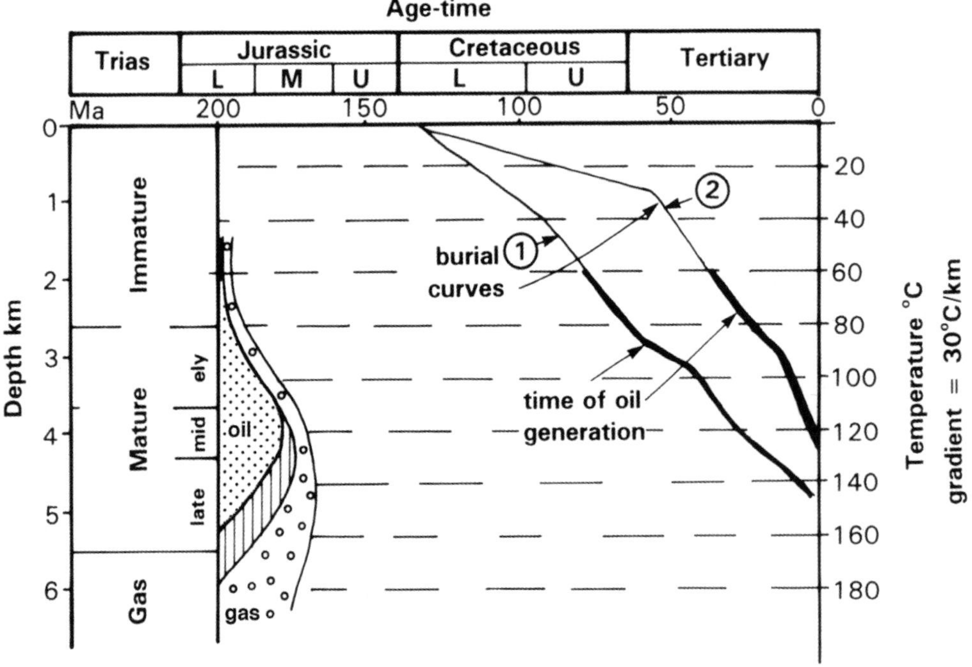

Figure 4.8 Source rock maturation plotted against geologic time. Well 1 shows oil generation from a lower Cretaceous source rock beginning in the Upper Cretaceous and continuing to the present. Well 2 shows the same source rock only beginning oil generation in the Mid-Tertiary and continuing to the present. The period of oil generation has been calculated using the method of Lopatin (Waples 1980) in which temperature is the major control through time. In this example the present day temperature gradient, derived from well logs, is extended back in time unchanged. The maturity scale to the left of the grid is schematic and based on temperature only.

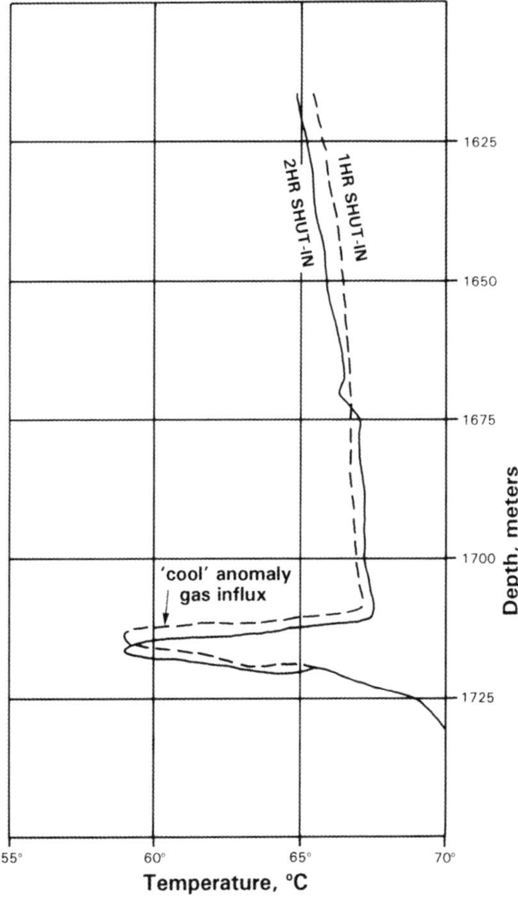

Figure 4.9 A borehole temperature anomaly caused by the influx of gas. The gas expands and cools on entering the mud-filled borehole (re-drawn from Hill, 1990 after McKinley 1981).

are extended back in time and combined with burial curves to arrive at a hydrocarbon generation curve (**Figure 4.8**). The temperature data used in this method generally come from simple BHT values, corrected to present day formation temperature (Section 4.4) and presented as a temperature gradient. This gradient is either extended back in time un-modified or, in more complex modeling, varied, based on geological arguments. The BHT measurements and corrections should obviously be as accurate as possible.

For detailed discussions on the use of temperature in organic matter studies and the use of time and temperature to predict maturity, specialist papers and books should be consulted (esp. Waples 1980).

Locating fluid movement and overpressure from temperature gradients

The typical, gradually increasing geothermal gradient measured down a (not circulating) drilling mud column, can be disturbed by any inflow of formation fluids (flow into the borehole) or outflow of drilling fluids (into the formation). A temperature anomaly is caused which may be either an increase or a decrease, depending on conditions. This type of examination requires continuous temperature profiling logged while running into the borehole.

For example, a sharp increase in temperature gradient downwards when drilling into high pressure shales (under compacted) has been reported (Lewis and Rose 1970). This increase is due to the high content of hot (i.e. at formation temperature) formation water in the overpressured shales. The formation water enters the borehole and causes the anomalous temperature rise in the mud. However, studies at a regional scale suggest that there is actually no statistical correlation between overpressure and temperature deflections (Kubala *et al.* 2003).

Nonetheless, if there is a direct, continuous flow of formation water or hydrocarbon fluids into the borehole, then the logged temperature will show a marked increase at the inflow point (Hill 1990). This is because the inflowing fluids are at formation temperature which, in a newly drilled well, is higher than the mud temperature (cf. **Figure 4.5**). If gaseous hydrocarbons enter the well, however, a cool anomaly is seen: the gas expands on entering the borehole, dropping rapidly in temperature (**Figure 4.9**).

In the same way as inflows to the borehole from the

formation produce temperature anomalies, so also does an outflow or loss of drilling fluid (Hill 1990). Typically, where the cooler drilling fluid enters into the formation, there will be a cool temperature anomaly. This effect is used to identify hydraulically fractured zones (i.e. purposely fractured for production) where a pre-fracturing gradient will contrast with the post-fracturing gradient, which shows a cool anomaly opposite the fractures (**Figure 4.10**). Multiple, closely spaced (in time) passes of the temperature log are especially effective in these cases and allow continuous changes in convection effects (fluid movement) to be monitored, which are rapid, as opposed to conduction effects, which are slow (Alm 1992).

The use of the continuous temperature log to detect fluid movement is most common in production logging (Hill, 1990) but the same principles can be used effectively in un-cased (open hole) exploration wells. This is not generally the case, strangely.

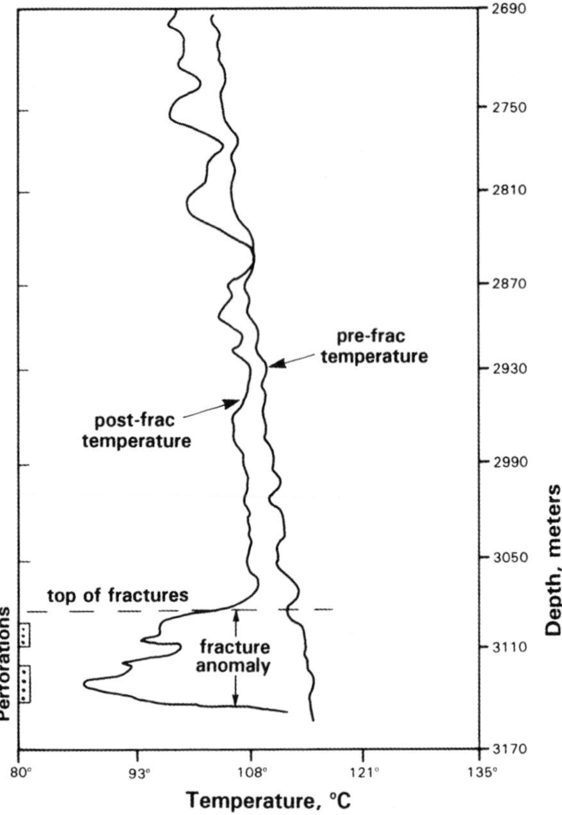

Figure 4.10 A borehole temperature anomaly created by hydraulic fracturing. Borehole mud enters the created fractures causing a cool anomaly which did not exist before fracturing was done (re-drawn from Hill, 1990 after Dobkin, 1981).

5
CALIPER LOGS

5.1 Generalities

Caliper tools measure hole size and shape. The simple mechanical (wireline) caliper measures a vertical profile of hole diameter (**Figure 5.1**). Wireline calipers with up to six independent arms give a more detailed assessment of borehole shape, while borehole geometry tools record the orientation of the caliper arms in addition. Acoustic calipers, which are integral to some tools, are a new generation of measurement in which acoustic signals are used to derive a very detailed, oriented borehole size and shape that can be displayed as 3-D images. Finally, a 'virtual' caliper can be calculated from some modern, multi-sensor tool responses as a secondary output. Some of these are also able to be displayed as 3-D images.

5.2 Caliper tools

Mechanical calipers

The mechanical caliper measures variations in borehole diameter with depth. The tools can only work in the wireline environment. In the simplest tool, the measure-

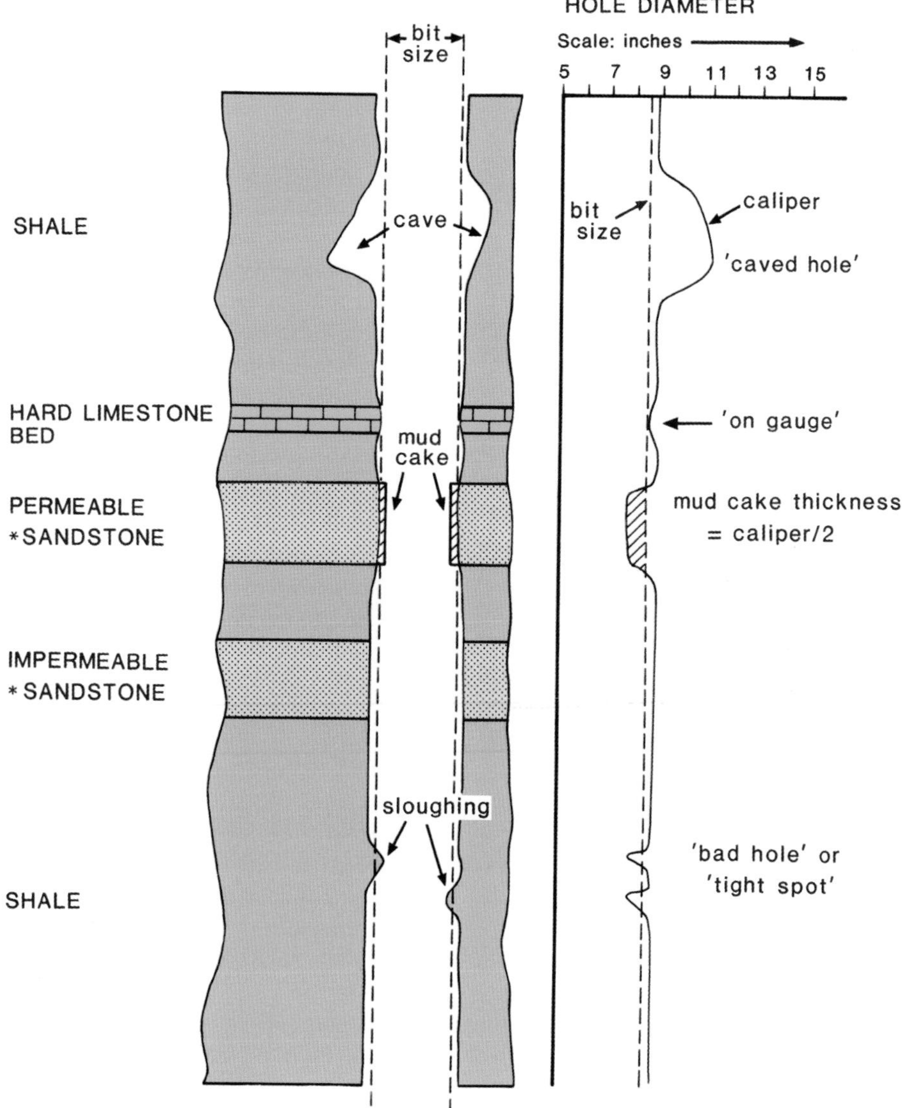

Figure 5.1 The simple wireline, mechanical caliper showing hole diameter and some typical responses. * Limestone, dolomite etc. equally applicable.

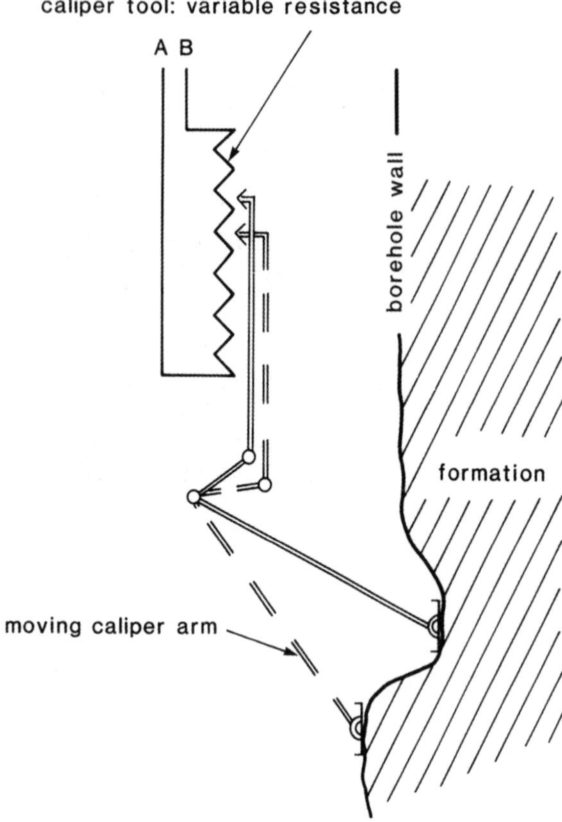

Figure 5.2 Schematic caliper tool showing the conversion of a mechanical movement to an electrical signal using a variable resistance (adapted from Serra 1979).

ments are made by two articulated arms pushed against the borehole wall. In the original design, the lateral movement of the caliper arms was linked to the cursor of a variable resistance, so that any movement was translated into variations of electrical output (**Figure 5.2**). Variations in electrical output can be translated into diameter variations after a simple calibration. In wireline tools where an arm is used to apply the sensor head to the borehole wall, such as in the electrical micrologs (Chapter 7) and in the density and neutron tools (Chapters 10, 11), a simple caliper measurement is integral to the response.

Dual caliper tools, such as the Borehole Geometry Tool of Schlumberger (wireline), exist specifically for measuring hole size and volume, although such information can be taken from dipmeter or imaging tools, which acquire geometry data in order to derive dip or an image (Chapters 14, 15). The geometry tools from Schlumberger have four pads fixed at right angles, opposite pairs being linked but independent of the perpendicular set. In terms of geometry, this gives two independent calipers at 90°. The tool also contains orientation equipment so that the azimuth (bearing) of the two calipers is constantly defined. Similar information, but from six independent caliper arms, comes from six arm dipmeters (i.e. the Halliburton SED), which give an even better assessment of borehole size, shape and orientation.

Acoustic calipers

The acoustic or ultrasonic caliper derives borehole size and shape using an ultrasound sound source (transducer), housed in the tool and used to reflect a signal off the borehole wall as it rotates (**Figure 15.11**). Either the tool itself rotates, as in the LWD environment, or a rotating source is used, as in the wireline acoustic image logs. The time it takes for the signal to travel from the tool and back (the emitter is also the receiver) is converted to hole size. The acoustic imaging tools acquire data in sufficient detail to be able to display hole shape in three dimensions, either as a wire-frame or an actual image (**Figure 5.3**).

In the LWD environment, mechanical calipers are not possible since tools generally rotate and extended arms would be quickly torn off. LWD density measurements are especially sensitive to *stand-off* (the distance between a sensor and the formation), so LWD density tools usually include an acoustic caliper transducer, or even 3 separate transducers, to measure this (Molz 2000). Sampling can be quite rapid, for example, every 125 milliseconds, and statistical combinations are used to produce data points (Dowla *et al.* 2006). In addition, the measurements are oriented using the tool's magnetometer information, so that as well as size, an accurate hole shape can be calculated related to true north and the tool's axis (**Figure 5.3**).

Any acoustic caliper calculation requires an accurate mud velocity under downhole conditions to be known. This is derived either from general algorithms or mud samples, and results can be quality checked against other methods of measurement or even tested inside the casing. Acoustic calipers and image logs are described in greater detail in the chapter on imaging (Chapter 15). They are an integral part of the output from the acoustic imaging tools.

Virtual calipers

Multi-sensor or multi-measurement tools can provide sufficient data for a 'virtual caliper' to be calculated. That is, borehole size and shape can be inferred from the effect that they have on a tool's signals. These are indirect effects and are not either a direct measurement or a primary output of the tool. Resistivity, neutron, density and photoelectric (PEF) measurements can all be used in this way. Such virtual caliper estimates are especially useful in the LWD environment where sensors rotate but, as pointed out, no mechanical measurements are possible. Only the generalities of virtual caliper derivation are given in this section: more details appear in the relevant tool chapters.

Modern LWD resistivity tools take many raw measurements and produce a large volume of data from

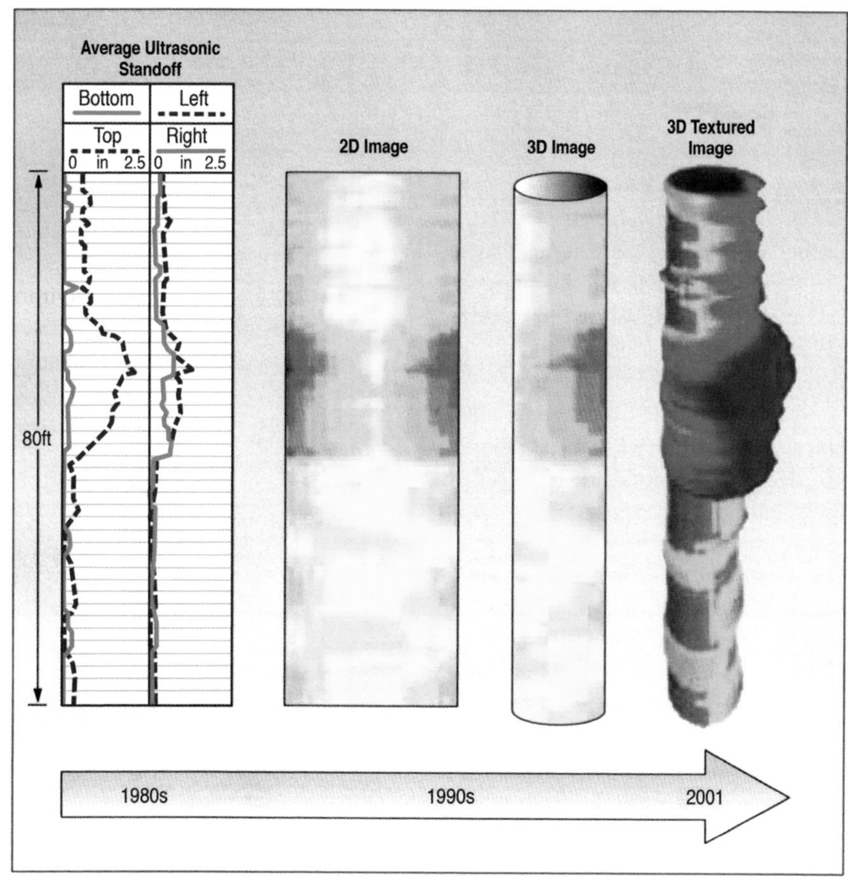

Figure 5.3 The progression from the single value, oriented acoustic calipers of the 1980s, to the 2-D and 3-D oriented images of the 1990s, and to the 3-D textured caliper images of the new millennium (from Inaba *et al.* 2003). *Copyright Schlumberger Ltd. Used with permission.*

which a virtual caliper can be calculated. This is because within this large volume of data are signals that are mainly influenced by the borehole immediately around the tool and others that are hardly affected at all. Special processing can enhance the borehole effect (Dowla *et al.* 2006), and when mud resistivity and temperature are known (water based mud must be used), and conditions are optimum, a stand-off and caliper can be calculated (**Figure 5.4**) (Chapter 7, Resistivity).

Nuclear measurements of density and neutron porosity are made by tools with two detectors, a near and a far (or short spaced and long spaced). The immediate borehole environment has a large effect on the near detector and this can be extracted to give, as with the resistivity, a stand-off and caliper. The LWD neutron caliper is calculated even if the tool does not turn, and represents a volume around the tool, but with no directionality. An oval hole, for example, cannot be identified. The LWD density tool, however, acquires density data by sector, normally 16, so that 16, individual, oriented caliper estimates can be calculated every time the tool turns. These data indicate hole size and (oriented) shape, and can be presented as a 3-D image (cf. **Figure 5.3**). Although processing is different, the photoelectric (PEF) measure-

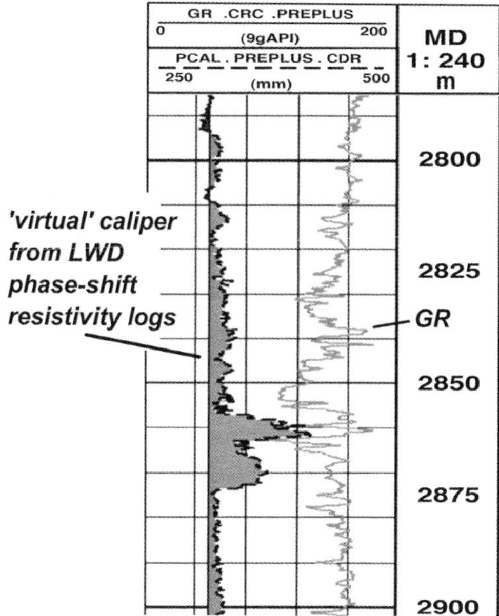

Figure 5.4 A 'virtual caliper' calculated from a set of LWD, 2 MHz phase shift (phase average), resistivity logs. Water based mud, good mud to formation resistivity contrast (modified from Dowla *et al.* SPWLA 2006).

ment, which is also acquired by the density tool, can similarly be used as a caliper image (Chapter 10, Density and PEF; Chapter 11, Neutron).

The rest of this chapter considers only the various mechanical, wireline calipers.

5.3 Log presentations

The caliper log is output simply as a continuous value of hole diameter with depth (**Figure 5.5**). The curve is traditionally a dashed line and usually plotted in track 1 of the API format (**Figure 1.8**). The horizontal scale is inches of hole diameter or, in the differential caliper, expressed as increase or decrease in hole diameter about a zero defined by the bit size (**Figure 5.5,2**). The standard caliper log is accompanied by a reference line indicating bit size. Almost always, the caliper measurement and the bit size are given in inches regardless of the depth units used for the well. This is because most drill bits and oilfield tubular goods are measured in imperial units.

The geometrical data from four-arm, dual-caliper tools, such as the dipmeter, are presented in various formats, only one of which is shown (**Figure 5.6**). The two, independent hole diameters measured by the two calipers are plotted along with the directional elements of tool orientation (P1AZ, pad 1 azimuth), amount of hole deviation (DEVI) and azimuth or direction (HAZI) of the deviation. An integrated hole volume may be added as horizontal ticks on the depth column, giving a continuous record of hole volume based on the caliper readings (not on the example).

The calipers of the example presented (**Figure 5.6**), show the geometry tool turning slowly as it moves upwards in a persistently oval hole with a small diameter of approximately 9″ and a large diameter of approximately 11″. The larger diameter is oriented nearly north

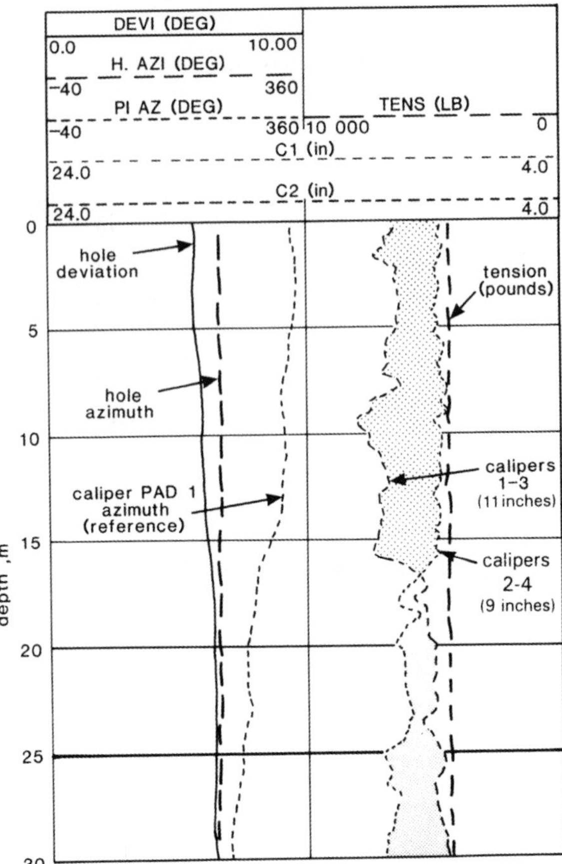

Figure 5.6 Wireline borehole geometry log presentation (*see* text for explanation).

to south as indicated by the pad 1 azimuth over the depth 0–15 m (calipers 1–3 in larger diameter). At depth 30 m, calipers 2–4 show the larger diameter (approx. 11″), with calipers 1–3 the smaller (approx. 9″). The rotation of the tool is indicated by the persistent change in the pad 1 azimuth (P1AZ) and explains the caliper cross-over at 17 m (where both calipers show the same diameter but the hole is still oval). Above this, calipers 1–3 follow the larger diameter (approx. 11″), while calipers 2–4 follow the smaller (approx. 9″).

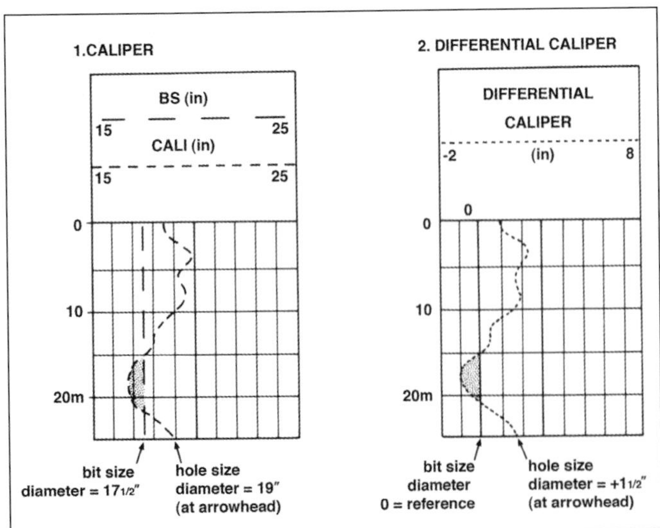

Figure 5.5 Presentation of the caliper log: (1), in ordinary format; (2), in differential format. BS = bit size.

5.4 Simple, two-arm, wireline caliper interpretation

Increase in borehole diameter

The simple caliper log records the mechanical response of the formation to drilling. A hole that has the same size (diameter) as the bit which drilled it is called *on gauge* (**Figure 5.1**). On gauge holes are the target for all drilling and essentially indicate good drilling technique. Holes with a much larger diameter than the bit size are *'caved'* or *'washed out'*. That is, during deepening of the hole, the

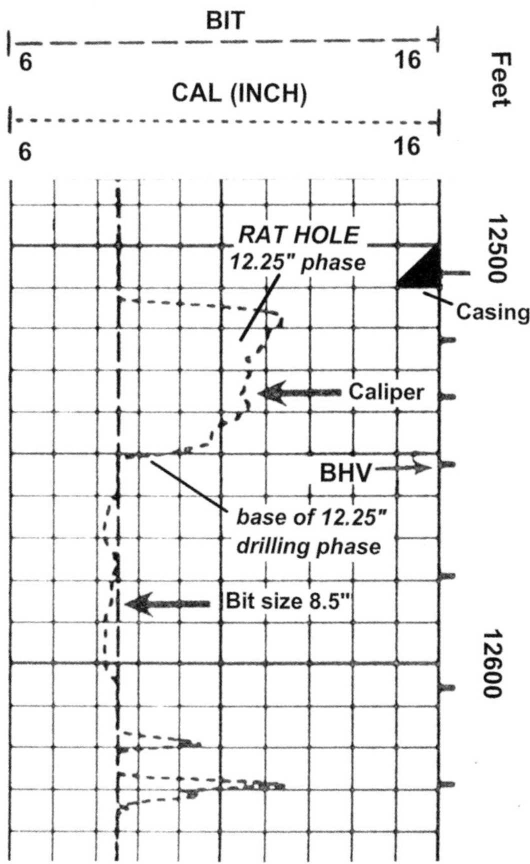

Figure 5.7 The 'rat hole' below a 12.25" casing shoe at the top of an 8.5" drilling phase. The 12.25" drilling was stopped at 12,550 ft and the casing set 40 ft above. BIT = bit size (8.5"); CAL = caliper; BHV = borehole volume. Each tick is separated by 10 ft³ of hole volume.

borehole walls cave in, are broken by the turning drill pipe, or are eroded away by the circulating borehole mud. This is typical of intervals of shales or clays, especially when they are geologically young and unconsolidated, so that caving can have a general lithological significance (**Figure 5.1**). However, caving is also typical of certain specific lithologies such as coals or organic shales, which are often finely laminated. In some fields, even with varied drilling fluids and drilling techniques, it is found that certain stratigraphic levels habitually cave – generally for mechanical (textural) reasons.

A special case of oversized borehole exists below casing (**Figure 5.7**). When a larger drilling phase is changed, casing is set before the deeper, smaller phase is begun. However, casing is not set at the bottom of the larger phase, a section of the hole is left open below the casing shoe (the bottom of the casing) to allow work, such as cementation, to take place. This is called the '*rat hole*' and can be anything from 10 m–30 m (50 ft to 100 ft) (**Figure 5.7**). The rat hole will be filled with cement when the drilling of the following phase begins, but this usually works loose and leaves it appearing to be a large cave. Log quality over the rat hole is poor.

One particular type of hole that can develop under badly configured drilling conditions is that of a spiral hole. This is identified on the caliper as a consistent, wavy diameter with a specific wavelength (**Figure 5.8**). It is caused by a vibration during drilling between the bit and the stabilizers of the bottom-hole assembly (BHA) and brought into play when a certain weight (too much) is put on the bit. The wavy caliper means that the hole has a cork-screw shape which makes it very difficult for many tools to log properly, especially those with sensors which need to be pressed against the borehole wall. Spiral hole is also accompanied by vibrations at the bit during drilling, which can cause LWD tool failure. It is effectively a result of bad drilling practice.

Decrease in borehole diameter

Wireline mechanical calipers may show a hole diameter smaller than the bit size. If the log has a smooth, regular profile, a mudcake build-up is indicated (**Figure 5.9,a**). This is an extremely useful indicator of permeability as only permeable beds allow mudcake to form. Sections of mudcake will indicate clearly the intervals of potential (permeable) reservoir, and build-ups will correspond to certain lithological responses seen on other logs. For example, a low gamma ray indicating a sandsone will also correspond to intervals of mudcake.

Mudcake thickness can be estimated from the caliper

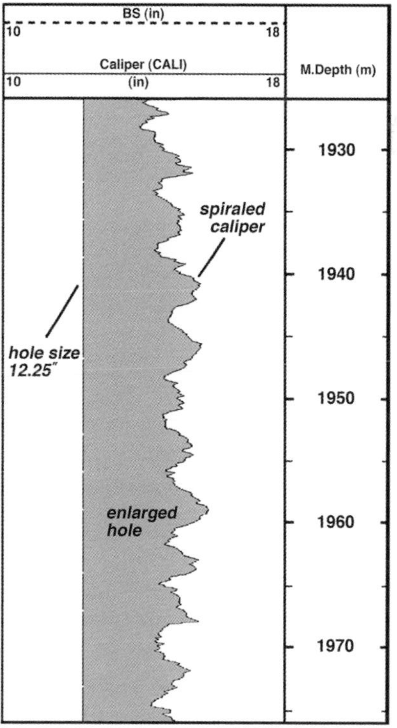

Figure 5.8 Caliper showing spiraled and caved borehole through a shale drilled with a 12.25" bit. The spiraling in this example continued until the bit and the bottom-hole assembly were changed.

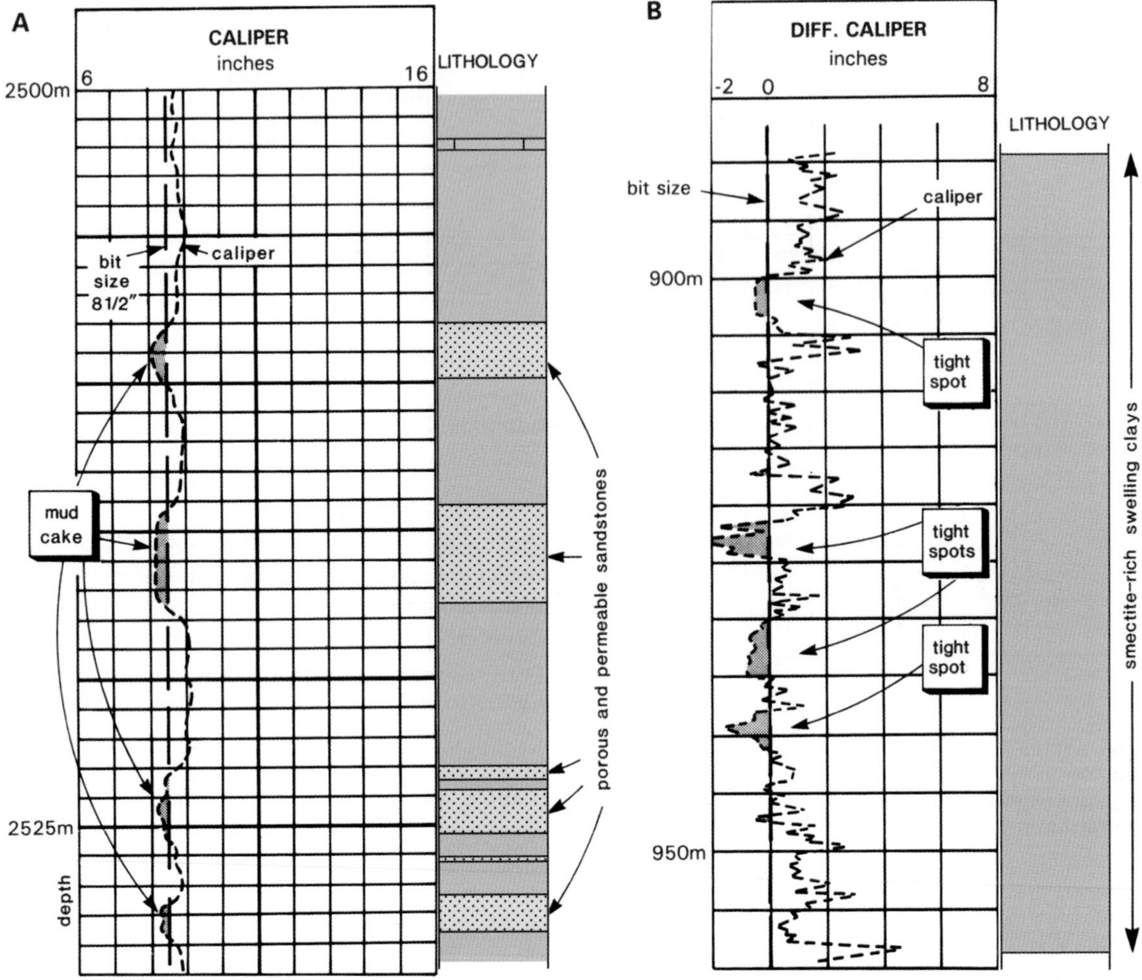

Figure 5.9 Hole size diminution seen on the simple caliper. A. Mudcake build-up opposite porous and permeable sandstones. B. Tight spots in a shale sequence caused by borehole wall sloughing in swelling, smectite rich clays.

by dividing the decrease in hole size by two (the caliper giving the hole diameter), i.e.

$$\frac{\text{bit size (diam)} - \text{caliper reading (diam)}}{2} = \text{mudcake thickness}$$

It should be remembered that this thickness may vary between tools. The caliper of an older wireline density tool, for example, was applied harder to the formation than the caliper of the wireline microlog, the former causing a groove in the mudcake and therefore giving a thinner, log derived mudcake thickness.

Boreholes with a smaller diameter than the bit size, but which are ragged and rugose, are probably sloughed (**Figure 5.9,b**). The intervals of reduced hole will be the 'tight spots' encountered during drilling, trips or logging. That is, it will be at these points that tools stick or the bit gets stuck while being pulled out of the hole. There will be no correspondence between the tight spots and lithological indicators of reservoir on other logs as in the case of mudcake. Sloughing will invariably occur in a shale interval and a frequent cause is abundant smectite in the clay mineral mixture of the formation. Smectite is a swelling clay which takes water from the drilling mud, increases in volume, breaks from the borehole wall and sloughs, or collapses, into the hole. The Gulf Coast 'gumbo', which often causes hole problems, is smectite rich.

Quality control using the caliper

An extremely important use of any type of caliper is in the quality control of logs in general. When caving is serious, the quality of log readings is impaired. In some tools, such as the wireline micrologs, a caliper is registered simply because the tool sensors are pad mounted. Lack of contact with the formation, a problem in rugose holes with any pad-mounted tool, is quickly seen by using the caliper. For modern tools without a mechanical caliper, the 'virtual caliper', or stand-off derived from processing, takes the place of an actual caliper in quality control (**Figure 5.4**).

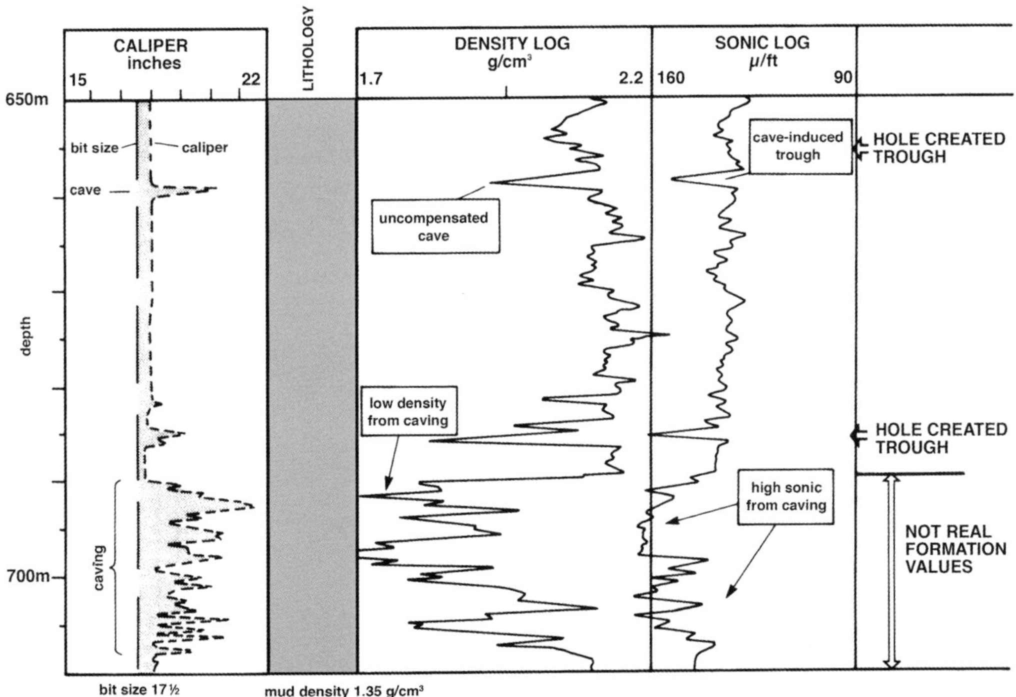

Figure 5.10 Poor hole conditions and caving causing zones of poor data quality where log readings do not represent real formation values. Above 680 m both the density and sonic are reading the formation. Below 690 m, because of the caving and irregular hole shape, they are both reading largely borehole mud values. The clay/shale lithology is consistent through the interval shown, being poorly consolidated.

The quality control example shows a wireline density and a sonic through an interval of poorly consolidated clay or shale (**Figure 5.10**). Below 690 m the hole is extensively caved and very irregular (rugose), with the logs badly affected. Both logs are reading values more indicative of the mud than the formation. Real formation values are represented by the readings above 680 m where the hole conditions are good. Caving often requires inordinately large corrections and the log values will be of little use. It is therefore essential to look at the caliper before beginning any interpretation

It should be noted that the simple, mechanical caliper attached to the wireline, open hole tools such as the micrologs and the density, will generally be pessimistic in terms of hole condition, because in oval boreholes a simple, mechanical caliper will naturally open to the maximum diameter (**Figure 5.11**). In this situation, while the log measurements recorded will be made across the larger diameter, the hole condition itself is not as bad as may first appear.

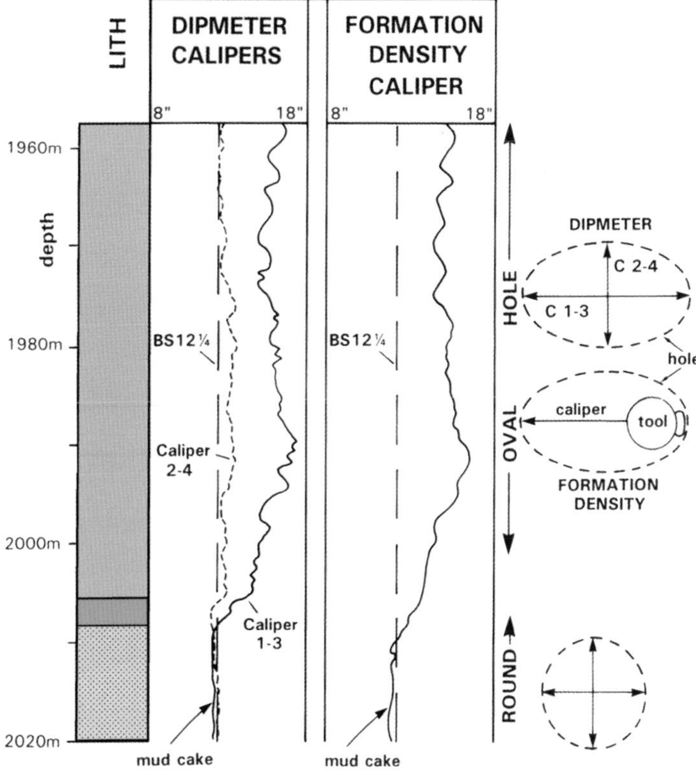

Figure 5.11 Comparison between the simple caliper of the formation density tool and the two-arm caliper of the dipmeter tool, in an oval hole. The simple caliper normally expands to the long axis in an oval hole.

5.5 Four-arm caliper interpretation

Breakouts

A great deal more information can be gained from the dual caliper, wireline, borehole geometry tools than from a simple caliper tool. As indicated previously, dual caliper information can be taken from the dipmeter (4 or 6-arm) or the electrical imaging tools.

Using just one caliper pair, borehole shape cannot be interpreted. With data from a multi-arm caliper, the shape can be much better defined. A hole can be seen to be 'on gauge' and round (**Figure 5.12,a**) or enlarged and oval due to various causes (**Figure 5.12,b,c,d**). Using a borehole geometry tool allows different shapes to be defined and classified and their causes interpreted. (Modern imaging tools give even greater caliper detail, even 3-D images, and are discussed in Chapter 15, Image Logs).

Three main types of elliptical borehole have been recognised, *'keyseats'*, *'washouts'* and *'breakouts'* (**Figure 5.12**). Washouts develop from general drilling wear, especially in shaly zones and dipping beds. On the geometry logs, a washout has a considerable vertical extent and both calipers are larger than the drill bit size, with one caliper being much larger than the other. Shape changes are variable and gradual (**Figures 5.12,c; 5.13,2**). Keyseats are asymmetric oval holes, formed by wear against the drill string at points where the borehole inclination changes (doglegs) (**Figure 5.12,b**). Both washouts and keyseats are general drilling phenomena: breakouts, however, have a specific cause.

Breakouts are recognised using the following strict criteria to avoid being confused with general drilling phenomena (**Figures 5.13,1; 5.14**) (i.e. Bell 1990):

1. The tool must stop rotating (ideally the tool should rotate before and after a breakout zone).
2. The calipers must separate to indicate an oval hole. The larger caliper should exceed hole gauge: the smaller caliper should not be less than hole gauge and its trace should be straight (the caliper difference should be larger than 6 mm (0.2") and the zone of elongation greater than 1.5 m or 5 ft). The limits of the breakout should normally be well marked.
3. The larger diameter of hole elongation and its direction should not consistently coincide with the azimuth of hole deviation.

Breakouts form as a result of the interaction between stresses around the borehole caused by drilling the hole, and the existing stress regime in the country rock (Bell and Gough 1979). Small brittle fractures (spalling) occur in the borehole wall around a rotating bit, which, if there are unequal horizontal stresses in the formation, form in a preferential direction, that of the minimum horizontal stress, Sh_{min} (**Figure 5.15,a**). In more precise terms, compressive shear fracturing of the borehole wall is localised in the direction of the minimum horizontal

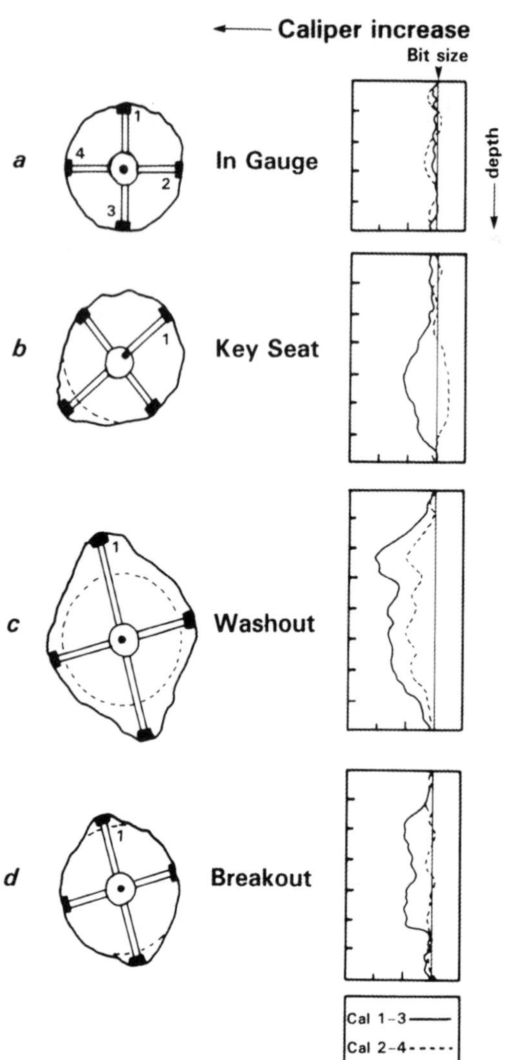

Figure 5.12 Diagrammatic representation of types of borehole shape and profile as identified on the two-arm caliper. a. Round, in-gauge hole. b. Key seat hole enlargement at a dogleg. c. Washout hole enlargement due to general drilling wear. d. Breakout, showing characteristic oval hole with abrupt vertical limits (re-drawn, modified from Plumb and Hickman 1985).

formation stress Sh_{min} and is the cause of breakouts (Bell 1990). Mud weight also has an influence (Lindsay *et al.* 2007). Laboratory experiments and empirical observations back up the theory (*see* Prensky 1992b for a review and references). Hence, breakouts indicate the present day stress-field orientation and are independent of lithology, dip and existing fractures or joints. They are often associated with drilling induced fractures. Breakouts only form in low permeability formations such as shales. Where there is mudcake and permeability, there are no breakouts.

Breakout studies to define *in-situ* stress fields have been carried out on many scales from the local (**Figure 5.16**) to the global (www-wsm.physik.uni-karlsruhe.de).

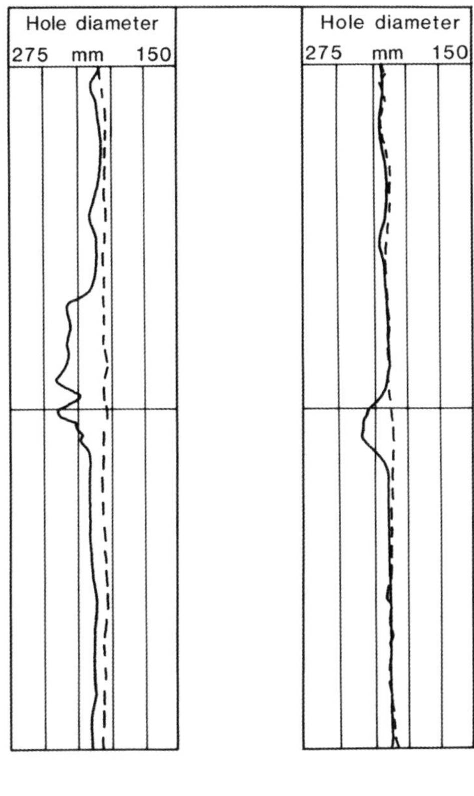

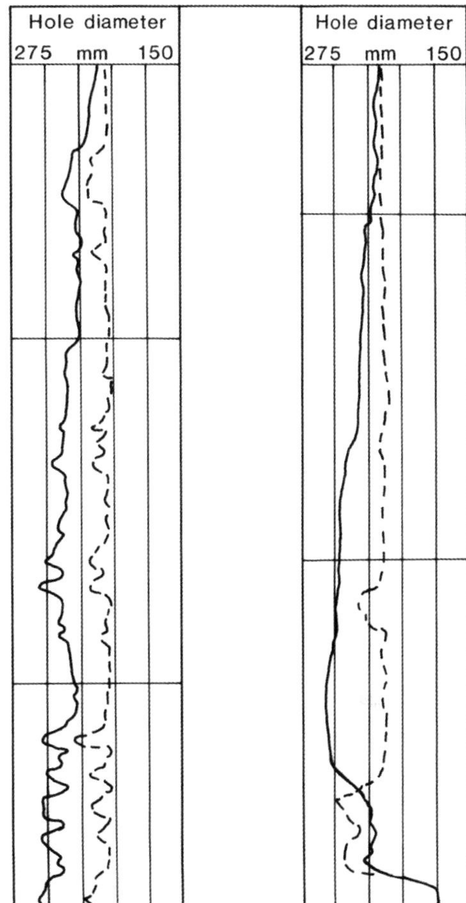

Figure 5.13 Field examples of hole size enlargement seen on the two-arm, dual caliper. 1. Breakouts, seen as well-defined, oval hole developments. 2. Washouts, seen as generalised hole ovality. Hole diameter increases to the left (from Cox 1983).

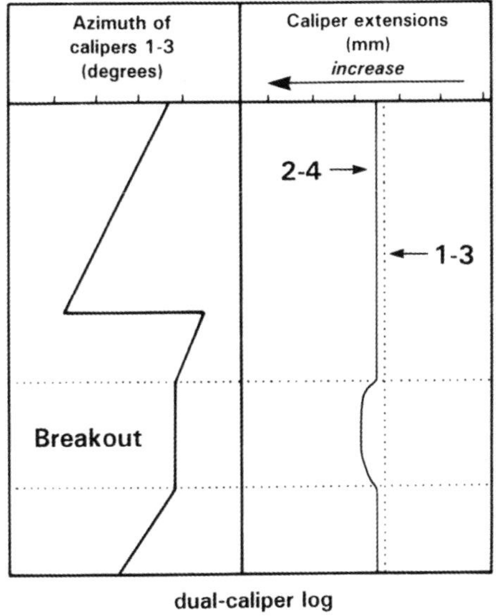

Figure 5.14 Schematic representation of the characteristics used to identify breakouts on caliper logs (re-drawn from Yassir and Dusseault 1992).

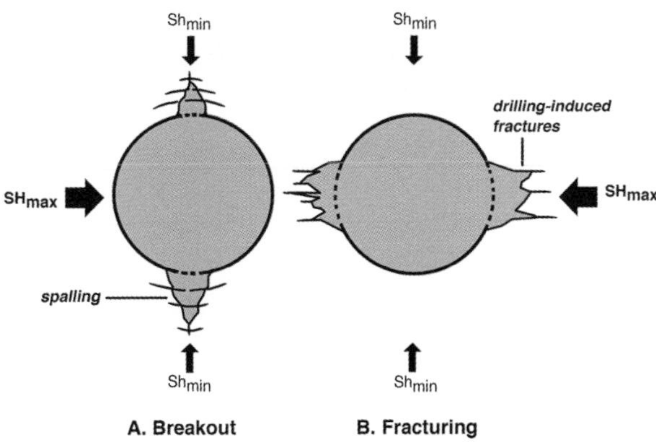

Figure 5.15 Horizontal stress-field relationship to borehole shape. A. Breakout formation due to spalling during drilling, in the direction of minimum horizontal stress (Sh_{min}). B. Hole enlargement along drilling induced extensional fractures or enlarged natural fractures oriented in the direction of maximum horizontal stress (SH_{max}) (re-drawn, modified after Dart and Zoback 1989; Hillis and Williams 1992).

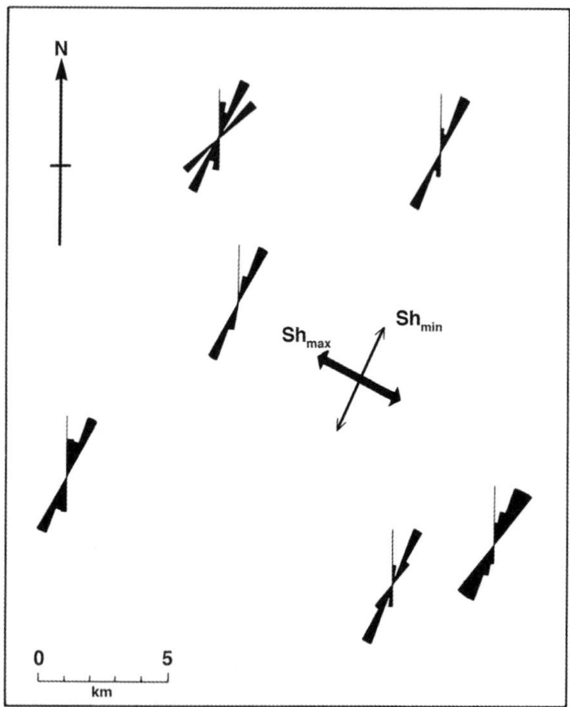

Figure 5.16 Consistently oriented breakouts identified from dipmeter caliper data in an offshore field, indicating the present day, horizontal stress-field. Depth of analysed interval from 2.5 to 3.5 kilometres (8000–11,500 ft). Sh_{min} = minimum horizontal stress, Sh_{max} = maximum horizontal stress.

On the global scale, breakout derived stress-field orientations are similar to those derived from earthquake studies and tend to indicate intra-plate tectonic stresses (**Figure 5.17**) (Zoback *et al.* 1989).

On a local scale, breakout studies have an importance for borehole stability and field development. Drilling related and induced artificial fractures are most likely to be oriented in the maximum horizontal stress direction Sh_{max} (i.e. normal to breakouts) (**Figure 5.15,b**). Artificial fracture connection between wells during field production is then more likely in this orientation (Bell 1990). Horizontal drilling is often more stable in the Sh_{max} (maximum horizontal stress) direction (Hillis and Williams 1992).

(Breakouts are also discussed under Borehole Imaging Tools, Chapter 15, and borehole stresses are described in Chapter 9, Sonic Log)

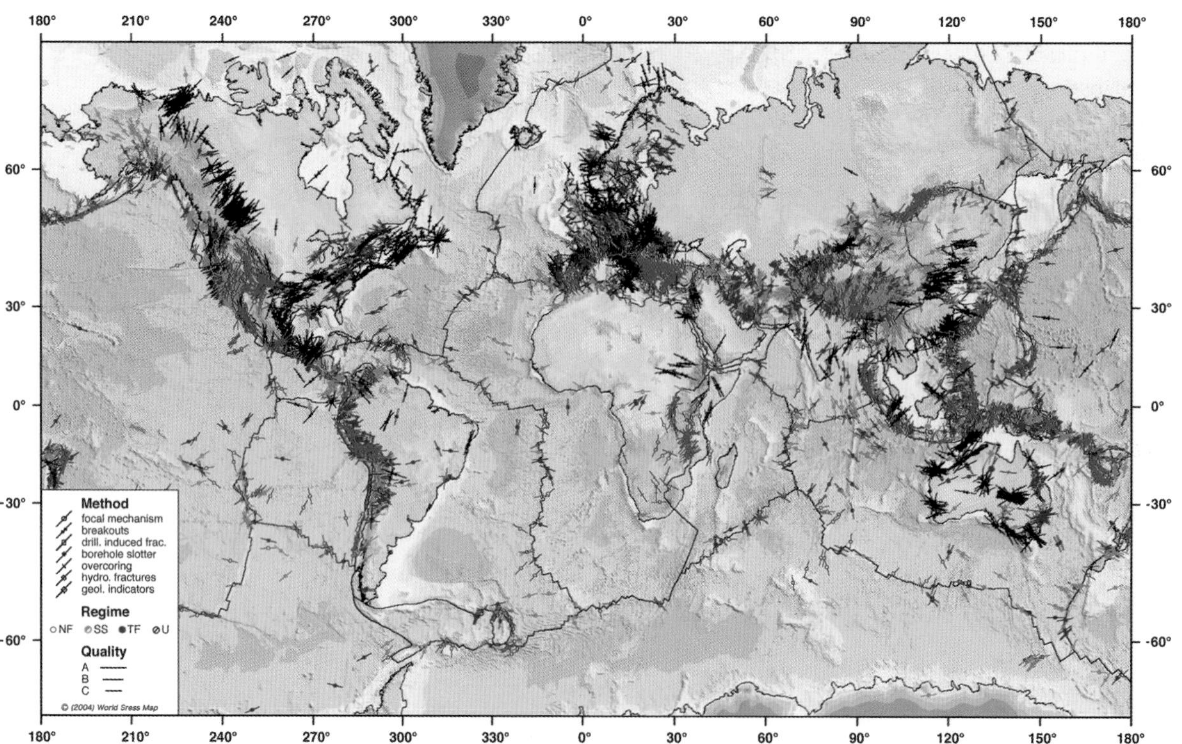

Figure 5.17 The World Stress Map constructed from borehole data, direct measurements, earthquake interpretation and other indications (*see* www-wsm.physik.uni-karlsruhe.de).

6 SELF POTENTIAL OR SP LOGS

6.1 Generalities

The log

The SP log is a measurement of the natural potential differences or self-potentials between an electrode in the borehole and a reference electrode at the surface: no artificial currents are applied (**Figure 6.2**). (The currents were actually called *'potentiels spontanés'*, or 'spontaneous potentials', by Conrad Schlumberger and Henri Doll, who discovered them.) They originate from the electrical disequilibrium created by connecting formations down the borehole (in the electrical sense) when, in nature, they are isolated. The SP only exists as a wireline tool and cannot function in oil based mud (OBM).

Principal uses

The principal uses of the SP log are to estimate shale volume (V_{sh}), identify fresh water and to indicate permeability. It was used (alone) in the past to calculate formation-water resistivity, although more recently it has been suggested that this is best done by inverting the SP with the resistivity logs (Salazaar *et al.* 2007). The SP can be used to indicate facies and, in some cases, for correlation (**Table 6.1**, **Figure 6.1**).

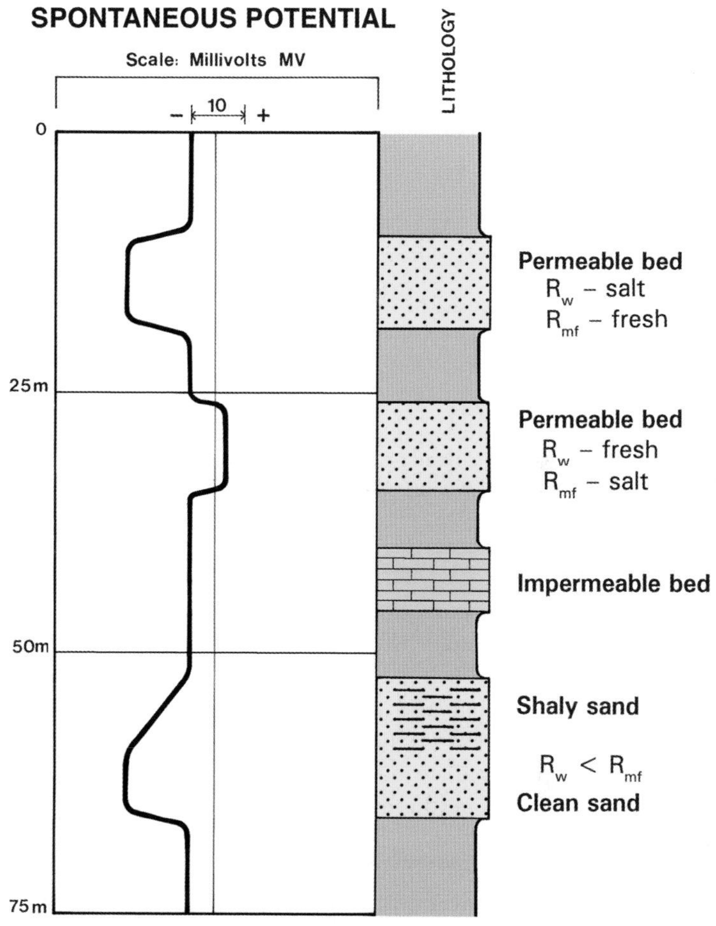

Figure 6.1 The SP log: some typical responses. The SP log shows variations in natural potentials. R_w = formation-water resistivity; R_{mf} = mud filtrate resistivity.

Table 6.1 The principal uses of the SP log.

	Discipline	Used for	Knowing
Quantitative	Petrophysics	shale volume (V_{sh})	SSP and shale line
		formation-water resistivity (salinity)	mud filtrate resistivity and formation temperature
		Rw and *m*	inversion with resistivity logs in a water zone
Qualitative	Petrophysics	permeability indicator Fresh Water	shale line mud filtrate salinity
	Geology	facies (shaliness)	clay/grain size relationships
		Correlation	

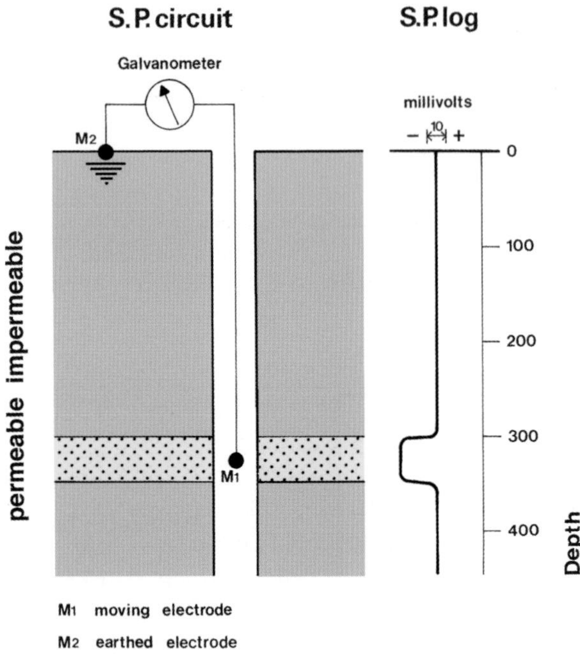

Figure 6.2 Illustration of the principle of the SP log. A natural potential is measured between an electrode in the well and an earth at the surface.

6.2 Principles of measurement

Three factors are necessary to provoke an SP current: a conductive fluid in the borehole; a porous and permeable bed surrounded by an impermeable formation; and a difference in salinity (or pressure) between the borehole fluid and the formation fluid. In oilfield wells, the two fluids concerned are the mud filtrate and (usually), formation water.

SP currents are created when two solutions of different salinity concentrations are in contact. There are two principal electrochemical effects; *diffusion or liquid junction potential* and *shale or membrane potential* (**Figure 6.3**). The diffusion potential (or liquid junction potential) arises when solutions of differing salinity are in contact through a porous medium. Sodium chloride, NaCl, is the most common cause of oilfield salinity, so that it is effectively two solutions of sodium chloride of different salinities that come into contact. Through the porous medium, mixing of the two solutions takes place by ionic diffusion. The Cl^- ion is both smaller and more mobile than the larger, slower Na^+ ion. (In fact, Cl^- is actually larger than Na^+ but, in the hydrated state applicable here, Na^+ attracts surrounding water molecules and is much larger). The ions mix (diffuse), therefore, at unequal rates, creating a charge separation. The Cl^- ion mixes the quickest, thus increasing its saturation in the more dilute solution. A potential is created between the negatively charged dilute solution with excess Cl^- and the positively charged, concentrated solution with excess Na^+ (**Figure 6.3,1**).

The shale potential arises when the same two solutions are in contact across a semi-permeable membrane. In the borehole, this, as the name suggests, is shale (actually a clay mineral rock) (**Figure 6.3,2**). Clay minerals which form shales consist of layers with a large negative surface charge. Because of charge similarity, the negative chloride ions effectively cannot pass through the negatively charged shale layers, while the positive sodium ions pass easily. The shale acts as a selective barrier. As Na^+ ions therefore diffuse preferentially across a shale membrane, an overbalance of Na^+ ions is created in the dilute solution, and hence a positive charge. A corresponding negative charge is produced in the concentrated solution (**Figure 6.3,2**). The shale potential is the larger of the two electrochemical effects.

The actual spontaneous potential currents which are measured in the borehole are, for the most part, a result of the combination of the two electrochemical effects described above. Consider a porous and permeable sandstone penetrated by a borehole: the mud filtrate (for the example) is less saline than the formation waters

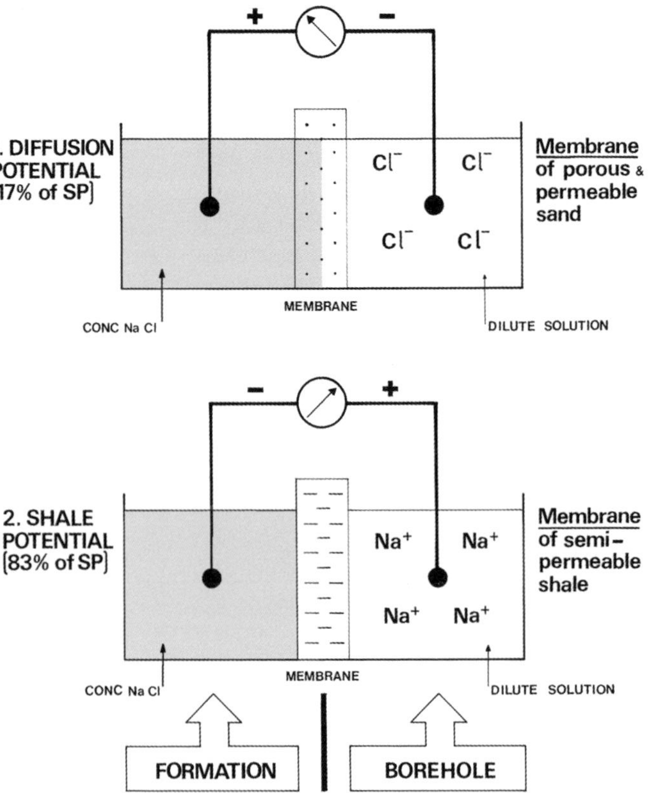

Figure 6.3 Schematic illustration of the main electrochemical SP effects. (1) Diffusion potential across a porous and permeable membrane; (2) shale potential across a membrane of semi-permeable shale (modified after Desbrandes 1968).

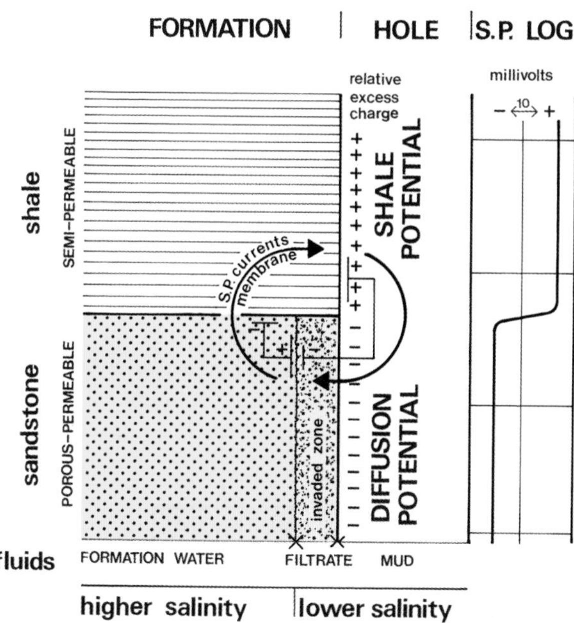

Figure 6.4 SP currents in the borehole. The effects of the shale potential and the diffusion potential act together at bed boundaries causing an SP log deflection.

(**Figure 6.4**). Opposite the sandstone bed (permeable membrane) the less saline solution, the mud filtrate, will become negatively charged as a result of the diffusion potential (cf. **Figure 6.3,1**). But above the sand, opposite the shale (semi-permeable membrane), because of the shale potential, the less saline solution, the mud filtrate, will become positively charged (cf. **Figure 6.3,2**). The excess charge is therefore negative opposite the sand and positive opposite the shale.

This couple works in a complementary sense and creates a spontaneous current flowing between the borehole (mud filtrate), the porous formation and the contiguous shale (**Figure 6.4**). The flow of current is focused at the bed junction. It is only here that there is a change in potential. This is important since SP measurements are made, not of absolute values, but of changes in values. It is only at the bed junctions that changes take place and will be recorded.

If a bed is not permeable, ions will not be able to move, there will be no current flow and thus no potential change: that means no SP. However, even the slightest permeability will permit current flow and an SP change will be recorded.

There is also an electrokinetic element to the SP and currents can be caused by a difference in pressure between the borehole mud and the formation fluids. These currents are usually insignificant in comparison to the electrochemical effects and are not considered further (for a discussion *see* Desbrandes 1968).

6.3 The SP tool

The SP tool approaches the simplicity of the circuit described (**Figure 6.2**) and consists simply of an electrode (lead) mounted on an electrically isolated bridle on the downhole tool. A 1.5 volt battery is included in the circuit to give a bucking current to bring the SP to the required scale. The tool's galvanometer records only changes in potential: it gives no absolute values. The surface electrode of the SP must be an effective earth (Wallace 1968).

Log presentation: units and scales

SP currents are measured in millivolts (1×10^{-3} volts) and the scale is in + or – millivolts, negative deflections to the left, positive to the right (**Figure 6.5**). The log is usually run in track 1 of an API format, along with a gamma ray or caliper log.

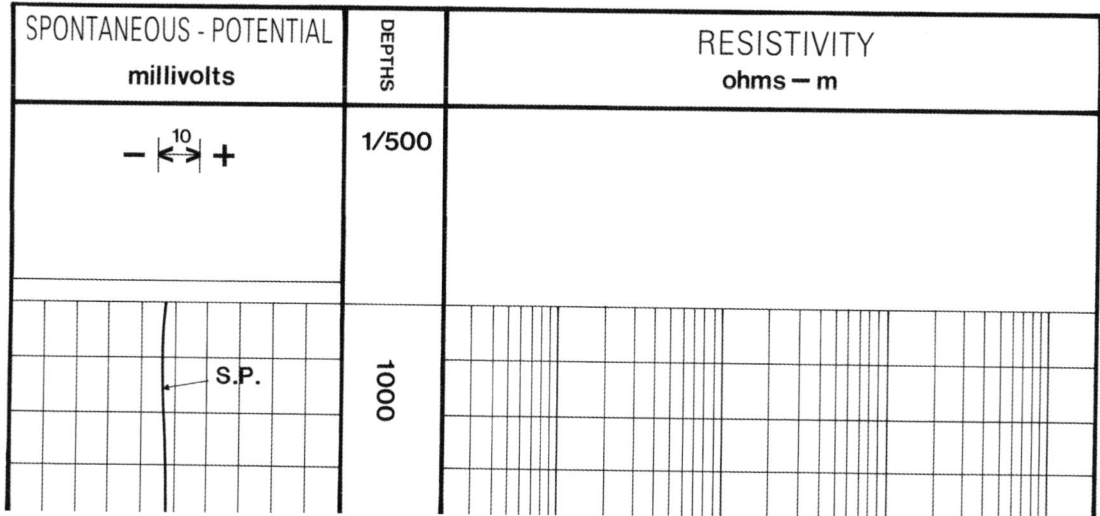

Figure 6.5 SP log presentation. The SP is in track 1. There is no absolute scale, only relative deflection – negative or positive. 1 division equals 10 millivolts.

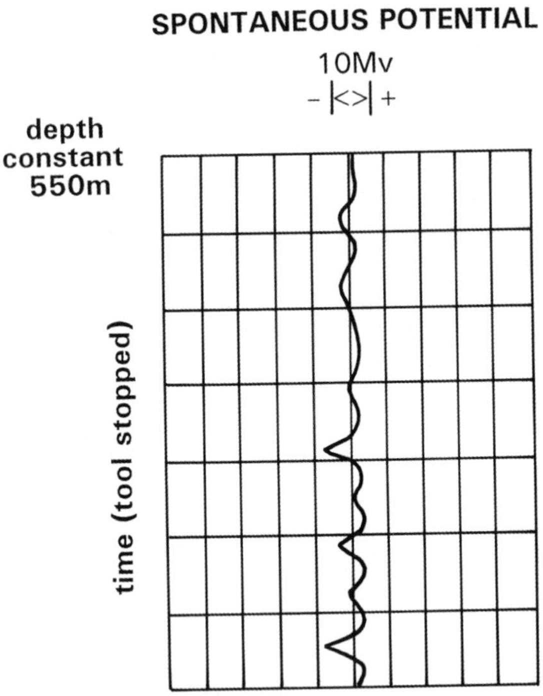

SPONTANEOUS POTENTIAL

10Mv

- |<>| +

depth constant 550m

time (tool stopped)

Figure 6.6 The SP log indicating sea state! For this test, offshore Louisiana, the SP tool was grounded to the rig and stopped at 550 m. The changes in SP potential occur with the passing waves, which were 2.5 m–3.0 m (8′–10′) crest to trough. The hole was cased (from Wallace 1968).

Unwanted logging effects

As indicated above, for the SP tool to work effectively it must be connected to an earth at the surface. For onland wells this causes no problem and an iron probe can be pushed directly into the (humid) soil. Offshore, however, no such possibility exists. Without an effective earth, the SP will not be recorded. The SP from many offshore wells, especially from floating rigs, is useless and mostly ignored. This is a pity. The SP is a cheap and useful log.

The search for an effective earth offshore is difficult. The one most commonly used on floating rigs is the riser, but this is usually in electrical connection to the rig, and any rig is electrically noisy. Using the rig legs is not helpful either since these are given a potential themselves to stop rusting, and as waves pass, this potential changes and causes a wavy SP, which is only indicative of sea state and not formation characteristics! (Wallace 1968) (**Figure 6.6**). Using the anchor chain produces a similar effect.

The SP may also suffer from 'rogue' electrical currents caused, for example, by a magnetization of the logging cable drum so that, as the tool is spooled-in during logging, a wave is seen on the log with a period equal to the drum's circumference.

The logging companies have given little thought to the offshore SP problem, perhaps because the SP is not an expensive hi-tech tool. However it produces a cheap, useful log and should be considered.

6.4 Log characteristics

Bed boundary definition and bed resolution

SP bed boundary definition is poor. The sharpness of a boundary will depend on the shape and extent of the SP current patterns. Generally, when there is a considerable difference between mud and formation resistivity, currents will be spread widely and the SP will deflect slowly; definition will be poor (Dewan 1983). The contrary also applies. When resistivities are quite similar, boundaries are sharper. In general, boundaries should not be drawn using the SP. If the log has to be used, the boundary should be placed at the point of maximum curve slope (i.e. maximum rate of change of the SP - **Figure 6.7**).

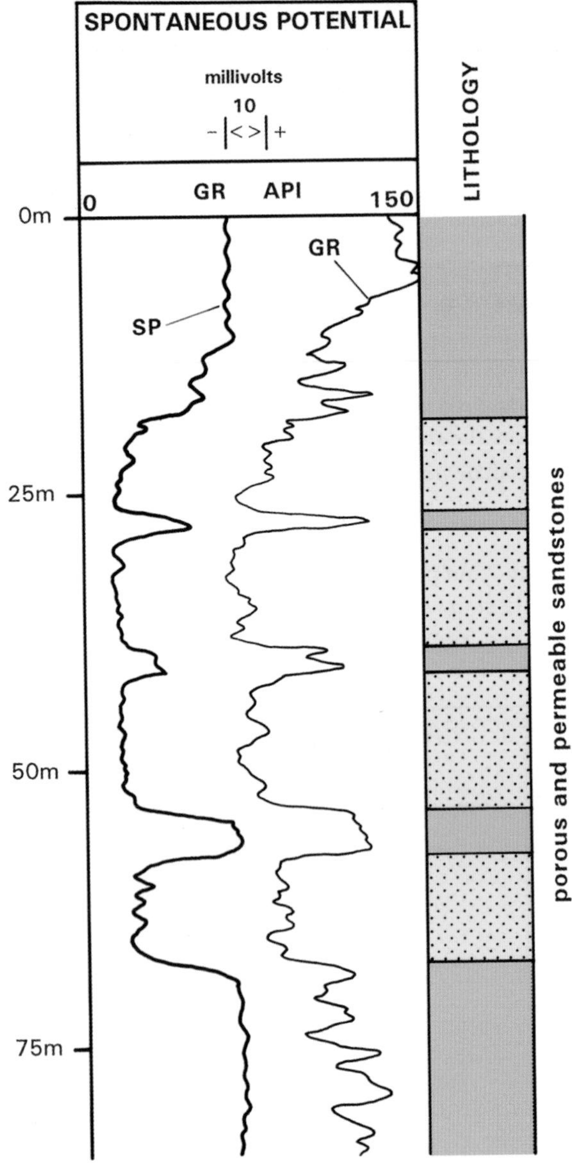

Figure 6.7 The bed definition and 'character' of the SP log compared to the gamma ray log. In most cases the gamma ray log gives much more formation information and better bed boundary definition than the SP.

SP bed resolution is also poor. For a full SP deflection (i.e. SSP or static SP, *see* Section 6.5) and proper bed resolution, as a rule of thumb, a bed should be thicker than 20 times the borehole diameter (Ellis 1987). The exact minimum SP bed resolution will obviously depend on depth of invasion and salinity differences in the same way as described above for bed boundary definition.

6.5 Quantitative uses

Methodology

Quantitatively, the SP log has been used in the past for the evaluation of formation-water resistivities although today this is best done by direct sampling (Chapter 3). It can also be used for shale volume calculation. Any quantitative use of the SP requires a special methodology which is described briefly below.

SP values for calculation - shale baseline and static SP

With no absolute values, the SP is treated quantitatively and qualitatively in terms of deflection, that is, the amount the curve moves to the left or the right of a defined zero. The definition of the SP zero is made on thick shale intervals where the SP does not move: it is called the shale baseline (**Figure 6.8**). All values are related to this line and care must be taken when defining it. The baseline will frequently 'drift' through the well, change

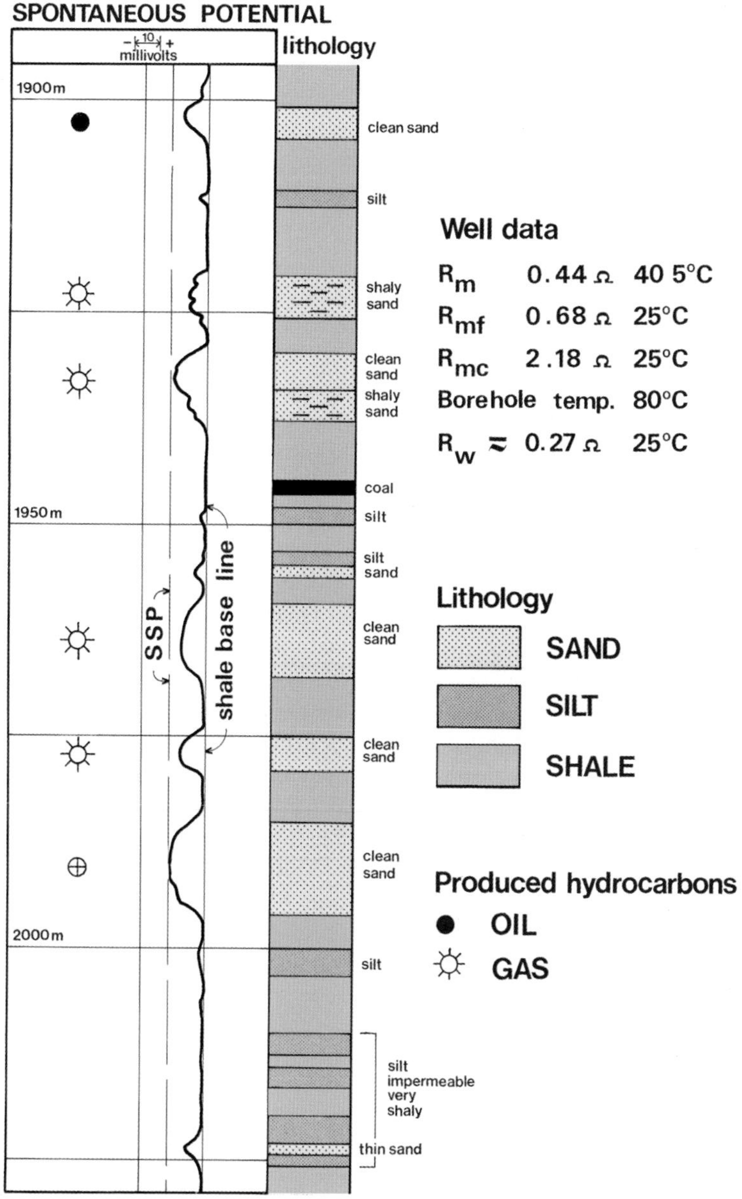

Figure 6.8 Example of the shale baseline and the SSP defined on an SP log. The shale baseline is the maximum positive deflection and is chosen over thick intervals of clean shale. The SSP is a maximum negative deflection and occurs opposite clean, porous and permeable water-bearing sandstones (in this example).

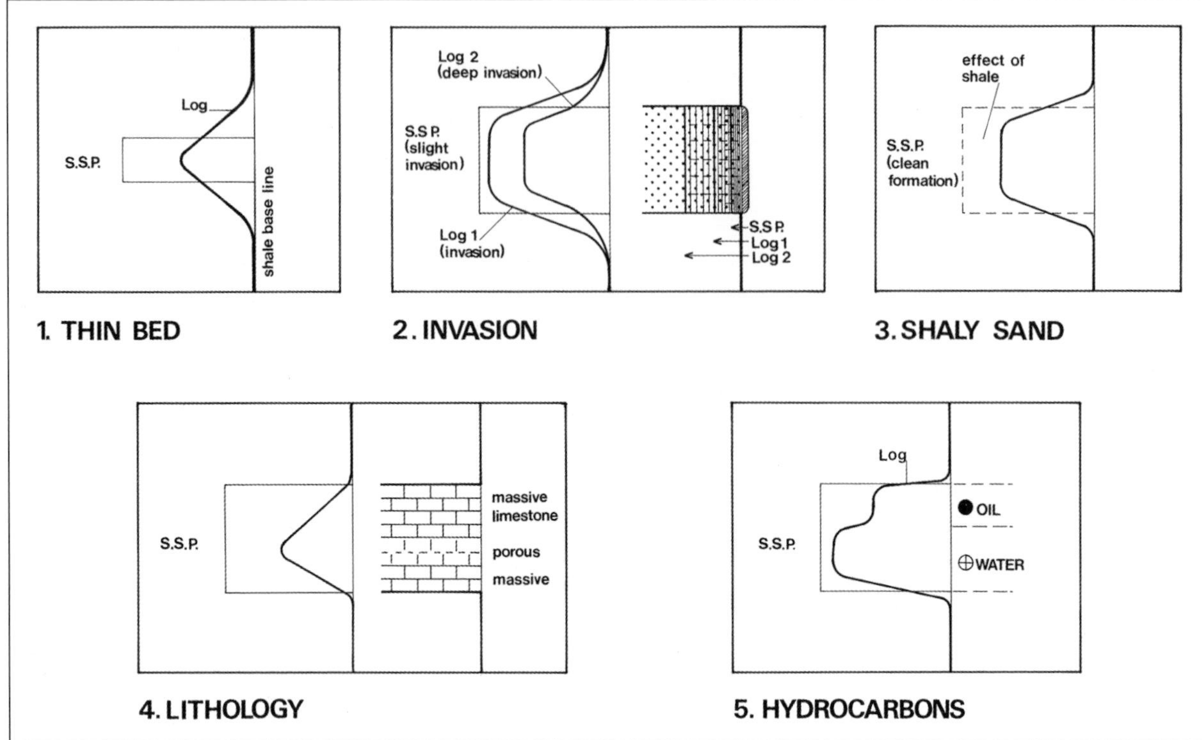

Figure 6.9 Some conditions causing aberrant SP values when the SSP is not attained.

as shale type changes, or change because different mud mixtures are being used. For quantitative use, the nearest baseline to the bed of interest should be taken.

The theoretical maximum deflection of the SP opposite permeable beds is called the static SP or SSP. It represents the SP value that would be observed in an ideal case with the permeable bed isolated electrically. It is the maximum possible SP opposite a permeable, water-bearing formation with no shale (**Figure 6.8**). It is only the log-derived SSP that can be used for the quantitative evaluation of R_W (the formation-water resistivity).

Frequently the SP does not show its full deflection for a number of reasons: the bed is not thick enough, there is shale in the formation, the invasion is very deep, there are adverse lithological effects (junction beds with high resistivity) or hydrocarbons are present (**Figure 6.9**) (Pied *et al.* 1966). These conditions must be considered when using SP values for calculation.

Water resistivity (R_w), quick look and calculations

Qualitatively, the greater the SP deflection, the greater the salinity contrast between the mud filtrate and the formation water. A rapid look at the SP over a certain series of beds in a sand-shale sequence will show water salinity changes. Generally these will be negative deflections, the formation waters being more saline than the mud filtrate. Deflections to positive values, however, occur with fresh formation waters (at least those fresher than the mud filtrate) (**Figure 6.10**). The SP is the only log that allows *categoric* identification of fresh formation water; the resistivity logs will be ambiguous. Typically, a positive SP deflection is much less marked than a negative one: the positive potential difference is much smaller (Taherian *et al.* 1992).

Quantitatively, the SP can be used to calculate formation water resistivity using the relationship between the resistivity and ionic activity. Ionic activity is the major contributing factor to the electrochemical SP, as explained previously. There is a direct relationship between ionic activity and the resistivity of a solution, at least for the most frequently-encountered values in logging (Gondouin *et al.* 1957) (**Figure 6.11**).

This relationship allows a mathematical expression of the amplitude of the SP deflection to be expressed in terms of formation-water resistivity in the following way.

$$(S)SP = -K \log \frac{(R_{mf})e}{(R_w)e}$$

S(SP) = SP value: this should be the SSP (static SP)
$(R_{mf})e$ = equivalent mud filtrate resistivity (for the SSP equation) closely related to R_{mf}
$(R_W)e$ = equivalent formation water resistivity (for the SSP equation) closely related to R_W.
K = temperature-dependent coefficient, as an average, 71 at 25°C ($K = 65 + 0.24 \times$ T°C; $K = 61 + 0.133 \times$ T°F) (cf. Desbrandes 1982).

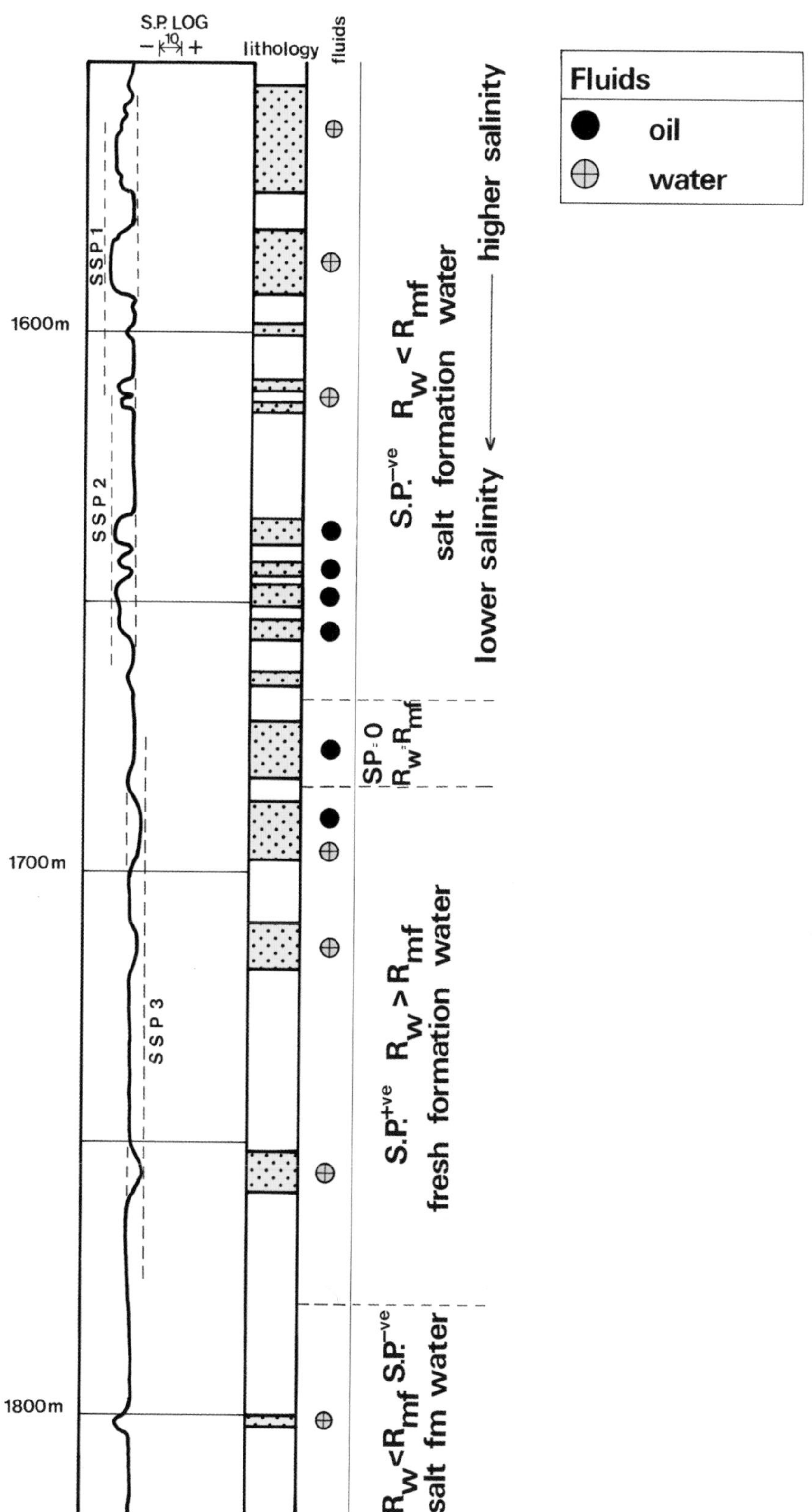

Figure 6.10 Behaviour of the SP in a sand-shale sequence with varying formation-water salinity. A zone of fresh water occurs between about 1680 m and 1775 m. Mud filtrate resistivity is constant.

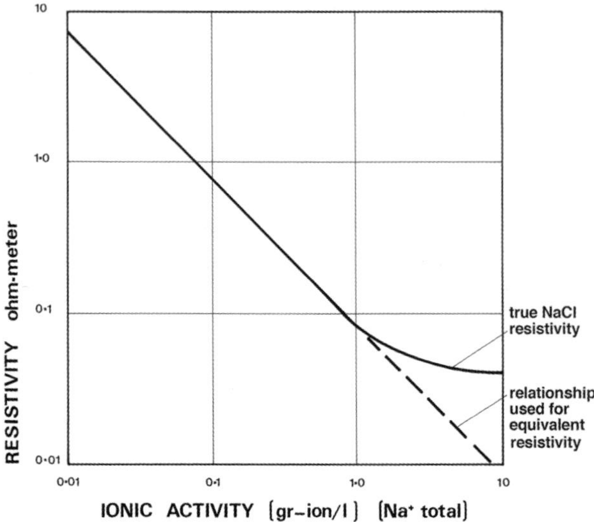

Figure 6.11 Graph of the relationship between water resistivity and SP deflection (ionic activity) for salt solutions. This is the basis for using the SP to calculate formation water resistivity, R_w (from Gondouin *et al.* 1957).

The preceding method allows an approximation of the resistivity of formation water (**Figure 6.11**). However, it is based on the ionic activity of NaCl solutions, even though it is generally observed that salinities of both mud filtrates and of formation waters are due to ionic mixtures and that calcium and magnesium as well as sodium ions are present. The effects of calcium and magnesium are especially important at high resistivities in 'fresh' waters and corrections must be made to the formulae shown above.

With the advent of wireline tools that allow multiple downhole fluid samples to be taken (Chapter 3), this calculation method using the SP is seldom used. However, it has recently been suggested that inverting the SP with resistivity logs can lead to a reliable estimation of water salinity and that today the SP is often wrongly ignored (Salazar *et al.* 2007).

Shale volume from SP (Pseudo-static SP)

It is considered that the volume of shale V_{sh} in a water-wet, shaly sandstone can be simply calculated using the SP as follows:

$$V_{sh}(\%) = \left[1 - \frac{\text{PSP}}{\text{SSP}}\right] \times 100$$

PSP = pseudo-static spontaneous potential = the SP read in the water-bearing *shaly sand* zone.
SSP = static spontaneous potential = maximum SP value in a *clean sand* zone.

This simply assumes that the SP deflection between the shale base line (100% shale) and the static SP in a clean sand (0% shale) is proportional to the shale volume and therefore linear (**Figure 6.12**). This relationship is certainly true qualitatively, but quantitatively it is not evident. The SP reaction to shale, that is, its membrane (shale) potential, is related to clay mineral cation exchange capacity (CEC) and this can be influenced by factors such as oil saturation. Membrane potential increases as the saturation in oil increases (Fan *et al.* 2002). The SP-derived V_{sh} is probably an over-estimation.

6.6 Qualitative uses

Permeability recognition

If there is even a slight deflection on the SP, the bed opposite the deflection is permeable. All deflections (with some rare exceptions) on the SP indicate, *a priori,* a permeable bed. The amount of deflection, however, does not indicate the amount of permeability: a very slightly permeable bed will give the same value as a permeable bed (other values being equal).

The reverse, unfortunately is not true and not all permeable beds give an SP deflection, although these cases are rare (**Figure 6.9**).

Mineral identification

The rare exceptions when the SP will deflect and the formation is not permeable are due to mineralizations. Pyrite is an example (**Figure 6.13**). It is also possible that the SP reacts to excessively reduced and excessively oxidized beds (shales or sandstones) which are not in subsurface electrical equilibrium (Hallenburg 1978). However, coals, which are extremely reduced, give a large negative SP deflection (**Figure 6.13**) or, quite

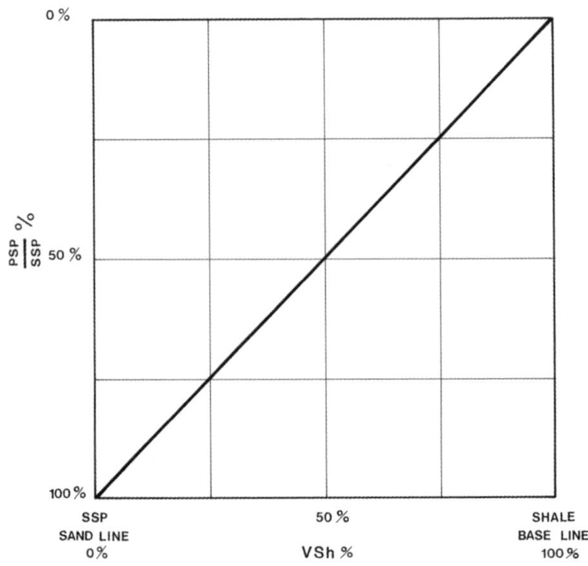

Figure 6.12 Graph of the clay volume-SP relationship. The shale baseline represents 100% shale and the SSP 0% shale. The relative deflection then depends on the clay volume as shown by the graph.

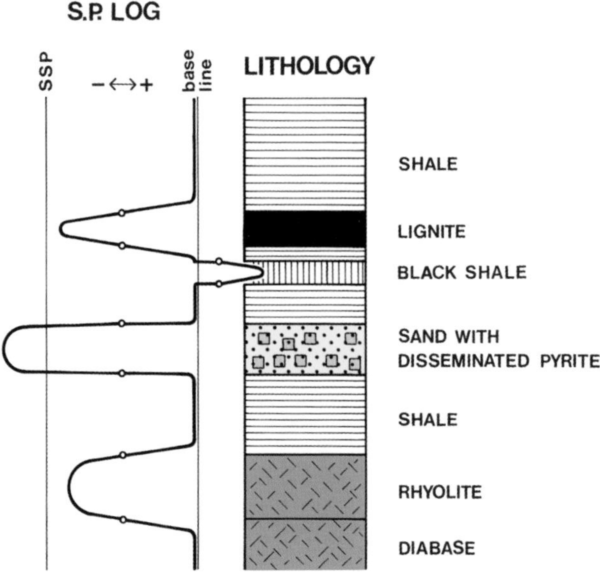

Figure 6.13 Identification of some minerals and lithologies using the SP curve. The log is idealised (re-drawn from Pirson 1963).

often, no deflection at all. The reasons are obscure. The SP should be used with caution for mineral or redox identification – other logs are much more diagnostic.

Facies

When it was introduced, the SP was to become one of the first logs to permit correlation in sand-shale sequences, principally because certain intervals had typical log shapes. This shape, in sand-shale sequences, is related to shale abundance, the full SP occurring over clean intervals, a diminished SP over shaly zones. The relationship is considered linear as discussed. Insofar as shaliness is related to grain size, the SP is a good facies indicator. The example (**Figure 6.14**) shows a well-marked channel sand: the coarse-grained base is clean while the finer grained top is shaly. The SP is, therefore, following grain-size change *(see also* Chapter 16).

The SP has now been largely replaced by the gamma ray log for facies identification: the gamma ray log has more character and is more repeatable (**Figure 6.7**).

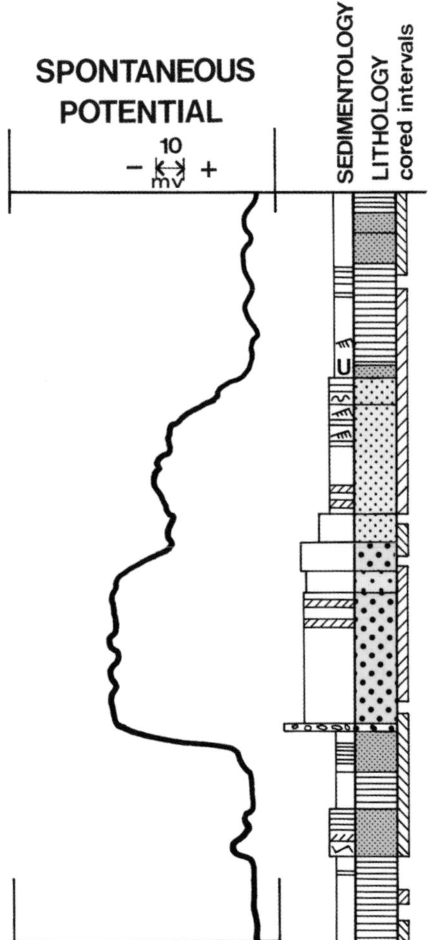

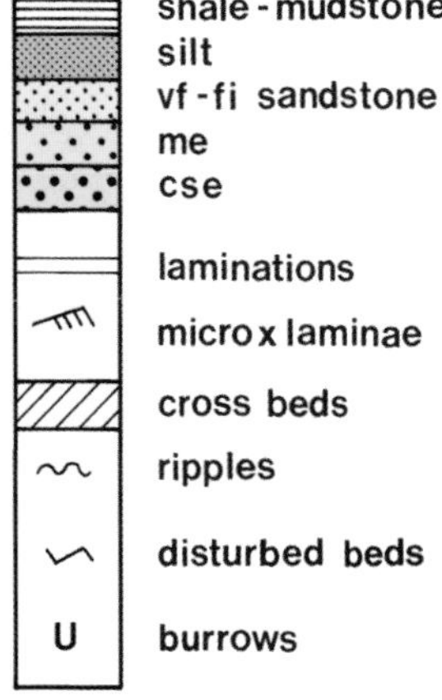

Figure 6.14 Facies identification using the SP log. A typical fining-upwards, channel sandstone giving a bell-shaped SP curve. From the Carboniferous, UK (after Hawkins 1972).

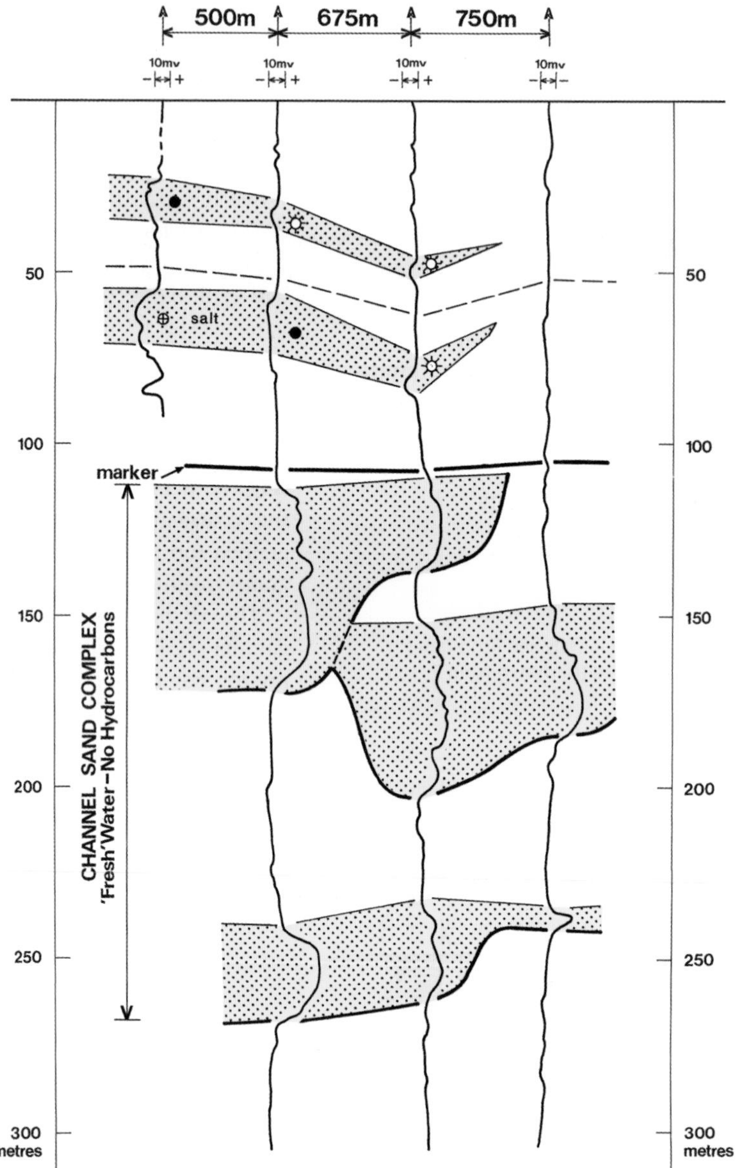

Figure 6.15 Correlation using the SP log. Changes in water salinity indicate which sand bodies can be correlated. Drilling-mud filtrate is similar in all wells.

Correlation

Previously, the SP log was used for correlation but, for the reasons just given above, it has now been replaced especially by the gamma ray log. The SP is still useful for correlation, however, in areas of varied water salinities. If wells are quite close (and drilling mud fluids are similar), correlation should only be made between sands with similar salinity values (**Figure 6.15**). For this the SP is the only log that can be used as a guide.

7 RESISTIVITY LOGS

7.1 Generalities

The log

Of all the logging tools, those that measure resistivity are archetypal. It was with surface resistivity measurements that Conrad Schlumberger started his company in 1919 and the first log to be run was a resistivity log **(Figure 1.1).**

Resistivity is an intrinsic property of matter that quantifies its ability to conduct electricity. The higher the resistivity the more difficult it is to pass a current of a particular magnitude. The resistivity log is a measurement of this in subsurface formations. As a downhole measurement, resistivity is distinguished from most, if not all, other properties in that it can be measured in several different ways. This means that resistivity can be measured by LWD tools in both conductive and non-conductive muds during drilling, and by wireline tools post-drilling

Nearly all the minerals and fluids that are encountered in the subsurface have very high resistivities. In fact logging tools are simply not designed to be able to

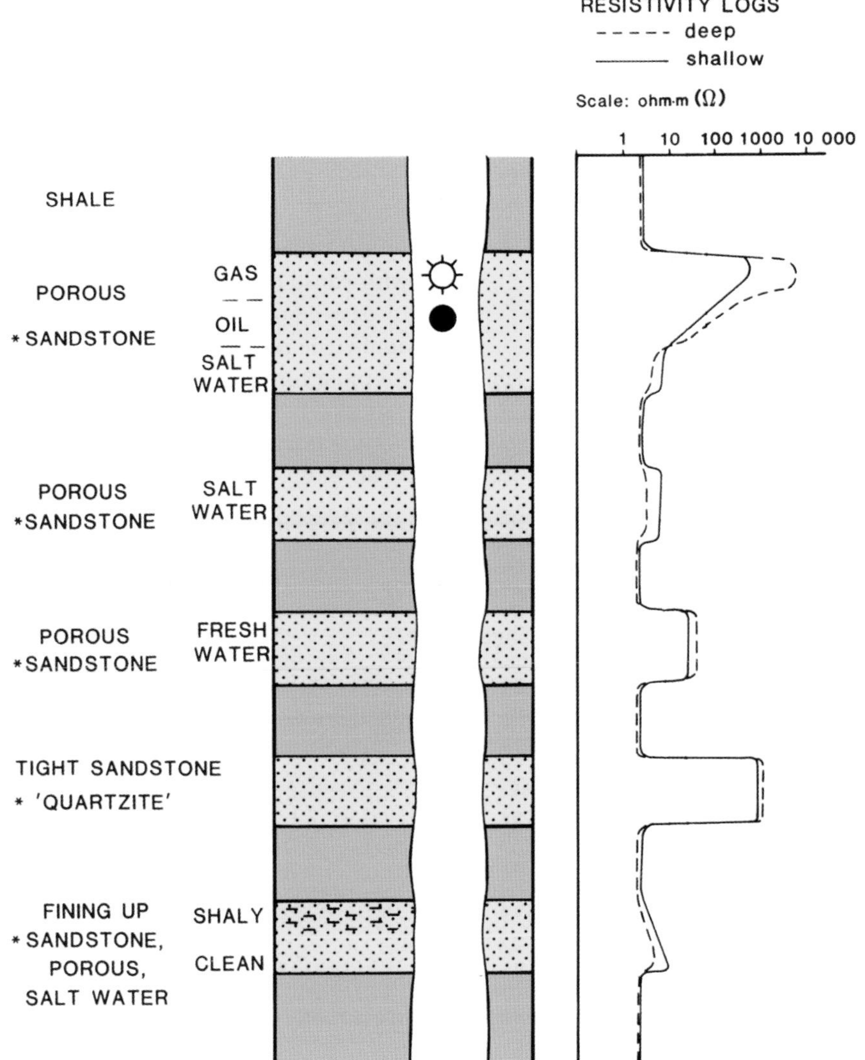

Figure 7.1 The resistivity log: some typical responses. The resistivity log shows the effect of the formation and its contained fluids on the passage of an electric current. *Limestone, dolomite, etc., equally applicable.

measure them. The most important exception is water. Most of the time, formation resistivity is controlled by its amount and distribution. When a formation is porous and contains salty water (which is conductive) the overall resistivity will be relatively low. However, when this same formation contains hydrocarbons, its resistivity will be higher. It is this difference that is exploited by log analysts when they estimate hydrocarbon volumes by calculating the water saturation from resistivity logs. But high resistivity values only *may* indicate a porous, hydrocarbon-bearing formation; they may simply indicate a low porosity (**Figure 7.1**).

Principal uses

It was realised very early by Henri Doll and Conrad Schlumberger that resistivity logs could be used to detect hydrocarbons. This is still their principal use: resistivity logs furnish the raw data for saturation calculations. As will be explained, resistivity can be quantitatively related to the volume of water in the formation. If porosity is estimated using some other means, the water saturation can be found. However, as will also be seen below, a formation's resistivity depends on more than simply the amount of water it contains, it can also contribute information on conductive minerals, texture, lithology, facies, compaction, overpressure and source potential. The log is used for correlation and geosteering **(Table 7.1).**

7.2 Theoretical considerations

Earth resistivity and conductivity

The laws which govern electrical resistance in a simple electrical circuit apply equally to currents flowing in the earth. The basic measurement, whether in a laboratory or in a borehole, consists of imposing a voltage drop across a sample of known dimensions and measuring the resulting current. Either the voltage or the current can be controlled, and their ratio is the Resistance.

$$\text{Resistance} = \text{Voltage Drop/Current}$$

Resistance is an extrinsic property, meaning that it depends on the size and shape of the sample. *Resistivity* is a more fundamental, intrinsic property, and is independent of sample size and shape: it is the property that is measured in subsurface logging.

For a sample that is prism shaped (such as a cube or a cylinder), with current passing along the prism's axis, resistance and resistivity are related by:

$$\text{Resistance} = L \times \text{Resistivity}/A$$

Re-arranging and using the normal symbols used by petrophysicists and log analysts this becomes:

$$\text{Resistivity} = \frac{r \times A}{L}$$

Where: R = resistivity in ohm-m, r = resistance in ohms
A = the prism's cross-section in m^2
L = it's length in m.

In this realationship, a prism is any parallel-sided solid with constant cross-sectional area, and the current has to pass perpendicular to this area for the formula to apply. The relationship will be more complex than this for more complicated sample shapes and in, practice, it may not be possible to derive a simple equation connecting resistance and resistivity. The current paths em-

Table 7.1 The principal uses of the wireline and LWD resistivity logs.

	Discipline	Used for	Knowing
Qantitative	Petrophysics	Fluid saturations Formation (S_w) Invaded zone (S_{xo}) i.e.detect hydrocarbons	Formation water resistivity (R_w) Mud filtrate resistivity (R_{mf}) Porosity (Ø) (and F) Temperature (BHT)
	Reservoir property	permeability	permeability to resistivity relationship
Semi-quantiative and qualitative	Geology	textures Lithology Conductive minerals Correlation	calibration with laboratory samples, cores rock resistivities mineral resistivities
	Sedimentology	Facies Bedding characteristics	general lithologies tool limitations
	Reservoir geology	Compaction Overpressure and Shale porosity	normal pressure trends
	Geochemistry	Source rock identification Source rock maturation	sonic and density log values formation temperature
	Drilling	Geosteering	reservoir and seal resistivities

ployed by logging tools, for example, are far more complicated than a simple cylinder or cube. This is handled by noting that, in general, resistance and resistivity are proportional. For the simple prisms introduced above, the constant of proportionality K is:

$$K = L/A$$

Which can be found from first principles. The equation still holds true for the far more complex geometries employed by logging tools (K is then known as the 'tool constant'). Providing K can be found, by calibration for example, resistivity can always be calculated.

(It is worth noting that physicists give resistivity the symbol 'ρ' but in all logging applications it is given the symbol R, which unfortunately is more widely used (for example by electrical engineers) to mean resistance! Fortunately, from now on we will only be concerned with resistivity and so no confusion should arise.)

In the subsurface, we invariably measure the resistivity of mixtures of minerals and fluids. The precise value depends on the relative amounts of these components, their individual resistivities, and the way they are distributed. In general, this means it can depend on the direction the current is passed (for example parallel or normal to the borehole axis). Resistivity also depends on the frequency of the current that is used to measure it. This means that, although resistivity is the oldest of the logging measurements, it is also one of the most difficult to interpret (a fact which is often forgotten).

Sometimes it is helpful to discuss the flow of current in the formation in terms of conductivity. This is simply the reciprocal of resistivity.

$$\text{resistivity (ohm-m)} = \frac{1000}{\text{conductivity}} \quad \text{*milliSiemen/m (mS/m)}$$

*The SI unit Siemen replaces the older mho.

So a 'very conductive' formation or material has a low resistivity and vice versa. It may seem an unnecessary complication to introduce another property which gives no more information, but using conductivity can make some of the equations used in quantitative analysis easier to handle and understand. It can also sometimes make the description of current flow a bit more concise. We will use both properties in this book.

As we have seen, the basic resistivity measurement involves generating a voltage drop through a fixed volume of formation. There are two basic ways to achieve this, and logging tools have been developed which exploit both. There are advantages and disadvantages to both types of tool. Arguably the simplest way is to pass a current from an electrode, through the formation, and back to a return electrode. This method is exploited in the laterolog logging tools and laboratory measurements. In the second method, a current is induced in the formation by a high frequency electromagnetic field. The nature of the field depends in a predictable way on the formation resistivity, and different ways have been developed to measure this. This technique is exploited by the induction logging tools and the LWD propagation tools, as discussed below.

Rock resistivity: why do rocks conduct?

As previously stated, rock materials are essentially insulators and have a very high resistivity (like all generalities this is a half-truth, and will be modified later). However, porous rocks consist not just of rock materials, but also voids or pores. In the subsurface the pore spaces are principally filled with water and it is this that carries the current (**Figure 7.2**). Formation waters vary from fresh to very saline: usually they are saline and salinity can increases with depth (e.g. Dickey 1969). For oilfield purposes, salinity is usually quoted in NaCl equivalent salinity, although formation water brines in reality have a variety of dissolved solids (normally salinity is expressed as the ratio of the mass of salt(s) dissolved in unit mass of solution. This is known as 'weight-weight' or w/w). Sea water has an average salinity of 35,000 ppm (parts per million of dissolved solids) while a formation brine may have a salinity of anywhere from a few thousand ppm to 300,000 ppm **(Table 7.2).** Other factors remaining constant, the more saline a solution is, the greater the conductivity (the lower the resistivity). The electric current is carried by dissociated ions, e.g. Na^+, Cl^- in a salt solution and the more of these there are, the lower the resistivity. The same formation containing salt water shows a far higher conductivity (much lower resistivity) than if it contained fresh water (**Figure 7.3**). Fresh water actually has a very high resistivity (pores, of course, may also be filled with hydrocarbons, which are also not conductive).

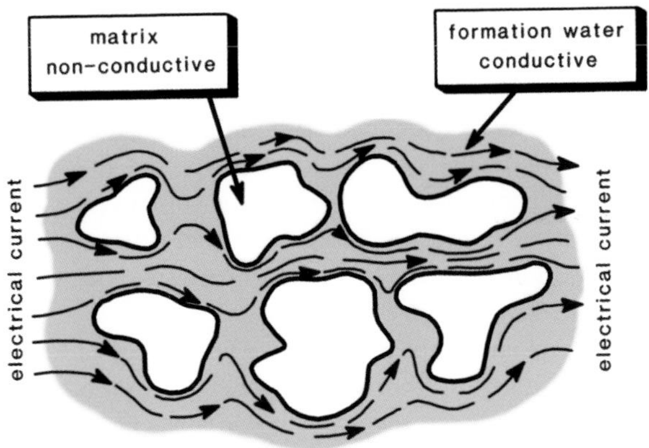

Figure 7.2 Formation conductivity – schematic. The electrical current is restricted to the formation fluids (formation water): the matrix is non-conductive.

Table 7.2 Some typical formation-water salinities.

Origin	Total salinity	Type (ppm)	R_w * ohm-m
Sea water	35,000		0.19
Lagunillas, Venezuela	7,548[1]	fresh	0.77
Woodbine, E. Texas	68,964[1]	saline	0.10
US average	94,000[2]	saline	0.08
Burgan, Kuwait	154,388	saline	0.053
Simpson sd., Oklahoma	298,497[1]	very saline	(0.054)[3]

*Approximate R_w (formation water resistivity) at 24°C (75°F)
(1) From Levorsen 1967
(2) From USGS
(3) Near the saturation limit

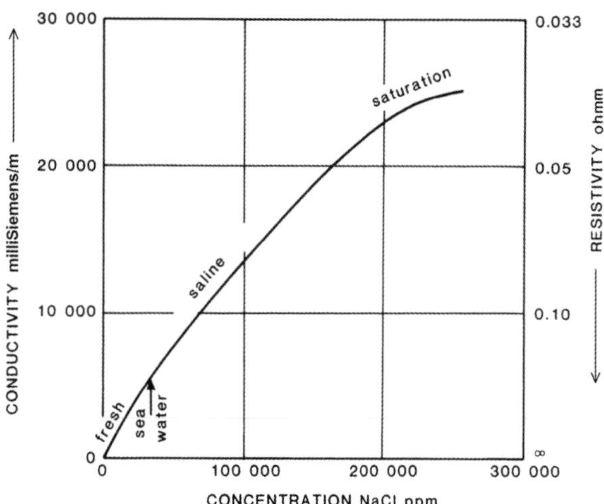

Figure 7.3 Relationship between conductivity (resistivity) and concentration in a salt (NaCl) solution, at 24°C (75°F) (modified from Serra 1979).

The resistivity of formation water is an important property in quantitative analysis. It is given the special symbol R_w (resistivity of water) **(Table 7.2).**

Rock resistivity: formation resistivity factor 'F'

If, as suggested above, it is only the formation waters that are conductive, two predictions can be made about the resistivity – or conductivity – of a porous rock.

The conductivity of the rock is expected to be less than the conductivity of the water it contains (i.e. the resistivity of the rock will be greater than R_w).

The more resistive the formation water, the more resistive the rock as a whole.

This is found to be the case for a large range of rocks. The resistivity of the rock is generally proportional to the resistivity of the water it contains. This can be written as:

$$R_o = F \times R_w$$

The constant of proportionality F is known as the *Formation Factor* or *Formation Resistivity Factor* (*FF* or *FRF*) and is always greater than one (alternatively one could say the formation factor for pure water is one). It is the ratio of the resistivity of a water saturated rock to the resistivity of the water and is therefore dimensionless. The symbol R_o is another standard symbol in quantitative log analysis: it is the resistivity of the rock when it is saturated with water.

Roughly speaking F increases as porosity decreases but the precise relationship with porosity varies between rocks. So although the rock plays no active part in determining resistivity, it plays an important passive one (**Figure 7.2**). As we will see, this passive role is basically dependent on rock texture or more specifically on the geometry of the pores and pore connections (**Figure 7.4**). A good analogy is that of a comparison between conventional roads and motorways. Vehicles will travel far more quickly and in greater volume between two towns down a wide, straight motorway than along a narrow twisting conventional road. Thus, in rocks, the easier the path through the pores the more current that passes. The expression of this passive

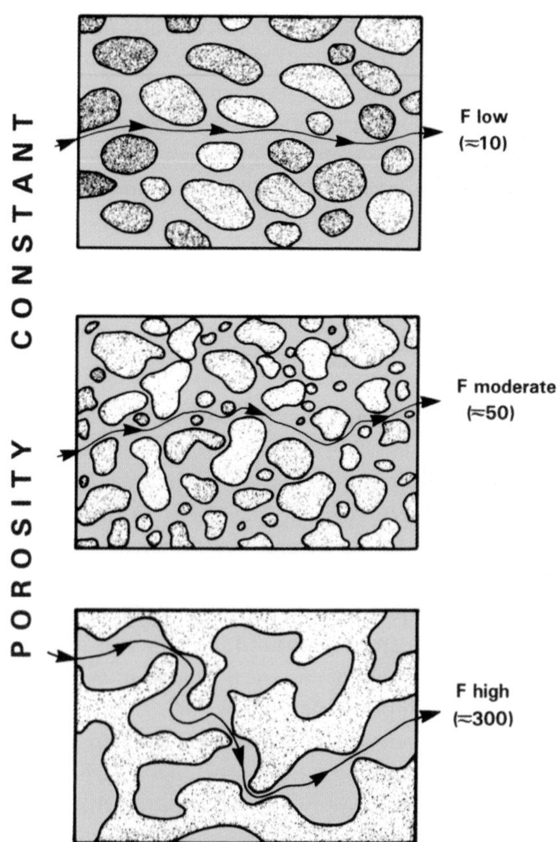

Figure 7.4 Schematic illustration of three formations which have the same porosity but different values of formation resistivity factor, *F*. The role of the matrix is evident: less at low values of *F* (top), greater at high values of *F* (bottom).

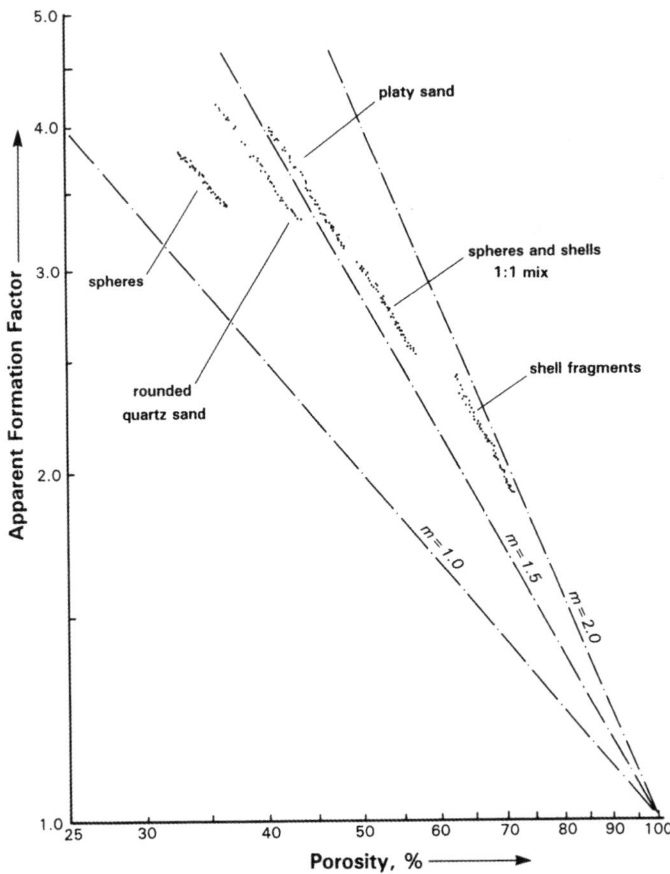

Figure 7.5 Graph of formation resistivity factor, *F* and porosity showing their relationship to grain shape (texture) illustrated by analyses of laboratory samples. A predictable relationship between *F* and porosity only exists for one type of grain population. m = cementation factor (re-drawn from Jackson *et al.* 1978).

behaviour is *F*. When the passive role of the rock is small, meaning pore throats are large, *F* is small: when the rock has a large inhibiting effect, *F* is large (**Figure 7.4**).

To understand *F* better it is useful to examine the influence porosity has upon it. In any one rock formation, *F* and porosity can show a consistent relationship (**Figure 7.5**). However, porosity is not the only influence on *F*, and the *F* to porosity relationship varies from one rock to another. Laboratory work with artificial mixtures shows that in any grain population with similarly shaped grains, the *F*-porosity changes are mathematically predictable (follow Archie's law, Section 7.8) (Jackson *et al.* 1978). But when grain shape is changed, the relationship changes, although still in a predictable way (**Figure 7.5**). *F* is therefore strongly influenced by grain shape (theoretically because of changes in pore throat geometry). However, in geological terms, grain shape is an element of texture, along with other factors such as size and arrangement (sorting). Geologically then, *F* becomes a texturally related term, an aspect which will be considered in more detail when the geological applications of resistivity logs are illustrated (Section 7.9).

For petrophysical purposes it is necessary to quantify the relationship between *F* and porosity (porosity being measurable by other logs). Fundamental work by Gus Archie established an empirical relationship (Archie 1942), which has been confirmed by subsequent work (e.g. **Figure 7.5**). However, as indicated above, the relationship varies with each population of grains and to establish a universally applicable relationship has proved elusive (e.g. Winsauer and McCardell 1953; Maute 1992). Presently available formulae still give only a good estimate (*see* 'Basic, simple equations of petrophysics' Section 7.8).

F usually lies between 5 and 500, with the higher numbers corresponding to lower porosity and/or fewer conductive paths through the rock. Well sorted, high porosity sandstones will have an *F* value of 10 or less. A vuggy limestone may have a value around 300–400 (particularly if it has a porosity of less than 10%) (**Figure 7.4**).

For most rocks, the *F* value is independent of the resistivity of the fluid filling the pores. This means that *F* will not vary with changes in formation water salinity which entail overall rock resistivity changes (**Figure 7.6**). Importantly, it also means that the *F* value is constant between the reservoir containing oil and the same reservoir containing water. This concept will be used below when discussing invasion.

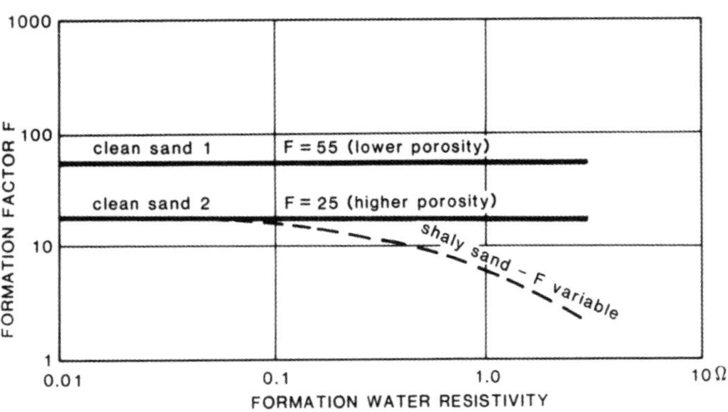

Figure 7.6 The effect of changes in formation-water resistivity on *F* (formation resistivity factor). *F* will not change with different water salinities in a clean formation. In a shaly formation, *F* will constantly change (schematic).

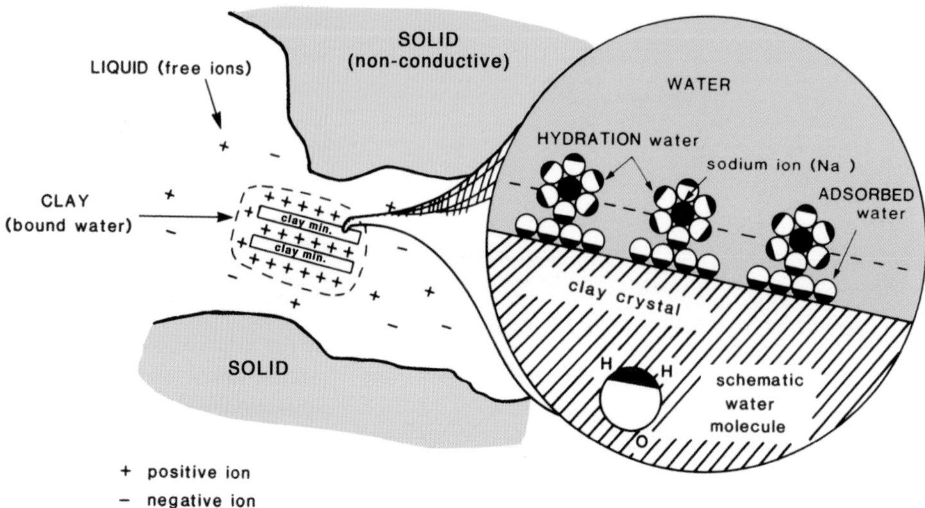

Figure 7.7 Models of the conductivity capacity of clay minerals (modified from Wyllie 1963; detail Clavier *et al.* 1977).

Resistivity (conductivity) of clays

It was stated above that 'most' rocks play no active part in determining resistivity, and that the formation factor, F, is independent of the resistivity of the formation water. However, the part played by the rock skeleton is not always passive. If some mineral(s) exist which have a significant electrical conductivity, then they can carry some of the current and the resistivity will be reduced. The conductive minerals are said to introduce *excess conductivity*.

The best known minerals for introducing excess conductivity are the clays. They contribute in two ways. Firstly, they typically introduce a lot of water in to a rock, and this will conduct electricity in exactly the same way as has been described, the clay simply behaving as a porous rock with the 'dry clay' playing the passive role and the water carrying the current. The volume of water introduced can be high and may lead to porosities as high as 40% by volume in Pleistocene clays and claystones but diminishes rapidly through compaction to a more normal 20% or less in older formations

Secondly, the interface between water and certain clay minerals can be electrically conductive and therefore produce some additional conductivity. Clay consists of stacked silicate layers which, in the presence of water, become negatively charged. Clay may be considered to act like a salt, dissociating into an immobile, negatively-charged framework and positive, current-conducting ions (Wyllie 1963). However, it is only at the surface of the clay-mineral layers that the dissociation occurs and a current is able to be carried (**Figure 7.7**). Clay behaves like an inverted electric cable; the inside is non-conductive while the outside conducts electricity. The conducting layer, however, is complex. Adsorbed water clings to the immediate clay layer while the positive ions (Na^+ in a salt solution) surrounded by hydration water, form a further outer layer (Clavier *et al.* 1977) (**Figure 7.7**). The external water, called 'bound water', is chemically free but physically bound.

In clay-sand mixtures (shaly-sands), clays can contribute to excess conductivity. The magnitude of this depends on the type of clay (it is especially marked in smectite), the salinity of the formation water and temperature (**Table 7.3**). However, very generally, the higher the resistivity of the formation fluids, the greater the current carried by the shale. This has the effect of changing F: it diminishes as fluid resistivity increases (**Figure 7.6**). Importantly, in oil zones where the formation fluids have high resistivities, clays are conductive. This means that in oil-saturated shaly-sands, resistivities may be quite low and explains why log analysts are interested in clay mineral conductivity. For an accurate, quantitative log analysis, excess conductivity caused by shale does need to be accounted for.

Summary: earth resistivity

The conductivity of most rocks is due to interstitial pore waters (formation waters) which contain dissociated, current-carrying ions. The rock skeleton is a non-conductor but plays an inhibiting role expressed quantitatively by $R_o = F \times R_w$. In mixtures of clay and

Table 7.3 Clay mineral properties (from Dewan 1983).

Clay mineral	CEC (meq/g)	Av. CEC
Smectite	0.8–1.5	1.00
Illite	0.1–0.4	0.25
Chlorite	0.0–0.1	0.04
Kaolionite	0.03–0.06	0.04

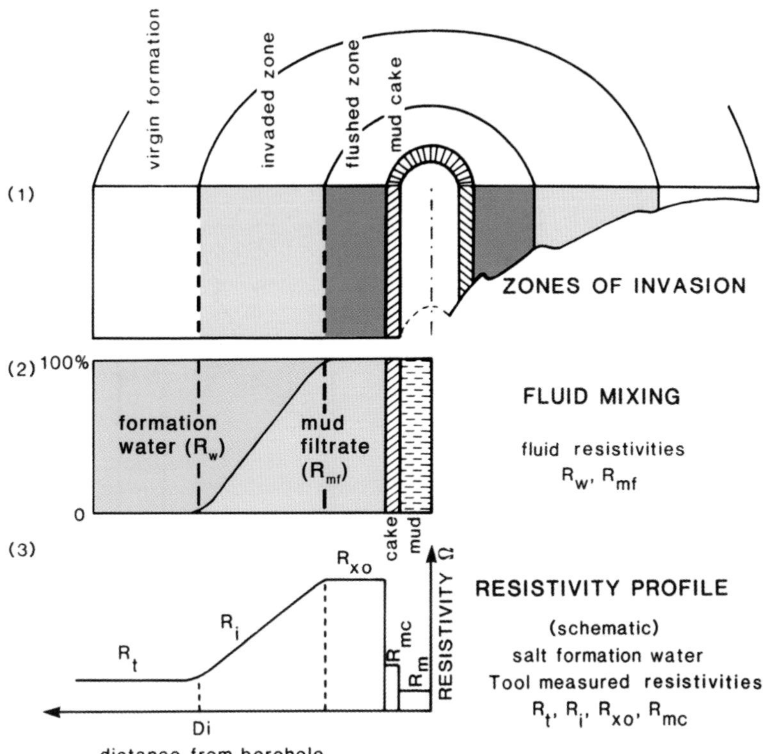

Figure 7.8 (1) Zones of invasion about a borehole; (2) equivalent schematic representation of fluid mixing: (3) resistivity profile. R_w = resistivity water: R_{mf} = resistivity mud filtrate: R_t = true resistivity: R_{xo} = flushed zone resistivity: R_i = invaded zone resistivity: R_{mc} = mudcake resistivity: D_i = diameter of invasion.

non-conducting materials, conductivity is provided by the formation water but also by the clay itself.

7.3 Zones of invasion

Resistivity profiles

The concept of invasion has already been described (Chapter 2) and it is all-important to the understanding of borehole resistivity. The essential target of resistivity logging is that of the true resistivity of the formation (R_t) and, especially, its saturation in hydrocarbons. To this end, it is necessary to consider the invasion of mud filtrate (with a certain salinity and hence resistivity, R_{mf}) into a permeable formation.

For convenience, the invasion of a porous and permeable bed by mud filtrate is divided into zones: the flushed zone, the invaded zone and the virgin formation (**Figure 7.8,1**). In reality the zones probably grade one into the other. Closest to the borehole, immediately behind the mudcake, is the flushed zone where the mud filtrate has replaced all but a small fraction of the formation fluids. Moving further from the borehole wall, it would be expected that the mud filtrate makes up a smaller and smaller fraction of the pore space (**Figure 7.8,2**). This is the transition or invaded zone. Eventually a point is reached that is sufficiently far from the borehole wall for no mud filtrate to be present. This is, of course, the un-invaded, virgin formation. Note that sometimes the term 'invaded zone' is used to describe the entire thickness of formation that has mud filtrate in it (i.e the sum of what are defined as the flushed and invaded zones above). Note also that although the above description assumes that the proportions of mud filtrate and reservoir fluids vary continuously with distance from the borehole wall, there are circumstances where a more piston-like displacement of reservoir fluid by filtrate occurs. The transition will then be quite abrupt.

The change in fluid composition away from the borehole can give rise to an accompanying change in the resistivity of the overall formation, resistivity varying with distance from the borehole. These variations can be conveniently depicted by a graph of resistivity against distance from the borehole at each depth level (**Figure 7.8,3**), the profile assuming that the variations are due entirely to changes in fluid content. That is to say, *F* does not vary away from the borehole wall (this may not always be true).

To understand invasion better, changes can be observed in the time domain by comparing LWD resistivity measurements made just after the formation is drilled, with wireline resistivities made much later, when invasion may have reached its maximum extent. A particularly good example shows a series of LWD measurements made at intervals from 'while drilling' to 300 hours later

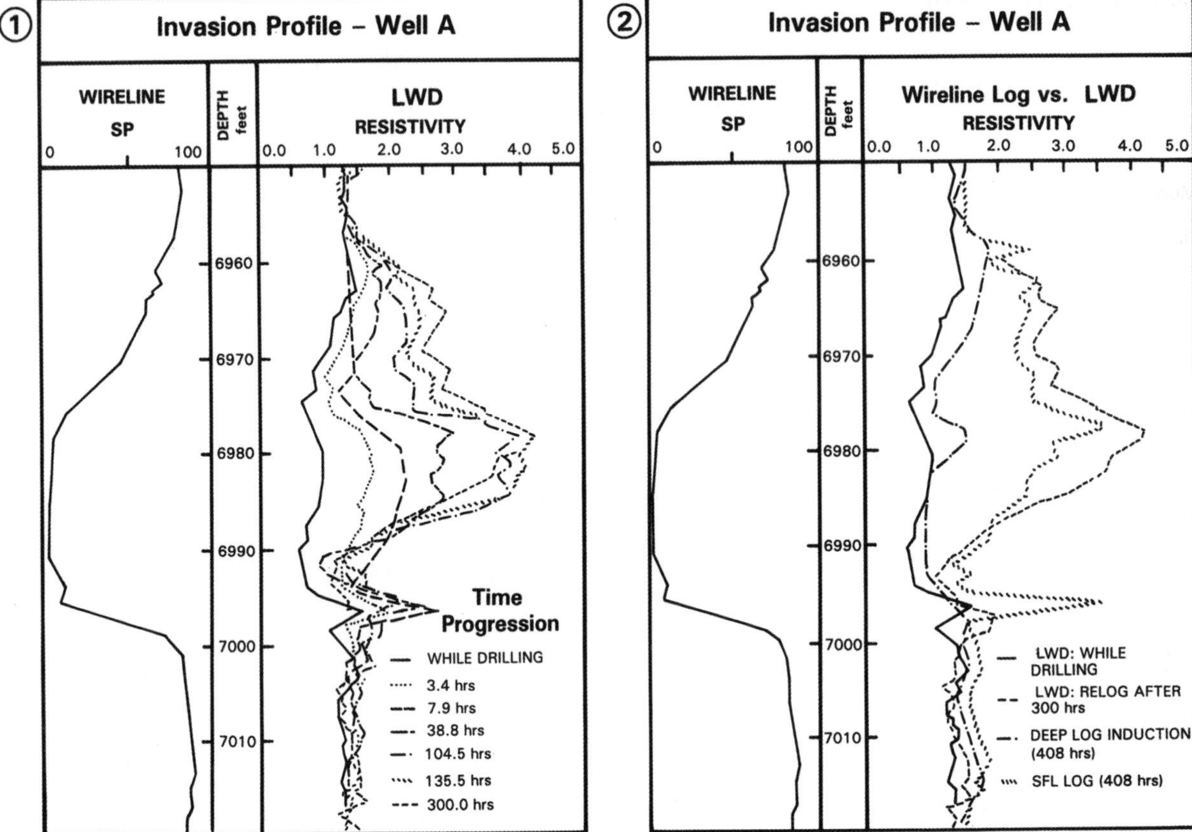

Figure 7.9 Progressive formation invasion demonstrated by LWD and wireline resistivity logs run over a porous, salt water bearing sandstone interval. 1. LWD resistivity logs measured repeatedly over the interval from 3.4 hrs after drilling to 12.5 days (300 hrs). 2. LWD logs (first and last) compared to wireline resistivity logs run 17 days (408 hrs) after drilling. The deep induction wireline measurement compares with the first LWD measurement (no invasion, R_t), the shallow wireline SFL measurement compares with the final LWD measurement (flushed zone, R_{xo}) (from Cobern and Nuckols 1985).

(12.5 days) (**Figure 7.9,1**). The first, while drilling measurement, shows the formation with the original salt formation water: there is no invasion. The resistivity progressively increases for the next 104.5 hours (4.3 days) as invasion progresses, the invading fluid having a higher resistivity than the in-place, salty formation water. After the 4.3 days (104.5 hours) the invasion stabilises and logs acquired over the next 8 days are similar (**Figure 7.9,1**) (Cobern and Nuckols 1985). For comparison, wireline logging took place 17 days (407 hours) after drilling. The wireline resistivity representing the flushed zone (the SFL) is similar to the stabilised LWD log (at maximum invasion), while the wireline log representing the virgin formation (deep induction) is similar to the first LWD log measured before any invasion took place and the reservoir contained only salt formation water. A typical resistivity profile is developed which, in this case, shows a decrease from the more resistive flushed zone containing less saline mud filtrate close to the borehole, to the virgin formation containing a more saline original water deeper into the formation. It is truly with such a set of logs that invasion can be monitored (it takes a surprisingly long time in this case) and the depth of investigation of the resistivity tools empirically evaluated. It is clear that resistivities depend on both where (in relation to the borehole) and when (in relation to the drilling) they are measured (Chapter 2, Section 2.2 and 'Fluid movement', *below*).

The zones of invasion, associated fluid resistivities and corresponding zone resistivities all have accepted notations (**Table 7.4**). These will be used henceforth.

Oil (hydrocarbon) zone resistivity profiles

The previous discussion assumes 100% water saturation in a porous and permeable formation, the resistivity variations being due to mud filtrate and formation water mixing, a two phase system of miscible fluids. When hydrocarbons are present, the system has three components, filtrate, hydrocarbon, formation water, and is more complex. The mud filtrate will displace the oil and/or gas immediately around the borehole, thereby reducing their saturation throughout the flushed zone (**Figure 7.10,1**). In a very simple case, a resistivity profile across a hydrocarbon zone will show a flushed zone with a moderate to low resistivity filled with mud

Table 7.4 Resistivity notation.

Zone	**Resistivity notation** (tool measured)	**Fluid resistivity** (sample measurement and/or log calculated)	**Fluid saturation** calculated
Hole		R_m (m = mud)	
Mudcake		R_{mc} (mc = mudcake)	
Flushed zone	R_{xo}	R_{mf} (mf = mud filtrate)	S_{xo} (saturation in mud filtrate)
Invaded zone (transition)	R_i (i = invaded)	R_z (R_{mf} + R_w mixed)	(S_{wi})
Uninvaded zone	*R_t (t = true)	R_w (w = formation water)	S_w = 1 (saturated in formation water) S_h = 1-S_w (with hydrocarbons) S_{wirr} = irreducible water saturation
	**R_o (o = original) theoretical value, not measured		S_w = 100%

*R_t = true, uninvaded formation resistivity of the reservoir which may contain hydrocarbons. Target of deep resistivity tool measurements.
**R_o = Original, theoretical formation resistivity with 100% formation water saturation. R_t (should) = R_o when S_w = 100%

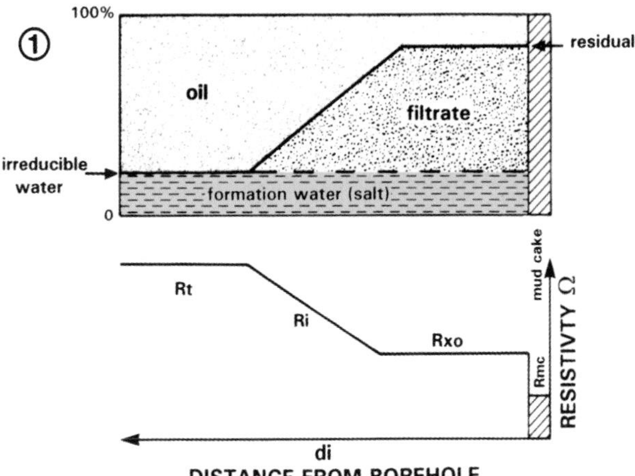

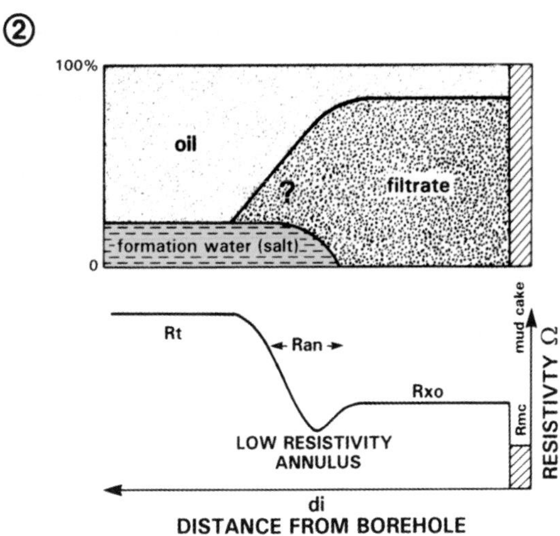

Figure 7.10 Schematic oil zone resistivity profiles. 1. Simple invasion model. 2. Model with low resistivity annulus but it is not certain if this zone really exists and if it does, for how long. R_{an} = annulus resistivity. For symbols *see* Table 7.4.

filtrate, a transition zone, and the virgin formation with a high resistivity because of the high (original) saturation in hydrocarbons. (Both oil and gas are infinitely resistive and show the same effect on resistivity logs.) The resistivity profile therefore shows a big increase away from the borehole, the exact reverse of a water zone (**Figure 7.10,1**). This increase in resistivity away from the borehole and deeper into the formation, is expressed very distinctly on the logs. Shallow investigating tools which read in the flushed zone show (relatively) low resistivity values, while deep reading tools show high resistivities (**Figure 7.11**) The separation between the curves from the shallow and deep tools, plotted on the same resistivity scale, is diagnostic of hydrocarbons. It is sometimes called the *hydrocarbon separation* and is used in the 'quick look' technique for locating oil or gas. A quick look, however, must be verified by calculation since real cases are more complicated than the simple case above.

In practice, the way the resistivity varies through a hydrocarbon zone depends on the relative resistivities of formation water and mud filtrate and how the hydrocarbon saturation varies from the borehole wall to the virgin zone. If the resistivity of the mud filtrate is less than or equal to the resistivity of the formation water (R_w) then the flushed zone will always have a relatively low resistivity and the virgin zone will have the highest resistivity (as the example above). The transition zone will have a resistivity that is intermediate between the flushed and virgin values. (Note, however, that this type of profile does not in itself prove that a hydrocarbon zone is present, it may simply reflect the increase in resistivity of the water filling the

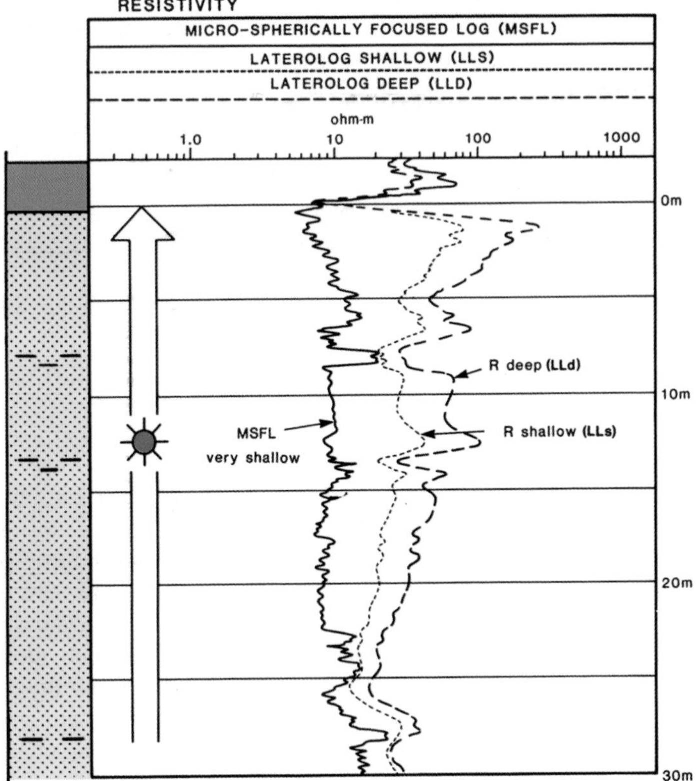

Figure 7.11 Strong separation of resistivity logs in a gas zone, the so-called 'hydrocarbon separation'. Porosity is around 15%.

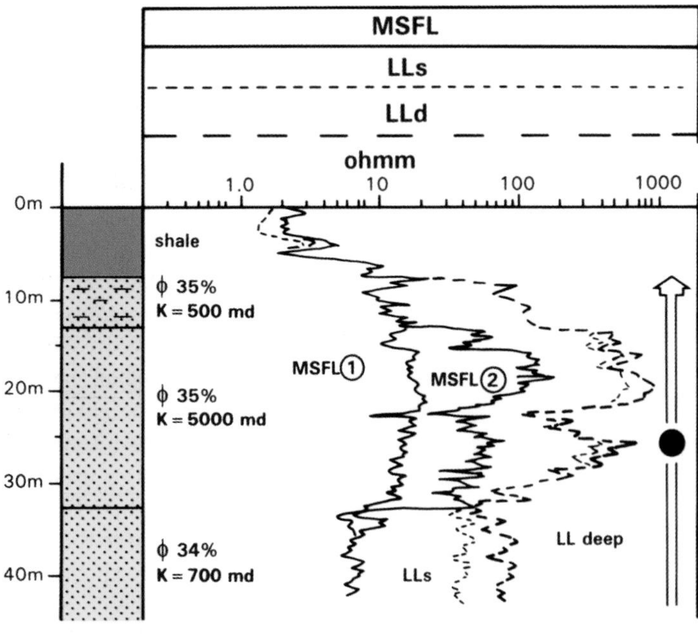

Figure 7.12 Active fluid movement during logging shown by a comparison between a main run and 'repeat' section. MSFL 1, the 'repeat' section, was run 1.5 hours before MSFL 2, the main run. The comparison shows that hydrocarbons are re-migrating into the flushed zone, measured by the MSFL, over the extremely permeable section (see text for explanation).

pore space). For other combinations of R_{mf} and R_w the invaded zone may have a value that is the lowest or highest observed. The latter situation occurs when fresh filtrate replaces a more saline formation water and at the same time displaces some of the hydrocarbon. Although the water saturation in the invaded zone is higher than in the virgin formation, because the invading water is fresher, it is more resistive. The reduction in resistivity expected from the increase in water saturation is offset by its higher resistivity.

Hydrocarbon zone invasion therefore hides complex events. It has been pointed out recently that filtrate will behave differently towards miscible formation water and immiscible hydrocarbons (Bonner *et al.* 1991). Filtrate will push hydrocarbons away from the borehole creating a 'saturation front' but will mix with the formation water to create a 'salinity front'. The two fronts will become separated and may create a low resistivity annulus in the volume between them (**Figure 7.10**,**2**). There are other explanations for this annulus but it is not uncommonly observed on the logs (Threadgold 1971; Oberkircher 1993). How long it persists is uncertain.

Fluid movement

With the data sets now accumulating, from the comparison of LWD, MAD and wireline measurements (i.e. **Figure 7.9**), it is clear that there is considerable fluid movement not only during drilling when invasion occurs, but also when drilling ceases. The fluid equilibrium which existed before drilling, attempts to re-establish itself when drilling ceases and gravity effects become important, notably in gas filled reservoirs, those with very high permeabilities and importantly in horizontal wells (Chapter 2). The example shown (**Figure 7.12**) is of a vertical well with a very highly permeable, light oil reservoir. The well was drilled with a salt water mud and logged by a resistivity tool combination of a very shallow (MSFL), medium (LLs) and deep (LLd) devices (DLL-MSFL tool of Schlumberger). A (repeat) run of the tool was made 1.5 hours before the same interval was logged during the main run. In that 1.5 hours, the mud filtrate has moved down in the reservoir under gravity to make space for a re-migration of the hydrocarbons back towards the wellbore.

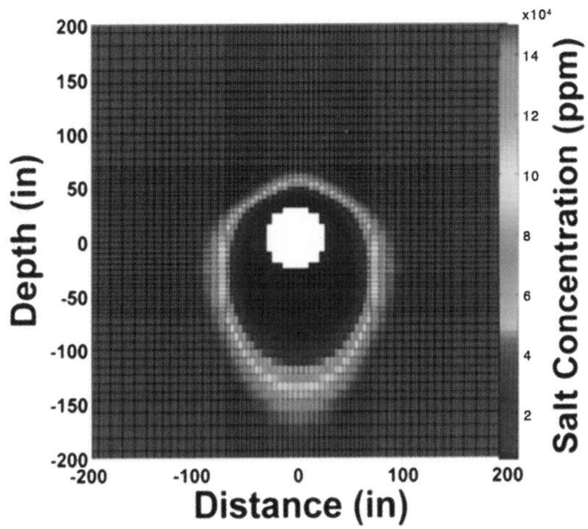

Figure 7.13 Invasion in a horizontal well showing the effect of gravity. Modeled concentration of salt after 3 days invasion. Formation 150,00 ppm, filtrate 5000 ppm NaCl (from Mendoza *et al.* SPWLA 2007).

The increasing flushed zone resistivity (MSFL) over the central part of the reservoir shows this. The two deeper logs (LLd and LLs) are unchanged as is the shallow reading (MSFL) in the upper and lower reservoir zones (**Figure 7.12**). In this case, no doubt, the re-migration of the hydrocarbons and movement of the mud filtrate were helped by the huge permeability of 5000 mD in the affected reservoir.

Although such effects are not always easy to see in vertical wells, they are more evident in horizontal wells, and logs can be affected even at the time they are acquired, mud filtrate having already moved under gravity away from the top of the borehole thus creating a pear shaped invaded zone (**Figure 7.13**) (Salazar *et al.* 2006; Mendoza *et al.* 2007). It is more and more evident that even wireline logs are taking a 'snapshot' of a dynamic situation and what is measured, as already suggested, depends on when it is measured. More discoveries in this area remain to be made.

Types of mud

Since the variations in resistivity about a borehole are due to the influence of mud filtrate, it is as well to be aware of the typical types of mud mixture that are available. Mud types in use today can be classed generally as saltwater muds, freshwater muds (which are both water-based, WBM), synthetic-based muds (SBM) and oil-based muds (OBM).

Water-based muds (WBM) consist of solid particles suspended in a solution of salts in water. To mix water-based muds, sea water is generally used offshore and fresh water onshore, simply because that is what is available. The water component of the mud has a tendency to react with the formation being drilled. This can cause major problems and if not controlled can lead to the loss of the hole. The mud engineer therefore tries to adjust the composition of the water to minimise the reaction and this involves controlling the concentration of the salts. If the source of the water is fresh, salts will always be added. For a sea water supply, salts may again be added but it is also possible that the salinity will need to be reduced by adding fresh water. Adding salt(s) to water reduces its resistivity. Mud filtrates therefore have finite resistivities (R_{mf}) which can vary from several ohmm for a very fresh mud, to fractions of an ohmm for a mud based on salt saturated water. In reality, more often than not, mud filtrates are more resistive (less saline) than the formation water (**Table 7.5**).

Oil-based muds (OBM) consist of solid particles and water droplets suspended in a refined oil. A typical oil-based mud will contain around 50% oil and 20% water along with surfactants as emulsifiers, salts and a weighting agent such as barite and a wetting agent to make cuttings oil wet. They are not conductive because, although they contain water, oil is the continuous phase. This means that tools that rely on an electrical contact with the formation will not work (laterologs and the older resistivity tools as well as the SP and many of the electrical imaging tools). The advantage of OBMs is that the filtrate, which is basically just the oil phase, does not react with the formation (i.e. reduces water loss), is a good lubricant and often reduces drilling time considerably

In recent years oil-based muds have been replaced by so-called synthetic-based muds (SBM). As far as resistivity tools are concerned these behave the same way. The continuous phase

Table 7.5 Variations in mud filtrate and formation-water resistivity values, as indicated by resistivity tools (*see also* Figure 7.9).

	Formation water salinity	
	Fresh formation water	Saline formation water
Saltwater mud (usual offshore)	$R_{mf} < R_w$	$R_{mf} > R_w$
Freshwater mud	$R_{mf} > R_w$	$R_{mf} > R_w$
Oil-based mud	$R_{mf} > R_w$	$R_{mf} > R_w$
	(Oil filtrate has a high resistivity so R_{mf} is large. When hydrocarbons are present $R_{mf} = R_t$ and only indirect resistivities can be measured)	
*Synthetic mud	generally the same as for oil-based mud.	

*Most synthetic muds are not conductive, although specialist forms exist that can be moderately conductive (see text).

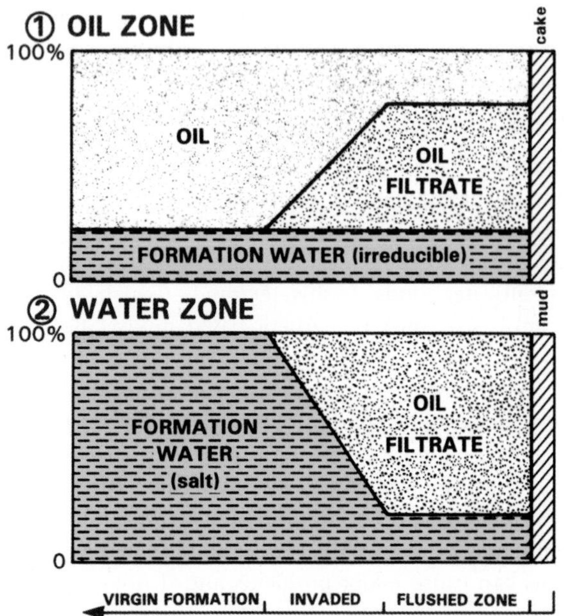

Figure 7.14 Fluid mixing in a well drilled with oil-based mud. 1, Oil zone. 2, Water zone (modified after Boyeldieu *et al.*1984).

consists of non-conductive organic compounds such as alphaolefins. These are chosen because they are considered to be less damaging to the environment than the base oils used in OBM. Conductive SBMs have been developed specifically to allow logging tools that need an electrical connection to the formation to be run (Cheung *et al.* 2001). It is fair to say these have not been very successful, they are expensive and, whilst they do conduct, they have a resistivity that is high enough to still adversely affect the tool responses (tens of ohmm).

The fluids used in the borehole and their characteristics should be sumarised on the log heading with the older style logs and in the LAS or DLIS listings for digital logs.

Oil-based mud resistivity profiles

Many modern wells are now drilled with oil-based mud (OBM) for the reasons given above. Clearly, the invasion behaviour of an oil filtrate is quite different from a water filtrate. Oil filtrate is miscible with the hydrocarbons in a hydrocarbon zone but is immiscible with water, the exact reverse of water-based mud (**Figure 7.14**). In an oil or gas zone, invasion will be difficult to identify as the oil filtrate mixes with or displaces the formation hydrocarbons but has no effect on the water (the water remains at the same saturation and has the same composition). The resistivity will therefore be the same in the flushed zone, invaded zone and the virgin formation. In normal situations, this will appear on the log as all the resistivity curves superposed (**Figure 7.15**) (La Vigne *et al.* 1997).

In a water-bearing reservoir on the other hand filtrate will displace water and the water saturation will increase with depth into the formation. The resistivity will be higher in the flushed zone than the virgin reservoir. Oil mud filtrate is immiscible with the formation water and, historically, oil-based mud has been considered to show shallow invasion. In fact, it tends to show

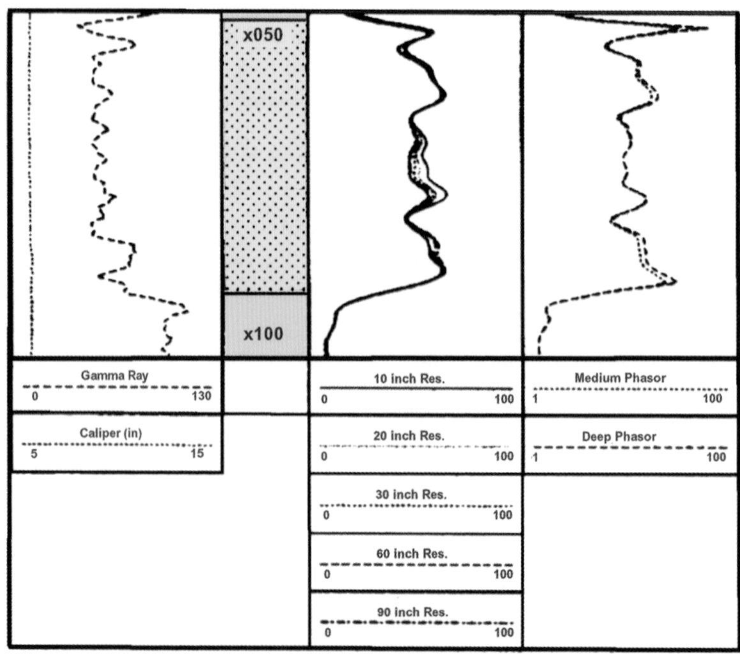

Figure 7.15 Array induction and Phasor induction resistivities in an oil reservoir drilled with oil-based mud (OBM). The resistivities at all depths of investigation are essentially the same (re-drawn from La Vigne *et al.*1997).

more of a piston-like displacement. In other words, the filtrate invades a few centimetres into the formation and then its concentration falls abruptly to zero. Modern array tools confirm that shallow OBM invasion is the most common situation, but not always (La Vigne *et al.* 1997 *op. cit.*).

As has already been indicated, boreholes in which oil-based muds are used cannot be logged by the contact resistivity tools: only induction or propagation devices can be used. Typically, an array induction tool will be used for wireline logging; the propagation type resistivity tools are used in the while drilling domain. The tools are described below.

7.4 Resistivity tools

Two types of measurement

Two different arrangements for measuring the resistivity of subsurface rocks were introduced at the beginning of this chapter:

1. Direct electrical connection between the tool and formation in which current flows from the tool to the formation and back.
2. Indirect methods in which electromagnetic fields are induced in the formation by a transmitter in the tool. The resistivity is measured or calculated from the behaviour of these fields (Section 7.1). As explained below, there are two fundamentally different ways this is achieved.

Tools using the first method are often described as 'resistivity tools' and the second as 'conductivity tools'. (These terms are not really meaningful because, as has been explained, resistivity and conductivity amount to the same thing. Nevertheless, the terms are so common that they will be used in this book.)

The earliest tools were 'resistivity tools' and used the direct electrical connection method. Almost all the present generation of tools that use this method are called *laterologs*. They always require a conductive, water-based mud in the borehole to ensure an electrical connection between the tool and the formation. The current could be DC but, in order to avoid some artifacts and to make the instrumentation simpler, it is normally a low frequency alternating current (similar to domestic electricity supplies). In principle the measurement could be made with just two electrodes, but in practice far more are needed to produce an accurate measurement. The current normally passes between two electrodes, at least one of which is located in the downhole tool, and the second may actually be the cable armour or even a separate electrode at the surface. Different electrodes are used to monitor the voltage drop which is input to the resistivity equation.

Tools using the indirect methods induce an electromagnetic field in the formation and then monitor how the field behaves by its effect on one or more receiver coils. In order to get a measurable response these tools have to work at high frequencies. Within the broad area of non-contact arrangements there are two distinctly different tool types. The first was developed in the 1950s to allow resistivity to be measured in wells filled with a non-conductive medium. These are the *induction tools* that work by using a transmitter, operating at a few kHz, to induce a current to flow around the borehole (**Figure 7.16**). The strength of this induced current depends on the conductivity of the formation and hence tools using this method are sometimes also called 'conductivity tools'. They will function in any non-conductive medium including oil-based mud, diesel oil, fresh water or air but they will also work in conductive muds (however, as will be explained below, large holes filled with very conductive muds can significantly reduce their accuracy).

The second type of non-contact tools are known as *propagation tools*. They were developed to allow LWD tools to measure resistivity which, because they are part of the drill string, have to be made almost entirely of metal. They work on a principle which is similar to RADAR and emit short pulses of radio waves. These are more strongly attenuated in low resistivity media than resistive rocks and so, by measuring their attenuation, resistivity can be inferred. Like the induction tools, they can be used in wells drilled with either oil-based or water-based mud.

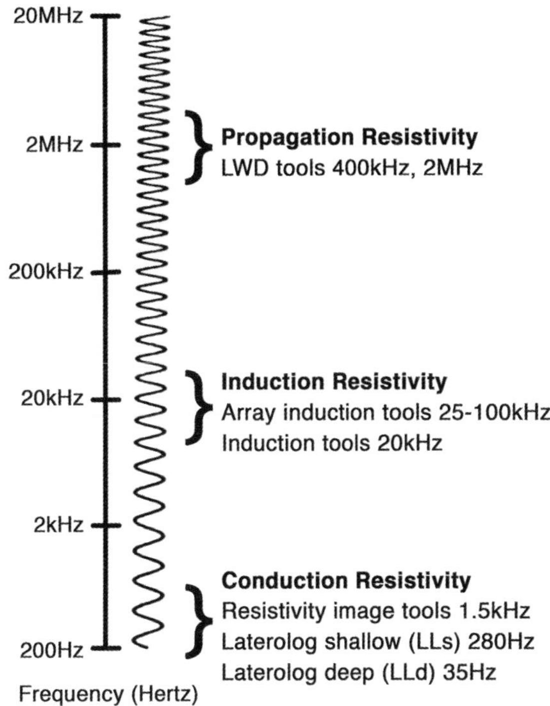

Figure 7.16 The range of electromagnetic frequencies used in the classic conduction tools, the induction tools and the newer LWD propagation tools (re-drawn, modified after Rodney *et al.* 1983; Bonner *et al.* 1996).

7.5 The different types of resistivity tools

Wireline, contact resistivity tools (laterologs and their predecessors)

The basic principles of the direct contact resistivity tools were established by Conrad Schlumberger in 1927. In his arrangement a current was passed between two electrodes, one in the borehole, one on the surface and the potential difference was a measured drop between two other electrodes. Again, one of these was on the tool in the borehole. Tools using this arrangement were called the *normal* devices. A slightly different arrangement of electrodes, known as a lateral array, was developed shortly afterwards. In this, a constant current was passed between an electrode in the borehole and one at surface but the potential difference was measured between two electrodes in the well (Schlumberger 1989a). Both arrangements give rise to very simple tools that consist of little more than the electrodes, mounted on an insulating tool body, and the conductors that connect them with the surface. Because they are simple they can continue to function in the most hostile environments including some hot, very deep research wells.

The main problem with the lateral and normal tools is that the current path in the formation depends on the size of the borehole and what it contains. If the well penetrates a relatively resistive formation, then most of the current will flow in the borehole. Conversely, if the formation is relatively conductive then more of the current will flow there. In order to get the current to follow the same path regardless of the relative resistivities of borehole and formation, a system known as current focusing is used (**Figures 7.17**). This involves more than four electrodes, and most tools need some sophisticated downhole instrumentation to control the currents. These tools began to appear in the 1940s and are generally called the laterologs (**Figures 7.18**). They are the commonest type of direct contact tool in use today. The older normal and lateral tools are obsolete as wireline tools, but in recent years they have made a come-back as near bit LWD tools.

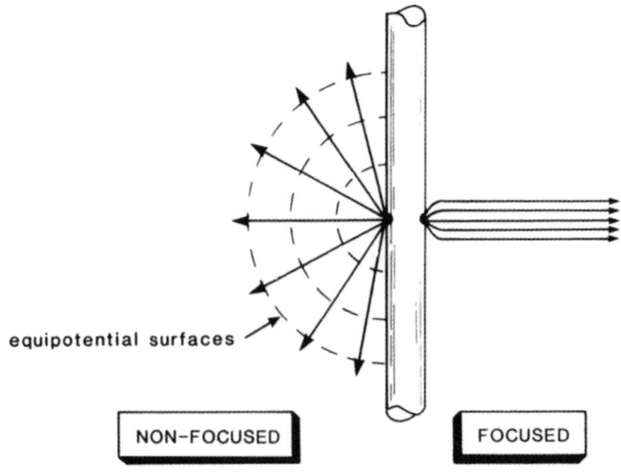

Figure 7.17 Schematic drawing of focused and non-focused electrical current distribution about a logging tool. The old Electrical Survey tools were not focused: modern Laterologs are focused.

Laterologs (and their predecessors) can be designed to have a depth of investigation that varies from a few centimeters to hundreds of metres (the latter, ultra-deep reading tools are operated as stationary measurements and the resistivity profiles are derived after the survey

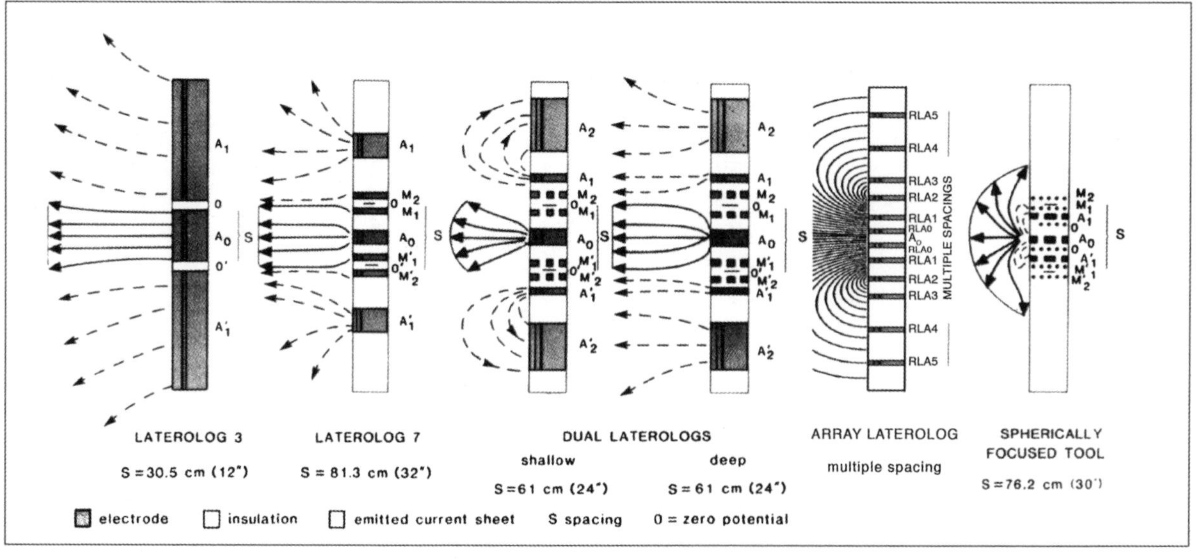

Figure 7.18 Schematic electrode disposition in several older and newer, wireline resistivity tools from Schlumberger. A = electrode, M = monitoring electrode (re-drawn after Schlumberger).

Table 7.6 Resistivity measuring tools from the main companies. (From Serra 2000, 2008, Baker Hughes™ (Atlas), Halliburton and Schlumberger documents.)

Type of tool	Schlumberger	Baker Hughes™ (Atlas)	Halliburton	output
Pad devices	ML	ML	ML	microlog, mud cake
	PL	MLL		
	MSFL	MSL	MSFL	micolaterolog, flushed zone
	MCFL		HFDT	
		TBRT		thin bed, deep reading
Electrical tools (wireline)	DLL (1972)	DLL	DLLT	deep & shallow laterolog
	SFL	PROX		shallow resistivity without pad
	HALS (1996)	TBRT	DFL	high resolution resistivity
	HRLA (1998)	*HDLL	HEDL	array laterolog
	*ARI (1992)			azimuthal laterolog (+image)
Induction tools (wireline)	DIL	IEL	DILT	deep & medium induction
	DIT	DPIL	HRI + DFL	
	IDPH (Phasor)	HDIL	HRAI	high resolution induction
	*AIT (1990)	DIFL	ACRt	array induction
	3Dex-3DExplorer			vertical & horizontal resistivities
	RTscanner			
LWD tools	CDR (1988)	*MPR (Autotrak™)	CWR (1993)	multiple propagation logs
	ARC (1996)	NaviGator™	EWR-M5 (2003)	
	EcoScope	OnTrak™		
	PeriScope	AziTrak™	ADR	deep looking resistivity
	*RAB (geoVISION) (2006)			contact WBM tool with images

*described briefly in the text
for acronyms use www.spwla.org

has been completed). The modern laterologs can simultaneously make measurements at several different depths of investigation and this means that they can investigate formation resistivity anywhere from the flushed zone to the un-invaded formation. The deeper 'looking' devices are hole-centred (**Figure 7.18**) while the shallow investigating devices, like the microlog, are mounted on a pad pressed against the borehole wall (**Table 7.6**, **Figure 7.19**).

In the logging suite, the body-mounted laterologs tend to be the deepest looking water based tools and most likely to give the virgin formation resistivity, R_t.

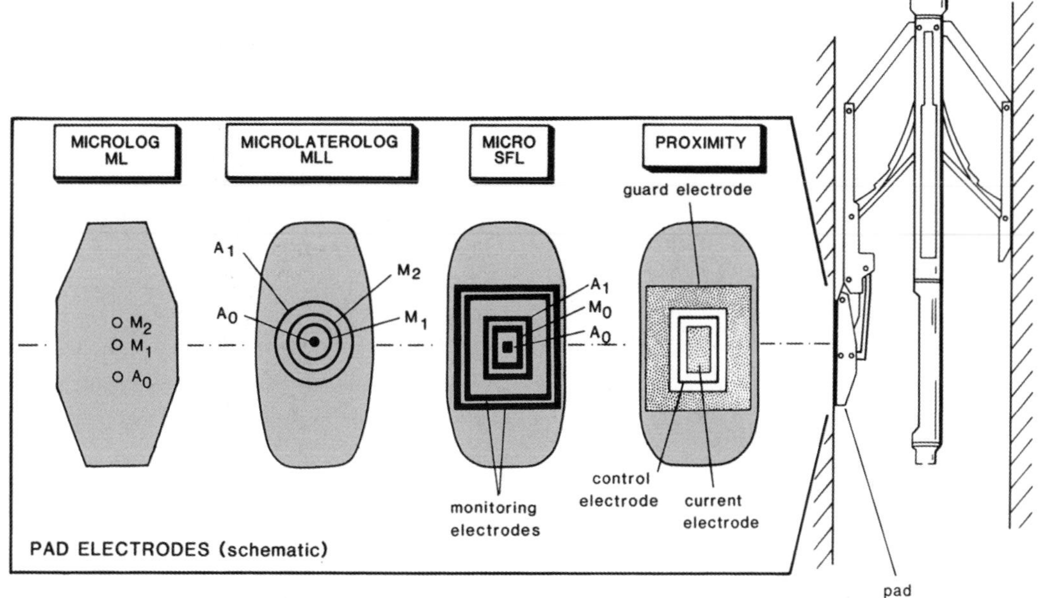

Figure 7.19 Schematic drawings of electrode dispositions on several older, wireline, pad-type resistivity tools. One tool (MSFL) is shown in the hole. SFL = spherically focused log. A, M, electrodes. (Modified from Schlumberger documents).

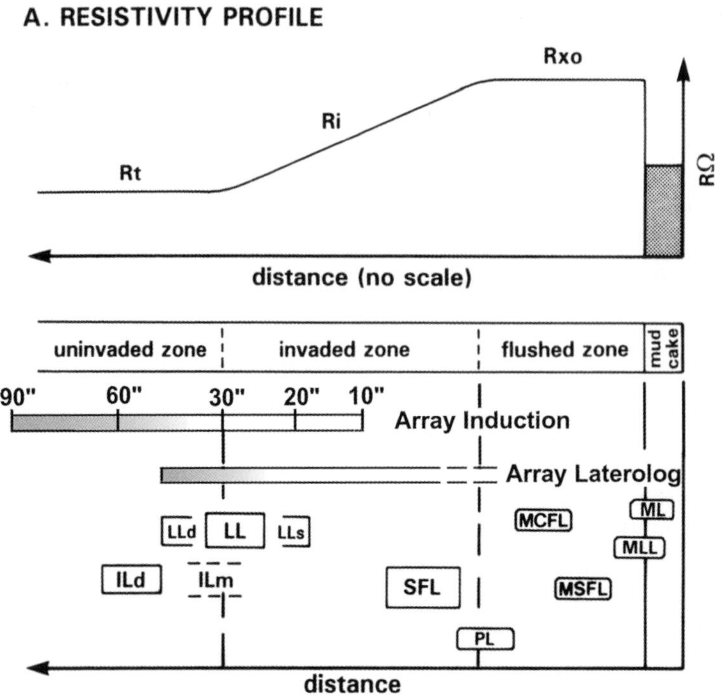

Figure 7.20 The resistivity measured by the various tools and compared to a typical salt water invasion profile. IL = induction log, deep-medium; LL = laterologs, deep, shallow; SFL = spherically focused log; PL = proximity log; MCFL = micro-cylindrically focused log: MSFL = micro-spherically focused log; MLL = microlaterolog; ML = microlog

The Dual Laterolog tool, that first appeared in the late 1960s but is still in service, provides a deep measurement for R_t (LLd) and an intermediate one for the resistivity of the transition zone R_i (LLs) (**Figure 7.18**). The tool has a depth of investigation of 1.25 m (50″) and vertical resolution of 61 cm (2 ft). The flushed zone resistivity R_{xo}, comes from a very shallow reading, pad-mounted electrode array, that is basically a miniature version of the laterolog. Examples of the latter are the Microlaterolog (MLL) and the Micro-spherically focused log of Schlumberger (MSFL)(**Table 7.6**, **Figure 7.20**). Pad tools can have a vertical resolution of 5–7.5 cm (2″–3″) and a depth of investigation of a few centimeters. A consequence of this finer vertical resolution is the shallower depth of investigation; a typical trade-off with logging tools. (Note that in the literature, depth of investigation usually refers to the detection of 50% of the signal, i.e. Theys 1991).

The basic hardware for the laterolog tools changed little from the 60s to the late 80s. However, in the late 80s the availability of better electronics, down-hole telemetry and well-site computing power, allowed tools with multiple depths of investigation to be developed. An early example was the array laterolog of British Plaster Board (BPB) which gave a pad micro-resistivity, an intermediate resistivity and conventional shallow and deep resistivities. Another approach simplified the down-hole tool to little more than an array of electrodes, the currents and voltage drops at each electrode being measured at each depth. The resistivity at five or six depths of investigation can then be derived by modeling the tool response. This requires a lot of computation but this is now cheap and easy to provide at the well-site. The trend towards multiple values with different depths of investigation continues today since it allows the direct observation of the invasion profile and greater processing possibilities.

While some tools were developed for multiple depths of investigation, others were being designed to examine oriented sectors of the borehole. In a horizontal well it is necessary to know whether a value is from the top of the hole or the bottom; whether it is from an upward looking sensor or downward, hence the requirement for azimuthal data. This trend too continues today.

Wireline induction tools

All the laterolog type tools need a conductive fluid in the borehole to function, such as water-based mud. However, from the earliest days of the oil industry, wells have been drilled also with non-conducting fluids (for example air, mineral oil and oil-based mud). In 1949 the induction tool was introduced to the industry by Henri Doll of Schlumberger to allow these holes to be logged. During the Second World War he had worked on mine detection and his new tool concept originated from this (Dorozynski & Oristalgio 2007).

A basic induction sonde consists of two coils within an insulating tool housing, a transmitter coil driven by a high frequency oscillator and a receiving coil. The coils are typically mounted about 1 metre apart on an insulating mandrel. A constant amplitude sinusoidal current at a fixed frequency of about 10 kHz is applied to the transmitter coil. This creates an electromagnetic field in the vicinity of the tool and this, in turn, induces currents in the formation that flow in a circular path around the moving tool (**Figure 7.21**). The induced currents create a secondary electromagnetic field which induces an alternating current in the receiver coil. The formation current is 90° out of phase with the transmitter current and the receiver current is a further 90° out of phase. In other words, the transmitter and receiver currents show a 180° phase shift. This measured current is the so-called *R-signal*. There is also a much stronger current, caused by a direct coupling of the transmitter and receiver coils, which is 90° out of phase with the transmitter current: this is the *X-signal* and is an approximation of the so-called 'skin effect' or tool distortion of the signal. Because the phase relationships of the *R*- and *X*-signals are known, the latter can be distinguished and eliminated. The original tools did this using analogue instrumentation but more up-to-date tools actually measure both the *R*- and *X*-signals, principally because the *X*-signal can be used in subsequent signal processing (these are sometimes named 'Phasor Induction Tools').

Commercial logging tools have always had more than two coils. For example, the Dual Induction Tool of Schlumberger, which was introduced in 1962 had a series of secondary, paired, reverse wound coils in addition to the transmitter and two receiver coils. The former were precisely placed to eliminate or 'buck' out the unwanted *X*-signal. The two receiver coils gave the tool two depths of investigation (in addition a laterolog type device mounted in the same tool gave a third, shallow reading resistivity). It was generally considered that the induced current in the formation flows between 1 m and 5 m from the borehole and that the vertical resolution was about 2.5 m (8 ft) (Schlumberger 1995). The corresponding average depth of investigation for the medium or shallow induction was 0.8–1.5 m (i.e. detection depth of 50% of the tool signal) with a vertical resolution of about 1.5 m (5 ft).

The induction tool has been progressively improved since that time but the basic construction with the principal coils being set 1 m (40") apart has not changed greatly. Like most tools, the induction has benefited from improved computing power, both at the well-site and in the research centres where the coil arrangements are developed. It has already been noted that tools now exploit the *X*-signal. Other developments include using multiple transmitter frequencies, so while the original tools used a fixed frequency of 20 kHz, later tools gave a choice of 10, 20 and 40 kHz.

An advance on the dual induction or IES survey was the introduction of better signal processing along with some tool modifications. Schlumberger introduced the Phasor Induction (mentioned previously) in the late 80s and although the standard resolutions for the deep and shallow readings were 7 ft (2.0 m) (IDPH) and 5 ft (1.5 m) (IMPH) respectively (the same as the older ILD and ILM), with processing these measurements could be reduced to 3 ft (90 cm) and eventually 2 ft (60 cm). The smaller resolutions however could be adversely affected by hole conditions being mostly based on the raw shallow reading. These were the first digital induction tools to be introduced by Schlumberger.

A significant new tool, the Array Induction Tool (AIS), was introduced by British Plaster Board (BPB) in 1983 (Martin *et al.* 1984). It consisted of one emitter coil and four receiver coils, the raw signals being processed mathematically using electromagnetic theory to produce multiple investigation depths calculated from the tool response. These were then used to reconstruct an invasion profile, though the shallowest reading was still

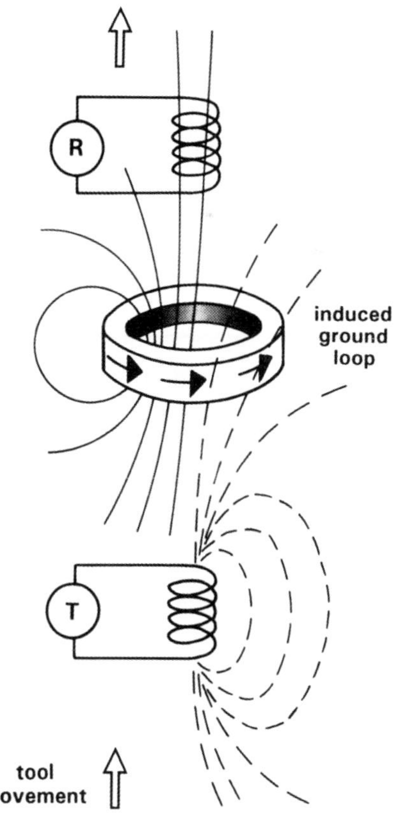

Figure 7.21 The principle of the simple induction tool. The vertical component of the magnetic field from the transmitting coil, T, induces a ground loop in the formation, which in turn is detected by the receiver coil, R (re-drawn, modified from Ellis 1987).

too deep to measure the flushed zone (Head *et al.* 1992) (**Figure 7.22**). This was an important advance because deriving invasion information was impossible with the 2-value induction tools. This approach is now used in almost all commercial induction tools most of which give resistivities at six or more depths of investigation from 25 cm to 300 cm (10″–120″). Induction tools are still under active development.

LWD resistivity tools

The first LWD resistivity tools to be introduced in the early 80s required water-based mud and used the simple principle of passing a current from an electrode on the tool to a return electrode. These were replaced in the late 80s by tools using a laterolog type configuration and others using axial current generation. This type of tool has continued to evolve as a near bit and/or resistivity image device (see below). However, most LWD resistivity tools in use today are based on the propagation principle. They can be used in conductive or non-conductive muds.

It is difficult to build LWD versions of laterologs and induction tools because the housing for the electrode or coil array has to be non-metallic. An LWD tool, because it is part of the drill string, has to be constructed mainly from metal. To produce a reliable, deep reading resistivity tool a new measuring principle had to be employed: electromagnetic propagation. Tools using this principle first appeared in the early 1980s. Propagation tools create a high frequency electromagnetic field around the tool using a transmitter which operates at radio frequencies (**Figure 7.16**). This makes sense when one considers that radio transmitters and RADAR dishes are made almost completely of metal. The problem of creating an electromagnetic field near a metal tool is therefore eliminated. The earliest tools invariably worked at 2 MHz (this is generally considered the high frequency band in communications and is used in commercial AM radio, amateur radio transmitters and also in very long range RADARs). Most tools in current use work at 2 MHz and 400 kHz simultaneously: the lower frequency increases the depth of investigation.

The basis of the measurement is that electromagnetic fields are more strongly attenuated in low resistivity media. The tool therefore has two or more receiver antennae that are typically positioned a few tens of centimetres apart and a few tens of centimetres from the transmitter. The ratio of the near to the far signal amplitude can then be converted to resistivity. Phase shift is also dependent on resistivity, so measuring the shift between the two transmitters allows a second estimate of resistivity. The wavelength of the radio waves is typically a few metres, so the receiver spacing has to be large enough to produce a measurable difference but still be less than one wavelength. The receiver spacing also dictates the vertical resolution, so a variety of factors really constrain the tool design and, not surprisingly,

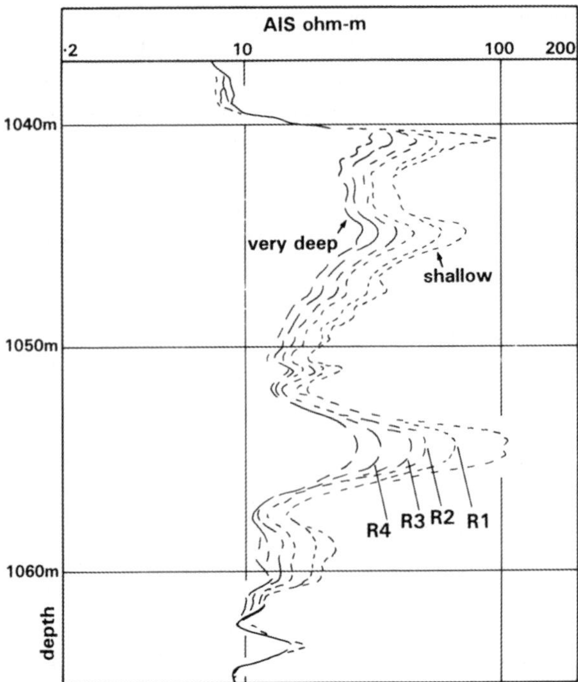

Figure 7.22 Invasion profile indicated by the BPB AIS, array induction tool in a water-filled limestone drilled with oil-based mud. The 4 raw induction tool readings (R1–R4) have been resolution matched and modeled to give the invasion profile. The results may be presented as a colour image (from Elkington 1995).

all the commercial tools have similar dimensions. In many respects, the functioning of these tools is more analogous to a sonic tool than the traditional wireline resistivity tool.

As noted above, the depth of investigation depends on the frequency. It also depends on whether the resistivity measurement is based on phase shift or attenuation and the transmitter-receiver spacing (**Table 7.7**). Most modern tools actually have four or more spacings (although for practical reasons they normally have only one or two receivers and several transmitters, the net effect is the same). The combination of two frequencies, several receiver-transmitter spacings, and the possibility of making resistivity measurements using phase shift

Table 7.7 Notional depths of investigation of the propagation signals from a two-frequency resistivity tool. Actual depths of investigation depend on formation conductivity (Meyer 1995).

Propagation Signal	Depth of Investigation
2 MHz phase difference	SHALLOWEST
400 kHz phase difference	
2 MHz attenuation	
400 kHz attenuation	DEEPEST

and attenuation, means that these tools can produce about twenty different resistivity readings. These do not necessarily all correspond to different depths of investigation so one combination of type, frequency and spacing may give the same depth of investigation as a different combination of type, frequency and spacing (analogous to the gears on a mountain bike, there may be 21 different combinations of front and rear cogs but a lot of the combinations will give a very similar gear ratio!). Furthermore, some combinations simply will not work in some conditions: low frequency attenuation measurements, for example, typically fail completely for resistivities above a few 10s of ohmm. Nevertheless, there is normally a sufficient range in depth of investigation to see, for example, invasion .

The question sometimes asked is why the propagation principle is not employed in wireline tools. If nothing else, it would avoid the necessity of using fiberglass tool bodies, which normally represent a weak point in a tool string. Unfortunately, propagation tools have two undesirable characteristics. First and foremost, the depth of investigation for any combination of spacing, frequency and measurement type, depends on the resistivity of the medium. In particular, the depth of investigation decreases with resistivity. Secondly, if the well intersects a feature at a low angle the measurement is dominated by a phenomenon known as polarisation. This manifests itself as large resistivity spikes at or near the point where the tool crosses the boundary (often called 'current horns'). For vertical wells crossing more or less horizontal bed boundaries, polarisation will not occur but it is likely to be a problem with steeply dipping beds or fault planes and fractures. It is most commonly observed in high angle wells and, in fact, it can actually be usefully exploited to geosteer wells as the spikes tell the driller when the well is at, or close to, top reservoir (*see* 'Current horns etc.' *below*). Even so, propagation has actually has been exploited to produce shallow reading wireline tools for use in oil-based mud.

LWD propagation resistivity tools are often run in the top-hole sections of deepwater wells that are otherwise not logged. In this part of the hole, logs are generally only used to assist in correlation and, by using LWD, a day or more of rig-time can be saved. In fact, the propagation tools are generally considered to be accurate enough for quantitative log analysis, so many operators use them in place of wireline tools, even in the reservoir section.

7.6 Modern Resistivity tools: some examples

This section does not attempt to describe every tool available on the market. Instead, it selects one or two tools to describe as being typical. Service companies have their own fact sheets, often available on-line. First described are modern wireline resistivity tools, then modern induction tools and finally LWD tools now in use. The LWD tools are accompanied by some special remarks.

Array laterolog (wireline, water based, multi-depth)

The High-Definition Lateral Log™ (HDLL) from Baker Hughes™ is one of the multi-electrode resistivity or array type tools for water-based muds (Hakvoort *et al.* 1998). It has a single current injecting electrode and 18 potential measurement electrodes (**Figure 7.23).** The current and voltage of the injecting electrode along with 8 electrode potentials (normal) and 16 first-potential differences (lateral) between consecutive (i.e. neighbouring) electrodes, are measured by high resolution

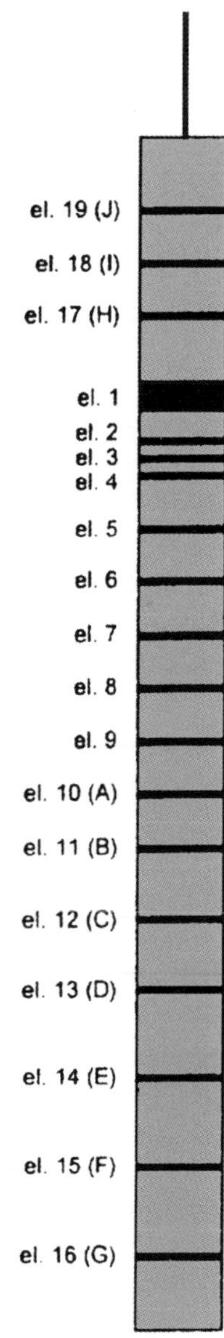

Figure 7.23 The multi-electrode configuration of the array laterolog tool the High Definition Laterolog™ (HDLL) from Baker Hughes™ (from Hakvoort *et al.* SPWLA1998).

signal processors and 14 second potential differences are calculated between groups of electrodes. From these measurements, an array of normal and lateral curves can be constructed and a set of synthetic resistivity curves generated. The short electrode spacings give shallow readings which have good vertical resolution, while the long spacings give deep readings, but with less vertical resolution, effects originally exploited by the classic normal and lateral tools.

The results from the different electrode spacings can be combined in such a way as to produce synthetically focused curves, a shallow, a medium and a deep response. The detailed measurements from the tool can be inverted using either 2D (layered formation including borehole and invasion effects) or 3D (dipping layers and deviated borehole and invasion) modelling algorithms. These algorithms first construct an earth model using bed boundary detection from the shallower looking data. This earth model is then used to construct a shallow resistivity structure which is refined before constructing a deep resistivity structure. From these results, the R_{xo}, R_t and the depth of invasion (L_{xo}) are constructed (**Figure 7.24**). It is considered that, with this processing structure, the array laterolog can accurately assess beds as thin as 30–45 cm (12"–18") and give a valid invasion profile. Measurements are taken every 3.8 cm (1.5") (8 per foot) for the calculations. In general, calculated R_{xo} compares with microlog resistivities, but the derived R_t is better defined and more accurate than a deep laterolog (Hakvoort *et al.* 1998 *op. cit.*).

This example is typical of array tools in that signal processing is almost as important as the acquisition of the data itself. The large volume of acquired data must be processed in order to become interpretable and processing requires as much data as possible. Probability limits can be put on the accuracy of predictions (Frenkel and Mezzatesta 1998).

Azimuthal resistivity log (wireline, water-based, full cover images)

The Azimuthal Resistivity Imager (ARI) of Schlumberger provides oriented electrical images from a laterolog type tool, using deep looking signals (Schlumberger 1993a). It is based on a standard dual laterolog sonde with a modified upper electrode which has 12 small electrodes positioned azimuthally round the tool (**Figure 7.25**). Current from each of these electrodes is electrically focused into the formation to provide a deep resistivity representative of 30° of borehole wall. A standard dual laterolog tool operates simultaneously at both 35 Hz for the LLd and 280 Hz for the LLs measurements. The azimuthal currents use a 35 Hz signal and so have a relatively deep investigation and because they have their own monitoring and feedback electrodes can be used as calibrated resistivity curves (*below*). The azimuthal electrodes also use a 71 Hz signal for a very shallow measurement, which is essentially a mud signal. This can be used to correct the azimuthal signal for borehole irregularities and tool eccentricity and also to construct an electrical stand-off (tool to borehole wall distance) from which borehole size and shape can be derived provided mud electrical characteristics are known (Schlumberger 1993 *op. cit.*).

Because the tool uses a general purpose orientation (GPIT) sonde, the 12 azimuthal measurements are displayed as a 360°, north referenced image (Chapter

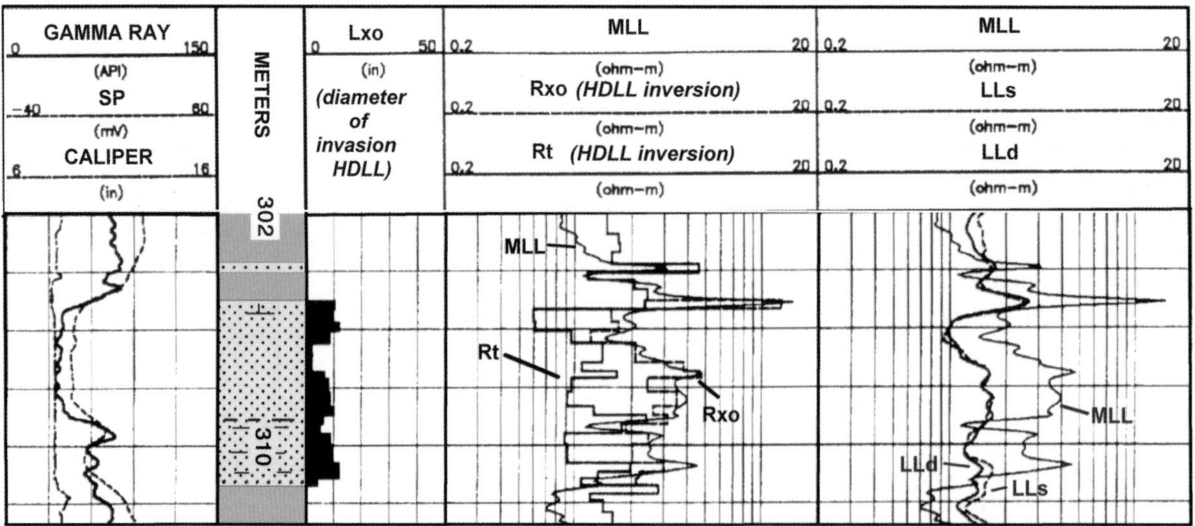

Figure 7.24 Inversion of HDLL (multi-electrode laterolog) measurements to produce 'synthetic' R_{xo} and R_t curves and their comparison to classic MLL (micro-laterolog), LLs and LLd measurements (laterolog shallow and deep). The 'synthetic' curves show more detail and are more accurate. Sampling over the interval shows mud filtrate (R_{mf}) is more resistive than the formation water (R_w) (modified from Hakvoort *et al.* SPWLA1998).

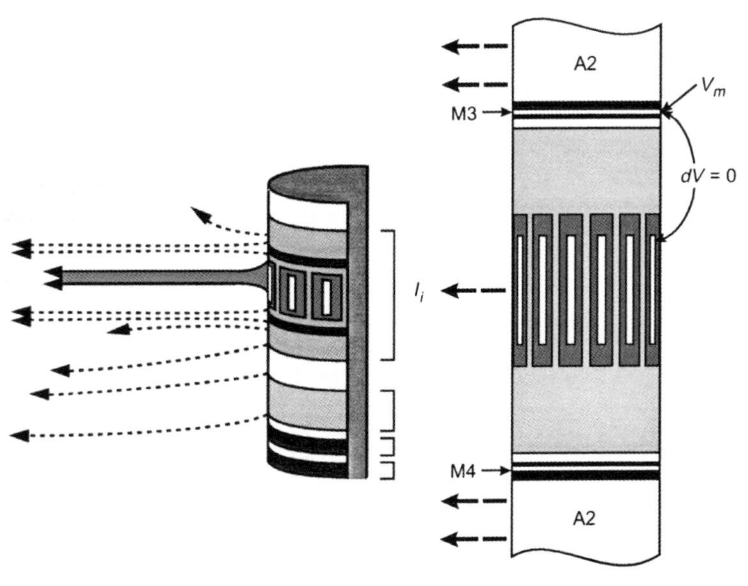

Figure 7.25 Electrode configuration and schematic current paths of the Azimuthal Laterolog (ARI, azimuthal resistivity imager) of Schlumberger (modified from Schlumberger 1993a). *Courtesy of Schlumberger.*

15, Image logs). This image is normally in colour (brown-yellow scale), with the shade representing the resistivity value (lighter colours are higher resistivities). Besides producing an image, the 12 resistivities can be averaged into a single, calibrated curve to give a standard deep laterolog, but with a vertical resolution of around 20 cm (8″) instead of the usual 61 cm (24″) for the standard tool (White 1993).

Array induction (wireline, non-conductive muds, multi-depth)

The Array Induction Tool (AIT) from Schlumberger is a typical multi-depth induction resistivity tool (Schlumberger 1995). It has 8 receivers which work at multiple frequencies and which are at different distances from the single transmitter. The receiver array provides 28 raw resistivity measurements which can be processed to give 5 curves receiving at least half their signal from five different depths of investigation, namely 10″, 20″, 30″, 60″ and 90″ (25 cm – 2.3 m). These depths of investigation do not vary with formation resistivity. In previous tools, depth of investigation measured directly changed as the formation changed. All the major logging companies have similar tools to the AIT.

The new aspect of this array induction tool is that, unlike previous tools, the curves provided are calculated, 'virtual' curves, rather than observed curves which have been corrected (similar to the array laterolog). Thus, the 28 raw curves are subjected to considerable correction and manipulation before the five, virtual curves are computed. The correction manipulations include, mud and hole corrections, radial response analysis, resolution matching and dip and speed correction.

The vertical resolution of the array tool is normally given as 1.2 m (4 ft) but it can be reduced by calculation to 60 cm (2 ft) and, less reliably, even to 30 cm (1 ft). This is achieved by modeling and hence relies on a number of assumptions. If these do not apply, the high resolution curves will be inaccurate to some degree. The tool can also provide an estimate of the inner and outer limits of invasion, that is the limits of the zone from fully flushed formation to un-invaded or virgin formation and the width of the invaded zone (**Figure 7.26**). For effective calculation the tool measurements are sampled every 7.6 cm (3″) of depth (4/foot, about 13/metre).

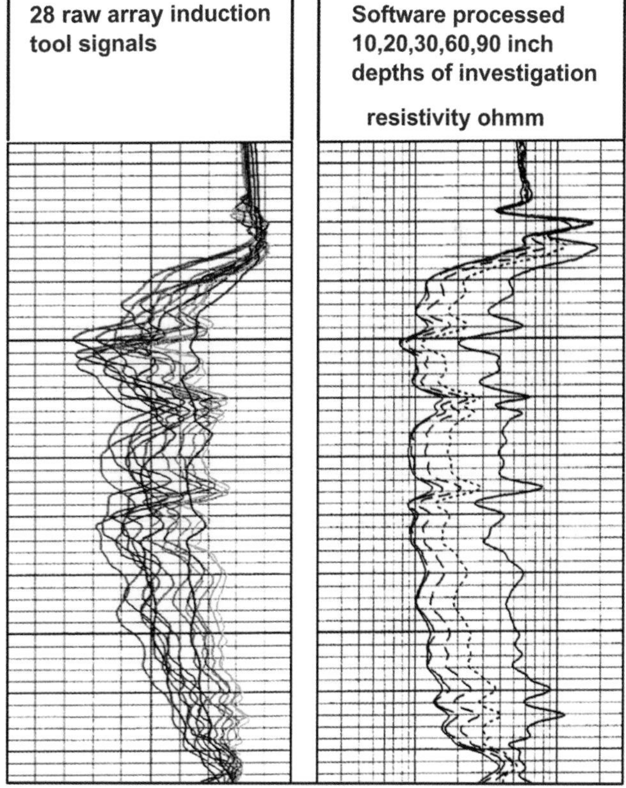

Figure 7.26 The Array Induction Imager Tool (AIT) raw signals and processed results, 5 curves with 10 to 90 inch depths of investigation. The interval shows a lower, deep resistivity (R_w salt water) with a higher resistivity flushed zone (less salty mud filtrate R_{mf})(Schlumberger AIT tool brochure 1992). *Courtesy of Schlumberger.*

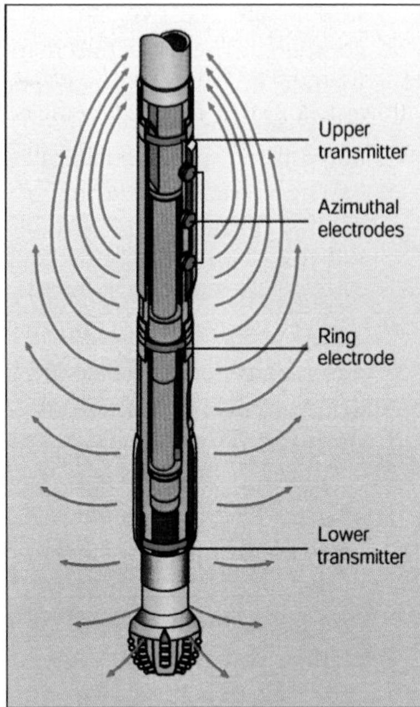

Figure 7.27 Design and current paths of the Resistivity At Bit (RAB) tool from Schlumberger, which can produce electrical images at three depths of investigation as well as other measurements, while drilling (from Bonner *et al.* 1996). *Copyright Schlumberger Ltd. Used with permission.*

Because of the large amount of data received from the tool and the presence of additional sensors that monitor borehole conditions, borehole corrections are much better than for older induction tools and even a tool stand-off can be calculated. Borehole corrections are important for induction tools, especially in conductive muds. With measurements from previous induction tools 'tool error' was common but this is no longer the case. Future advances in the array tools will be as much about software as about the design of the tool itself.

Resistivity at Bit (RAB) (LWD, water-based, full-cover images)

One of the more useful LWD water-based tools in use today is the Schlumberger Resistivity at Bit (RAB) tool (now re-branded as the GeoVISION), which provides 5 resistivities: one through the bit; a ring resistivity with a 23 cm (9") depth of investigation located typically 1.5 m (5 ft) behind the bit; and three azimuthal measurements with depths of investigation of 1", 2" and 3" (2.5 cm, 5.1 cm, 7.6 cm), from button electrodes higher up the tool (Bonner *et al.* 1996). The electrodes are driven by two emitters, one just above the bit and the other at the top of the tool (**Figure 7.27**). The button and ring electrodes all use the axial principle and the current from the upper transmitter leaves the tool radially, passing into the formation at 90 degrees, and is effectively electrically focused.

The lower toroidal-coil transmitter, 30 cm (1 ft) from the bottom of the tool, provides a 1500 Hz alternating current that induces a voltage in the collar below, the current passing through the collar and the bit. In this way, the resistivity at the bit is measured. The through bit resistivity is said to have a 60 cm (2 ft) resolution in a vertical well but only the diameter of the borehole in a horizontal well. This is therefore a true 'logging while drilling' measurement, unlike most LWD measurements, which may actually may be made an hour or more after the bit has drilled the formation.

The ring electrode, with a depth of investigation of 23-30 cm (9" – 12") depending on the formation, can be used to give an R_t. As it is about 5 ft (1.5 m) behind the bit, the R_t estimate can be made as soon as 2.5 minutes after drilling (for an ROP up to 36.5 m/hr – 120 ft/hr) but this figure clearly depends on drilling rate and the bottom hole assembly (BHA). However, it means the tool can be used for geosteering.

The azimuthal button measurements are collected into 56 directional quadrants and images are produced. The button electrodes have a diameter of 2.54 cm (1") and produce an electrical field with a diameter of about 3.8 cm (1.5") (Chapter 15). Low resolution images are produced real-time while drilling but the higher resolution can be replayed from stored data. To record images, rotation must be more than 30 rpm (Bonner *et al.* 1996 *op. cit.*).

The images can be used to identify hydrocarbon contacts (**Figure 15.13**), for drilling decisions, dip calculation while drilling and geosteering, especially locating interfaces (Chapter 15, Image logs).

Multi-propagation resistivity (MPR™) (LWD, multi-depth, non-conductive muds)

While drilling resistivity tools, as has been described, now produce many simultaneous measurements, and multiple depths of investigation are provided by 'virtual curves' that are calculated rather than directly measured (*see* LWD resistivity tools). An example of this type of tool is the Multiple Propagation Resistivity™ tool of Baker Hughes™ INTEQ. It has upper and lower transmitter sets and two receivers, all with digital electronics, inset into a drill collar (Meyer *et al.* 1994). The tool has 35" and 23" (89 and 58 cm) spacings, uses 2 MHz and 400 kHz frequency signals, records both amplitude change and phase shift, and produces 32 raw measurements which, after signal processing, are reduced to 4 calculated curves with fixed depths of investigation (**Figure 7.28**).

For computation, environmental corrections are first applied. 2 MHz signals are more affected by borehole conditions than the lower frequency 400 kHz, so the higher frequency 2 MHz signals are given importance at this stage. The 32 raw data curves are compared to 8 derived resistivities, environmental effects evaluated and 8 standard, compensated resistivity curves with different depths of investigation produced.

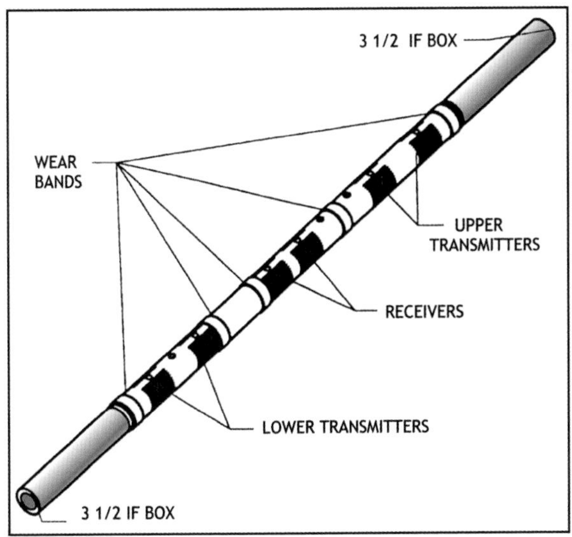

Figure 7.28 The Multiple Propagation Resistivity™ (MPR) tool from Baker Hughes™ which measures 8 basic resisivities while drilling (LWD), that is amplitude ratio and phase difference at 2 MHz and 400 kHz for both 35 inch and 23 inch spacings (re-drawn from Meyer *et al.* SPWLA 1994).

Raw and compensated values are compared as a next step, inverted to remove shoulder effects and then resolution matched. Because anisotropy affects propagation tools when dips are high (over 55°), specific R_h and R_v terms are derived (horizontal and vertical resistivity). These are calculated independently for each data set (*see* next paragraph). Similarly, individual corrections are applied for invasion and dielectric effects and a linear combination is made of all 16 curves. From these, the four fixed depths of investigation curves are calculated, 10″, 20″ 35″ and 60″ (25.5 cm – 1.52 m).

Notionally, 400 kHz *attenuation* measurements are the deepest measurement while 2 MHz *phase differences* are the shallowest. A 2 MHz *attenuation* measurement is usually deeper than a 400 kHz *phase difference* measurement although, in practice, only calculated values from LWD logs are usable **(Table 7.7)**. It is suggested that the deepest measurements compare with the wireline deep resistivities (such as LLd) and the shallowest compare with a shallow resistivity (such as LLs) but are not as shallow as the pad type devices (such as MSFL).

Current horns, dielectric effects, and anisotropy on LWD propagation logs

In addition to the usual unwanted environmental effects present in the close borehole (invasion, drill damage etc.), LWD propagation type logs are affected by some additional, formation related effects. This section looks at current horns, dielectric effects and anisotropy.

Current (polarisation) horns are a feature, especially of LWD propagation type logs in non-vertical wells, as has been suggested previously (*see* Section 7.5 'LWD resistivity tools'). The logging signal used in propagation type tools causes a secondary charge to form at bed boundaries. This secondary charge is seen as horns on the logs. In vertical wells, bed boundaries are parallel to the tool current loops, and there are no secondary effects but in non-vertical wells, generally above about 45° but certainly above 55°, the current loops from the tool cross bed boundaries, they then behave as a secondary source and horns are produced (Anderson *et al.*1992). Horns become more marked the greater the deviation of the well and the larger the resistivity contrast between the shoulder beds (Bonner *et al.* 1992). They are more marked on phase shift curves (**Figure 7.29**), and can

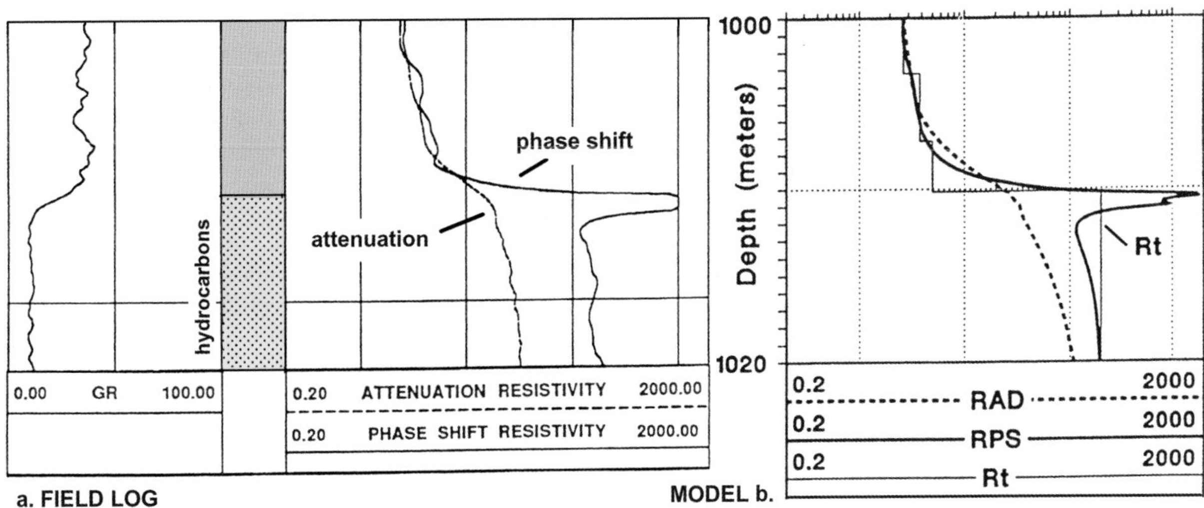

Figure 7.29 Polarisation-horn seen on the attenuation and phase shift resistivities of a. field logs from an LWD electromagnetic wave propagation (EWR) tool, the compensated dual resistivity (CDR of Schlumberger) in a 75° deviated well and b. the modeled responses showing the bed boundary position. RAD = modeled attenuation resistivity, RPS = modeled phase shift resistivity. The sands contain hydrocarbons (modified from Anderson *et al.* SPWLA 1990).

be more apparent on the deeper reading than shallower logs. In horizontal wells, horns can be used as an indication of an approaching bed boundary (Bourg *et al.* 2007).

Dielectric effects are seen on the LWD propagation type logs (as they are on wireline induction logs) especially at high values of R_t. A dielectric is a material having a low electrical conductivity but that can be polarised. A *dielectric constant* (ε) in logging is a measure of the formation's ability to store an electric charge. Fresh water, for example, has a dielectric constant of about 80, quartz 4.65. The dielectric constant of shale varies strongly with the frequency of the electromagnetic field applied and also with mineral content. Thus, a typical shale with a dielectric constant of up to 10,000 at an induction log frequency of 10–40 Hz, has a dielectric constant of 100 to 200 at an LWD frequency of 2 MHz (Bonner *et al.* 1992). The amplitude measurement is more affected than the phase measurement. In processing, the dielectric constant is either assumed to be constant, or varies with resistivity but is often under-corrected for. When the actual value is greater than the assumed value, attenuation resistivities read too high, phase resistivities read too low and curve separation is the result (**Figure 7.30**). A constant value of 10 is sometimes assumed (Schroeder 2001).

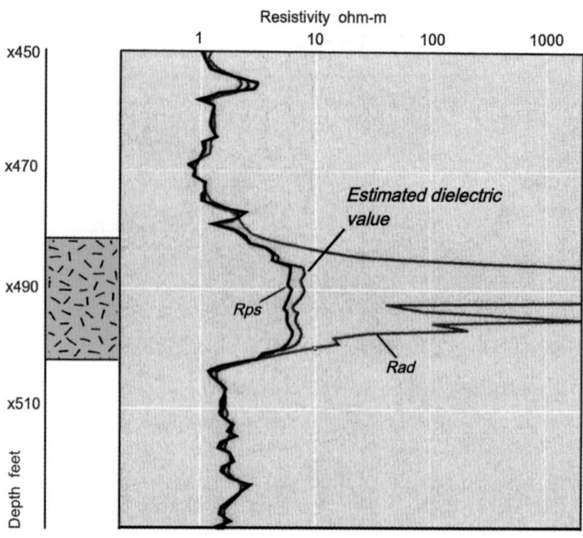

Figure 7.30 A pronounced dielectric effect on a deep attenuation resistivity measurement from a volcanic rock in the North Sea. The dielectric constant was assumed to be 50 while it was in fact over 500. Rps = resistivity phase shift – shallow; rad = resistivity attenuation – deep (modified from Bonner *et al.* 1992). *Copyright Schlumberger Ltd. Used with permission.*

Although anisotropy affects many logs, much effort has been put into recognising its effect on LWD resistivity logs. It affects these logs more than the older wireline induction logs. The anisotropy normally considered is that caused by thin beds, for example, thin sands within bedded shales, as commonly found in turbidite environments. In such bedded formations, the horizontal resistivity component (R_h), is very different from the vertical resistivity component (R_v). In a vertical well only the horizontal component (R_h), is measured and anisotropy is not an influence (Anderson *et al.* 1997). However, with progressive deviation, especially above 45°, the difference between the components begins to have a greater and greater influence. The affected logs show a separation that looks like invasion, the deeper the measurement the greater the effect, the separation increasing with deviation (**Figure 7.31**). Phase change measurements are more affected than attenuation measurements. Anisotropy can be detected during log processing and is usually satisfactorily corrected (Li *et al.* 2003), but examples are coming to light where this is not the case (*see next section*).

Laterolog, induction or propagation, which is best?

With modern tools there is inevitably overlap in the ranges when laterolog and induction tools can be used effectively. Traditionally the laterologs have been used in conductive, water-based muds and particularly with high resistivity formations such as limestones. In oil-based mud there is no alternative to using Induction logs but they are also often used in moderately conductive muds with low resistivity formations such as porous sandstones containing salty formation water (at least if only wireline is available). For the wireline tools, these are still the core considerations for each type of tool, although modern induction tools will give reliable readings in a much wider range of hole conditions. Other considerations are tool length and possibly where in the tool string the resistivity tool can be located. The induction tools are shorter than the laterologs and so may allow a shorter 'rat-hole' to be drilled (this is not just a rig-time issue, sometimes it is vital to avoid drilling into an over- or under-pressured sand below the primary target). Additionally, borehole conditions of mud type, hole size and so on, should be considered. Charts are available online to make the choice, when expected mud type and formation resistivity are known and are input (**Figure 7.32**).

For LWD there is little alternative to the propagation tools for conventional, quantitative analysis, even for wells drilled with very conductive muds. In fact, large holes filled with conductive muds are not a great disadvantage for LWD tools because each hole size has a dedicated tool. For example an 8½" hole will typically be logged with a 6¾" diameter tool whereas a 12¼" hole would use a 9" diameter tool (compare this with wireline where the same 3⅝" tool is used for all hole sizes above 6").

Nevertheless, it is true that in areas where laterolog and propagation type tools have both been run and compared, some startling differences have been found. Propagation LWD tools are in general affected by the same factors that influence any resistivity tool:

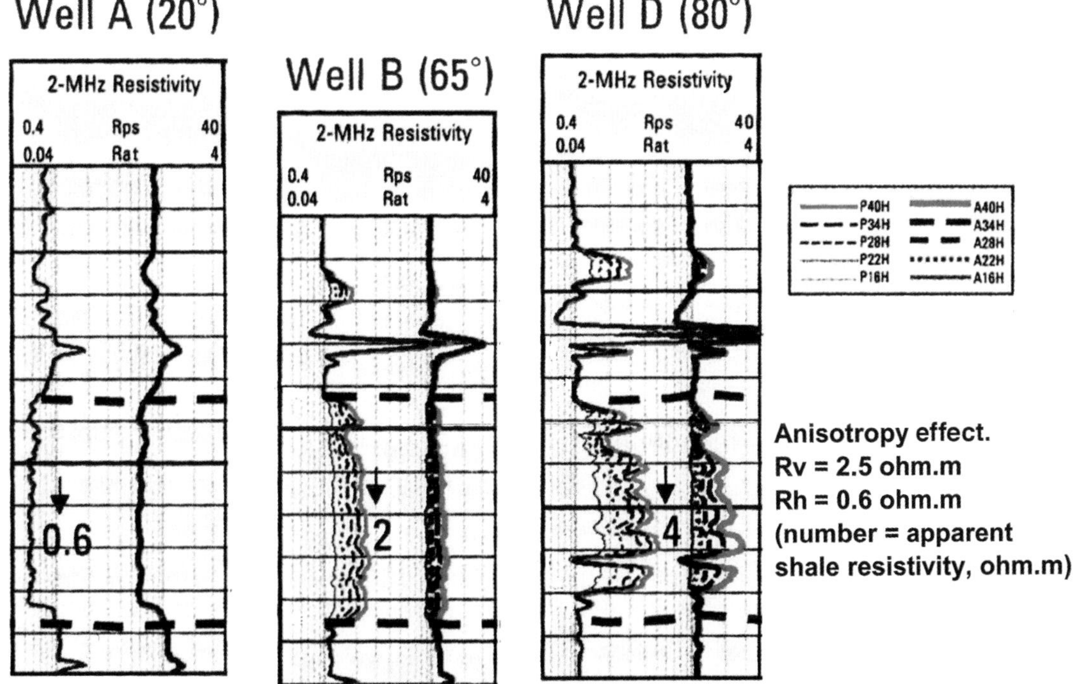

Figure 7.31 The effect of anisotropy illustrated on 2 MHz propagation resistivities in a shale zone as deviation increases. The wells A, B and D are approximately 500 m apart with deviations of 20°, 65° and 80° respectively. The plots are true vertical depth (TVD) and the same shale is between the dashed lines. The log separation resulting from the anisotropy increases as the deviation increases but well A is near enough to the vertical that only *Rh* is measured. Vertical resistivity (*Rv*) = 2.5 ohm.m, horizontal resistivity (*Rh*) = 0.6 ohm.m, water based mud in the hole (modified from Quiming *et al.* SPWLA 2003).

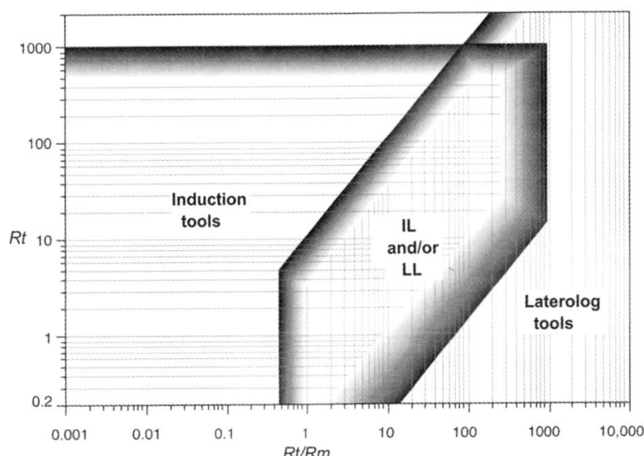

Figure 7.32 Indication of tool preference, induction or laterolog, based on expected formation (Rt) and mud (Rm) resistivities. Specific company charts should be consulted (Schlumberger 1992). *Courtesy of Schlumberger.*

mud filtrate invasion, bed boundary effects, shoulder bed effects, resistivity anisotropy, dielectric properties and tool eccentricity (Quiming *et al.* 2003). These tend to affect different tools in different ways and may be more significant for some measurements than others.

For example, in the Orinoco heavy oil area, sands have high resistivities (200–400 ohm-m) but are highly laminated with thin, conductive beds of shale (2.5–6 ohm-m) (Bourg *et al.* 2007). LWD propagation logs in this area, in both horizontal and highly deviated wells, show the sands to be highly invaded with a corresponding invasion profile. LWD laterologs, however, show invasion to be small. Wireline laterologs in near-by vertical wells also show little invasion and are to be believed; deep invasion into heavy oil is unlikely. The LWD propagation logs are therefore very misleading. It appears that the propagation logs are highly influenced by the conductive, interlaminated shale beds (2.5 × 6 ohm-m) and the formation anisotropy (**Figure 7.31**). Modeling and manipulating these characteristics produces an invasion profile, which correction is not able to eliminate (Bourg *et al.* 2007 *op. cit.*). Clearly, this environment requires a laterolog type tool.

This example involves formation anisotropy. It is an important aspect of resistivity; in general it is anisotropic. This means it can matter in which direction the current flows and so, for example, an induction tool, in which the current flows normal to the borehole axis, can give a very different read-

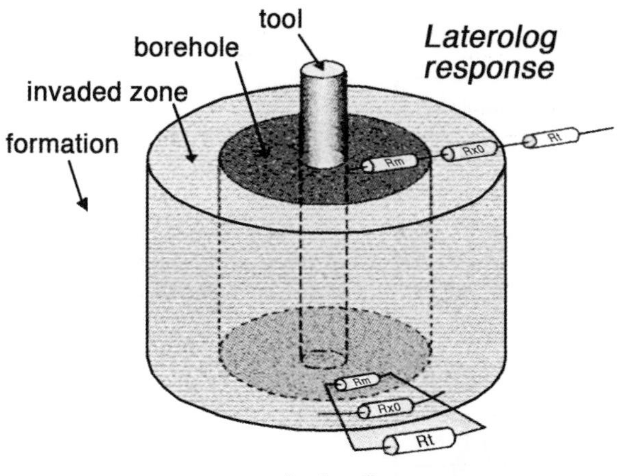

Figure 7.33 The difference between multiple laterolog and induction resistivities. The laterolog responses are series equivalent, the induction responses parallel equivalent (from Grifiths *et al.* SPWLA 2000).

ing to a laterolog, which is passing current parallel to the borehole.

So it is useful to recognise that the different types of tool are measuring different resistivities. The laterolog tool can be imagined as measuring resistivity in series, the resistivity of one zone affecting the next, for instance, the flushed zone affecting the measurement of the invaded and subsequent zones (**Figure 7.33**). The induction tool, on the other, hand measures zones in parallel, separately, so that one zone measurement does not affect the next (Griffiths *et al.* 2000). With LWD propagation tools the situation is, if anything, even more complicated and, it is probably fair to say, still not fully understood. These observations may help in understanding which tool is likely to be the most effective.

7.7 Log characteristics

Log format and scales

The unit of resistivity logs is ohms m^2/m, which is invariably reduced to ohm meter (ohm-m) (Section 7.1). The reduced annotation is used here. (This is an unusual instance of the oil industry using an SI unit and the rest of the world not. Most people use ohm-cm.) Resistivity logs are plotted on a logarithmic scale, either in track 2 alone, or in tracks 2 and 3 on an API format (**Figure 7.34**). The values are usually 0.20–20.0 ohm-m for one track, or 0.20–2000 ohm-m when two tracks are used together. For some reason LWD resistivity logs are often plotted on a three cycle grid: 0.2 - 200 ohm-m.

The old style, API format, log plot example (**Figure 7.34.1**) shows the results from the Schlumberger Dual Laterolog tool, the logs plotted being the deep laterolog (LLd), shallow laterolog (LLs) and the micro-spherically focused (pad) log (MSFL). The modern array tool plots have a variety of styles, although the basic API format seems to persist. The example shows 13, while-drilling resistivities from a propagation type tool, the EcoScope from Schlumberger, along with an LWD gamma ray and drilling information (**Figure 7.35**). The logs are in colour as the amount of information displayed is very large. On the older style ISF-SONIC combination shown in the example (**Figure 7.34.2**), the deep induction log (ILD) is plotted directly in resistivity units alongside the spherically-focused device (SFL). On this display, the original conductivity values of the induction measurement, in millimhos/m, are also plotted, athough this is rarely the case today (remember conductivity and resistivity are basically the same property). The scale of 0–2000 mmho is used, a unit that has now been replaced by the SI unit of milliSiemen/m (i.e. 1 mmho = 1 mS)

The display of resistivity logs as images is described in Chapter 15, along with some of the other colour enhanced displays.

Bed resolution generalities

In practical terms, bed resolution for a resistivity tool can be defined as the thinnest bed that the tool can resolve to give a true formation resistivity, R_t (or R_{xo}). This is not the scientific definition (*see* section 2.4 and **Table 2.3**). The wireline, pad mounted, micro-resistivity tools are capable of resolving the thinnest features of any of the standard logging tools. At the other extreme, the original induction tools probably had the worst vertical resolution of any conventional tool. Logs recorded with these tools typically produce very lazy, slowly varying curves. They generally needed beds at least 2 m thick to produce an accurate reading and even then the contrast with the surrounding beds had to be relatively low. Modern tools, like the array induction discussed previously, have far better vertical resolution and the shallower reading curves can produce an accurate reading in beds that are 1 m thick. This is a result of better sonde design and computer processing of the raw data. It is still true, however, that bed resolution is related to depth of investigation: the finer the bed resolution the shallower the depth of investigation.

For petrophysical calculations, it is important to know minimum bed resolution for true formation resistivity measurements (**Figure 2.12**). **Table 7.8** gives the approximate bed resolutions for petrophysical purposes. For beds thinner than the minimum resolution, correction charts or calculations can sometimes be used to find the true resistivity values. These methods are based on theoretical models which make assumptions like planar bed boundaries that are perpendicular to the well. If these assumptions do not apply, the calculated resistivity will be wrong.

For geological purposes, the resistivity curves should be used with a full understanding of their vertical resolution. The micro-resistivity logs give too fine a resolution

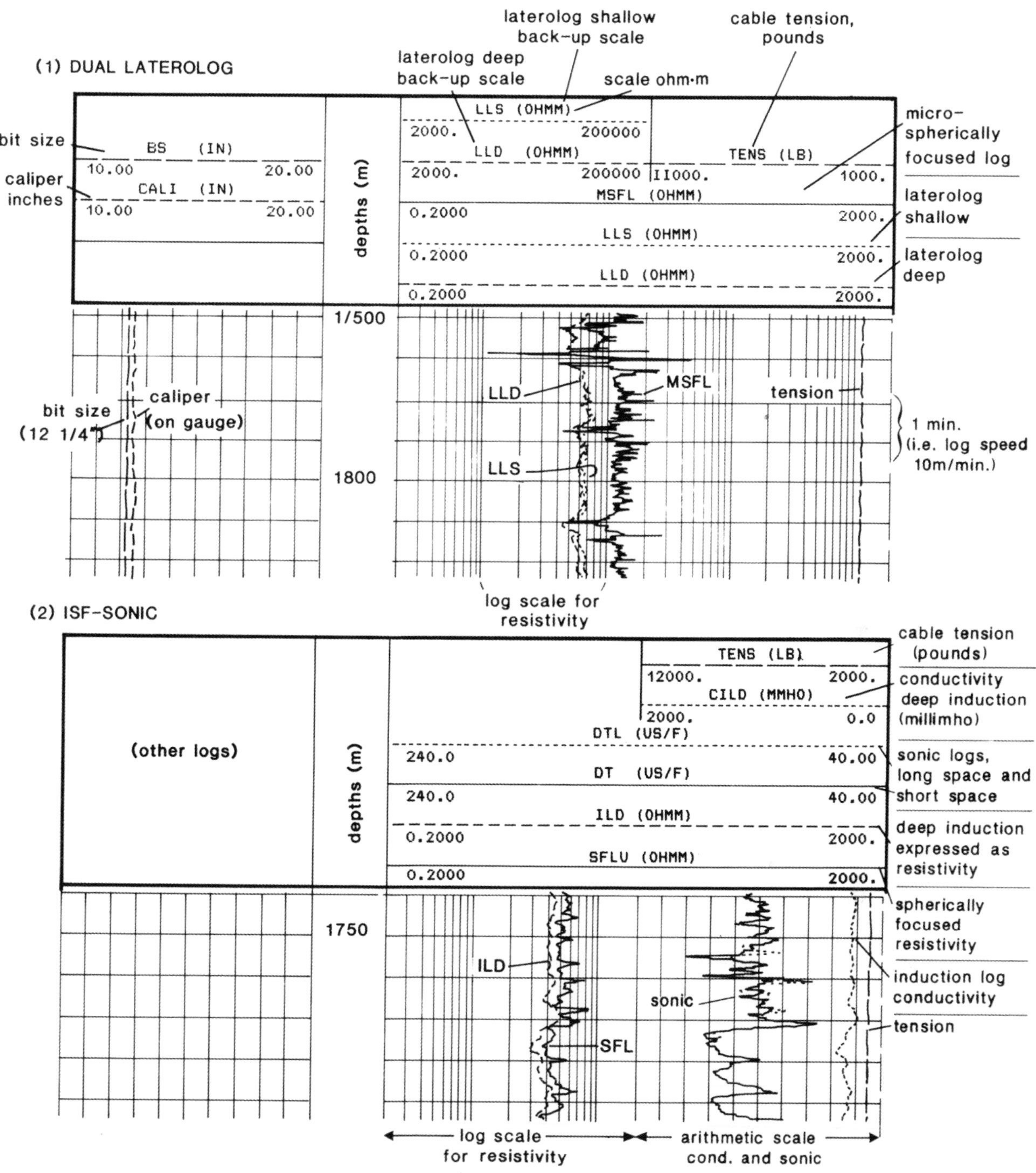

Figure 7.34 Typical resistivity log formats. (1) Dual laterolog combination; (2) induction, spherically focused log combination. Both wireline tools from Schlumberger.

for general practical, lithological bed interpretation and are best used for defining bedding characteristics, textural heterogeneities and even facies. The laterologs, however, resolve beds at the right scale for general bed-boundary and lithological interpretation (**Figure 7.36**). Ideally they should be used in conjunction with other logs to do this, although in the intermediate and top-hole sections of a well they are often the only logs run. The older induction logs give poor bed-boundary resolution but, at the same time, they average all the bed effects in such a way as to make lithology trends stand out (**Figure 7.36**). Modern induction tools, as we have seen, are normally as good as the laterologs at resolving features.

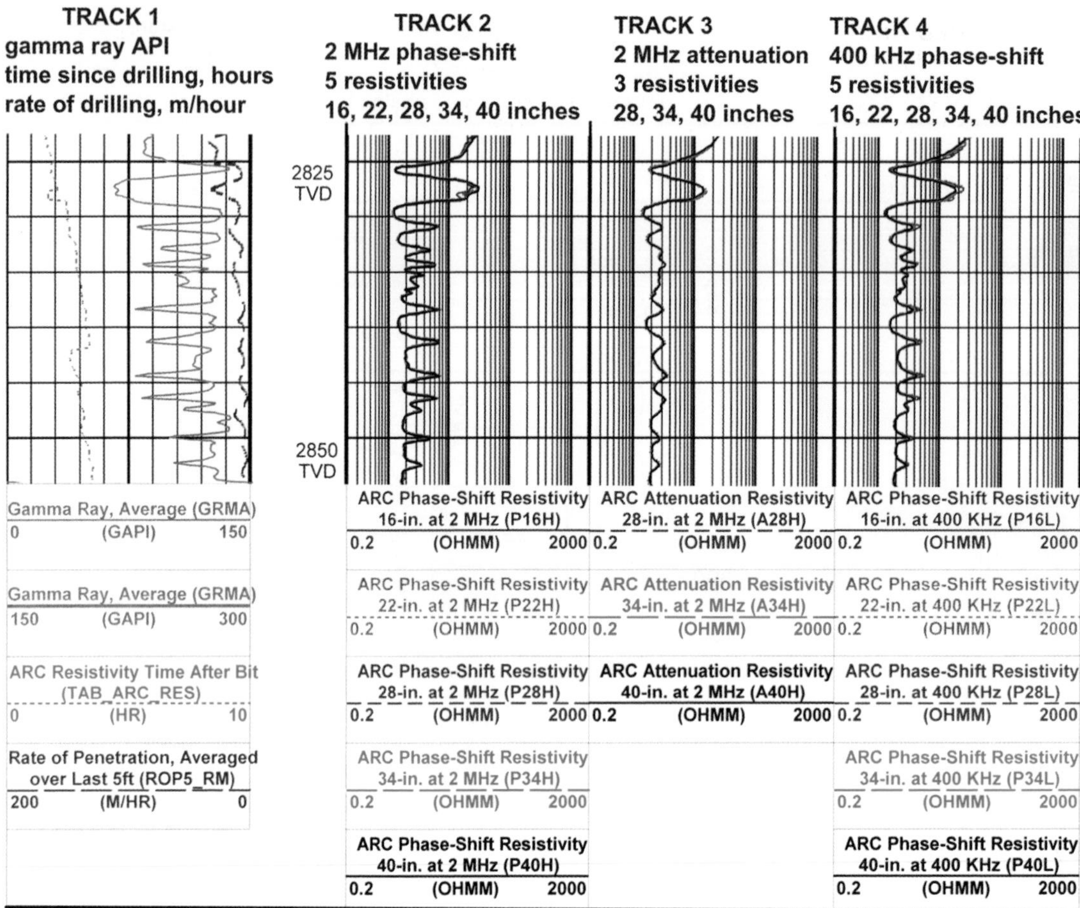

Figure 7.35 Typical LWD propagation log plot. Memory plot from the EcoScope, dual frequency tool of Schlumberger. Plotted in meters true vertical depth (TVD). Some drilling parameters are usually plotted along with the geophysical measurements, as in track 1. ARC = Array Resistivity Compensated.

Table 7.8 Vertical resolution and depth of investigation of some resistivity tools (*see also* Figure 7.20 and symbols in Table 7.4).

Logging tool frequency	output log	sample	vertical resolution	DOI	measurement	reference
	MLL	5 cm (2″)	5.0–10.0 cm (2–4″)		R_{xo}	Theys 1991
PEX	MSFL	15 cm (6″)	5.0–7.6 cm (2–3″)		R_{xo}	Theys 1991
DLL	LLD	15 cm (6″)	61.0 cm 24″(28″ Serra)	1.25 m	R_t	Theys 1991
	LLS	15 cm (6″)				
HDLL™		3.8 cm (1.5″)	30–45 cm (12–18″)			
ARI		15 cm (6″)	20.3 cm (8″)			Serra 2000
HALS		15 cm (6″)	20.3–40.6 cm (8–16″)			Serra 2000
HRLA		5 cm (2″)	30.5 cm (12″)	127 cm (50″)		Schlumberger brochure 2000
DIT	IDPH	15 cm (6″)	2.0 m (84-96″)			Theys 1991
	IMPH	15 cm (6″)	1.5 m (60-72″)			Theys 1991
	Processed		91.4 cm (36″)			Serra 2000
	SFLU	15 cm (6″)	7.6 cm (30″)			Theys 1991
AIT		15 cm (6″)	1.2m (4ft) 46 cm (18″)			Serra 2000
		7.5 cm (3″)	0.3, .61, 1.21 m (1,2,4ft)	25.4 cm–2.28 m (10, 20, 30, 60, 90″)		
CDR	phase	[15 cm (6″)]				
	Attenuation	[15 cm (6″)]				
RTscanner						
LWD	older tools		20 cm (8″)	1.2 m (47″)		
LWD	MPR	time based		25.5 cm–1.52 m (10, 20, 35, 60″)		
	RAB			2.5, 5.1, 7.6 cm (1″, 2″, 3″)		

DOI = depth of investigation

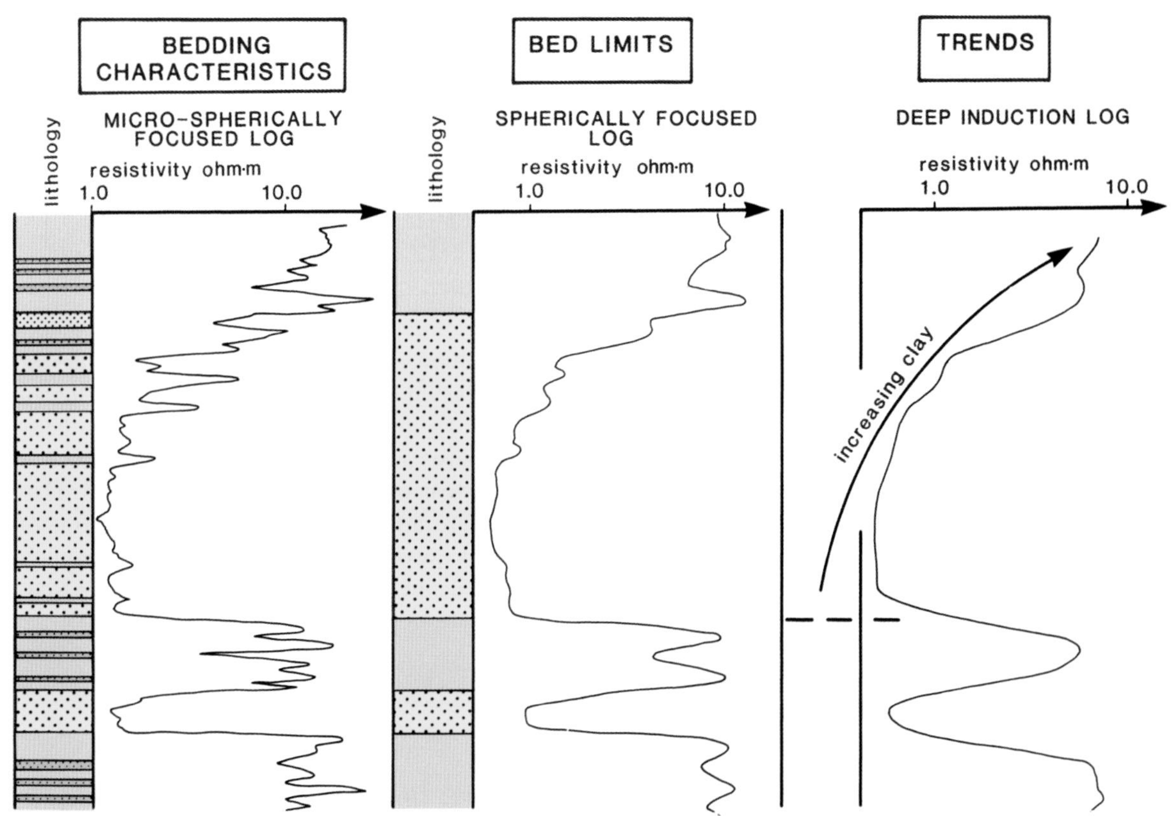

Figure 7.36 Contrasting bed resolution characteristics of the resistivity tools and their geological application *(see text)*.

Depth of investigation, geological implications

The depth of investigation of the resistivity tools has been discussed previously as related to tool design and invasion detection (**Figure 7.20**). A large source to receiver spacing was equated to deep investigation, a short spacing to shallow investigation (Section 2.4). Although this is true in general, it is a considerable over-simplification and, in detail, depth of investigation depends on the precise current paths or the way the fields interact with the formation. For example, an electrically focused laterolog reads much deeper than its electrode spacings, and the investigating depth of a propagation resistivity measurement depends on its frequency, and whether it is a phase difference or attenuation measurement. However, depth of investigation is an important aspect of a tool's capabilities and although designed for petrophysical needs, also has geological significance (**Figure 7.36**).

The logs from deep-reading devices, especially the induction logs, are best used for gross formation characteristics in which individual beds are unimportant. Such is the case with shale porosity trends and correlation. The deep-reading logs should not be used for absolute bed values or characteristics in formations where there are rapid vertical changes. Texture-related changes are best seen on the logs from tools mainly influenced by the invaded zone, such as the pad mounted micro-logs. In permeable intervals there is a mixing of formation water and mud filtrate in the invaded zone, and the way in which it takes place is very dependent on formation texture. Such changes cannot, in general, be seen on the logs from deep-reading devices. Even in impermeable zones, micro-logs are still effective. For example, the identification of thin source beds, typical of the Cretaceous oceanic events, is only possible with the logs from the micro-tools.

The use of the resistivity logs for geological interpretation should thus make use of the general indications as follows: gross characteristics – deep logs; bed boundaries – intermediate logs; texture and bedding detail – micro-logs.

Signal processing: some general comments

Prior to the mid-1980s, tool design was the principal way tools evolved. Post-1990 it has as much to do with signal processing as it does with the tool itself. In fact, tools can now be designed specifically to make use of signal processing techniques, the two being co-dependent. Some processing techniques have been described under tool description headings but there are also general comments to be made. These apply especially to the LWD resistivity logs, but also have general significance. As stated in the introduction to this chapter, the main goal of the resistivity tools is to measure the resistivity of the virgin formation, R_t. With signal processing they can do much more than this.

There is a consistent problem of resolution to be solved by any array tool with variable emitter-receiver spacings. The volume of formation being investigated by the several sensors is not the same; a deeper measuring signal senses a larger volume than a shallow measurement. This implies that a deeper measurement has a greater formation signal while the shallow signal is more influenced by the borehole. The problem for processing is that the shallow reading, having a far better vertical resolution than the deeper reading, is used to provide the bed structure. Resolution matching, therefore, attempts to use the shallow reading to improve the deep reading resolution, but the deep reading to improve the formation signal in the shallow reading. Various routines exist and are automatically applied to give the tools the best resolution possible.

The manipulation of raw log measurements was originally a 'correction': effects not desired would be eliminated in an effort to enhance the desired (usually formation) readings, such as a correction for borehole size, mud type or temperature. This is still the approach with some calculations. However, the modern approach is to make a large number of raw measurements so that they may be combined and manipulated to provide a new set of calculated or 'virtual' curves. This is the case with the array tools, especially the indirect measurement, array type tools, as has been described. From the user's point of view, it is difficult to judge the quality of the results which depends both on the quality of the raw measurements but also the applicability of the algorithms used in processing. When there are conflicting results, it is hard to know how to recognise a 'right' measurement. Comparisons with other logs and experience of an area are perhaps the only recourse (e.g. Bourg *et al.* 2007).

In the effort to interpret formation characteristics from raw log responses, two approaches can be used; *forward modeling* and *inverse modeling* (Anderson *et al.* 1997). A forward model is an algorithm that uses a synthetic description of a formation's bedding and bed properties, to calculate the log that would actually be recorded in such a formation using the tool's known characteristics (cf. **Figure 2.14**). A detailed algorithm that solves the fundamental equations governing a tool's physics in certain geometrical situations may be used or, more commonly, a simpler type of linear approximation to the tool's response, called a *convolution filter* (Passey *et al.* 2006). If the modeled log does not fit the recorded log, then the proposed model can be changed until both responses are similar.

Inverse modeling is the *'reconstruction of a formation property profile consistent with the measured data'* (Dyos 1987). It consists of predicting realistic formation values from the tool recorded values by mathematically satisfying the calculated effect on the tool signal, of the proposed formation. This type of modeling does not have a unique solution because several formation combinations may satisfy the actual response. Forward and inverse modeling are now integral to resistivity log interpretation (Section 2.5).

7.8 Quantitative uses of the resistivity logs

The quantitative use of log resistivity measurements is at the heart of the whole domain of quantitative well-log interpretation – the domain of petrophysics. Resistivity was the parameter depicted on the first well log and it was also the first parameter to be used quantitatively. The principal use of well logs is to detect hydrocarbons; the principal use of the resistivity log is to quantify those hydrocarbons, that is, to give the volume of oil and gas in a particular reservoir, or, in petrophysical terms, to define the water saturation, S_w. When S_w is not 100%, there are hydrocarbons present:

$$1\text{-}S_w = S_{hc}$$

Where: S_{hc} = saturation in hydrocarbons.

The basic, simple equations of petrophysics

Below, the simple, fundamental equations of petrophysics appear in a specific order, followed by an explanation and comment on their computation. The intention is simply to show where the numbers for log calculations come from. Today, calculation is inevitably computer-based and the derivation of the numbers used is not obvious. The formulae shown below are never used in their simple form but illustrate their origins.

$$R_o = F.\ R_w \qquad (1)$$

Overall rock resistivity (100% water saturated) = the formation resistivity factor (F) × resistivity of the formation fluid (*see* 'Rock resistivity: formation resistivity factor', Section 7.2). Rock resistivity consists of two elements, the passive but constricting formation (F) and the conductive formation fluids (R_w). As Wyllie wrote in 1956 (Wyllie 1963*), This is perhaps the most important single relationship in electric log interpretation and must be committed to memory.*

$$I = \frac{R_t}{R_o} \qquad (2)$$

The *resistivity index* = the resistivity of a rock containing hydrocarbons divided by the resistivity of a rock with 100% water. R_t = deep, measured resistivity which may indicate contained hydrocarbons. The equation introduces the notion of the ratio (in one particular reservoir) of the resistivity when it is entirely water-saturated (I = 1), as opposed to the resistivity in the presence of hydrocarbons ($I > 1$).

The Archie Equation

$$S_w{}^n = \frac{F.R_w}{R_t} \qquad (3)$$

Where: S_w = water saturation; n = *'saturation exponent'*, usually 2. It reflects changes in the way an electrical current passes through the formation (electrical tortuosity) with changes in water saturation (S_w).

$F.R_w$ is the same as R_o when a formation is 100% water-saturated (*see* equation 1). Thus, equation (3) can be written:

$$S_w{}^2 = \frac{R_o}{R_t} \qquad (3a)$$

The water saturation (squared) = the rock resistivity with 100% water saturation divided by the rock resistivity with possible hydrocarbons. The equation is more commonly written:

$$S_w = \sqrt{\frac{R_o}{R_t}} = \sqrt{\frac{F.R_w}{R_t}} \qquad (3b,c)$$

This equation, due to G.E. Archie of Shell, makes use of the ratio of resistivities from equation (2).

Invaded zone resistivities – movable hydrocarbons

$$S_{xo} = \sqrt{\frac{R_{xo}\text{ (100\% mud filtrate)}}{R_{xo}\text{ (with residual hydrocarbons)}}} \qquad (4)$$

Where: S_{xo} = flushed zone saturation
R_{xo} = flushed zone resistivity

Flushed zone saturation = the square root of the flushed zone resistivity in a 100% water zone, divided by the flushed zone resistivity with possible residual hydrocarbons. Residual hydrocarbon saturation, $S_{hr} = 1 - S_{xo}$ The equation gives the saturation in unmoved or residual hydrocarbons of the invaded zone. This is the same Archie Equation as above, but here uses the resistivity ratio in the flushed zone. Comparison of S_w and S_{xo} in a hydrocarbon zone is considered to give movable hydrocarbons. That is $S_{xo} - S_w$ is equal to the fraction of movable hydrocarbons in the formation. The percentage volume in terms of the reservoir is given by multiplying the term by the porosity, i.e. % volume of reservoir with movable hydrocarbons = $(S_{xo} - S_w) \times Ø$ (where Ø = porosity).

Formation resistivity factor-porosity relationships

$$F = \frac{a}{Ø^m} \qquad (5)$$

Where: F = formation resistivity factor
Ø = porosity
m = so-called *'cementation factor'*, dependent on rock type and related to texture, not cementation (**Figure 7.5**). It reflects changes in electrical tortuosity with changes in porosity.
a = a constant (the tortuosity factor).

The equation indicates that the formation resistivity factor is a function of porosity and rock type (m). Archie discovered this relationship between F and porosity (*see* **Figure 7.5**) and equation (5) is the result. Subsequent research and empirical correlations show that the global relationship varies; average figures used for the relationship are (**Table 7.10**):

$$F = \frac{a}{Ø^2} \quad \text{ideal sandstones (default Archie)} \qquad (5a)$$

$$F = \frac{0.81}{Ø^2} \quad \text{most consolidated sandstones} \qquad (5b)$$

$$F = \frac{0.62}{Ø^{2.15}} \quad \text{typical unconsolidated sandstone} \qquad (5c)$$

– this is the *Humble Formula*

$$F = \frac{1}{Ø^2} \quad \text{compact formations, chalks (default Archie)} \qquad (5a)$$

$$F = \frac{1}{Ø^m} \quad \text{where } m = \text{variable (usually 1.75 to 4)} \qquad (5d)$$

In limestones, the F to porosity relationship is quite variable.

Practical average Archie Equation

$$S_w = \sqrt{\frac{0.62 \times R_w}{Ø^{2.15} \times R_t}} \qquad (6)$$

This is a general equation for finding the water saturation. The values for the unknowns are obtained as shown in **Table 7.9.** Some typical values of tortuosity factor, a, saturation exponent, n and cementation factor, m, are shown in **Table 7.10.**

There are two simple graphical methods that can be used to see whether a zone is likely to be hydrocarbon-bearing or wet. The Hingle plot and the Pickett plot. They are both plots of porosity against resistivity, are based on the Archie formula and make assumptions about the variables a, m, and n (**Figure 7.37**). Hingle uses a linear porosity scale but a log scale for R_t chosen for a particular a and m. The 100% water line will cross the porosity axis at the matrix point. Pickett uses stan-

Table 7.9 Construction of the basic Archie Formula.

Symbol	character	derived from
Ø	porosity	density log, neutron-density crossplot, NMR, (sonic sometimes), cores
F	formation resistivity factor	$\frac{0.62}{Ø^{2.15}}$ calculated from empirical formulae (e.g. Humble Formula) using porosity as above
R_w	formation water resistivity	laboratory measurements of downhole (wireline, test) samples, occasionally SP log, approximation from resistivity logs in obvious water zone
R_o	Formation resistivity saturated 100% with formation water	$R_o = F \times R_w$ (can only be calculated cannot be measured by logs)
R_t	True formation resistivity	deep Laterolog, deep Induction, calculated Array resistivities
S_w	% water saturation of pores	target of the Archie calculation. $S_w = 1$ = 100% water, $S_w = 0.5$ = 50% hydrocarbons

dard log scales for both resistivity and porosity values. The slope of the constructed lines give a value for m and where the 100% water line crosses the no porosity line (Ø = 0), is the value of $R_w \times a$. (A good description of these plots is given by Asquith and Krygowski 2004).

7.9 Qualitative uses

General indications for resistivity log interpretation

To interpret the geological significance of resistivity logs, it is essential to realise that the same porous bed can have a range of resistivity values depending on fluid content (**Figure 7.38**). In petrophysical terms, F will remain constant while R_t varies (*see* **Figure 7.6**). No porous bed can be said to have a typical resistivity: this is a general principle for qualitative geological work.

General notions of depth of investigation and bed resolution, as previously described (*see* 'Log characteristics'), must also be considered. The indications for interpretation are: gross indications – deep logs; texture – intermediate logs; texture and structure – micrologs (**Figure 7.36**).

Textures

The resistivity of a rock is intimately related to texture. The simplest expression of this is the variation of resistivity with porosity changes. When the porosity decreases, the resistivity increases, all other things being equal (**Figure 7.39**). This is in fact the basis of the porosity-resistivity cross-plots (**Figure 7.37**), in which a departure from a constant porosity to resistivity relationship indicates a change in water saturation and the presence of hydrocarbons.

However, as discussed previously (Section 7.2), the influence a rock (as opposed to fluids) has on resistiviry can be expressed by F, the formation resistivity factor, and porosity is only one element of its makeup (**Figure 7.40**). An earlier example (**Figure 7.5**), illustrated F as sensitive to grain shape which, it was suggested, showed F to be texturally related (Section 7.2). But shape is just one element of texture. Others such as size, composition,

Table 7.10 Cementation factor, saturation exponent and tortuosity factor values for some common lithologies.

Rock type	a = tortuosity factor	n = saturation exponent	m = cementation factor	Notes
Ideal clean sandstone	1.0	2.0	2.0	'default' (for intergranular rocks)
Typical unconsolidated sandstone	0.62	2.0	2.15	The 'Humble Formula'
Typical consolidated sandstone	0.81	2.0	2.0	
Carbonates	1.0	2.0	2.0	with Archie behaviour
Practical experience	1.0	2.0	1.75 – 4 (increases with porosity)	Kennedy 2002 & refs

Saturation exponent is the variation in electrical tortuosity with changes in saturation n = 1.8 – 2.5 (default 2)
Cementation factor is the variation in electrical tortuosity with porosity

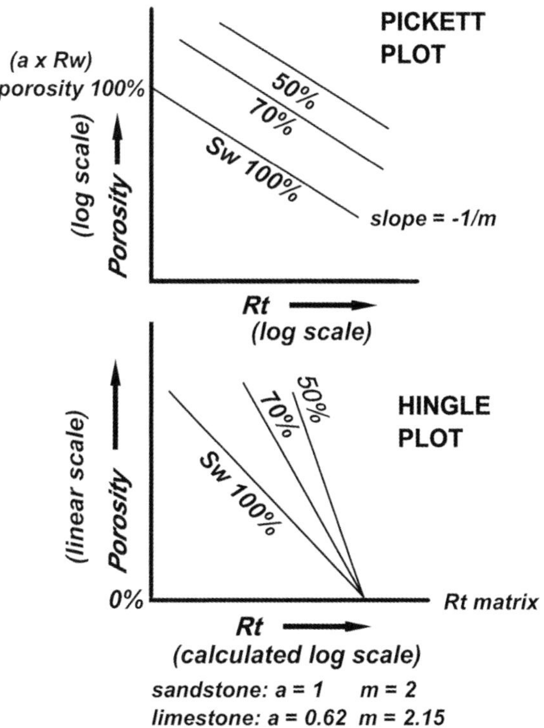

Figure 7.37 Schematic representation of two of the most common graphical methods for solving for hydrocarbon saturation based on Archie relationships. The Pickett plot uses a log scale of *Rt* plotted against a log scale of porosity. The Hingle plot uses a specially constructed log scale of *Rt* (depending on the *a* and *m* chosen) and a linear scale of porosity.

orientation and arrangement (sorting) also have their influence on *F*, and hence – resistivity (**Figure 7.40**). In reality, each lamina has a different texture and hence a different *F* value. The changes in texture (and *F*) may be small in absolute terms, but are still significant enough to affect the high resolution resistivity tools such as the dipmeter and the electrical imaging tools. Indeed, they are the reason resistivity can be used to form high resolution images. For example, electrical images show variations related to cross-bed laminae, even in the most permeable reservoir, and they are clearly not responding to changes in water salinity. Since $R_t = F \times R_w$ and R_w is not varying, the electrical images are showing changes in *F* (Chapter 15).

The geological importance of the link between *F* and resistivity in terms of texture, and the way in which this may be exploited, is nicely shown by the next example.

The Rodessa limestone of the East Texas Basin shows different porosity characteristics in different sub-facies, depending on grain type. Ooid limestones tend to have bimodal porosity, skeletal limestones tend to have unimodal porosity (Keith and Pittman 1983). The effect of each of these facies on the resistivity log is quite distinct. Thus, for the same porosity value, the unimodal porosity facies (skeletal) shows a higher resistivity than the bimodal (ooid). This is brought out by plotting density log porosities against resistivity from the shallow laterolog (corrected for invasion) (**Figure 7.41**). The difference in texture between the facies is most distinctly shown by their behaviour to invasion, so that plotting corrected

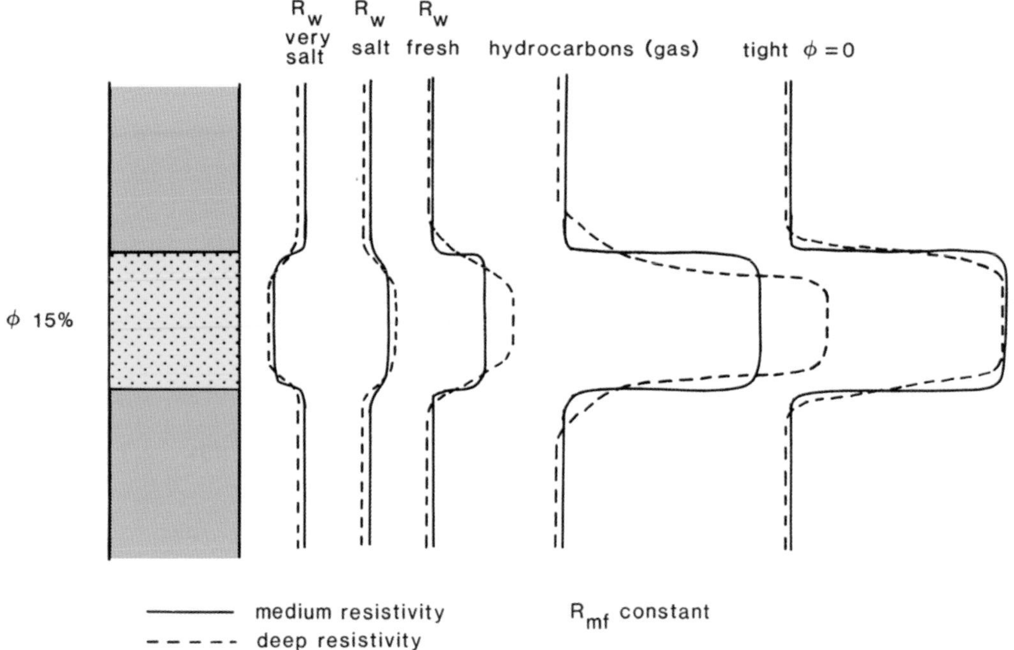

Figure 7.38 Schematic illustration of the behaviour of resistivity logs over the same reservoir bed but with different fluids and, in the last case, no porosity.

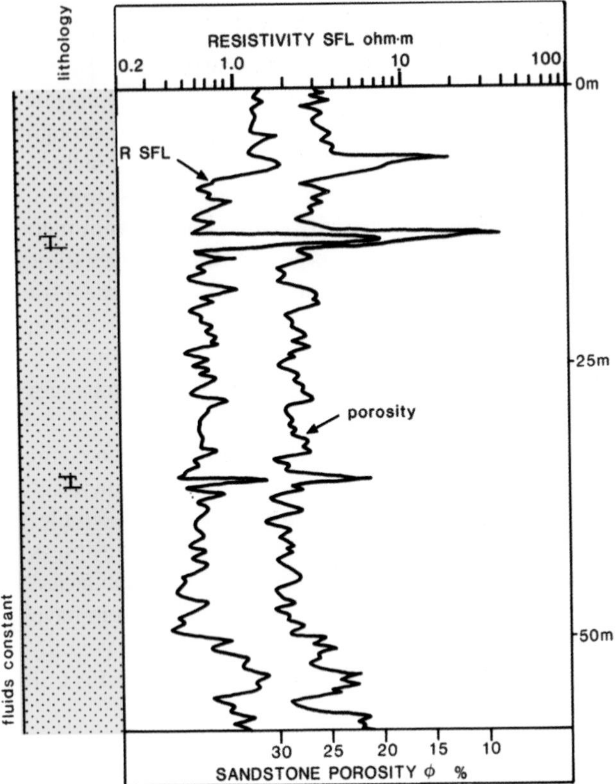

Figure 7.39 The close relationship between resistivity and porosity in a water-bearing sandstone. Resistivity from a spherically focused log (SFL): porosity is log-derived.

invaded zone resistivities against R_t, (un-invaded formation resistivity) clearly separates them. The authors found that resistivity, especially from the invaded zone, was a better discriminator of facies than porosity.

This example of the Rodessa limestone simply shows that the two porosity populations have different values of *F*. If porosity is facies related, so is *F*, and the resistivity log becomes an excellent facies discriminator. (*see also* Chapter 15, Images, Section 15.6 'Sedimentary interpretation' and Chapter 17, Sequence Stratigraphy, Section 17.5, 'Carbonate sequence stratigraphy'.)

Gross lithology

Resistivity logs cannot be used for a first recognition of the common lithologies; there are no characteristic resistivity limits for shale, or limestone or sandstone. The values depend on many variables such as compaction, composition, fluid content and so on. However, in any restricted zone, gross characteristics tend to be constant and the resistivity log may be used as a discriminator. For example, in sand shale sequences, shale characteristics may be constant and sands may be similar and with constant fluid salinities (**Figure 7.42**). The resistivity then becomes an excellent log for lithological distinction. Indeed, this is especially the case in younger, unconsolidated sediments and in the top sections of offshore boreholes where the quality of other logs may be poor. The deep resistivities (and propagation LWD resistivities) can still be used.

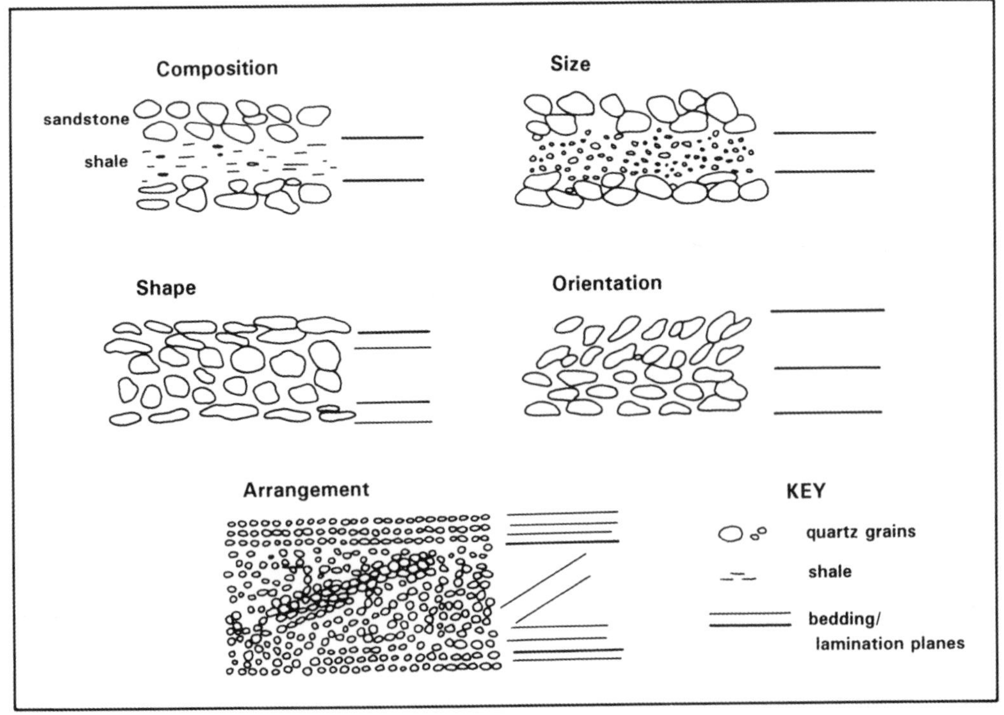

Figure 7.40 The influence of texture on the formation resistivity factor, *F*. Each thin bed or lamina has a different *F* value. This figure should be compared to Figures 7.4 and 7.5 (modified from Nurmi 1984).

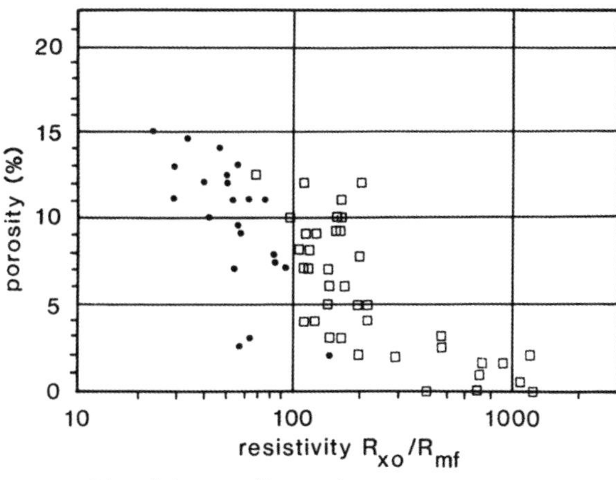

Figure 7.41 Textural patterns indicated on the resistivity log in the Rodessa Limestone, East Texas. Porosity is density-log derived: resistivity is from the shallow laterolog (From Keith and Pittman 1983).

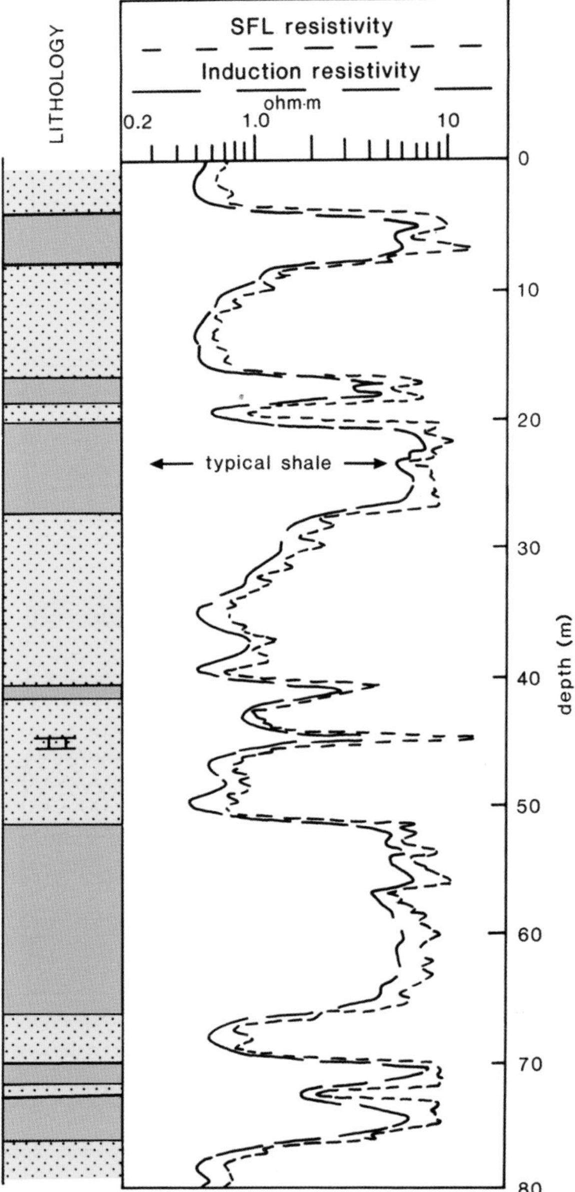

Figure 7.42 Shale intervals shown on the resistivity logs. In most sand-shale sequences, shales tend to have a constant, typical value.

In certain specific cases, however, the resistivity logs can be used to suggest a lithology and certain minerals have distinctive, but not exclusive, values. High resistivities, for example, may be diagnostic of salt, anhydrite, gypsum and coal (**Figure 7.43**, **Table 7.11**), although high resistivities are also associated with tight limestones and dolomites. Low resistivities are generally not diagnostic and, although shales generally have low values, so too do brine-bearing porous rocks (**Figure 7.43**).

Conductive minerals

Electronic conductivity (as in metals) as opposed to ionic conductivity (as in solutions) can occur when certain minerals are abundant in a formation **(Table 7.11)**. The effect can be seen with pyrite, especially when concentrations are higher than around 7% (**Figure 7.44**) (Theys, 1991) and are observed in detail on electrical image logs as patches of low resistivity (dark image) (Chapter 15). Pyrite concentrations affect modern LWD resistivity logs in a particular way because of the high frequency of their signal: the higher the frequency the lower the resistivity measured. Thus, a laterolog with a signal frequency of 35 Hz (deep) and 280 Hz (shallow) will show higher resistivities than the 2 MHz LWD resistivity tool (Kennedy 2004). In the example which shows this (**Figure 7.44**), the interval of abundant, high density pyrite is indicated by a very low resistivity, especially on the LWD logs. Electronic conductivity is the cause.

Resistivities may also be affected by two other iron minerals: glauconite and chamosite. They both reduce resistivity when they are abundant.

Glauconite is classed as a potassium and iron-rich mica. It is relatively common as a minor mineral in marine sandstones and limestones. When it is abundant in the form of grains or pellets, the sediment is termed a 'greensand'. The mineral is stable in sea water and greensands, by definition, have very high percentages of glauconite. It has a high density and, if not accounted for, will lead to under-estimates of porosity derived from the density (Chapter 10). It will also affect the neutron because it contains iron, a high thermal neutron absorber (Chapter 11). The Senonian (Upper Cretaceous) of Egypt contains clays and sands with abundant glauconite (greensands). In a study of samples that analysis showed contained between 13% and 81% by volume, it was found that the mineral caused a suppression of the resistivity. This was considered to be caused by a high

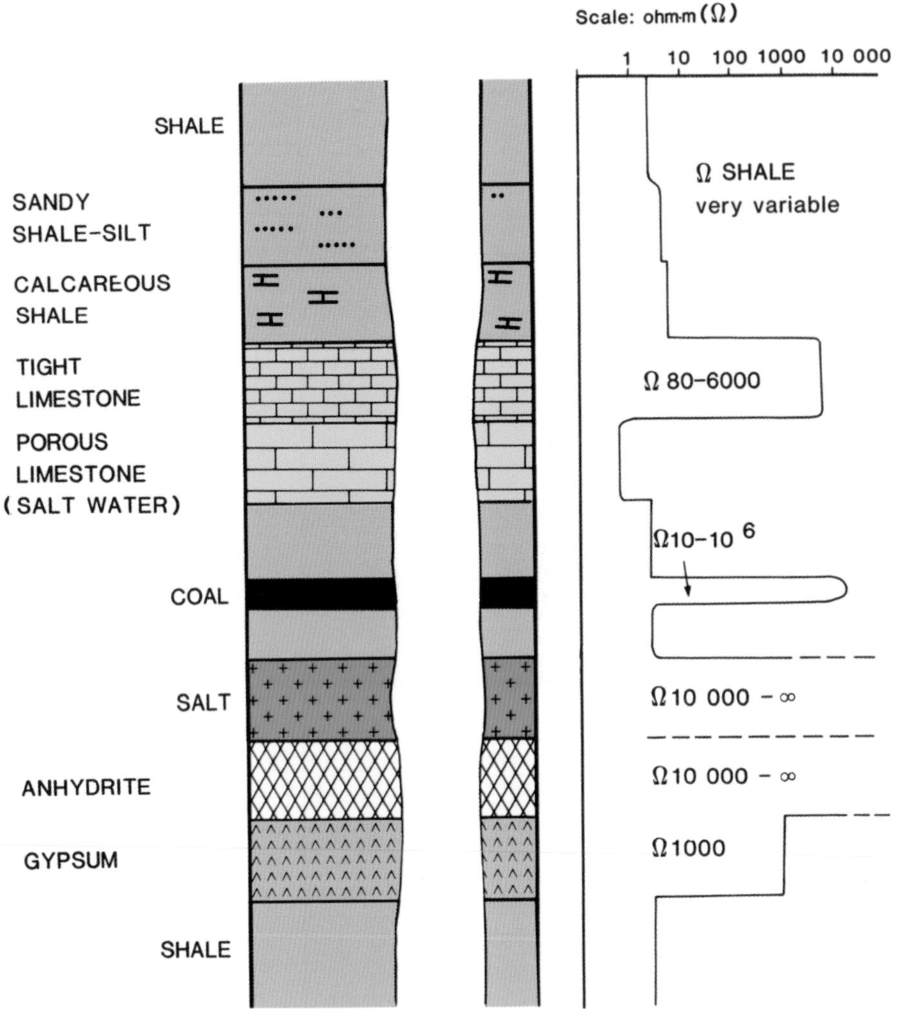

Figure 7.43 Responses on a deep resistivity log of some minerals and some typical, distinctive lithologies. To these mineral values should be added the following fluid values: pure, fresh water (26.7°C) = ∞, salt-saturated water (26.7°C) = 0.03251, methane = ∞.

Table 7.11 Some typical lithology resistivity values (mainly from Serra 1972).

Lithology/Mineral	Resistivity	Resistivity range ohm-m
Shale	moderate	extremely variable 0.50–1000.00
Limestone	generally high	variable – depends on porosity and formation water salinity
Dolomite	generally high	
Sandstone	moderate–low	
Salt	very high	10,000–infinity
Anhydrite	very high	10,000–infinity
Gypsum	high	1000
Coal	high (variable)	10–1,000,000
Pyrite	very low	0.0001–0.1

CEC and it should therefore be treated as a clay for the purpose of saturation analysis, rather than an inert grain (Patchett *et al.* 1993).

Chamosite, a hydrated iron silicate, can also have a distinctive effect on the resistivity. Thick beds, rich in chamosite, occur in the Lower Jurassic of the North Sea. They are recognised as having very high densities and high neutron porosity values but a low resistivity, which is unusual (**Figure 7.45**). High density normally corresponds to a high resistivity so that high density and low resistivity can be used as diagnostic (see *also* Chapter 11, **Figure 11.30**). Although chamosite occurs as oolites, it is not associated with porosity and it is not clear what is causing the conductivity.

Subtle lithological variations

Although resistivity logs do not allow the direct identification of common lithologies, they are nonetheless very sensitive lithology indicators. This is

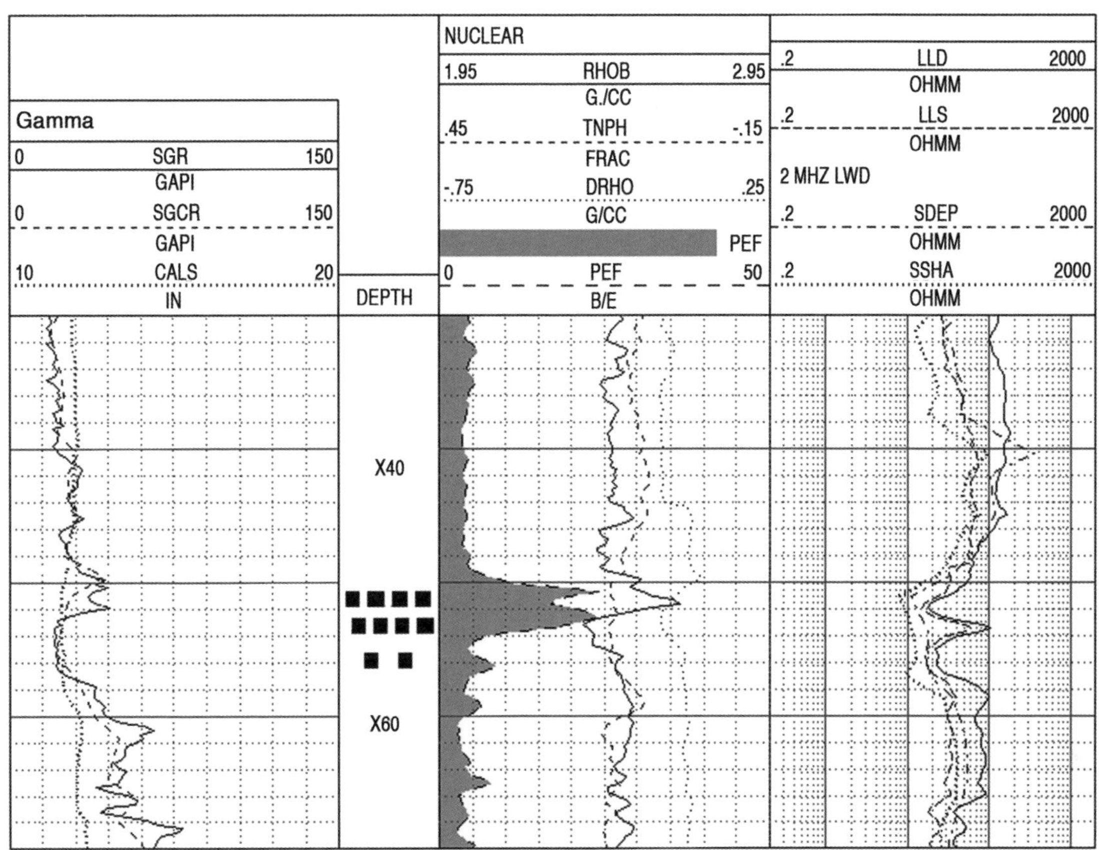

Figure 7.44 The effect of pyrite on resistivity logs. At high concentrations the electrical conductivity of pyrite is seen and log resistivity values are significantly lowered, especially of the 2 MHz, LWD resistivity logs. LLD, LLS = deep and shallow wireline laterolog: SDEP, SSHA = deep shallow 2 MHz LWD resistivity (modified from Kennedy SPWLA 2004).

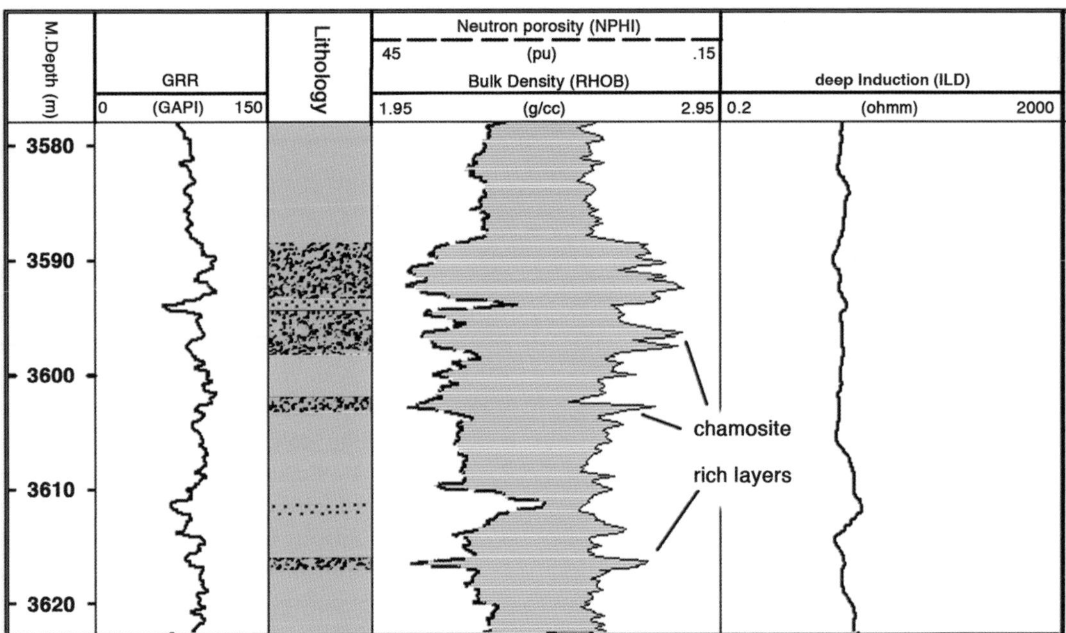

Figure 7.45 Chamosite-rich layers in the Lower Liassic shales of the North Sea. High density with high neutron porosity values indicate chamosite but the high density does not have a correspondingly high resistivity, as is normally the case. Low resistivity with a high density is characteristic of chamosite. GRR = gamma ray.

illustrated by a set of resistivity logs through a shale with numerous siderite rich stringers and concretions (**Figure 7.46**). The lithology is known from cores and consists in general of bedded shales with very thin beds, bands and concretionary beds of sideritic shale. Even the thinnest siderite-rich interval is recorded on the resistivity curves. Of the example logs (**Figure 7.46**), the SHDT (dipmeter) curve, with a 2.5 mm sample spacing, shows the fine detail. This detail is slightly smoothed out by the MSFL log, and greatly smoothed by the deep induction log (both sampled at 15 cm). Nevertheless, the sensitivity of these resistivity logs to the small variations in the shales is clear. The logs are, in fact, responding to two things, both quite subtle: changes in *texture* and changes in *composition*. The textural effect is caused by siderite filling the shale porosity and the compositional effect is a result of the siderite (iron carbonate) itself.

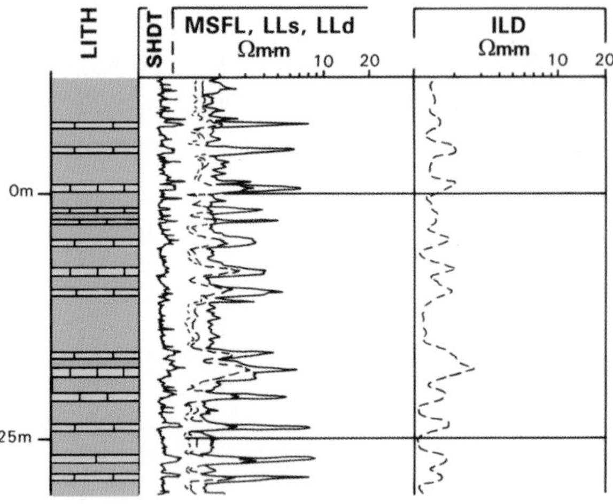

Figure 7.46 Siderite stringers in a shale sequence as seen on resistivity logs. The SHDT dipmeter curve (2.5 mm sampling) shows that these are very thin, often concretionary layers.

This sensitivity of the resistivity logs is emphasised in a second example in which there are bulk changes in a shale, probably in texture as well as composition, brought about by a series of marine flooding events (**Figure 7.47**). The shale, which is rich in organic matter, shows a low resistivity. It is probably well laminated (*see below*) and was deposited in deep water (it is a condensed deposit). Analysis of palynodebris shows that most of the organic material is structureless, indicative of an anoxic environment. The overlying shales are slightly silty, probably laminated, and contain woody organic matter, typical of more open, oxygenated waters. These then grade upwards into silty shale (**Figure 7.47**). These gradual changes are recorded in the resistivity logs.

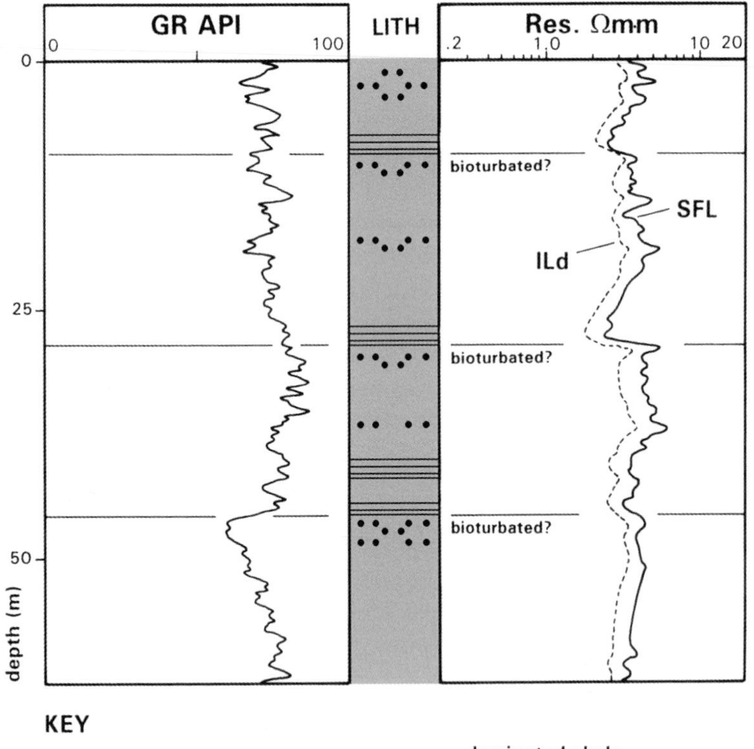

Figure 7.47 Subtle textural and compositional variations in shallow marine shales indicated on the resistivity logs. Compositional changes are noted in the organic matter content and in the amount of silt. Textural variation is seen in the fine lamination of the organic rich shales which causes distinctive, low resistivities. Note the separation between the shallow (SFL) and deep (ILd) devices (*see* text).

This example also illustrates how bedding characteristics can affect the resistivity logs. In normal circumstances, when there is no permeability, *shallow* and *deep* resistivity measurements should show similar values related to the formation lithology. It has been observed, however, that in certain fine-grained or crystalline formations, the resistivities show significant separation. Research has shown that the separation is due to the presence of microscopic permeability paths associated with bedding lamination (fine-grained rocks) or small scale vertical fractures (crystalline rocks). These have a selective effect on the electrical behaviour of the shallow and deep signals (Pezard and Anderson 1990). *Deep* reading, focused devices have current fields which use horizontal permeability paths, such as bedding; *shallow* devices tend to use vertical permeability paths such as vertical fractures or joints. Thus, in well bedded shales, deep measurements tend to be the lower, following the bedding permeability. When vertical joints or fractures

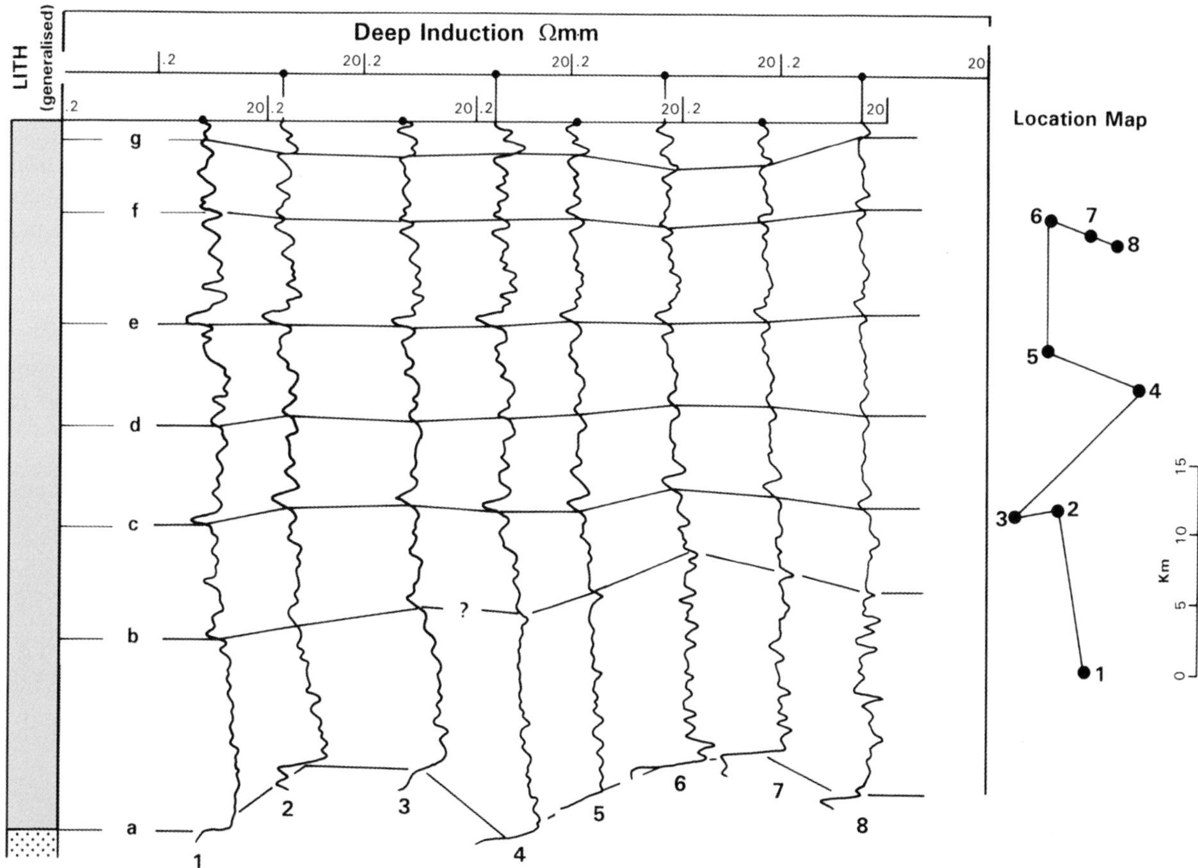

Figure 7.48 Correlation using deep induction logs (resistivity plots). The interval is one of thick, seemingly characterless, marine shales. The logs show persistent, subtle changes which allow excellent correlation over a distance of 30 km.

are present the reverse is true: *shallow* measurements are lower. These effects are analogous to the anisotropy effects already illustrated for more permeable formations (**Figure 7.31**). In the example (**Figure 7.47**), the *shallow* device (SFL) is consistently reading higher than the *deeper* device (ILD). This effect is caused by persistent horizontal bedding.

Correlation

The sensitivity of the resistivity logs to subtle lithological changes is the basis for their use in correlation. Ideally, logs which correlate well are those which are more sensitive to vertical changes than to lateral variations. Within a limited geographical extent, this is often the case with the resistivity logs, especially in shale or silt intervals. Distinctive shapes, trends or peaks over shale zones are related to subtle compositional changes reflecting original patterns of sedimentation (i.e. **Figure 7.47**) and as such can be correlated. The best log for this purpose is usually the deep induction log (**Figure 7.48**).

Despite its frequent (and successful) use for correlation, mainly as a result of its availability, the resistivity log has drawbacks for this task. It is influenced by changes in formation compaction, pressure and interstitial water salinity which are non-stratigraphic, post-depositional features and tend to obliterate the original depositional characteristics (cf. **Figure7.52**).

Facies

From the shale example illustrated previously (**Figure 7.47**), it is clear that facies and facies changes can be followed on the resistivity logs. Indeed, it can be argued that the subtle lithological changes discussed previously are, in fact, a facies changes.

One of the principal uses of the resistivity log in facies analysis is its ability to register changes in quartz (sand) -shale mixtures. This is especially so in the fine-grained rocks, such as shales and silts. The example (**Figure 7.49**) shows small-scale deltaic cycles 15–20 m (50–65 ft) thick, picked out by resistivity trends. The increase in resistivity corresponds to an increase in the silt (quartz) content. Even slight, sub-cyclic events are visible on the logs.

Within sands themselves, it is suggested that through hydrocarbon-bearing zones, different resistivity values can be correlated with differences in grain size. For example, a coarser grained sand will generally have a lower irreducible water saturation, and hence higher

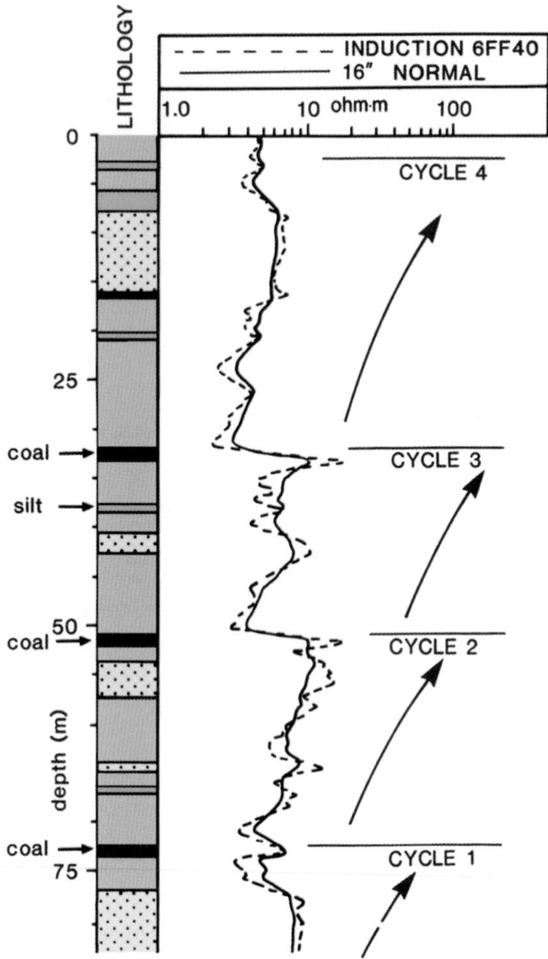

Figure 7.49 Resistivity logs showing small-scale deltaic cycles. The resistivity varies with changes in the sand-shale percentages.

resistivity, since the saturation in hydrocarbons is higher (**Figure 7.50**). A fine-grained sand will have a higher irreducible water saturation and show a lower resistivity. A clean, fining-upwards sandstone filled with hydrocarbons, therefore, will show a regular upwards decrease in resistivity.

Compaction, shale porosity and overpressure

The normal compaction of shale, seen along a borehole, shows up in a plot of shale resistivity against depth. As compaction increases, so the resistivity increases (in a homogeneous shale) (**Figure 7.51**). This trend is especially apparent on logs such as the deep induction. Using the standard log scale for resistivity values, a plot against depth shows a near-linear distribution corresponding to a persistent, normal compaction (Macgregor 1965). The reason for this trend is the relationship between conductivity and shale porosity: a more porous shale is more conductive (**Figure 7.52**). A similar relationship to shale porosity is shown by the sonic log, which also gives persistent trends with shale compaction (**Figure 7.51**).

In some wells, a reversal in shale conductivity with depth is present which can be associated with overpressure. When a zone of overpressure is encountered, shale conductivity will increase, sometimes abruptly, before resuming the normal, decreasing trend with depth (**Figure 7.52**). Overpressure is related to, and causes, an increase in shale porosity and it is this porosity change that the conductivity responds to (Schmidt 1973). Plotting shale conductivity with depth, therefore, brings out normal pressure and compaction trends, and abnormally pressured zones with increased porosity. Care must be taken with such plots to ensure that the changes are not due to variations in shale composition or the salinity of the associated water (cf. **Figure 7.47**). If enough data are available in a particular region, tables can be constructed to give quantitative estimates of overpressure from resistivity values (Ichara and Avbovbo 1985). This relationship gains in importance in the LWD environment since resistivity (conductivity) anomalies can be detected during drilling (Rasmus and Voisin 1990).

A break in a continuous conductivity-depth trend may also be used to indicate a geological unconformity or a tectonic break. In rapidly-deposited or stratigraphically continuous zones, compaction will be persistent and regular, as in the previous example (**Figure 7.51**). However, when there is a break in sedimentation or, more importantly, an unconformity, such regular compaction trends will be interrupted and so will resistivity trends. Abrupt changes in resistivity trends can therefore be used to diagnose geologically significant breaks (*see* Chapters 16, 17).

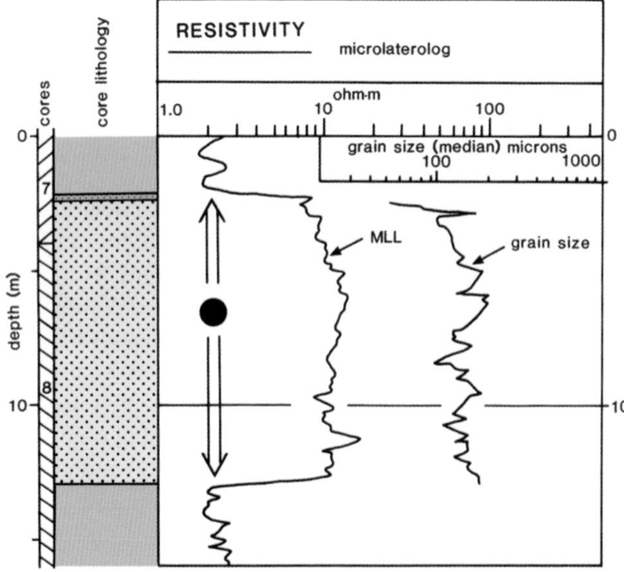

Figure 7.50 Grain size-resistivity relationship in an oil zone. The resistivity variations are related to grain-size changes (*see* text).

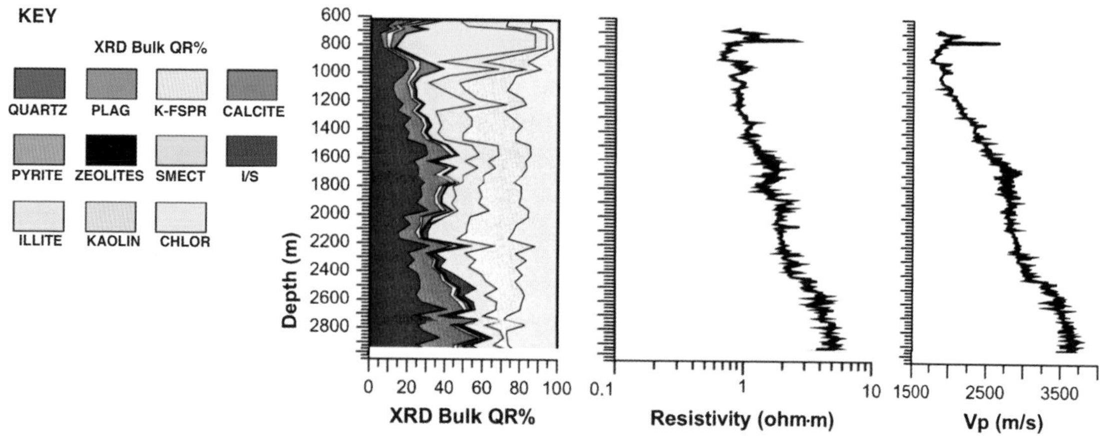

Figure 7.51 Shale resistivity trends with depth. The example shows normal compaction trends in an offshore Norway well. The composition is from X-ray diffraction (XRD). The resistivity trend is shown with the corresponding sonic compressional velocity (Vp) (modified from Peltonen *et al.* 2008).

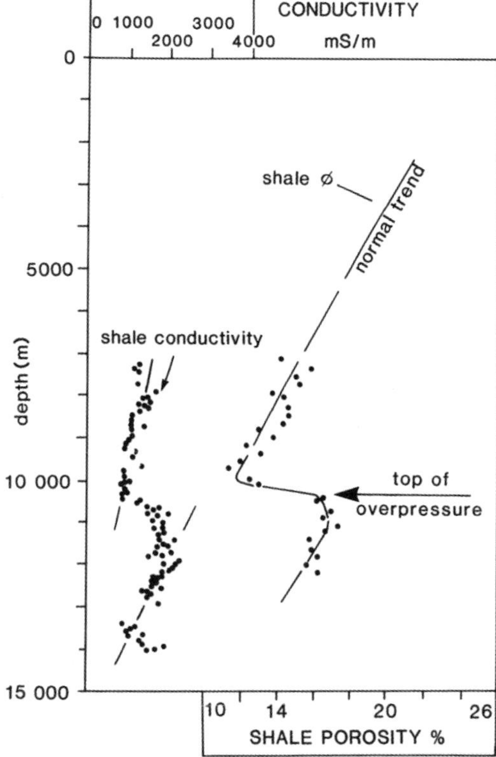

Figure 7.52 Indication of overpressure on a conductivity plot. Conductivity changes correlate with changes in shale porosity (data source, Schmidt 1973).

Source-rock investigation

The resistivity log may be used both qualitatively and quantitatively to investigate source rocks.

The effect a source rock has on the resistivity log depends on the maturity of the organic matter: it has little effect when the source is immature, but causes a large increase when it is mature (**Figure 7.53**). Immature source and non-source shale cannot be differentiated using the resistivity alone. A typical shale, which is not a source-rock, consists of a matrix of clays and lesser amounts of other minerals, and a certain water filled porosity. A source shale also contains both matrix and porosity but typically 4%–12% of the matrix is organic matter (**Figure 7.54**). If the source is immature, the pore space is only filled with water, but if the source is mature, the pores contain both water and free hydrocarbons (**Figure 7.54**). It is the free hydrocarbon fluids that affect the resistivity. Some authors indicate that the numerical size of the resistivity increase is related to the degree of source maturity (Passey *et al.* 1990). However, this implies that the amount of hydrocarbon in the pores is related to the maturity, an effect which has not been proven.

To investigate source-rocks the resistivity log cannot be used alone: a high resistivity in a shale interval may be caused by several textural or compositional effects. For example, a carbonate-rich zone where porosity is blocked, or silica cementation, both cause high resistivities. If the hydrocarbon effect is to be isolated, these compositional and textural effects must be identified. This is done by comparing the resistivity log to a log which is principally affected by texture and composition and not by pore fluid, logs such as the sonic and the density.

Based on these ideas and using analyses of source rocks from around the world, it was shown that if resistivity log values are cross-plotted with either sonic or density log values, then a sample can be reliably identified as either source or non-source (Meyer and Nederlof 1984). The quantitative application of this method is discussed in Chapter 9, Sonic Log, Section 9.6, Source-rock identification.

Another method suggests that it is even possible to calculate the amount of organic matter in a source-rock using the resistivity and the sonic. This method requires that the sonic log is plotted on a normalised scale

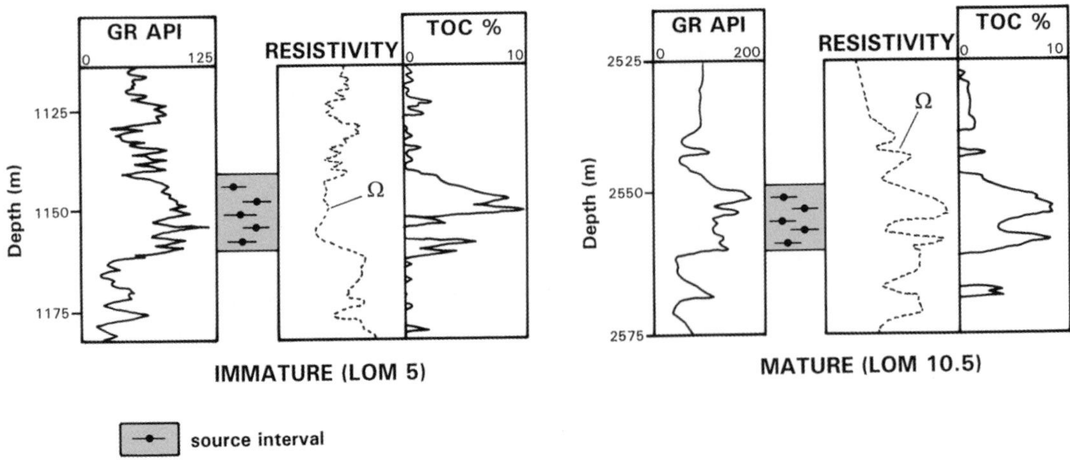

Figure 7.53 Resistivity log characteristics in source rocks. When a source rock is immature, no resistivity anomaly is seen. When it is mature, high resistivities are measured. TOC = total organic carbon. LOM = level of maturity (re-drawn from Passey *et al.* 1990).

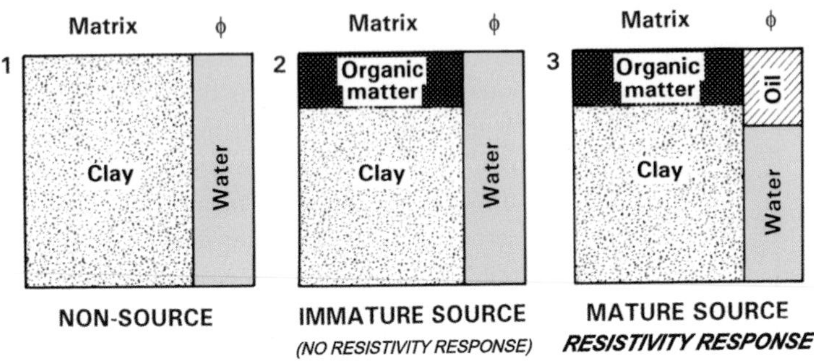

Figure 7.54 Schematic volumetric content of an argillaceous, 1. non-source, 2. immature source and 3, mature source. The mature source contains oil in the pore space which causes high values on the resistivity log as illustrated in Figure 7.53 (re-drawn from Passey *et al.* 1990).

with the resistivity log (the quantitative aspects of this method are also discussed in Chapter 9, Section 9.6). When the normalised scales are used and adjusted, the sonic and resistivity logs 'track' one another in non-source intervals but separate when a source rock is present (Passey *et al.* 1990). The degree of separation is said to be related to both degree of maturity and the total organic (source) abundance (TOC%), so that, if the level of maturity (LOM) is known, the TOC% can be calculated (for details *see* Chapter 9, Section 9.6; methods using the density log are discussed in Chapter 10, Section 10.6, Source rock evaluation).

Methane hydrates

Methane hydrate is the enclosure of methane in ice (actually in the ice structure) and has been studied using logs since the 1980s, especially by Ocean Drilling Project (ODP) teams. Recently, hydrate occurrence was studied and production attempted in the Mallik 5L-38 test well in Northern Canada (Anderson *et al.* 2005). Hydrates can be recognised on a suite of logs. The resistivity is high (10–120 ohmm), the sonic is high, both compressional (2.5–3.6 kms/sec) and shear (1.1–2.0 km/sec.) and the density is lowered but can still be used to derive a porosity, while the neutron is difficult to use (**Figure 7.55**) (Mathews 1986). The responses from the resistivity and the sonic logs can be used to quantify hydrate saturation but require some specific corrections (Collett 1998).

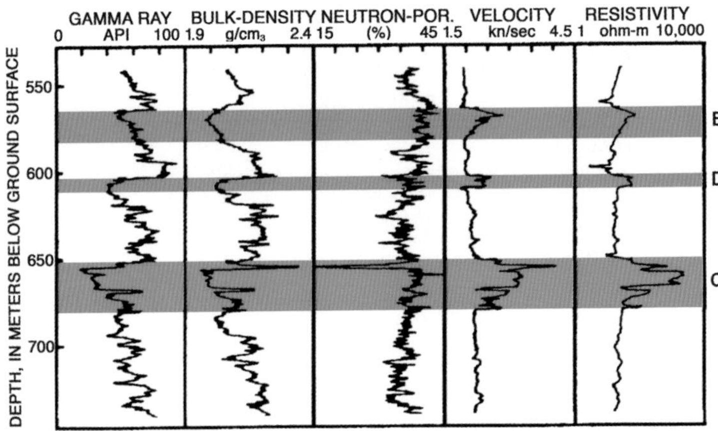

Figure 7.55 Gas hydrate log responses from the test well Northwest Eileen State-2. Zones C, D and E have high hydrate saturations (modified from Collett SPWLA 1998).

8
THE GAMMA RAY AND SPECTRAL GAMMA RAY LOG

8.1 Generalities

The log

The gamma ray log is a record of a formation's gamma radioactivity. The radiation emanates from naturally-occurring uranium, thorium and potassium *(see below)*. The simple gamma ray log cannot distinguish the contributions from these three individual elements and simply outputs a total count rate. A log from a more sophisticated tool, the spectral gamma ray, gives the volume fraction of each individual, contributing radioactive element.

The geological significance of radioactivity lies in the distribution of the three elements. Most rocks contain traces of gamma-emitting elements and are radioactive to some degree; igneous and metamorphic rocks more so than sedimentary rocks. However, amongst the sediments, shales normally have the highest gamma activity. It is for this reason that the simple gamma ray log has been called the 'shale log', although modern thinking shows that it is quite insufficient to equate the gamma ray value with shale content. Not all shales are radioactive and not all that is radioactive is necessarily shale (**Figure 8.1**).

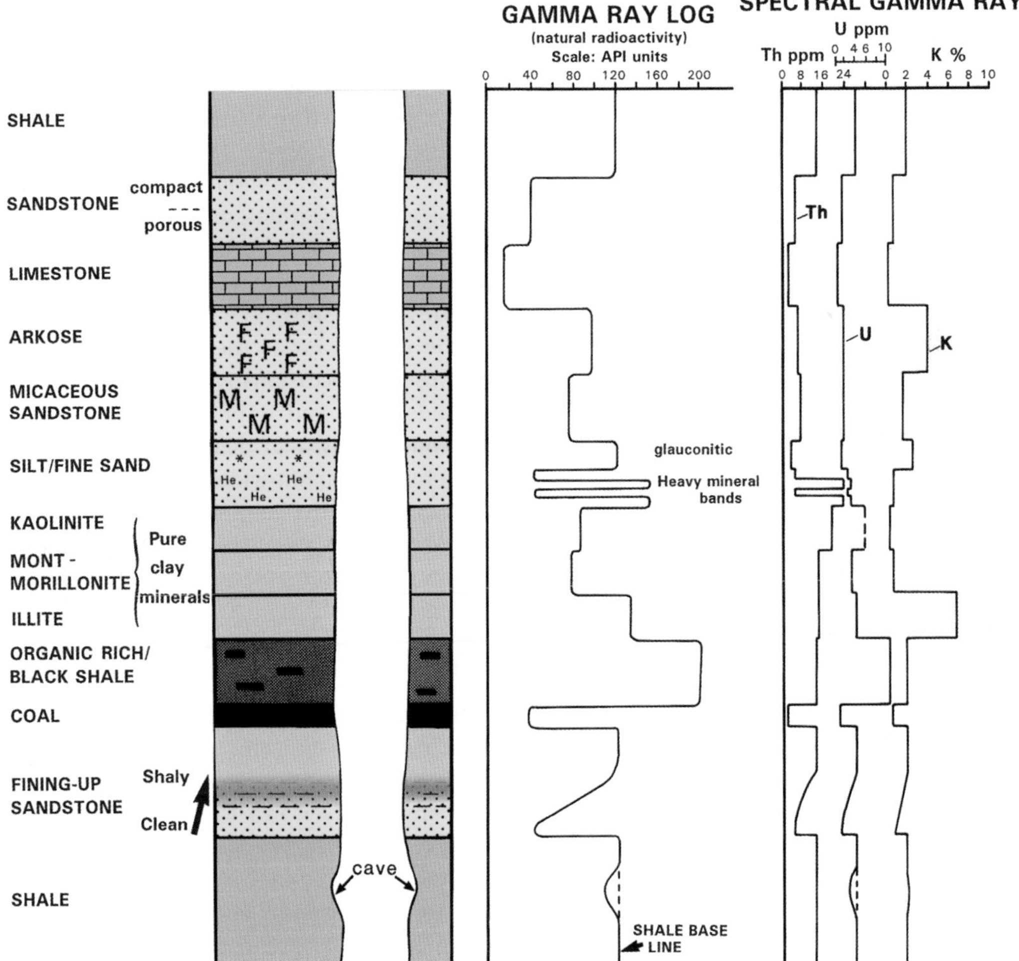

Figure 8.1 The gamma ray log and spectral gamma ray log: some typical responses. The gamma ray log shows natural radioactivity. The spectral gamma ray log gives the abundances of the naturally radioactive elements, thorium (Th) and uranium (U) in parts per million (ppm) and potassium (K) in %. F = feldspar, M = mica, * = glauconite, He = heavy minerals.

Table 8.1,a Principal uses of the simple gamma ray log.

	Discipline	Used for	Knowing
Quantitative	Petrophysics	shale volume (V_{sh})	gamma ray (max) = shale line gamma ray (min) = clean line
Qualitative	Geology	shale (shalyness)	shale line, clean line
		lithology	typical radioactivity values
		mineral identification	mineral radioactivity
	Sedimentology	facies	clay/grain size relationship
	Stratigraphy	correlation	interval characteristics
		unconformity identification	
	Sequence stratigraphy	parasequence, sequence id.	clay/grain size relationship
		flooding surfaces	organic matter radioactivity
		condensed sequence id.	organic matter radioactivity
	Climatology	Milankovitch sequences	spectral content of curve, age
Drilling	Wireline & LWD	depth control	previous log runs
	LWD only	geosteering	gamma ray as image log

The gamma ray tool is a very simple device (section 8.3). This means it can be easily combined with almost any other tool and nowadays a gamma ray is generally included in every logging. It is combined with tools such as the wireline pressure measurement devices (Chapter 3) and wireline sidewall core guns (Chapter 12) to provide a depth match to existing logs. Its simplicity means it can be made into a very rugged device (the reason why it was one of the first tools to appear in LWD form), so that gamma ray logs can be acquired in almost any well, no matter how hostile the conditions. The gamma ray may even be the only log that is achieved. Furthermore, gamma rays are capable of penetrating several inches of steel so that a gamma ray log can be acquired in cased holes (in fact, if necessary, it can be logged through several casing strings). This general availability of the log affects its many uses.

Principal uses

The principal use of the gamma ray log is in correlation, in the widest sense. That is, during drilling it is often used on its own to pick formation tops, especially in the overburden where it may be the only log available. Post drilling, in a single well, it provides a link between the open hole logs and the completion. Because of its availability, it is commonly used as a depth reference.

Quantitatively, the most important use of the gamma ray is as a shale indicator, although it must be emphasised, as explained below, that this relationship is not straightforward. Qualitatively, in its simple form, it can be used to help identify lithology (as well as shalyness), to suggest facies and sequences, to identify key stratigraphic surfaces and to stratigraphically correlate. The LWD gamma ray is used in addition to geosteer. The spectral gamma ray, which only exists as a wireline tool, can be used to derive a quantitative radioactive mineral volume and a more accurate shale volume. Qualitatively it can indicate dominant clay mineral types, give indications of depositional environment, help to localise source rocks and major sequence stratigraphic surfaces and occasionally to indicate fractures (**Tables 8.1,a**, **8.1,b**).

The gamma ray is the work horse for those who only use logs occasionally. It seems to be a simple log to understand and is practically always available. It is frequently used to demonstrate local or well stratigraphy and basin-wide correlations. This chapter will show that the gamma ray response is a lot more complex than is usually assumed, something which is known by petrophysicists but not by the occasional, geological user.

8.2 Natural gamma radiation

Gamma rays are a highly energetic form of electromagnetic radiation and are created in nuclear reactions, either natural or artificial. The energies of gamma rays are normally given in kilo or Mega electron volts (keV or MeV). These are not SI (Système International) units but are commonly used in nuclear physics. Most naturally produced gamma rays have energies of a few MeV, although by the time they are detected, these energy levels may have been considerably reduced as a result of Compton scattering (explained below).

Natural gamma radiation in rocks comes essentially from just three elemental sources: the radioactive ele-

Table 8.1,b Principal uses of the spectral gamma ray log.

	Discipline	Used for	Knowing
Quantitative	Petrophysics	shale volume (V_{sh})	CGR shale line, CGR clean line
		shale volume V_{sh} (*Th*)	Th (max), Th (min) for pure shale
		Radioactive mineral volume	V_{sh} (*Th*), K (max), K (min) for pure shale
Semi-quantitative and qualitative	Geology	dominant clay mineral	Th, U, K content of individual clay mineral species
	Sequence stratigraphy	condensed sequence id.	Th/U ratio and normal U content of shales
	Geochemistry	source rock analysis	uranium content of organic matter
	Reservoir geology	fracture detection	uranium in pore water (rarely used now)
	Volcanology	lava flow analysis	potassium content of flows

ments of the thorium family, of the uranium-radium family and of the single isotope of potassium ^{40}K (Adams and Weaver 1958). All three have half-lives that are similar to the age of the earth, which means that, while a significant amount of the original material is present in the earth's crust, it is still decaying fast enough to be measureable.

Quantitatively, potassium is by far the most abundant of the three elements (**Table 8.2**) but, because only the rare ^{40}K isotope is radioactive, its contribution to overall radioactivity in relation to its weight is small. Uranium and Thorium are rare and exotic elements by any standard, and occur in sedimentary rocks only in trace amounts. However, the reality is that the contribution to the overall radioactivity of the three elements is of the same order of magnitude, the abundance seeming to be the inverse of the contribution: a small quantity of uranium has a large effect on the radioactivity, a large quantity of potassium a small effect.

Each of the three sources emits gamma rays spontaneously. That is, they emit photons with no mass and no charge but great energy (this being the definition of a gamma ray). The energy, in the case of uranium, thorium and potassium emissions, occurs in the spectrum from 0–3 MeV. The radiation from ^{40}K is distinct, with a single energy value of 1.46 MeV (**Figure 8.2**). Thorium and uranium both emit radiations with a whole range of energies but with certain peak energies correspond-

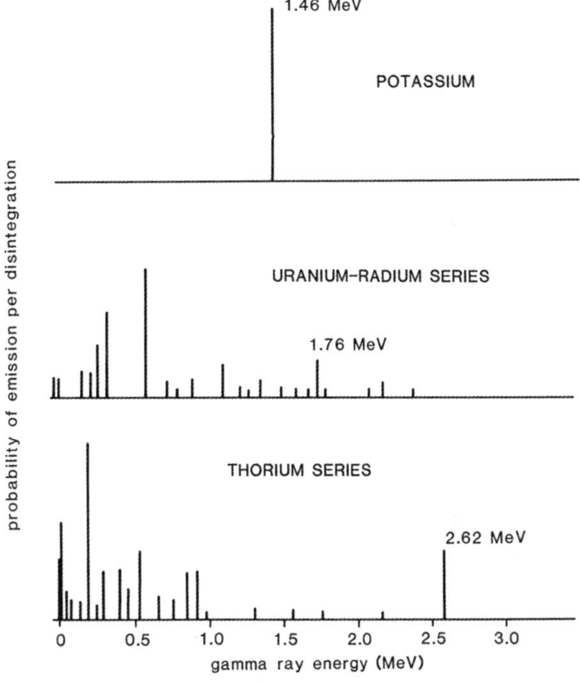

Figure 8.2 The gamma ray emission spectra of naturally radioactive minerals. The principal peaks used to identify each source are indicated. MeV = million electron volts (after Tittman *et al.* 1965 from Schlumberger 1972).

ing to daughter products. At the higher energy levels of 2.62 MeV for thorium and 1.76 MeV for uranium, these peaks are especially distinct (**Figure 8.2**). In fact, the energy of any primary gamma ray is diagnostic of the element that produced it.

The spectra and the energy levels illustrated (**Figure 8.2**) are those at the point of emission. One of the characteristics of gamma rays is that when they pass through any material their energy is progressively changed. The effect is known as Compton scattering and is due to the collision between gamma rays and electrons. At each collision the energy of the gamma ray is reduced

Table 8.2 Abundance and relative radiation activity of the natural radioactive elements.

	K	Th	U
†Relative abundance in the earth's crust	2.59%	~12 ppm	~3 ppm
*Gamma rays per unit weight	1	1300	3600

†Serra (1979), Serra *et al.* (1980)
*Adams and Weaver (1958)

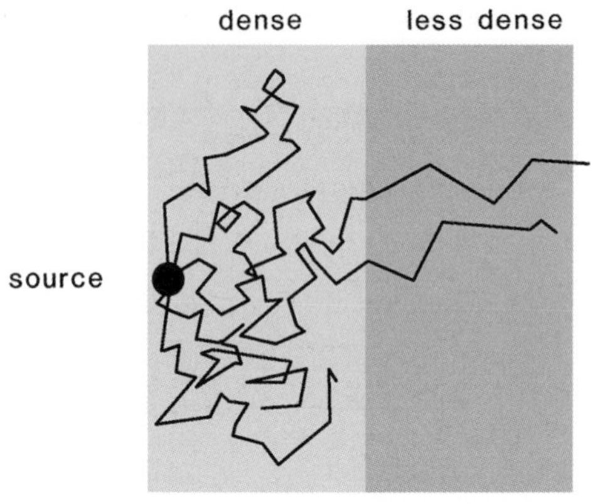

Figure 8.3 Schematic drawing of the Compton scattering of gamma rays. The effect is more marked in denser matter (cf. Lavenda 1985).

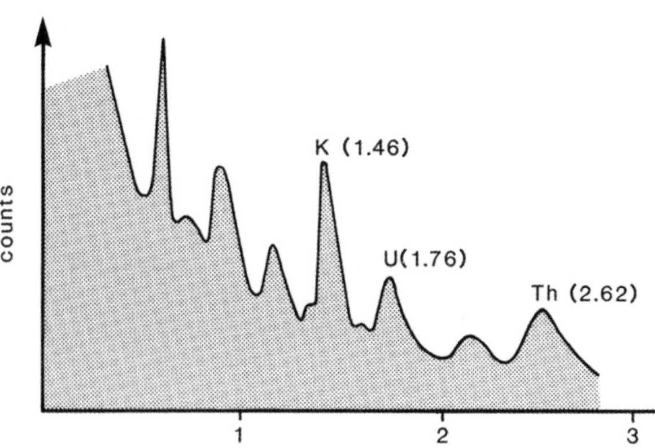

Figure 8.4 Complex spectrum observed from a radioactive source containing potassium, thorium and uranium, after Compton scattering (after Hassan *et al.* 1976).

(**Figure 8.3**). The higher the common density through which the gamma rays pass, the more rapid the degradation or loss of energy (in reality it depends on the material's electron density, which is related to common density Chapter 10).

In borehole logging, when gamma rays are detected by the tools, they have already passed through the formation, some drilling mud and the tool housing (especially in LWD tools), all of which cause Compton scattering. Thus, the original discrete energies of the primary gamma rays are reduced to a continuous spectrum of values (**Figure 8.4**). When more than one radioactive element is present, their contributions become mixed and the resulting spectrum is very complex. An additional difficulty is that, when a detector is heated, it smears the spectrum, which is why in laboratories detectors are cooled to cryogenic temperatures. In well logging, the detector is at or above borehole temperature.

However, despite these problems, a glance at the original spectra (**Figure 8.2**) will show that the final complex, mixed energy spectrum, even after Compton scattering, still contains the diagnostic peaks. The original distinct peaks of potassium at 1.46 MeV, uranium at 1.76 MeV and thorium at 2.62 MeV still exist and can be used to identify the original source of the radiations. This is the principle used in the spectral gamma ray tool.

8.3 Tools (Table 8.3)

Wireline tools

Simple gamma ray tool

The simple gamma ray tool is a sensitive gamma ray detector consisting of a scintillation counter attached to a photomultiplier tube (**Figure 8.5**). The scintillation counter is typically a crystal of sodium iodide (NaI) with minor impurities of thallium, 2 cm in diameter and 5 cm long (0.8" × 2"). When gamma rays pass through the crystal, they cause a flash of light. The light flash is converted to an electrical pulse by the photomultiplier and is either amplified and transmitted to surface or,

Table 8.3 Typical modern gamma ray tools.

Type of tool	Schlumberger	¹Baker Hughes™	²Halliburton	Output
Simple tools (wireline)	GR HGNS SGT	GR	GR HNGR NGRT	total gamma ray radioactivity logged at 3600 ft/hr (1100 m/hr) Schlumberger or 1800 ft/hr (550 m/hr) Halliburton
Spectral tools (wireline)	NGS *HNGS	SPECTRALOG™ (SL)	SGR CSNG	Th, U, and K abundances, SGR, CGR logged at 1800 ft/hr (550 m/hr) Schlumberger or 600 ft/hr (180 m/hr) Baker and Halliburton
LWD tools	GR (images)	GR (images)	Dual GR (images)	tools have 4 or 16 sectors that provide images

From Serra 2000, Baker Hughes™ (Atlas), Halliburton and Schlumberger documents

[1]LWD tools marketed by Baker Hughes™ INTEQ
[2]Marketed by Halliburton Sperry-Sun
*tool has BGP (bismuth germinate) sensors. All other tools have NaI (sodium iodide) sensors.

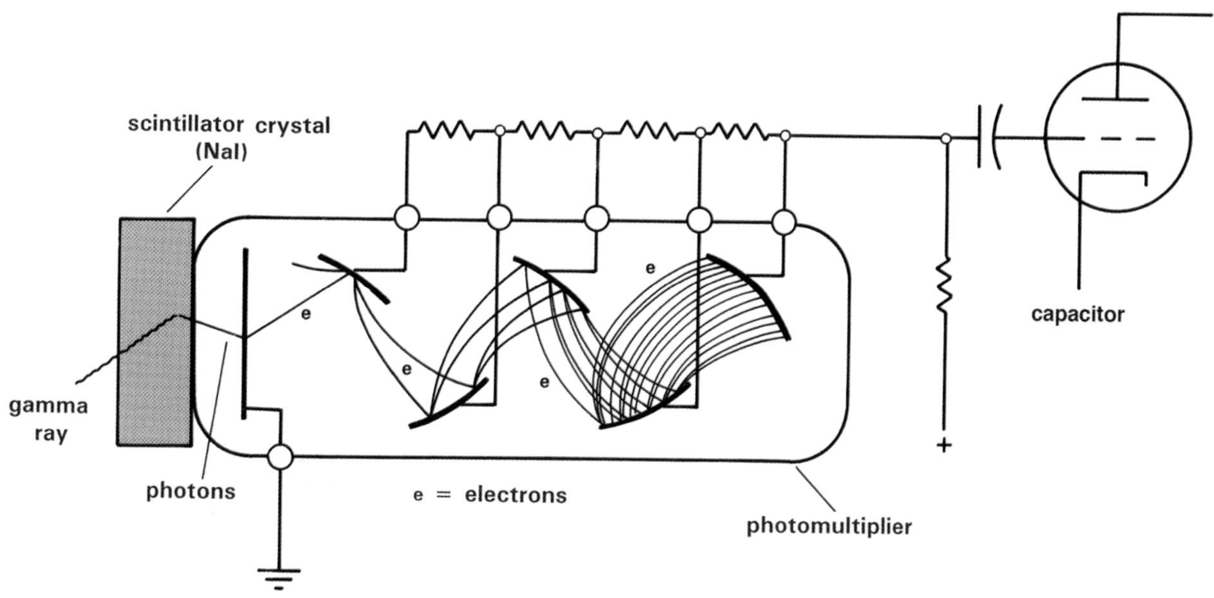

Figure 8.5 Schema of a gamma ray tool (re-drawn from Serra 1979 after a Lane Wells document).

more likely in modern tools, counted down hole. The count rate is then transmitted using the tool's normal telemetry system or, in the case of LWD tools, written to memory. Sodium iodide was for a long time the material of choice for gamma ray detectors because it is optically transparent and it is dense. The high density helps to ensure that most of gamma rays entering the crystal are completely absorbed.

Spectral gamma ray tool

The spectral gamma ray tool, like the simple tool, consists of a scintillation counter and photomultiplier. However, in the spectral tool the scintillator crystal has a much greater volume being about 4.5 cm in diameter and 30.5 cm long (1.75″ × 12″) and even two combined crystals can be employed, thus giving the tool a much better 'counting' sensitivity. Bismuth germinate (BGO) may be used for these larger crystals as it is even denser than sodium iodide, and therefore gives better counting rates. However, BGO is sensitive to temperature and is enclosed in a dewar flask in the tools using it, and must be cooled before a logging run.

When a gamma ray passes through a scintillator crystal, it not only causes a flash of light, but the intensity of that flash is proportional to the energy of the incident gamma ray. This characteristic is used by the spectral gamma ray tool, with its large scintillator crystals, to identify the energy level of the gamma radiations. In older tools, radiations were allocated to fairly broad, predefined energy bins, or 'windows', designed to separate the distinctive energy peaks of the 3 individual radioactive elements (**Figure 8.4**), namely 2.62 MeV for thorium, 1.76 MeV for uranium and 1.46 MeV for potassium.

Table 8.4 Ratios of radioactive to non-radioactive material in normal elemental mixtures (Serra *et al.* 1980).

	^{40}K	^{232}Th	^{238}U	^{235}U	^{234}U
% radioactive isotopes in normal mixtures	0.0199	100	99.27	0.72	0.0057
	$\frac{^{40}K}{K_{total}}$	All	$\frac{^{238}U}{U_{total}}$	$\frac{^{235}U}{U_{total}}$	$\frac{^{234}U}{U_{total}}$

The tendency now, however, is to analyse the entire spectrum from a large number of channels (256) and to use software algorithms that allow all energy counts to be used and 'allocated' to each element. In some tools, the very lowest energy level emissions are not used as they can be affected by photoelectric absorption, which modifies counts (Flanagan *et al.* 1991).

The relative count contributions of the three radioisotopes measured by the tool are related to their abundance. Using the known ratios of these radioisotopes to non-radioactive isotopes in normal elemental mixtures (**Table 8.4**), the gamma ray counts are converted to the actual abundances of each element. Thus, the quantitative, elemental abundances of thorium, uranium and potassium are plotted as the output logs from the spectral tool (Section 8.4, **Figure 8.9,b**).

LWD tools

LWD gamma ray tools are of the simple type with rugedised sensors (both scintillator crystal and Geiger-Müller) and were amongst the earliest to be introduced into the while drilling environment. The principles of measurement are the same as for the wireline tools but in the LWD tools the scintillator crystal (or other sensor),

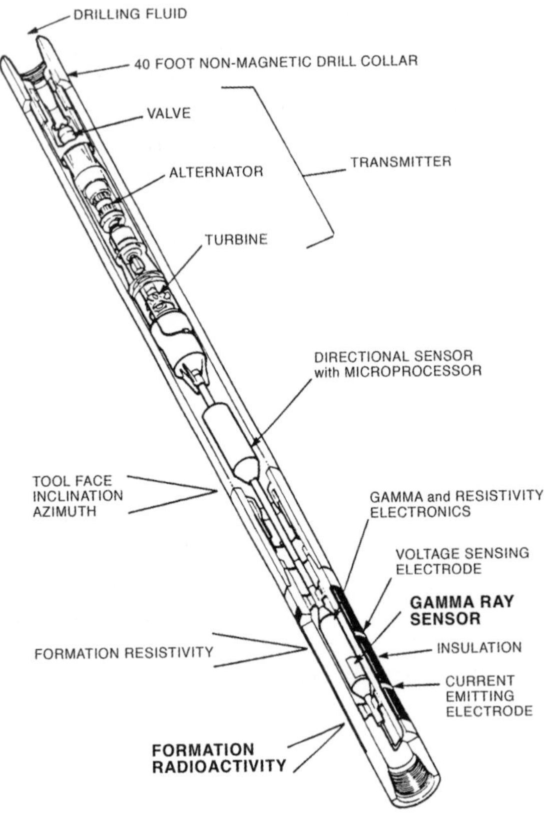

Figure 8.6 Diagram of an early LWD gamma ray (and resistivity) tool with a 7¼ inch radius. The tool is connected to drill-collars or the bit as part of the bottom hole assembly (from Cobern and Nuckols SPWLA1985).

is contained within the body of the drill-collar housing the tool and behind 5 cm (2″) or more of steel (**Figure 8.6**). This decreases the radiation reaching the tool by a factor of 5 to 10 depending on tool design (Coope 1983). However, this is countered by the fact that the LWD sensor will typically read about 30 cm (1 ft) of formation per minute, while a wireline tool will read 30 cm (1 ft) in only 1 second. With normal rotation speeds and rate of drilling (*see* 8.4, Logging speed), this sampling frequency provides a better quality count rate for the LWD gamma ray than for the wireline measurement. However, after processing, filtering and smoothing, the LWD logs are given the same sample rate as the wireline tools, namely 1 sample every 6″ (15 cm) and generally show similar curve activity (**Figure 8.7**) (Weller *et al.* 2005).

LWD gamma ray sensors may be directionally focused. That is, sensors are set in a shield (often tungsten) in which a limited window, a 90° slit, is left for radiation to enter (Jan and Harrell 1987). Since the LWD tool is turning, the window radiations can be allocated to bins, oriented around the borehole (**Figure 2.21**). The modern tendency is to use these oriented bins to create a real-time, gamma ray image which can be used for geosteering, especially if the sensors are placed near to the bit (**Figure 8.8**). Depending on the tool, 16 sectors (Schlumberger GeoVISION) or 8 sectors (Baker Hughes™ INTEQ) are used, which gives a nominal pixel size (Baker) of 6″ (15 cm) (Meyer *et al.* 2005).

8.4 Log characteristics

Calibration, log presentation, units and scales

Simple wireline gamma ray log

The accepted unit for radioactivity logging is the API (American Petroleum Institute) unit. It is defined in a reference pit in the grounds of the University of Houston, Texas. The pit contains specially mixed, high radioactivity cement surrounded by equally special low radioactivity cement. An API unit is 1/200 of the difference between the two radioactivities (Belknap *et al.* 1959). If a particular gamma ray tool is tested, the API unit for that tool is 1/200 of the difference between the low and high values. Thus, not only does the Houston pit serve as a standard for the API unit, it also serves to calibrate a tool. This scale is designed so that an 'average shale' reads 100 API units.

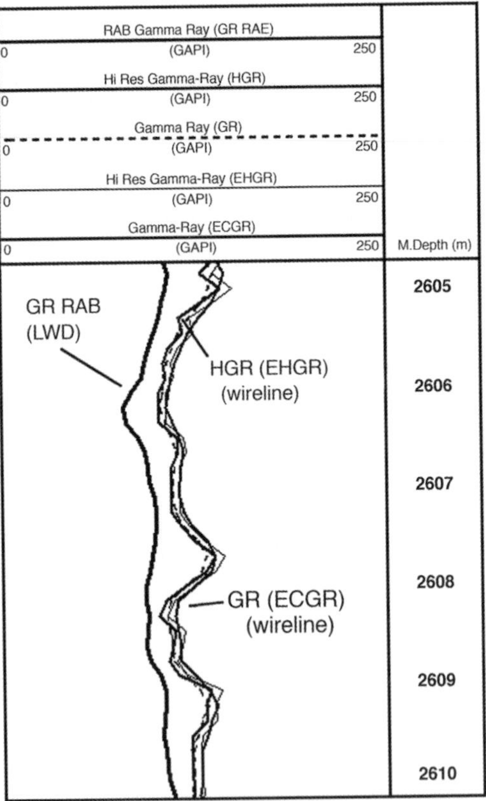

Figure 8.7 Raw, processed and corrected wireline gamma ray and LWD gamma ray curves compared. GR,RAB = LWD gamma ray: GR = raw wireline gamma ray: ECGR = environmentally corrected GR: HGR = high resolution gamma ray: EHGR = environmentally corrected HGR. The effective comparison is between the GR,RAB (LWD) and the raw GR (wireline); GR,RAB is lower in value and has less detail in this case.

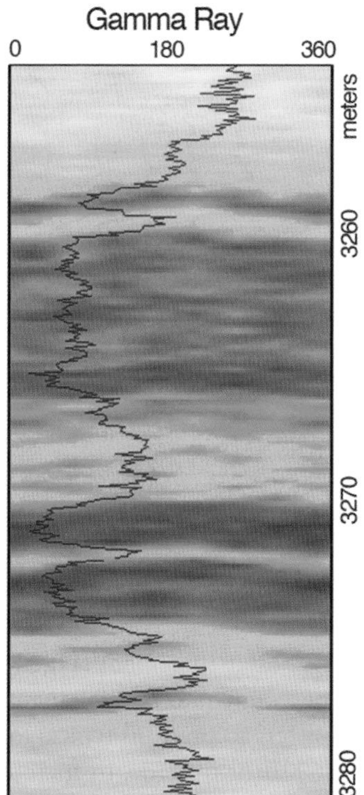

Figure 8.8 An image log generated from an 8 sector LWD gamma ray tool and superimposed curve, run in an 8½" hole in the Gulf of Mexico. On the log curve, gamma ray values increase to the right, so on the image sands are dark and the shales are light (Stamm *et al.* SPWLA 2007).

Locally, when a tool is serviced at a base, or is about to be used on a logging job, an in-place calibration can be made by placing a wrap-around 'blanket' or jig, with a known API rating, over a sensor. Such local calibrations are used for both wireline and LWD tools.

On the API log format (**Figure 1.6**), the simple gamma ray log is usually recorded in track 1 along with the caliper. Scales are chosen locally but 0–100 or 0–200 API are common (**Figure 8.9,a**).

LWD gamma ray log

The LWD gamma ray tools are notionally calibrated to the API gamma ray pit. Only notionally, because they are too big to be actually put in it. Thus, a typical shale should read 100 API units which means that LWD and wireline values should be comparable. However, with the LWD sensors being behind steel casing, there can be differences and, furthermore, the LWD tool will almost certainly occupy more of the borehole than the wireline equivalent so the effect of the mud will be different (*see* unwanted borehole effects, *below*).

Since the LWD gamma ray is of the simple type, the measurements can be presented in the same way as the wireline tool curve. However, because the sensors rotate, as described, the oriented values can be presented as an image (**Figure 8.8**). Image colours represent gamma ray values, but are not given any absolute scale, and are simply lighter or darker. Colours are generally chosen so that high API values are light. Shales, therefore, have

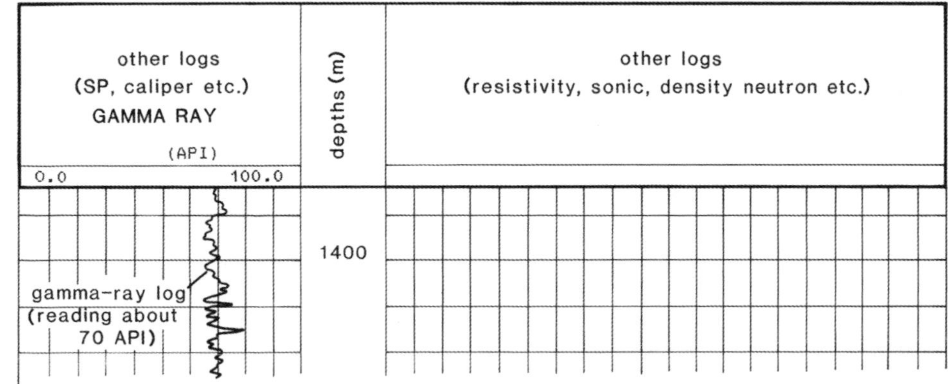

(B) SPECTRAL GAMMA RAY LOG

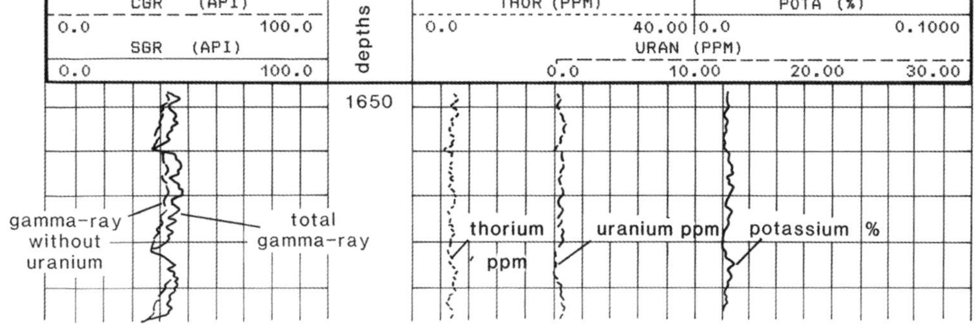

Figure 8.9 Typical gamma ray and spectral gamma ray log headings in API format.

light tones, while reservoirs with low gamma ray values have dark tones.

Spectral gamma ray log

The main results of the spectral gamma ray tool are elemental abundances derived, as described above. The calibration facility for the spectral tools is the same pit in the University of Houston that is used for the simple gamma ray tool. This is because the high activity cement of this pit has known quantities of uranium (13.1 ppm), thorium (24.4 ppm) and potassium (4.07%), which contribute to the overall radioactivity (ppm = parts per million) (Belknap *et al.* 1959). The individual channels of the spectral tool can be empirically calibrated. (It should be noted that these quantities are approximately twice the 'average shale' values, **Figure 8.18**).

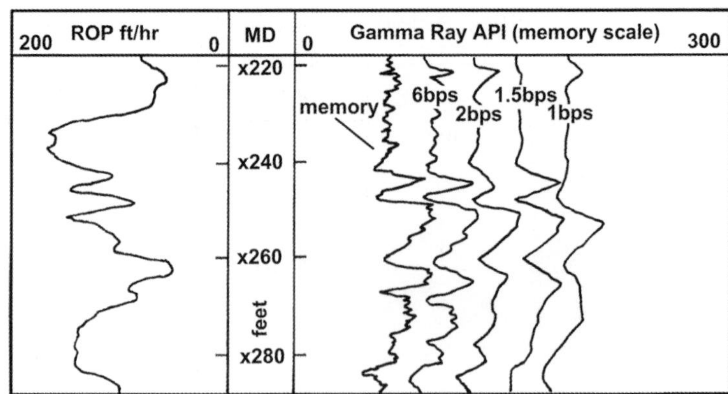

Figure 8.10 The effect of real time data rate transfer and ROP (rate of penetration) on an LWD gamma ray. The memory curve is from 10 second updates. bps = bits per second.

There are several common presentation formats for the gamma ray spectral log, but the simplest, and probably the best, is a straightforward plot of elemental abundances across tracks 2 and 3 on arithmetic scales (**Figure 8.9,b**). Thorium and uranium are given in ppm while potassium is given in per-cent (i.e. parts per hundred).

Track 1 of this (Schlumberger) presentation (**Figure 8.9,b**) shows two curves, the CGR and SGR. The SGR, or standard gamma ray, is the total contribution of the three elements in API units. That is, it is the same as the simple gamma ray log, but re-constructed from the elemental values plotted on tracks 2 and 3. To arrive at this value (for the Schlumberger NGT-A), the following multipliers are used: 1 ppm U = 8.09 API units, 1 ppm Th = 3.93 API units, 1% K = 16.32 API units. Thus, 3 ppm of uranium in a mix contributes 24.27 API units (3 × 8.09), and so on. The SGR is therefore the sum of these API contributions (and can be remembered as the Sum Gamma Rays). The CGR, or computed gamma ray curve, represents the contributions of only the thorium and potassium in API units. Hence, the difference between the SGR and the CGR is the contribution, in API units, of uranium. For reasons explained below (Section 8.9), the CGR is considered to be an improved clay volume indicator to the SGR or total value (and can be remembered as the Clay Gamma Ray). In formats not shown here, curves of the different elemental ratios are displayed.

Logging speed

Simple wireline gamma ray

As a result of computerisation, tool sample measurement in wireline logging is depth based. For the modern gamma ray tool this means that a count rate measurement is applied to a depth increment, for example the standard 6" (15 cm). To achieve this, the tool is interrogated at each 6" cable increment (**Figure 2.27**). The effect is that the count rate is unchanged by logging speed, it is simply less accurate. At typical logging speeds of 18 m/min (3600 ft/hr), the depth increment of 6" is logged in 0.5 seconds. If logging speed is only 9 m/min (1800 ft/hr), the increment will be logged in 1 second and the count rate will be more accurate because more counts will have been considered. However, the rate will be approximately the same.

LWD gamma ray

For LWD tools, logging speed restrictions are clearly not relevant. In the while drilling domain, log quality is affected by the relationship between drilling rate of penetration (ROP), rotation rate (RPM), tool count rate and, for the real time logs, the rate of data transfer (Baker Hughes™ INTEQ 2006) (**Figure 8.10**). However, a high rate of drilling (ROP) such as 100 m/hr (300 ft/hr), is still a lot less than a wireline logging speed, so that real-time log quality is mainly dependent on the mud-pulse system. LWD gamma ray logs are usually edited to give 2 measurements per foot (the same as typical wireline logs). With current count rates and rates of data transfer (between 6–12 bps bits per second), this sample rate can generally be achieved real time without limiting drilling rate. However, if a good LWD log is required (for example to pick a coring point) the ROP can be limited to suit the mud-pulse limitations.

Spectral gamma ray

The spectral tool (wireline) is very sensitive to logging speed effects because the count rate of the individual energy detection windows or energy levels is very small. Lower logging speeds make for more accurate values, so that the sonde is often attached to other slowly run tools such as the imaging devices (Chapter 15), and logging speeds of 4.5 m/min (900 ft/hr) are common. Despite these recommendations, many, if not most, of the pre-

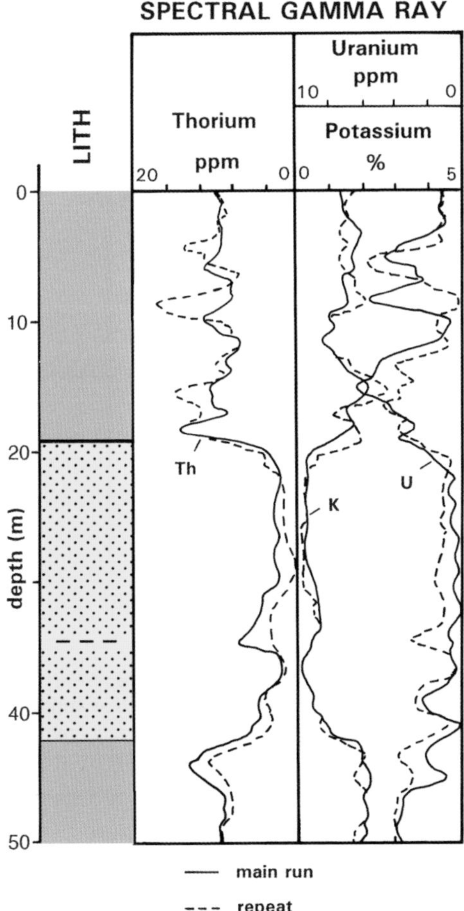

Figure 8.11 Repeatability of the spectral gamma ray. Precise repeatability is generally poor but it should be noted that the quantities being detected are parts per million (ppm).

1990 spectral logs have poor repeatability (Hurst 1990 and **Figure 8.11**), which may be, in part, a result of logging speed and, in part, the sensitivity of the tool itself. Experience actually suggests it is probably the latter. Tool errors are greater when abundances are below 1.0% K, 4 ppm Th and 1.8 ppm U (Gendron 1988). It is good practice to run a repeat section with every spectral log so that the variability can be judged empirically. Moreover, quantitative interpretation methods must take into account the inherent limits of accuracy of the measurement.

Depth of investigation and vertical resolution

Simple wireline gamma ray

The depth from which radiations can be detected by the simple wireline gamma ray tool is generally small but difficult to be precise about. One experiment found that 75% of radiations detected came from a 14 cm radius and 25 cm (5.5" & 9.8") vertically above and below the detector. This was for gamma rays with a single energy of 1.76 MeV and the detector centralised in a 15 cm (6") diameter hole filled with 1.2 g/cm³ density mud (Rhodes and Mott 1966). From theoretical calculations, Ellis (1987) found investigation radius values of 15–18 cm (6–7") for 2.0–3.0 g/cm³ material and 1.46 MeV energy radiations. Clearly, natural conditions vary greatly from these specific cases. In addition, although the volume of investigation about a gamma ray tool is spherical (the size depending on the sensors), because the tool is moving, the sphere becomes elongated for a depth based log. As a rough guide for the wireline tool, the volume of investigation can be considered to be approximately 20 cm (8") vertically above and below the detector (along the borehole) and 10 cm (4") radially (**Figure 8.12,a)**.

Other influences on investigation and resolution include formation density, statistical variation of radiations and signal filtering. Formation density affects investigation because lower density formations absorb fewer gamma rays. The depth of investigation of a gamma ray tool is greater in a lower density formation than it is in a higher density formation (**Figure 8.12,b**)

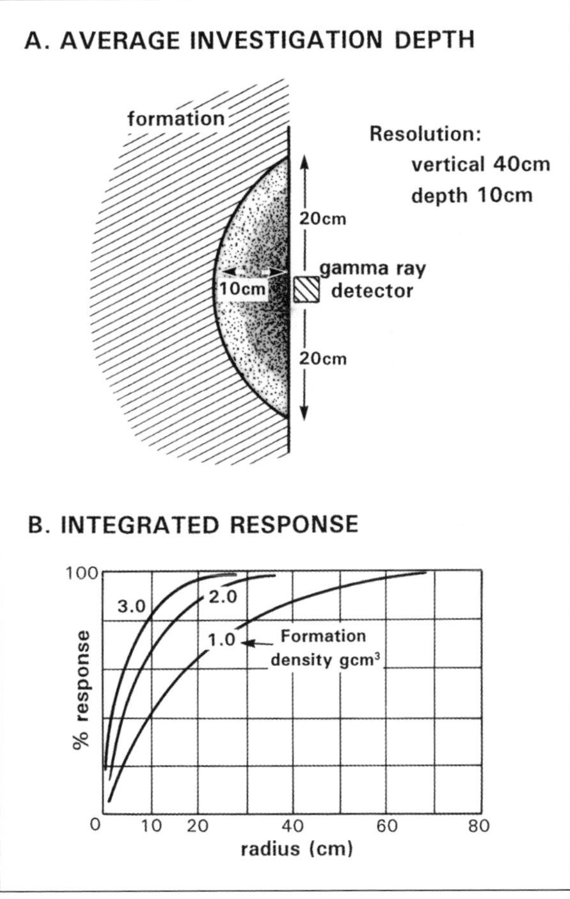

Figure 8.12 Depth of investigation of the gamma ray tool. (A) Average volume from which radiations are detected. (B) Depth of investigation shown to be dependent on formation density. Investigation depth is less in dense formations (graph B, re-drawn from Hallenberg 1992).

(cf. Hallenburg 1992). Statistical variation is the natural property of gamma ray emissions to vary unpredictably. These are only minor variations in count rate, but they cannot be avoided. And finally, signal filtering affects the final gamma ray log because raw measurement values are generally smoothed to take out unwanted variations. The filter may even be a simple moving average. The overall result is that the simple gamma ray log does not repeat in the very minor variations, blurs bed boundaries and has a rather poor thin bed definition (Chapter 2). In practical terms, the vertical resolution of the gamma ray can generally be taken as 45 cm (18″) or more (Goldberg *et al.* 2001).

The frequent combination of the simple gamma ray sonde with other tools has been mentioned. In practice, it means that the wireline version is run both with tools that are centred in the borehole (i.e. sonic and resistivity tools) or eccentred and against the borehole wall (i.e. density and neutron tools). Because of Compton scattering in the drilling mud, the log made with the sonde against the borehole wall and in direct contact with the formation, will always show a higher reading and a higher amplitude of variations than the borehole centred version immersed in the mud (**Figure 8.13**).

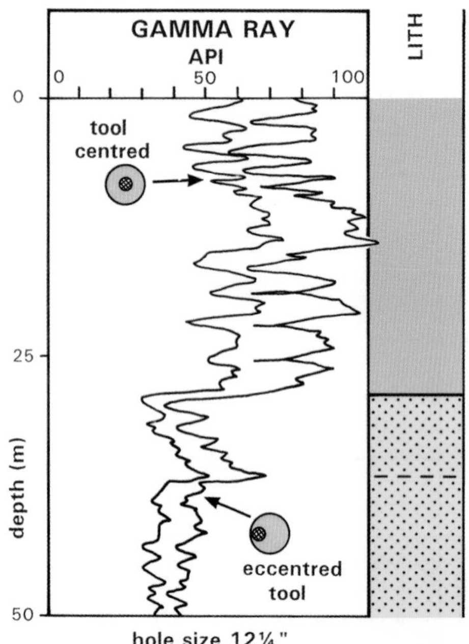

Figure 8.13 Comparison of a gamma ray log from a hole centred wireline tool (DLL-MSFL-GR logged at 10 m/min) and an eccentred tool (LDL-CNL-GR logged at 4 m/min). The eccentred tool shows higher values and greater sensitivity.

LWD gamma ray

For the LWD tools, the depth of investigation will be similar to the wireline tool but the vertical resolution will depend on the drilling rate, the while drilling tool sampling 30 cm (1 ft) in 1 minute as opposed to 30 cm in 1 second for the wireline tool. Theoretically, therefore, the LWD gamma ray can have a better vertical resolution than the wireline. However, the LWD gamma ray log is processed (smoothed) to resemble the wireline log (Coope 1983) so that the vertical resolution after processing is similar, namely 45 cm (18″).

Spectral gamma ray

Although the spectral gamma ray tools are run more slowly than the simple tools, and process a greater number of counts, their resolution is limited by detector size and is probably around 50 cm (20″). Schlumberger, in collaboration with ODP staff, have developed a spectral tool with 4, smaller sized, 5 × 10 cm (2″ × 4″), independent detectors (the Multi-sensor Gamma ray Tool, MGT) which gives 3–4 times better resolution than a tool with a 30.5 × 4.5 cm (12″ × 1.75″), detector

Table 8.5 Unwanted environmental effects - gamma ray logs.

Factor	Effect on log	Remedy
Simple Tool		
Caving	lowers values, bigger the cave, lower the value	corrected for if minor to moderate
Barite in mud	lowers values especially in thick mudcake	corrected for
KCl in mud	significant increase in 'background'	corrected for
Spectral tool		
Caving	lowers value in caves, If tool eccentred reduced effect	corrected for
Barite in mud	increase in calculated thorium and uranium	corrected for
KCl in mud	increase in calculated potassium (and uranium)	corrected for
LWD tools		
Steel casing	reduces counts	
	attenuates uranium and thorium more than potassium	included in processing routine
Barite in mud	reduces counts	
KCl in mud	increase in calculated potassium (and uranium)	corrected for

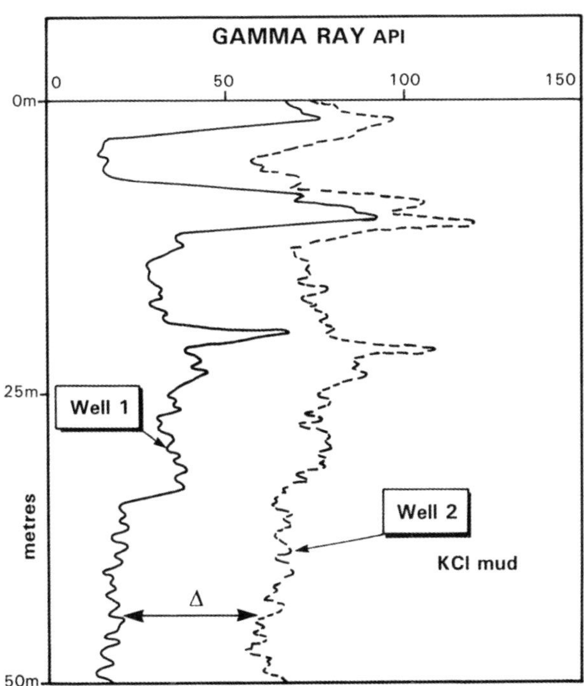

Figure 8.14 The effect of KCl in the drilling mud on gamma ray values. Well I, with ordinary mud, well 2 with KCl mud. The formation values should be the same. Δ is the difference created by the KCl content. The wells are 3 km apart.

(Goldberg *et al.* 2001). The vertical resolution achieved is around 10 cm (4"), but the tool is seldom run by the oil industry.

Unwanted borehole effects

Simple wireline gamma ray

The simple gamma ray log is relatively unaffected by small-scale borehole irregularities, but it is affected by large caves (**Table 8.5**). The effect is due to the increased volume of drilling mud between the formation and the gamma ray detector, which causes increased Compton scattering and a consequent diminution in the log value, as described previously. Most logging companies publish charts to correct for borehole size for various mud weights. These do however assume fairly simple situations: tool perfectly centred or completely eccentred in a perfectly circular hole.

A quite different effect is caused by the use of the radioactive mud additive KCl. The potassium radioactivity of the KCl is detected by the gamma ray tool and the usual result is a marked increase in the absolute values (**Figure 8.14**). It is sometimes proposed that this is simply a 'base line shift', because the mud volume through the hole is relatively constant and there will only be a constant increase in the background, implying that relative amplitude changes will remain unaffected. This is not the case, especially when there is invasion and KCl-rich mud enters into the formation and the mudcake. Such a situation will cause an invaded reservoir to show too high a gamma ray reading (*see also* the spectral log below). LWD readings may precede invasion and so circumvent the problem.

LWD gamma ray

The gamma ray scintillator sensor in an LWD tool, as described, is housed behind the thick steel of a drill-collar. Steel absorbs the higher energy uranium and thorium radiations more effectively than lower energy potassium radiations. That is, steel spectrally filters radiation energies. The LWD tools are, by inference, calibrated to the API pit where the 'average shale' reads 100 API units (6 ppm U, 12 ppm Th, 2.0%K).

This means that although the 'average shale' will read the same on LWD and wireline logs (100 API), because of the spectral filtering of the steel, formations with high uranium and thorium content will read lower on the LWD logs than the wireline (Coope and Hendricks 1984). This is the case with the uranium (organic) rich Kimmeridge Formation of the North Sea shown in the example (**Figure 8.15**) (Kirkton 1993). The converse is

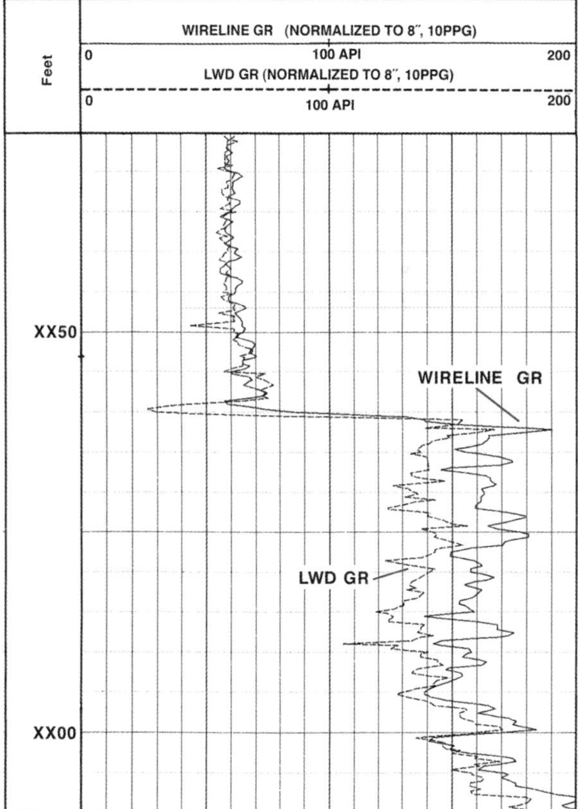

Figure 8.15 The comparison of an LWD gamma ray to a wireline gamma ray through a uranium rich shale, the Kimmeridgian of the North Sea. The LWD log reads less than the wireline because the steel of the LWD tool selectively filters the high energy, uranium radiations (from Meisner *et al.* SPWLA 1985).

also true, that formations with a high potassium content will read higher on the LWD than on the wireline logs.

Spectral gamma ray

The spectral gamma ray tool is run held near the borehole wall by a bow-spring to reduce the borehole effects that occur when a tool is centred. However, this does not eliminate mud effects entirely and the spectral log is affected by the mud additives barite and KC1 (**Table 8.5**). The effects vary depending on tool design (Company), and the algorithms used to derive abundances. If only the three energy windows around the high energy gamma ray emission peaks are used, as with the pre-1990 tools, barite does not affect the result, while KCl will only affect the potassium result and can be corrected for. But when the low energy part of the gamma ray spectrum is used, the barite effect on the low energy radiations causes an increase in thorium and decrease in uranium. KCl causes an increase in the potassium (as to be expected) but also a decrease in the uranium. Modern tools reading the 256 channel gamma ray energy spectrum can be processed without the lower energy counts and this eliminates the effects of barite.

8.5 Geochemical behaviour of potassium, thorium and uranium and natural radioactivity

The old tenet that the gamma ray log is a 'shale log' was based on its use as a black box, not understanding what was inside. In modern interpretation, an understanding of the mineralogy and geochemistry leading to radiation is taken into account. For this reason, the natural occurrences of the radioactive minerals and their geological significance are described below.

Potassium

Potassium is both chemically active and volumetrically common in naturally occurring rocks. Because of its chemical activity it is generally chemically combined. In the clay minerals, for example, it (and invariably its radioactive isotope) occurs in the clay silicate structure. In rock-forming minerals such as the feldspars, it is also chemically combined in the silicate structure, while in the evaporites potassium occurs chemically as a salt. The behaviour of potassium can therefore be considered in terms of chemical composition, as can its contribution to radioactivity.

Table 8.6 Potassium in clay minerals: chemical content. From Serra (1979); Dresser Atlas (1983).

	†Potassium content		
Mineral	% by weight	Average %	Construction
Illite	3.51–8.31	5.20	K, Al, Silicate
Glauconite	3.20–5.80	4.50	K, Mg, Fe, Al, Silicate
Kaolinite	0.00–1.49	0.63	Al, Silicate
Smectite	0.00–0.60	0.22	Ca, Na, Mg, Al Silicate
Chlorite	0	0	Mg, Fe, Al Silicate

†Average shale = 2% potassium

Table 8.7 Potassium content of evaporites.

Species	Formula %	Potassium by weight*	Typical gamma ray value API†
Sylvite	KCl	52.5	500
Carnallite	$KCl. MgCl_2(H_2O)_6$	14.1	200
Polyhalite	$K_2SO_{4.}MgSO_{4.}$	12.9	190

*Serra *et al.* 1980
†Serra 1979.

The potassium content of the various clay mineral species varies considerably. Illites (which are micas) contain by far the greatest amount, while smectite and kaolinite have little or none (**Table 8.6**). The consequence of this is that clay mixtures with a high kaolinite or high smectite content will have lower potassium radioactivity than clays made up essentially of illite (mica) (**Figure 8.1**). However, since most clays are mixtures of several clay minerals, the differences discussed above are muted. The average shale is considered to have a potassium content of 2% (**Table 8.6**).

Potassium is present in many rock-forming minerals besides the micas, considered above as clay minerals. The most important of these are the feldspars. Microcline contains approximately 16% potassium by weight, and orthoclase approximately 14%: such percentages render the feldspars highly radioactive in geological terms *(see* **Table 8.12**). Feldspathic sediments may therefore be detected by their radioactivity.

Finally, potassium is found in some of the less commonly occurring evaporites but in sufficient quantities to have an important effect on the radioactivity (**Table 8.7**). In these salts there is between 10% and 50% potassium by weight. When it is considered that the average shale contains only 2% potassium, the very strong radioactivity of these potassium evaporites is understandable (**Table 8.7, Figure 8.30**).

Uranium

Acid igneous rocks, on average, contain 4.65 ppm of uranium and are the principal original source for the element. It forms soluble salts, especially in the uranyle form (U^{6+}), being stable in oxidising conditions. As the oxide UO_2^{2+} (the uranyle ion) it is transported in river water (the uranous form U^{4+} also exists and is stable in reducing conditions, but is less common), which contains on average 0.6 µg/ml of uranium in solution. However, it is suggested that most uranium (around 90%) in rivers is actually carried attached (loosely?) to clay particles and not in solution (Durrance 1986). This is suggested

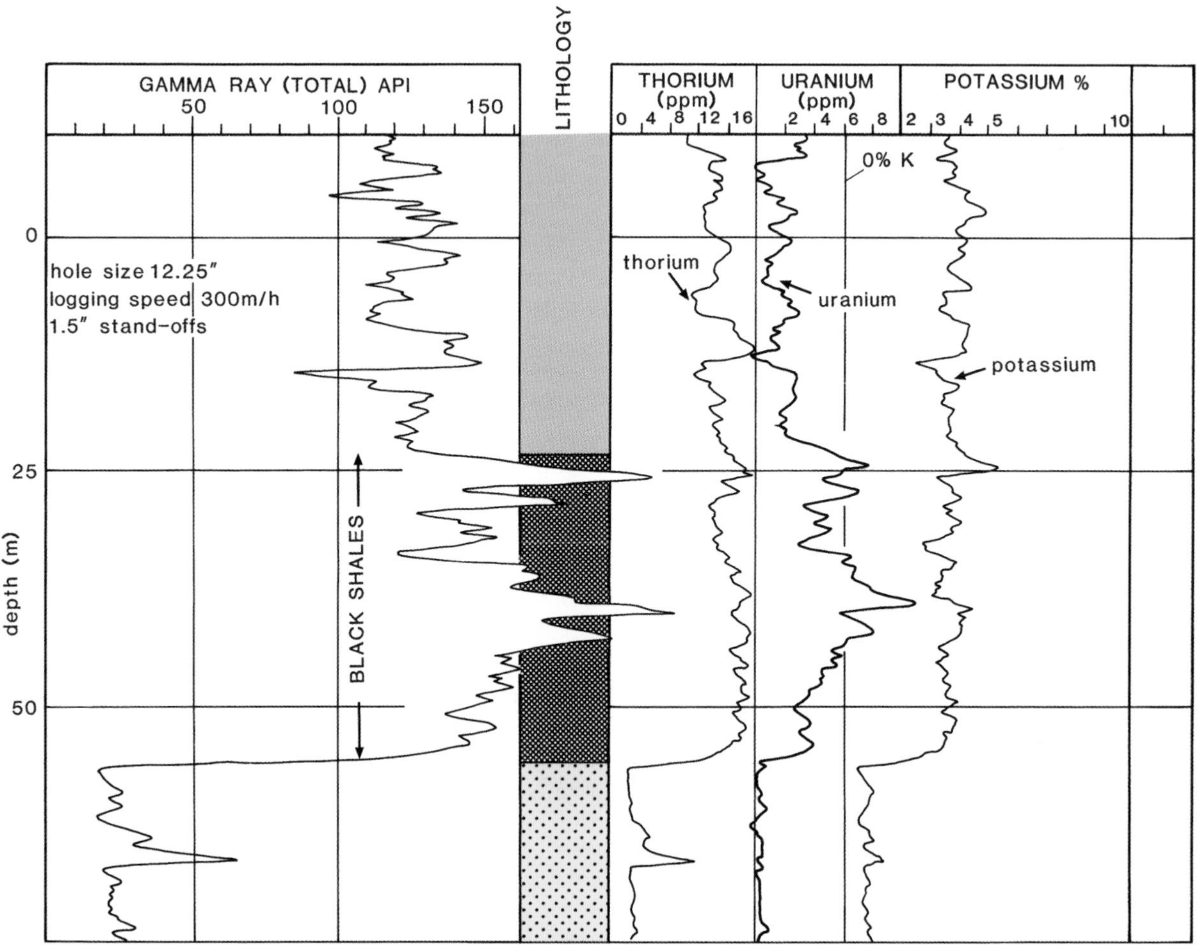

Figure 8.16 'Black shale' radioactivity. A spectral gamma ray log over the Upper Jurassic, Kimmeridgian black shales of the North Sea showing the high uranium contribution.

Table 8.8 The abundance of the radioactive elements and their relative contributions to the overall radioactivity of the 'typical shale' of Figure 8.18 and the black shale example of Figure 8.16 (values calculated for the peak at 40 m). Note the large contribution of Thorium and the variable uranium contribution.

Element	Content	gamma ray API equivalent	% gamma ray value
'TYPICAL' SHALE (Figure 8.18 average)			
Uranium	1.8 ppm	14.6	14.8%
Thorium	12.3 ppm	48.3	48.9%
Potassium	2.2%	35.9	36.3%
		98.8	100%
BLACK SHALE (Figure 8.16 peak at 40 m)			
Uranium	11.0 ppm	89.0	41.0%
Thorium	18.0 ppm	70.7	32.6%
Potassium	3.5%	57.1	26.4%
		216.8	100%

because suspended river sediment contains approximately 3 ppm of uranium, while the bedload sediments have much lower values. Sea water, on average, contains about 3 ppb (parts per billion) of dissolved uranium and acts as a reservoir from which the element is extracted.

There are three principal ways in which uranium is taken from sea water and passed into sediments (Serra 1979): 1, chemical precipitation in acid (pH 2.5–4.0), reducing (rH 0–0.4) environments; 2, adsorption by organic matter, or living plants and animals; 3, chemical reaction in phosphorites (phosphate rich rocks).

The extremely acid, reducing conditions required for the direct chemical precipitation of uranium (pH 2.5–4.0, rH 0–0.4) are found in few natural environments. They do occur, however, in stagnant, anoxic waters with a relatively slow rate of sediment deposition, which typically produce black shales (Adams and Weaver 1958). The high gamma radiation values of typical 'hot shales' such as the North Sea Upper Jurassic or the North African Silurian, both typical black shales, come from a high uranium content, some of which was probably chemically precipitated (**Figure 8.16**, **Table 8.8**) (Bjørlykke *et al.* 1975; Lüning *et al.* 2005).

Probably a more common way of introducing uranium into sediments is in association with organic matter. It has been established experimentally that carbonaceous material can extract uranium from solution

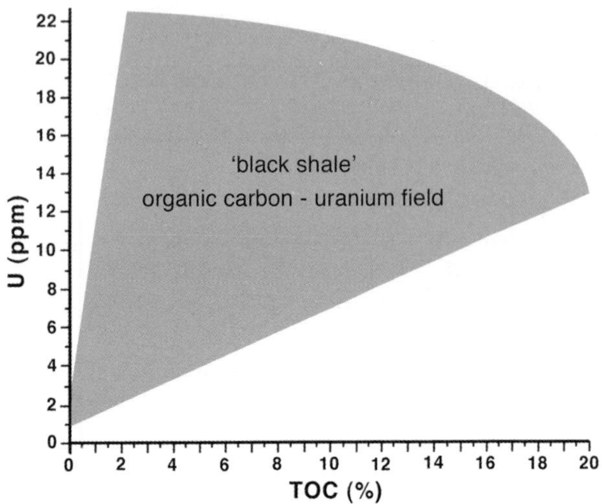

Figure 8.17 Widespread variation in the richness of the uranium content of 'black shales'; some are uranium rich, others are not. The shaded area includes data provided by shales from the following areas: Frasnian, Algeria: L. Jurassic, Germany: L. Jurassic, France: L. Jurassic, U.K.: L. Jurassic U.K.: Cenomanian, USA: Cenomanian, Morocco: Coniacian, offshore Ivory Coast: U. Miocene, Mediterranean: Cenomanian, Atlantic: U. Carboniferous, U.K. (for details see Lüning & Kolonic 2003).

Table 8.9 Average weight (%) of organic matter in sediments (from Shaw 1980).

Sediment	Average weight %
Shales	2.90
Carbonates	0.29
Sandstones	0.05

very efficiently, especially over the range of pH 3.5–6.0 (acidic) (Durrance 1986). Organic-rich shales often (but not always) contain large amounts of syn-genetic uranium (i.e. extracted locally), in which case they are associated with high gamma ray log values (e.g. Schmoker and Hester 1983) (**Figures 8.1**, **8.31**). It is the large size and high charge density of the uranyle ion which allows this, and it is thought that the process eventually involves an ionic bonding. The urano-organic complexes produced may form coatings on organic or inorganic particles or be disseminated through the sediment mass. However, the exact relationship between organic matter and total uranium content is not easy to establish since high organic matter content is not always related to high uranium content (Meyer and Nederlof 1984; Lüning and Kolonic 2003) (**Figure 8.17**). Empirically, the presence of organic matter in shales (**Table 8.9**) suggests that uranium adsorbed by organic matter is a common, though variable, contributor to overall shale radioactivity (*see* Section 8.6).

The third way of introducing uranium into sediments principally concerns phosphates and associated deposits. The uranium present in phosphatic rocks is generally syn-genetic and is found within the phosphates. Primary uranium minerals are absent. The very variable valence behaviour of uranium means, that under the right conditions, it forms complex ions with carbonate, phosphate, hydroxide and others, and it is assumed that U^{4+} substitutes for calcium in the carbonate-fluorapatite generally found in marine phosphorites (Durrance 1986). The correct chemical conditions for this type of reaction may be very localised, such as exist in hardgrounds, as is discussed below (Section 8.8, Radioactivity in carbonates).

In general, uranium behaves as an independent constituent: it is not chemically combined in the principal clay minerals like potassium, but is loosely associated with secondary components such as organic matter. For this reason it has a very irregular distribution in sediments. Moreover, its continued solubility in the subsurface, which is a function of its loose attachments, renders it susceptible to leaching and re-deposition, making its distribution even more unpredictable.

Typically, on the logs, uranium is shown by irregular, high peaks corresponding to its uneven distribution. Due to the unusual requirements of its original deposition, these peaks are associated with unusual environments, such as are found in condensed sequences or unconformities.

Thorium

Like uranium, thorium has its origin principally in acid and intermediate igneous rocks. However, it is extremely stable and, unlike uranium, will not go into solution. For this reason it is found in bauxites (residual soils). Although there is a possibility that thorium is adsorbed onto clay minerals (Durrance 1986), it is generally transported to sites of sediment deposition as clay fraction detrital grains. These are of heavy minerals such as zircon, thorite, monazite, epidote and sphene (**Table 8.10**), which are all very stable and insoluble.

Because of its detrital nature and its transport by water in the clay-grain sized fraction, thorium shows an affinity for terrestrial sediments and minerals. For example, it shows higher concentrations in kaolinites (of terrestrial origin) than in glauconites (of marine origin) (Hassan *et al.* 1976; **Figure 8.1**, **Table 8.11**). In the coarse- grained

Table 8.10 Thorium-bearing heavy minerals (Serra *et al.* 1980; Bhuyan and Passey 1994).

	Composition	ThO_2 content (ppm)
Monazite	Ce, Y, La, PO_4	40,000–120,000
Thorite	Th, Si, O_4	250,000–630,000
Zircon	Zr, Si, O_4	10,000
	Uranium (ppm)	**Thorium (ppm)**
Apatite	50–150	2–150
Epidote	20–50	50–560
Sphene	100–700	100–600
Zircon	300–3000	100–2500

Table 8.11 Thorium abundance in clay minerals (from Hassan *et al.* 1976; Dresser Atlas 1983)

Mineral	Thorium ppm (approximate average)	
Bauxite	8–132 (42)	More continental
Kaolinite	18–26	↑
Illite-muscovite	6–22	
Smectite	10–24	↓
Glauconite	2–8	More marine

sediments, thorium minerals may be found as silt-sized heavy mineral concentrations or placer deposits (see 'sandstone radioactivity' below).

Despite its lack of solubility, or probably because of it, thorium is widely and relatively evenly distributed in sediments. So much so that in shales it is used as a base level from which the relative abundance of the other radioactive elements, especially uranium, is measured (Section 8.10).

8.6 Radioactivity of shales and clays

Some definitions

Before discussing the nature of clays and shales, it is necessary to define some terms.

Clay has two meanings. By size it is a detrital particle below 4 μ (microns). By mineralogy, it is a hydrous aluminium silicate, in other words, a clay mineral, such as kaolinite, smectite or illite. Clays (by size) are composed of a percentage of clay minerals.

Shale is a fine-grained detrital sedimentary rock formed by the compaction of clay (by size and mineralogy), silt or mud. Shales are often laminated. They are not as indurated (compacted) as slates. Shales are composed mainly of clay to silt sized particles (below 63 μ). Clay minerals comprise most of the clay sized fraction, but these typically make up only 50% – 70% of the rock, the remaining particles being mainly quartz. The clay mineral components of a shale are the target of the log derived V_{sh} used for petrophysical calculations, as explained below (Section 8.7).

V_{sh} and V_{cly} are often used interchangeably. This is not useful. In order to be more rigorous, this book uses V_{sh} to indicate rock volume and V_{cly} to indicate the volume of clay minerals.

Clay minerals and radioactivity

In petroleum borehole logging, the commonest natural radioactivity (by volume) is found in shales (the rock) and clays (by size). A high gamma ray value frequently means shale. A typical shale analysed by a spectral gamma ray tool shows that each of the three elements, U, Th and K, is contributing (**Figure 8.18**), and an analysis of shales in general shows the relative contribution of each element to the overall radioactivity (**Table 8.8**). The 'average shale' of the API pits has 6.5 ppm U, 12 ppm Th and 2% K.

But the gamma ray log should not be used as a 'black box' shale indicator either qualitatively or quantitatively, as is commonly the case. The behaviour of the individual radioactive elements in clay minerals and shales in general is so different, as the preceding geochemical descriptions indicate, that there is a need for more understanding.

Potassium is involved in the chemical make-up of clay mineral structure and, despite the variations of this in specific clay mineral species (**Table 8.6**), has a fairly consistent content in most shales of around 2%. This is the case since shales are generally a mix of several of the clay mineral types. Potassium, therefore, is a moderately good 'shale indicator'. However, potassium also occurs in detrital minerals such as feldspars and micas as well as the clay minerals (**Table 8.12**), so that in sand-shale mixtures, potassium may occur in both the shales and the sands and cannot be used alone as a shale indicator and descriptor (see Section 8.9) (**Figure 8.25**).

Uranium distribution is very irregular, as has been shown, because its affinity is to secondary components and not to the main rock forming clay minerals. Thus, in the average shale, it may contribute only 10% – 30% of the total radioactivity but in certain cases this can increase dramatically (**Table 8.8**, **Figure 8.41**). Since its distribution is not related to clay mineral volume, uranium is a poor 'shale indicator'. This is the reason

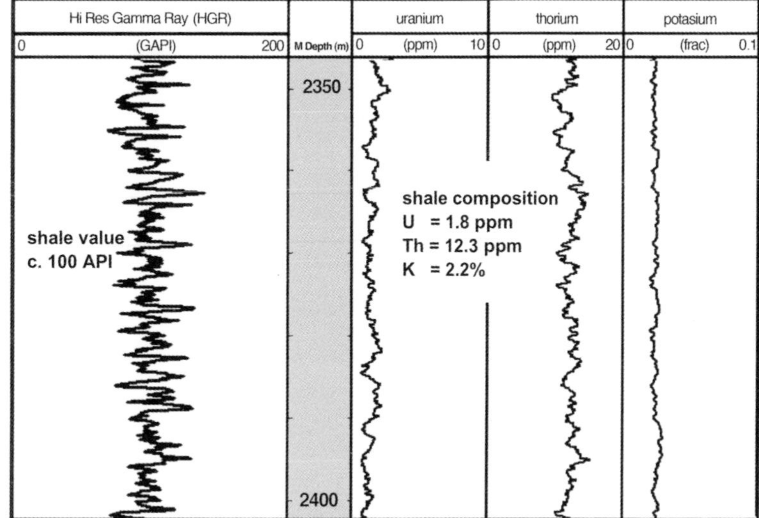

Figure 8.18 A typical shale interval analysed by a spectral gamma ray tool. The log shows the individual contributions of thorium, potassium and uranium to the overall shale radioactivity, which is expressed in API units. The accepted 'average shale' has a value of 100 API contributed by U = 6.5 ppm, Th = 12 ppm, K = 2% (see text). The shale in this example has less uranium than the average.

Table 8.12 Potassium content of some common detrital materials (from Serra 1979; Edmundson *et al.* 1979; Dresser Atlas 1983; Schlumberger 1985).

	Mineral species	% potassium by weight	Average %	Gamma ray value (API)
Micas	Glauconite*	3.2–5.8	4.5	75†–90†
	Muscovite	7.9–9.8	9.8	140†–270
	Biotite	6.2–10.1	8.7	90†–275
Feldspars	Microcline	10.9–16.0	16.0	220–280†
	Orthoclase	11.8–14.0	14.0	220–280†

*Detrital or authigenic
†For 8" hole, 1.2 g/cm$_3$ mud, 3⅝" NaI scintillator

for plotting the CGR, the curve without the uranium content, on spectral gamma ray logs; it gives a better shale volume estimate (section 8.4).

The behaviour of thorium in shales is not fully understood. Experience shows that despite its varying content in clay mineral species (**Table 8.11**), it has a constant value in almost all naturally occurring shales. The average value is about 12.0 ppm (range 8–18 ppm) for a typical shale, contributing between 40%–50% of the overall radioactivity (**Table 8.8**). This common occurrence of thorium in shales may be related to its insolubility which allows it to be recycled many times in sedimentary systems. Considering its constant average value and the high percentage contribution to the overall radioactivity, thorium is a very good 'shale indicator'. In mixtures of sand and shale, or carbonate and shale, thorium will occur essentially in the shale fraction (except in rare instances).

To summarise: as shale indicators, thorium may be used in most cases, potassium in many cases, but uranium should not be used at all. This obviously has implications for the simple gamma ray log: it is not necessarily a good 'shale indicator'.

8.7 Quantitative use of the simple gamma ray log

Shale volume

The gamma ray log can be used quantitatively to derive shale volume because even though the gamma ray value for shales varies enormously, in any one area or well, or zone of a well, the values for pure shale can often be constant (**Figure 8.19**). Thus, if one considers the maximum average gamma ray log value to be pure, 100% shale (i.e. shale line, **Figure 8.19**), and the lowest value to indicate no shale at all, 0% (i.e. sand line, **Figure 8.19**), a scale from 0–100% shale can be constructed. If the scale is considered to be linear, any value (GR) of the gamma ray log will give the volume of shale from the simple calculation

$$\text{volume of shale } (V_{sh})\% = \frac{\text{GR (log) value} - \text{GR (min)}}{\text{GR (max)} - \text{GR (min)}} \quad (1)$$

GR (max) = 100% shale (shale line)
GR (min) = 0% shale, i.e. clean formation (sand line, clean limestone line).
GR (log) = gamma ray log value of interest.

This value is sometimes called the gamma ray index (GRI) (Bhuyan and Passey 1994). Generally, the value is not very accurate and tends to over-estimate the volume of shale (V_{sh}) (Adeyemo *et al.* 2005) and hence clay minerals. Moreover, there is no scientific basis for assuming that the relationship between gamma ray value and shale volume should be linear. A modification of the simple linear relationship used above has been proposed as a result of empirical correlation (Dresser Atlas 1982). The relationship changes between younger (unconsolidated) rocks and older (consolidated) rocks (**Figure 8.20**):

for pre-Tertiary (consolidated) rocks,

$$V_{sh} = 0.33(2^{\,2V_{sh}} - 1) \quad (2)$$

for Tertiary (unconsolidated) rocks,

$$V_{sh} = 0.083(2^{\,3.7V_{sh}} - 1) \quad (3)$$

where V_{sh} = shale volume from these formulae (**Figure 8.20**).

Another way to treat the gamma ray V_{sh} or gamma ray index (GRI) is to use the knowledge that shales only consist of about 60% clay minerals (range 50%–70%). It is the clay minerals that are the object of the V_{sh} calculation because they affect resistivity responses (Section 8.2). The figure (**Figure 8.21**) shows a comparison between the actual weight % clay in a formation from analysis and the gamma ray index from equation 1. The GRI is far too large but the clay60 curve, that is 60% of the gamma index response (i.e. GRI × 0.6), is much closer to reality (Bhuyan and Passey 1994). The clay60 relationship produces a much more reasonable clay mineral volume from gamma ray readings (i.e. V_{cly}).

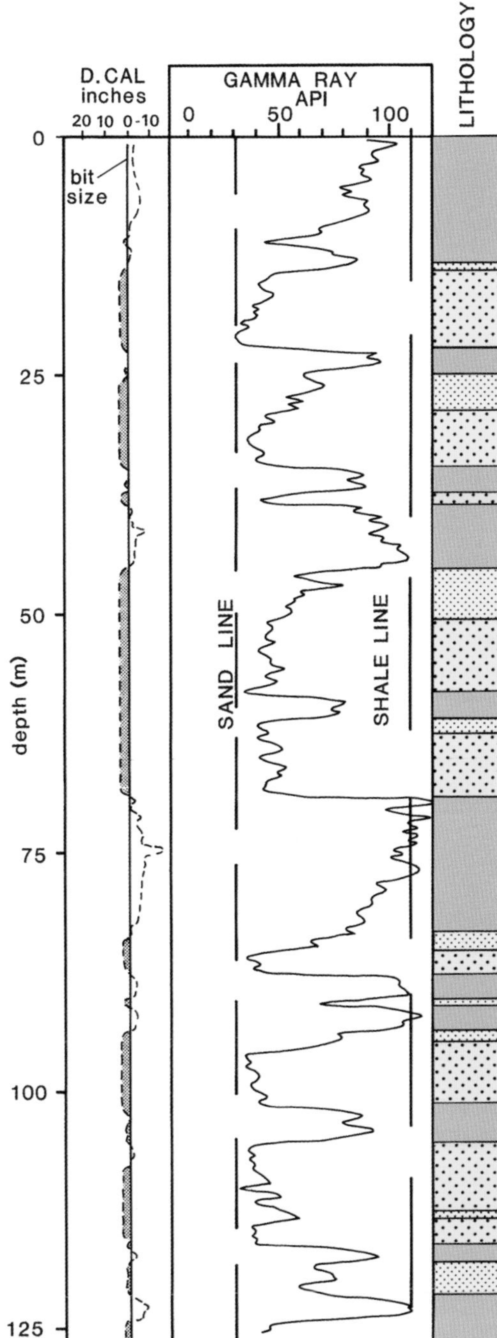

Figure 8.19 Sand line and shale line defined on a gamma ray log. These 'baselines' are for the quantitative use of the log, and may be reasonably constant in any one zone.

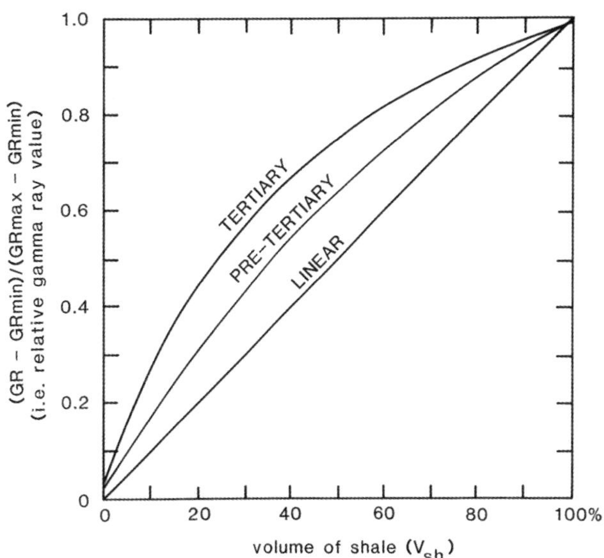

Figure 8.20 Graphical representation of the relationship between relative gamma ray deflection and shale volume (from Dresser Atlas 1982).

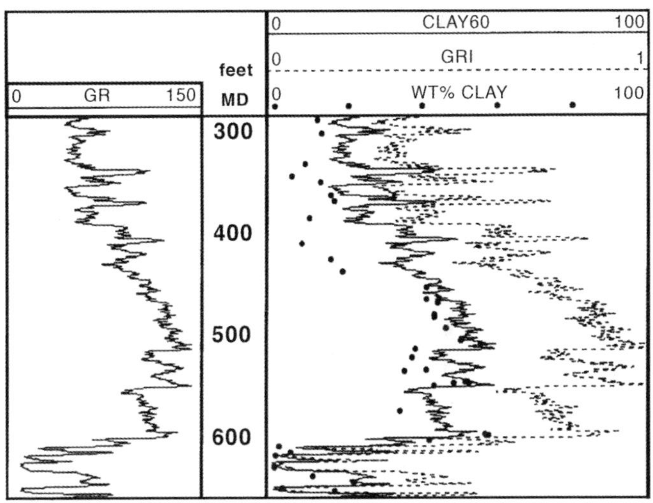

Figure 8.21 Plot showing the closer correspondence between actual clay (clay mineral) content from core (WT% clay) and the gamma ray at 60% (clay60), rather than the raw gamma ray (GRI) (from Bhuyan and Passey SPWLA 1994).

8.8 Qualitative use of the simple gamma ray log

Lithology

As a first indicator of lithology, the gamma ray log is extremely useful as it suggests where shale may be expected (**Figure 8.1**). Moreover, as shown above, frequently the higher the gamma ray value, the higher the percentage of shale (**Figure 8.20**). But the log is only a first indication. The radioactivity of some typical lithologies other than shale is now considered. This shows that any lithology indicated by the simple gamma ray log must be confirmed by other logs or by other means. There are many unexpected results.

Radioactivity of sandstones and other arenaceous rocks

Quartz, the principal component of the coarse-grained detrital rocks, shows no radioactivity. Sandstones, consequently, usually show low gamma ray values (**Figure 8.1**). However, associated detrital minerals are

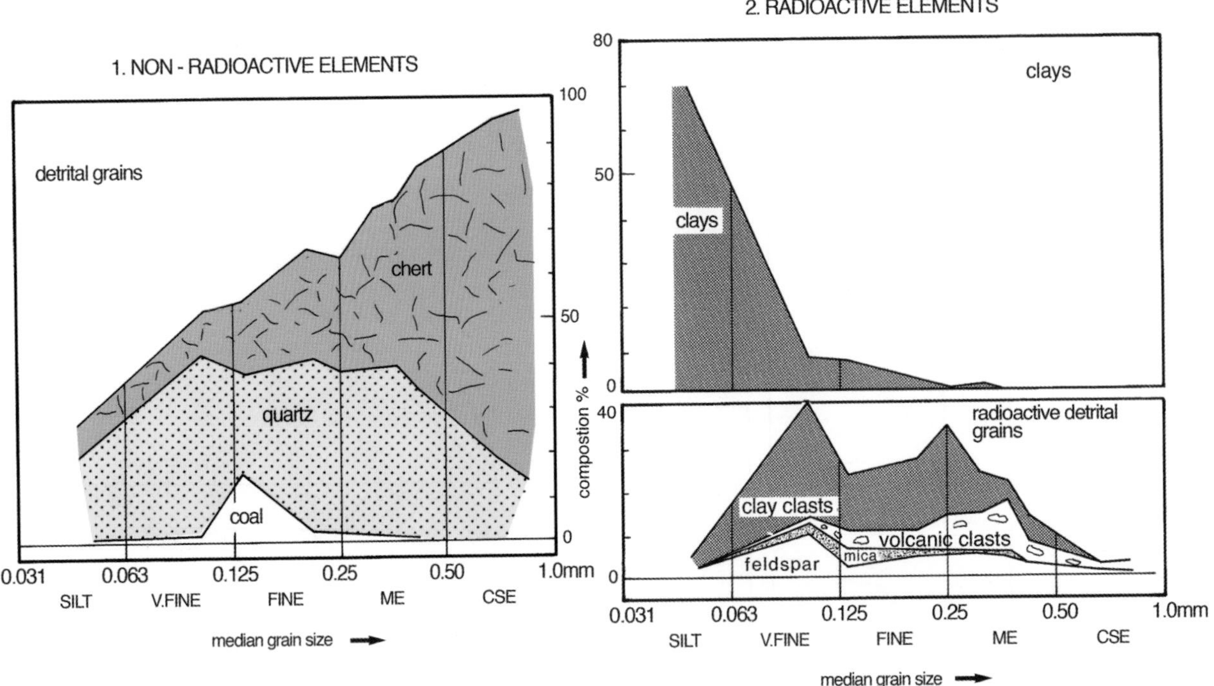

Figure 8.22 Radioactive elements in detrital rocks. Typical sandstone composition shown against grain size for the Reindeer Formation, Mackenzie Delta, Beaufort Sea. Radioactive elements vary with grain size. It is a deltaic sand of Lower Tertiary age (re-drawn from Nentwich and Yole 1982).

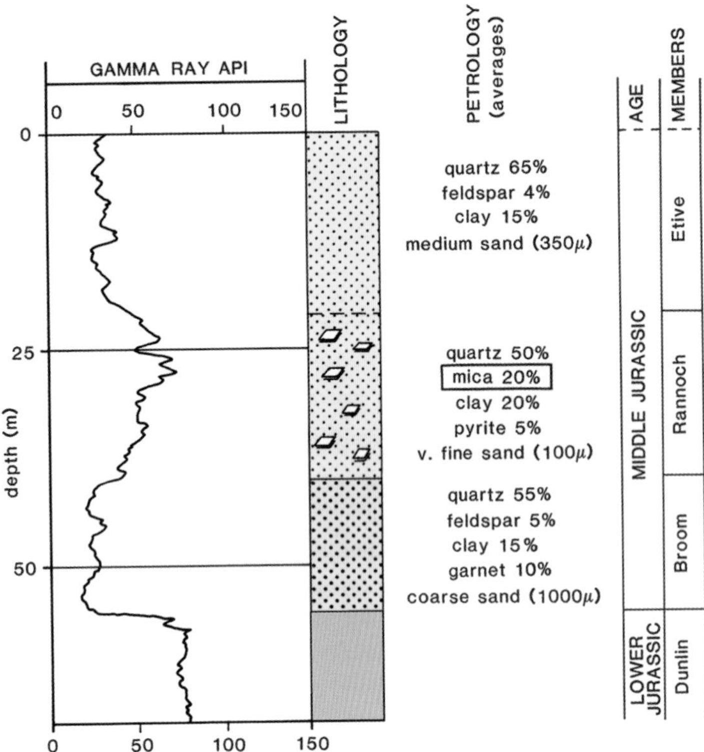

Figure 8.23 Radioactive sand, the 'mica sands' of the North Sea Jurassic. They are fine-grained shallow marine sandstones with perhaps 20% clay but 15–30% mica, mainly muscovite, which causes the radioactivity.

radioactive. The most common of these are feldspars, micas, heavy minerals and lithic fragments (**Figure 8.22**). The first two groups contain potassium (**Table 8.13**), the third thorium (**Table 8.10**) and the last contains shale. These all cause sandstones with high to moderate gamma ray values.

There are many examples of radioactive sandstones that may be quoted. The fine-grained mica sands of the North Sea (Nyberg *et al.* 1978) are a typical, well-known example (**Figure 8.23**). Marine sands often contain glauconite and, if the concentrations are sufficiently high, render them radioactive (**Figure 8.24**). A spectacular example is shown by a granite wash which forms a reservoir but contains abundant granite pebbles and feldspars (**Figure 8.34**). Another example shows a sandstone reservoir containing gas (**Figure 8.25**). The interval could be mistaken for shale, but contains clean sandstones with radioactive minerals (feldspars and heavy minerals) and is clearly saturated with hydrocarbons over the upper interval, as indicated by the resistivity logs and the neutron-density combination. In fact, radioactive sandstones are far more common than realised. Arkoses (>10% feldspar) are radioactive by definition.

Table 8.13 Radioactivity in sandstones.

Species	Mineral	Radioactive element
Mica sand	Muscovite/biotite	^{40}K
Glauconite sand	Glauconite	^{40}K
Arkose	Postassic feldspar	^{40}K
Placer silt	Heavy minerals	Th

Thorium, as previously described, is present in heavy mineral suites. Placer silts (concentrations of heavy minerals) are frequently radioactive, often producing a spiky aspect to the gamma ray log (**Figure 8.26**). However, this is the only case and, in general, detrital grain radioactivity is caused by potassium (**Table 8.13**).

For sandstone reservoir studies, identifying clay as opposed to non-clay radioactive elements, is important. Neglecting radioactive sandstone intervals and interpreting them as being shales means missing essential pay (**Figure 8.25**).

The fact that most detrital mineral radioactivity in sandstones is caused by potassium-rich minerals (**Tables 8.12, 8.13**) is used in the interpretation of the spectral gamma ray log and allows shale radioactivity to be separated from detrital grain radioactivity (*see* Quantitative uses of the spectral gamma ray).

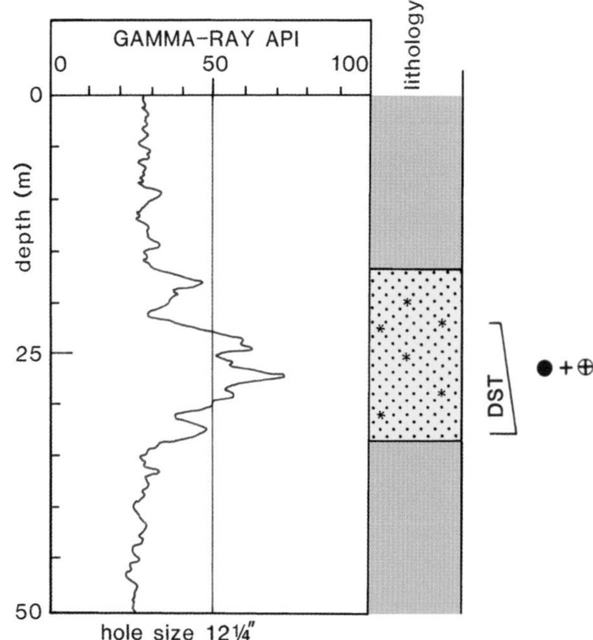

Figure 8.24 Glauconite causing radioactivity in a sandstone interval. Silty shales envelop this marine, glauconite-rich sand giving the sands higher gamma ray log values than the shales. An oil flow confirms the reservoir characteristics. DST = Drill Stem Test. *Glauconite.

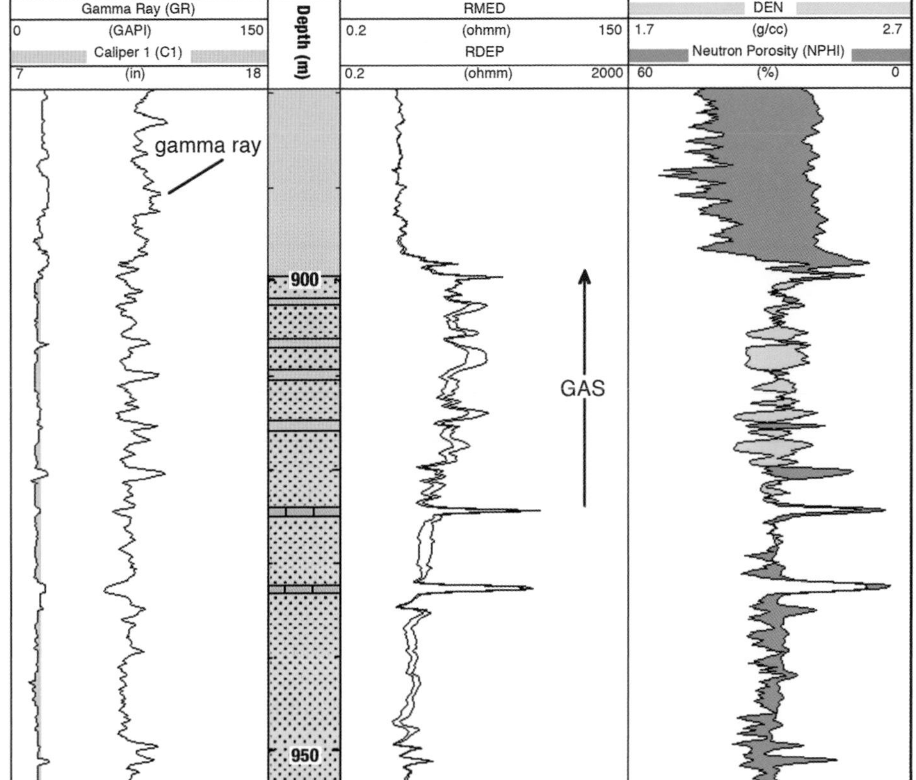

Figure 8.25 High gamma ray values caused by radioactive minerals (feldspars and heavy minerals) in a reservoir zone. Using the gamma ray to interpret shale volume, in this case, would eliminate the entire reservoir, even the interval containing gas. Note that the caliper indicates mudcake, despite the gamma ray.

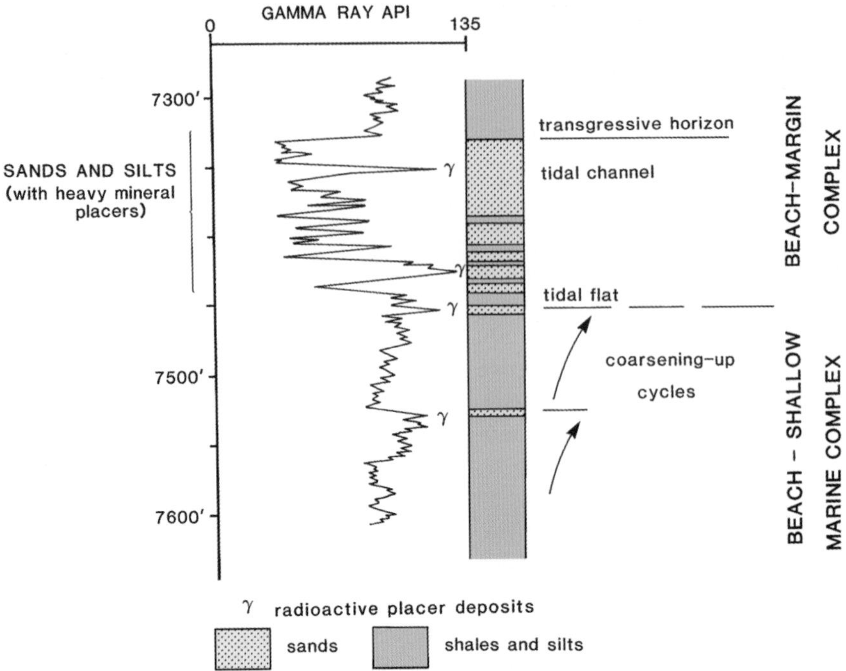

Figure 8.26 Heavy mineral concentrations (placer deposits) causing a spiky gamma ray log. Shales have lower gamma ray values than the heavy mineral deposits (Nigeria) (re-drawn from Serra 1974).

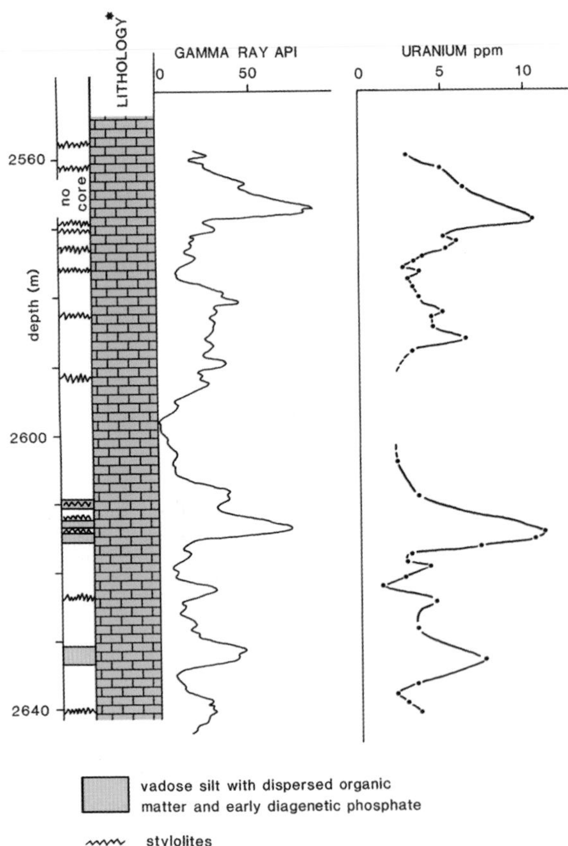

Figure 8.27 Radioactivity of Ypresian (Eocene) Limestones, Tunisia, related to uranium concentrations. The uranium is associated with early diagenesis, organic matter and phosphatic concentrations (re-drawn from Hassan 1973).

Radioactivity in carbonates

As a general rule, pure calcium carbonates are not radioactive and this aids in their identification (**Figure 8.1**). However, pure carbonates do show intervals of radioactivity, most frequently due to uranium. There seem to be three types of occurrence and cause.

The first is when organic matter is present. In the example shown (**Figure 8.27**), the organic matter is concentrated in stylolytes, but other occurrences of organic matter equally contain uranium (Hassan 1973). It is suggested, however, that uranium-rich organic matter does not occur in shallow water carbonates (Lüning and Kolonic 2003). A second occurrence is in thin surfaces that represent very slow deposition, or even erosion, and exposure such as palaeosols, karsts or sequence boundaries, but also maximum flooding surfaces (**Figure 8.28**). The form of uranium in these levels is not clear. Echinoid spines in maximum flooding surfaces have been quoted as being uranium rich (Raddadi *et al.* 2005), while palaeosols and karsts seem to contain uranium associated with phosphates (Ehrenberg and Svånå 2001).

A third and more difficult uranium occurrence is in association with dolomites and dolomitisation. The behaviour of uranium is partly controlled by the environment of deposition, as in the case with organic matter and palaeolsols, but also partly by subsequent mobilisation in the subsurface caused by its solubility. It is this solubility that makes the behaviour of uranium so variable in carbonates. It is even true that recent corals concentrate uranium while they are living but, by the time they are fossilised it is no longer there.

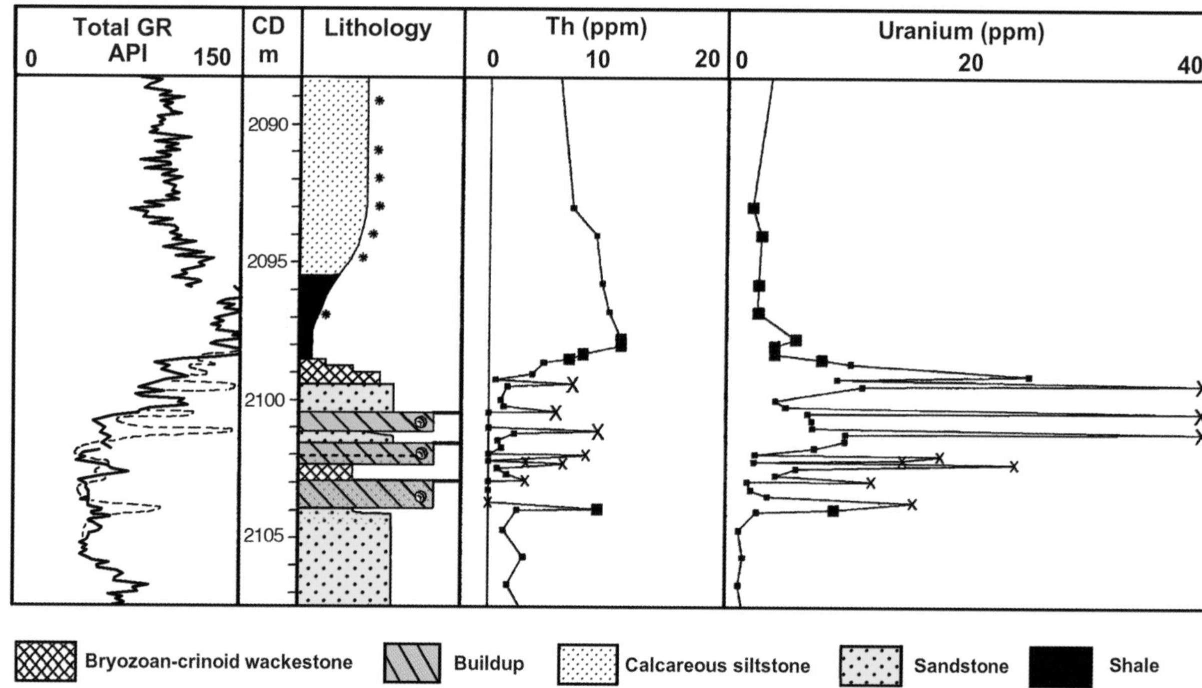

Figure 8.28 Bulk chemical analyses of uranium and thorium through Permian carbonates, showing high uranium values in palaeosols and exposure surfaces. Gamma ray: solid line = wireline, dashed line = core (modified from Ehrenberg & Svånå 2001). *AAPG © 2001 reprinted by permission of the AAPG whose permission is required for further use.*

Shaly carbonates or carbonate and shale mixtures have a radioactivity which is related, as expected, to clay mineral distribution. Thorium and potassium are the best indicators of these clays (Dull *et al.* 2006). Triassic, carbonate ramp deposits in Germany have been extensively researched (Aigner *et al.* 1995; Ruf *et al.* 2005). The frequent, shallowing-up cycles (from muddy to purer carbonate), of the deep and shallow ramp areas are well marked on the gamma ray logs (**Figure 8.29**). The logs in the example, because they are acquired at outcrop, can be confidently tied to the sedimentology and lithology. Other work has equally shown that it is the potassium and thorium content of the clays that are the cause of the radioactivity (Ehrenberg and Svånå 2001; Raddadi *et al.* 2005).

In summary, carbonate radioactivity is best measured with the spectral gamma ray tools because clay content is recognised by thorium and potassium radioactivity while uranium radioactivity is associated with either organic matter, karsts, palaeosols, sequence boundaries, maximum flooding surfaces or diagenesis and dolomitisation. However, workers familiar with carbonates indicate that very often there is no apparent relationship between the gamma ray and the carbonate facies (**Figure 17.32**) (Ruppel and Jones 2006).

Radioactivity in evaporites

The most common evaporites, such as salt and anhydrite, show abnormally low values on the gamma ray log. The occasional occurance of high radioactivity in

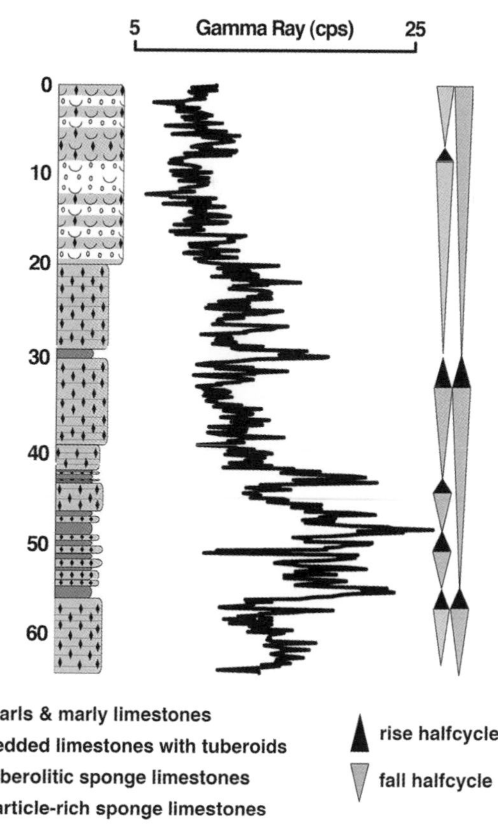

Figure 8.29 Outcrop gamma ray log showing shallowing-up (cleaning-up) carbonate/shale sequences in a ramp envrironment in the Upper Jurassic of Northern Germany (Pawellek & Aigner 2003).

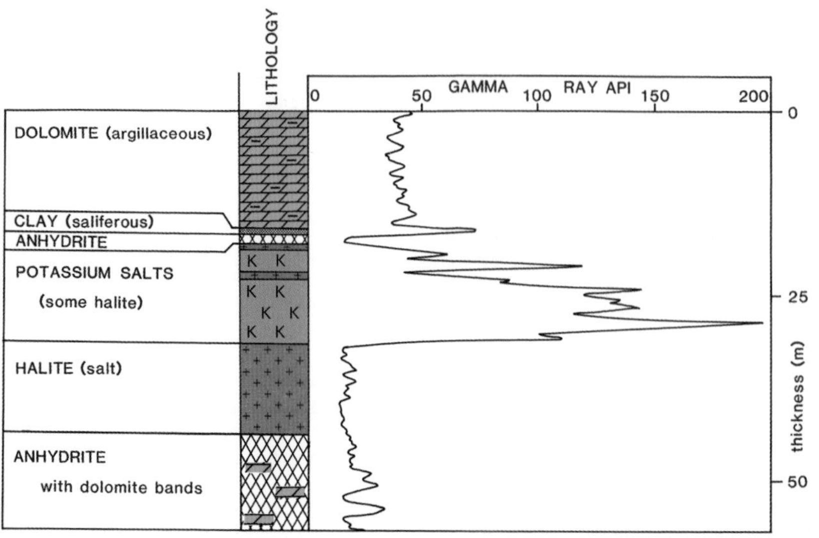

Figure 8.30 Potassium salts causing very high peaks of radioactivity in an evaporite sequence. (The lithology comes from an interpretation of combined logs and cuttings). Permian, North Sea.

evaporites is caused by potassium content, as has already been mentioned (**Table 8.7**). The log example shows a typical aspect of this evaporite radioactivity where there are frequently extreme contrasts between the potassium and non potassium-bearing zones (**Figure 8.30**). Volumetrically, potassium-rich evaporites are rare.

It is considered that, in logging potassium salts, the percentage of K_2O can be estimated from the gamma ray response. Thus, for a 6.25 inch, liquid-filled hole, a correlation of 12.6 API units per 1% K_2O was found (Edwards *et al.* 1967). Obviously, the logs must always be calibrated before making generalisations of this kind.

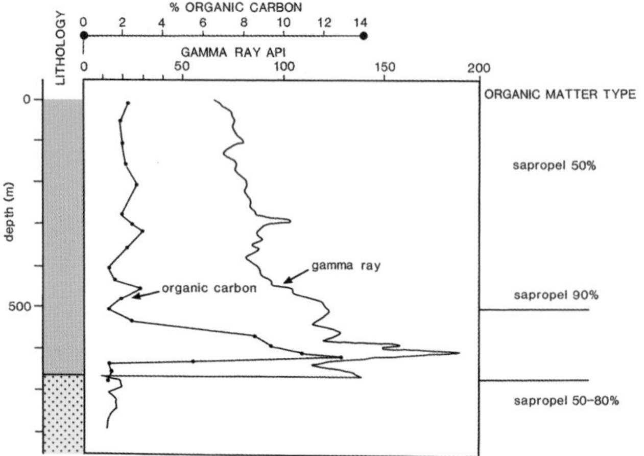

Figure 8.31 High organic carbon values and the total gamma ray giving good correlation, in this case due to uranium associated with organic matter.

Coal and organic rich shale (source rock) radioactivity

The relationship between organic matter and uranium enrichment is the basis for trying to identify organic rich shales (source-rocks) using the gamma ray log, and has been discussed (Section 8.5). In practice, although high gamma ray values often correspond to organic matter rich source-rock intervals (**Figure 8.31**), it is by no means certain (i.e. Schmoker 1981 and Section 8.10 below). The relationship is variable (**Figure 8.17**).

Coals have low gamma ray values (**Figures 8.1**, **8.32**). The contrast in this response between pure coal and organic shale is remarkable, especially when, in typical cyclic deltaic sequences, a low gamma ray coal is immediately overlain by a high gamma ray, organic-rich shale (**Figure 8.32**). It appears that uranium, which is adsorbed by organic matter in reduc-

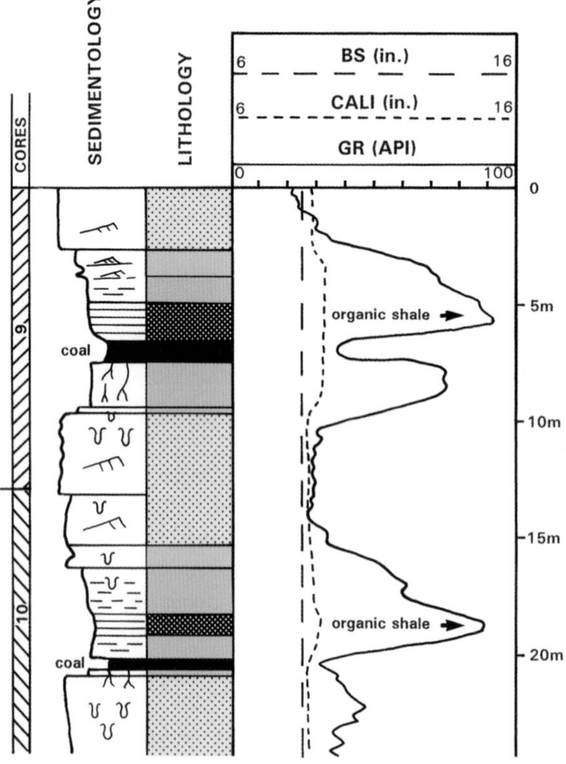

Figure 8.32 Gamma ray characteristics of coal (very low values) and organic rich shale (very high values) in a deltaic sequence.

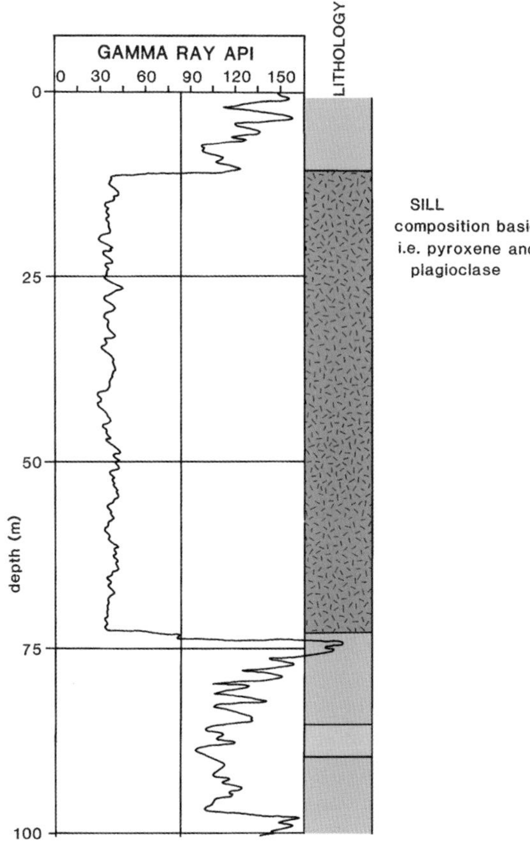

Figure 8.33 Low gamma ray values through a basic sill. It may be confused with a sandstone interval.

ing conditions (aided by bacteria), and causes the high gamma ray values in organic rich shales, is not adsorbed by organic matter in terrestrial swamps where no clay is present. Although water salinity may play a part, clay seems to be the catalyst for this adsorption. Thus, pure coals have a typical low gamma ray response while shaly coals have a gamma ray value, which depends on the amount of shale (or ash content in coal logging terms) (Kayal and Christoffel 1989).

Igneous and volcanic rock radioactivity

Igneous rocks are not volumetrically important in petroleum wells but occur sufficiently frequently to be a necessary element in the lithologic vocabulary. On occasions they even contain hydrocarbons. Both uranium and thorium originate in the acid to intermediate igneous rocks, but their distribution is very irregular since they are associated with secondary minerals such as apatite. Potassium is present, especially in the acid igneous rocks, principally in the alkali (potassic) feldspars. The net result is that basic igneous rocks have low radioactivity, while the intermediate and acid types show progressively higher values (Keys 1979; Sanyal *et al.* 1980) (**Table 8.14**). This can be related to the progressive fractionation that produces the intermediate and then

Table 8.14 Radioactive elements in igneous and volcanic rocks (from Serra, *et al.* 1980; figures approximate).

Rock type	Th (ppm)	U (ppm)	K_2O%	Typical radioactivity
Acid intrusive	1–25	1–8.4	2.00–11	High
Acid extrusive	9–25	2–7	2.00–6.00	
Basic intrusive	0.5–5	0.3–2	0.90–2.20	Low
Basic extrusive	0.5–10	0.2–4	1.40–2.50	
Ultrabasic	–	0.0001–0.03	1.6	Very low

acid igneous rocks from an original basaltic magma. Radioactive minerals become more abundant as fractionation progresses, and are therefore related to silica content. The examples show near end members of this series, a typical basalt sill, which may be confused with sand (**Figure 8.33**), and a granite pebble conglomerate, which may be confused with a shale (**Figure 8.34**).

Unconformities

Unusually high gamma ray values often occur as narrow, isolated peaks (Serra 1972). Considering the geochemistry of the radioactive minerals, these peaks are often associated with uranium concentrations. As discussed (*see* 'Uranium', Section 8.5), uranium concentrations indicate extreme conditions of deposition. Experience shows that these conditions frequently occur around unconformities (including sequence boundaries) where

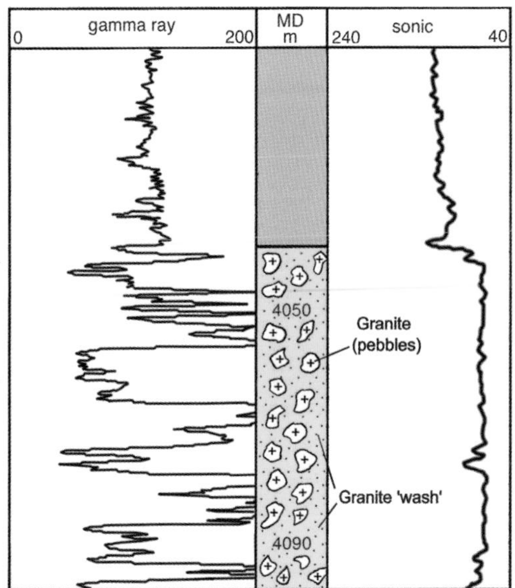

Figure 8.34 Very high gamma ray values in 'granite wash', being sand sized grains derived from granite, and granite pebbles. The interval has reservoir qualities despite the gamma ray, as indicated by the sonic (J. Garnham pers. comm.).

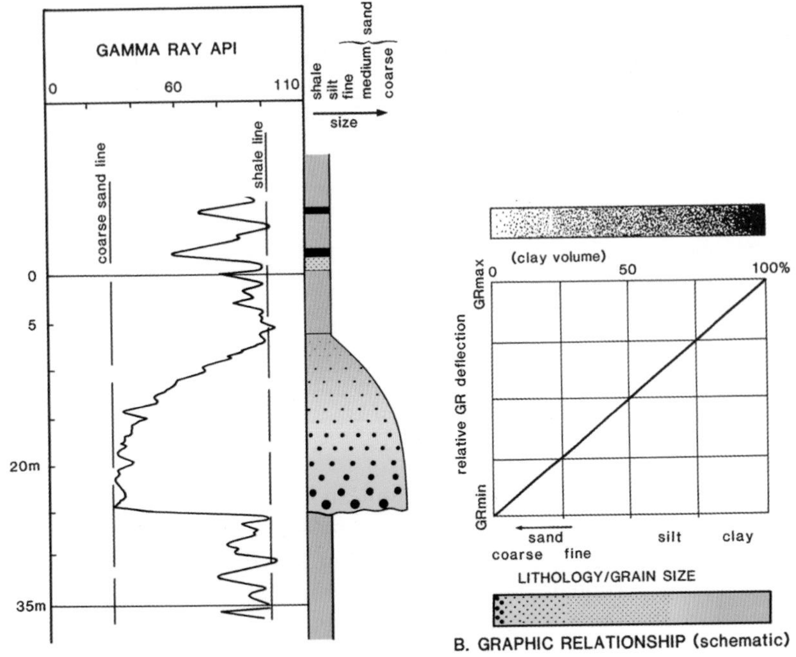

Figure 8.35 Facies from the gamma ray log. (A) The changes in sandstone grain size are reflected in changes in the gamma ray value. This allows a facies to be suggested. (B) Graphic representation of the variation of grain size with gamma ray value. Here it is expressed as a straight line but the relationship is very variable. It should represent the clay volume change.

a long passage of time is represented by little deposition. This observation applies as well to the hardgrounds mentioned previously (*see* 'Radioactivity in carbonates' above). The minerals associated with these latter horizons can be uranium-enriched phosphates or thorium-enriched heavy minerals (**Figure 17.14**).

Facies and grain size

An interesting and fairly comprehensive scheme for facies identification in detrital sediments (sand-shale) has been developed using gamma ray log shapes. The ideas have been extended for use in sequence stratigraphy (Van Wagoner *et al.* 1990). The basis for these schemes is the relationship between grain size and shale content. It is shale content that the gamma ray log indicates, but this is interpreted in terms of grain size. For example, a coarse-grained sand will have a very low shale content, a medium-grained sand some shale, and a fine-grained sand is often very shaly. The changes in grain size will be followed by changes in gamma ray value (**Figure 8.35**).

However, this method of interpreting facies using the gamma ray log is not straightforward. The relationship between grain size and shale content is variable, as is the relationship between shale volume and gamma ray value (Section 8.7 'Shale volume'). Empirically, if the gamma ray log shows a typical shape it can be taken as indicating grain-size changes. A lack of shape is not evidence for lack of grain-size change: it cannot be interpreted (Rider 1990).

A very interesting, and more original approach, to variations in the gamma ray log is proposed by Nio and

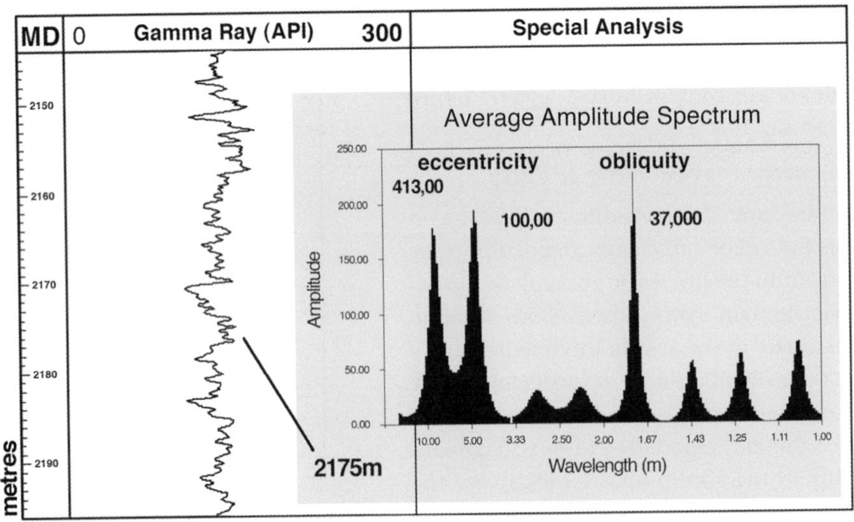

Figure 8.36 Spectral analysis of a gamma ray log from a Lower Jurassic shale interval. The analysis shows a cyclicity which corresponds to Milankovitch periodicities at 413,00 and 100,000 years (eccentricity) and 37,000 years (obliquity). Analysis by Cyclolog software from ENRES.

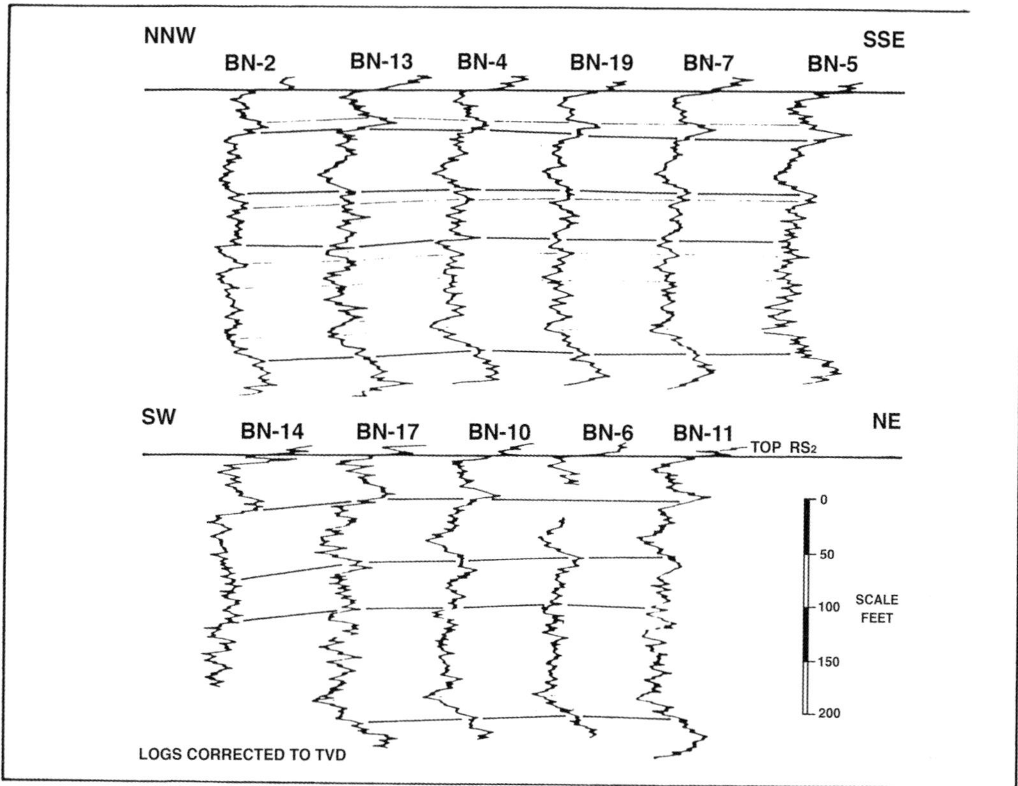

Figure 8.37 Correlation using the gamma ray log. Baronia field, Sarawak (from Scherer 1980).

others who apply spectral analysis to the curve (Nio *et al.* 2006). They consider that many of the log variations, despite lithological and grain size changes, are in fact related to climate change. Importantly, they interpret the gamma ray curve in terms of geological time, as represented by Milankovitch periodicities (**Figure 8.36**). They call their analysis cyclostratigraphy.

Facies interpreted from the gamma ray log and cyclostratigraphy are both fully described in Chapters 16 and 17.

Correlation

The gamma ray log is one of the most frequently used logs for correlation. It has 'character', is repeatable, is not affected by depth (except in very shallow sections), it gives some indication of lithology and is simple (**Figure 8.37**). Moreover, it is almost always run, as either wireline or LWD (or even both) and the sensitivity scales are relatively similar. Because it is used for correlation, it is generally reproduced on the well completion log, the document used to reassemble the essential drilling and geological data at the end of a well *(see* Chapter 12).

Besides its availability, the gamma ray log has inherent advantages for correlation, especially when this concerns shales. The gamma ray value of shale formations is often variable, depending on the various amounts of clay, minerals, carbonate and organic matter present. At the same stratigraphic level (horizontally as it were), these various elements tend to show only moderate variability in the complex mix, i.e. the depositional environment which controls the mix is laterally persistent. This complexity does not persist vertically, that is through geological time. There are changes in climate, sea level, source area and so on, as suggested by the cyclostratigraphy analysis. Thus, the gamma ray log value in shales can be relatively constant laterally but rapidly changing vertically. These are ideal characteristics for correlation and, indeed, are used in cyclostratigraphy (Nio *et al.* 2006).

Recently, correlation with the gamma ray log has taken on a new significance. It is suggested that gamma ray 'spikes' in shale sequences represent condensed sections, (maximum flooding surfaces in sequence stratigraphic parlance) which are effective time lines and should be correlated. This subject is considered in detail later in the book (Chapter 17) and in more detail in terms of the gamma ray below (Section 8.10).

In sandstones, gamma ray log shapes are often used to correlate. However, the shape is a facies characteristic and can lead to errors (e.g. **Figure 17.37**). Log shapes in carbonates are generally related to shale distribution and, as such, are more reliable for correlation, although care should be taken not to be misled by uranium concentration as discussed above *(see* 'Radioactivity in carbonates').

Although it has many advantages for correlation, the

gamma ray log also has disadvantages. The fine detail on the logs is generally noise and statistical variation (Section 8.4) and a comparison between any log and a repeat section shows to what extent this has an effect. Fine peaks therefore cannot be used for correlation. The second disadvantage is that the simple gamma ray cannot be calibrated (cf. Chapellier 1992) and absolute values should not be used. The values on the logs are relative to hole size, tool and method of measurement (Section 8.4, **Figure 8.13**). To be entirely comparable, the simple logs should be 'normalised' (Chapter 12). Spectral logs, however, because they measure abundances, will be more consistent from well to well in absolute values.

8.9 Quantitative use of the spectral gamma ray log

The spectral gamma ray log, like the simple gamma ray, is used to calculate shale volume. It can also be used to calculate the volume of radioactive minerals.

Shale volume

In the description of shale radioactivity given previously (Section 8.6), it was shown that the three naturally radioactive elements are not distributed evenly in shales. Spectral logs are therefore generally plotted with a computed potassium + thorium radioactivity, the CGR curve, as a better shale indicator (**Figure 8.9**). However, as described, potassium can occur in detrital minerals such as micas and feldspars so that thorium can be considered as the best shale indicator (section 8.6 and Fertl 1979a; Schenewerk *et al.* 1980). The shale volume calculated from the spectral gamma ray log may therefore be based entirely on the thorium values.

The mathematical relationship between thorium value (in ppm) and shale volume is taken as linear, the same relationship as between the simple gamma ray and shale volume. The equation becomes:

$$V_{sh}(Th) = \frac{\text{Th (log value)} - \text{Th (min)}}{\text{Th (max)} - \text{Th (min)}} \qquad (4)$$

Th (min) = thorium value in clean formation (ppm); Th (max) = thorium value in pure shale (ppm), and $V_{sh}(Th)$ = shale volume from thorium values.

As with the simple gamma ray, an empirical, exponential relationship to clay volume may be used instead of the simple linear one shown above (Fertl 1979), i.e. for consolidated and Mesozoic rocks:

$$V_{sh} = 0.33(2^{2V_{sh}(t)} - 1.0) \qquad (5)$$

and for Tertiary clastics

$$V_{sh} = 0.083(2^{3.7V_{sh}(t)} - 1.0) \qquad (6)$$

where $V_{sh}(Th)$ = shale volume from thorium values.

Radioactive mineral volume

Attempts to quantify the presence of radioactive minerals such as feldspars or mica are based on two assumptions: (1) all thorium radioactivity is from shale, and (2) radioactive detrital minerals show only potassium radioactivity.

For the quantification, the potassium values are normalised for shale volume using the maximum and minimum method, as for thorium. The normalised potassium value will give shale volume + radioactive minerals volume. Subtracting the shale volume derived from the thorium log will leave the volume of radioactive minerals (Schenewerk *et al.* 1980).

Volume of radioactive minerals =

$$\frac{K(\text{log value}) - K(\text{min}) - V_{sh}\,[(K(\text{max}) - K(\text{min})]}{a} \qquad (7)$$

where K(min) = potassium % in clean formation; K(max) = potassium % in pure shale and a = empirical factor for the formation concerned.

These two strictly quantitative methods are essentially used in petrophysical applications. Other, geologically applicable, qualitative and semi-quantitative uses of the gamma ray spectral log are described below.

8.10 Qualitative and semi-quantitative uses of the spectral gamma ray log

Shale and clay minerals

A certain amount of literature exists on the possibility of identifying clay mineral species using the spectral gamma ray log. Most results have either only local significance, are inconclusive or not usable. The intent is always to discover whether the variations of the individual radioactive elements enable the individual clay mineral species to be identified qualitatively, and eventually quantitatively.

The interval of the Muddy 'J' formation of Eastern Wyoming has been studied by Donovan and Hilchie (1981). They found a fairly good correlation between potassium radioactivity and illite content. However, they also found that, while there was no correlation between clay mineral content and total gamma radiation, there was a strong correlation between total counts and uranium content. The essential radiation was therefore coming from uranium. The evidence suggested that the uranium source was principally smectite, its presence being caused by the exchange of the uranyl ion from the formation waters. Uranium radioactivity therefore indicated the presence of smectite. Almost exactly the opposite was found in the analysis of shales around the North Sea (Dypvik and Eriksen 1983). The authors found that potassium and thorium were the dominant contributors to gamma ray activity with uranium being of minor importance (cf. **Table 8.8**).

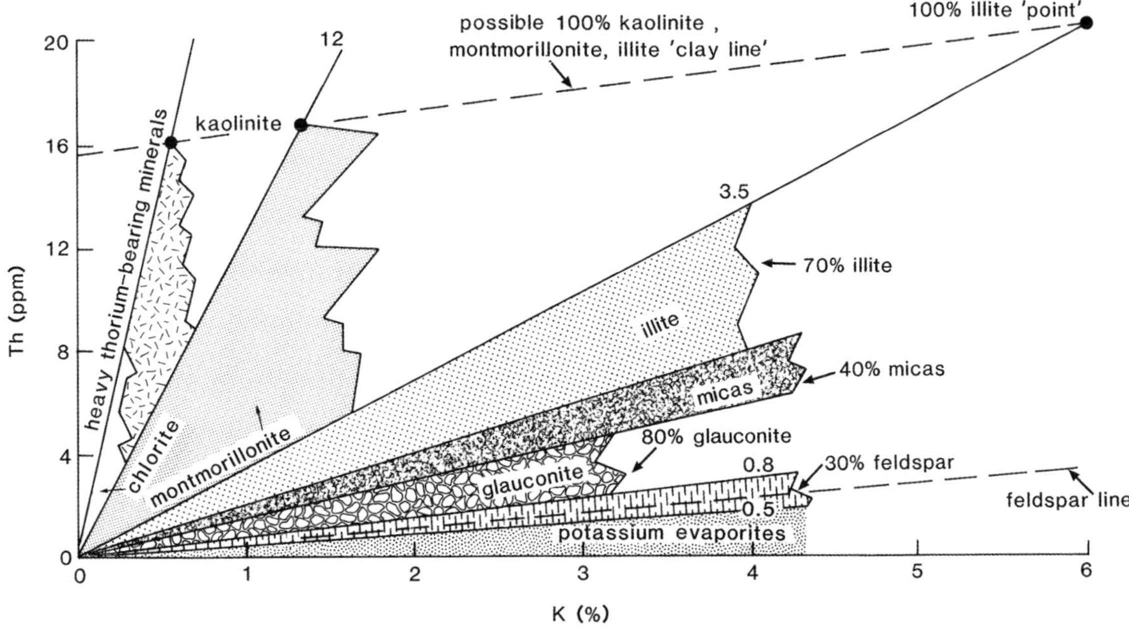

Figure 8.38 Graph of the theoretical distribution of clay minerals, heavy minerals and evaporites, in terms of potassium and thorium content (re-drawn from Quirein *et al.* 1982).

A complex quantitative approach to clay mineral identification has been proposed (Quirein *et al.* 1982). The authors suggest that clay mineral species, along with feldspar and evaporites, can all be identified relatively simply by their Th/K ratios (**Figure 8.38**). There is a tendency for this behaviour to be true (cf. **Tables 8.6, 8.11**), and it is the basis for using just thorium as a shale indicator (Section 8.9). However, individual clay minerals do not fall into such a simple classification which demands a strict chemical control for the distribution of the elements. As discussed, potassium is chemically involved in the clay lattice but the exact behaviour of thorium in terms of clay mineral composition is not clear. This quantitative method has no experimental confirmation and its use for the identification of specific clay minerals is not justified (Hurst 1990).

Dominant clay mineral and detrital mineral content: use of the ThlK ratio

The method described for quantifying radioactive mineral volume (Section 8.9) was based on the proposition that thorium occurs effectively only in clays and is thus a clay volume indicator, while potassium occurs in both clays and radioactive minerals. The method was applied quantitatively to sandstones but may be used semi-quantitatively for both sandstones and mudstones: the lithologies should be interpreted separately.

In sands, the Th/K ratio (effectively a measure of the potassium richness), will be largely a function of potassium rich, detrital mineral content. In shales, the same Th/K ratio will be a measure of clay mineral content (in that these are potassium rich). In both lithologies, the usual value for the Th/K ratio is 4-6 (Myers, pers. comm.), and deviations from this band will be the result of certain detrital mineral or clay mineral abundances. For example, a sandstone with a low Th/K ratio (of less than 4), will generally be dominated by feldspars, micas or glauconite: high ratios, (greater than 6), are likely to be dominated by heavy minerals. In mudstones, a similar low Th/K ratio (of less than 4), probably indicates that illites dominate the clay minerals, while high ratios (more than 6) probably indicate that kaolinite dominates.

These are not precise, quantitative relationships, only semi-quantitative indications. For example, a study of the Permian to Cretaceous of central Kansas (Doveton 1991), shows that low Th/K ratios (high potassium) are typical of the aeolian Permian shales and silts, where the high potassium content comes from feldspars, rock fragments and illites, while high Th/K ratios (low potassium) occur in the marine, Lower Cretaceous because the shales are dominated by kaolinite, with some chlorite, smectite and mixed layer clays, all generally low in potassium.

In practice, where ratios change progressively upwards through a shale, it can be an indication of climate change (it is, in effect, a progressive change in clay mineralogy). Similar progressive changes in a sandstone, however, are more likely to indicate mineralogical variations, for instance, channel lags often show a high Th/K ratio because of the heavy minerals they contain.

The interpretation of the Th/K ratio must be care-

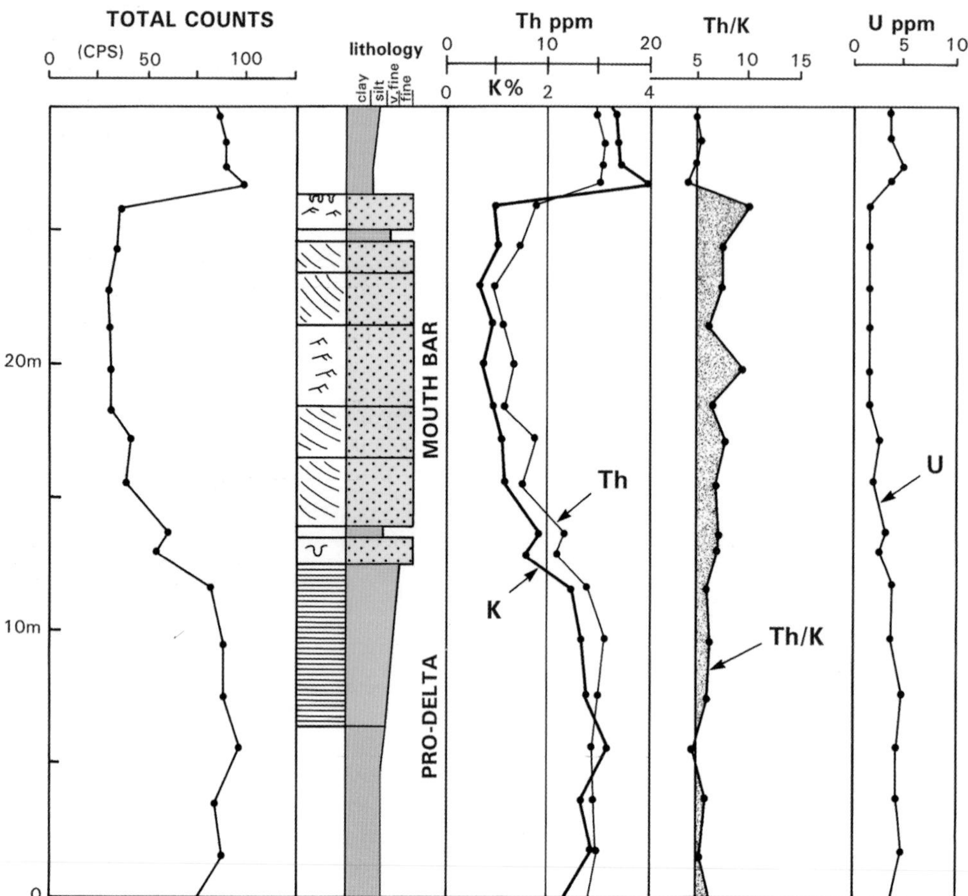

Figure 8.39 Thorium/potassium, Th/K ratios in silts and sands associated with change in grain size. Thorium is relatively more abundant in coarser grained fractions when sediment source is constant (Namurian outcrop, Co. Clare, Ireland, from Myers 1987).

fully controlled and, as suggested as a general rule, sandstones and shales should be studied separately. This is necessary because the ratio is often seen to be related to grain size. Thus, in coarsening-up sequences the Th/K ratio will change between the fine grained clays and silts and the coarser grained sandstones, generally increasing upwards into the sandstones (**Figure 8.39**). Another factor which must be considered is that potassium distribution changes during diagenesis. If there is dissolution of potassic feldspars and consequent redistribution of the potassium, the present-day Th/K ratio will not be related to original mineralogical content.

Source rocks: uranium content and gamma ray response

The theory of uranium adsorption by organic matter has already been discussed (*see* Uranium, Section 8.5) and illustrated (**Figure 8.16**) and explains why source-rocks are often identified by their uranium content and consequent overall high gamma ray value. This is the case with the marine Upper Jurassic, Kimmeridgian of the North Sea area, where organic matter levels are high (TOC = 5%+): there are high levels of uranium and the gamma ray values are correspondingly high (Bjørlykke *et al.* 1975, **Table 8.8**). It is equally the effect seen spectacularly in the Silurian graptolite rich, marine shales of the North African and Arabian platforms (Lüning *et al.* 2005). Although marine source rocks are seen with high gamma ray values (high uranium content), lacustrine source rocks have no gamma ray signature and are not uranium enriched (Meyer and Nederlof 1983). It appears that lakes do not have reserves of dissolved uranium available to be adsorbed by organic matter, while oceans do.

An additional complexity in the relationship between uranium and organic matter has been discovered recently. As source rocks mature, and the organic material slowly disintegrates and 'disappears', uranium can be left as a 'ghost', showing what previously existed but is now entirely unrelated to present organic richness (Lüning *et al.* 2005). Even though a link may have existed in the past, the present day gamma ray and uranium signature do not indicate organic matter content. Such a situation also occurs when organic matter is oxidised and burnt away: high uranium values (and gamma ray) remain but the organic material does not. In fact post-depositional changes in both uranium content and organic matter are common and add to the variability in the gamma ray

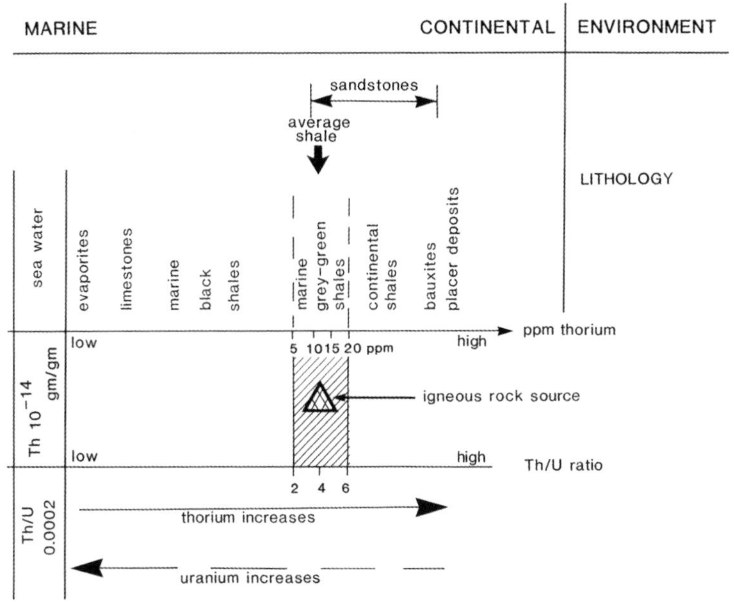

Figure 8.40 Schematic representation of the use of the Th/U ratio to indicate environment of deposition (source of data, Adams and Weaver 1958).

to source rock relationship (Lüning and Kolonic 2003). This means that neither total gamma ray response nor uranium content are consistently reliable source rock indicators (Kubala *et al.* 2004).

Using high gamma ray values to indicate source intervals should be applied with caution.

Depositional environment and condensed sequences: use of the Th/U ratio

Efforts to relate depositional environment to radioactive mineral content are generally based on thorium and uranium content and their inter-relationships. The affinity of uranium for sediments and shales of marine origin can be demonstrated (Koczy 1956), as can the affinity of thorium for terrestrial sediments (Hassan *et al.* 1976). Consequently, the contrast between thorium and uranium content should indicate the relative marine or relative continental influence (Adams and Weaver 1958). Analysis of a wide range of mainly mudrocks, shows that the 'normal' Th/U ratio is 3 – 6, higher ratios (higher thorium) occurring in 'continental' environments, lower values (higher uranium) in more marine environments (**Figure 8.40**).

Using these ratios to define depositional environments across a broad range has not been successful, there are too many variables involved, although work in central Kansas does show that there can be a ratio contrast between generally transgressive and generally regressive intervals (Doveton 1991). It is suggested, however, as outlined below, that a less comprehensive and selective application of the idea is more practical and practicable.

From a study of Upper Jurassic Kimmeridge clay outcrops in England, Myers and Wignall (1987) suggest that thorium content can be used as a quantitative reference level when studying variations in uranium content, as expressed by the Th/U ratio. Their analyses indicate that the typical Th/U ratio for shales is 3.9 ± 0.7, similar to the value of 3.8 ± 1.1 found by Adams and Weaver (1958) from analyses of American shales. If then, the expected, normal ratio is set at Th/U = 3 (i.e. slightly low), this can be used as a basis for an interpretation of abnormal ('excess') uranium content and eventually the identification of condensed sequences as explained below. In the method described, high Th/U ratios, i.e. with higher than expected thorium content, are not interpreted, although Doveton, after Weaver, considers ratios above 7 as indicating 'leached uranium' (Doveton 1991).

The Th/U ratio in 'normal' shales, then, is set at 3 for the interpretation method. Variations away from this set value (effectively the 'norm') are essentially a result of variations in uranium and not thorium. Setting the ratio at 3 means that only significantly high amounts of uranium will be signalled (or significantly low amounts but see end of previous paragraph). A ratio of less than 3, less than the 'norm' (high uranium), can then be said to contain more uranium than expected, or 'excess' uranium. Thus:

$$\frac{\text{Th log}}{3} = \text{U norm (ie Th/U ratio = 3, expected ratio)} \qquad (8)$$

$$\text{U log} - \text{U norm} = \text{U xess} \qquad (9)$$

(uranium log value less the calculated 'normal' value based on (1)

Where:
U norm = 'normal' shale uranium (calculated)
U xess = 'excess' shale uranium
U log = uranium log reading in shale of interest
Th log = thorium log reading in shale of interest

To take an example. From the spectral log a shale is found to contain 18 ppm thorium and 11 ppm uranium, then:

U log = 11 ppm   Th log = 18 ppm

$$\frac{18\,\text{ppm}}{3} = 6\,\text{ppm (U norm)} \qquad \text{(from 8)}$$

$$11\,\text{ppm} - 6\,\text{ppm} = 5\,\text{ppm} \quad \text{(U xess)} \qquad \text{(from 9)}$$

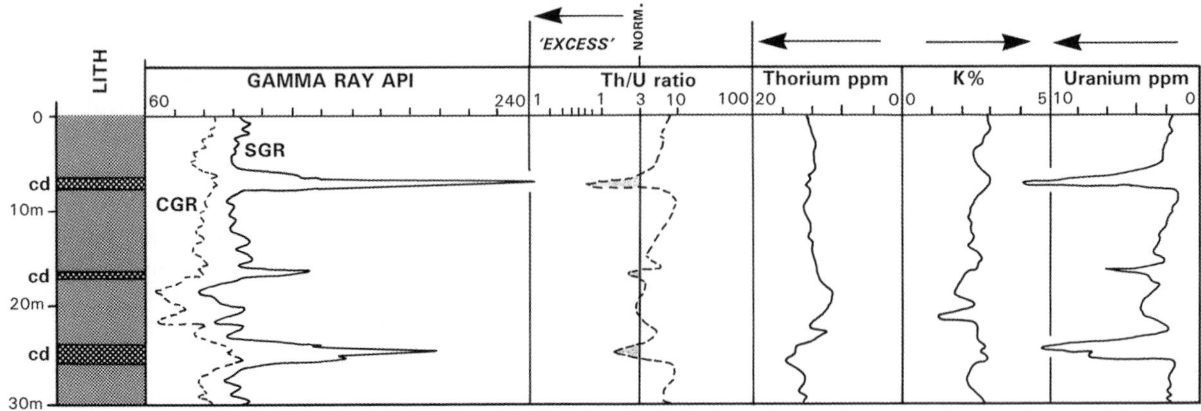

Figure 8.41 Condensed shale sections showing very low thorium/uranium, Th/U ratios due to 'excess' uranium content. Most shales have a Th/U ratio of 3–6, the 'norm'. In condensed sections, where organic matter is concentrated, uranium values are abnormally high and cause Th/U ratios of less than 3. The low ratio can be diagnostic.

There is therefore 5 ppm more uranium than would be expected from the thorium content.

(NB. The method outlined above, as proposed by Myers and Wignall (1987), uses the terms detrital uranium instead of 'normal', and authigenic uranium instead of 'excess'. To avoid suggesting that all sediments with high values of uranium (i.e. with a low Th/U ratio) contain authigenic uranium rather than any other form, and that correspondingly low values are detrital, the terms 'excess' and 'normal' respectively are used in this book.)

Shale zones recognised as having 'excess' or higher than normal uranium will have a high organic matter content in most cases (but see previous section). This in turn suggests an environment where the organic matter is preserved, typically deposited in an anoxic environment.

The method described above may be used to identify possible marine condensed sequences, important in themselves but doubly important in a sequence stratigraphic analysis (Chapter 17). Condensed sequences in marine areas arise when the detrital influx into an environment is low. This causes a relative increase in the *in-situ* material over the externally derived detritus. In-place material typically consists of the shells of pelagic macro- and micro-fauna and locally derived organic material, all of which simply falls to the depositional surface to form a slowly accumulating, organic-rich sediment. Provided that there is a low rate of dissolution, (i.e. that the environment is oxygen deficient = anoxic) the amount of organic matter in the condensed sequence will be high and in a marine environment, will have high adsorbed uranium. On the gamma ray spectral log, this high uranium content will show up as a low Th/U ratio. That is, using the methodology proposed above, condensed sequences will show 'excess' uranium (**Figure 8.41**). Using this ratio based method is more accurate and selective than simply using high overall gamma ray (i.e. gamma spike) or even high uranium values (Chapter 17).

Fracture localisation

In older studies, the spectral gamma ray log was used to identify zones of high uranium radiation which were associated with fractures or faults, the radioactivity coming from the high uranium content of formation waters (Fertl 1979; Fertl and Rieke 1980). Modern fracture studies are mostly undertaken using image logs (Chapter 15).

9
SONIC OR ACOUSTIC LOGS

9.1 Generalities

The log

Sonic tools measure the acoustic characteristics of a formation, the log giving a formation's slowness or interval transit time, designated Δt (delta-t), the reciprocal of the velocity. It is a measure of the formation's capacity to transmit sound waves (**Figure 9.1**). This is basically accomplished by measuring the time for a pulse of sound to travel a known distance through the formation. At its simplest, a logging tool therefore consists of a transmitter and one or more receivers a known distance apart. As will be seen below, however, the reality of making a measurement in a borehole is more complicated.

Sonic measurements were suggested by Conrad Schlumberger in 1934 although the tools were only introduced in practice and commercially in 1954. When the relationship between acoustic response and porosity was realised (publication by Gulf Oil in 1956), the sonic became one of the mainstay tools. Tool design was continuously improved and in 1963 the borehole compensated sonic (BHC) tool was introduced and became the

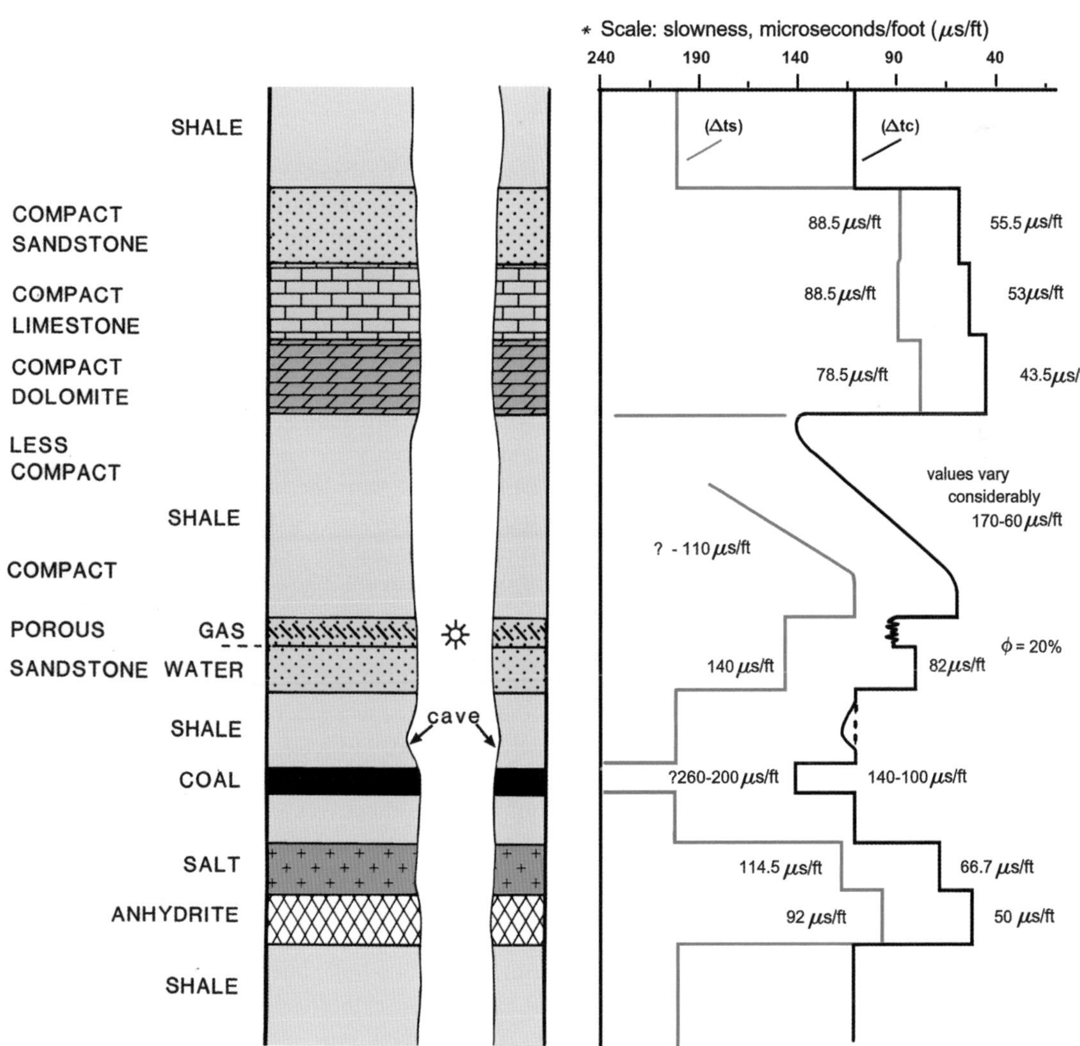

Figure 9.1 The sonic log: some typical responses. The sonic log shows a formation's ability to transmit sound waves. It is expressed as Slowness or Interval Transit Time, Δt. $*(1 \times 10^6) / \Delta t$ = sonic velocity ft/sec.; Δtc = compressional slowness; Δts = shear slowness. Values indicative only.

Table 9.1 The principal uses of the sonic log (wireline and LWD)

	Discipline	Used for	Knowing
Qantitative	Petrophysics	Porosity Pore pressure Gas detection Permeability	Matrix velocity, fluid velocity Density, *Vp/Vs* ratio Stoneley slowness
	Seismic	Interval velocity Seismic calibration Synthetic seismogram Acoustic impedance Elastic moduli Seismic attributes	Integrated travel time, seismic markers Check shots Density, calibration *Vp* + density log *Vp* + *Vs* + density log Elastic moduli
Qualitative and Semi-quantitative	Geology	General lithology texture Correlation	Matrix and mineral velocities Core calibration Sonic character
	Reservoir geology	Compaction and overpressure Fracture identification	Normal compaction trends density porosities (old method)
	Geochemistry	Source rock evaluation	Resistivity log values
	LWD only	Hydrate measurement	Hydrate physical characteristics
Drilling	Wireline & LWD	Rock strength, hole stability Wellbore damage	density log + *Vp* + *Vs* *Vs* dispersion

workhorse sonic from then on. But it was an analogue tool and could only measure the compressional or P wave. In 1986 the wireline, digital, array sonic tool was introduced, a fundamentally new design. This tool could digitally capture a full wave-train, and the compressional and shear arrivals were measured, along with the following Stoneley arrivals (Arroyo France *et al.* 2006). Almost all the wireline tools run today are of the full wave-train, array type. The most recent introduction has been an LWD sonic, equally with an array type design. Although this tool has had a difficult debut, it is (at the time of publication) now generally being accepted.

Principal uses

Sonic logs are now principally used as an aid to seismic investigations. The log can be simply used to tie a well to the seismic which then allows an accurate depth conversion, interval velocity and velocity profile to be calculated. It is used to make an acoustic impedance log when combined with a density log, the first step in producing a synthetic seismogram. Importantly, the log can be used to help in seismic processing and attribute analysis. Although the sonic log was previously used to calculate porosity, this is now secondary.

Geologists generally still only use the compressional wave velocity despite the shear wave velocity frequently being available. The compressional wave velocity is sensitive to subtle textural variations (of which porosity is only one) in sands, limestones and, importantly, shales (**Figure 9.1**). The compressional sonic log can help to identify lithology, indicate source rocks, normal compaction and overpressure, and is frequently used in correlation. The array, dipole sonic can be further used to identify permeability, quantify wellbore damage, calculate formation mechanical properties and elastic moduli, and identify gas and gas hydrates (**Table 9.1**).

Acoustic waves in a borehole

Three principal acoustic waves are detected in borehole logging, the *compressional* or *P* wave, the *shear* or *S* wave and the *Stoneley* (*St*) wave. Older sonic tools could only measure the compressional wave arrival (still the case with the seismic), but the modern sonic tools measure a full, digital wave-train and provide the compressional, shear and Stoneley wave arrival times (*P, S, St*) (**Figure 9.2**).

The compressional or *P* wave is caused by particle movement in the direction of propagation. It has high energy but small amplitude, and is the first movement to arrive at the receiver, or receivers, from the transmitter. It can travel in solids and liquids. The shear wave is associated with particle movement at 90° to the sense of movement, and arrives after the compressional wave. It cannot travel through liquids. The Stoneley wave arrives after the shear wave, has less energy but a high amplitude, which varies with frequency (i.e. is dispersive) and is a type of surface wave. The Stoneley wave is complex but, in the borehole, forms a tube wave, meaning that it exists in the cylindrical environment of the borehole.

The simplest type of monopole sound source (*see below*) produces a pressure pulse that spreads out spherically from the logging tool. When the sphere encounters the borehole wall, it is refracted (bent) and the pulse that is going to be detected turns parallel to the borehole

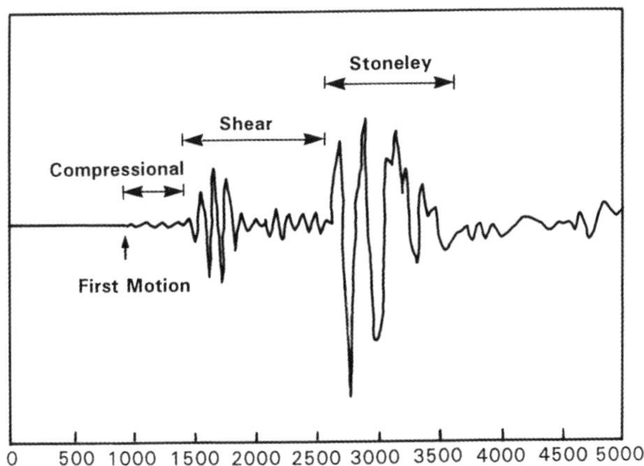

Figure 9.2 The full acoustic waveform that may be recorded in a borehole. The older sonic tools recorded only the first arrival of the compressional (*P*) wave. Array sonic tools now record the full waveform and compressional (*P*), shear (*S*) and Stoneley arrivals (*St*) (modified from Ellis 1987, after Schlumberger).

wall. This wave then travels along the interface with a velocity related to the formation. This is the so-called 'head wave'. As it moves along the borehole it creates disturbances like the wake of a boat. It is this 'compressional head wave' that is detected by a receiver and recorded as the *P* wave arrival. This is the first signal to arrive from the transmitter and the time it has taken is used as a measure of the formation compressional wave slowness or interval transit time.

When it encounters the borehole wall, the original pressure pulse is split into two, a compressional wave, as just described, but also a shear wave. Shear waves always have a lower velocity than compressional waves and they cannot be transmitted by fluids. The behaviour of the shear wave, however, is similar to the compressional wave in that it moves up the borehole-formation interface, albeit at a slower speed. It is also associated with a head wave and subsidiary disturbances and it is these that are recorded as the shear wave arrival. Once the technology existed to record the entire wave-train, the shear arrival could be identified and the shear slowness measured. This is now done routinely in what are known as 'fast formations', defined as formations in which the formation shear wave velocity is greater than the mud wave velocity (Haldorson *et al.* 2006).

Formations in which the shear velocity is slower than the mud velocity are known as 'slow formations'. These cause a fundamental problem for measuring shear slowness in a borehole. In fact, a shear head wave cannot form in the mud column when slow formations are present and so shear slowness cannot be directly measured. This is because the contrast in velocity between the mud and the lower formation shear velocity means that the shear wave actually refracts away from the borehole (Snell's law).

However, a shear wave slowness can be estimated if a dipole source is used (explained *below*). A dipole source produces what is known as a flexural wave at the borehole wall. Flexural waves propagate down the borehole wall, and so do produce a head-wave that can be detected by the tool. Over low frequencies, flexural wave velocity is the same as the true shear velocity. Flexural waves however are dispersive, that is to say, their velocity changes with frequency, and, in order to estimate the shear velocity, this variation needs to known. As a result of computer modelling, the relationship between flexural wave frequency and velocity is now known, so that the measured flexural wave slowness allows the shear wave slowness to be estimated. Shear wave detection was sometimes difficult in older tools (in other words unreliable) but, with more modern tools and techniques, there is a greater reliability. The majority of wireline tools are now equipped with at least one dipole source, even if they are used exclusively in fast formations.

The third type, the Stoneley wave, is a type of Rayleigh movement, or surface movement, like the waves that cause damage after earthquakes. The wave forms at the surface of the borehole wall, a solid to liquid junction. However, because the borehole is cylindrical, the complex behaviour of the waves causes constructive interference and a wave is formed, a tube wave, that travels up inside the borehole. Tube waves are the cause of 'hammer' noises in water pipes. In rigid boreholes, a Stoneley wave is produced. Stoneley waves are slightly dispersive, that is, there are small changes in velocity with frequency, meaning that at high frequencies the velocity will vary across the borehole but at low frequencies it is more or less constant (Haldorson *et al.* 2006 *op. cit*). It is at the low frequencies that the Stoneley wave is claimed to be sensitive to formation permeability and borehole size: high values of both cause energy loss. In reality, Stoneley wave energy is generally one of the poorest log based permeability predictors. Arguably, the wave is simply a by-product of the dipole source, the primary purpose of which is to produce a reliable shear slowness in slow formations.

Types of sound source

Three types of sound source are in use: monopole, dipole and quadrupole (**Figure 9.3**). In addition, some of the latest and more specialised wireline tools are equipped with a chirp source (essentially a miniature vibroseis source). For compressional, Stoneley and fast formation shear wave detection, a monopole source is sufficient. The pressure pulse emitted is omni-directional, meaning that it spreads out in all directions, forming a sphere around the point source, like a stone dropped in water. It is the type of source that was used in the older sonic tools. Dipole sources are used for shear wave detection in slow formations. A dipole source emits a directed pulse, forming a compression on one side of the borehole linked to a rarefaction on the opposite side (**Figure 9.3**). The source shakes the borehole, as it were, from side to side. It produces a flexural wave in the surface of the borehole wall that is similar to a shear wave and, as explained above, can be used to estimate the true shear velocity.

Logging while drilling tools mostly use monopole sources and so in general can only measure compressional slowness in slow formations. At least one contractor, however, uses quadrupole sources. Like the dipole source, they were developed to measure shear wave velocities in slow formations. The source can be described as distorting like a rubber ball with simultaneous opposite rarefactions and orthogonal and opposite compressions (**Figure 9.3**).

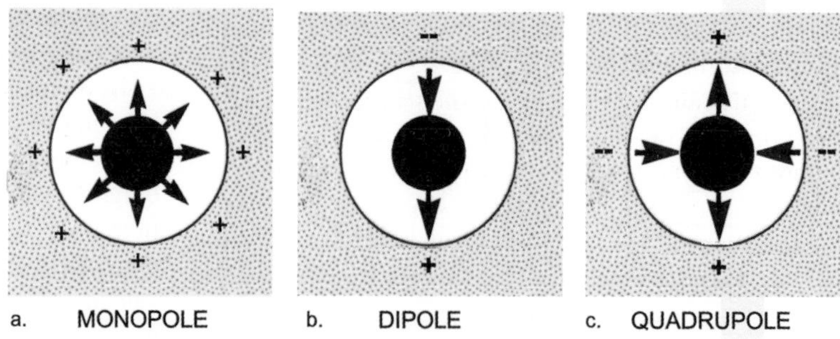

Figure 9.3 Types of transmitter sound source. a) monopole transmitter providing a multi-directional pulse; b) dipole transmitter giving a directed pulse; c) quadrupole transmitter providing an LWD sound source.

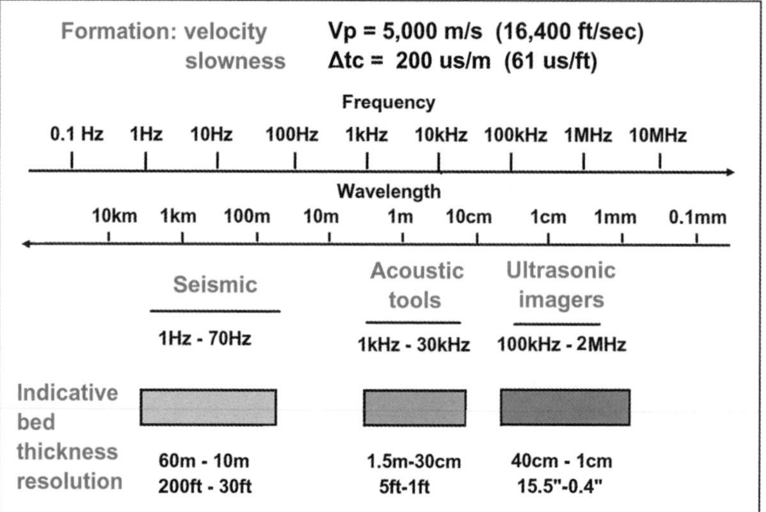

Figure 9.4 Compressional wave (*P*) wavelengths, frequencies and typical bed thickness resolutions for seismic, acoustic logging and ultrasonic imaging methods. Formation of average velocity, Vp, 5000 m/s (16,400 ft/sec).

All sources produce short pulses of sound at regular, approximately tenth of a second intervals. The individual pulses last about one tenth of a millisecond. Sonic logging generally uses frequencies between 500 Hz and 30 kHz (500–30,000 cycles per second). (This is in the range of human hearing and, if the tool is operated at the surface, the 'clicks' it produces can be clearly heard.) For typical subsurface formations, with compressional velocities between 1500–7500 m/sec (5000–25,000 ft/sec), this corresponds to wavelengths of between 5 cm and 25 cm (2″–9.8″) (for a frequency of 30 kHz) (Serra 2000) (**Figure 9.4**) (wavelength = velocity/frequency). The pulses contain a band of audio frequencies but the exact nature of the pulse varies between the type of source and between wireline and LWD tools. As a general rule, the average frequency of the dipole sources is significantly lower than the monopole sources (perhaps 1 kHz and 10 kHz respectively). LWD tools also use lower frequency sources to reduce the influence of drilling noise. This is mostly from the circulating drilling mud and has frequencies in the range 500 Hz–4 kHz (Market 2007). One LWD tool uses 2–5 kHz and 9–15 kHz bands for the compressional measurement and a quadrapole source at 2 kHz (Tang *et al.* 2004). For monopole sources, another tool uses 8–30 kHz and 12,15 or 25 kHz modes (**Tables 9.3**, **9.4**). Regardless of the particular source, the frequencies used by logging tools are much higher than those that make up a typical seismic signal (sonic and seismic velocities are routinely compared). These use much lower frequencies of around 10–50 Hz (10–50 cycles a second) and wavelengths of 30–750 m (100–2500 ft) (see Section 9.8, Seismic applications).

Sonic tool sources or transmitters (transducers) are either magnetostrictive (common for dipole sources) or piezoelectric (usual for monopole sources) and translate an electrical signal into a sonic pulse. That is, the application of an electrical charge to a piezoelectric transmitter causes a change in volume, which is translated into a pressure pulse. A common piezoelectric material used is lead zirconate titanate or PZT. Receivers, too, are also usually piezoelectric. They convert pressure waves into an electromagnetic charge. Piezoelectric materials have a type of structure which, when a stress (in this case a pressure pulse) is applied, shows separation of centres of negative and positive charge, thus creating a polarisation charge. It is this, amplified, which gives the electrical logging tool signal. They can operate satisfactorily at any temperature that is likely to be encountered in an oil well.

Units

Although sonic logs primarily measure velocity, the log is conventionally expressed as Δt, the *slowness* or *interval transit time*. The standard unit on a log is either Microseconds per foot (μs/ft) or Microseconds per *metre* (μs/m) (3.281 μs/ft = 1 μs/m). Typical values for formation slowness in the subsurface are 50–150 μs/ft (150–450 μs/m) (1 μs (1 microsecond) = 1×10^{-6} seconds). It is quite common for the former to be used even when the vertical, depth scale of a log is in metres. The slowness is simply the reciprocal of velocity (i.e high slowness is equivalent to low velocity):

$$\text{Velocity ft/sec} = \frac{1}{\Delta t\,\mu\text{s/ft} \times 10^{-6}}$$

So for a $\Delta t = 40\,\mu\text{s/ft}$ from the sonic log:

$$\text{Velocity} = \frac{1}{40 \times 10^{-6}} = 25{,}000\,\text{ft/sec} = 7{,}620\,\text{m}$$

Interval transit time is the older term for the sonic measurement. Slowness is the newer term, which means the same thing, and is used for the measurements made by the modern array tools. These provide logs of the compressional wave (Δtc or DTC), shear wave (Δts or DTS) and Stoneley wave (Δtst or DTSt) slowness. In the following text, slowness will be used as it seems to be the modern tendency.

9.2 Older, compressional wave, wireline sonic tools (pre-1985)

The description of sonic tools is divided into three sections. The first, this section (Section 9.2) deals with the older, first generation wireline tools and their characteristics, the second (Section 9.3) deals with the newer, wireline, array sonic tools and their characteristics, and the third (Section 9.4) with the present generation of LWD acoustic tools (**Table 9.2**). The first generation tools are now virtually obsolete but as their operation is reasonably easy to understand and there are many of their logs in databases, it is worth spending time describing them. In any case, the basic physics of sound propagation in the borehole and the formation is the same for all tools. The main difference between the first generation tools and the current ones is that in the former most of the wave-train was 'thrown away' whereas now it is stored and analysed. Furthermore, many of the components used in the current tools have not changed a great deal from those used in the original tools.

Borehole compensated sonic tool (BHC)

The first sonic tools simply measured the time taken for a sound pulse to travel between a transmitter and a receiver mounted a set distance apart and separated by a rubber section to stop sound travelling along the tool itself. The problem with this arrangement is that the travel time depends on the size of the borehole and the fluid it contains. So this design was quickly modified to a transmitter and two receivers at different spacings, or two transmitters and a single receiver but, otherwise, the design was similar. Although the addition of an extra receiver or transmitter did not make a great deal of difference to the size or complexity of the tool, it had a profound effect on the consistency of the measurement. None-the-less, these early tools were significantly affected by borehole conditions and this led to the design

Table 9.2 Sonic tools (wireline and LWD). From Serra 2000, 2008, Baker Hughes™ (Atlas), Halliburton and Schlumberger documents.

1. Wireline Sonic BHC (older tools)

Name	Acronym	Company
Borehole Compensated Sonic Long Spaced Sonic	BHC LSS	Schlumberger
Borehole Compensated Acoustilog Long Spaced BHC Acoustilog	AC ACL	Baker Hughes™ (Atlas)
Borehole Compensated Sonic Long Spaced Sonic	BCS LSS	Halliburton

2. Wireline Dipole, Array Sonic

Name	Acronym	Company
Array-Sonic Service Dipole Shear Sonic Imager Sonic Scanner	ASS DSI	Schlumberger
Digital Array Acoustilog Cross Multipole Array Acoustilog Multipole Array Acoustilog	DAC™ XMAC™ MAC™ -B and -F1	Baker Hughes™ (Atlas)
BHC Sonic DITS Wave Sonic Full Wave Sonic Tool Pulsed Power Multipole Acoustic Low Frequency Dipole Tool	BCDT FWS XACT LFDT	Halliburton

3. LWD sonic tools

Name	Acronym	Company
SonicVISION		Schlumberger
SoundTrak™		Baker Hughes™ INTEQ
Bi-modal Acoustic	BAT	Halliburton/Sperry-Sun

of a borehole compensation system that allowed the unwanted borehole effects to be largely eliminated. This borehole compensated design gave reliable measurements of formation values even in quite poor borehole conditions. The simple two transmitter-one receiver arrangement, however, was widely used in the former Soviet Union and its client states and, in the west, was commonly used in tools designed for use in small holes and hostile environments.

The borehole-compensated sonic tool (BHC), which was the acoustic workhorse for many years, had two opposing transmitter-receiver sets instead of just the one: one was inverted, and each set consisted of a transmitter and two receivers, a near and a far (**Figure 9.5,a**). The receivers measured only the first arrival, that is the compressional sound pulse arrival. This sonic was generally run hole-centred, so any pulse transmitted from the tool passed first into the mud. It would then be refracted at the borehole wall and travel through the formation but close to the borehole. As explained (acoustic waves in the borehole), it was the associated compressional head wave that would be detected at the receiver. A significant part of the trajectory in the compensated design is in the borehole mud but, when a set of two receivers is used (a near and a far), the effects of the mud can be eliminated. This is simply achieved by measuring the time taken for the signal to reach the near receiver and then subtracting this from the time taken to reach the far receiver. The path from tool to borehole wall and back, in the mud, and the path between the transmitter to the near receiver are effectively common to both trajectories and are eliminated on subtraction. What is left is the time taken between the two receivers (i.e. **Figure 9.5,a,** R1–R3). This is the formation (compressional) reading: the value required.

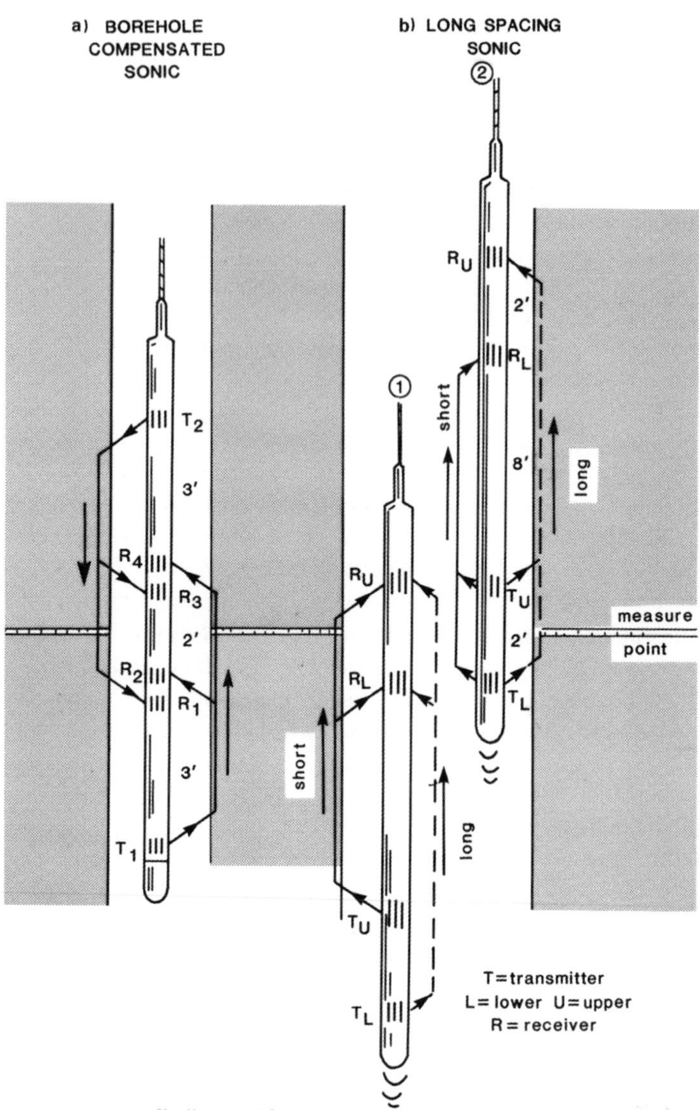

Figure 9.5 Schematic representations of the older wireline, sonic tools. (a) The borehole-compensated sonic tool (BHC) with 2 transmitter-receiver sets, one inverted. (b) The Long Spacing Sonic Tool (LSS) (Schlumberger) which gives long and short-spaced readings using a dynamic (i.e. position based) compensation. Positions (1) and (2) are both relative to the same measure point (modified from Thomas 1977; Purdy 1982).

Since tool tilt and hole size may make the common parts of the trajectory unequal, a second, inverted array (with a downward moving signal), is averaged with the first (with the upward moving signal) to provide compensation. Because this was an analogue tool, it meant that a single value recorded on the sonic log was the result of a sequence of four separate transmitter to receiver readings, two from the lower transmitter (to its near and far receivers) and two from the upper transmitter (to its near and far receivers) (**Figure 9.5,a**). Typical distances from the transmitter were 3 feet to the near receiver and 5 feet to the far receiver: 2 feet separated the receivers. These, of course, determine the vertical resolution of the measurement. The lower limit of the transmitter-receiver spacing is really determined by the relative speeds of sound in the mud and formation. The distance has to be great enough so that it takes longer for sound to travel from transmitter to receiver directly through the mud than to travel a few centimetres from transmitter to the borehole wall, a certain distance through the formation (at a high speed) and then back through the mud to the tool.

A single, BHC transmitter pulse lasted between 100μs–200μs (microseconds). The gap between these pulses was 50ms (milliseconds), so that 20 pulses were emitted per second, allowing five complete sequences of four individual transmitter-receiver readings each second. At a typical sonic tool logging speed of 1500 m/h (5000 ft/h), (i.e. approximately 40 cm/sec or 16 inches/sec) each complete sequence of four readings would give one log reading for every 8 cm (3") of borehole. The output from each receiver would be amplified and transmitted up the logging cable for processing at the surface.

Long-spaced sonic tool (LSS)

The borehole-compensated (BHC) sonic tool described above had a 'static' compensation, meaning that the compensated set of readings were effectively all taken with the tool at one depth. It worked well. In the late 1970s it was suggested that longer transmitter to receiver distances might help, under certain borehole conditions, to give a better formation reading, and the long-spaced sonic was designed. This tool had two receivers two feet apart separated by eight feet from two transmitters also two feet apart (i.e. the LSS of Schlumberger, **Figure 9.5,b, Table 9.2**). Like the BHC sonic, it measured only the compressional slowness. However, it provided a near reading with 8–10 foot spacings (2.4–3 m) and a far reading with 10–12 foot spacings (3–3.6 m). Because of its considerable length, the long-spaced sonic had a 'dynamic' compensation system where depth memorisation was used. To complete a full, compensated sequence for both the near and far readings, the tool had to record a full transmitter-receiver sequence at two different depth positions separated by 10 feet, the tool's compensation shift. For the transmitters and detectors available at the time, this tool was too long, and often produced erroneous results. At the time, it was not a good design. The dynamic compensation system is diagrammatically illustrated (**Figure 9.5,b**).

Log presentation and scales

The sonic log scale of slowness (interval transit time), from left to right, is generally from 240 μs/ft–40 μs/ft, or 140 μs/ft–40 μs/ft, and, since slowness (transit time) is the reciprocal of velocity, this means that fast formations will plot on the right. For operators that use metric units the most frequently used scale is 450 μs/m–150 μs/m. The scale is linear. On the old API format, a sonic tool run on its own would be presented over the full width of tracks 2 and 3 (**Figure 9.6,a**). The sonic tool was frequently run in combination with resistivity logs (e.g. Schlumberger ISF-Sonic tool; Atlas (Baker Hughes™) Wireline Acoustic-Resistivity tool). When combined with other tools, the log appeared on only one track often with the sensitivity scale of 140 μs/ft–40 μs/ft (**Figure 9.6,b**). Sonic logs are now frequently run as part of a 'quad-combo', that is together with density, neutron and resistivity tools. In this case, the sonic slowness is either plotted in the same track as the nuclear logs or is assigned its own track on a non-API (4 track) format.

An integrated travel time (or TTI) was recorded simultaneously with most sonic logs (it is still calculated, but is seldom plotted). It gives the time it would take for a sound wave from the sonic tool to travel a certain distance along the borehole. It is derived from the average velocity of the formation logged (the integrated area under the log curve) and plotted over the vertical depth of the interval in milliseconds (10^{-3} seconds), each millisecond appearing on the inside depth column as a tick or bar. Each 10 ms is a longer tick (**Figure 9.6**). Adding the milliseconds and dividing by the thickness of the interval covered gives the velocity. The TTI milliseconds can simply be added together to compare to the travel times on the seismic section: seismic sections are in two-way time, that is TTI × 2 (Section 9.8). Nowadays, the integration can be quickly performed, as and when needed, using standard log analysis software, so the 'ticks' have become obsolete (in addition, an integrated transit time curve is normally stored digitally as the log is recorded).

Depth of investigation (and borehole damage)

Notionally, the depth of investigation of the older sonic tools depended on the transmitter to receiver distance, but the true picture is more complicated. It was originally considered that the sound pulses detected by the borehole sonic tools penetrated very little into the formation (Dewan 1983; Chemali *et al.* 1984; Ellis 1987). However, a consideration of the way sound propagates shows that this cannot possibly be the case, and laboratory experiments and computer models have now shown that a compressional wave travels up a borehole at least 3 wavelengths inside the formation behind the borehole wall (Serra 2000). This is simply a result of the nature of wave propagation. When the initial disturbance in the mud hits the borehole wall, it sets up a secondary compressional wavefront in the formation. This spreads in all directions, including away from the borehole and, by the time the head-wave reaches the receiver, it will have penetrated a significant distance into the formation. It is tempting to argue that the part of the wave-front that has moved perpendicular to (i.e. away from) the borehole cannot influence the wave-front which is moving parallel and close to the borehole wall and generates the head wave. Unfortunately wave mechanics suggests otherwise, and the net effect is that the concept of depth of investigation is even more nebulous with sonic tools than the other logs.

But to give some example figures. With formation velocities of between 1500–7600 m/sec (5000 and 25,000 ft/sec) and signals with a frequency of 20–30 kHz, pulses will travel between 15 cm–1.0 m (5.9–39.4") into the formation (wavelengths 5–37.5 cm (2.0–13.8"), λ = velocity/frequency) (Serra 2000). For a particular signal frequency, penetration is greater in higher velocity formations. However, the higher the signal frequency

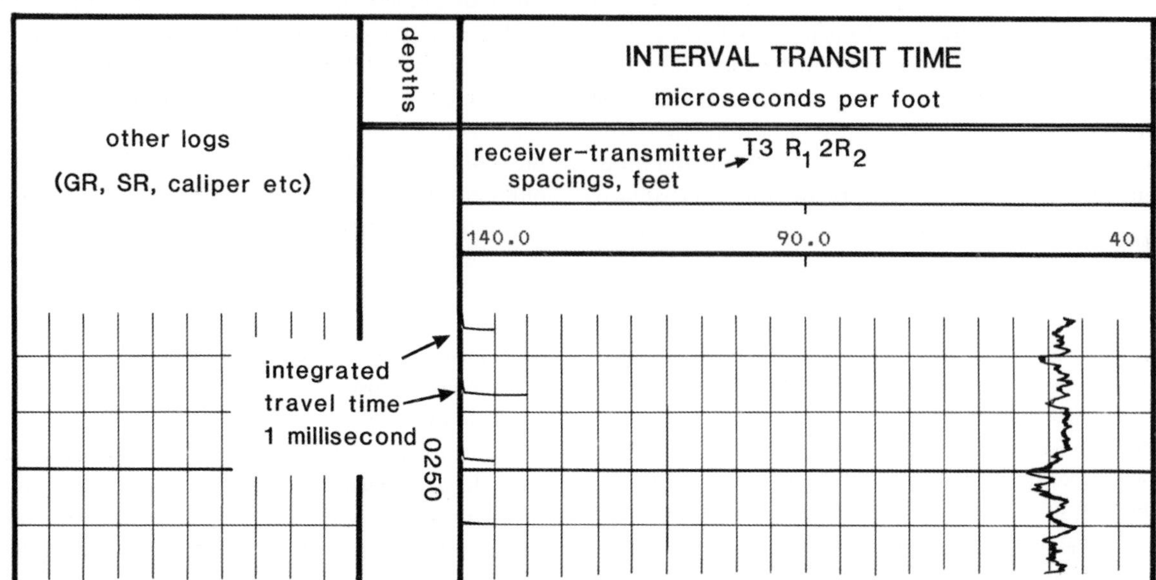

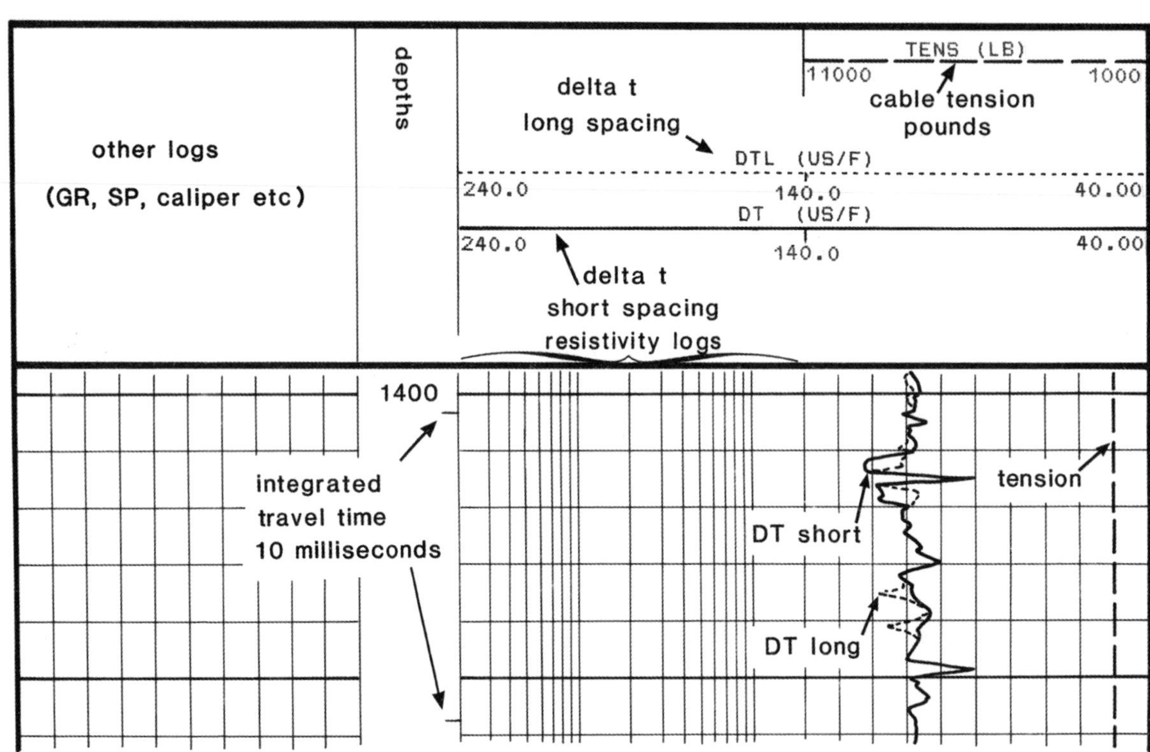

Figure 9.6 Typical sonic log API format headings. (a) BHC tool; (b) long spacing tool (on the ISF-sonic combination of Schlumberger). The scale on the older logs is 'Interval Transit Time': it is the same as 'Slowness', the modern term.

used, the less the penetration for the same formation. A rough rule of thumb is that the depth of investigation in inches, is the same as the transmitter receiver spacing in feet.

Comparison between seismic and sonic velocities has shown that there are often differences between the two that cannot be accounted for by the frequency difference (dispersion) (**Figure 9.4**). The differences are considered to exist because sonic velocities are affected by chemical and mechanical damage immediately around the borehole (Section 9.7).

Chemical damage is caused by a reaction between the drilling mud and the formation, especially when montmorillonite (smectite) or swelling clays are present. The example (**Figure 9.7**) shows the effect on sonic measurements of a progressive chemical reaction between the mud filtrate and swelling clays in a well in Colombia, exposed to the mud for between 3 and 35 days (Blakeman 1982). The example is extreme, but the long-spaced sonic tool was introduced to overcome the problem. Increasing the transmitter to receiver distance, as in the long-spaced sonic tool, theoretically increases the signal penetration (Ellis 1987). The increased depth of investigation occurs because the compressional wave in the damaged zone has a lower velocity, or is more attenuated (looses more energy), than the wave in the undamaged formation. If the transmitter-receiver distances are large enough, the deeper penetrating wave is detected as the first arrival (this same principal determines the lower limit on the transmitter-reciever spacing in a conventional tool, *see* above). This depth can be greater than 30 cm (1 ft) (Ellis and Singer 2007). The reservations about the long-spaced tool have been mentioned.

The second form of borehole damage is mechanical, and has become evident as modern image logs have been acquired. Many of the images show drilling induced fractures and mechanical damage in the vicinity of the borehole (Chapter 15). The damage is caused by the change in pressure and stresses introduced by the drilling process. Some of this damage worsens with time; some improves. Comparisons between LWD and wireline sonic logs show that LWD velocities are commonly higher than wireline velocities (Bean *et al.* 1998). The differences are probably caused by a combination of the mechanical and the chemical damage around the borehole, and suggest that a sonic measurement made as soon as possible after drilling is going to be more reliable.

Bed resolution

The vertical resolution of the older sonic tools was the span between receivers both for the borehole compensated tools and the long-spaced tools. This was frequently 61 cm (2 ft) for the BHC, and 61 cm (2 ft) and 120 cm (4 ft) for the long-spaced shallow and deep configurations respectively. Beds of less than 60 cm thickness (or less than 120 cm on the LSS deep configuration) would be registered on the log, but a true velocity not measured.

Unwanted logging effects

The conventional borehole compensated sonic (BHC) was very robust, even in poor and over-sized holes: the compensation system was very effective (cf. Ellis 1987). However, in extremely poor holes, cycle skipping would sometimes occur. It was caused when the first (compressional wave) arrival was too attenuated (weak) to activate the receiver, which would only be tripped by a subsequent arrival: the recorded time was therefore too long (slowness too large) (**Figure 9.8,a**). The reverse situation occurred when strong noise signals tripped a receiver out of sequence and caused noise spikes, a feature found in hard formations such as limestones (**Figure 9.8,b**). In fact, in some environments, recording a good log was heavily reliant on the skill of the engineer. For example 'road noise' generated by the tool scraping against the borehole wall could often be eliminated by increasing the logging speed. As will be seen below, array tools largely eliminate these problems because the processing uses a significant part of eight or more wave-trains rather than just the first breaks from two.

While the conventional sonic was robust, the long-spaced sonic was not. The tool had two weaknesses; signal attenuation and dynamic compensation. Attenuation occurred because the tool was too long, and resulted in signals too weak to trigger a receiver, thus causing cycle skipping. With a dynamic compensation system, a single error in one of the eight readings comprising a full measurement sequence would be propagated

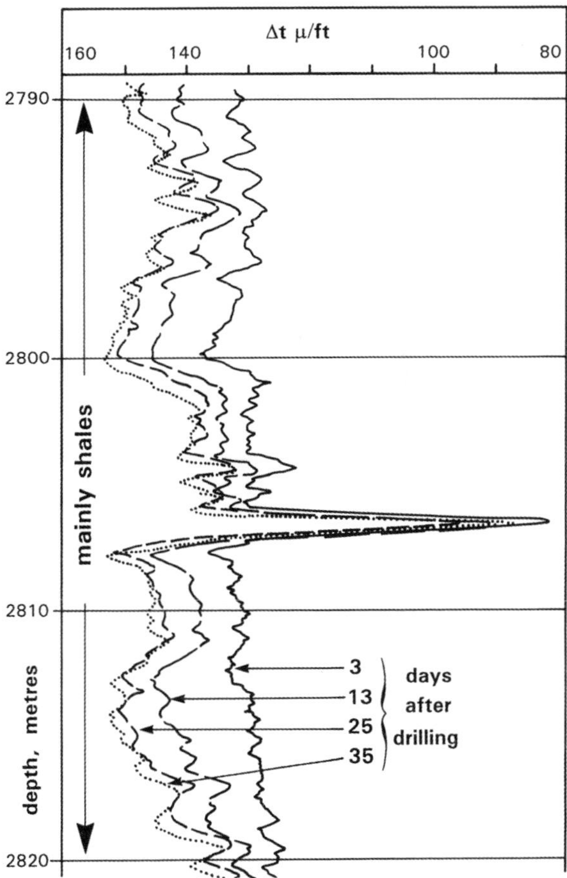

Figure 9.7 Shale alteration affecting slowness (interval transit times) in a well offshore Columbia (No. 1-1 Punta Gallinas). Successive passes of the sonic were made over 35 days and show a persistent increase in interval transit time (decreasing velocity) indicating shale alteration and deterioration. Note there is little change in the hard band at 2807 m (re-drawn from Blakeman 1982).

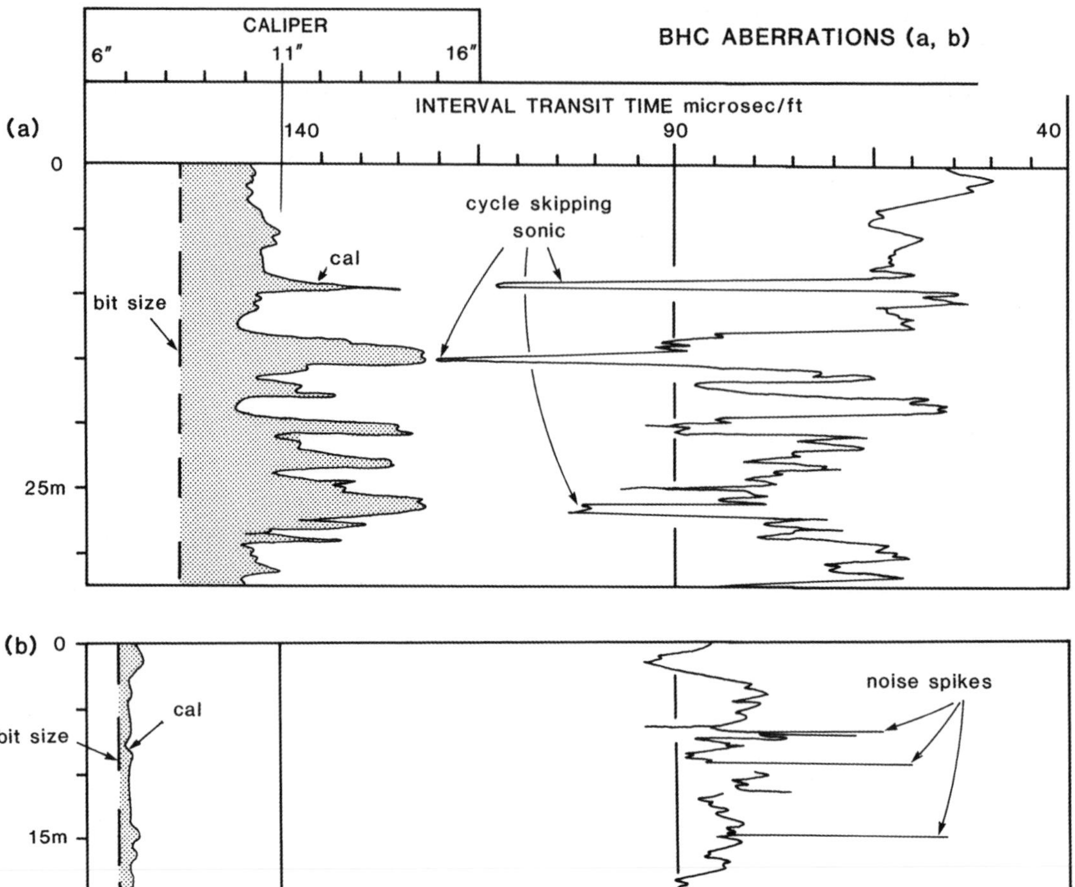

Figure 9.8 Unwanted environmental effects on the older, wireline sonic log. (a) BHC tool, cycle skipping; (b) BHC tool, noise spikes. Interval transit time = slowness.

through the entire set. The result was paired errors on the log (**Figure 9.9**) which were frequent on many long-spaced sonic records despite computer 'smoothing' (Purdy 1982).

9.3 Full waveform array, dipole, wireline sonic tools

Generalities

Array-type, 'dipole' sonic tools are in normal use today (they are often informally named 'dipole sonics' but, as explained above, the dipole source is only really necessary in slow formations). They differ from the earlier tools in that they record a full sonic wave-train from each receiver every time the transmitter fires (this represents a huge amount of data and these tools can generate gigabytes of information on a single log run). These are processed to derive the slowness (or

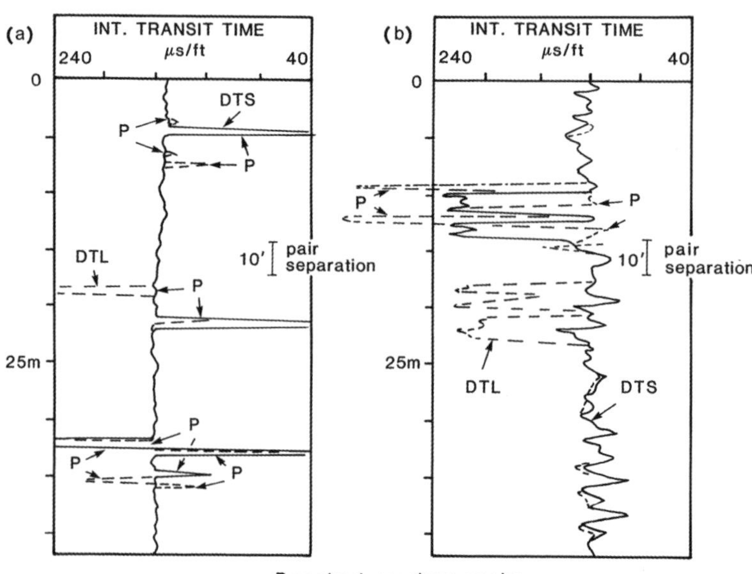

Figure 9.9 Unwanted effects on the older, wireline long spaced sonic log (LSS). (a, b) long-spacing tool, paired aberrations; DTS = short-spaced sonic, DTL = long-spaced sonic. The pairs are separated for the most part by 10 ft (3 m), the compensation shift distance. Interval transit time = slowness.

Table 9.3 Wireline, array dipole sonic tools from the major companies; some details (Serra 2008; Baker Hughes™, Halliburton and Schlumberger documents).

	Tool acronyms	T	T No	Frequency kHz	R No	T-T ft	T-R ft	R-R ft	S.I μs	DOI inches
Schlumberger	ASS	M (A)	2	5–18	2+ 8 (A)	2	3,5 & 8,11.5	2, 0.5	5,10,20	
	DSI	M	1	5, 9–30	8		9	0.5	10–32.7	
		D	2	0.08–1.5		0.5	11,11.5			12–24
	Sonic scanner	M D (A)		wide range						5–12
										6-6 ft
Baker Hughes™	DAC™		2	low	12					
	XMAC™	M	2		8	30				
		D	2		8	12				
	MAC™	M	2	2–15, 8	8				8	
		D	2	1–3	8				8,16,24,32	6
Halliburton	FWS	M,D (A)	1M,2D	AGC	4		long	1		
	XACT	M	2	1–10, 15	4 sets of 2	1				
		D	2	0.5–5, 1						
	LFDT	M	1	15	1,12,13,14	4			4–8	3 ft
		D	2	1.5	1,12,13,14	4			16	

T = transmitter; R = receiver; S.I. = sample interval; DOI = depth of investigation; M = monopole; D = dipole; (A) = array; AGD = automatic gain control; Tool acronyms, *see* Table 9.2.

interval transit time) of the compressional, shear and Stoneley wave arrivals. Full wave-train tool designs vary between companies but a common feature is the use of an array of receivers, between 8 and 13 (**Table 9.3**). At least 8 receivers seem to be preferable (Smith *et al.* 1991). The other common thread is the use of monopole and dipole transmitters. The acquisition of shear and Stoneley measurements, in addition to the compressional measurement, has broadened the possible applications of the sonic log, especially in the seismic and rock mechanics fields, at the same time as providing better quality measurements.

The Schlumberger Dipole Shear Sonic Imager (DSI) and sonic scanner are used as examples.

Dipole Shear Imager (DSI) and Sonic Scanner

The Dipole Shear Imager (DSI) of Schlumberger is fully digital (Schlumberger 2002, tool brochure), that is to say the waveforms are converted to digital form down-hole prior to being transmitted to surface, rather than simply being amplified as was the case with the BHC type tools. It has a monopole source and two, orthogonal (crossed) dipole sources, all separated by an isolation section from an array of 8 receivers. The sources are between 9 and 11.5 feet (2.7–3.5 m) from the nearest receiver, and the receiver array is 42" long (107 cm) (**Figure 9.10**).

The omni-directional monopole source can use a low frequency pulse (1 kHz) for Stoneley wave, and a high frequency pulse (8–30 kHz) for compressional and (fast) shear wave measurement. The transmitter is 9 ft (2.7 m) from the nearest receiver. The two orthogonal dipole sources, 11.5 ft and 11 ft (3.5 and 3.35 m) from the nearest receiver, are used for shear wave logging. For this, they use a low frequency signal, usually below 4 kHz (80 Hz–5 kHz), to create flexure waves. The receiver section has eight hydrophone pairs, each pair in line with one of the dipole transmitters. Each pair can be recorded separately for dipole, shear measurements, but summed for monopole recording. The entire array spans 3.5 ft (107 cm) with receivers separated by 6" (15 cm) (Schlum-

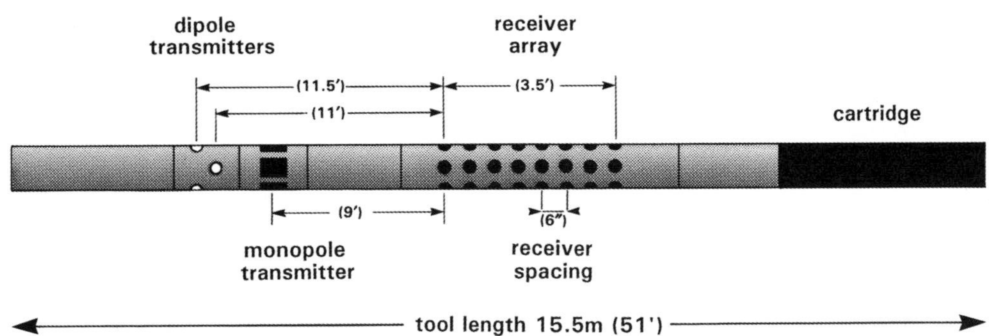

Figure 9.10 The Dipole Shear Imager (DSI) tool of Schlumberger (re-drawn from Schlumberger document).

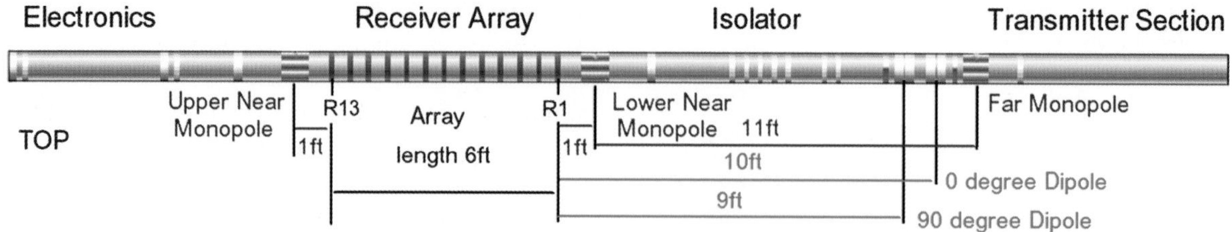

Figure 9.11 The Sonic scanner tool of Schlumberger with monopole and crossed dipole transmitters and a receiver array of 13 levels, each with 8, independent, azimuthal receivers (modified from Pistre *et al.* SPWLA 2005).

berger 2002). Depending on the frequency of the signal, waveforms are sampled digitally into 512 samples. A full waveform lasts around 5ms (maximum 10ms) and can be sampled at 5 μsec, 10 μsec or 20 μsec (**Table 9.3).**

The DSI can operate in any one or all of six modes: upper dipole mode, lower dipole mode, crossed dipole mode, Stoneley mode, *P* and *S* mode and first-motion mode **(Table 9.3).** The tool is run hole-centred as large eccentring effects can occur. Logging speed depends on the information required. In general mode, logging speed can be 1100 m/hr (3600 ft/hr), similar to nuclear tools. If all six possible firing modes are used, logging speed should be 300 m/hr (1000 ft/hr) and if high resolution 15 cm (6″) results are required, 275 m/hr (900 ft/hr) (Schlumberger 2002 *op. cit.*).

The Sonic Scanner (Pistre *et al.* 2005) is a technical advance on the DSI. Its development was stimulated by the demand for reliable rock mechanics data, which is used to predict borehole stability and sanding potential in development wells. The tool can provide all the information that the DSI and earlier tools provided, plus a lot more. It is a modular tool so it can be customised for a particular application, and new technology can be introduced as a new module rather than requiring the design of a whole new tool. In its basic form, it has near and far monopole transmitters, 0.3–3.35 m (1 ft and 11 ft) from the nearest array receiver, which measure near and far formation compressional slowness (**Figure 9.11**). The tool is thus able to compare slowness in the near borehole section, which can be altered by drilling, using a 30 cm and 2.1 m (1 ft and 7 ft) spacing, and in the far formation which is more likely to be unaltered, using an 3.35–5.2 m (11 ft–17 ft) spacing. The actual depths of investigation are about 15 cm (6″) for the shallow signal and 1.8 m (6 ft) for the far signal, but these will vary with signal frequency and formation slowness (Serra 2008). The tool also contains two orthogonal dipole sources (at offset depths), at 2.7 m and 3 m (9 ft and 10 ft) respectively from the nearest receiver of the array, and they are used for shear wave measurements and shear wave splitting (anisotropy) evaluation. The frequency of the dipole sources is between 300 Hz and 8 kHz, the actual frequency that gives the measurement being the optimum for that formation and used automatically.

The Sonic Scanner receiver section contains 104 sensors which make up 13 depth stations each with 8, azimuthal sensors. The stations are 15 cm (6″) apart and so form an array 1.8 m (6 ft) long (**Figure 9.11**). The array is therefore able to measure inline dipole signals (X-X), and orthogonal (Y-Y) signals, and their opposing pairs (X-Y, Y-X), or the azimuths of any arrival. Monopole receiver records can be stacked together to improve signal to noise ratios or can be treated separately to provide 8 radial monopole arrivals. As noted above, tools like the Sonic Scanner are really a kit of parts that can be put together to create a tool that is customised for a particular application, the challenge for the end user is to measure what is needed, and to avoid making measurements just because the tool can (e.g. modelling seismic attributes or predicting sanding potential).

Processing, picking slowness

All array tools acquire a number of receiver (or transmitter) common waveforms at each depth station (**Figure 9.12**), the number of individual waveforms depending on the number of receivers and/or transmitters used. Receiver threshold detection, as used in the older tools, is inadequate and inappropriate for a full waveform analysis. Instead, filtering and gathering techniques are used to analyse the entire, digital waveform from all the receivers of an array at each depth station. Sampling depths are normally the same as the separation distance between the receivers of the array, mostly 15 cm (6″), similar to other standard logs. The point of measurement is the mid-point of the array. Various algorithms exist for extracting slowness values from a series of wave-trains, and are mostly adapted from general signal processing theory. Schlumberger use a method called Slowness Time Coherency (STC); Baker Hughes™ use semblance. The methods are similar to the semblance method of seismic processing and will be briefly described (Block *et al.* 1991; Schlumberger 2002).

A fixed, small time length window is used to compare parts of a waveform across the receiver array using a linear moveout. In this context, moveout is the time difference at which the same signal arrives in each receiver across the array, corresponding to the distance between them. Ideally, the parts of two wave-trains from

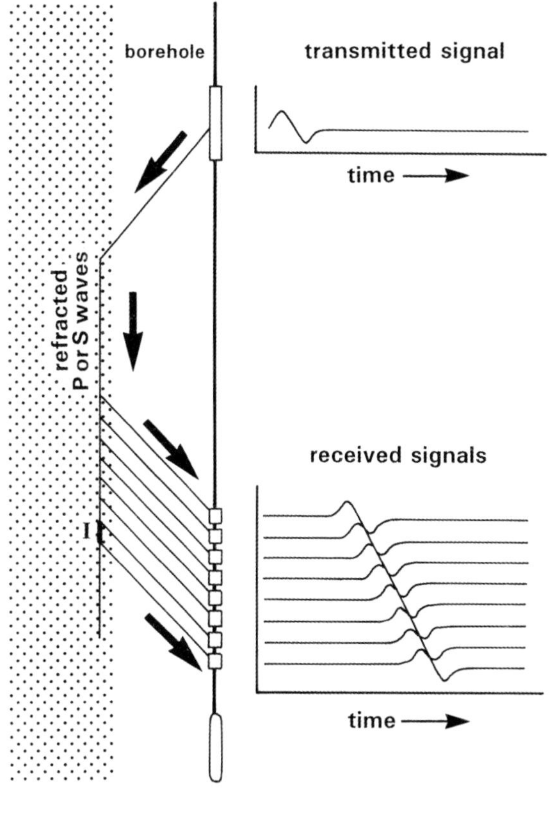

Figure 9.12 Array sonic sampling system. At any depth, a series of transmitter-common readings are made, with different offsets. Sequences of readings are gathered in various ways (*see* text and Figure 9.13) (from Smith *et al.* 1991).

adjacent receivers will be identical except for a shift in time, given by slowness multiplied by receiver spacing. On a display of all the equally spaced waveforms, the linear moveout can be represented as a straight line with a constant angle across the plot. The gradient or angle is proportional to the slowness: the steeper the slope the greater the slowness (i.e. the lower the velocity) (**Figure 9.13,a**). In reality, the compared parts of the wave-train will never be completely identical. A wave-train gets distorted as it travels further through the formation, and noise (electronic or mechanical) may adversely affect individual trains. In practice, the outputs from all the receivers are compared and the slowness that gives the best match is chosen. By using eight or more wave-trains the influence of noise can be drastically reduced (compare this with the older BHC tools where a single noise spike on one of the receivers could corrupt the measurement).

With slowness time coherency processing (STC), the comparison is made across the array from the fastest time expected to the slowest (i.e. shallowest to steepest angle on **Figure 9.13,a**). For each comparison, a coherence function is calculated which is an expression of how similar the waveforms are in the particular time window. When a moveout corresponds to a particular wave arrival time, say the shear arrival, waveforms will be more similar and the coherence function will be high. If the arrival is hard to pick, the coherence value will be low. At any one depth, the full waveform is explored in this way and a plot can be made of arrival times against slowness. The corresponding coherence function can be represented on the Z axis and contoured (or coloured) to make a semblance contour (or colour) plot (**Figure 9.13,b**). As described below, these results can be represented on a log plot to give an indication of the robustness of a measurement (**Figure 9.16**).

Most tools normally estimate compressional slowness using first arrival detection as well. This is a useful

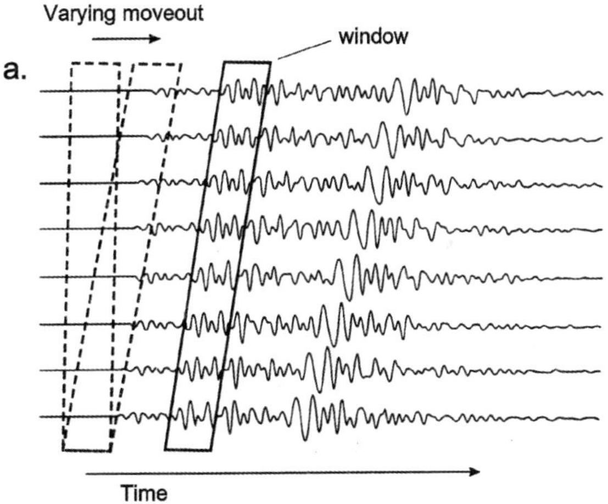

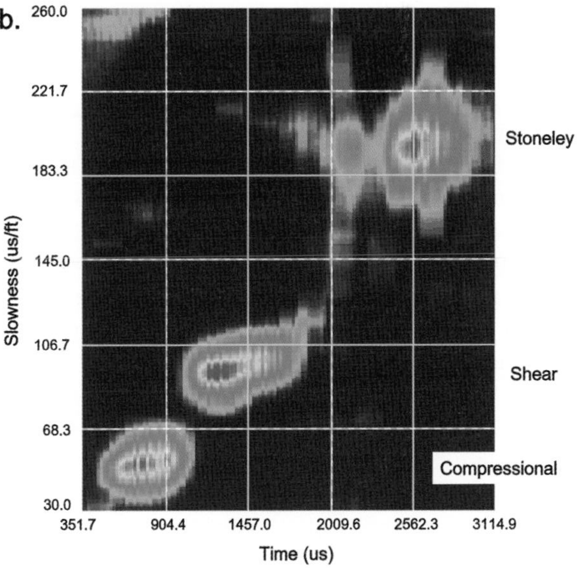

Figure 9.13 Picking arrival times on array waveforms. a) Using a small window and a linear moveout. b) Using slowness time coherency (STC) processing to build a contoured time-slowness plot with coherency as the Z axis (modified from Schlumberger 2002; Kessler *et al.* SPWLA 2004). *Courtesy of Schlumberger.*

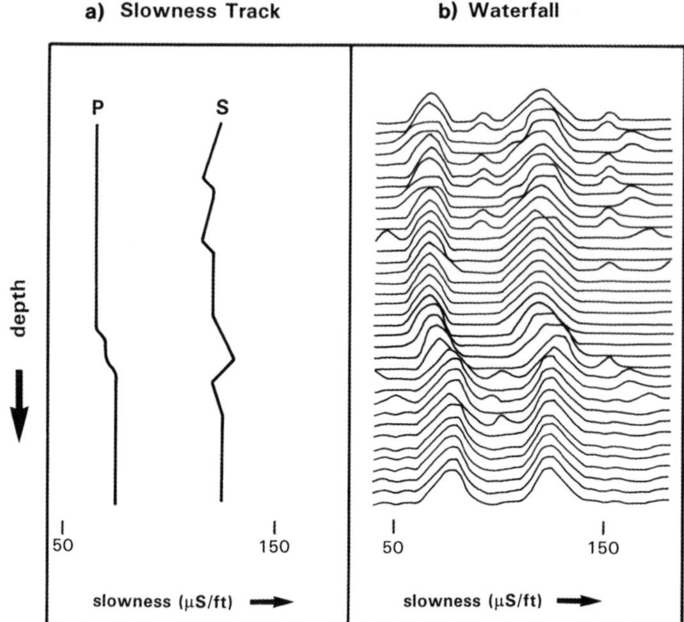

Figure 9.14 Array sonic displays. a) Individual slowness logs of discrete, picked values against depth, b) 'waterfall' waveform display of illustrative waveforms at selected depths (re-drawn from Smith *et al.* 1991).

independent check on the compressional slowness and, ideally, the curves produced by the two different methods should agree well. In fact, array sonic tools typically produce several different compressional and shear slowness curves, with curve names that typically give little information on how they were computed. The end-user needs to consult the log header or the logging companies literature to find which curve is which.

Displays and data output

The values from the full waveform processing can be plotted as single, discrete slowness values for each of the compressional (*P*), shear (*S*) and Stoneley (*St*) arrivals, in the same way as other logs are plotted (**Figure 9.14,a**). This is the simplest form of plot from the full waveform tool and, for compressional slowness, uses the same format and scales as have always been used (in particular slowness increases from right to left). However, additional types of display are available, which try to include more of the acquired data, not just a single value, and give some visual idea of the quality of the measurement. Three of these more complex plots are: the edited waveform display (waterfall plot); the variable density display; and the slowness-coherence display. There are others.

The edited waveform display shows an actual waveform (edited) from a particular receiver at selected, regular depths (**Figure 9.14,b**). Typically, about 1ms of data is plotted, which is sufficient to capture the compressional, shear and Stoneley arrivals with a transmitter-receiver spacing of 2m (the waveform would typically be plotted only from an elapsed time of 0.5ms, as before that no formation signal will appear). This type of plot is not limited to array sonic tools and, in fact, was in use long before these tools appeared, and has been available as long as computer logging units have been in service (ca. 1980).

The variable density display (VDL) shows the same information as the edited waveform but was actually in use even before computer units appeared. It also uses an edited, complete waveform from a single receiver but displays it in a different way. Instead of plotting individual wave-trains, the individual peaks and troughs from all the individual traces are amalgamated as continuous stripes. The positive areas are coloured black, the negative white, in a similar way to the shading of a seismic trace (**Figure 9.15**). The shaded area may be one solid colour (i.e. black) as in this example, or a colour graded by amplitude. The horizontal scale is time, and may include an actual waveform trace. The plot is an attempt to represent as much information as possible about the full waveform. Both types of waveform display (edited waveform and variable density) can provide simple quality checks of the reliability of the compressional and shear slowness picks. To do this, the slowness curves are superimposed on the waveform display using appropriate scales (VDL or Waveform are equally suitable). If the slowness values are reliable they will track the leading edge of the waveform (compressional), or the first higher amplitude arrival (shear).

The third display is one in which the picked slowness is shown along with the value of the coherence or semblance for that pick. It is a very quick quality check

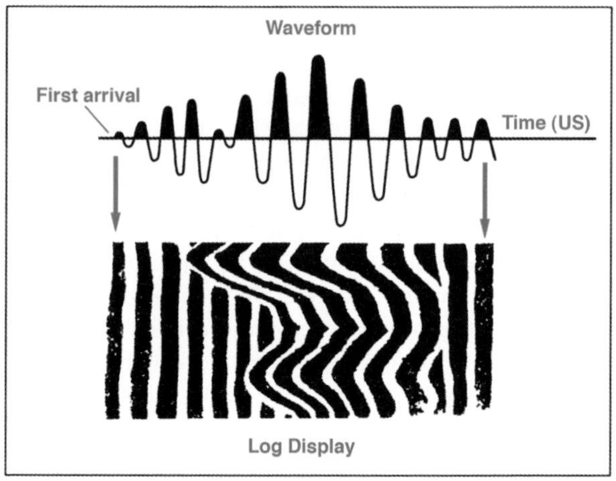

Figure 9.15 Origin of the variable density display of array sonic waveforms (modified from Serra and Serra 2000, courtesy Serralog).

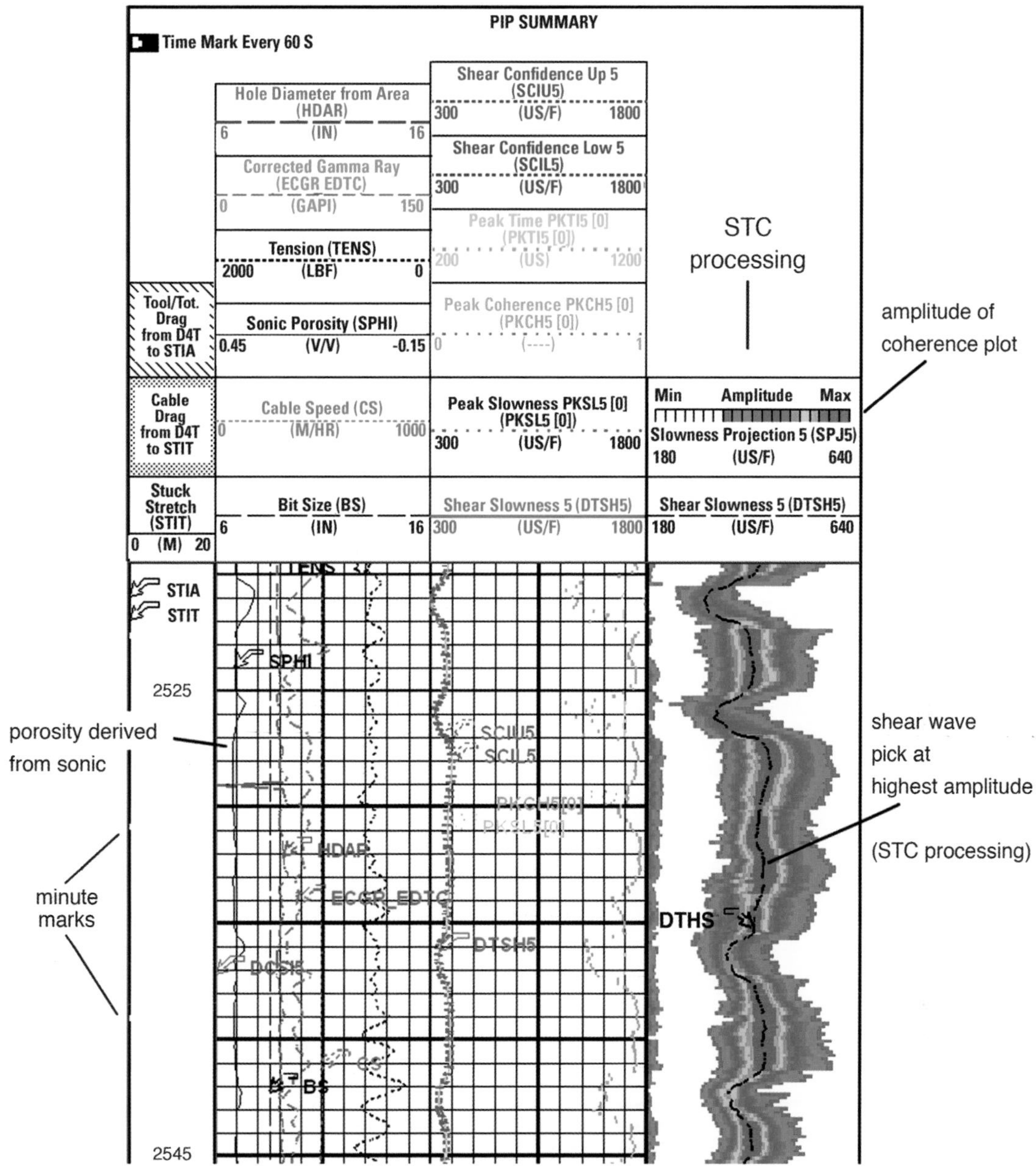

Figure 9.16 Log display of shear sonic slowness from slowness coherency (STC) processing (output from a Schlumberger SonicScanner tool).

on the reliability of the slowness curve. The slowness has the horizontal scale of μsec/ft (usually) but is often reversed (i.e. lower values to the left) and the limits expanded to include the very slow values for shear and Stoneley arrivals. The coherence value for the pick is represented by a colour scale across the entire track, typically red for high values, green and blue for low (**Figure 9.16**). Normally, the actual slowness curve is superimposed on this so that the user can see how reliable the pick is. If the curve coincides with a red part of the plot, the coherence is high and the pick is probably reliable. If the curve coincides with a green coloration, the coherence is weak. The coherence value is taken from the STC or other waveform processing, as explained previously, and the horizontal scale on the coherence is the same slowness scale as for the plotted log curve. Other presentations exist which show the confidence level of the pick.

Depth of investigation and vertical (bed) resolution

The depth of investigation of the array tools depends on the same factors that influence the depth of investigation in the older tools, namely transmitter to receiver spacing, formation slowness, wave type and signal characteristics. Compressional waves have a deeper depth of investigation than shear waves. In addition, the depth of investigation of any wave is greater at lower frequencies.

The general assumption, as discussed, is that the depth of investigation of compressional waves varies over the range of 15 cm – 1.0 m (5.9" – 39.4"). As will be discussed (*Wellbore stability*, Section 9.7), deeper investigation is preferred because the immediate borehole environment may be mechanically and chemically altered. The depth of investigation of the Dipole Shear Imager (DSI) is said to vary between 30.5 cm and 1 m (12" and 3 ft) for the compressional wave and 13 cm and 30.5 cm (5" and 1 ft) for the shear wave (Serra 2008). For the Sonic Scanner, the dipole signal has a depth of investigation of between half the borehole diameter (short wavelength) and 2–3 borehole widths (long wavelengths) (for example 10–60 cm (4" to 2 ft) in an 8.5" hole) (**Table 9.3**) (Pistre *et al.* 2005). It varies with frequency.

The vertical resolution of an array type sonic is the vertical height of the receiver array. For the Schlumberger Dipole Shear Imager (DSI), this is 1.07 m (3.5 ft) (**Figure 9.17**) and the measure point is the mid-point of the array. For the Sonic Scanner, it is 1.82 m (6 ft) (the height of the receiver array) with 15 cm (6") sampling (the distance between the receivers) (Schlumberger 2005). A bed that is thinner than the array gather will still be detected, and at its real depth position, but it will not be fully resolved (Hsu and Chang 1987). Generally, all the receiver information will be included in one gather. Borehole compensation may be applied by using transmitter stations through the receiver array section (**Figure 9.17**).

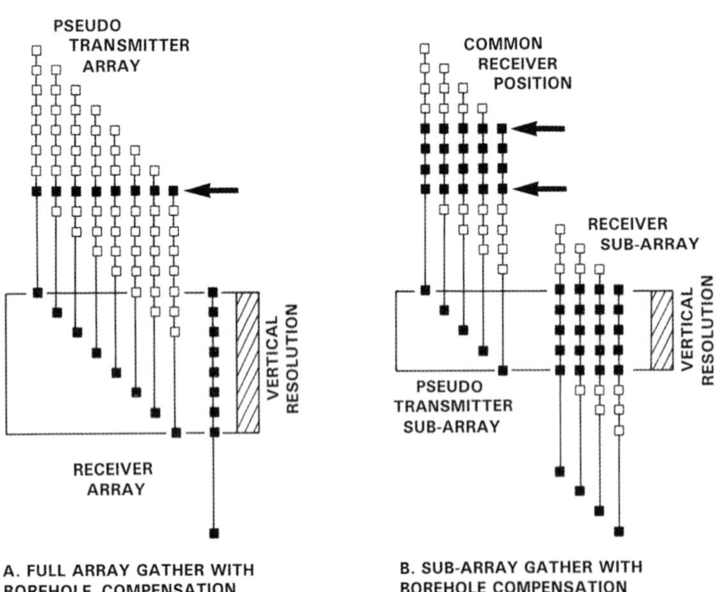

Figure 9.17 Data gathering methods for the array sonic used by Schlumberger. a) Gather using one transmitter position and an array of 8 receivers. b) Gather using 4 transmitter positions and an array of 5 receivers. The vertical resolution of the measurements will be the vertical height of the array or sub-array (re-drawn modified from Hsu and Chang 1987).

Methods exist for achieving a smaller vertical resolution by not using the entire array for the processing sequence. A method devised by Schlumberger is said to give a resolution equal to the receiver spacing, 15 cm (6"). The method consists of using just two receivers for one depth but with the tool at varying depths, so that the receiver pair progressively changes (Schlumberger 2002). For this type of information the tool must be run slowly.

9.4 LWD sonic tools

Generalities

The conversion of the sonic log to an LWD measurement was probably the most challenging of all the wireline to LWD transfers. It was the last of the basic measurements to appear in LWD. The obvious challenge was to distinguish the sonic pulse from the loud background noise generated by the drilling process. First arrival detection simply would not work in this environment and so LWD sonic tools had to be array tools from the outset. However, there are normally fewer receivers in the LWD array than in the wireline tool, although a minimum of four are needed to allow a sonic signal to be extracted from the background noise.

In the LWD environment it is not realistic to transmit complete waveforms in real time, so the tools perform processing downhole and only transmit to surface a single value for the compressional slowness curve. This is a significant difference with the wireline tools. LWD waveforms are stored in memory and can only be downloaded when the tool returns to the surface but, at that point, they can be re-processed using exactly the same techniques that are applied to wireline logs.

Because of the complex and noisy environment in which LWD sonic logs are acquired, there has been an assumption that the LWD sonic is inherently not very accurate. This is no longer true. There are two difficult elements in the design of an LWD sonic, a transmitter signal that is not influenced by noise and the acoustic isolation between the transmitter and receiver sections. Early LWD design used a high frequency monopole source, and receivers were placed close to the transmitter to try to enhance the signal to noise ratio and minimise the direct signal through the tool. Only the compressional arrival was measured, and analysis indicates that the error level of these early tools was 2 or 3 times greater than the same vintage wireline tools (Tang *et al.* 2007). New electronics, new designs and acquired experience mean that LWD sonic tools are now gen-

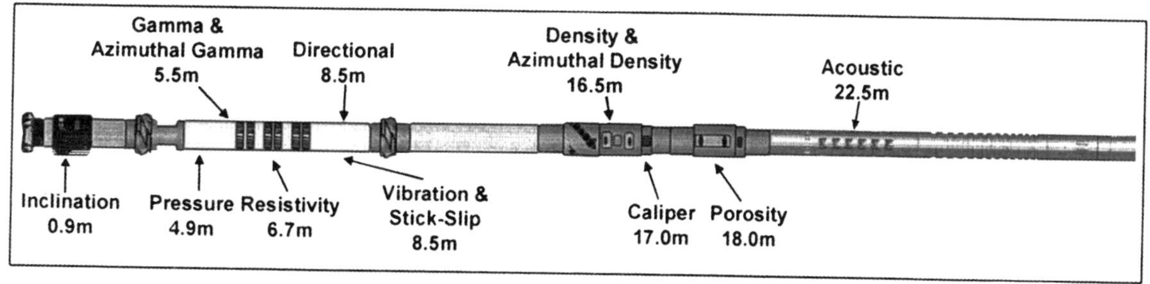

Figure 9.18 An LWD borehole assembly which includes the Acoustic Properties eXplorer™ (APX) of Baker Hughes™ INTEQ. It has been placed behind the other sensors in this BHA (from Gravem *et al.* SPWLA 2003).

erally as good as their wireline counterparts. Normally, the sonic section of an LWD bottom-hole assembly (BHA) is run behind the more familiar tools. In the illustrated BHA, the sonic sensor is 22.5 m (74 ft) behind the bit, coming behind the gamma ray, resistivity and neutron-density tools (**Figure 9.18**). This reflects the use to which the tool is put; it is often run as a wireline replacement. However, the distance behind the bit may be changed at will, and this is only an example.

The SoundTrak™ or Acoustic Properties eXplorer™ (APX) from Baker Hughes™ INTEQ will be described as typical of the present generation of LWD sonic tool, but all major companies have their own (**Table 9.4**).

SoundTrak™ or Acoustic Properties eXplorer™ (APX™)

The Acoustic Properties eXplorer™ tool module is 9.9 m (32.5 ft) long and consists of a transmitter section which has modular transmitters for monopole, dipole and quadrupole signals, an isolation section, and a receiver section with 6 lines of wide spectrum receivers, segmented into four orthogonal, independent sets (Gravem *et al.* 2003). The distance between the transmitter and the nearest receiver is 3.25 m (10.66 ft) and the measure point (centre of the receiver array) is 2.16 m (7.08 ft) from the bottom of the tool (Joyce *et al.* 2001).

The segmented transmitter functions in either monopole, dipole or quadrupole modes over a wide frequency range, including the 10–18 kHz band for which the system was designed (Joyce *et al.* 2001 *op. cit.*). A more recent tool (Tang *et al.* 2007) uses a segmented source which operates between 2–5 kHz and 9–15 kHz. The higher frequency is used for fast and slow formations, and the lower frequency for ultra-slow, unconsolidated formations. There is a low frequency quadrupole excitation at 2 kHz which is used for a direct shear velocity measurement.

In monopole mode, and at a high and low frequency, the transmitter provides a signal for the compressional and Stoneley measurements respectively. In a quadrupole mode, at both high and low frequency, it provides a signal for shear measurement in respectively fast and slow formations. A high transmitter power is required to minimise the signal to noise ratio. Measuring shear arrivals in slow formations is difficult with the wireline tools but is especially difficult in the LWD environment. Slow formations have a shear slowness greater than the compressional slowness of the mud (i.e. a slower velocity), meaning greater than 190 μsec/ft in water or up to 240 μsec/ft in oil based mud (Gravem *et al.* 2003). The high transmitter power enables the receiver section to have an offset of 3.25 m (10.66 ft), a greater distance than in the early LWD tools, and now enables a better depth of investigation, equivalent to the wireline tools. The central section of the tool is an acoustic isolator consisting of a series of rings around the drill collar. They stop the transmitter signal from reaching the receivers directly along the drill collar itself. The compressional

Table 9.4 LWD sonic tools from the major companies; some details (Serra 2008; Baker Hughes™, Halliburton and Schlumberger documents).

	Tool	T	Frequency kHz	RA	R-R inches	meas type	acous aper ft
Schlumberger	SonicVISION		wide	4		Δtc, Δts	2
Baker Hughes™	SoundTrak™ (APX™)	1Q	M 10–18 Q 2–6	4 × 6A	9	Δtc, Δts, Δtst	45″
Halliburton	Bi-modal BAT	2	6–8 & 12–15 In phase or opposite phase	2 of 7A	6	Δtc, Δts	

T = transmitter; R = receiver; RA = receiver array; M = monopole; Q = quadrupole; (A) = array AGD = automatic gain control; acous aper = acoustic aperture. See also Table 9.2.

wave from the monopole transmitter can be affected by the tool at certain frequencies, but the quadrupole signal is not affected (Tang *et al.* 2002).

Each of the four orthogonal, azimuthal receivers, in the six rows of the receiver array section, is aligned along the tool with the sectors of the transmitters. The six receiver rows are spaced 23 cm (9″) apart along the tool, making the receiver section 1.14 m (45″) long (Joyce *et al.* 2001 *op. cit.*). Each of the 4 azimuthal receivers at each level of the array is independent, so that four receiver waveforms can be combined into a compound waveform in order to minimise unwanted noise and decentralisation effects. At each depth level, six compound waveforms representing the entire receiver array, can be processed downhole. Typically compressional arrival time is collected in real time. Processed results and raw monopole, dipole and quadrupole waveforms are stored downhole, and full data are only downloaded from memory once the tool returns to the surface (*see* processing)

Depth of investigation and vertical resolution

The nominal vertical resolution of the LWD sonic will be the same as for the wireline tool, namely the width of the receiver array. Thus, for the APX, vertical resolution will be 1.14 m (3 ft 9″). No figures are available for the depth of investigation (DOI) of the LWD sonic tools, although modelling is based on a 10 cm (4″) investigation.

Processing: while, and post drilling

Processing of the LWD sonic is critical. Realtime use requires the data to be processed downhole to reduce the volume of data sent uphole. This will normally mean that only the compressional arrival will be available in realtime. When the tool is brought to the surface, compressional, shear and possibly Stoneley data will become available. Acquiring realtime data does not compromise the subsequent processing.

Displays

Displays and output are similar to the wireline logs except that drilling parameters are frequently included, such as rate of rotation (RPM), rate of drilling penetration (ROP) and time after drilling.

Comparison with wireline logs

One of the difficulties of the LWD sonic has been its perceived unreliability. Results from the most recent tools, however, compare well with wireline tool results. LWD sonic tools can be run with objectives related to real time acquisition or with the objective of simply replacing the wireline tool. In the second case, post drilling processing is in order but for real time results, downhole processing must be used. The comparison (**Figure 9.19**) shows real time LWD sonic measurements, post drilling processed logs and other LWD measurements. The qualitative similarity of the results over a range of slownesses from carbonates to coals is clear simply from visual inspection. As a general rule, LWD and wireline compressional slowness agree well in fast formations (e.g. any of the North Sea Plays). A lot of LWD tools only have monopole sources and so cannot measure shear slowness in slow formations. Data from the classic, unconsolidated sands from West Africa and the Gulf of Mexico, for example, often have to be re-processed, even to get a reliable compressional slowness, so obtaining a shear slowness is more than extremely difficult.

However, a number of attempts have been made to measure the accuracy of the LWD sonic in a rigorous, scientific manner (Tang *et al.* 2007; Plona *et al.* 2005). One accuracy analysis found that wireline compressional measurements have errors of around 2%, occasionally up to 5% (Tang *et al.* 2007 op. cit.). Using the same method, early compressional LWD logs showed errors around 3%–7% but present compressional logs are routinely 2%, the same as for wireline. The calculations confirm experience.

9.5 Porosity determination from the sonic log

Porosity from compressional wave slowness (DTC)

It was the realisation (in 1958) that the sonic log could be used to calculate porosity that established it as one of the essential logging measurements. Other logs are now preferred for this, notably the density and NMR but, under some circumstances, the sonic compressional wave can be, and still is, used to calculate porosity. This normally only occurs when there is no alternative, for example, if hole conditions are bad or a potential reservoir has been intersected in part of the hole where it was not expected.

Because there is no universal relationship linking sonic slowness and porosity, empirical and semi-empirical equations have to be used. The simplest example is the Wyllie equation, which is based on a very, arguably over-simple model (Wyllie *et al.* 1956). It is semi-empirical and has become known as the '*Wyllie time average*' equation:

$$\frac{1}{V} = \frac{\text{Ø}}{V_{fl}} + \frac{1-\text{Ø}}{V_{ma}} \qquad (1)$$

which can be re-written, replacing Δt for V and solving for porosity as:

$$\text{Ø} = \frac{\Delta t - \Delta t_{ma}}{\Delta t_{fl} - \Delta t_{ma}} \qquad (2)$$

Where, V = tool-measured compressional velocity (*Vp*); V_{fl} = velocity (compressional) of the interstitial fluid; V_{ma} = velocity (compressional) of the matrix material; Ø= porosity; Δt = tool measured compressional slowness (interval transit time) (DTC); Δt_{fl} = slowness (compressional) of interstitial fluid; Δt_{ma} = slowness (compressional) of matrix material.

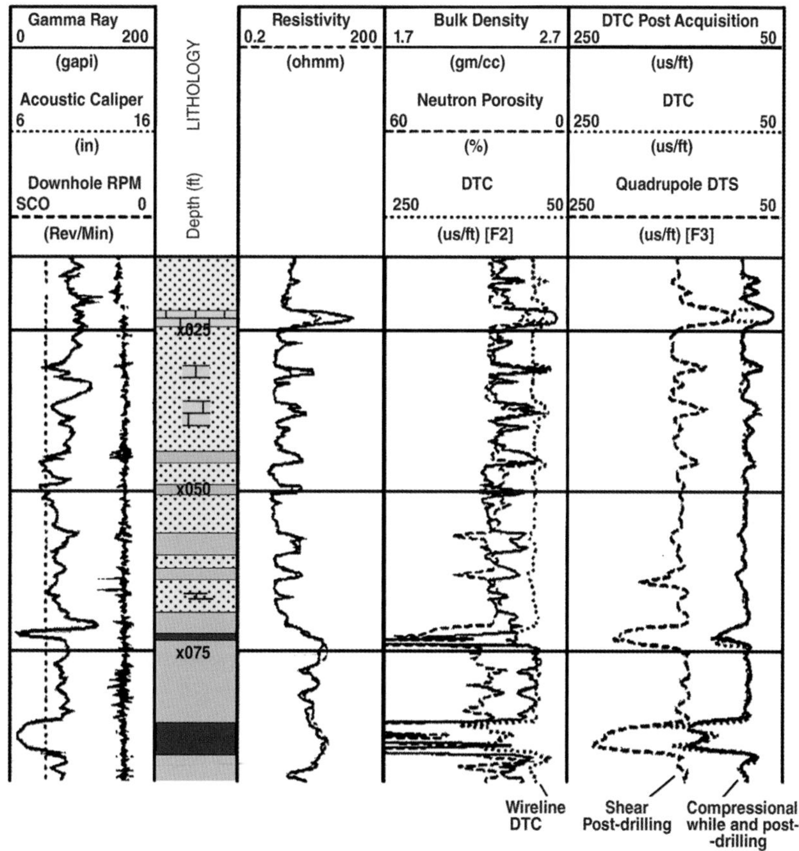

Figure 9.19 Wireline and LWD acoustic logs compared. Over the wide range of slownesses logged, there is a good correspondence (modified from Gravem *et al.* SPWLA 2003). DTC = compressional slowness.

Equation (2) simply states that the compressional slowness measured by the tool is the sum of the time spent in the solid matrix and the time spent in the fluid (Wyllie *et al.* 1956). The overall slowness is a function of the matrix compressional velocity (V_{ma}), the fluid velocity (V_{fl}) and their relative volumes (i.e. porosity) (**Figure 9.20**). The matrix type must therefore be known before applying the equation: it must be known whether the rock is a sandstone, limestone, etc. The relationship is seen on cross-plots, the measured slowness having a linear relationship with porosity (**Figure 9.21**). This relationship will vary depending on the velocity of the matrix material (fluid velocities varying little by comparison). Some of the more common matrix compressional (and shear) velocities are shown in **Table 9.5**.

Given the simplistic model on which the Wyllie equation is based, it gives good results in a surprisingly wide range of reservoirs. It is typically at its best in lower porosity, well cemented sands but, on the other hand, nearly always seriously over-predicts porosity in high porosity unconsolidated sands (**Figure 9.22**). Because of this, a large number of alternatives have been proposed which range from simple modifications to Wyllie, to completely different models. Furthermore,

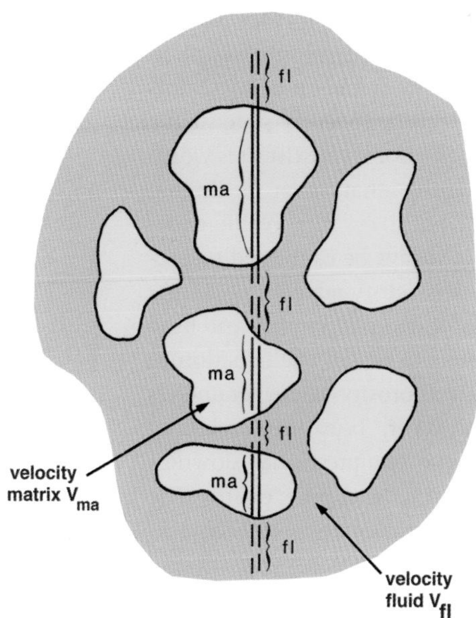

Figure 9.20 Diagrammatic representation of the path of *P* waves through a rock, showing the relationship between time spent in the matrix (V_{ma}) and time in the fluid (V_{fl}), giving the basis for the calculation of porosity from sonic velocities.

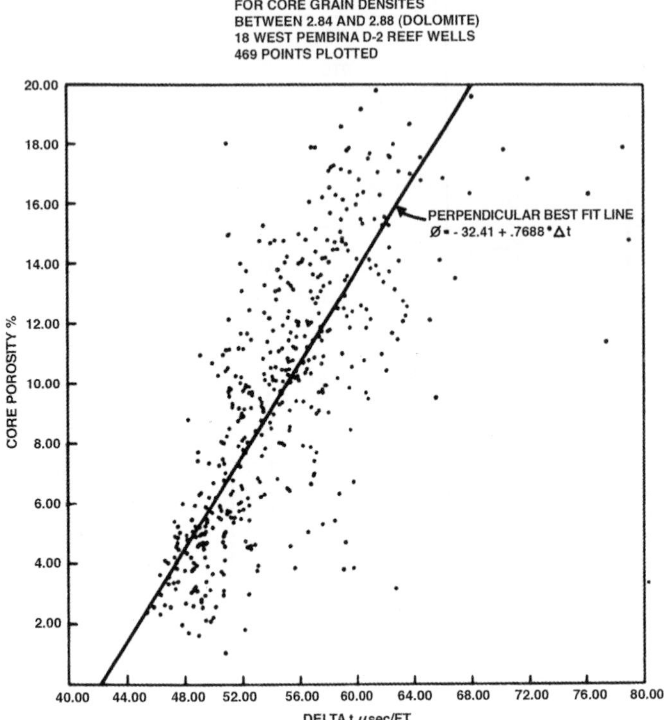

Figure 9.21 Slowness compared to measured core porosity in a dolomite (from McFadzean 1973).

some equations are intended to have wide application whereas others have clearly been developed for one particular play in a restricted area. There is no reason to expect that a universal relationship between porosity and slowness exists, in fact, on the contrary, the propagation of sound in rocks is controlled by so many factors that one can confidently state such a relationship does not exist. It is worth remembering that, over a limited range of porosities, the Wyllie equation can always be calibrated to produce a satisfactory match: it is simply a matter of choosing matrix and fluid parameters to match the equation to the known porosity. These parameters may, however, bear little relationship to the compressional slowness of pure water and pure quartz. The simple schematic representation illustrated (**Figure 9.20**) of a straight wave path through a sediment is, not surprisingly, incorrect: there will be much reflection and refraction. If an incorrect ray path is the cause of the general error, then the path through the fluid is longer than expected (or shorter through the matrix), and there is an overestimation of porosity. This is only one possibility.

The opposite is found in vuggy carbonates: the sonic often underestimates the total porosity as detected by the density log (Chapter 10). The explanation is that the compressional sonic wave that is detected always takes the simplest (fastest) path through the formation. This path will skirt the vugs (although the complexity of pore shapes will also influence velocity, Weger *et al.* 2009). The difference between the sonic and density (or other nuclear log) porosity is called the *secondary porosity index* (SPI). Although attractive, this is almost certainly too simplistic, and there are plenty of examples of vuggy carbonates where the sonic porosity is higher than the density porosity (ie the SPI is negative!) (e.g. Kennedy 2000). For unconsolidated sediments, most logging companies provide compaction correction coefficients, based on cross-plotting sonic porosities and density- or neutron log porosities. It is, however, best to avoid using the sonic log to calculate porosity in these formations (Sarmiento 1961).

When gas replaces liquid in the formation, the time average graph no longer applies (i.e. V_{fl} is replaced by $V_{fl} + V_{gas}$). Even though the sonic pulse does not penetrate deeply into the formation and, in the presence of gas is supposed not to enter the virgin (gas) zone (Serra 2000), there is often sufficient gas in the invaded zone to affect the velocity. Indeed, the effect can be used to identify gaseous

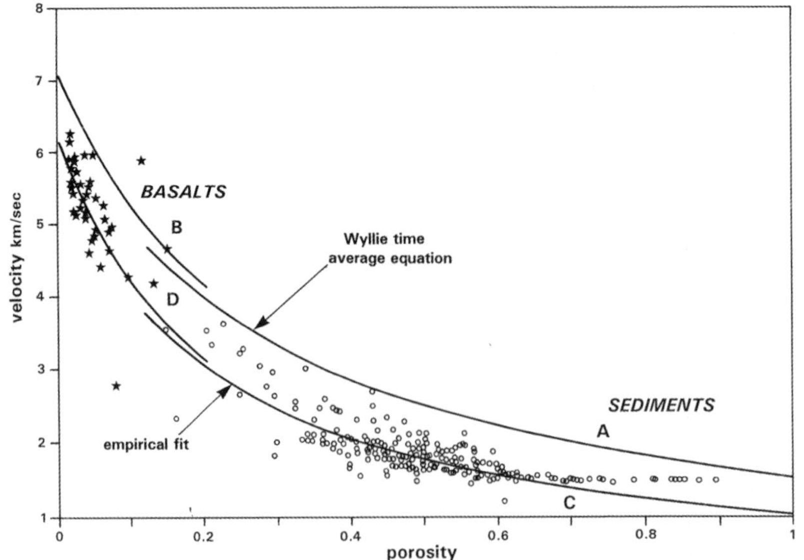

Figure 9.22 Porosity predictions from the 'Wyllie time average equation' in (A) sediments (calcareous oozes), (B) oceanic basalts. Empirical curve fit for (C) sediments and (D) oceanic basalts. The indication is that the Wyllie equation overestimates porosity across a wide range of values (from Brereton and McCann 1990).

Table 9.5 Some typical sonic matrix compressional and shear slowness, velocities and *Vp/Vs* ratios (*see also* Figure 9.24) (Wylie *et al.* 1956; Schlumberger 1972; Ellis and Singer 2007;Serra 2008).

Species	Δ*tc* (μs/ft)	*Vp* (m/s)	*Vp* (ft/s)	Δ*ts* (μs/ft)	*Vs* (m/s)	*Vs* (ft/s)	*Vp/Vs* (Δ*ts* / Δ*tc*)
Sandstones (Ø 5–20%)	51–55.5	5,029–3,505	16,500–11,500	88.0	2,895–1,830	9,500–6,000	1.6–1.8
Quartz	52.9	5,760	18,900	83.3	3,660	12,000	1.57
Limestones (Ø 5–20%)	47.5–53	5,640–3,960	18,500–13,000	88.5	2,895–2,130	9,500–7,000	1.86–1.9
Calcite	45.9	6,400	21,000	88.7	3,383	11,100	1.93
Dolomites (Ø 5–20%)	38.5–43.5	6,100–4,570	20,000–15,000	78.5	3,353–2,286	11,000–7,500	1.80
Dolomite	41.5	7,010	23,000	77.0	3,870	12,700	1.86
Shales	62.5–167	5,180–2,130	17,000–7,000				

Δ*tc* (μs/ft) = compressional slowness; Δ*ts* (μs/ft) = shear slowness; *Vp* = compressional velocity; *Vs* = shear velocity

hydrocarbons when a gas/water contact is present (**Figure 9.23**). To estimate the real porosity in the presence of gas, the porosity calculated from the raw sonic log should be multiplied by between about 0.7– 0.8, but this is only an estimate since even small amounts of gas can drastically slow the velocity. In fact, for example, the velocity of unconsolidated sands are quite insensitive to gas saturation and the slowness of the formation is almost the same whether it contains 5% or 90% gas.

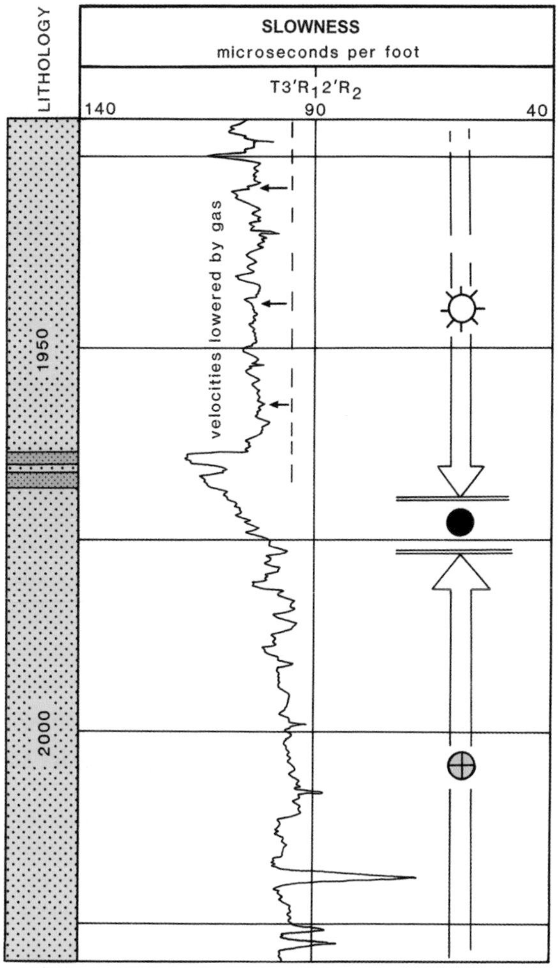

To calculate porosity in the presence of shale, the sonic log must be corrected for a shale volume derived from other logs. This adds further complications and options to the porosity-slowness equations.

Figure 9.23 The effect of gas on the BHC sonic log. The velocity (*Vp*) in this porous sandstone is lowered by about 8%.

Porosity from shear wave slowness (DTS)

Formuli similar to the time average equation have been proposed using shear wave slowness instead of compressional slowness. They are not widely accepted, although the shear slowness has the advantage that it is hardly affected by the presence of gas. The sonic shear (DTS) relationship to porosity is non-linear but can be approximated as linear below about 36% porosity (Perarnau and Payne 2006). The equation proposed by these authors is:

$$\Delta t_{shear} = 2.72\, Ø + \Delta t_{shear\ matrix} \quad (3)$$

The practical use of this equation is in the identification of gas where no other logs are available. When gas is present, the porosity calculated using the shear wave is essentially unaffected, while the porosity from the compressional wave will be over-estimated. Therefore, a separation between Δt_{shear} (DTS) and Δt_c (DTC) will indicate gas, even though the actual porosities may be wrong (Perarnau and Payne 2006 *op. cit.*). This approach is being used increasingly to demonstrate the presence of gas at low saturations, too low to be detectable with a resistivity or neutron log and therefore probably not of any economic value. It is nevertheless of interest (*see Gas and the Vp/Vs ratio,* Section 9.7).

9.6 Qualitative and semi-quantitative uses of sonic logs (non-seismic)

Lithology identification

The compressional velocity of the common sedimentary rock types is rarely diagnostic of lithology: there is too much variation within each type and too much overlap between types (**Table 9.5**, **Figures 9.24**, **9.25**). How-

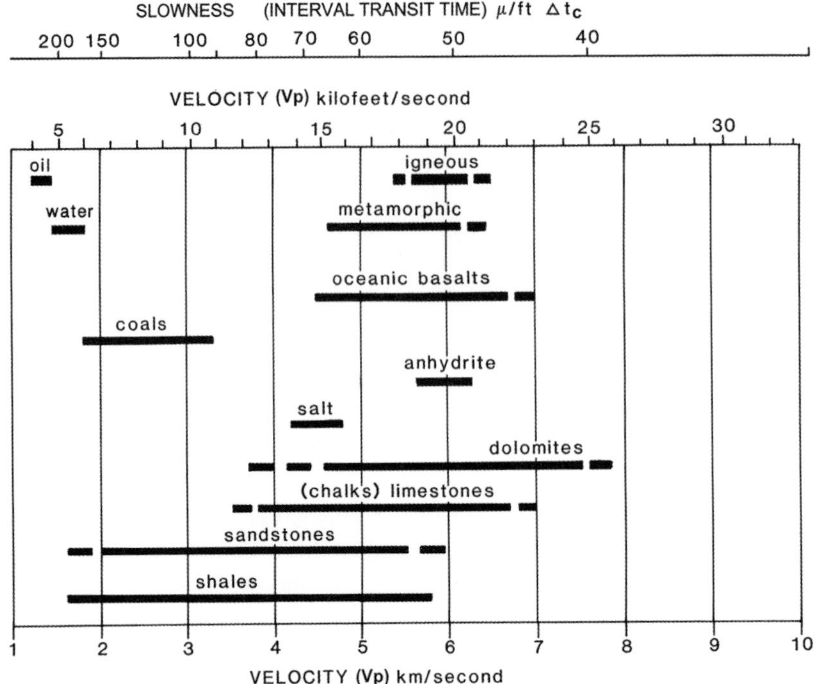

Figure 9.24 The average velocity (*Vp*) ranges of common lithologies compared. The considerable amount of overlap indicates that compressional velocity alone is seldom diagnostic of lithology (values are for depths typical of oil exploration wells). See Table 9.5 for matrix velocities and Table 9.6 for mineral velocities.

ever, such is the natural occurrence that high velocities are more likely to be associated with carbonates, middle velocities with sands and shales and low velocities with shales (**Figure 9.24**).

Certain lithologies, nonetheless, have diagnostic velocities. Coals have unusually low velocities (higher slowness times) (**Figure 9.26**). Most evaporites also have diagnostic velocities because they are essentially chemically pure substances with predictable physical properties, such as halite (rock salt), gypsum and anhydrite (**Table 9.6**). Moreover, halite velocities do not vary with depth, a fact which distorts seismic sections and is well known by geophysicists.

The use of the shear velocity in combination with the compressional velocity to identify lithology is considered below (*Seismic attributes*, Section 9.8).

Texture

Although sonic response may generally not be diagnostic in terms of lithology, it is very sensitive to rock texture, even to subtle changes. The way in which compressional waves travel through a formation is intimately associated with *'matrix, matrix materials, grain size distribution and shape, and cementation'* (Wyllie *et al.* 1956), in other words, texture (**Figure 9.20**). This is

Table 9.6 Some typical mineral and fluid compressional and shear slowness, velocities and *Vp*/*Vs* ratios (*see also* Figure 9.25) (Wylie *et al.* 1956; Schlumberger 1972; Ellis and Singer 2007; Serra 2008).

Species	Δ*tc* (µs/ft)	*Vp* (m/s)	*Vp* (ft/s)	Δ*ts* (µs/ft)	*Vs* (m/s)	*Vs* (ft/s)	*Vp*/*Vs* (Δ*ts* / Δ*tc*)
Pure water	205.5	1,463	4,800				
Salt water	165–200	1,585	5,200				
Halite	66.7–67	4,572	15,000	114.5	2,438	8,000	1.73
Anhydrite	54–50	6,096	20,000	97.5	3,475	11,400	1.81
Gypsum	52–53	5,791	19,000				
Anthracite	90–120	3,386–2,540	11,110–8,330				
Lignite	140–180	2,176–1,690	7,140–5,550				
Casing (steel)	57.8	6,096	20,000	105.2	2,895	9,500	

Δ*tc* (µs/ft) = compressional slowness; Δ*ts* (µs/ft) = shear slowness; *Vp* = compressional velocity; *Vs* = shear velocity

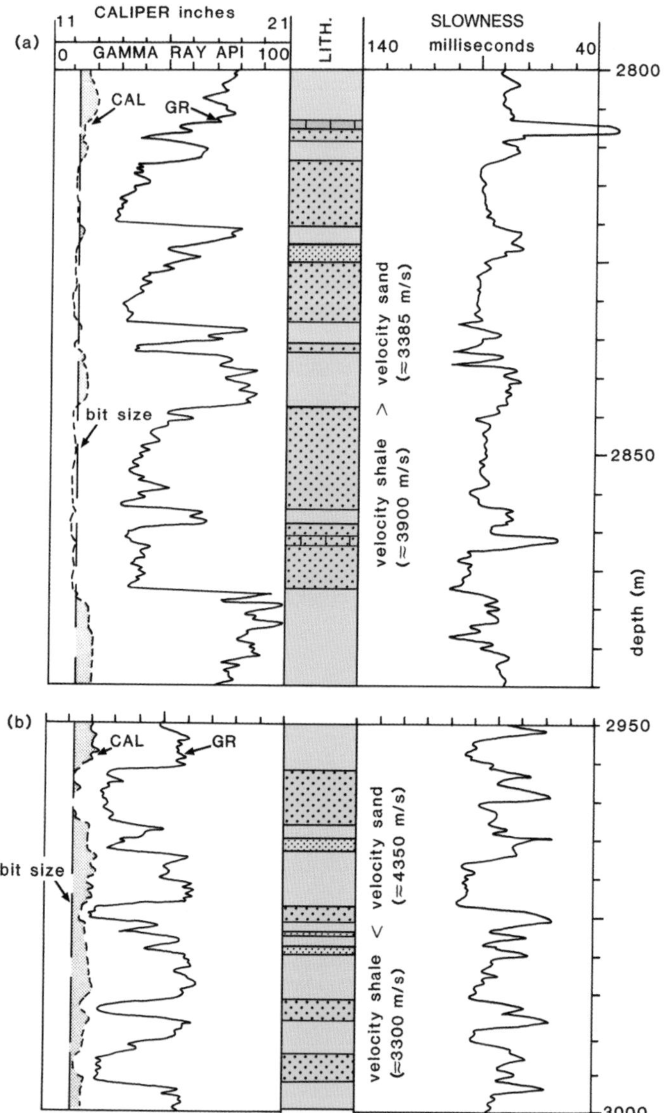

Figure 9.25 Sonic log (DTC) in a sand-shale sequences. (a) The sands have a lower sonic velocity (*Vp*), about 3385 m/sec (11,100 ft/sec) than the shales, 3900 m/sec (12,795 ft/sec). (b) The reverse, where the sands have higher velocity (*Vp*), about 4350 m/s (14,270 ft/sec) than the shales 3300 m/sec (10,825 ft/sec). Sonic velocities are therefore not diagnostic of lithology.

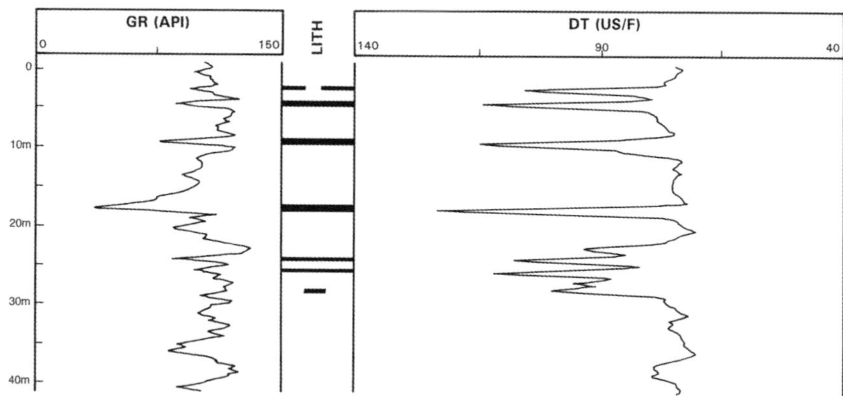

Figure 9.26 Distinctive sonic log (DTC) response in coals. The slowness is characteristically very high (low velocity, *Vp*) (cf. Figure 9.24).

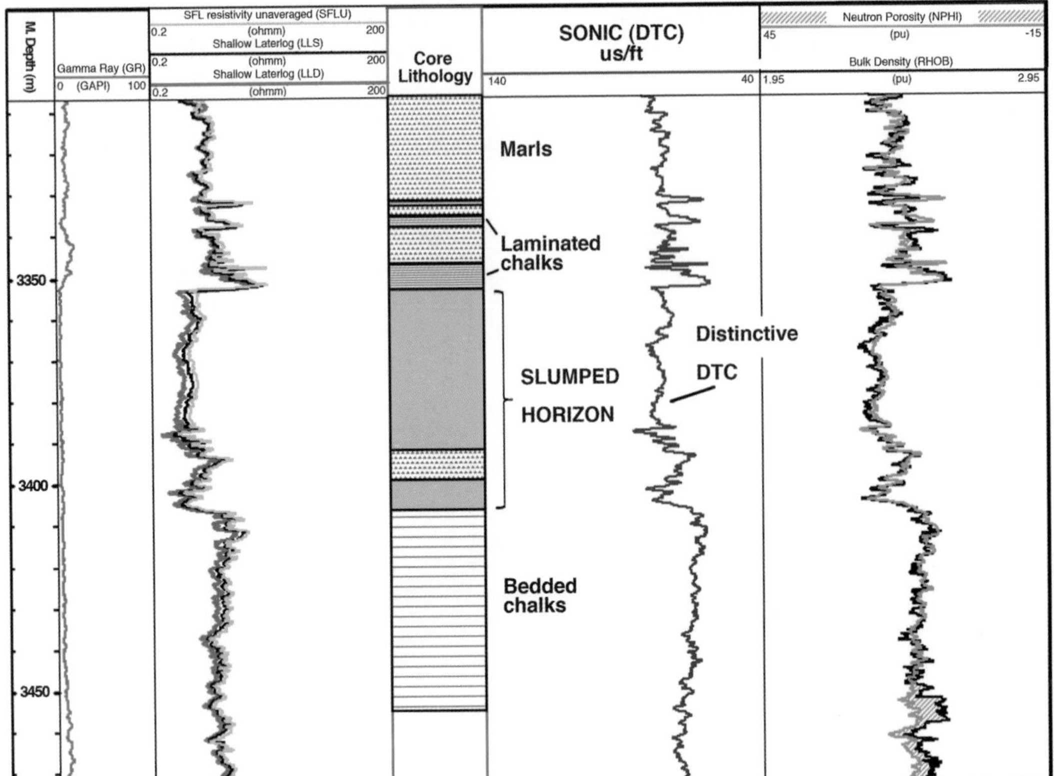

Figure 9.27 The top Upper Cretaceous slumped horizon showing a distinctive, higher compressional slowness (DTC) than the bedded, undisturbed chalks below. Cored interval, North Sea Well.

true for most lithologies and, in fact, extends upwards in scale to include larger structural characteristics such as bedding. For example, the sonic (DTC) has a very distinctive response to slumped, debris flow intervals in the Upper Cretaceous chalks of the North Sea. Over a cored interval, where the chalk bedding characteristics can be detailed, the interval of slumping and debris flow, which has chaotic textures and no bedding, shows distinctly higher compressional slowness times (lower velocity) than normal chalk, which is generally thin-bedded (**Figure 9.27**) (Hatton 1986).

It is probable that the sensitivity of the sonic to bedding, as well as to texture at a smaller scale, is because the detected signals physically travel through the formation. Any horizontal feature, such as bedding, must be crossed and will affect the response. This is well illustrated in shales where finely laminated intervals have a different response to massive intervals. The example (**Figure 9.28**) shows a shallow marine shale cycle in which the laminated section at the base shows higher compressional slowness times (lower velocity) than the more massive, upper section. It may also explain,

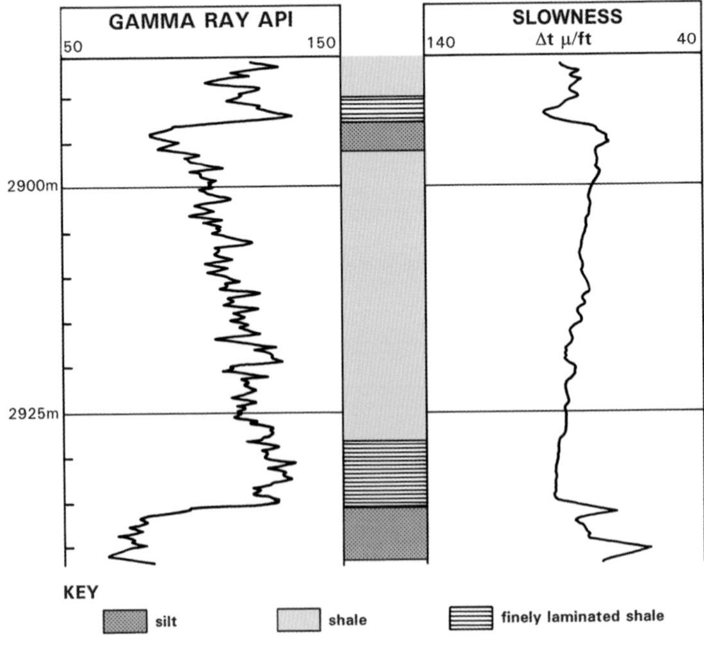

Figure 9.28 Sonic (DTC) response to shale structure in a shallow marine, coarsening-up sequence. The finely laminated shales at the base of the sequence show a high slowness (low *Vp*), while in the more massive, bioturbated, silty upper parts of the sequence, slowness is lower (higher compressional velocity, *Vp*).

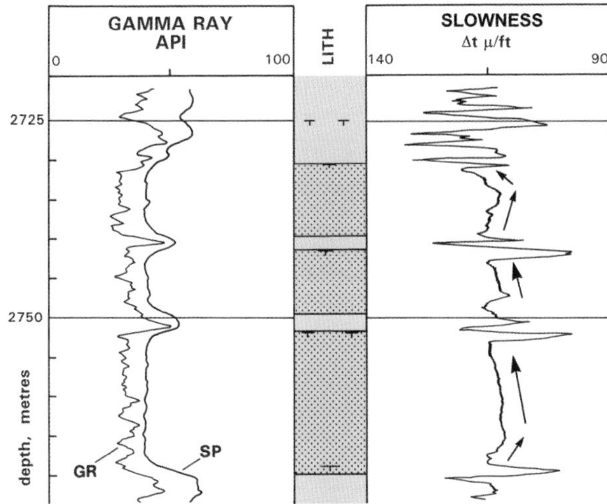

Figure 9.29 Subtle textural and structural variations in deep sea, turbidite sands, shown on the sonic log (DTC). The log changes indicate variations in grain-size, texture and sedimentary structure. Which feature is dominant in this example is not known.

in part, why coals are so distinctive on sonic logs (**Figure 9.26**).

In many cases, the exact textural effects causing the sonic log response may not be known, and the difficulty in calculating porosity from the sonic (DTC) is a demonstration of this. An example of textural changes in turbidites is an illustration (**Figure 9.29**). The consistently low gamma ray response suggests that there are no compositional changes, and yet the sonic shows distinct variations. Undoubtedly porosity change occurs, but there are also changes in grain size and bedding (sedimentary structures). It is not possible to extract and separately identify the individual influence of each.

Correlation - sonic log character

The slowness of a formation, especially of the compressional arrival, is a very distinctive characteristic even though, as indicated, the precise textural and lithological causes are difficult to define. Rather like colour, it is not diagnostic of a particular lithology but, in some formations, it is very typical and slight changes indicate subtle formation changes. The sequence illustrated (**Figure 9.30**) is entirely shaly: cuttings and side-wall cores find only shale. The sonic log, however, picks out subtle variations, probably in texture, carbonate content and quartz content, to show a very distinct stratigraphic interval despite depth differences. It is this characteristic which makes the sonic log excellent for correlation, and even for identifying specific stratigraphic intervals, especially in fine grained sequences. There are many examples in the literature (i.e. Whittaker *et al.* 1985; Michelsen 1989).

Compaction in shales

As shale is buried, it becomes compacted and its compressional slowness (DTC) decreases (velocity increases) (**Figure 9.31**). The effect is most obvious when sonic

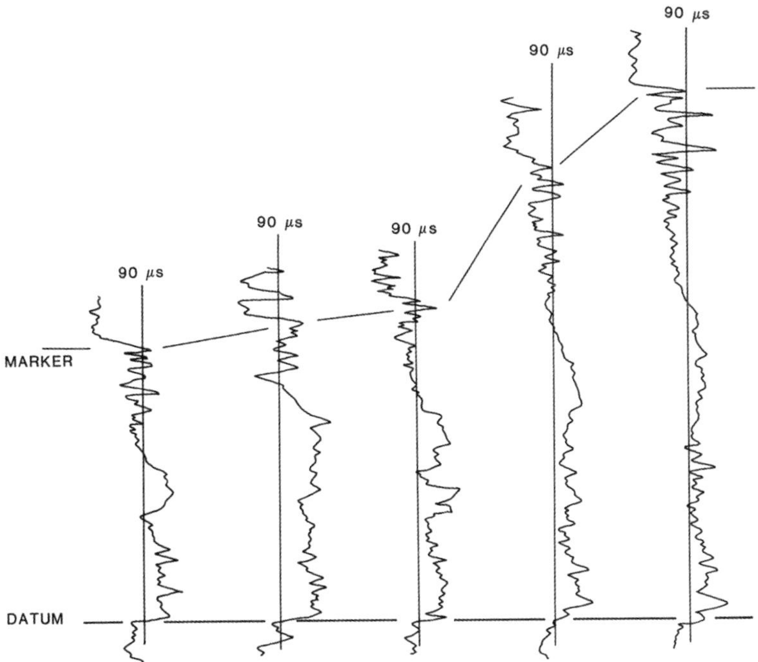

Figure 9.30 The 'character' of the sonic log (DTC) used for correlation. The log is sensitive to subtle changes in texture (and composition) as indicated by the logs in this fully shale sequence. The outside wells are 40 km apart and the zone is between 40 m and 75 m thick (130–230 ft).

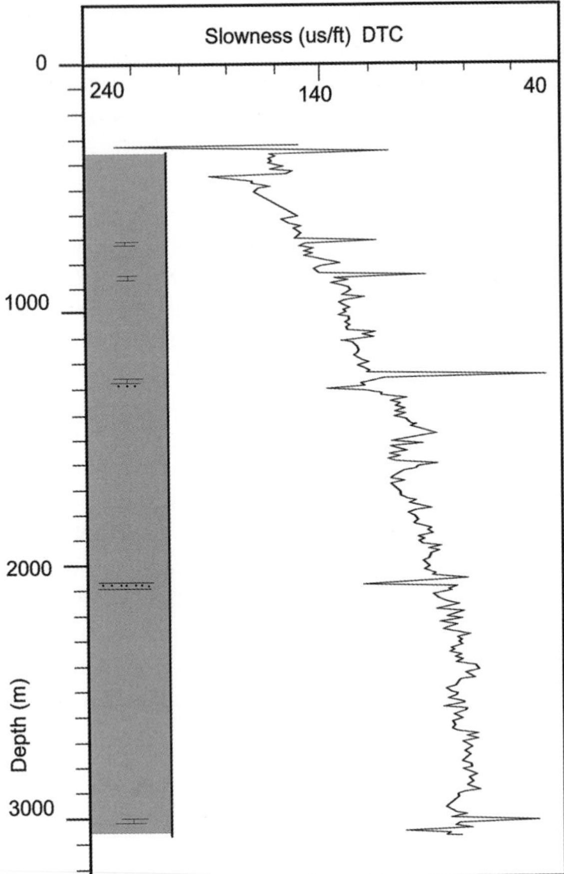

Figure 9.31 Compaction in a shale sequence shown by a regular decrease in compressional slowness (DTC), or increase in velocity (*Vp*) with depth. The velocity (*Vp*) increases from approximately 1,950 m/sec (160 μ/ft) to 3,730 m/sec (80 μ/ft) over a thickness of 3,000 m (from 6,250 ft/sec to12,500 ft/sec over 9,840 ft).

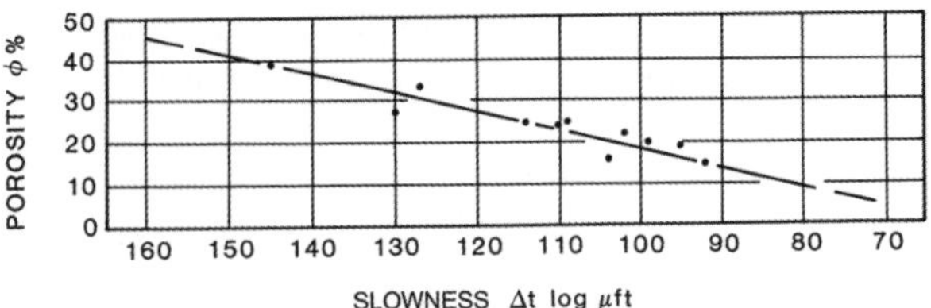

Figure 9.32 The relationship between mudstone porosity (Ø %) and slowness in Miocene mudstones, Japan (from Magara 1968).

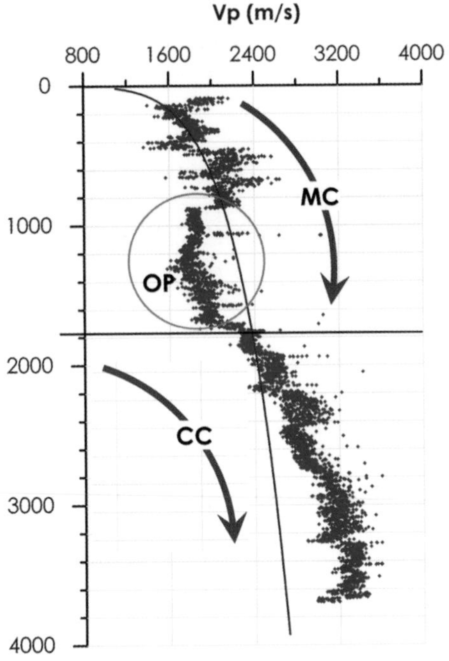

Figure 9.33 Compaction in North Sea mudstones affected by siliceous stiffening. MC = mechanical compaction; CC = 'chemical' compaction; OP = overpressure (Mondol *et al.* 2008).

logs are plotted with a compressed vertical scale and, over long (thick) shale intervals, compaction is seen to cause a regular increase in velocity downwards. In extremely homogeneous intervals, when slowness is plotted on a logarithmic scale and depth on an arithmetic scale, there may be a straight-line relationship, representing very regular compaction indeed (Hottman and Johnson 1965). Regular compaction trends of this kind are often seen on the depth-slowness plots of Tertiary clays in many parts of the world (e.g. Magara 1968; Herring 1973; Issler 1992; Mondol *et al.* 2008).

Shale compaction is physically a decrease in porosity, hence the decrease in compressional slowness (**Figure 9.32**). The decrease in porosity is generally thought of as a result of physical squeezing: as a shale is buried, it is squeezed by the overburden (Burst 1969). Recent research, however, seems to suggest that there are more effects than just simply physical squeezing, and that chemical effects also play a part. Like physical effects, they depend on depth, but also on temperature and time (**Figure 9.33**) (Mondol *et al.* 2008).

Although compaction effects can be seen qualitatively on compressed vertical scale slowness plots, graphical methods have their limitations and compaction can be characterised quantitatively by calibrating measured shale porosities with their corresponding log derived slowness (Magara 1978; Issler 1992) (**Figure 9.32**). Using such data from Japan and Eastern Canada, Magara (1978) proposed an empirical relationship:

$$Ø = 0.466\Delta t - 31.7 \qquad (4)$$

Where, Ø = shale porosity; Δt = sonic compressional slowness (DTC).

To calculate shale porosity, other authors have used both the Wyllie time average equation (i.e. Bulat and Stoker 1987, see (1) above for the formula) and the 'acoustic formation factor' approach (Raiga-Clemenceau *et al.* 1988). The latter method in the Beaufort-Mackenzie Basin gave the following results (Issler 1992):

$$\emptyset = \frac{1-(\Delta t_{ma})\ 1}{(\Delta t\ )\ x} \qquad (5)$$

Where, Ø = shale porosity; Δt = sonic log value (DTC); Δt_{ma} = matrix (compressional) slowness (67 µs/ft); x = acoustic formation factor (2.19) (the figures are applicable to the Beaufort-Mackenzie Basin).

However, the Wyllie 'time average' and the 'acoustic formation factor' formulae were intended for sandstones. The compaction characteristics of shales and sandstones are different, shales responding more to physical forces than sandstones (Magara 1980). Thus, applying either the Wyllie formula or the acoustic formation factor to shale compaction is theoretically incorrect. In addition, general formulae tend to ignore shale mineralogical variations. Abundant organic matter will give higher porosities than actually exist (next section) and shales with abundant kaolinite have been found to behave differently to shales with abundant smectite (Japsen 2000). All this suggests that simple methods should be used with care, and only for approximations.

Using general compaction trends, it is possible to estimate erosion at unconformities or the relative amount of uplift (Lang 1978; Magara 1978; Vorren *et al.* 1991; Hillis 1995). Shale compaction is generally accompanied by diagenetic effects which are irreversible (e.g. Schmidt 1973) and stay 'frozen' during uplift. The compaction of a sediment, therefore, represents its deepest burial. Using the general compaction curve for a particular interval, any 'over-compaction' at a shallower depth can be explained by uplift. Tracking back to the general curve gives the amount of uplift (**Figure 9.34**). (Unloading effects are said to exist (Lubanzadio *et al.* 2006) but they are small compared to loading effects)

Using the same thinking, any 'jumps' in compaction, as at unconformities or faults, when compared to general well trends, can give some idea of the amount of missing section. However, it should be stressed that such generalities should only be applied to one stratigraphic interval at a time, and then in a relatively consistent facies, so that only one lithology is being considered (cf. Hillis 1995). In addition, if there are several subsidence and uplift episodes, different intervals will show different histories (Japsen 2000). The method, therefore, has irregularities and should be used with circumspection, but, in general, the sonic is the best log for compaction and uplift studies.

Compaction is considered in more quantitative detail below, under 'overpressure identification'.

Source-rock identification

By itself, the sonic log cannot be used to indicate source-rock potential. However, the presence of organic matter, especially in shales, lowers sonic velocities, apparently in direct relation to abundance and, when combined with the resistivity log value, the velocity is a good qualitative, and possibly quantitative, source indicator (*see* Chapter 7, Resistivity). Several methods of quantification exist: two are described below.

Based on an analysis of source rocks from around the world, a general formula has been derived for simply separating source from non-source rocks using a sonic-resistivity combination (Meyer and Nederlof 1984). A regression line on a sonic-resistivity cross-plot is said to separate source rocks from the non-source, both shale and limestone (**Figure 9.35**). The linear equation for this discriminant D, is:

$$D = -6.906 + 3.1861\log_{10}\Delta t + 0.4871\log_{10} R75° \qquad (6)$$

Where, D = the discriminant,; Δt = compressional sonic µs/ft (DTC); R75° = resistivity log equivalent at 75°F (**Figure 9.35**).

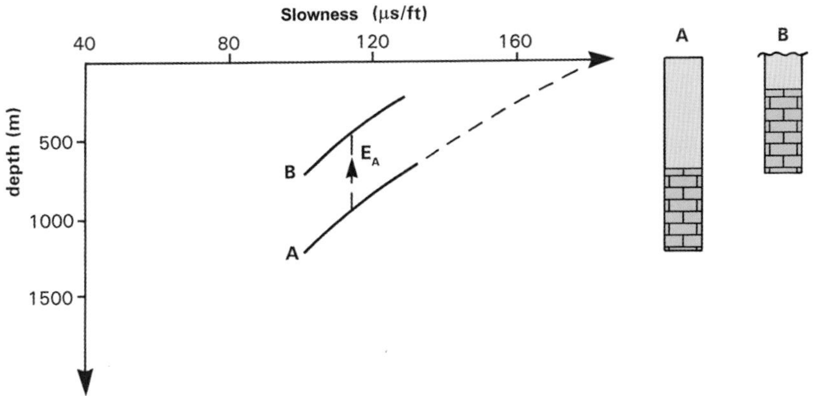

Figure 9.34 The sonic (DTC) used to estimate uplift. Well A shows a normal compaction (curve A). Well B shows 'over-compaction' relative to well A at the same depth, because of uplift and subsequent erosion (curve B). The amount of uplift and erosion (Ea) is the vertical distance (depth difference) between curve A and curve B. Curves represent chalk compaction (re-drawn from Hillis 1995).

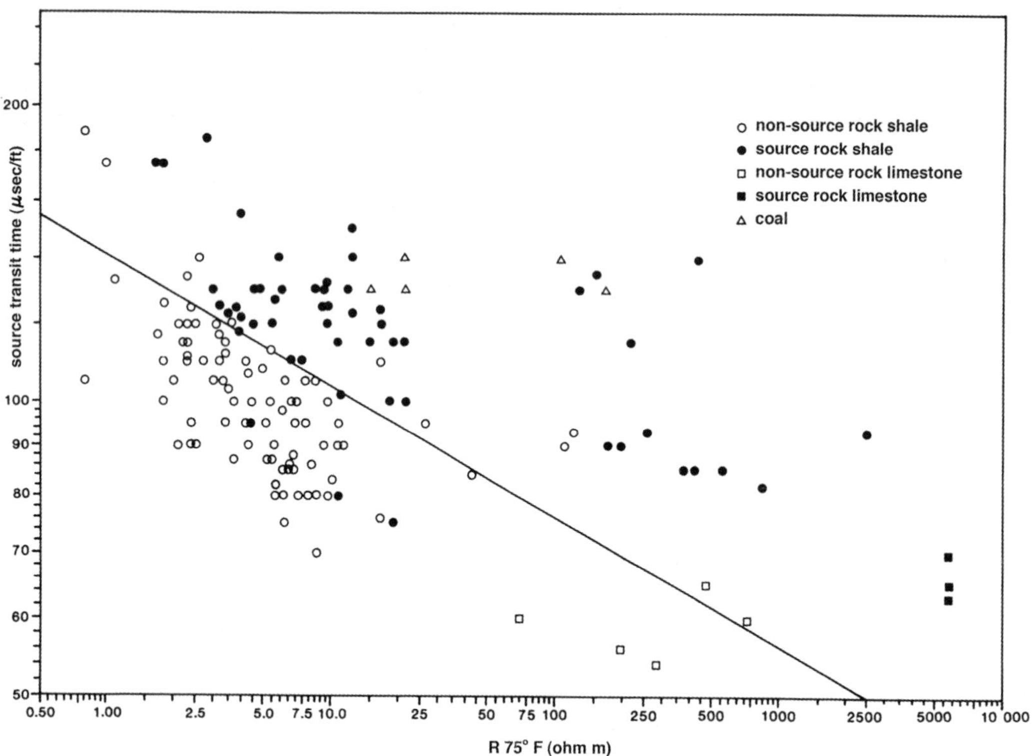

Figure 9.35 The identification of source-rock intervals on a cross-plot of resistivity against sonic slowness (DTC). The oblique line is D = 0, from discriminant analysis using points of known source-rock potential (from Meyer and Nederlof 1984).

A second, rather unusual, empirical method, is considered to enable actual values of TOC (total organic carbon) to be derived (Passey *et al.* 1990). The sonic and a resistivity log are used in a standard depth plot format, but the method requires two essential steps to make them 'compatible' before they can be interpreted. First, both logs are 'scale normalized' by plotting the sonic log on a scale where 50 μs/ft = 1 logarithmic cycle on the resistivity log (for example 50 μs/ft = .01 to 0.1 ohm.m). Second, a non-source shale interval is located (in the stratigraphic interval being considered) and the two logs made to plot one over the other through that interval (**Figure 9.36**). The authors call this a Δ log R plot (Passey *et al.* 1990 *op. cit.*). When the two logs are plotted like this, they will track each other over all non-source shales, regardless of compaction and compositional changes. In source intervals, there will be a marked separation (**Figure 9.36**). There will also be a separation in hydrocarbon reservoirs and in coals but these can be eliminated on lithological grounds using, for example, the gamma ray. If the level of maturity is known, then the TOC% can be derived. The empirical equation for this is:

$$\text{TOC\%} - (\Delta \log R) \times 10^{(2.297 - 0.1688 \times \text{LOM})} \qquad (7)$$

Where, TOC% = total organic carbon in %; LOM = level of maturity (Hood *et al.* 1975); Δ log *R* = curve separation in resistivity units.

The level of maturity must be known for the quantification since the resistivity log responds to the amount of liquid hydrocarbons in the shale pores, not the amount of solid hydrocarbon, as discussed in the chapter on the resistivity log (Section 7.9). For example, a mature source rock is marked by a sonic low and resistivity rise; an immature source has an equally low sonic but no change in resistivity (**Figure 9.36**). However, that the amount of free hydrocarbon fluid in the pores of a shale is quantitatively related to the degree of maturation of the organic matter, which this method implies, remains to be proven.

This method seems to be useful qualitatively but quantitatively cumbersome and doubtful. Moreover, as the authors point out, with just the sonic log, it is impossible to separate low sonic values due to organic matter and low sonic values due to porosity changes (such as overpressure). This is a frequent dilemma in much log interpretation; separating the compositional effects from the textural effects. For log-based source-rock quantification, the density log appears to be simpler to use (Section 10.6).

Fracture identification

There are two simple ways of using the sonic log to identify fractures: by comparing compressional sonic (DTC) to density porosities and by using Stoneley wave plots. Both methods were developed before image logs became available. Using Stoneley waves has

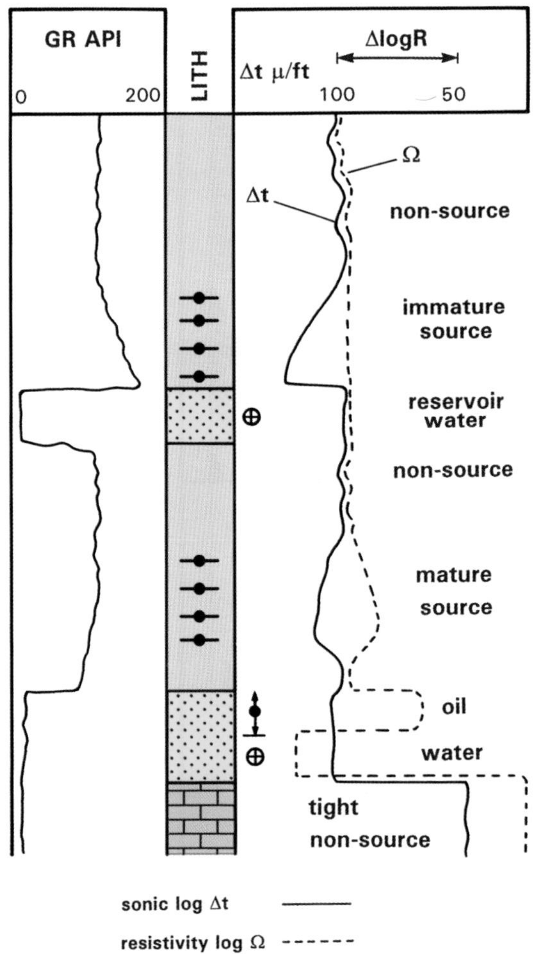

Figure 9.36 Schematic representation of sonic (DTC) and resistivity log responses in source, non-source and reservoir intervals using the delta log R method (modified from Passey *et al.* 1990).

evolved, and can now be applied quantitatively.

The presumed travel paths of the compressional sonic signals suggest that the log will be insensitive to high angle fractures and vugs, as previously discussed (Section 9.7, *Porosity*). And, as suggested, this is because the compressional waves detected are the fastest (first arrivals), and will avoid open fractures or void spaces. On the contrary, a porosity from the density log will include void spaces and open fractures (i.e. give total porosity). Thus, when a porosity based on the sonic response is compared to a porosity from the density log, and significant open fractures are present, the density log porosity will be markedly greater (**Figure 10.27**). The logs may be simply overlain to observe the effect. This method, originally used in the Austin Chalk, is now redundant as image logs can be used to identify fractures (Chapter 15).

As explained previously (Section 9.1), at low frequencies, Stoneley waves are sensitive to formation permeability which, in the present context, means open fractures. Under the right conditions, open fractures can be detected and also some estimate of their permeability be made (Hornby *et al.* 1992). Although research has tended to concentrate on fractures in crystalline rocks and hard formations (i.e. Paillet 1991; Hornby *et al.* 1992), work shows that the experience gained in these formations can be applied to sedimentary successions (e.g. Mari *et al.* 1994).

Full waveform sonic measurements can be usefully combined with borehole images (**Figure 9.37**), core analysis and, where available, test flow rate information (Paillet 1991; Al-Khatib and Al-Adani 2009). On a simple visual level, chevron reflections seen on variable density displays of full sonic waveforms, are diagnostic of secondary reflections coming from open fractures (**Figure 9.38**) (Donald and Bratton 2006). Their strength is

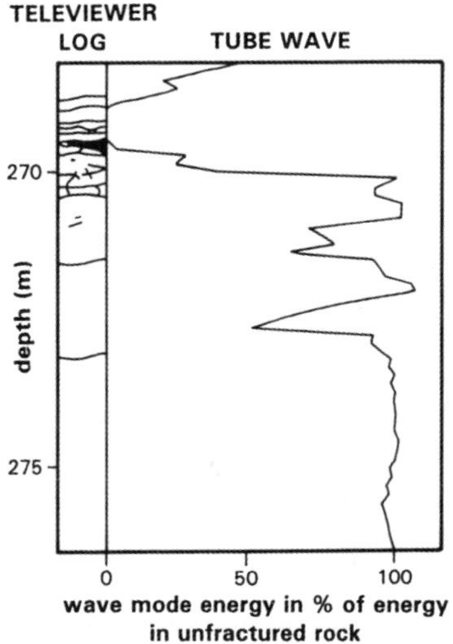

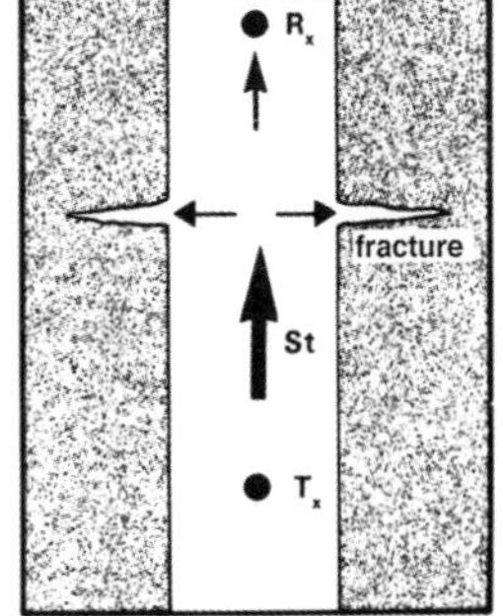

Figure 9.37 The effect of an open fracture on Stoneley (tube) waves. A) Energy loss shown on a log compared to open, horizontal fractures interpreted from a borehole televiewer. B) Schematic illustration of Stoneley waves attenuated across an open fracture (modified from Paillet 1991).

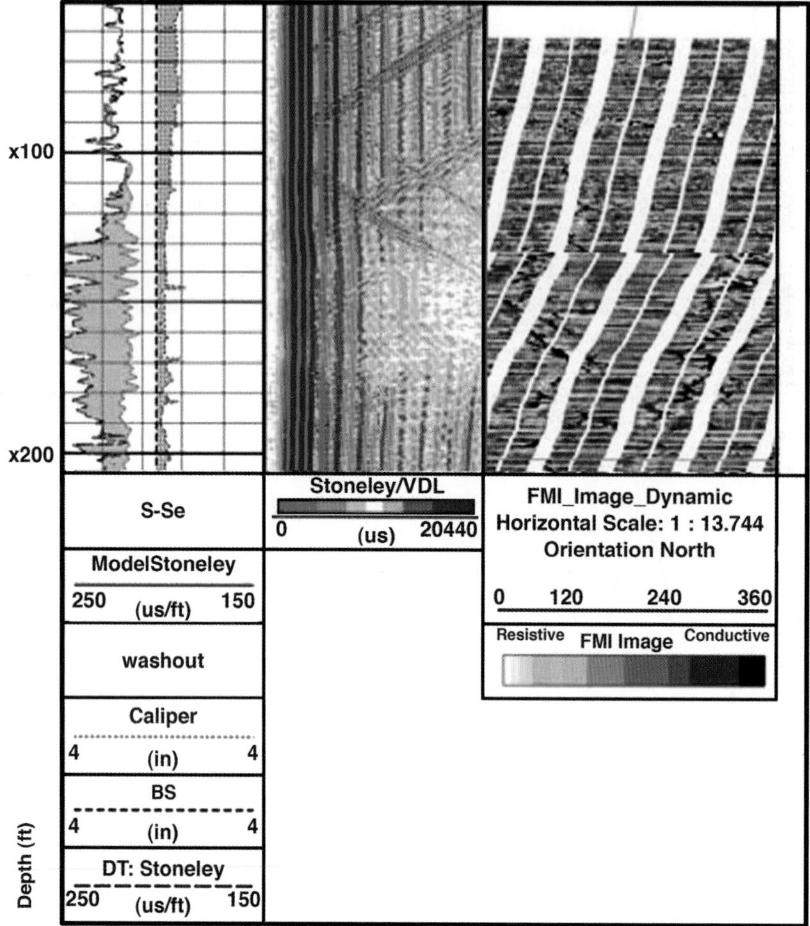

Figure 9.38 Stoneley waves reflected from open fractures in the formation forming chevrons on a VDL display of Stoneley slowness (Schlumberger processing). The apex of the chevron shows the position of the facture, while direct arrivals form the strong reflections parallel to the log trace. The formation electrical images (Schlumberger FMI) in the right-hand column, show open fractures at the borehole wall (dark traces) (modified from Donald and Bratton SPWLA 2006).

related to the amount of pressure released. If the presence of Stoneley chevrons can be compared to image logs, then the presence of open fractures becomes more certain. Images logs only look at the borehole wall and do not easily allow open, penetrative fractures to be differentiated from shallow fractures, which can be drill related. The Stoneley wave response, however, is caused by effects a little deeper in the formation and can potentially indicate penetrating fractures.

The quantitative uses of the Stoneley wave are discussed next.

9.7 Quantitative uses of sonic logs (non-seismic)

Permeability

The use of Stoneley waves, a type of tube wave, to derive permeability has been explored for some time. The association between tube-wave attenuation and permeability in porous sediments, but especially fractured crystalline rocks, is well established in the literature (Paillet *et al.* 1991; Brie *et al.* 1998; Haldorson *et al.* 2006) and many studies are reported in which attempts are made to use Stoneley measurements for permeability at the borehole scale (cf. Paillet 1992) (**Table 9.7**, **Figure 9.37**).

One reason for trying to use the Stoneley wave to derive permeability is that most permeability measure-

Table 9.7 Acoustic information used to investigate porosity, lithology, fluids, permeability and fractures (after Paillet *et al.* 1992).

Characteristic	Compressional Slowness	Shear Slowness	Stoneley Slowness
Porosity	***	+	–
Lithology	***	***	–
Fluids	***	***	–
Permeability	+	+	***
Fractures	–	+	***

*** required, + often useful, – not needed

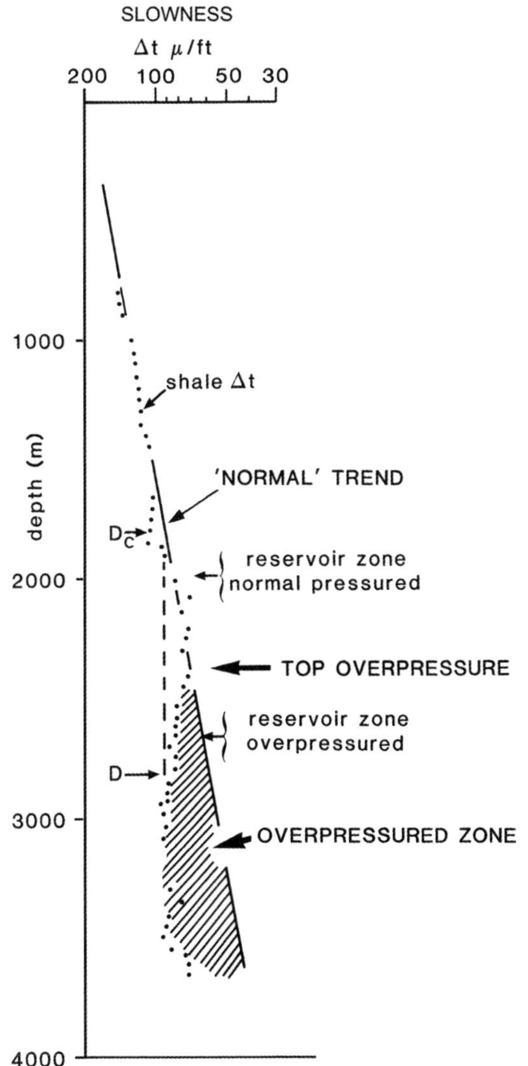

Figure 9.39 Overpressure indicated by a decrease of shale interval slowness (DTC) with depth. A downward decrease from the normal compaction trend indicates overpressure. (D and Dc are for overpressure calculations, see text).

ments are punctual, such as from pressure tools, and having a continuous curve would be very useful. However, the calculation is very complex and not reliably proven. The continuous permeability from a modern NMR tool is easier to use, has been shown matching with core, and is usefully associated with a reliable porosity (Chapter 13). It is hard to recommend the Stoneley method.

Pore pressure and overpressure calculation

The prediction of pore pressure using the sonic log relies on recognising the relationships between compaction, shale porosity and the evolution of pore pressure. If pore pressure can be estimated in a shale seal, then the underlying reservoir pressure can be predicted (assuming continuity). The graphic and semi-quantitative use of the compressional sonic to identify and describe normal shale compaction has been discussed (Section 9.6, *Compaction in shales*). It was suggested that, other things remaining constant, an increase in velocity (decrease in DTC) accompanies normal compaction, which in shales indicates a decrease in shale porosity. Overpressure is indicated by a reversal of this trend, by an increase in shale porosity with depth, indicated by a decrease in sonic velocity. A plot of shale slowness through an overpressured zone shows a break in the normal compaction trend (**Figure 9.39**). The reason for the increase in shale porosity, and accompanying overpressure, is that pore fluids, unable to escape during compaction, preserve porosity by supporting part of the overburden. This was described in Chapter 3 (Section 3.2).

It is considered possible to estimate pore-pressure quantitatively, and the amount of overpressure, using a normal compaction trend and the deviation from this trend respectively (**Table 9.8**) (Hottman and Johnson 1965; Japsen 1998, 2006). A very approximate average compaction trend from the sonic compressional velocity is:

$$Vp = 1477 + 0.57\,(Z) \qquad (8)$$

Where Vp = compressional velocity (m/sec), Z = depth in meters.

This formula suggests that porosities depend on vertical effective stress (lithostatic or overburden load minus pore pressure), and that any deviations will be the result of overpressure (Japsen 2006). Other authors suggest that there is no general velocity to depth function for shales, and that it will vary with mineral content, especially smectite and kerogen content (Storvoll *et al.* 2005). Some authors additionally use density and gamma ray logs in the derivation of Vp and not just the sonic. They also indicate the importance of local variations and the influence of unloading (Lubanzadio *et al.* 2006).

To avoid some of these problems, overpressure may be calculated by using a limited interval, the so-called

Table 9.8 Approximate overpressure estimates from sonic (DTC) deviations (after Hottman and Johnson 1965).

Δt difference from average trends (μs/ft)	0	20	40	60
Equivalent mud weight (g/cm³)	1.07	1.84	12.16	≈2.3
Gradient (psi/ft)	0.465	0.800	0.935	≈1.00
(bar/m)	0.105	0.181	0.212	≈0.226

Pressure = gradient × depth
Equivalent units: psi/ft × 0.68947 = bar/m; ppg × 8.34523 = g/cm³

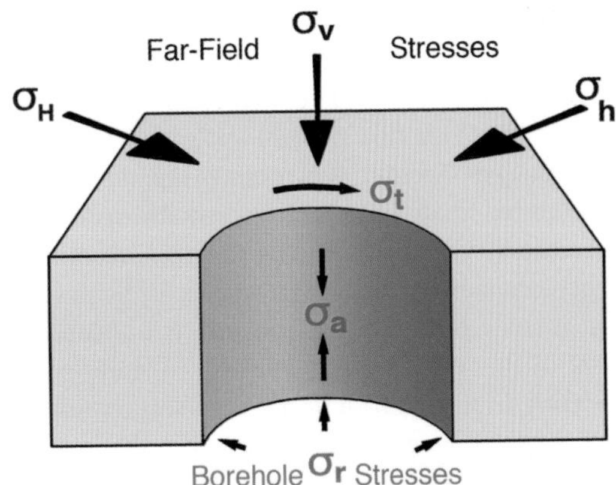

Figure 9.40 Stresses around borehole. Formation stresses are represented by σ_v vertical, σ_h minimum horizontal and σ_H maximum horizontal stresses. Borehole stresses are represented by σ_a axial, σ_r radial and σ_t tangential or hoop stresses (re-drawn after Bratton *et al.* SPWLA 2004).

equivalent depth method. The simplest such method gives the following formula (Magara 1978; Serra & Serra 2003):

$$Pp = \rho_w (Dc/10) + \rho_{fm} (D - D_c)/10 \quad (9)$$

Where, Pp = pore pressure (MPa); ρ_w = water (fluid) density (g/cm^3); ρ_{fm} = average overburden density (g/cm^3); D = depth of interest (m); *Dc* = equivalent depth (m) with same slowness (i.e.compaction). As defaults, the following can be used: $\rho_w = 1.05\,g/cm^3$; $\rho_{fm} = 2.31\,g/cm^3$ (Serra & Serra 2003).

D_c is a point in the section at normal pressure which has the same slowness as the point being measured. An example of D to D_c equivalence is marked on the Δt shale depth plot (**Figure 9.39**). The above calculation assumes that the effective stress at the two depths is similar and that the pressure at *D* is the sum of the hydrostatic pressure to D_c and the lithostatic pressure from *D* to D_c. This simple method is only a 'first estimate'. (If unloading mechanisms and fluid expansion contribute to overpressure, using the sonic alone may underestimate pore pressure). Obviously real time LWD data is the best way of exploiting the sonic measurement for pore prediction. Although the data still arrives after the overpressure has been drilled, it at least gives some warning that pressure is increasing. LWD sonic tools are often run solely for assisting with pore pressure prediction. Since it is only compressional slowness that is of interest, monopole tools are quite adequate.

Wellbore stability and formation damage (dispersion analysis)

Before drilling, a formation is under a stress regime, which can be described by three orthogonal stresses, a vertical stress (σ_v) and two orthogonal horizontal stresses one of which is usually larger, the maximum (σ_H), than the other, the minimum (σ_h). A borehole has a stress-field of its own, which can also be described (in a vertical well) by three orthogonal stresses, the axial (σ_a), radial (σ_r) and tangential (σ_t) also called the hoop stress, as it affects the circumference of the wellbore (**Figure 9.40**). The drilling of a borehole, therefore, modifies the far-field stresses in a formation, magnifying them and causing loading near the wellbore, the effects of which increase as the borehole stress regime is approached (**Figure 9.40**) (Bratton *et al.* 2004). The wellbore stress field is controlled by the driller, mainly through mud weight. If it is too low, the hole will slough and collapse, if it is too high, fractures may be induced in the formation and mud lost into them. This behaviour, the balance between the wellbore stress field and the far field stresses, depends also on the mechanical behaviour and rock strength of the formation. A knowledge of rock strength, therefore, is used for safe drilling, effective hydraulic fracturing and efficient reservoir production.

The behaviour of a particular borehole during drilling is now subjected to considerable specialised study. This section only points out that logging parameters are used in these studies, especially the measurements from the modern wireline and while drilling, full waveform sonic tools. The values of the sonic compressional (DTC), shear (DTS) and Stoneley (DTSt) waves are used to construct the various elastic property moduli of the formation, that is, properties that describe mathematically how a formation will respond to deformation. The most common moduli used are listed in the table (**Table 9.9**). The stress-field around the borehole is calculated from pore pressure, overburden pressure, Poisson's ratio, borehole directional data and orientation of the far-field stresses (Weiland *et al.* 2004).

In addition to the efforts to evaluate the original far field stresses, analysis has now turned to assessing the borehole stresses and associated mechanical damage, and how far they are indicative of actual formation behaviour (Bratton *et al.* 2004). Elastic wave velocities are sensitive to changes in stress, and this means that the measurements from the modern sonic with monopole and dipole transmitters and an azimuthally segmented receiver array (cf. Sonic-scanner) can be used to determine changes of stress in both radial distance from the borehole and their orientation. These stress changes are associated with mechanical formation damage (*Depth of investigation*, Section 9.2) and so can be linked to radial changes in damage away from the borehole and the orientation of the damage if the stress field is anisotropic (Bratton *et al.* 2004, *op. cit.*).

The origin of this method depends on the dispersion (change of slowness with frequency), especially of the flexural waves produced by dipole sources (Pistra *et al.* 2005; Plona *et al.* 2005). At low frequencies, flexural waves approach the slowness of shear waves but, as the frequency increases, so the slowness increases (velocity

Table 9.9 Some common elastic moduli derived from the sonic log (Helix RDS 2008).

V	Poisson's ratio	$\frac{\text{lateral strain}}{\text{Longitudinal strain}}$	$\frac{½ (\Delta t_s / \Delta t_c)^2 - 1}{(\Delta t_s / \Delta t_c)^2 - 1}$
E	Young's modulus (psi)	$\frac{\text{applied uniaxial stress}}{\text{Normal strain}}$	2G (1 + v)
G	Shear modulus (psi)	$\frac{\text{applied stress}}{\text{Applied strain}}$	$1.34 \times 10^{10} \frac{\rho_b}{\Delta t_s^2}$
K	Bulk modulus (psi)	$\frac{\text{hydrostatic pressure}}{\text{Volumetric strain}}$	$1.34 \times 10^{10} \rho_b \left(\frac{1}{\Delta t_c^2} - \frac{4}{3\Delta t_s^2}\right)$
β	Bulk compressibility (psi^{-1})	$\frac{\text{volumetric deformation}}{\text{Hydrostatic pressure}}$	$\frac{1}{K}$

Units: Δt = μs/ft, ρ_b = g/cm^3
Δtc = DTC, compressional slowness, Δts = DTS, shear slowness

decreases). The different frequencies are also associated with different depths of investigation; at low frequencies the flexural wave has a deeper investigation; at higher frequencies a shallower investigation (**Figure 9.41**) (Pistra *et al.* 2005, *op. cit.*).

Both stress and formation damage increase towards the borehole wall, and therefore progressively affect the high frequency, near borehole flexural waves, but in different, detectable ways (Bratton *et al.* 2004).

It has been found that, if there is stress anisotropy, such as that indicated on image logs by breakouts (Chapters 5, 15), the dispersion characteristics of the flexural wave are distinctive. In isotropic formations there is no stress anisotropy (i.e. horizontal stresses are all similar) and flexural wave dispersion from all orientations of the receiver array is the same (**Figure 9.41,a**). If the formation is inherently anisotropic, such as from textural sorting or even bedding, there will be orthogonal differences producing fast and slow flexural waves, but they will display a similar dispersion behaviour (**Figure 9.41,b**). However, if there is stress-induced anisotropy, the orthogonal fast and slow waves will display dissimilar dispersion behaviour and there will be what is called 'cross-over' (**Figure 9.41,c**). From the directions of the fast and slow flexural waves in the receiver array when there is cross-over, the orientation of the far-field stresses can be given, and possibly the value of the maximum horizontal stress (i.e. σ_H) (Sinha *et al.* 2008).

Gas and the Vp/Vs ratio ($\Delta ts/\Delta tc$)

The presence of gas was discussed previously in terms of porosity calculations (Section 9.5). Free gas at over 10% by volume, or light (compressible) oil, will sharply decrease the compressional wave velocity in porous formations (**Figure 9.23**), especially un-consolidated sands, but there will be little (or a slight positive) effect on shear wave velocity, because shear waves do not propagate in either fluids or gases (Williams 1990). This effect is noted in Poisson's ratio, the ratio of lateral strain to longitudinal strain, which is derived from the

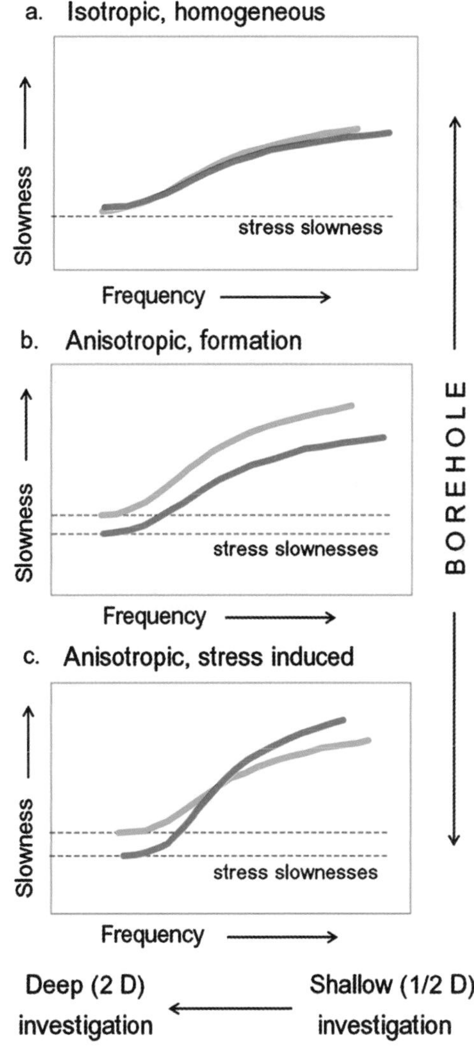

Figure 9.41 Acoustic dispersion in fast and slow shear arrivals. a. Homogeneous, isotropic formation. b. Anisotropic formation with parallel dispersion. c. Stress-induced anisotrpic dispersion: the fast and slow directions 'cross-over'. Red and blue = orthogonal directions. D = hole diameter (modified from Murray *et al.* SPWLA 2004).

P and S wave velocities (**Tables 9.5, 9.9**). However, the gas effect can also be seen in simple cross-plots of the *Vp*/*Vs* ratio against compressional slowness (DTC) (**Figure 9.42**) or shear slowness (DTS) (Williams 1990). The generalised version of the *Vp*/*Vs*-DTC plot shows the distinctive gas region as well as the lithology and porosity fields (Brie *et al.* 1998). In order to just identify gas in clastics, a calculated, water bearing *Vp*/*Vs* ratio can be compared to an actual, measured *Vp*/*Vs* ratio. If the measured ratio is significantly lower than the water-bearing calculated ratio, the presence of gas is indicated (Williams 1990 *op. cit.*).

By the same token, when porosities calculated using DTC are compared to porosities using DTS, they will be similar in a water zone but will show separation in a gas zone, where the compressional porosity will be higher than the shear porosity. (**Figure 9.43**). (Perarnau and Payne 2006). However, the derivation of porosity from the shear velocity, as discussed, is not yet accepted, and the actual porosities calculated are generally not real (Perarnau and Payne 2006 *op. cit.*).

The *Vp*/*Vs* ratio will be considered again under seismic applications (Section 9.8)

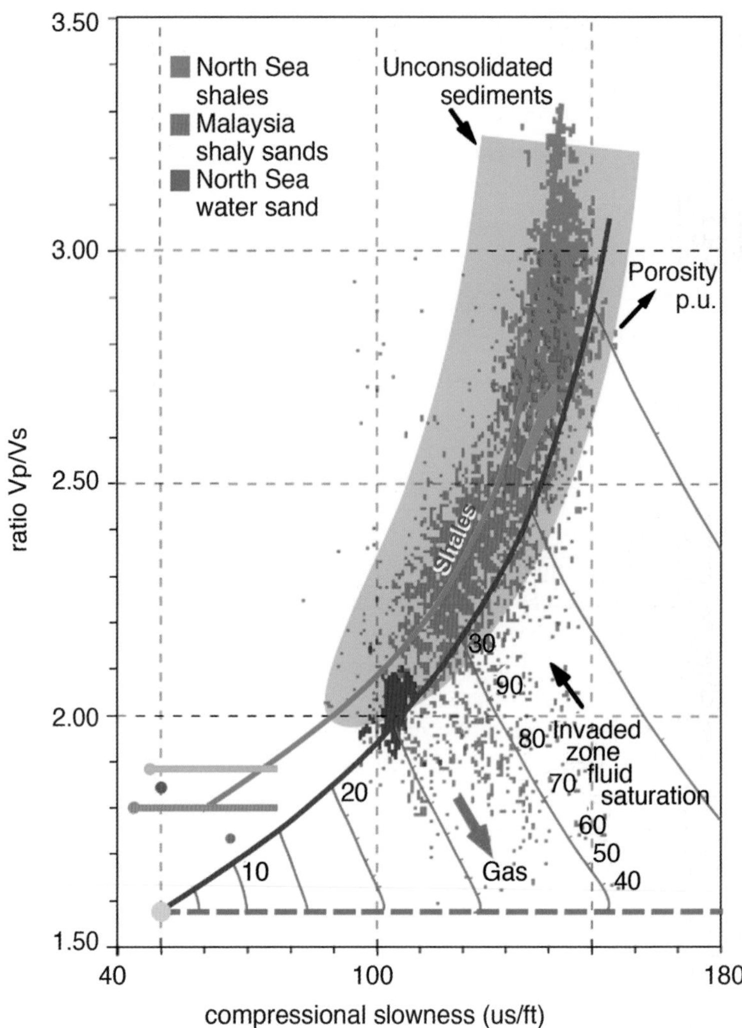

Figure 9.42 The *Vp*/*Vs* ratio of shales and gas sands plotted against compressional slowness (DTC). Compacting sediments (decreasing porosity) show consistent trends: gas sands show a distinct departure from the trends (from Brie *et al.* 1998). *Copyright Schlumberger Ltd. Used with permission.*

Gas hydrates

Methane hydrates, methane entrapped in ice molecules, are a potential future gas resource and their presence can generally be qualitatively detected. Their quantitative evaluation is possible but, at present, rather uncertain and is still being worked on (**Table 9.10**).

Hydrates are found at very shallow depths (0–600 m) in permafrost zones on land and offshore in deep water, mainly outer continental margins and relatively close to the sediment-water interface. Offshore, they are identified as causing the commonly recognised bottom simulating reflector (BSR), which marks the base of the hydrate zone. It is estimated that 98% of hydrates are of the offshore marine type and only 2% are on land (Birchwood *et al.* 2010). To form hydrates requires either low temperatures and little pressure or moderate pressures and low to moderate temperatures. Being solid, they can be considered as either replacing pore water or as pore-filling cement (Williams *et al.* 2008). Because they are generally found at shallow depths in the sediment column, they are associated with unconsolidated,

Table 9.10 Methane hydrate physical properties (from Collett 1998; Akihisa *et al.* 2002; Murray *et al.* 2005).

Property	Value(s)
Formula	$CH_4(H_20)_6$
Density	0.91 g/cm^3
Pe	0.319 barn/g
U	0.328 barn/cm^3
Hydrogen Index	1.06
ØN	67%
Δ*tc*	80 μs/ft (92.4–84.7 μs/ft)
Δ*ts*	181–169 μs/ft
Vp	3.3–3.6 km/sec
Vs	1.68–1.80 km/sec
Slowness	decrease
Resistivity	10–155 ohmm (insulator)
K, Bulk modulus	6,400 MPa
G, Shear modulus	2,550 MPa

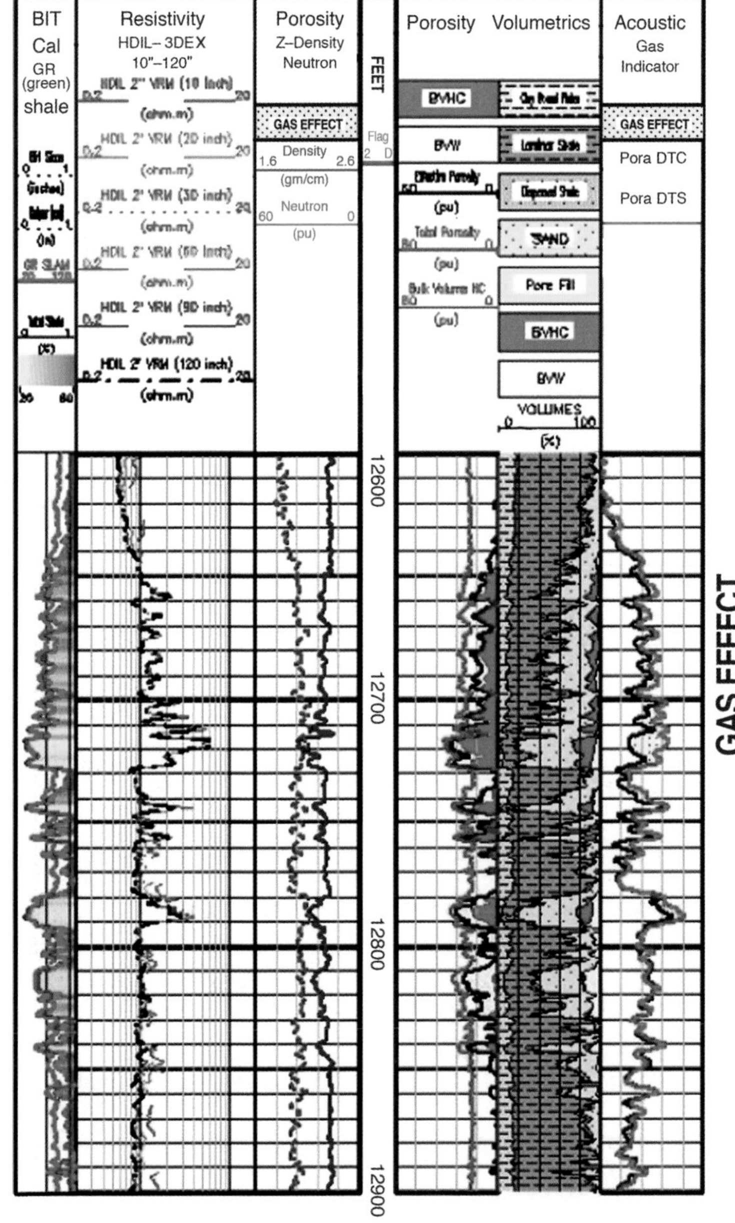

Figure 9.43 Porosity from compressional slowness compared to porosity from shear slowness. When gas is present DTC overestimates porosity while DTS is essentially unaffected. Separation of the two porosities indicates gas (Perarnau and Payne SPWLA 2006).

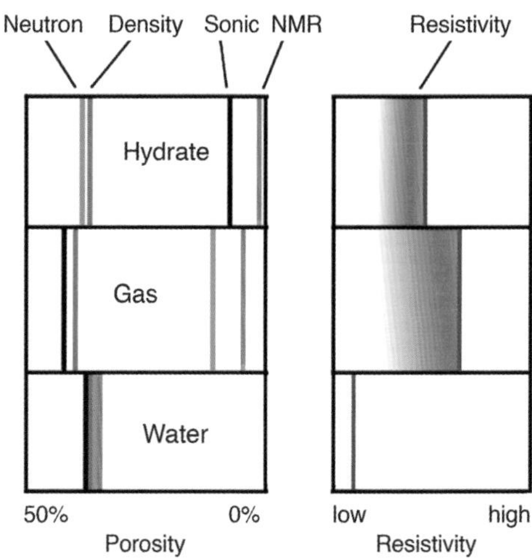

Figure 9.44 Schematic responses to methane hydrate, gas and water of the main porosity logs, neutron; density; sonic; NMR and resistivity (re-drawn after Murray *et al.* SPWLA 2005).

very high porosity formations, but the actual lithology is very variable. A typical offshore zone was explored by the Ocean Drilling Project (ODP) team on Blake Nose Plateau (Goldberg and Saito 1998).

The most diagnostic logs for hydrate detection are the resistivity and sonic logs (Collett *et al.* 2000) but density, neutron, NMR and dielectric logs can also be used (Worthington 2010). The best suited logs are more influenced by the hydrate presence than by lithology. A sub-permafrost hydrate deposit in Northen Canada has been drilled by the Mallik test wells (Anderson *et al.* 2005). In these wells, a low sonic compressional and shear slowness (high velocity) is associated with a high resistivity over the hydrate zones and the response is considered typical (**Figure 7.55**). However, hydrates should also be identifiable on the neutron log (high from the hydrogen in ice and methane) and from the lack of response by the NMR (invisible to the NMR because protons cannot be re-oriented in a solid, **Figure 9.44**) (Worthington 2010 *op. cit.*). In fact, the comparison of lack of effect on the NMR log with a standard porosity effect on the density log, seems to offer a useful approach to quantification. (The dialectric log is also useful in some situations, but is not covered in this book).

As indicated, a reliable quantitative evaluation of hydrates is still being developed. A significant problem is the measurement of hydrate saturation in cores since, as soon as they are brought to the surface, they dissociate and change condition. In situ measurement is at present considered the only way to evaluate real hydrate saturations, and this is done using logs. There is therefore no way at present to evaluate log-based calculations against core-based measurements, as is the case in conventional reservoirs. A second problem is that, if wireline logs are used, dissociation in the near wellbore, where most log measurements are made, will probably have already taken place. A solution to this is to use LWD logs which

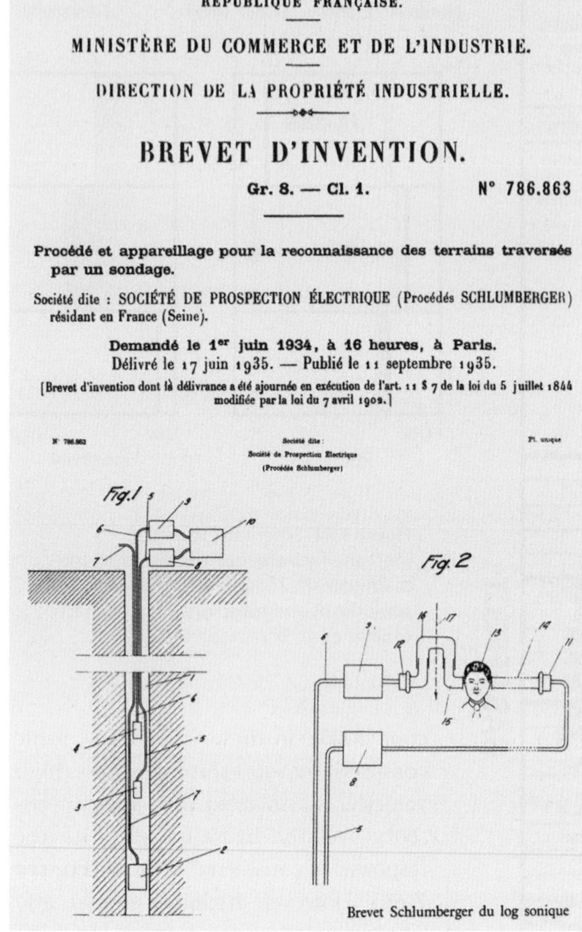

RÉPUBLIQUE FRANÇAISE.

MINISTÈRE DU COMMERCE ET DE L'INDUSTRIE.

DIRECTION DE LA PROPRIÉTÉ INDUSTRIELLE.

BREVET D'INVENTION.

Gr. 8. — Cl. 1. N° 786.863

Procédé et appareillage pour la reconnaissance des terrains traversés par un sondage.

Société dite : SOCIÉTÉ DE PROSPECTION ÉLECTRIQUE (Procédés SCHLUMBERGER) résidant en France (Seine).

Demandé le 1er juin 1934, à 16 heures, à Paris.
Délivré le 17 juin 1935. — Publié le 11 septembre 1935.

[Brevet d'invention dont la délivrance a été ajournée en exécution de l'art. 11 § 7 de la loi du 5 juillet 1844 modifiée par la loi du 7 avril 1902.]

Figure 9.45 The *brevet d'invention* for the sonic log deposited by Schlumberger in Paris, June 1934 (from Allaud and Martin 1976).

may be able to take measurements soon enough to avoid these local changes (Worthington 2010 *op. cit.*). New technical core measurement innovations and new log techniques will certainly be found in the future, so that this very valuable resource will be able to be reliably evaluated. But logs will remain crucial.

9.8 Seismic applications of sonic logs

The sonic log was originally invented as an aid to seismic prospection, as is seen by Conrad Schlumberger's *Brevet d'Invention* registered in Paris in June 1934 (**Figure 9.45**) (Allaud and Martin 1976). Following its commercialisation, the sonic log became a tool for petrophysicists and geologists. Today, however, the modern array sonic tools, with their ability to measure compressional (*Vp*), shear (*Vs*) and Stoneley (*VSt*) velocities, are reverting to their origins and are increasingly used for seismic work. Seismic methods are not the subject of this book, but there are certain observations on the use of sonic logs in seismic work that are relevant: these follow.

Seismic v. sonic velocities

The frequency of sound pulses now used in sonic logging are in the range 1.5–30 kHz; while the equivalent pulses in seismic work are 10–100 Hz (**Figure 9.4**). The sonic tool can detect beds down to about 40 cm or thinner; the seismic wave can resolve, typically, down to about 10m in shallow section but only 60 m in deep sections, depending on velocity and wavelength (amongst other things). Seismic resolution, then, is approximately 1/100 that of the sonic log (Sheriff 1980). The difference is well illustrated when seismic and sonic traces are directly compared (**Figure 9.46**).

Borehole damage is mentioned frequently throughout this book as affecting near borehole log measurements (esp. Chapters 5, Caliper, and 15, Images) and, in this chapter and as discussed, was the reason for the introduction of the long-spaced sonic. In the seismic context, it is sufficient to note that damage frequently affects sonic measurements; velocities in the damaged, near wellbore are generally lower than in unaffected formation. This will clearly affect comparisons between

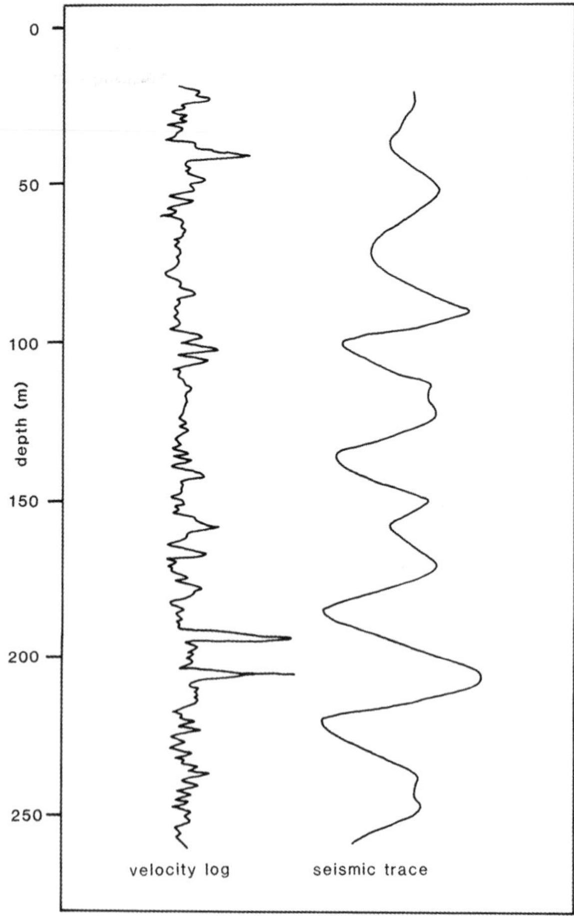

Figure 9.46 The contrasting frequency content of the sonic log and a seismic trace. Compare to Figure 9.4 (re-drawn from Sheriff 1980).

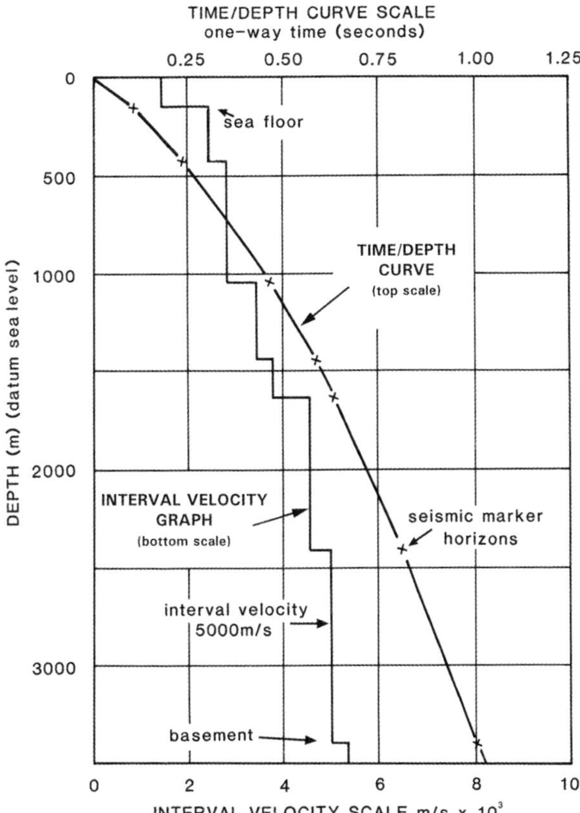

Figure 9.47 The presentation of sonic velocity (*Vp*) data as a time-depth curve and interval velocity graph to match the time scale of the seismic data. The two horizontal scales (time/depth scale curve and interval velocity scale) are independent: the depth scale is common to both curves.

seismic and sonic velocities. Even though modern sonic measurements can be processed to assess and even quantify borehole damage, as has been described (*Wellbore stability*, Section 9.7), it is measurements that are unaffected by borehole damage that are required for seismic work.

When the sonic log is compared in general to the seismic, the differences in frequency content, and borehole damage effects, must be considered.

Interval velocities

The results of sonic logging may be presented in several ways so that they can be used in seismic interpretation. Two presentations, which are complementary, are the interval velocity and the time-depth curve.

To find interval velocities, the sonic velocity is averaged over important stratigraphic intervals, or intervals likely to be indicated on the seismic section (**Figure 9.47**). On the older, analogue sonic logs, the interval velocity is found by counting the integrated travel-time marks over the interval concerned (**Figure 9.6**), and then dividing by the depth covered by the time. For instance, if 200 marks are counted (i.e. 200 milliseconds) between 2400 m and 3400 m (thickness 1000 m), the interval velocity is $1000/200 \times 10^{-1}$ m/s = 5000 m/s. On modern logs the integrated travel time is generally not plotted and the log can be simply averaged. Interval velocities are usually presented in histogram form against depth (**Figure 9.47**).

The time-depth curve represents the accumulated interval velocities: the accumulated milliseconds being plotted against depth. The first cross on the time-depth curve (**Figure 9.47**) is 150 milliseconds (0.15 sec, upper horizontal scale) from the origin and at 200 metres depth (an interval velocity of 200/0.15 = 1333 m/sec, lower horizontal scale). The co-ordinates of the next cross are 250 milliseconds (+100 millisecs) at 450 metres (+250 m) depth (an interval velocity of 250/0.1 = 2500 m/s). The presentation on the time axis (top horizontal scale) then becomes compatible with the seismic section. A normal time-depth curve is taken from zero time and zero depth (i.e. corrected from well KB to a surface datum, which is mean sea level offshore) to the well TD. From this can be read the average time to any particular depth or stratigraphic horizon, and this value can then be used to convert seismic time maps (isochron maps) to depth maps (isobath maps). The example given is a very simple one, and it should be remembered that time-depth curves are usually in one-way time and seismic sections and isochron maps are in two-way time (the time it takes for a seismic signal to go from the surface to the reflector and back).

Originally, when a well was completed a series of 'check shots' were run to calibrate the sonic log. A geophone was lowered into the well, a shot fired at the surface and the time taken for a compressional sound pulse from the surface (first arrival) to reach the geophone was recorded. The precise depth of the geophone was known and, therefore, also the precise time to this depth. Today, the check shot survey can still be run (the technology has improved) but is often replaced by a technique which measures a seismic like wave train, generally in three dimensions and at a great number of depths. This is the vertical seismic profile or VSP and it can be processed into a seismic-like response. For the simple use being discussed here, the VSP can be considered as simply supplying a series of depths (every 10–50 m) with precise first arrival (compressional) times from the surface datum. The VSP is generally run at TD but can be run at mid-well as a 'look-ahead'.

Just using the check shot data, a time-depth curve can be made for a well which is independent of the sonic-derived time-depth curve. Alternatively, the check shot depths may be used by combining them with the sonic log, the latter then being squeezed or stretched from time-depth point to time-depth point so that the average velocities between shot points correspond to the average velocities on the sonic log (Goetz *et al.* 1979). With the

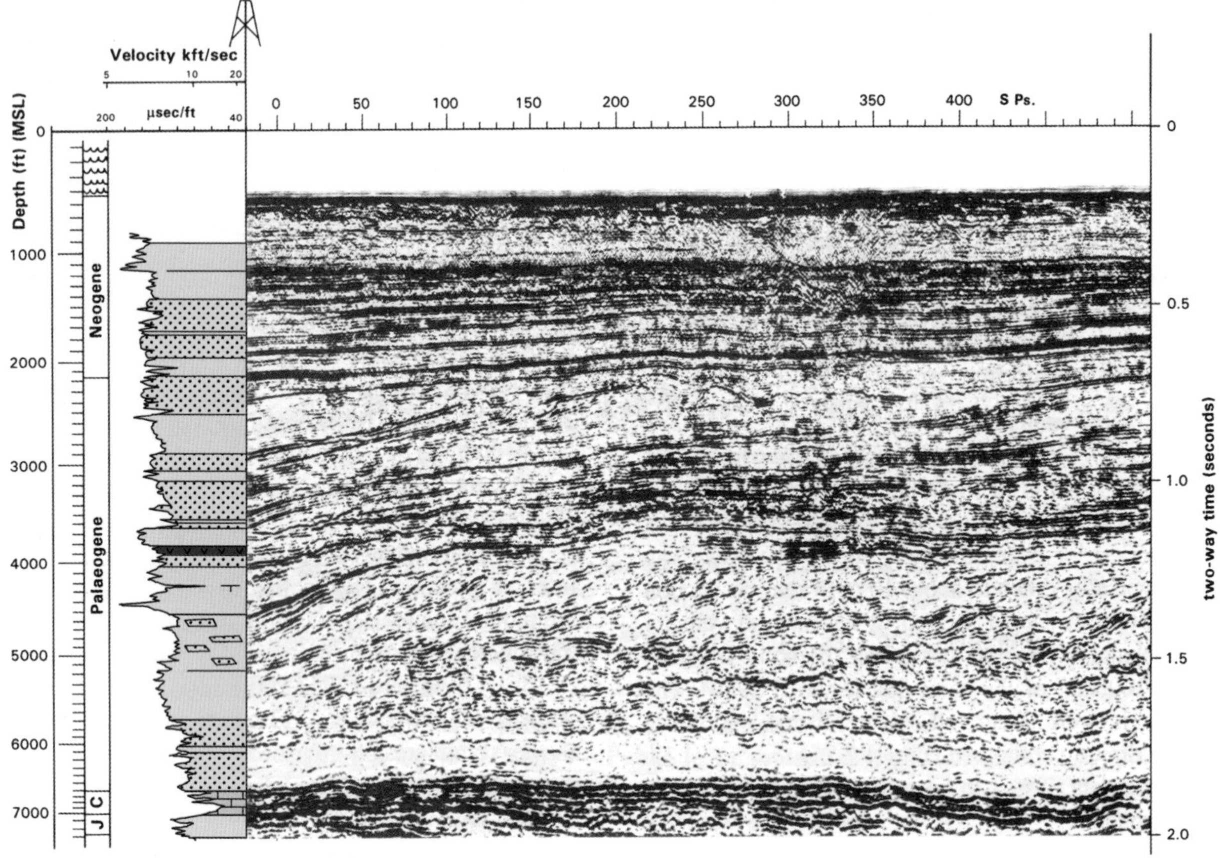

Figure 9.48 A sonic log (DTC) furnished with lithology and stratigraphy and replayed with the time scale of a seismic section. The time scale conversion log provides an accurate visual geology for the seismic section.

achieved precision, the sonic log may now be re-plotted on a linear time scale similar to that of a seismic section, having been converted from the original linear depth scale as recorded in the well (**Figure 9.48**). A geological and stratigraphic representation on a timescale log is a powerful tool for both geophysicist and geologist, and most geophysical interpretation packages allow the direct import of such logs into the seismic domain. The seismic section is now furnished with detailed, accurate, geological information (**Figure 9.48**).

Synthetic seismic logs

A synthetic seismic log is a presentation of the data contained in a sonic log in the form of a seismic trace. It is calculated using the sonic compressional data, check shot type information and the density log.

A seismic section is the result of (compressional) acoustic reflections from subsurface strata. The reflections depend on the contrasts of the acoustic impedances (i.e. velocity × density) of adjacent layers, that is, the reflection coefficient (R):

$$R = \frac{\text{acoustic impedance below} - \text{acoustic impedance above}}{\text{acoustic impedance above} + \text{acoustic impedance below}}$$

$$\text{i.e.} \quad \frac{\rho_2 V_2 - \rho_1 V_1}{\rho_2 V_2 + \rho_1 V_1} \qquad (10)$$

Where: V = compressional velocity
ρ = density

When both sonic and density logs are available, the acoustic impedances of the layers logged can be calculated (**Figure 9.49**). This acoustic impedance log represents the logged section as it would be sensed by a seismic pulse.

A simple Richter wave or a modelled synthetic seismic signal is passed digitally through the acoustic impedance log. This digital signal is distorted, just as it would be if it were going through the same layers in the subsurface. Recording the signal distortions, the computer constructs a synthetic seismic response (**Figure 9.49**). In this way, the original sonic data have been converted into a seismic-like trace. Even though the VSP provides a more sophisticated seismic model, the simple synthetic seismic log is still useful for 'tying' wells to the seismic, demonstrating the effective bed resolution on the section and explaining the simpler reflection responses (**Figure 9.50**) (Hernández *et al.* 2007).

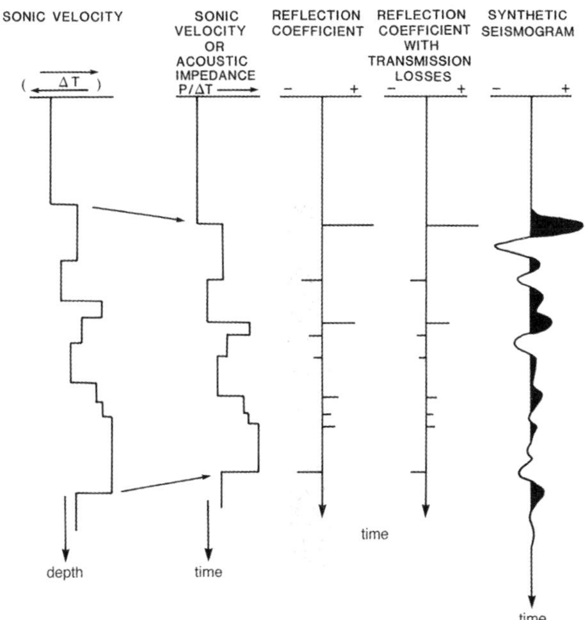

Figure 9.49 Diagrammatic representation of the construction of a synthetic seismic trace from the compressional sonic log velocity (*Vp*) and density log (from Thomas 1977).

Seismic attributes : AVO and more

A seismic attribute is any quantifiable transform of seismic trace data and may be trace related or horizon related. Attributes are used to extract interpretable information from the seismic, such as changes in amplitude with offset, changes in reflection coefficients with depth, changes in amplitude with fluid content and so on. For this kind of work, there is a growing tendency for well information to be used quantitatively by geophysicists (Kittridge *et al.* 2008). Amplitude variation with offset (AVO) studies, for example, that try to detect reflection amplitude changes caused by fluid variations, lithology variations or both with increasing reflection offset (**Figure 9.51**), make use of well derived, log parameters.

AVO work necessitates using both *Vp* and *Vs* along with the density to characterise a reflection. Typically, various responses are modelled using different thicknesses of reservoir, different porosities and shalyness, and different fluids. The modelled results are then compared to the actual seismic. For this work the lithology, porosity, fluid and velocity characteristics can be taken from the well. For example, sand /shale net to gross, reservoir porosity and fluid saturations, are all familiar properties to the petrophysicist, but can be used by the

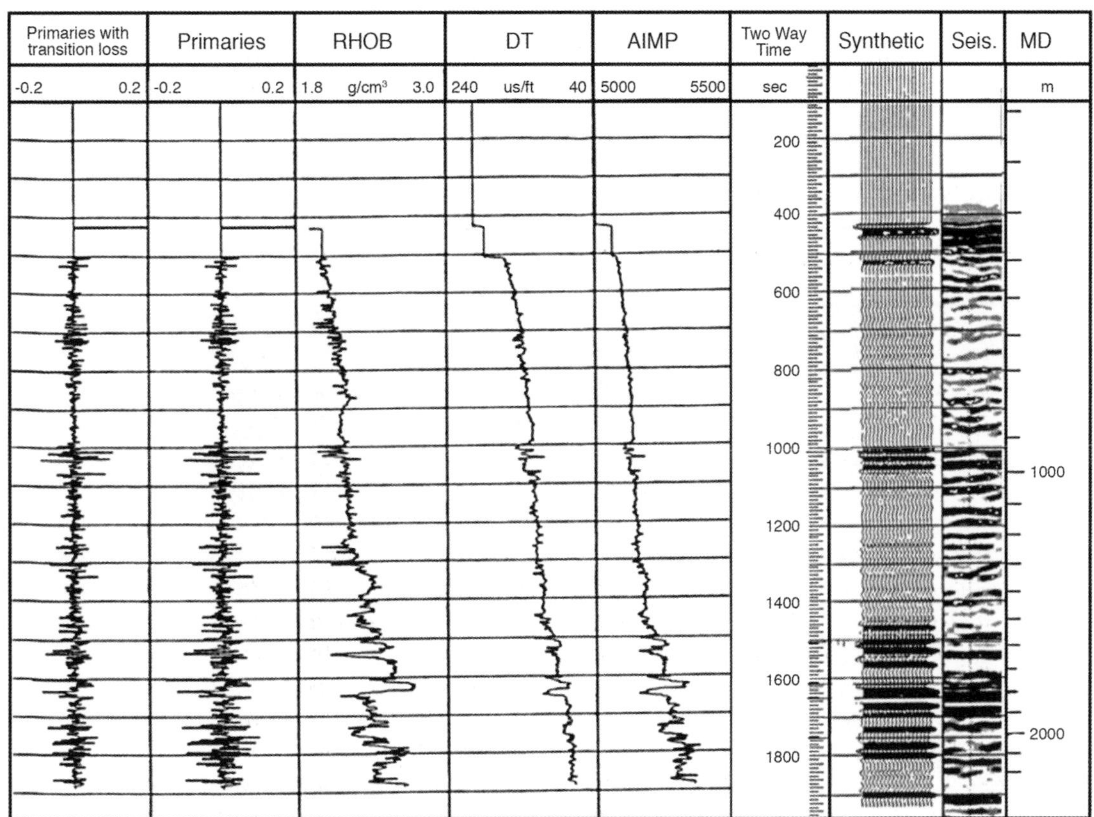

Figure 9.50 Example of the data used, and the derived synthetic seismic, compared to the actual seismic. RHOB = log density; DT = log slowness (DTC); AIMP = acoustic impedance (RHOB × DTC); Primaries, Primaries with transmission loss = mathematical models of the sub-surface.

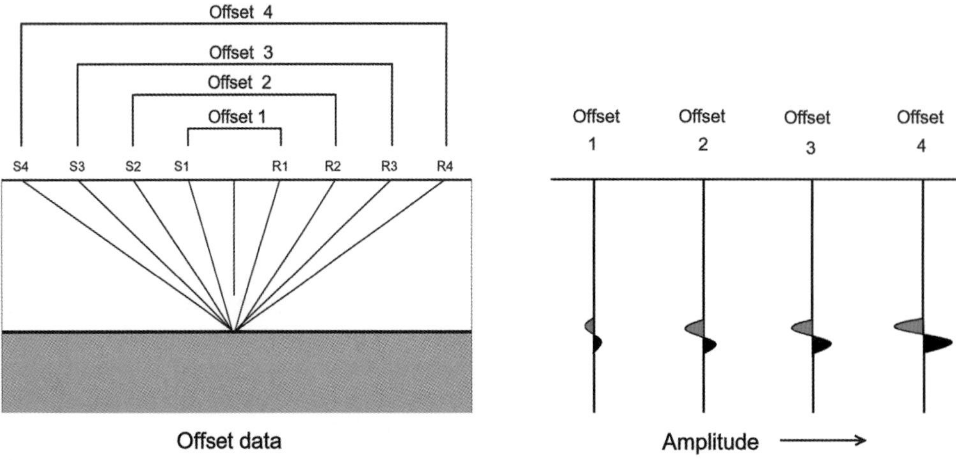

Figure 9.51 Schematic illustration of amplitude variation with offset (AVO) acquisition (left panel) which uses log based formation acoustic measurements to construct the model of amplitude variation (right panel).

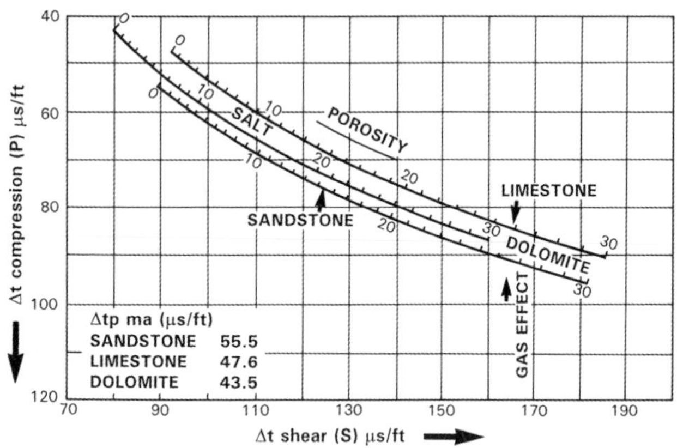

Figure 9.52 Graph of compressional against shear slowness derived from the array sonic. The graph shows separate sandstone, limestone and dolomite fields over the porosity range 0–30%, an effect that can be applied to seismic interpretation (from CGG document).

geophysicist in AVO calculations. There is a clear effort to extend information away from the well and into the seismic domain.

One example of the use of well data in seismic analysis is the application of the *Vp*/*Vs* ratio to characterise lithology. A simple plot of compressional slowness (*Vp*) against shear slowness (*Vs*) shows different lithology fields (Pickett 1963; Leslie and Mons 1982). Sandstones generally show *Vp*/*Vs* ratios between 1.6 and 1.75, while limestones have a ratio of approximately 1.9 (**Figure 9.52**, **Table 9.5**) (Leslie and Mons 1982). These ratios may change locally, and with depth, and so must be locally derived, especially if shale is included. One example showed a *Vp*/*Vs* ratio in water bearing sandstones of 1.182 + .00422 Δ*ts*, while in shales ratio was 1.276 + 00374 Δ*ts* (Williams 1990). Similar plots were previously discussed being used for gas detection (Section 9.7) but, as can be seen, they also contain lithology information and can be used for seismic interpretation.

A second example is fluid substitution. AVO is frequently carried out to identify horizons likely to contain hydrocarbons as opposed to water. If a well encounters a reservoir containing water, the same reservoir can be modelled containing oil or gas using, for example, the Gassmann substitution equations (e.g. Batzle and Wang 1992). For these equations, rock and fluid characteristics such as density and bulk moduli, and for fluids, viscosity, are required. Rock characteristics can be derived from the logs, fluid characteristics from laboratory analyses of well samples.

A final example is the way that mudrock behaviour can be used as input to rock physics. For this, both *Vp*-density and *Vp*-*Vs* relationships are relevant. Mudrocks compact in a different way to sands (Section 9.6, *Compaction in shales*) and this has significance for seismic reflections. In simple terms, sands may give either a positive (sand higher than shale) or negative (shale higher than sand) reflection and this can change with depth and compaction. Plotting *Vp* against *Vs* and *Vp* against density (porosity) over a range of depths will characterise these compaction effects. The *Vp, Vs* and density values can be taken either from the nearest well or from regional trends, based on multiple wells (i.e. Smith and Sondergelg 2001), but the data, importantly, are well derived.

10 THE DENSITY AND PHOTOELECTRIC FACTOR LOGS

10.1 Generalities

The log

The density log is a continuous record of a formation's *bulk density* (**Figure 10.1**). This is the overall density of a rock including solid matrix and the fluid enclosed in the pores. Geologically, bulk density is a function of the density of the minerals forming a rock (i.e. matrix) and the volume of free fluids (and gases) which it encloses (i.e. porosity). For example, a sandstone with no porosity will have a bulk density of 2.65 g/cm^3, the density of pure quartz. At 10% porosity the bulk density is only 2.49 g/cm^3, being the sum of 90% quartz grains (density 2.65 g/cm^3) and 10% water (density 1.0 g/cm^3).

Principal uses

Quantitatively, the principal use of the density log is to derive porosity and many operators prefer to use the density on its own to calculate it. This is because, as explained below, there is a simple relationship between

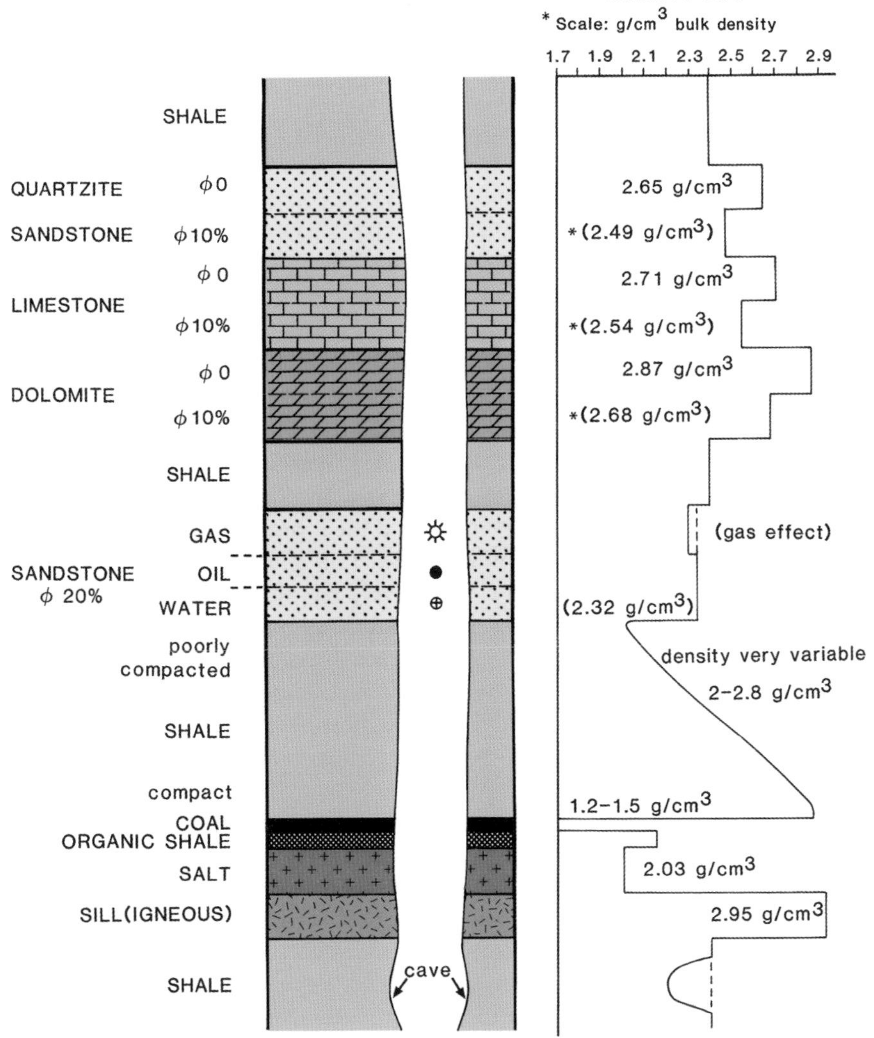

Figure 10.1 The density log: some typical responses. The density log shows *bulk density*.
*Density and porosity with fresh formation-water density 1.0 g/cm^3 (cf. Figure 11.1, which is on a compatible scale of neutron porosity).

Table 10.1 The principal uses of the density log.

	Discipline	Used for	Knowing
Quantitative	Petrophysics	Porosity	Matrix density Fluid density
	Seismic	Acoustic impedance Elastic moduli	density log + sonic *Vp* density log + sonic *Vp* + *Vs*
Qualitative and Semi-quantitative	Geology	General lithology Shale texture changes Mineral identification	Combined with neutron Average compaction trends Mineral densities
	Reservoir geology	Overpressure identification Fracture recognition	Average trends Sonic porosities (old method)
	Geochemistry	Source rock evaluation	Density of organic matter
Drilling	LWD only Wireline & LWD	Geosteering Hole condition Rock strength, hole stability	Log image format Standoff density log + *Vp* + *Vs*

density and porosity that is rigorously true. Furthermore, the density log has excellent vertical resolution in comparison to most other conventional logs. The tool is designed to operate in formation densities between 2 to 3 g/cm^3, and in this range the claimed accuracy of modern tools is typically ±0.01 g/cm^3 (it is lower at high densities). This corresponds to an accuracy of ± 0.5 pu (porosity units) in a typical porosity calculation. It is also used to calculate (indirectly) hydrocarbon pore volume and hydrocarbon density. It is cross-multiplied with the sonic log to produce the acoustic impedance log, which is used to model seismic responses (Chapter 9, Section 9.8). Increasingly, it is also used with modern full-waveform sonic tools to estimate rock strength and borehole stability, essential inputs to successfully drilling and completing expensive high angle production wells.

Qualitatively, it is a useful lithology indicator. It can be used to identify certain minerals, and can help to assess source rock organic matter content (even quantitatively), and may help to identify overpressure (**Table 10.1**). It is generally combined with the neutron (Chapter 11) for both quantitative and qualitative interpretations.

The measurement has been available in LWD form since the 1990s and modern wireline and LWD tools often use common components. LWD density measurements can exploit the fact that the sensor rotates with the drill string, and produces an image of the borehole wall. These images can be used to geosteer wells.

10.2 Principles of measurement

All density tools exploit so-called 'gamma-gamma' scattering to measure density. A radioactive source emits a continuous beam of high energy gamma rays into the formation. Some of these are scattered back to a pair of gamma ray detectors located a maximum distance of 50 cm (20") from the source. The term 'gamma-gamma' refers to the fact that the tool both emits and detects gamma rays. The density of the formation is measured because the count rate at a detector depends on the density of the material between it and the emitter. Although gamma detectors and electronics have improved over the years, the basic gamma-gamma principle has not changed since the first tools appeared in the 1950s. Furthermore, exactly the same technique is exploited in both wireline and LWD tools.

In detail, the tool physics is more complicated than suggested above. The gamma rays are generated by a radioactive isotope of caesium (^{137}Cs) which emits gamma rays with an energy of 662 keV (kilo electron volts, *see* Chapter 8). These are emitted in all directions, but the source is surrounded by heavy shielding except for one small window. Most of the gamma rays are therefore absorbed before they ever leave the tool (and critically before they get anywhere near the detectors). However, those that escape from the small window form a beam of gamma rays travelling away from the tool and directed into the formation. These collide with electrons in the formation and both lose energy and change direction. A very few of these collisions results in the scattered gamma ray traveling back to the tool, where it will be detected. The measurement is extremely wasteful: most gamma rays are absorbed before they even leave the tool and, of those that are emitted into the formation, it is very unlikely that they undergo precisely the right collision to send them back to a detector. Fortunately, ^{137}Cs is commonly available and even the feeble sources used in logging produce a huge number of gamma rays. A typical logging source produces 50 billion gamma rays every second, but only a few hundred end up being detected!

As noted above, it is the electrons in the formation that are responsible for scattering the gamma rays. That is, the attenuation and gamma ray flux loss is a function of the formation's electron density (i.e. the number of electrons per unit volume or electrons/cm^3) and this in turn, is very closely related to common density (g/cm^3) (**Table 10.2**). The physical mechanism responsible for

Table 10.2 Density, electron density and tool given density for some common compounds (from Schlumberger 1989a; Minette 1996).

Compound	Formula	Actual density ρ_b g/cm³	Tool density based on electron density (ρ_e), g/cm³	*Density given on log, g/cm³
Quartz	SiO_2	2.654	2.650	2.648
Calcite	$CaCO_3$	2.710	2.708	2.710
Dolomite	$CaCO_3MgCO_3$	2.850	2.863	2.850
Halite	NaCl	2.165	2.074	2.032
Gypsum	$CaSO_42H_2O$	2.320	2.372	2.351
Anhydrite	$CaSO_4$	2.960	2.957	2.977
Sylvite	KCl	1.984	1.916	1.863
Coal bituminous		1.200	1.272	1.173
		1.500	1.590	1.514
Coal anthracite		1.400	1.442	1.355
		1.800	1.852	1.796
Fresh water	H_2O	1.000	1.110	1.000
Salt water	200,000 ppm	1.146	1.273	1.135
Oil	$n(CH_2)$	0.850	0.970	0.850
Methane	CH_4	0.000677	0.00084	
Gas	$C_{1.1}H_{4.2}$	0.000773	0.00096	

*Density given on log = 1.0704 (ρ_e) – 0.1883

the attenuation is called Compton scattering (Chapter 8, Section 8.2). A second type of scattering, named Photoelectric absorption, is also exploited in modern density tools and produces another log, the *Pe* or PEF (this is discussed in Section 10.7).

In dense formations, Compton scattering attenuation is high and fewer gamma rays have the energy to reach the tool's detectors, while in less dense formations, the number is much higher. The change in counts with change in density is exponential over the range of the average logging density (about 2.0–3.0 g/cm³) (**Figure 10.2**). Detector counts are converted directly to bulk density for the log printout (**Figure 10.9**). Although electron density as detected by the tool and real density are closely related, there are differences, notably when hydrogen and chlorine are involved (*see* evaporites). The density log is calibrated to give actual values for a water-filled limestone (calcite 2.71 g/cm³ and pure water 1.00 g/cm³) (**Table 10.2**). The precise transformation from count rates to density is unique to a particular tool. It is checked every month by placing the tool in an Aluminium block and, if necessary, a new transform is computed. A more detailed calibration is performed at manufacture where individual tools are calibrated in 1.738 g/cm³ (magnesium), 2.70 g/cm³ (aluminium) and other blocks.

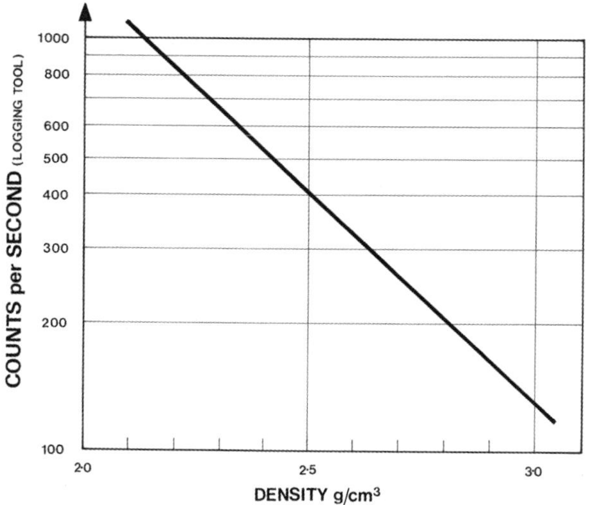

Figure 10.2 Correlation between the density tool radiation count (counts per second) and bulk density. A high density gives a low count (re-drawn from Desbrandes 1968).

10.3 Tools

Wireline tools

The standard density tools have a collimated gamma ray source, usually radiocaesium (^{137}Cs), which emits gamma rays at 662 keV, as described, and two scintillation type gamma ray detectors, a near at less than 6 inches (15 cm) and a far between 12–18 inches (30–45 cm) from the source (Flaum *et al.* 1989, Wraigt *et al.* 1989). The combination of two detectors allows for the compensation of borehole effects, the far detector being influenced more by the formation while the near detector is dominated by borehole effects. When the readings are compared and combined in a calculated ratio, unwanted borehole effects such as mudcake can be corrected for and the real formation effects enhanced (*see* processing). The Platform Express density tool from Schlumberger has a third detector to improve this mudcake correction.

Density tools (**Table 10.3**) use efficient scintillation detectors which can separate high (hard) and low (soft) gamma ray energy levels (**Figure 10.3**). This allows a good evaluation of borehole effects, an accurate density measurement and the additional measurement of the photoelectric factor value (Section 10.7). Source and detectors are mounted on a plough-shaped pad or skid which is pressed hard against the borehole wall so that they are as close to the formation as possible during logging (to minimise stand-off) (**Figure 10.4**). Wireline density tools, as a consequence, only measure along one sector of the borehole, i.e. only in one, limited direction.

LWD tools

LWD density tools work on the same principles as the wireline tools in that there is the same gamma ray source (^{137}Cs) and two shielded detectors (**Figure 10.5**). However, in the while-drilling environment the source and detectors rotate, which brings both advantages and challenges.

The main challenge for the LWD density tool is that during drilling the source and sensors are necessarily separated from the borehole wall, that i.e. there is stand-off (the distance between the measurement device and the formation). Stand-off has a considerable effect on density measurements and must be corrected for. To minimise stand-off, some LWD density tools have the source and detectors mounted in stabilisers although

Table 10.3 Modern density tools. (From Serra 2000, 2008, Baker Hughes™ (Atlas), Halliburton and Schlumberger documents

Name	Symbol	Company
1. Wireline Density measurement (older tools)		
Formation Density Compensated	FDC	Schlumberger
Compensated Densilog	CDL	Baker Hughes™ (Atlas)
Spectral Density Logging Tool	SDLT	Halliburton
2. Wireline Density and Photoelectric measurement		
Litho-Density Tool	LDT	Schlumberger
(other forms)	LDS, HLDT, PEX	"
Compensated Z-Density	ZDL	Baker Hughes™ (Atlas)
Compensated Densilog	CDL	"
Spectral Density Log	HSDL, SSSL	Halliburton
3. LWD tools		
Azimuthal Density Neutron	ADN VISION	Schlumberger
Compensated Density Neutron	CDN	"
Density	LithoTrak,	Baker Hughes™ INTEQ
Optimal Rotational Density	ORD	"
Stabilised Litho-Density	SLD	Halliburton/Sperry-Sun
Azimuthal Litho-Density	ALD, ASLD	"

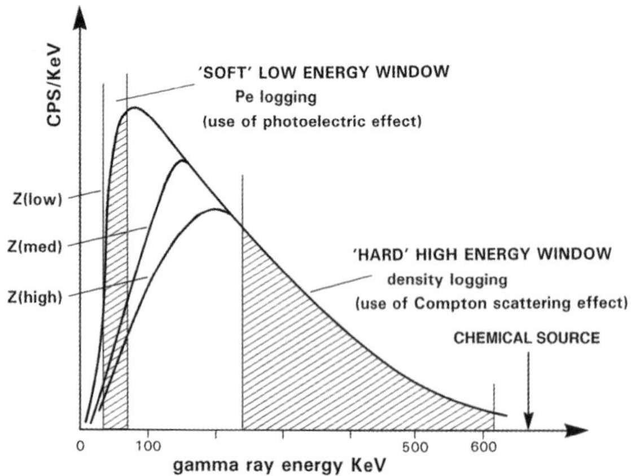

Figure 10.3 Density and lithodensity (photoelectric) logging in relation to gamma ray energy. Density logging uses the high energy regions where Compton scattering occurs. Photoelectric logging uses the low energy region where the photoelectric effect is dominant. CPS = counts per second. KeV - kilo electron volts. Z = atomic number (modified from Ellis 1987).

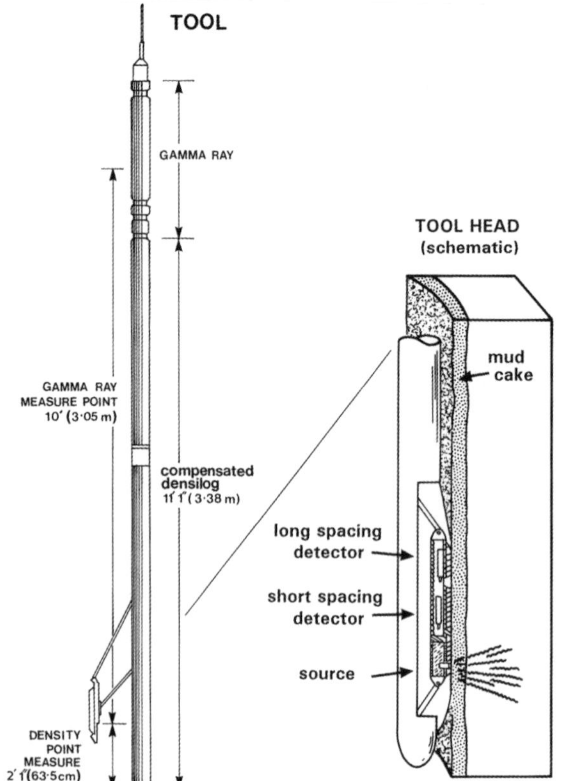

Figure 10.4 A density tool (Densilog from Atlas Wireline) and a tool head (modified from Dresser Atlas 1982 and Ellis 1987).

others are so called 'slick', and source and detectors are within the tool itself (**Figure 10.5**). Both of these tools, however, need a stand-off correction and since a direct hole measurement by an extended arm caliper is not possible in the while-drilling domain (the arm would be quickly ripped off), LWD tools have an ultrasonic 'acoustic caliper', which measures stand-off indirectly (Chapters 5 & 15). The raw density data itself can also be used to calculate a 'virtual' caliper (see processing *below*).

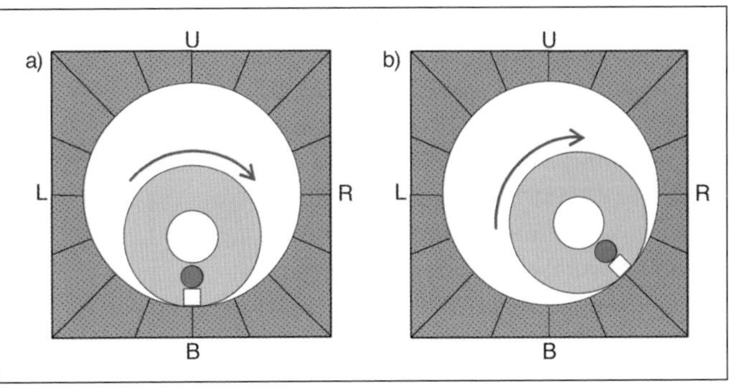

Figure 10.6 The behavior of a rotating LWD density tool in a horizontal well. a) normally the tool settles on the bottom under gravity and the best formation density is from the bottom sectors. b) a slick tool may mount the borehole wall as it rotates so the best formation densities will be in the bottom, right-hand sector. The 16 sectors of the density signal are indicated (re-drawn after Radtke *et al.* SPWLA 2003).

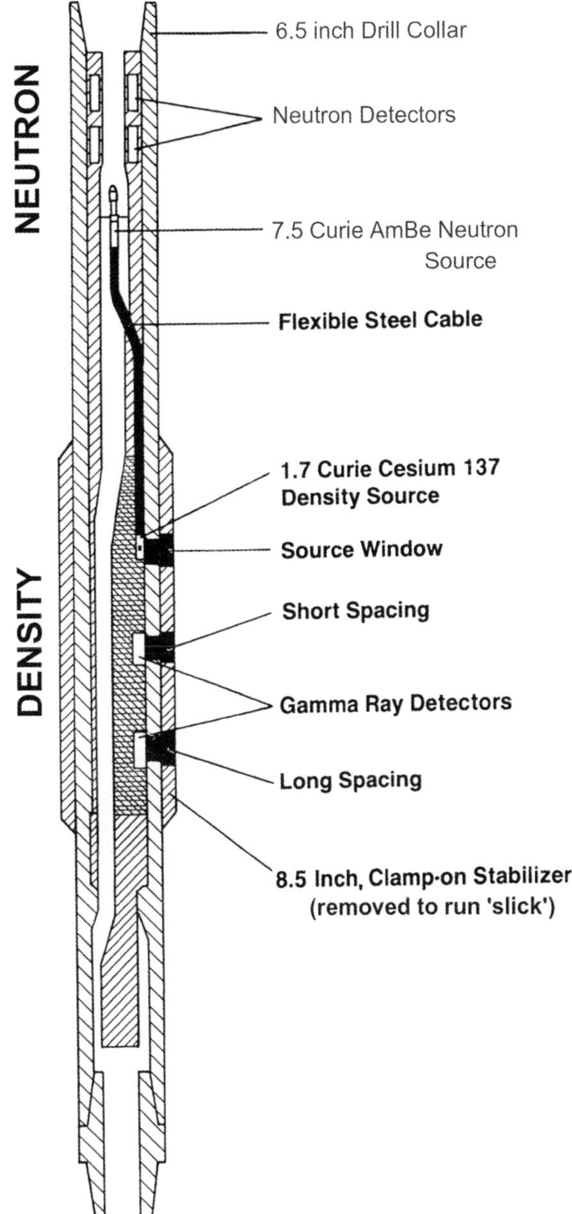

Figure 10.5 The layout of a typical LWD density (and neutron) tool. The tool may be run with the stabilisers to reduce stand-off (as in the diagram) or with the stabilisers off when it is said to be 'slick' (from Wraight *et al.* SPWLA 1989).

Being sensitive to stand-off and having rotating sensors, the LWD density measurements must be oriented to be useful. In the earliest LWD density tools, orientation was achieved by allocating the density readings to four quadrants, up, down, left and right, in horizontal or highly deviated holes and the 'best' density selected from the four results to represent the formation (Carpenter *et al.* 1997). However, the most recent tools provide the density in the form of an image built up from measurements in 16 oriented sectors of 22.5° (**Figure 10.10**) (Radtke *et al.* 2003; Meyer *et al.* 2005). Detector counts in each of the 16 sector bins are collected as the tool rotates, typically during 10 seconds. The accumulated bin counts are then recorded before being emptied for the next count. If a single curve is required, the 'best' density can be selected from the bins, as is done, for example, for the IDD or image derived density of Schlumberger. This 'best density' is often, but not always, from the quadrant on the bottom of the borehole (**Figure 10.6**). Density image logging is only effective in holes with more than about 10° of deviation.

If the density images are to be used for image interpretation rather than density analysis, the resolution of the pixels is important. The compensated density itself has a nominal resolution of 3.5" (8.9 cm) but this can be improved by using the near detector, when a 1.5" (3.8 cm) nominal pixel size can be achieved (Meyer *et al.* 2005).

Processing

Formation density is calculated from an analysis of the near and far detector counting rates. If the tool is flush against the borehole wall and there is no formation alteration in the near wellbore region, the near detector and far detector should give the same density. A non-zero value indicates the two detectors are reading different densities and the difference (known as the density correction or 'Delta-rho', DRHO) could be because:

1. The tool is not flush against the borehole wall.
2. There is mudcake between the tool and the formation.
3. There is invasion by filtrate which affects the near detector more than the far detector.
4. The tool is not working properly.

The density correction is therefore a very useful quality control (QC) check.

If the tool is working properly, the density correction is actually used to improve the density measurement. In practice, the tool actually exploits the fact that every combination of far and near detector count rates corresponds to a unique combination of density and density correction. This mapping is traditionally known as a 'spine and ribs' plot (**Figure 10.7**). A response with no correction will fall on the 'spine' and any departure indicates a correction is required (represented by the 'ribs'). Note that the correction has already been applied to the displayed density and should not be applied again. The correction is plotted on the log variously as DRHO, ZCOR, DENCOR etc. (**Figure 10.9**).

With the advent of computers, tools can produce far more curves than can be presented on a log. In the digital record, one will typically find a whole series of density curves that are generated from just one of the detectors, or even just a subset of counts from one detector. (e.g. S1RH is the density from just the short-spaced detector of the Schlumberger tool). Modern signal processing actually uses the energy spectrum of each sensor as a selective input and sensors are provided with a reference peak to assure their accuracy (**Figure 10.8**). Corrections for mudcake, borehole, barite and rugosity and alpha processing (resolution matching) are all applied to the count rates before a final compensated, formation density is computed (Theys 1991).

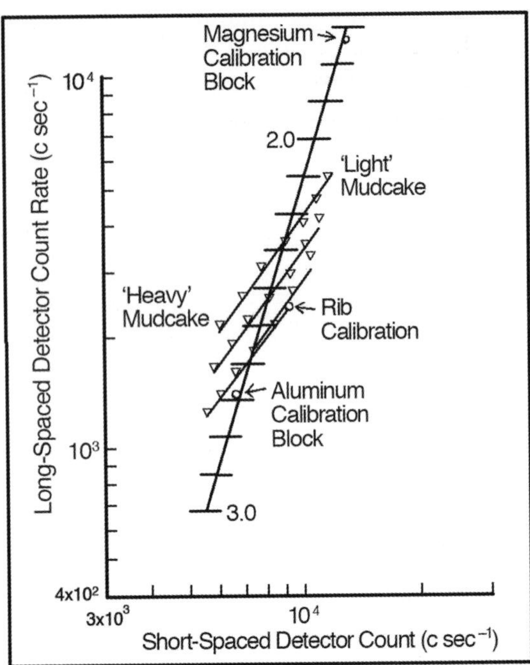

Figure 10.7 An example of the 'spine and ribs' plot for correcting the compensated density tool for mudcake and stand-off. The spine is an average ratio of the long and short spaced detector counts when there is no correction. A correction is applied when there is departure from the spine, based on the ribs and depends on mud weight and stand-off. It is applied automatically to the main bulk density (RHOB) curve (usually a subtraction for mud cake) and is plotted on the log as DRHO as on Figure 10.9.

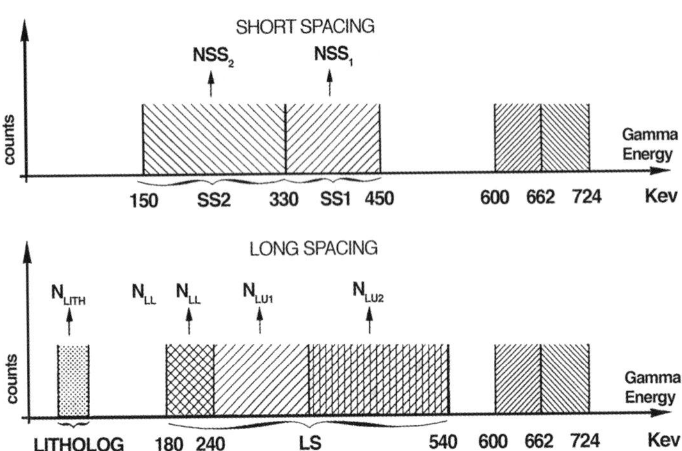

Figure 10.8 The gamma ray energy spectra windows used in the litho-density tool detectors. Lower energy windows are affected by barite and may not be used. The highest energy windows are reference peaks to monitor the source. The acronyms are Schlumberger channel identifiers (from Theys 1991) *Courtesy of Schlumberger*.

In the LWD environment, because stand-off is important, a 'virtual' caliper can be calculated. The compensated formation density that is calculated from the two detectors is compared to the apparent formation density from the far detector alone. Any difference can be accounted for by a gap filled with mud of a certain density. Using a known mud density, the gap, which is the stand-off, can be given dimensions and quoted as hole size. For this to be effective there should be a reasonable density contrast between the formation and the mud (Dowla *et al.* 2006). Since the LWD density is recorded by sector, the caliper derivation is also calculated by sector and can be represented as a 3-D image (Chapter 5).

Log presentation, scales and units

The density log is normally plotted on a linear scale of bulk density in g/cm^3 (**Figure 10.9**). If an API format is used (**Figure 1.6**), the log is run across tracks 2 and 3, most often with a scale between 1.95–2.95 g/cm^3 (Although in forma-

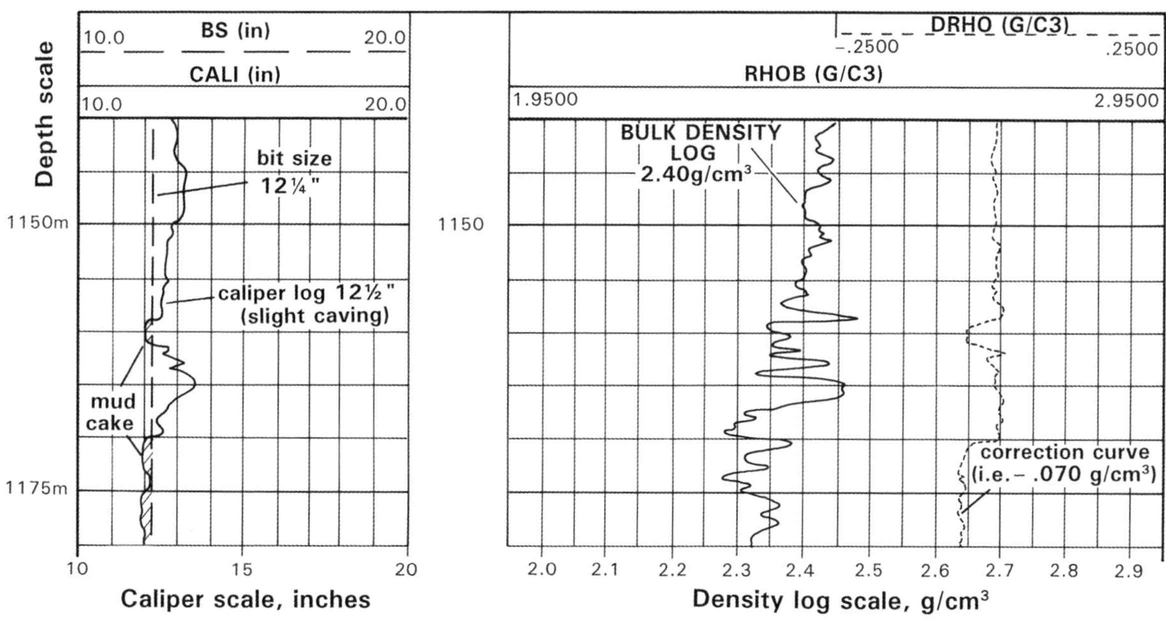

Figure 10.9 Typical heading of a density log. The density log is over tracks 2 and 3: the scale is in g/cm³. Any mud weight correction is shown in log form (dashed) and has been automatically applied. It is based, in this example, on a barite mud containing 272 ppm barium and with a density of 1.84 g/cm³.

tions where average densities are low, for example deepwater tertiary sands, a scale of 1.7–2.7 g/cm³ is often used). The main wireline log is accompanied by a curve indicating the borehole and mud-cake corrections (eg. DRHO) that have been automatically applied, as explained (*see* processing). The wireline logs usually also have a record of cable tension as the density tool tends to stick while the LWD density logs are plotted with drilling information such as rate of penetration and time since drilling.

Both wireline and LWD density tools are typically run as a density-neutron combination along with (at least) a gamma ray, resistivity and caliper, the so-called 'triple combo'. The caliper (mechanical or ultrasonic) is an essential accompaniment to the density log for reasons of stand-off and quality control as explained.

The older LWD density logs from high angle and horizontal wells, as explained, were displayed as four values, up, down, left and right, and used the standard scales. The tendency now, as described, is to display the LWD density measurements as an oriented image, denser formation in lighter colours (**Figure 10.10**). The density caliper may also be displayed (**Figure 5.3**).

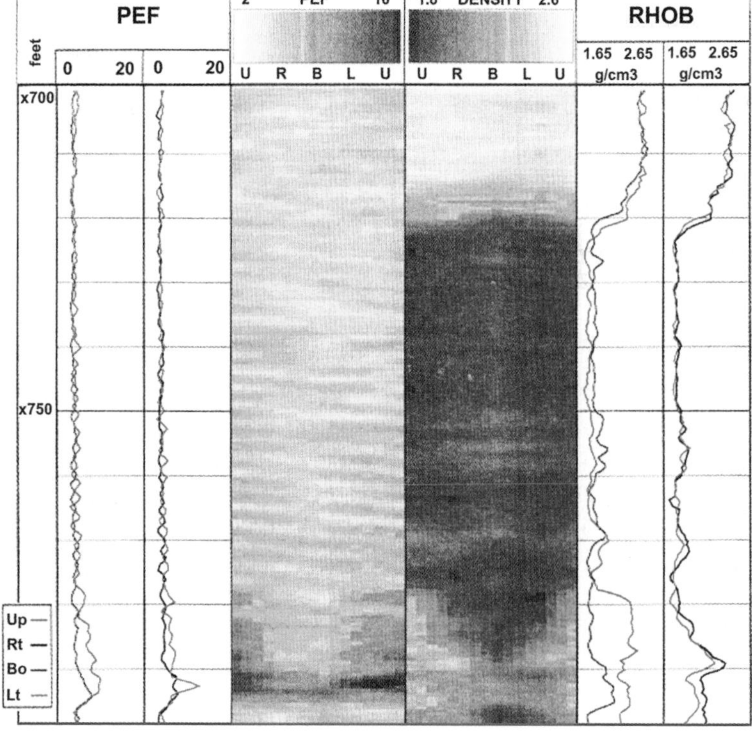

Figure 10.10 An image created from oriented density (RHOB) and photoelectric (*Pe*) measurements from an LWD tool (the ADN, azimuthal density log of Schlumberger). The dark, lower density image is a clean, gas bearing sandstone, the lighter, higher density image is shale. The PEF image shows only hole spiraling. Gulf of Mexico well, flat bedding, 52° deviation, 1.65 g/cm³ (10.3 lbs/gal) mud. The four quadrant logs are plotted beside the corresponding image track i.e. Up, Rt (right), Bo (bottom) and Lt (left) (modified from Carpenter *et al.* SPWLA 1997).

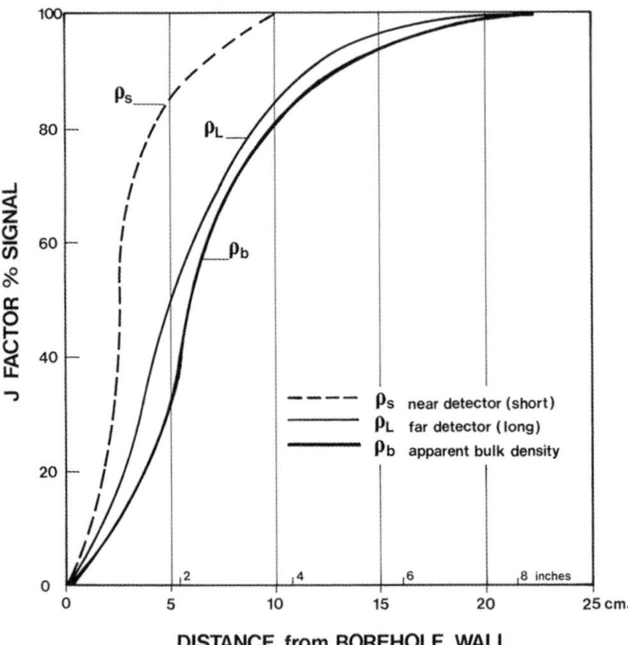

Figure 10.11 The depth of investigation of the density tool is very shallow. The graphs show experimental results for a 35% porosity, water-filled sand (re-drawn from Sherman and Locke 1975).

10.4 Log characteristics

Depth of investigation

The depth of investigation of a density tool is largely determined by the source to detector spacing and so the short-spaced detector alone has a shallower depth of investigation than the long spaced. This fact is exploited in the density correction as discussed.

Research into the density tool's characteristics shows that its depth of investigation is very shallow. **Figure 10.11** shows that 90% of the original Schlumberger FDC response probably originated from 13 cm (5") or less from the tool. These are experimental results using a sand with a 35% porosity and a bulk density of 2.07 g/cm^3 (Sherman & Locke 1975; Wiley & Patchett 1994). In normal logging, the investigation depth will probably be less, especially for the more modern tools, and around 5–10 cm (2–4") for average formation densities (Tittman 1986; Badruzzaman 2004) although investigation will vary with formation density, being shallower in denser formations. This means that the density tools, both wireline and LWD, are easily affected by hole conditions. Moreover, in porous zones where the tool has its principal petrophysical use, it will be measuring the invaded zone, and there is little chance of the wireline tool detecting original formation water or oil in place. The LWD tool, however, measures the formation before significant invasion has occurred and tool responses show that it frequently detects gas and light hydrocarbons (*see also* Section 11.5) (Benfield *et al.* 2004).

Vertical, bed resolution

While the depth of investigation of the density tool is small, the bed resolution is good (an example of the trade-off between depth of investigation and vertical resolution that affects nearly all logging tools). The vertical resolution of the older wireline density tools is the distance between the detectors, namely around 25 cm (10") (Serra 2000) and, under ideal conditions, true densities measured in beds down to about 40 cm (16") (Theys 1991). Individual sensors, however, have intrinsic bed resolutions of long spaced 30.5–38 cm (12–15"), short spaced and *Pe*, 5.0 cm (2") (Mathis and Gearhart 1989). At higher sampling rates and modern processing, by using the short spaced detector definition, it is considered possible for the wireline tools to resolve beds down to 10 cm (4") or less. A partial reaction from the density tool can be caused by even thinner beds, however, especially if they have a very high or very low density contrast. For example, calcareous nodules 5 cm (2") thick are seen as high spikes and coals down to around 8 cm (3") are seen as low spikes.

The LWD density probably has a slightly better bed resolution than its wireline counterpart because of binning and filtering. However, this resolution of the LWD density tools depends not only on tool design but also on drilling conditions. As explained in the introduction, LWD densities can be displayed as an image (**Figure 10.10**), and these can be derived either from a compensated density based on near and far count ratios (as for the wireline) or from the near detector alone (the image normally costs significantly more than a single density curve so, although it is always available, it is not always bought). Vertical resolution for the compensated density images is 8.9 cm (3.5") and for the images from the near detector alone, 3.8 cm (1.5") (Meyer *et al.* 2005). These are nominal values and, if the stand-off is large, they will not be realised, especially for the finer resolution from the near detector.

In summary, density tools can resolve beds down to perhaps 10 cm, and certainly below 40 cm. This good bed resolution makes the density log useful for drawing bed boundaries.

Unwanted logging effects

The shallow depth of investigation of the density tool makes it very susceptible to stand-off and hole conditions. This is especially seen in the LWD tool response. Automatic compensation and corrections are applied to the density log but these cannot cope with a large stand-off. The wireline density log should be interpreted along with its corresponding caliper log and the LWD along with any hole size estimates. The use of density images helps in the quality control of the LWD logs and, as has

Table 10.4 Unwanted environmental effects – density log

Factor Name	Effect on log	*Severity
Caved or rough hole (stand-off)	Decrease in formation density to approach a drilling mud density value	Common (corrections attempted)
Barite in the drilling mud	Automatically corrected in the tool	Rare (corrections satisfactory)
Mudcake	Automatically corrected in the tool (spine & ribs)	Rare (corrections satisfactory)

*When the effect makes the log reading unusable. Ratings: frequent, common, present, rare.

been explained, a best quality density derived: it is verifiable visually (Radtke *et al.* 2003). The most frequently encountered unwanted logging effects are shown in **Table 10.4.**

10.5 Quantitative uses

Porosity calculation

The density log is used to calculate porosity, its principal use. The fact that the bulk density of a mixture is the volume weighted average of the components is exploited to do this. The density may also be used indirectly to derive hydrocarbon pore volume and hydrocarbon density.

To calculate porosity from log-derived bulk density, it is necessary to know the density of all the individual materials involved. The density tool sees global (bulk) density, the density of both the grains forming the rock and of the fluids enclosed in the interstitial pores (**Figure 10.12**). As an example, if the tool measures a bulk density of 2.5 g/cm^3 in a salt-water-bearing formation (fluid density 1.1 g/cm^3 [as seen by the tool]) we can interpret any of the following:

Lithology	**Grain density**	**Porosity**
Sandstone	2.65 g/cm^3	10%
Limestone	2.71 g/cm^3	13%
Dolomite	2.87 g/cm^3	21%

Of course, if the grain (matrix) density and the fluid density are known, the equation that gives porosity from the summation of fluid and matrix components can be solved (**Figure 10.12**). For example,

$$\text{bulk density } (\rho_b) = \text{porosity } (\varnothing) \times \text{fluid density } (\rho_f) + (1-(\varnothing) \times \text{matrix density } (\rho_{ma})$$

When solved for porosity this equation becomes:

$$\text{porosity } \varnothing = \frac{\rho_{ma} - \rho_b}{\rho_{ma} - \rho_f}$$

where ρ_{ma} = matrix (or grain) density, ρ_f = fluid density and ρ_b = bulk density (as measured by the tool, and hence includes porosity and grain density).

The relationship between the bulk density (as measured by the tool) and porosity can be extremely close when the grain density remains constant (Patchett and Coalson 1979). The example shows a reservoir of ortho-quartzite composition and a quite constant grain density of 2.68 g/cm^3 (**Figure 10.13**). The porosity derived from the bulk density log in this example corresponds well to the core porosity when a matrix density of 2.68 g/cm^3 and tool-registered fluid density of 1.1 g/cm^3 are applied. The density tool is considered to have an accuracy of the order of 0.013 g/cm^3 which, as explained previously, means an accuracy of approximately +/−0.5 porosity units (pu) (Granberry *et al.* 1968). The

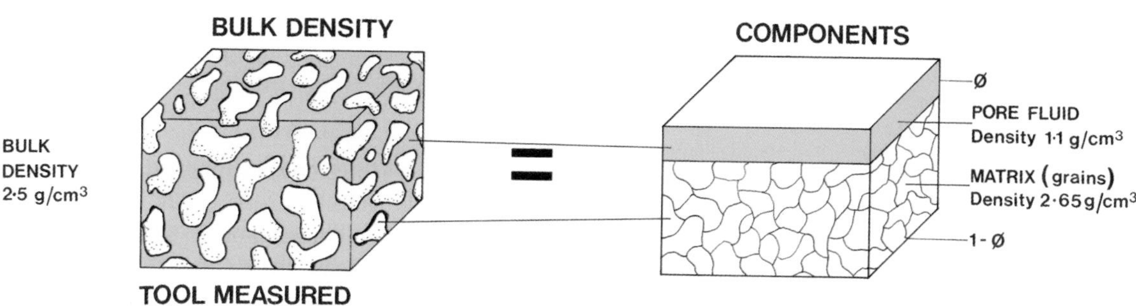

Figure 10.12 Tool measured bulk density and a visualisation of the derivation of the porosity component. The numbers are for a sandstone with 10% porosity.

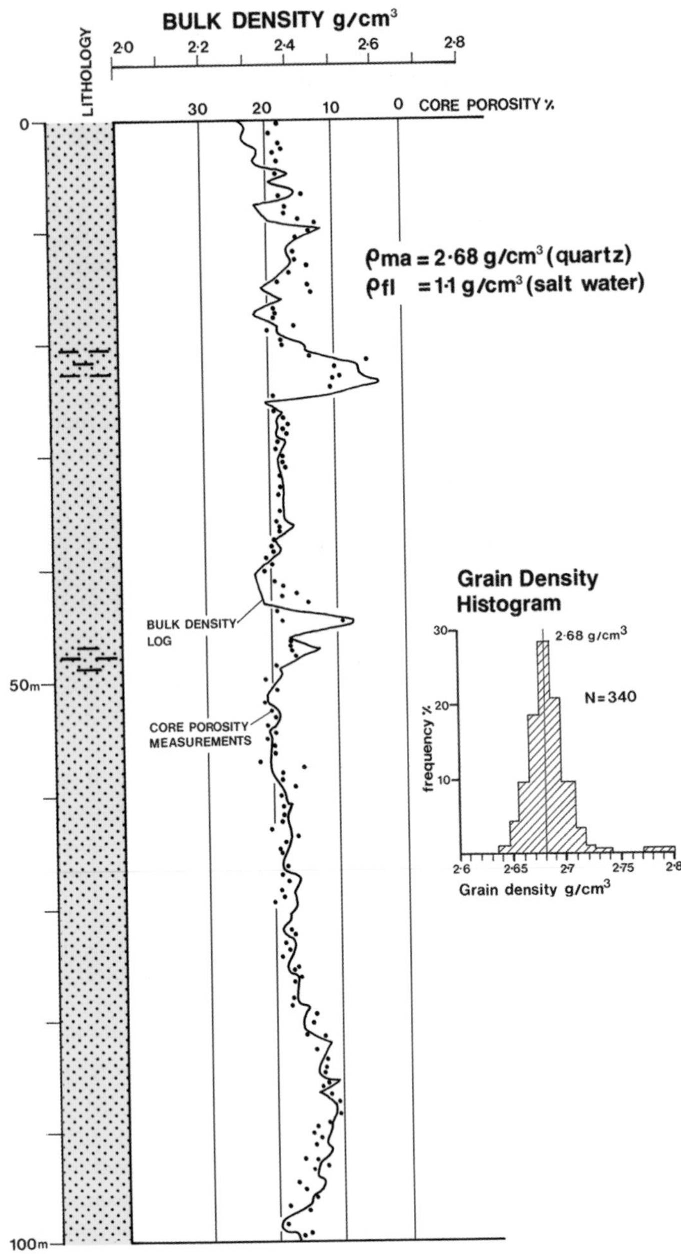

Figure 10.13 Close correspondence between the bulk density log and core-measured porosity in an orthoquartzite. The bulk density can be converted to porosity using a matrix density of 2.68 g/cm³, as indicated by the inset histogram.

density log porosity is generally considered to be the most accurate of the logs.

If constant grain density figures are applied to a formation and the grain density is *not* constant, the porosity calculated is inaccurate and errors of porosity units may occur. Such errors can occur in the North Sea Jurassic sands where up to 30% mica can increase the average grain density to 2.84 g/cm³ (mica density 2.82–2.99 g/cm³) so that, when too low a grain density is used, the porosity is underestimated by the density log (**Figure 10.14**).

Erroneous porosities may also be calculated when the fluid density changes. This can happen when a rock is saturated with gaseous hydrocarbons. As shown above, the porosity equation is furnished with a grain density and a fluid density. The latter is 1.0 g/cm³ for fresh water and 1.1 g/cm³ for salt water (but may vary with temperature). In the presence of gas (typical density 0.0007 g/cm³) the fluid density drops dramatically. As the example shows, the density log gives too high a porosity (**Figure 10.15**). If the porosity (and water saturation) can be calculated by other means, the density log can be used to calculate the hydrocarbon pore volume and density (Theys 1991).

When oil is present, the porosity given by the density log is essentially correct. This is because the density tool investigates the flushed zone (*see* 'Depth of investigation', Section 10.4) where only a small volume of oil remains. Moreover, the density of oil is quite close to that of water (about 0.7 g/cm³). Gas, however, is more mobile and can occur in the flushed zone (or before flushing in the LWD domain) where, because of the large density difference with water, has the effect of diminishing the bulk density as described above.

Acoustic impedance and rock strength

The density log is used in conjunction with the simple sonic log to calculate acoustic impedance and with the full waveform sonic, to calculate rock strength.

The subjects are briefly described in Chapter 9 (The sonic, Section 9.7).

10.6 Qualitative uses

The density tool gives a continuous log of the formation's bulk density and thus needs no interpretation since the character (density) is given directly. The qualitative use of this log therefore depends on the geological significance of the density of a formation.

Lithology identification

The densities of the more common lithologies (shale, sandstone and limestone) are rarely diagnostic since there is too much overlap and too much of a spread caused by differences in composition and texture. Shales, for example, may have densities ranging from 1.8 g/cm³ to 2.7 g/cm³: the density difference between a plastic clay and a compacted shale (**Table 10.5**). Most oilfield densities are between 2.0 g/cm³ and 3.0 g/cm³ and the common lithologies span the whole of this

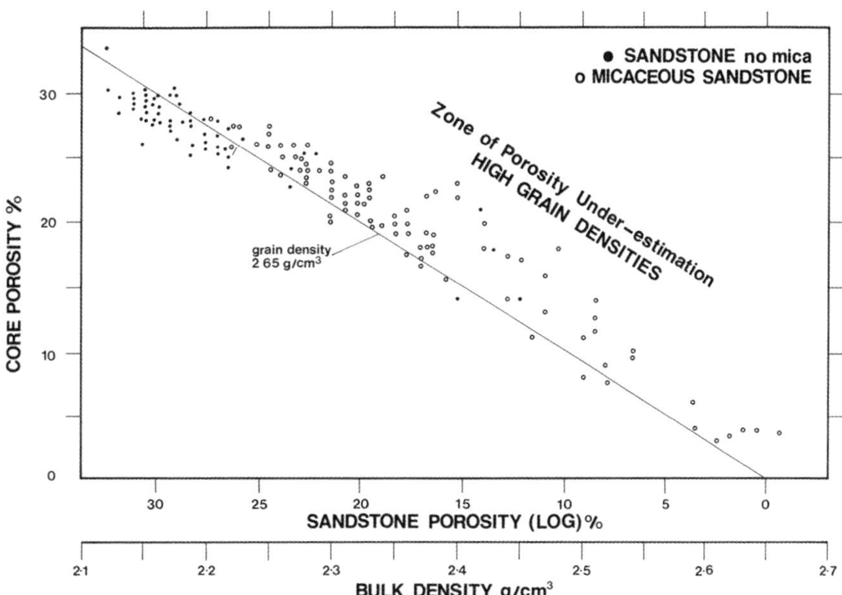

Figure 10.14 The effect of mica on porosity values derived from the bulk density log. For the graph a matrix density of 2.65 g/cm³ was used (giving the diagonal line). For the micaceous sands, core-measured porosities are consistently higher than those given by the log, because the grain density is too low at 2.65 g/cm³. Mica has densities up to 3.10 g/cm³ (re-drawn from Hodson 1975).

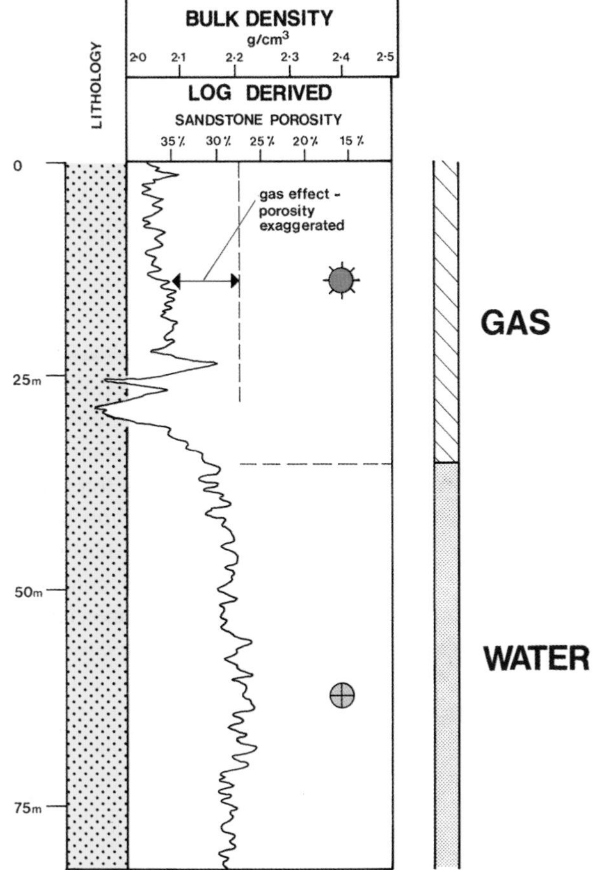

Figure 10.15 The effect of gas on the density log. In this example the gas zone reads about 35% porosity: it should read 27% porosity.

Table 10.5 Densities of common lithologies (see *also* Figure 10.16).

Lithology	Range (g/cm³)	Matrix (g/cm³)
Clays-shales	1.8–2.75	Varies (av. 2.65–2.7)
Sandstones	1.9–2.65	2.65 (quartz)
Limestones	2.2–2.71	2.71 (calcite)
Dolomites	2.3–2.87	2.87 (dolomite

range although, as described below, certain diagnostic lithologies fall outside these limits (**Figure 10.16**).

(Although the density log alone is generally a poor indicator of lithology, combined with the neutron log it becomes excellent. In fact, the neutron-density log combination is probably the best qualitative indicator of general lithology, especially in the presence of a valid *Pe* curve. The subject is described in Chapter 11, *see* 'Neutron-density combination').

Shale compaction and composition

The compaction of shales with burial is a well-known phenomenon and it can be followed on the density log. Shale compaction involves a series of textural and compositional changes resulting in a progressive decrease in porosity and corresponding increase in density (e.g. Burst 1969). For example, shallow, uncompacted clays have densities around 2.0 g/cm³ while, at depth, this figure commonly rises to 2.6 g/cm³ or more. Changes due to compaction are gradual and, when seen in one well, occur over a considerable thickness of sediment (**Figure 10.17**). To see clay compaction changes, the density log is best viewed at a compressed vertical scale

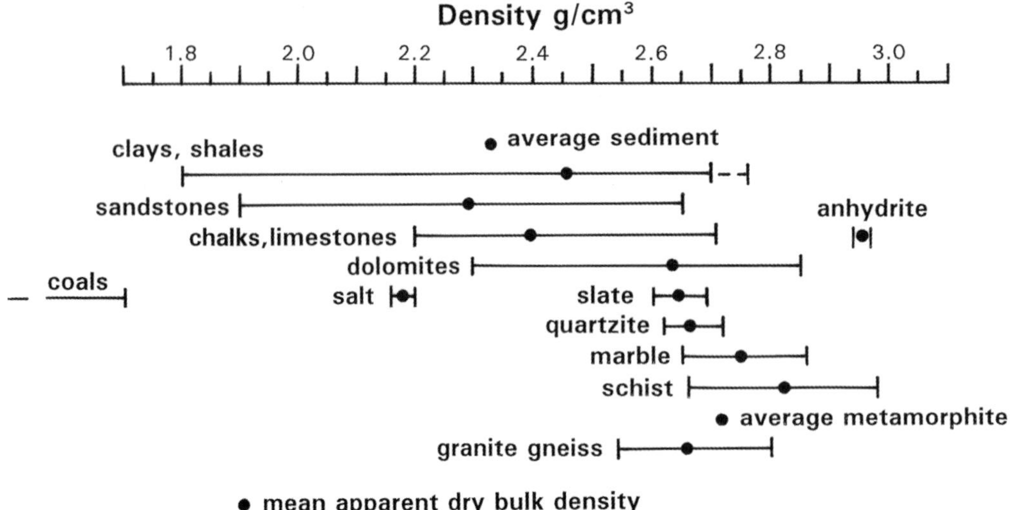

Figure 10.16 Density ranges of some common lithologies. Note the similar ranges of clay/shale, sandstone and limestone (modified from Jackson and Talbot 1986).

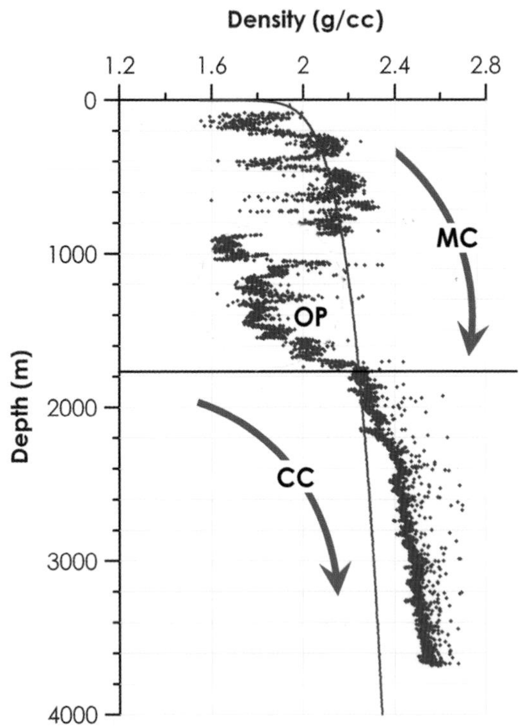

Figure 10.17 Shale compaction with depth seen on a bulk density log plotted at a compressed vertical scale. MC = mechanical compaction; CC = chemical compaction; OP = overpressure (from Mondol *et al.* 2008).

(say a screenful), which allows the effect to be examined even in shale-sand or shale-lime sequences.

The physical and chemical aspects of shale compaction have been examined in detail on the Norwegian Shelf over the last few years. Researchers have found that physical 'squeezing' due to overburden dominates in the near sub-surface at low temperatures (**Figure 10.17**, MC = mechanical compaction). Deeper in the subsurface, below about 2 km (6500 ft) and at higher temperatures (above about 60°–80°C when smectite is transformed into illite), silica is released, forms micro-quartz grains and the clay fabric becomes stiffened by the chemical precipitation (**Figure 10.17**, CC = chemical compaction) (Thyberg *et al.* 2009). The changes are clearly related to temperature and time as well as depth. Although the density logs show such changes, they are best seen on the sonic logs as discussed in Chapter 9.

Shale age and unconformities

Although it is by no means diagnostic, shale density is often indicative of age. In general, older shales are more dense. Palaeozoic clays or Tertiary shales are rare. The increase in shale density during compaction, although essentially due to a decrease in porosity, is accompanied by irreversible diagenetic changes as explained (**Figure 10.18**). Compaction trends, therefore, become 'fossilised' (Shaw 1980). This means that, in the subsurface, an abrupt change in compaction will indicate a change in age, in other words an unconformity (**Figure 10.19**) or fault. Beyond this, if general compaction curves for a region can be established, the maximum depth of burial of a formation can be estimated. The methodology is similar to that described using the sonic log (*see* 'Compaction', Chapter 9). For compaction studies, the density log must be used carefully as it is affected by small local changes, and the sonic log is preferred.

Shale composition

Shale density changes due to compaction are gradual, while small-order, local variations are more likely due to changes in shale composition. For example, an in-

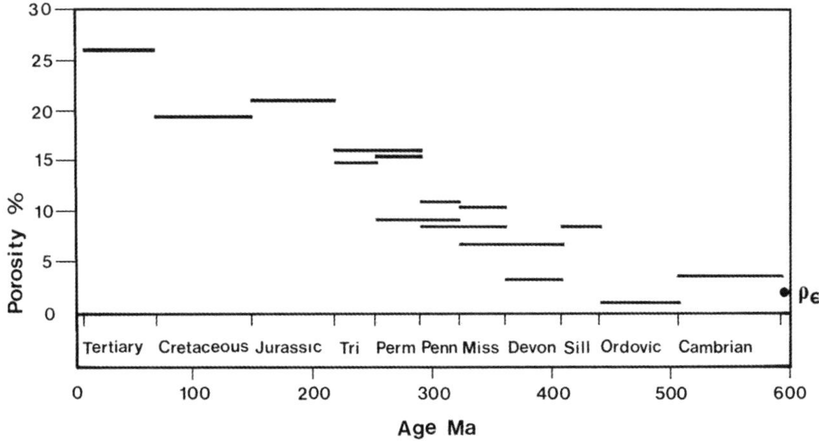

Figure 10.18 Shale porosity compared to geologic age. It generally decreases, the older it gets.

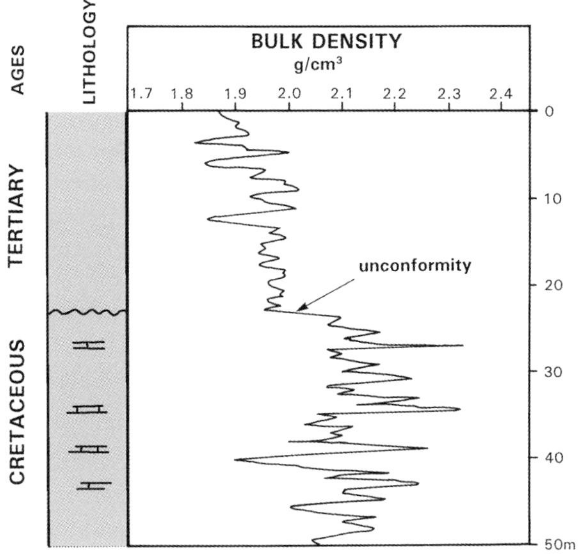

Figure 10.19 Tertiary shales unconformably overlying dipping, eroded, Cretaceous shales. The abrupt change in density marks the unconformity.

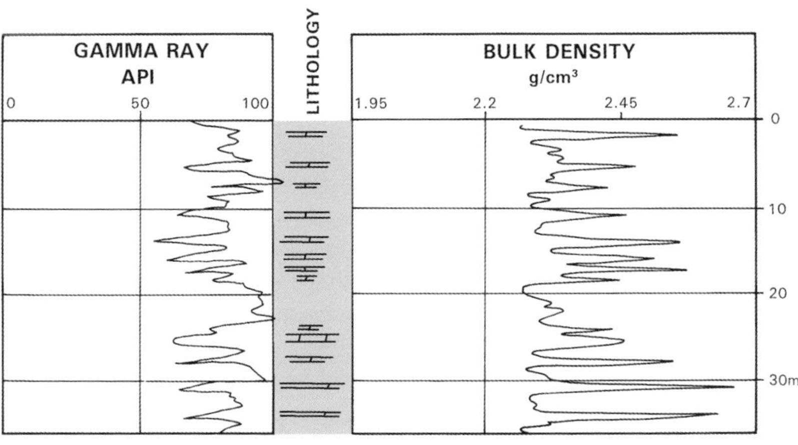

Figure 10.20 Thin, carbonate/siderite cemented horizons in shale. The intervals may be thin continuous bands or irregular, nodular horizons.

crease in calcium carbonate content generally fills the shale porosity and causes an increase in the shale bulk density (**Figure 10.20**). The increase in density is even more marked when iron carbonate (siderite) is involved (density when pure, 3.89 g/cm³). When organic matter is present, the reverse occurs and the density diminishes, organic matter having a very low density (of around 1.2 g/cm³, **Figure 10.28**). This relationship may be quantified (*see* 'Source rock evaluation' *below*).

The density log in sandstones – composition and diagenesis

Bulk density variations in sandstone generally indicate porosity changes. However, as explained above, this is not true when there are changes in grain density. Pure quartz sands are considered to have a grain density of 2.65 g/cm³ but, in reality, such sands are only the ideal case (i.e. orthoquartzite) and grain density will change depending on the non-quartz constituents. Sands are commonly mixed with feldspars (density 2.52–2.74 g/cm³), micas (2.82–2.99 g/cm³), lignite fragments (0.5–I.8 g/cm³) and rock fragments (variable density). Heavy minerals may also be a constituent (3.0–4.19 g/cm³). The well-known mica sands of the North Sea Jurassic reservoirs, as already discussed, contain up to 30% muscovite (**Figure 10.14**). The density of muscovite (2.82 g/cm³) increases the average grain density from 2.65 g/cm³ up to in the region of 2.82 g/cm³ but, of course, this varies with the mica content (**Figure 10.21**). In clean sands, therefore, grain density can give some idea of sand composition.

Changes in grain density in sands are generally gradual and of

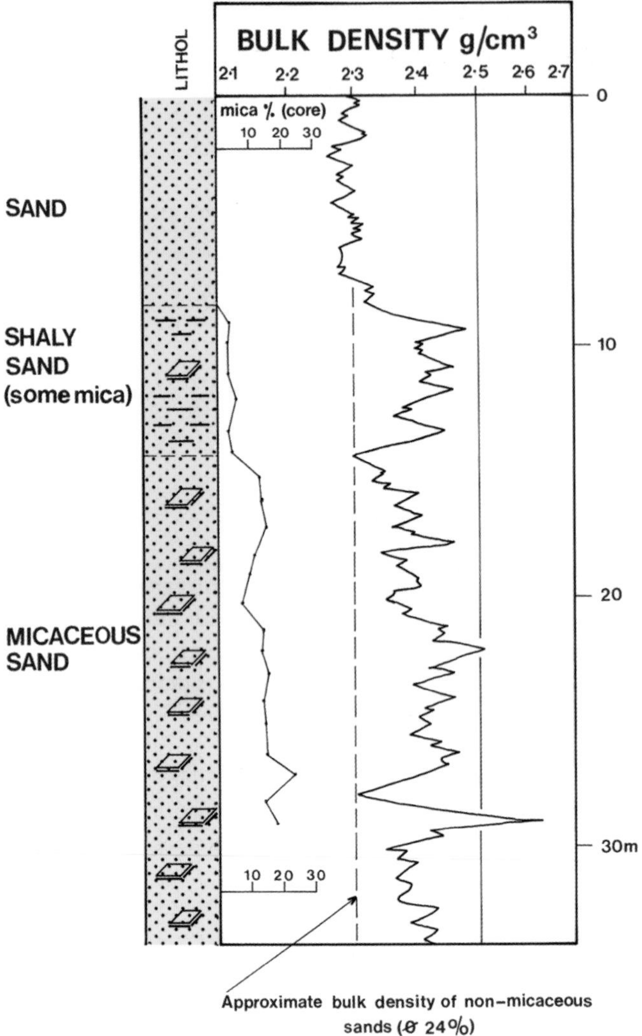

Figure 10.21 The effect of muscovite (grain density 2.76–3.1 g/cm³) on the bulk density log in micaceous sands. The increase in density below 15 m is due to the mica content. The percentage of mica indicated is based on thin-section analysis of core material.

a moderate order. Abrupt changes, especially in otherwise homogeneous beds, often indicate diagenetic or secondary changes. The example shows a sand with zones of secondary calcium carbonate cement in which porosity and permeability are near zero (**Figure 10.22**). In cores these zones are often seen to have abrupt limits. A similar phenomenon may also occur with secondary pyrite cement.

Mineral identification

Density becomes a criterion for lithological identification when it is either abnormally high or abnormally low (the average for sedimentary rocks in oil wells being about 2.3 g/cm³). Coals, for example, are identified by very low densities, between 1.2 g/cm³ and 1.8 g/cm³; pyrite, conversely, is identified by very high densities, between 4.80 g/cm³ and 5.17 g/cm³ (Kennedy 2004). The extreme values for these minerals may not be reached under natural conditions, but abnormally high and abnormally low peaks are still easily visible (**Figure 10.23**). The more common extreme and diagnostic densities are shown in **Table 10.6**.

Evaporite identification

Chemical deposits, because of their purity, may at least be suspected if not positively identified by their densities (**Table 10.7**). Care must be taken as evaporites may be impure and densities will be altered. However, most evaporites tend to give intervals of constant density with very little variation. This characteristic, when accompanied with a density near that of the pure mineral value, makes an evaporite identification probable (**Figure 10.24**). Using the density and a second log (e.g. sonic or neutron) is normally sufficient to unambiguously identify a particular evaporite.

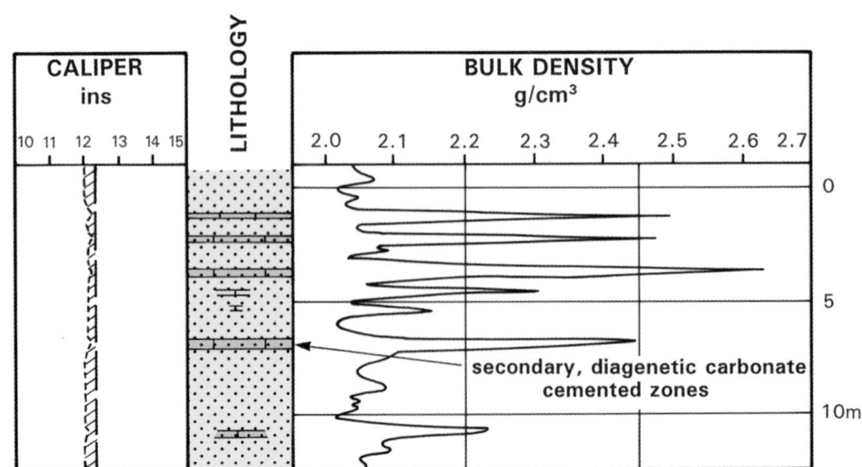

Figure 10.22 Secondary calcareous cementation in sandstone. The density log shows thin, cemented intervals which have little or no porosity, while the reservoir generally has 30%–35% porosity.

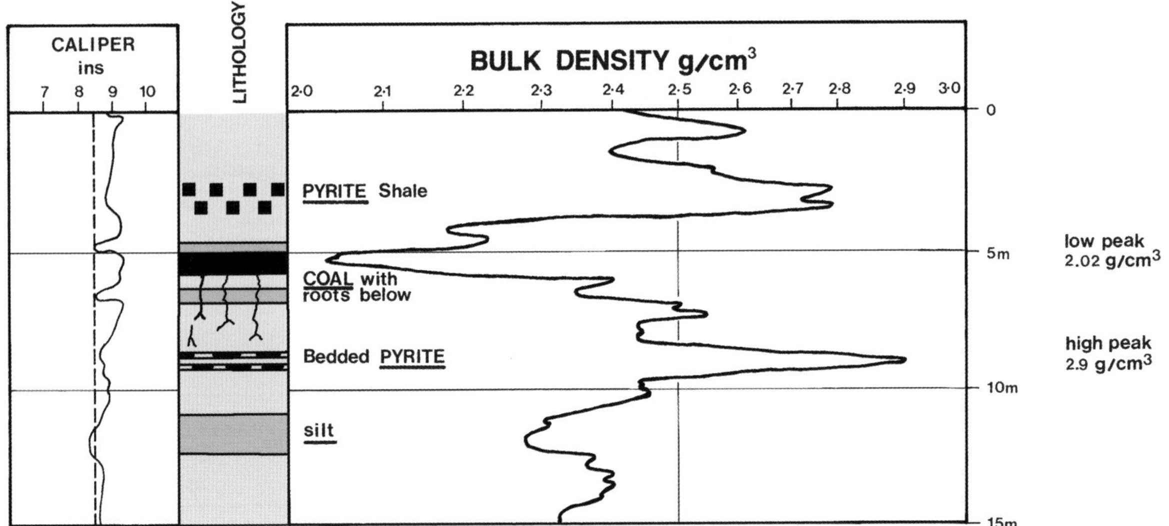

Figure 10.23 The identification of coal, with low density and pyrite, with high density, on the bulk density log. Lithology from core analysis.

Table 10.6 Diagnostic mineral and lithological densities (from Serra 1972, 1979; Gearhart 1983; Dresser Atlas 1983; Minette 1996).

		(g/cm³)
Low	Lignite	0.50–1.50
	Coal	1.15–1.70
	Anthracite	1.15–1.70
	Organic shale	1.80–2.40
High	Pyrite	4.80–5.17
	Siderite	3.00–3.89
	Basalt	2.70–3.20
	Gneiss	2.60–3.04

Table 10.7 Evaporite densities. Typical values as seen on the density log (Schlumberger 1989a).

Evaporites	Log Density g/cm³
Salt	2.04
Gypsum	2.35
Anhydrite	2.98
Carnalite	1.57
Sylvite	1.86
Ployhalite	2.79

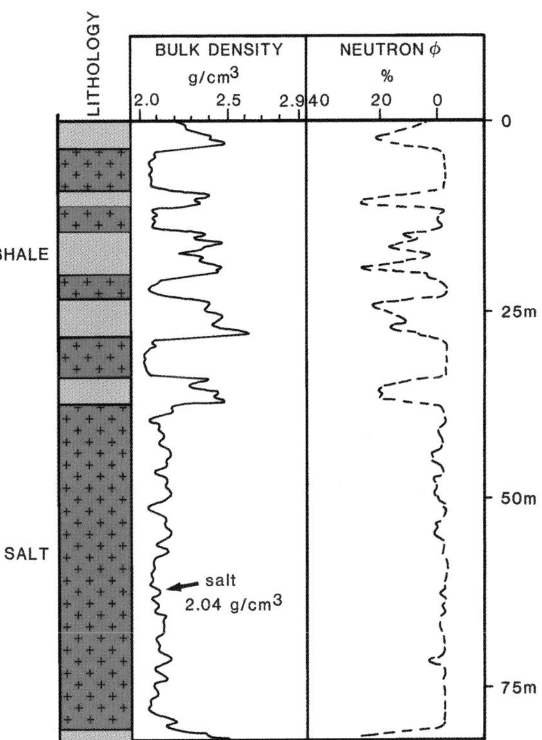

Figure 10.24 Bulk density log over a salt-shale series. The density log over the evaporite intervals tends to give constant values. The density log reads 2.04 g/cm³ in salt but the true density is 2.2 g/cm³ (see text). The neutron log assists in the identification of the evaporite intervals (ØN salt = −3 to 0).

It is worth noting that the bulk density of salt is not the same as its common density because of the presence of chlorine. The log gives a value of 2.04 g/cm³ while the real density is about 2.2 g/cm³ (**Tables 10.2,10.7**).

Overpressure identification

The general increase in shale density with depth of burial, time and temperature was described under the heading of compaction. The principal cause of this density increase is the diminution in shale porosity with increasing overburden (**Table 10.8**). Mudstone porosities may be as high as 50% near the surface, diminishing rapidly to below 20% from about 600 m downwards (**Figure 10.25**) (Magara, 1978). The actual figures and gradients vary from one region to another as the figure shows, although the normal trend of a progressive porosity loss is universal. When the reverse occurs,

Table 10.8 Some shale porosity values (1, 3, 4, from ref. 2).

	Approximate shale porosity			
Area	500 m	1000 m	2000 m	5000 m
1. Gulf Coast	45%	28%	22%	13%
2. Nagoka Plain Japan	45%	29%	17%	–
3. Venezuela	30%	24%	12%	–
4. Oklahoma	23%	13%	4%	(0)

1. Dickinson (1953) 3. Magara (1968)
2. Hedberg (1963) 4. Athy (1930)

and porosity shows an increase with depth, overpressure can be suspected.

The normal decrease in shale porosity is accompanied by an expulsion of both pore-water and interstitial water (Burst 1969). The fluids are gradually squeezed out during burial. If, however, the fluids cannot escape, once trapped they become overpressured: they begin to support some of the overburden (*see* Chapter 2). This has the effect of preserving porosity and it is this preservation which causes a reversal in the normal compaction and density increase trend shown by the log. The density decrease therefore identifies an interval of abnormal pressure (e.g. Fertl 1980) (**Figures 10.26, 10.17**).

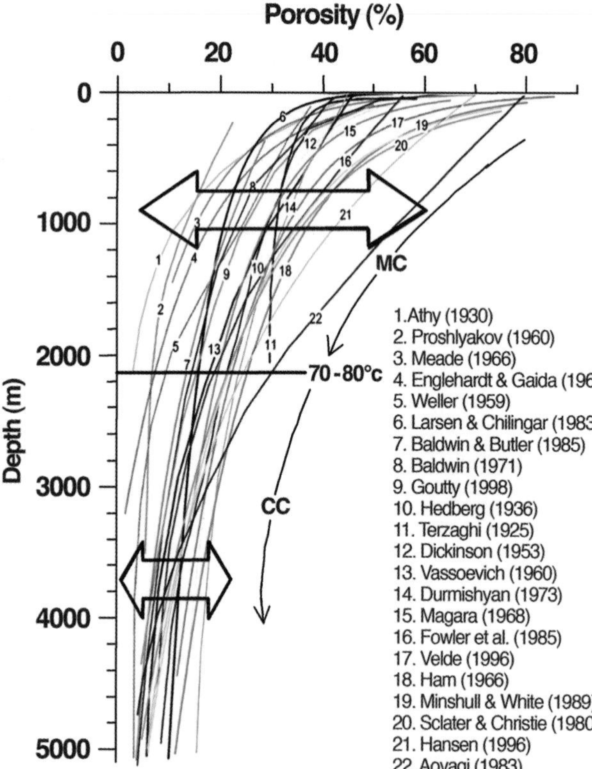

Figure 10.25 Diminution of mudstone porosity with depth. There are numerous 'trends' in the published literature. MC = mechanical compaction; CC = chemical compaction (from Mondol *et al.* 2008).

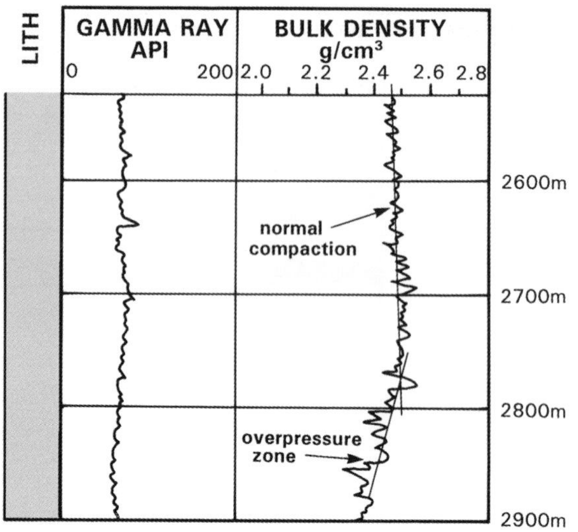

Figure 10.26 Overpressure seen by a bulk density drop and break in the normal compaction curve. The gamma ray shows the interval is shale.

Fracture recognition

Numerous methods have been proposed for the identification of fractures (Schafer 1980). One of these involves the comparison of density-log porosity with sonic-log porosity. The density tool records bulk density and, as such, will include both intergranular porosity and fracture porosity. For the sonic measurement, however, the sound waves (*Vp*) will take the quickest path from emitter to receiver. This path will avoid the fractures (if they are high angle). The sonic velocity (*Vp*) will therefore give only intergranular porosity. When the two logs are compared and the density derived porosity is much greater than the sonic derived porosity, the difference is due to the fracture porosity (Schafer 1980). The example shows this effect in a compact, upper Carboniferous sandstone and shale sequence (**Figure 10.27**).

In practical terms, the two logs should be normalized to permit a proper comparison. This may be done with the logs themselves or by cross-plotting core-verified values to define 'fracture fields' (Etnyre 1981). This method is interesting but has fallen out of use as fractures are now better identified and explored using image logs (Chapter 15).

Source rock evaluation

The presence of organic matter in shales lowers their density. The normal average matrix density

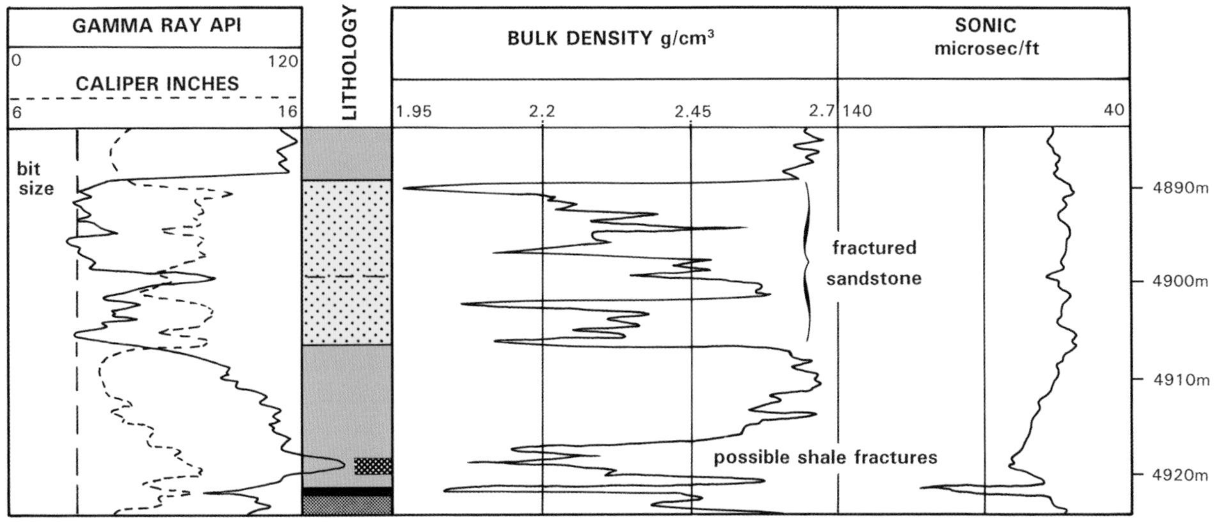

Figure 10.27 The contrasting effect of fractures on the density log and sonic log. The density log shows very low values over the fractured sandstone interval while the sonic is not affected. The shale interval may also show a similar effect. The caliper is from the density tool.

Table 10.9 Clay and clay-mineral densities (from Fertl, 1977: Johnson and Linke, 1978; Patchett and Coalson, 1982; de Andrè *et al.* 2004).

Species		density (g/cm³) range	typical
Smectite		1.98–3.00	(1.98)
Kaolinite		2.40–2.69	(2.52)
Chlorite		2.60–3.22	(2.71)
Illites		2.67–2.74	
	Muscovite	2.76–3.10	(2.81)
	Biotite	2.65–3.10	(3.02)
Glauconite		2.96	(2.96)
Average shale matrix		2.65–2.70	(2.70)

of a mixture of clay minerals is about 2.7 g/cm³ (**Table 10.9**), while organic matter has densities between 0.50 g/cm³–1.80g/cm³ (**Table 10.6**). The presence of organic matter therefore has a marked effect on the overall shale bulk density (**Figure 10.28**).

This organic matter effect on the density log can be quantified, as was recognised very early on (Tixier and Alger 1967), so that the log can be used to evaluate source rocks. Traditionally, to do this, the relationship between organic matter content and the density log is normalised using sample analyses (Schmoker and Hester 1983) (**Figure 10.29**). The normalised density log can then be used to interpolate between analysed points.

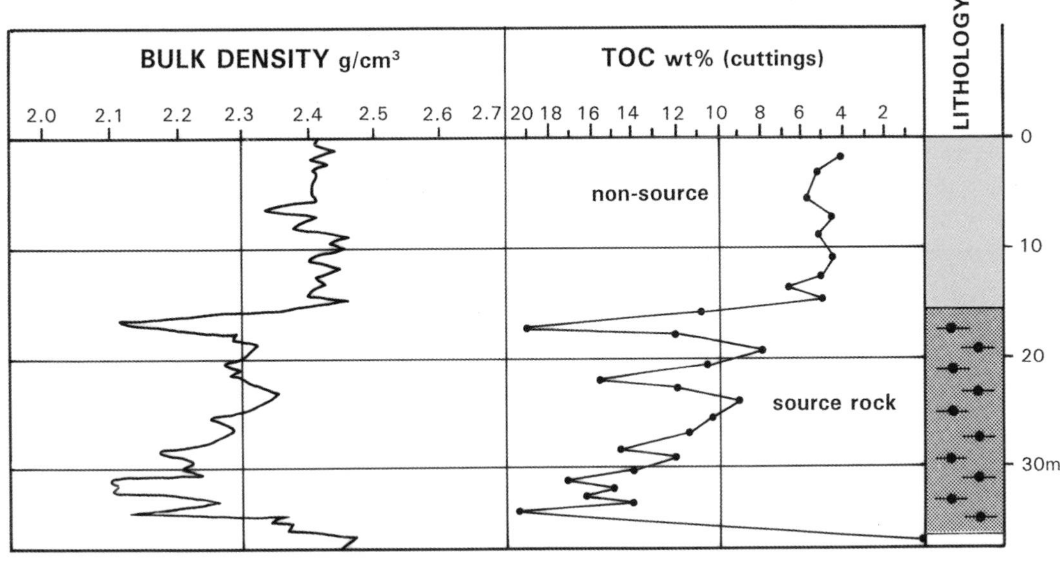

Figure 10.28 The effect of organic matter on the density log. The relationship may be quantified, the greater the amount of organic matter, the lower the density (*see* text).

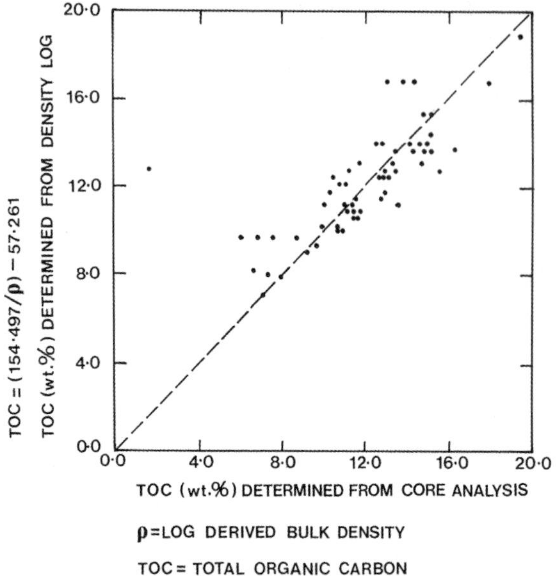

Figure 10.29 Comparison of the organic content derived from the density logs and from core analysis, Bakken Formation, Williston Basin. Dashed line shows ideal agreement (re-drawn from Schmoker and Hester 1983).

More importantly, in the same basin, a normalised log can also be used in wells where no analyses are available. Difficulties arise when the organic matter is mixed with a high density mineral such as pyrite (density 4.80–5.17 g/cm³, **Table 10.6**) since the high density of the pyrite masks the effect of the low density organic matter. Compaction must also be taken into account. These problems have led some workers to abandon the density log for source rock studies (Passey *et al.* 1990).

However, the density log has long been used in coal logging as an indicator of the ash (shale) content of the coal beds, with the result that log based calculations obviate the need for coring (Lavers and Smits 1977). Properly used, the density log is an excellent indicator of the amount of shale in coal or, *vice versa*, the organic matter in shale, and a robust and simple method for using it to estimate organic carbon content is explained below. It avoids the initial need for lengthy normalisation and allows TOC (Total Organic Carbon) values to be quickly derived (Myers and Jenkyns 1992).

The method is based on the proposition that non-source shale intervals are identical to source intervals apart from the organic matter content. To derive the quantitative organic matter effect on the logs over a source interval, it is sufficient simply to subtract the log values of a contiguous non-source interval. For instance, in **Figure 10.28**, the average density of the shales from 0 m to 13 m can be used to evaluate the source rock richness from 13 m to 35 m. The effect can then be converted to TOC%. In this way, depth and the general effects of compaction are automatically accounted for, the principal unknown being the density of the organic matter (kerogen). The method is presented below.

The following assumptions are made (for details see Myers and Jenkyns 1992):

1) The source rock is composed of mudrock (matrix density = 2.70 g/cm³), water filled porosity (density = 1.05 g/cm³) and kerogen (density = 1.1 or 1.2 g/cm³).
2) The non-source interval has the same mudrock matrix density, water density and water filled porosity as the source interval (**Figure 10.30**).

$$Ø_{fl} = \frac{\rho_{ns} - \rho_{ma}}{\rho_{fl} - \rho_{ma}} \quad (1)$$

$$Ø_{ker} = \frac{\rho_{s} - \rho_{ns}}{\rho_{ker} - \rho_{ma}} \quad (2)$$

$$TOC\% = \frac{0.85 \times \rho_{ker} \times Ø_{ker}}{\rho_{ker}(Ø_{ker}) + \rho_{ma}(1 - Ø_{fl} - Ø_{ker})} \quad (3)$$

Where:
ρ_{ns} = density non-source interval (average from log)
ρ_{s} = density source interval (from log)
ρ_{ma} = 2.70g/cm³, assumed mudrock density
$Ø_{fl}$ = water filled porosity, derived with equation (1)
$Ø_{ker}$ = kerogen filled porosity, derived with equation (2)
ρ_{ker} = 1.1 or 1.2 g/cm³, kerogen density
ρ_{fl} = 1.05 g/cm³, density water
TOC% = 0.85 × wt.% kerogen

The water filled porosity of the contiguous non-source interval is given by equation (1). The volume (porosity) filled with kerogen of a given density is given by equa-

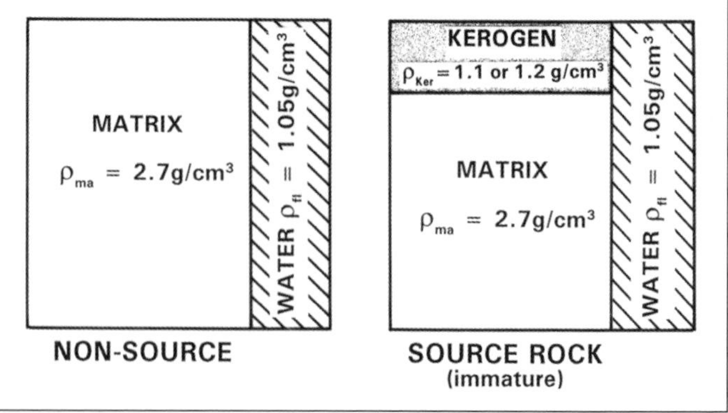

Figure 10.30 Schematic basis for using the density log quantitatively to derive total organic carbon, TOC. The matrix and water content characteristics are assumed identical in both the source and non-source. Kerogen is an additional part of the total volume in a source rock.

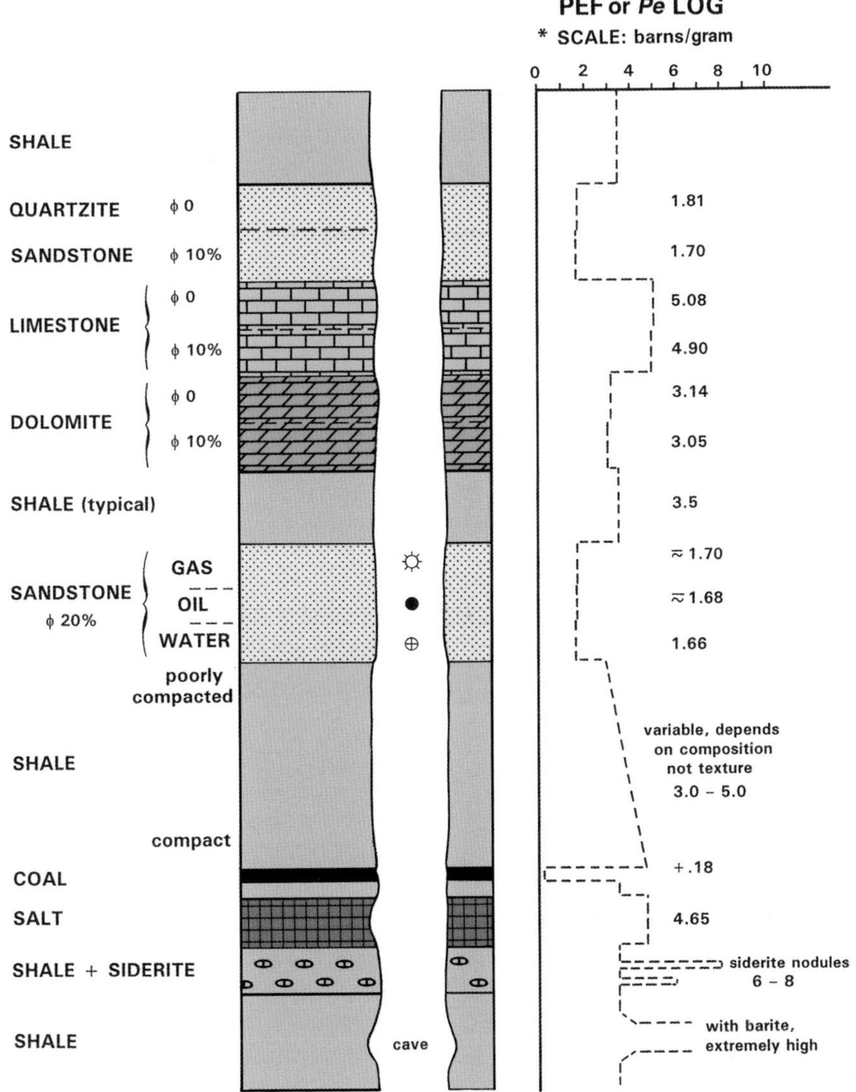

Figure 10.31 The Photoelectric Factor (*Pe* or PEF) log. The log is a measure of the combined atomic complexity of the formation so that porosity effects are minimal. The lithologies are comparable to those used in Figures 10.1 and 11.1.
* a Barn is 10^{-24}cm^2.

tion (2). The conversion of kerogen volume to weight and then TOC% using a weight % kerogen equivalence to weight % carbon of 0.85, is given by equation (3).

THE PHOTOELECTRIC FACTOR LOG (or Litho-Density)

10.7 Generalities

The log

The photoelectric factor, *Pe* (or PEF) log is a by-product of the density measurement that has been available since the mid-1980s (the Litho-Density log of Schlumberger). It is a continuous record of the effective *photoelectric absorption cross-section index* or *Pe* of a formation. The photoelectric absorption index is strongly dependent on the average atomic number, *Z*, (i.e. atomic complexity) of the constituents of the formation, which implies the composition and, by inference, the lithology: the effects of porosity are minimal (**Figure 10.31**). The *Pe* response to heavy, high atomic number elements, and even traces of very heavy elements, are disproportionate and can dominate a reading. In particular, iron containing minerals can give high *Pe* readings even when present at a few volume per-cent (Iron Z=26). The *Pe* is called the PEF by Schlumberger. They are the same quantity and *Pe* is used here.

The *Pe* is purposely defined to be only weakly dependent on porosity. It is actually derived from a more fundamental property, the photoelectric capture cross-section, *U*. This is a measure of how effectively a material can *absorb*, as opposed to simply scatter gamma rays. The normal unit for *U* is barn/cm^3 (yet another non-SI unit used in atomic, nuclear and high energy physics). The barn itself is a unit of area (10^{-24} cm^2). The efficiency of the photoelectric absorption depends on both the energy of the gamma ray and the elemental composition of the material. Absorption increases with atomic number and decreases with gamma ray energy. The highest absorption therefore occurs with low energy gamma rays (a few keV) interacting with heavy minerals. As explained below, *Pe* is the ratio of *U* to density and therefore has the non-SI. units of b/g (not b/electron as is always written in chart books and text books on logs). That is *Pe* = *U*/density.

As will be seen below, a modern density tool can simultaneously measure density and *U* and so can output *Pe* as a continuous curve. Pore space is mainly occupied by the light elements, hydrogen, water and carbon at relatively low densities and so *U* and density both decrease with increasing porosity. The ratio of the two, the *Pe*, is roughly constant, and this makes the *Pe* a very convenient way of quickly identifying matrix type. For instance, the photoelectric absorption index of a sandstone (quartz matrix) at 0% porosity is *Pe* 1.81 while at 35% fresh water filled porosity it is *Pe* 1.54. For limestone (calcium carbonate matrix) the figures are, at 0% porosity (i.e. matrix), *Pe* 5.08 and, at 35%, porosity *Pe* 4.23 (**Figure 10.32**) (Gardner and Dumanoir 1980). That is, the difference between the *Pe* values of the two matrix types (i.e. 3.27 units) is more significant than the variations within each individual matrix type caused by porosity changes (i.e. 0.27 and 0.85 respectively) (**Figure 10.32**).

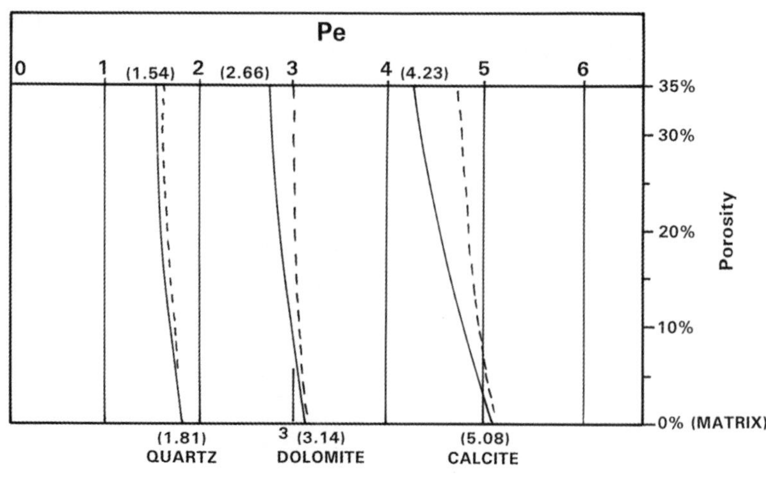

Figure 10.32 *Pe* values of quartz, dolomite and calcite over the porosity range from 0 to 35%. Porosity generally has only a subsidiary effect on the *Pe* value: matrix type is more important (modified from Gardner and Dumanoir 1980).

Table 10.10 Principal uses of the photoelectric factor (*Pe* or PEF) log.

	Discipline	Used for	Knowing
Quantitative	Petrophysics	Matrix identification	ρ_{maa} Ø
		U_{maa}	U_{ma} U_{fl}
Qualitative	Geology	Matrix type	mineral values
		Diagenetic minerals	elemental values

Principal uses

The photoelectric absorption index is used principally in a quantitative manner as a matrix indicator, either alone or, especially when cross-multiplied with the corresponding density log value, to give the value *U* (**Table 10.10**). Qualitatively, in the correct borehole environment, it can be used to indicate lithology and certain, mainly diagenetic, minerals. In the LWD domain, the photoelectric log can be imaged and used for geosteering, along with the density image itself. However, it is more indicative of hole condition than formation, as the example shows (**Figure 10.10**).

The use of the *Pe* curve is severely restricted by the fact that it has to be massively corrected in holes with barite weighted mud. This is a direct result of its particular sensitivity to heavy elements. Barium has an atomic number of 56 and so barite (barium sulphate) has a photoelectric absorption index that is nearly 150 times that of most of the common minerals. Even small amounts deposited in the mudcake will dominate the log response. If the log is to be used effectively, the drilling mud should not contain barite, although modern algorithms and signal processing can remove the effects of small amounts.

The litho-density log is sometimes, misleadingly, called the lithology log. It is not: it is a log of the effective photoelectric absorption index. Its response is no closer to the lithology than that of any other log.

10.8 Principles of Measurement

When gamma rays pass through matter, at most energy levels they lose energy through collision or Compton scattering (para 10.2). However, at low energies, below about 100 keV, the phenomenon known as photoelectric absorption is the dominant effect. In photoelectric absorption, low energy gamma rays are captured by an atom and the gamma ray is absorbed: it disappears. The capturing atom transfers the gamma ray's energy to a bound electron and, if the acquired energy is sufficient, the electron leaves its atomic orbit and is ejected, becoming ionised (**Figure 10.3**). The degree of absorption depends on the atomic number (*Z*) and the electron density (ρ_e) of the atoms, effectively their atomic complexity. It increases exponentially with Z which explains why heavy elements have a disproportionate influence on *Pe*. In geological terms, this is related to the chemical (mineral) composition of a formation and, indirectly to lithology.

A *Pe* measurement has been available from density tools since the mid-1980s. These tools exploit the same property of scintillators that is used in the spectral gamma rays: that is the intensity of the light flash is proportional to the energy of the incoming gamma ray. This allows the low energy gamma rays that are particularly susceptible to photoelectric absorption to be distinguished. A low count rate of these implies a relatively high concentration of heavy elements and hence a high *Pe*. The fact that the *Pe* measurement is based on only a small subset of the total scattered gamma ray population has some important practical consequences. Firstly, it is simply not very accurate: logging companies typically quote ± 0.1 b/g as the accuracy of a typical *Pe* reading of 2–3 b/g (the accuracy will drop as *Pe* increases). Secondly, in order to increase the count rates, most tools use the short-spaced detector to make the *Pe* measurement. This is very susceptible to bad hole and mudcake.

Apart from the fact that the *Pe* measurement uses only the low energy gamma rays, it comes from the two detector density tools already described (Section 10.3) and, as already mentioned, the *Pe* is just a by-product of the density measurement. In reality, the count rate in the low energy area is a combined result of the formation electron density effect of Compton scattering and the photoelectric absorption effect. That is, in the low energy area, *U*, (as previously discussed), is registered, which is the product of the electron density ρ_e, and the photoelectric factor, *Pe* (Gardner and Dumanoir 1980). *Pe*, the photoelectric factor, is therefore the ratio of the two:

$$Pe = \frac{U}{\rho_e}$$

Where:
U = photoelectric absorption cross section, per unit volume (low energy window count of tool),
ρ_e = electron density index, per unit volume (high energy window count), and
Pe = photoelectric absorption factor, per unit weight.

This means in effect that *Pe*, the photoelectric factor plotted as the log, is derived by stripping the electron density effect of the high energy window from the overall effect in the low energy window (**Figures 10.3, 10.8**).

It is worth noting that ρ_e is in electrons/cm^3, *Pe* is in barns(cm^2)/gram and *U* is in barns/cm^3, the effective photoelectric absorption cross section index per unit volume.

Log presentation, scales and units

The photoelectric factor log is called the *Pe* or PEF log (Photo Electric Factor). The scale used is barns per gram being a measure of the capture cross-section or capture efficiency. A barn is 10^{-24} cm^2.

The *Pe* curve is normally plotted combined with the density and neutron logs in tracks 3 and 4 (API format), the linear scale being from 0–20 or 0–15 barns, most of the common minerals having values below 6 (**Figure 10.33**, **Table 10.11**). Here it is recommended that the 0–20 scale is used, which tends to keep the *Pe* near the left of the track and away from the density and other curves. As the *Pe* is an inherently inaccurate measurement, there is little point using the full width of the track. Like the LWD density log, the *Pe* from the LWD tools can now be plotted as an image with a nominal pixel size of 3.8 cm (1.5") (Meyer *et al.* 2005). The response is very affected by hole conditions (**Figure 10.10**).

10.9 Log Characteristics

Depth of Investigation, vertical, bed resolution

The *Pe* curve has a considerably better resolution than the bulk density, the latter has an intrinsic vertical resolution of about 40 cm (15") while the *Pe* has a vertical resolution of 5 cm (2") with the modern spectral density tools (Theys 1991). With processing, however, these vertical resolutions can be reduced although the smaller values are not always robust. In addition, care must be taken with these resolutions since the *Pe* value is processed from algorithms involving both the long spaced detector, with a poorer (larger) resolution and the short spaced detector with a better (smaller) resolution (Smith 1990). This means that the depth of investigation and vertical resolution are dependent on the far detector characteristics and not just the near detector (cf. **Figure 10.10**).

Unwanted log effects

The photoelectric factor log has been in service for a number of years but was not used routinely in the 1980s–90s. The principal reason was the fact mentioned, that the log is heavily affected when barite muds are in the borehole. The *Pe* value for barite is 267 barns/gram while most common minerals have a *Pe* value of less than 6 (**Table 10.11**). The presence of barite swamps the true response (**Figure 10.34**).

Recent improvements in processing and correction algorithms have meant that the log is now routinely used, especially since the *Pe* is also available in the LWD environment where invasion is smaller, the effect of barite (theoretically) less of a problem and the image format more easily evaluated for quality (**Figure 10.10**).

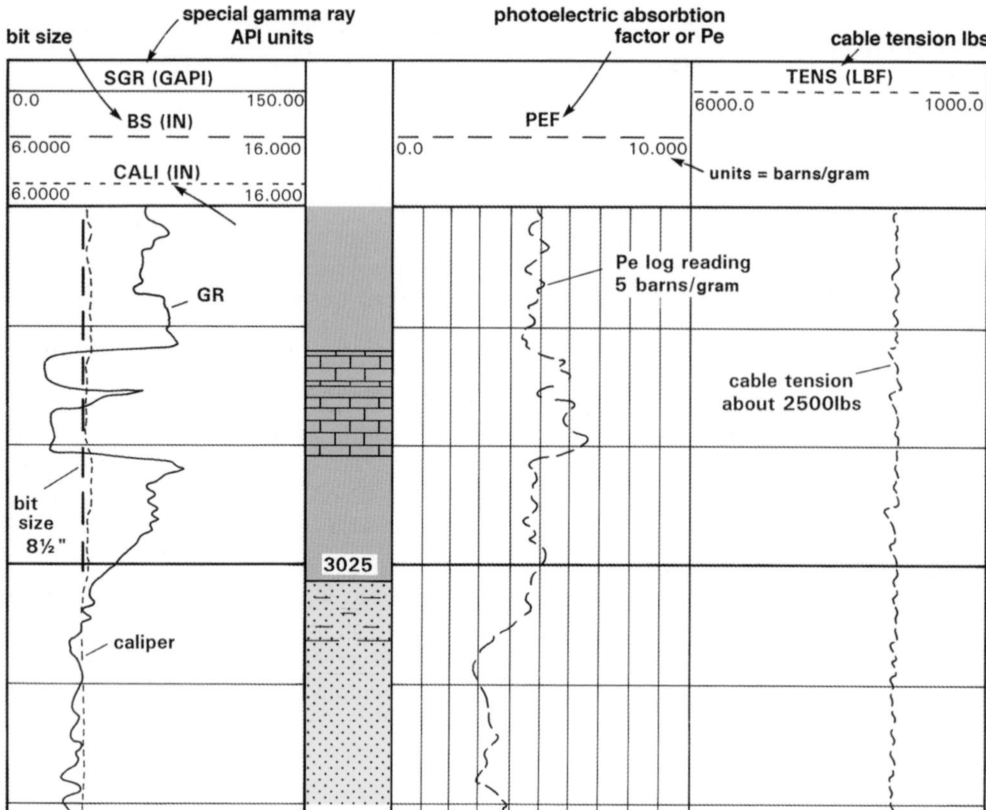

Figure 10.33 A typical *Pe* log through shale, limestone and sandstone. Note the similar gamma ray value of sandstone and limestone but very different *Pe* values.

Table 10.11 Common photoelectric factor and related log values (from Suau and Spurlin 1982; Ellis 1987; Schlumberger 1989a; Minette 1996).

Name	Formula	*Pe	$+U_{ma}$	$\#\rho_{ma}$
Quartz	SiO_2	1.81	4.79	2.65
Calcite	$CaCO_3$	5.08	13.77	2.71
Dolomite	$CaMg\,(CO_3)_2$	3.14	9.00	2.86
Barite	$BaSO_4$	266.8	1074.00	
Shale (av)		3.42	9.05	2.65
Shaly sand		2.70	6.52	2.41
Feldspar (K)		2.86	7.51	2.62
Muscovite		2.40	7.90	3.29
Biotite		6.30	21.03	3.34
Glauconite (wet)		5.32	21.00	3.95
Siderite	$FeCO_3$	14.69	56.00	3.81
Pyrite	FeS_2	16.97	82.00	5.00
Limonite		13.00	46.67	3.59
Halite	NaCl	4.65	9.65	2.04
Gypsum	$CaSO_4.H_2O$	3.42	8.11	2.37
Anhydrite	$CaSO_4$	5.06	14.95	2.96
Coal bituminous		0.18	0.26	1.47
Coal anthracite		0.16	0.28	1.75
Water		0.36	0.40	1.11
Salt water (120.000 ppm)		0.81	0.96	1.19
Oil CH_2 (variable)		0.13	0.12	0.97
Gas CH_4		0.095	$0.119.\rho$ gas	$1.25.\rho$ gas

*log PEF; $+U_{ma} = Pe.\rho_e$; #tool read density cf. Table 10.2

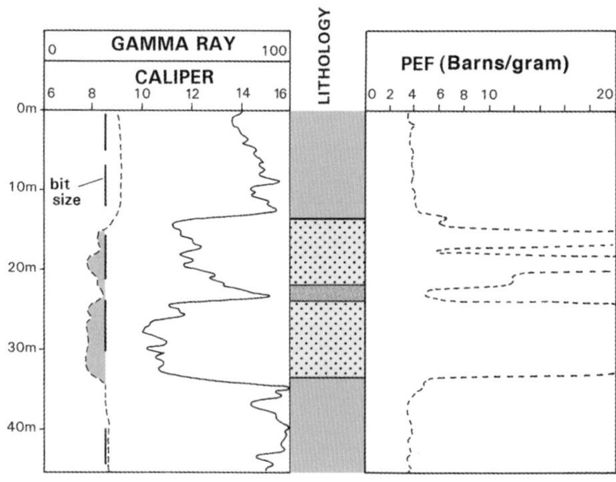

Figure 10.34 The effect of barite on the *Pe* (PEF) log. The barite in the mud cake causes very high *Pe* values and does not allow the log to be used for lithology identification.

10.10 Quantitative uses

Matrix identification – lithology

When only two matrix minerals (and porosity) are present, the photoelectric factor log values may be used to derive the volumetric fractions of each, the *Pe* value being plotted against the bulk density value (Gardner and Dumanoir 1980) (**Figure 10.35**).

The most effective use, however, is when three minerals are present (and porosity), the *Pe* value being used in combination with the density log value. The two are cross-multiplied to produce the factor *U*, the volumetric photoelectric absorption index (Gardner and Dumanoir 1980), discussed above (Section 10.8). The reasoning is that the *Pe* value is not volume but mass related and hence both the density and *U* are volume related. The *Pe* value and density value combined will therefore reflect both the lithology *per se* and the porosity effects which are lithology controlled. The methodology is generally found to be useful in areas of complex carbonate-evaporite lithology where porosity is lithology dependent, especially in the presence of gas which does not affect the *Pe* value (McCall and Gardner 1982). In sand-shale sequences the effect is less evident.

In practical terms, over the zone of interest, the ρ_{maa} (matrix density apparent) and porosity (Ø) are found from a density-neutron cross plot (**Figure 11.26**), while the U_{maa} (matrix volumetric absorption index apparent) is found either from a nomogram (Schlumberger, 1989a) relating *Pe*, ρ_b and porosity (Ø) to U_{ma} or from the following equation:

$$U_{maa} = (1 - Ø_a)\, U_{ma} + Ø_a . U_{fl}$$

Plots of U_{maa} against ρ_{maa} are considered to be indicative of lithology (Gardner and Dumanoir 1980). However, like most log calculations, it is seriously disturbed by shale.

10.11 Qualitative uses

Lithology

In the same way as the log is used quantitatively to identify matrix type, it can help identify lithology qualitatively, in that *Pe* values are matrix specific and unaffected by porosity variations (**Figure 10.32**). Usefully, the log can be used to separate clean sand from clean limestone (**Figure 10.33**) and clean dolomite, and can also be useful in limestone/dolomite mixtures. However,

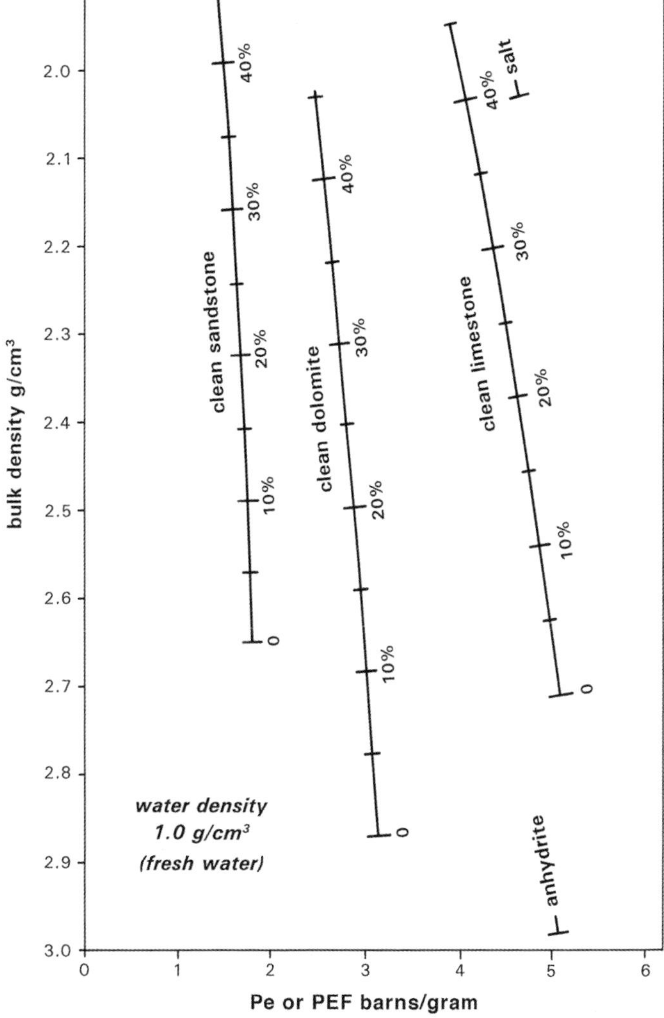

Figure 10.35 Matrix identification using the *Pe* and bulk density log values. Porosity values are indicated along the matrix lines. (From Schlumberger, 1989a).

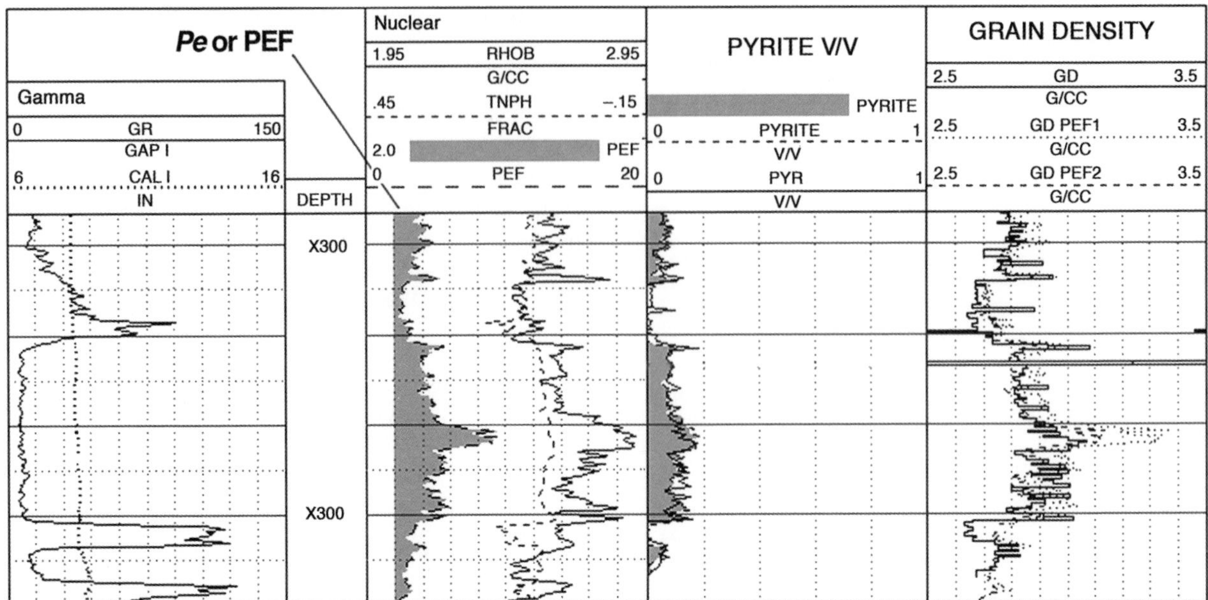

Figure 10.36 The effect of pyrite on the *Pe* and other logs in an oil bearing, sandstone reservoir. In track 4 the pyrite fraction is derived from the *Pe* (shaded) and from core grain density (solid line). In track 5 grain density is estimated from the *Pe* (dotted and dashed curves) and measured on core (solid line). The large effect pyrite (*Pe* = 17) has on the *Pe* log is evident (modified from Kennedy SPWLA 2004).

shale presence makes identification in shaly formations (calcareous or siliceous) difficult.

Diagenetic and other minerals

One of the more interesting uses of the *Pe* log is in the identification of certain, mainly diagenetic, minerals which contain an element, such as iron, with a high *Z* number (Fe, *Z* = 26). Mineralisation may be difficult to recognise on the standard logs. In the illustration, for example, pyrite occurs filling pores in an oil bearing, sandstone reservoir. The presence of substantial pyrite is evident principally from the *Pe* log reading because it has a value of 17 (**Table 10.11**) (**Figure 10.36**). When this high *Pe* value is combined with the high density, pyrite can be suspected. In the example, pyrite was verified from core. Once identified, the quantity of pyrite may be quite reliably calculated from the *Pe* log (**Figure 10.36**) (Kennedy 2004).

Another iron mineral, siderite (Fe_2C0_3), which frequently occurs in thin, nodular beds in sandstones and shales, may also be evaluated with the *Pe* log. The *Pe* value for siderite is high (*Pe* = 14.69, **Table 10.11**) but significantly the U_{maa} value, the volume related effective photoelectric absorption cross section, is very high (U_{maa} = 56.0, **Table 10.11**), so even small quantities have a marked effect on the log (Humphreys and Lott 1990). Haematite, another iron mineral, will have a similar marked effect (Suau and Spurlin 1982). In reasonable abundance (between 5–10% by volume), biotite and glauconite may also be detected (Humphreys and Lott 1990).

It has been suggested that cross-plotting *Pe* against potassium or the Th/K ratio of the spectral gamma ray log, can help to indicate clay minerals and micas. The plots have very little experimental backing and are best used with caution (to say the least).

11
THE NEUTRON LOG

11.1 Generalities

The log

The neutron log provides a continuous record of a formation's reaction to neutron bombardment (**Figure 11.1**). The measurement is given in *neutron porosity units,* which are related to a formation's *Hydrogen Index,* an indication of its hydrogen richness. Unlike most other measurements, the neutron porosity is not a well defined physical property. It is a measurement of neutron count rates.

There are several different types of neutron tool. All emit high energy neutrons into the formation but they differ in what precisely they detect. The tools that are principally considered in this chapter were developed in the 1960s and measure the number of neutrons that are scattered back towards the tool. They are intended to respond primarily to the amount of hydrogen in the formation. There are wireline and LWD versions, both very similar in design and function. Other neutron tools exist that measure the secondary gamma rays produced when neutrons collide with nuclei in the formation. These are the geochemical and neutron lifetime tools, briefly described at the end of the chapter.

The behaviour of neutrons will be noticeably modified in formations when they contain hydrogen nuclei which, in the subsurface, essentially means when they contain water (H_2O). The neutron log is therefore princi-

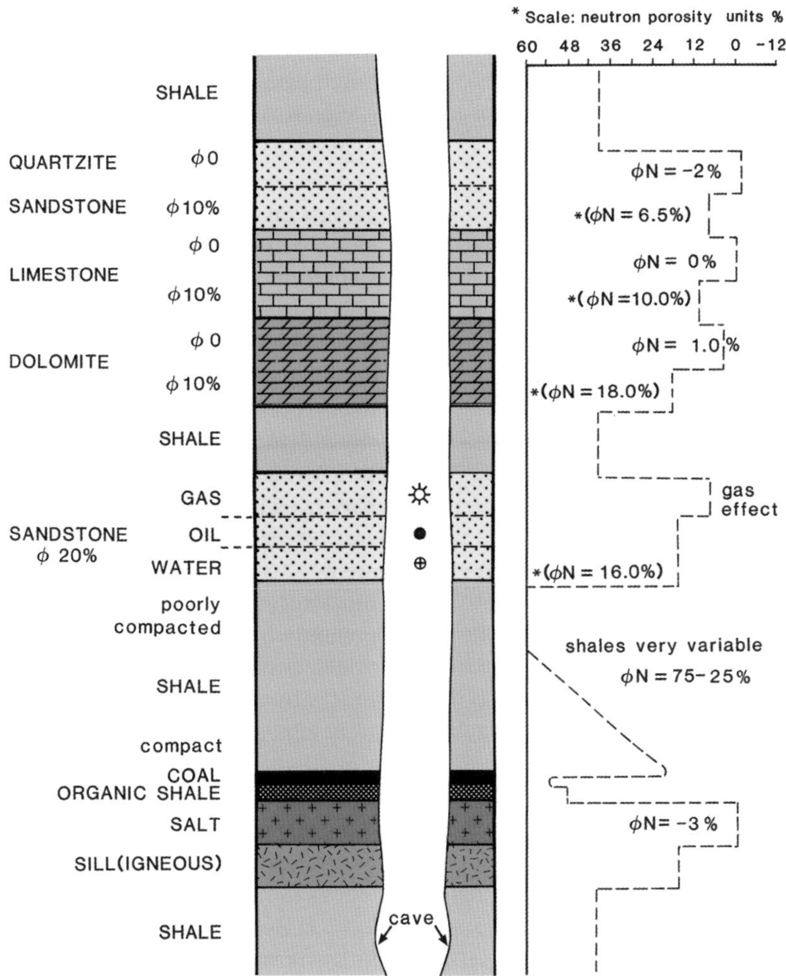

Figure 11.1 The neutron log: some typical responses. The neutron log records neutron counts which are converted to *neutron porosity units.* *Porosity with fresh water and a compensated neutron tool (cf. Figure 10.1 which is on a compatible scale of porosity, limestone scale).

Table 11.1 The principal uses of the neutron log.

Neutron only			
	Discipline	**Used for**	**Knowing**
Quantitative	Petrophysics	Porosity	Matrix Hydrogen Index
Qualitative	Petrophysics	Gas identification	Lithology
	Geology	Lithology – shales Evaporites Hydrated minerals Volcanic and intrusive rocks	Gross lithology Neutron evaporite values Calibration
Neutron – Density combined			
	Petrophysics	Porosity V_{sh}	Using cross-plot Using cross-plot 'shale point'
	Geology	Lithology Shale content	Using cross-plot and logs Using logs (cross-over)

pally intended to measure a formation's water content. This may be bound water, water of crystallisation or the free water in pore-space. The hydrogen content of a formation is quantified, as indicated, by the Hydrogen Index (HI), which by definition is unity in pure, liquid water. The index is therefore defined as the weight % hydrogen in the formation compared to the wt % hydrogen in water. (HI is also of significance for NMR logs, Chapter 13). Because most hydrogen in the subsurface exists as water, the hydrogen index can be directly related to porosity, and the neutron log output is now given directly in *neutron porosity units* (ØN). Neutron porosity is close to the true porosity, but it is only identical in clean, water bearing limestones. In other lithologies or limestones that contain hydrocarbons (especially gas, and/or impurities), the neutron porosity must be transformed to a true porosity. A neutron tool's response is calibrated to limestone, and so the log is sometimes called the Limestone Curve (**Figure 11.1**).

Principal uses

Quantitatively, the neutron log is used to derive porosity. Combined with the density, it can also be used for shale volume. Both these properties are closely related to the amount of hydrogen in the formation. Qualitatively, the log is an excellent discriminator between gas and oil (this may be quantified). It can be used geologically to identify gross lithology (especially shales), evaporites, hydrated minerals and volcanic rocks. When combined with the density log on compatible scales, it is one of the best subsurface lithology indicators (**Table 11.1**).

The geochemical tools that measure the proportions of certain key elements in a formation (e.g. iron, calcium, silicon), but are interpreted in terms of mineralogy, and the neutron lifetime logs, primarily used to monitor saturation in producing wells, are described briefly in a separate section at the end of the chapter (Section 11.8).

11.2 Principles of neutron measurement

Some generalities

The type of tool described in this chapter emits neutrons from a source and measures the count rates of neutrons that are scattered back. This arrangement seems very similar to the density tool, but using neutrons instead of gamma rays. However, the analogy is only superficial. The detectors at the heart of the density tool can count gamma rays with any energy, whereas neutron detectors will only really respond to neutrons whose energy has been mostly lost. In other words, it is not enough just to scatter neutrons back to the tool, they must also be slowed down to the point where they can be efficiently detected (**Figure 11.2**). This two stage process, scattering and slowing-down, is one of the main reasons why the neutron tool is hard to describe satisfactorily using simple analogies. A number of simple explanations have been produced over the years and, providing these are accepted as considerable over-simplifications, they are fine. The problem, however, is that if these simple models are taken too far, they can lead to a wrong interpretation of the data. This must be kept in mind.

The basic processes leading to the neutron measurement can be summarised as follows:

- *High energy* neutrons are emitted from a source (either chemical or a neutron generator).
- The high energy neutrons are slowed by 'scattering' from atoms in the borehole and formation. They are ultimately slowed by a factor of between a million and a billion.
- The *slow neutrons* 'diffuse' away from the source.
- The small fraction of slow neutrons that end up in the vicinity of the detector are counted. This count forms the neutron measurement.

The following paragraphs describe these processes in a little more detail.

Neutron interactions

Neutrons are subatomic particles which have no electrical charge but whose rest mass is almost identical to that of a proton (i.e. a hydrogen nucleus). Neutrons interact with matter and lose energy in two principal ways: *colliding* with and *scattering* from atomic nuclei; and *absorption* by atomic nuclei. Free neutrons are unstable and decay with a half life of about 15 minutes, but the processes of interest in logging tools are much shorter than this.

Neutron porosity measurements are based on scattering. Absorption actually interferes with the basic measurement and if the absorption of a neutron takes place, it will often produce a nucleus that is unstable, or in an excited state, and it will subsequently emit high energy gamma rays and possibly other high energy particles. Absorption is one of the factors that causes neutron porosity to differ from true porosity.

The scattering process itself (i.e. collisions) may be either *inelastic* or *elastic*. In elastic scattering (like billiard balls), the kinetic energy of the neutron and the nucleus that scattered it are conserved. But with inelastic scattering, some of the kinetic energy of the neutron is used to excite the target nucleus, which normally returns to the ground state by emitting a gamma ray with a characteristic frequency. At the end of the scattering event, the overall kinetic energy of the system is reduced.

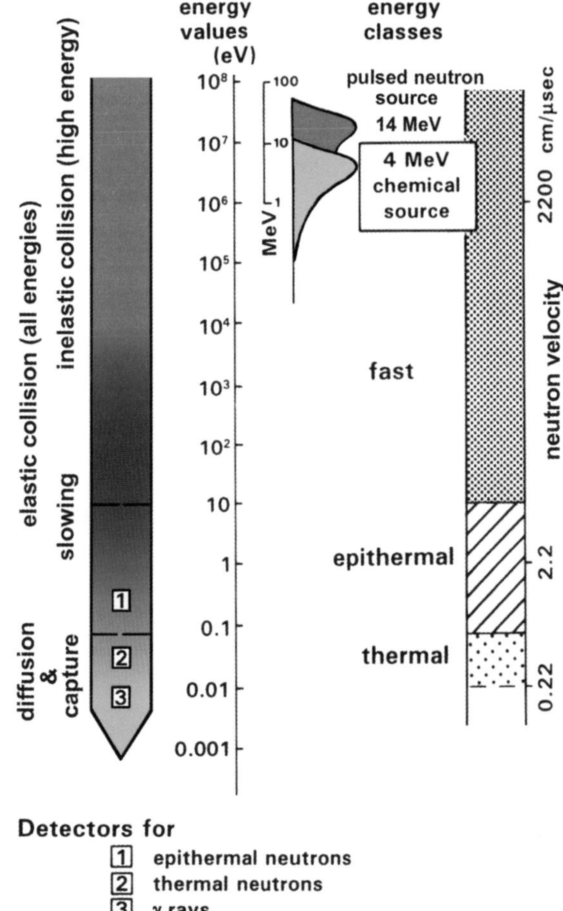

Figure 11.2 Schematic diagram of a neutron lifetime showing the energy loss after emission, and the neutron tool detector energy levels (from Owen 1960; Tittle 1961; Serra 1979).

Higher energy reactions

The neutrons emitted by logging tool sources have very high energies and hence high velocities. They are simply known as 'fast neutrons' and actually travel at a significant fraction of the speed of light. There are two types of source that are used to produce them: chemical sources and so-called neutron generators, which are effectively small particle accelerators (**Figure 11.2**).

High energy, fast neutrons can be scattered or absorbed by nuclei. Scattering (collision) causes the neutrons to lose energy and slow down (**Figure 11.3**). The amount of energy they lose at each collision depends on exactly what they collide with but, broadly speaking, the smaller the difference in mass between the neutron and the target nucleus, the greater the amount of energy they can lose. Two facts mean that heavier atoms are actually better at slowing down fast neutrons. Firstly, in inelastic scattering (the commonest type of interaction), some of the neutron's kinetic energy is used up in exciting the target nucleus. Secondly, in elastic collisions, the best nuclei for slowing down the neutrons are actually intermediate weight

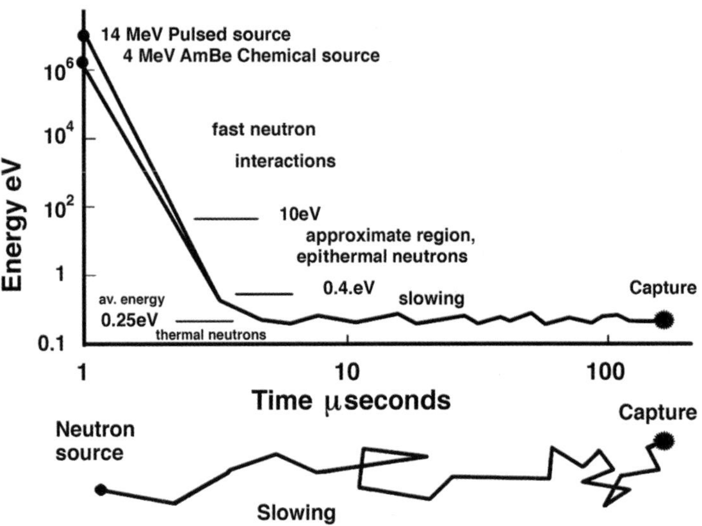

Figure 11.3 Neutron reactions in relation to time, from source to capture. Fast neutrons from a tool source lose energy very quickly, diffuse at thermal energy levels and are then finally captured (re-drawn modified from Ellis & Singer 2007; Serra 2008).

atoms like oxygen and carbon. This is because, at such high velocities, Special Relativity comes into play and the mass of the neutron is considerably greater than its rest mass. Hydrogen, the eventual target of the neutron measurement, is not particularly good at slowing down fast neutrons, because, at this stage, it is much lighter than the neutron.

Some fast neutrons may be captured, causing the capturing nucleus to become excited so that it has to emit a gamma ray(s) with a particular energy to return to the ground-state. These gamma rays are exploited in geochemical tools. The average amount of energy lost per collision, the average number of collisions needed to slow neutrons down to speeds so that they can be efficiently detected, and the typical distances that this takes place in, depend on what precisely is in the formation. There is a relationship between formation density and the behaviour of the neutrons at this stage. Some of the more advanced tools, therefore, attempt to estimate formation density from the slowing down behaviour (Quirein *et al.* 2005). This relationship may eventually be exploited in a source-less density tool, especially in the LWD environment but, for the moment, this measurement is secondary to the lower energy, porosity sensitive measurement and is simply not reliable or accurate enough to threaten the well proven 'gamma-gamma' density tool (Chapter 10).

Slowing down reactions

The lifetime of a free neutron begins with its generation by the tool and ends when it is either absorbed by a suitable nucleus or decays, about 15 minutes later to a proton, an electron and a neutrino (an enigmatic particle with little or no mass). The intervening time is spent losing energy or, equivalently, losing speed. It is at this stage that the interaction between neutrons and protons is important: at the slower speeds, the neutron and the proton now have nearly the same mass and collisions between the two cause a marked slowing of the neutron (**Figure 11.4**). As this happens, the particle passes through speeds described as fast, epithermal and, finally, thermal velocities. The latter refers to the fact that the neutron is in thermal equilibrium with its surroundings, meaning that on average it neither loses nor gains energy when it is scattered and is thought of as diffusing, behaving much like the ball in an old style pin-ball machine. Thermal neutrons are particularly important in logging because they can be detected and counted with high efficiency and, because they are the end product of the slowing down process, may be created in large numbers. Once created, they remain as thermal neutrons until the end of their life (higher energy neutrons only exist for a fleeting time between successive collisions) (**Figure 11.3).**

The moderating reactions which cause the velocity loss occur over a certain trajectory, called the *slowing-down length*, and happen over a certain *time* (**Figure 11.3**). The slowing-down length can be calculated from a knowledge of the combined stopping power of the material traversed (the formation). In a hydrogen rich medium, slowing-down length will be short compared to that in a hydrogen free environment (**Figure 11.4**, **Table 11.2**). Slowing-down length is an important concept in logging as it is used to place detectors at an optimum distance from the tool's neutron source. The slowing-down time for these reactions is also a function of hydrogen abundance.

The *fast neutrons* produced by the chemical sources used in neutron tools today have an initial energy of around 4 MeV, which means that they have an initial velocity of approximately 2800 cm/μsec (**Figure 11.2**). The neutron generator source produces pulses, or bursts of higher energy neutrons, at 14 MeV and with an initial velocity of 5200 cm/μsec. With en-

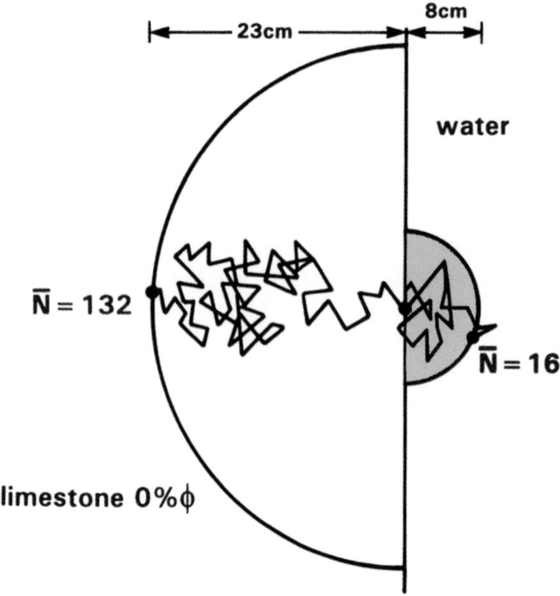

Figure 11.4 Schematic trajectories of a neutron in a limestone with no porosity, and pure water. The slowing down length in the water is shorter, and the number of collisions many fewer than in a pure limestone, for neutrons to be slowed to same energy level (modified from Ellis 1987).

Table 11.2 Neutron slowing-down parameters.

Moderator	*no of collisions
H	16
C	110
O	131
Ca	330
H_2O	22.5
Limestone 20%Ø	70
Limestone 0%Ø	138

(* number of collisions involved during change from 4.2 MeV to 0.4 eV)

ergies of 14 MeV or 4 MeV, neutrons have considerable penetration capabilities but, as described, after a few microseconds and successive collisions, the original fast neutrons have slowed down through epithermal to thermal levels with about 0.025 eV of energy and a velocity of around 0.22 cm/μsec. To reduce a neutron from 2 MeV (2200 cm/μsec) to 0.025 eV (0.22 cm/μsec) requires an average of 18 (elastic) collisions with hydrogen nuclei but 257 (inelastic) collisions with silicon and 368 with calcium nuclei (Serra 1979). Expressed in another way, elastic collision with hydrogen can take all of a neutron's energy but inelastic collisions with heavier elements cause an energy reduction of only around 10% to 25%: the effect of hydrogen is seen as dominant at epithermal energy levels (**Table 11.2**).

Capture

At the lower energy, thermal levels, the neutron is thought of as diffusing, (**Figure 11.3**) and, as described, can diffuse randomly for about 15 minutes (in a vacuum). In earth materials the time is significantly shorter and, for example, varies from 5 μsec in rock salt, 450 μsec in a limestone without porosity and 900 μsec in a quartzite (Serra 1979). The period of diffusion comes to an end as the neutrons undergo *absorption*. That is they are captured by other nuclei, which then change energy state (become excited) and become unstable. These may then spontaneously de-excite and emit gamma rays of capture, the so-called neutron-gamma capture radiation. Capture marks the end of the 'free' existence of the neutron. Neutron absorption (capture) depends on the thermal neutron *capture cross-section* of the absorbing nuclei of the formation, which is a measure of how effective they are at this. The quantity is sigma (Σ) or the macroscopic (bulk) thermal neutron capture cross-section of the formation and is given in *capture units* (c.u.), the contribution from 1 gm of the absorber per cm^3 (Ellis 2007). Although capture cross-section can form a measurement in itself, the principal interest in porosity logging is the capacity of thermal absorbers to modify count rates and so disturb the neutron porosity value. Elements such as chlorine, gadolinium and boron all have high thermal neutron capture cross-sections, and also iron if it is very abundant (**Table 11.3**).

Summary

In summary, at the very high energy level of the neutron sources, neutrons initially undergo interactions which reduce their energy rapidly but which are not especially sensitive to hydrogen presence. As interactions reduce the energy (velocity) of the neutrons they reach a level at which they interact dominantly with hydrogen nuclei. This is when they are sensitive to the formation porosity. From the number of neutrons backscattered and detected by the tool, hydrogen abundance can be deduced. And from hydrogen abundance, porosity can be derived: the tool's main output. Neutron absorption occurs which can distort porosity derivations. The effect depends especially on the capture cross-section of thermal neutron absorbers.

Table 11.3 Thermal neutron capture cross-sections of some elements.

Element	Capture cross-section, barns	*cross-section* / atomic weight
H	0.33	0.33
C	0.0034	0.00028
O	0.00027	0.000017
Na	0.53	0.023
Mg	0.063	0.0027
Al	.23	0.0085
Si	.16	0.0057
Cl	33.2	0.94
K	2.10	0.054
Ca	0.43	0.011
B	759	70.3
Gd	49,000	312
Cd (shield material)	2,450	21.9

11.3 Tools

Tool basics

The basic neutron porosity tool consists of a neutron source and two detectors. The source bombards the formation with fast neutrons, and the detectors count the number of low energy neutrons at two distances from the source (**Figure 11.5**). In short, this type of tool emits high energy neutrons and counts the low energy neutrons that are scattered back to it. The wireline and LWD tools work on the same physical principles but have slightly different designs. As noted above, there are other types of neutron tool that emit neutrons but count the secondary gamma-rays that result from their interactions with nuclei in the formation.

Two types of neutron source are in use, the so-called chemical one and a more recent electrical device known as a neutron generator. Most neutron porosity tools currently in service use the chemical source.

Chemical sources consist of a mixture of beryllium and a heavy radioactive element (more often than not an artificial element such as americium). Alpha particles from the latter collide with the beryllium nuclei and in the process produce high energy neutrons with energies up to 4.5 MeV (million electron volts). The emitted neutrons actually have a broad spectrum of energies and output is typically in the region of 10^8 neutrons per second, the particles travelling away from the source in all directions.

The neutron generator used in logging tools produces pulses of neutrons with an energy of 14 MeV (hence their generic name of pulsed neutron generators). They use a fusion reaction between deuterium and tritium to generate the neutrons and these fly away at 90 degrees

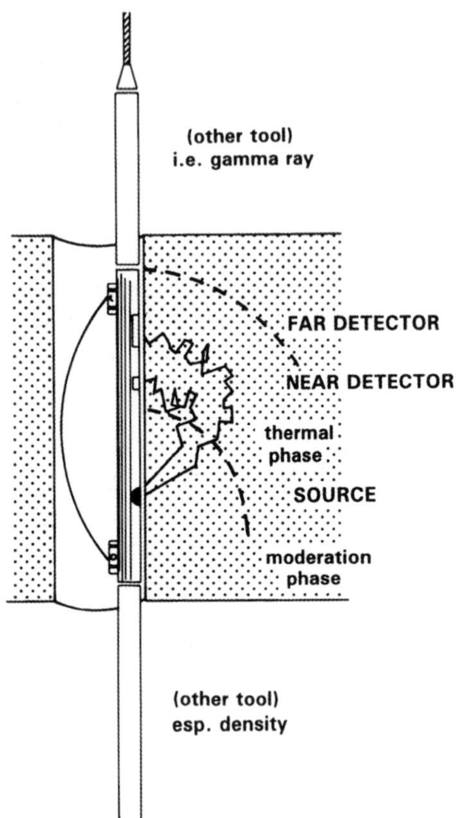

Figure 11.5 A schematic, compensated neutron tool. The source and detectors are held pressed against the borehole wall by a bow-spring.

to the tool axis (the same reaction is used in prototype fusion power reactors). Pulsed Neutron Generators were developed for neutron lifetime logs, which specifically require pulses of higher energy neutrons, but they can be used in any neutron tool and have the particularly desirable feature that the neutrons can be switched off when the tool is not in use.

The first neutron tools from the 1950s consisted of a source and a single gamma ray detector. The output was normally a simple count-rate which the analyst was left to transform to porosity. They were replaced by the tools with two neutron detectors, described above, in the 1960s. Neutron detectors are similar in construction to Geiger counters and the heart of the detector is a metal cylinder containing low pressure gas. The active component is normally Helium-3, which strongly absorbs low energy neutrons to form a proton and a 'triton' (a tritium nucleus). These are charged and, as they accelerate through the gas towards a wire with a large voltage applied to it, they create more ions and consequently a small pulse of electrical current. It is this which is ultimately what is counted. helium-3 is a very rare gas and world supplies are dwindling, so that the alternative gaseous neutron absorber, boron tri-fluoride can be used. Here it is boron-10 that strongly absorbs neutrons to produce lithium ions and alpha particles, after which the detection process is the same as for helium-3. Whichever neutron absorber is used, this type of detector is only really capable of detecting slow neutrons, the slower the better. The fast neutrons initially emitted by the source are virtually invisible to the detectors.

In fact, the efficiency of these counters varies inversely with the square root of the neutron energy. They respond primarily to thermal neutrons (lower energy) so that the most commonly used tools are effectively thermal neutron detection tools (**Table 11.4**). However, with the higher energy pulsed source, there are sufficient epithermal neutrons to be detected. Wireline sensors may be shielded with cadmium, a strong thermal neutron absorber (**Table 11.2**), to allow only the epithermal neutrons to be measured, while in the LWD tools the thick steel of the drill collars has the same effect (Burnett 1990). Using epithermal neutrons is considered preferable for deriving porosity.

The location of the detectors on a tool is chosen so that the count-rates show a large variation with changes in formation hydrogen index. Typically the near detector is positioned about 30 cm from the source and the far detector 60 cm. At these spacings, the count-rate falls with increasing hydrogen index (or porosity) (**Figure 11.9**).

Wireline tools

Thermal neutron tools

In the wireline tool with a chemical source, both source and detectors are incorporated in a simple cylindrical housing that is normally pushed against the borehole wall with a bow-spring (**Figure 11.5**). Normal open hole tools have a diameter of approximately three and a half inches, but slim-hole versions also exist. The names of these tools invariably involve the phrase 'Compensated Neutron'. This is a reference to the fact that they always have two neutron detectors which are designed to account for environmental factors (*see below*). The two detectors are placed along the tool about 30.5 cm and 61 cm (12" and 24") from the source and, as explained above, these distances are chosen to make the tool particularly sensitive to the hydrogen index. They are calculated from the slowing down length (Section 11.2) so that they are mainly in the area of thermal neutron energy in typical formations (**Figure 11.6**). The tool, therefore, counts thermal neutrons at two distances from the source. The neutron porosity is actually obtained from the ratio of the near detector to far detector counts. The use of the two detectors helps to reduce the effect of environmental factors such as hole size and mud weight, although the raw neutron porosity is still sensitive to them (**Table 11.6**). Each tool has a unique relationship between the ratio of the counts and neutron porosity, which is established by calibration. The calibration is performed at regular intervals in order to account for any changes in sensitivity of

Table 11.4 Neutron porosity tools (from Serra 2000, 2008; Baker Atlas, Baker Hughes™, Halliburton, Sperry-Sun and Schlumberger documents).

1. Wireline Neutron measurement (older tools)			
Name	Symbol	Company	
Dual Neutron Log	CNT-G (DNL)	Schlumberger	Th, Ep separately
Sidewall Neutron Log	SNP	"	Ep
Sidewall Epithermal Neutron	SWN	Baker Hughes™ (Atlas)	Ep
Epithermal Neutron	DSEN, SNL	Halliburton	Ep
2. Wireline Neutron measurement (most commonly used tools)			
Name	Symbol	Company	
Compensated Neutron Log	CNL	Schlumberger	Th
Accelerator Porosity Sonde	APS	"	(generator source)
Compensated Neutron	CN	Baker Hughes™ (Atlas)	Th
	NEU	"	
Compensated Neutron Tool	HDSN	Halliburton	Th
3. LWD tools			
Name	Symbol	Company	
Compensated Density Neutron	CDN, VISION	Schlumberger	
Compensated Neutron	CCN, LithoTrack™	Baker Hughes™ INTEQ	
Compensated Thermal Neutron	CTN	Halliburton/Sperry	Th
	CNP-CN	"	

Th = thermal neutron detector. Ep = epithermal neutron detector.

the detectors (normally at least monthly) and the ratio results are presented on the log as *neutron porosity units* (*see* Units of measurement *below*).

The neutron sonde has been traditionally combined with the density sonde into one tool string. As will be described, the density and neutron curves used together allow quick assessments of lithology and fluid type. Nowadays the neutron can be combined with almost any other tool and it is commonly run in a single string which includes all the standard open hole tools (density, resistivity, sonic and possibly NMR). Since the neutron source activates the formation, it can affect the gamma ray reading, and the neutron sonde should be placed below the gamma ray on the wireline string and behind it in the LWD assembly.

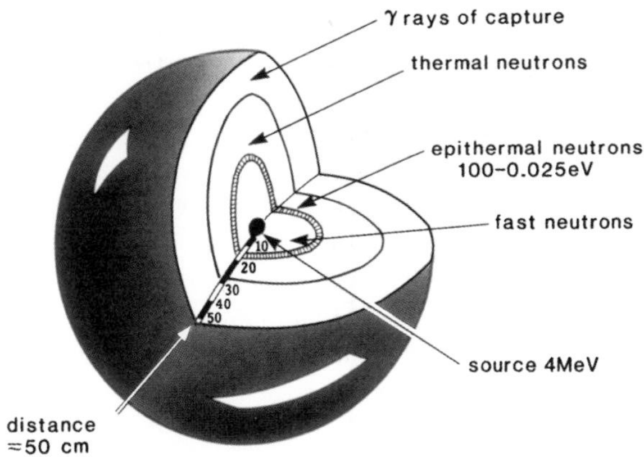

Figure 11.6 Spatial distribution of neutrons and disintegration products around a fast neutron source as used in logging tools (modified from Serra 1979).

Epithermal Neutron Tools

Epithermal neutrons have a slightly higher energy than the thermal neutrons used in most neutron porosity tools. For the temperatures we deal with in the Earth's crust, they have energies of a few electron volts rather than a small fraction of an electron volt (**Figure 11.2**). The main disadvantage to using thermal neutrons is that they are strongly absorbed by certain nuclei (e.g. cadmium and boron). Although these nuclei are only ever present at trace levels in sedimentary rocks, they absorb so strongly that this may be all that is required to significantly reduce the count rate (which will ultimately result in a reduced neutron porosity being calculated).

The problem could be avoided by counting epithermal neutrons exclusively, as their count-rate is not distorted by strong neutron absorbers. However, the difficulty in using epithermal neutrons is that they will always have a much lower count-rate than the thermal neutrons because they are an intermediate step on the way to thermal equilibrium. In other words, no sooner has one been created by the scattering of a higher energy neutron, than it undergoes another collision and becomes a thermal neutron. Nevertheless, epithermal neutron tools have been in use as long as thermal neutron tools (e.g. the pad type SNP from Schlumberger that appeared in the 1960s and, much later, the CNT-G which detected thermal and epithermal neutrons, **Table 11.4**). Making detectors that are selective for epithermal neutrons is easy: one simply exploits the strong thermal neutron absorbers which cause the problem in the first place. In practice, epithermal neutron detectors are simply neutron detectors that have been encased in cadmium, which absorbs all the thermal neutrons before they enter the detector proper.

As explained, the main problem with using epithermal neutrons is that the count rates are too low to give an accurate measurement. This could easily be overcome by using a stronger source, but this creates safety issues, which are almost insurmountable. Consequently, most tools designed to measure neutron porosity use a chemical source and count thermal neutrons.

In the early 1990s Schlumberger introduced the Array Porosity Sonde (APS), a true neutron porosity tool based on a pulsed neutron generator, that counted epithermal neutrons (**Figure 11.7**). This was a significant advance on the existing tools but, curiously, it never seems to have been recognised as such, and tools which have changed little from the 1960s are still being manufactured and are still the most common tool. An obvious advantage of using a pulsed neutron generator is that it can be turned off but, from a technical point of view, its greatest advantage is that a far greater neutron flux is generated and this means that accurate measurements based on epithermal neutrons are possible.

The APS has a pulsed neutron generator and four main neutron detectors at various distances along the tool, plus a small auxiliary detector (**Figure 11.7**). Like the compensated neutron tools described in the previous section, externally it is simply a cylinder that is pushed against the borehole wall by a bow-spring. Unlike the Compensated Neutron tools, most of the detectors are partially shielded so that only neutrons that have passed through the formation are counted. This is very reminiscent of the density tool and like the density tool, the volume of investigation is limited to a relatively narrow sector in front of the tool. The locations of these detectors have been carefully chosen for optimum sensitivity, but it is not simply the hydrogen index that the tool is designed to measure. Combinations of detectors are variously sensitive to hydrogen index and matrix composition and density. The auxiliary detector measures the decay of the neutron counts after the pulse has finished. This information allows the gap between the tool and the borehole wall to be estimated and so plays a similar role to the 'DHRO' curve produced by the density tool.

In short, the APS avoids the problem of thermal neutron absorption, has a comparable volume of investigation to the density tool, has in-built quality control measures and can, to an extent, account for matrix changes. It is indisputably a major improvement on the CNT type tools. As already mentioned, it is strange that the older tools are still in widespread use. One reason may be that the epithermal neutron response is unfamiliar in that it is less affected by shale than the traditional thermal neutron response (*see* Section 11.6, Neutron log in shales). The reduced effect of shales was originally considered an advantage but users found the new log difficult to compare with existing older logs. To counter this, the service companies attempt to model the thermal neutron response of the older tools from the epithermal response of the new tool (Fricke *et al.* 2008).

While drilling, LWD tools

Current tools

The LWD neutron tools currently in service generally use a chemical neutron source and are similar in design to the wireline tool. However, the LWD tool uses banks of sensors, which are about 30 cm (12") and 60 cm (24") from the source, and are either ^{3}He proportional counters, Geiger-Müller counters (more efficient at high energy), or occasionally lithium glass proportional counters. Because the steel casing surrounding the LWD sonde absorbs thermal neutrons, the sensors measure mainly the higher energy epithermal neutrons (Wraight *et al.* 1989). This is allowable because the tool is turning and, as it does so, logs the formation much more slowly and registers about 20 times more neutron counts than the wireline tool. The LWD neutron response is considered to be very close to the wireline counterpart (**Figure 11.8**).

(Even though the tool is turning, because of the nature of neutrons, the measurement cannot be sectorised or converted to an image).

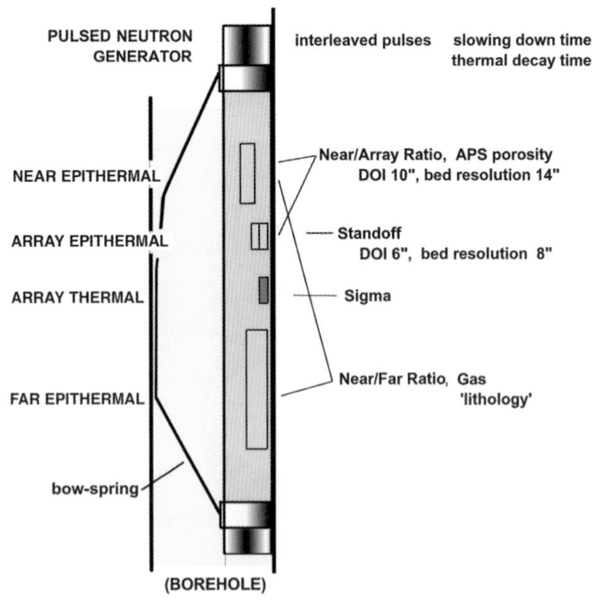

Figure 11.7 Schematic representation of the Schlumberger Array Porosity Sonde (APS), wireline tool, illustrating the variety of sensors used with the pulsed neutron source (based on Schlumberger 1993). *Courtesy of Schlumberger.*

Units of measurement

Neutron logs are plotted on a standardised arithmetic scale of *neutron (or limestone) porosity units* (ØN). These may be expressed as a percentage or a fraction. It was early shown (Archie 1950) that there is a relationship between neutron tool count-rates and porosity in clean, water-filled limestones (**Figure 11.9**). This allowed the count-rates to be converted to a more convenient value, the neutron porosity unit, which is related to the true porosity, but only under a special set of conditions. Neutron porosity is defined as equal to the true porosity *only* under standard (calibration) conditions of a clean, water-filled limestone (even then the limestone must be very pure and the water should be fresh). To find the real porosity in other lithologies and with other fluids in the pore space (i.e. other matrix types and fluids), the neutron log value must be converted by using algorithms or graphical solutions (*see* Quantitative uses *below*).

As noted, neutron porosity is not a fundamental physical property like density or sonic slowness. To be useful, it first needs to be related to a calibration standard. The primary calibration facility for neutron porosity is a test pit in the grounds of the University of Houston, Texas (it is in the same location as the test pits that represent the primary standard for the gamma ray log). It is here that the *neutron porosity unit* is defined. The pit contains three, 1.8 m (6 ft) zones of fresh-water wet limestone with a spread of porosities, one zone of Carthage Marble (porosity 1.9%), one of Indiana limestone (porosity 19%) and one of Austin Chalk (porosity 26%) and also a zone of pure (Houston) water (**Figure 11.10**) (Belknap *et al.* 1959). Limestones were chosen because, chemically they tend to be much simpler than clastics and can also be very homogeneous. Their use explains why the tool is calibrated to give the true porosity in limestones and not, say, clastics.

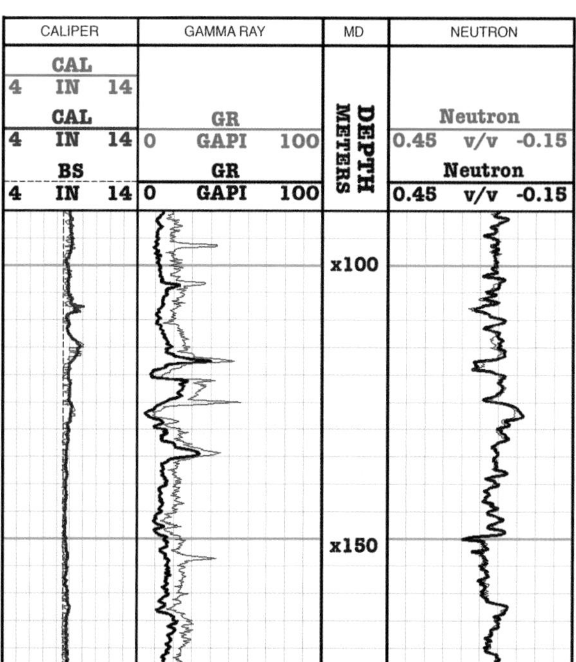

Figure 11.8 Neutron logs from a wireline and an LWD tool compared: both used a chemical source. The logs show good similarity in this example from Kazakhstan (from McCalmont *et al.* SPWLA 2008).

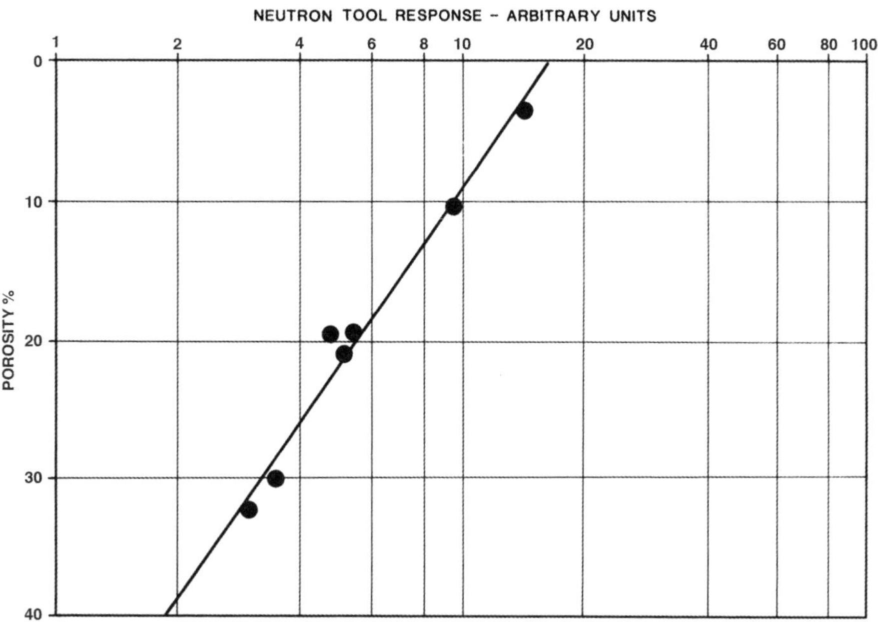

Figure 11.9 Graph showing the consistent relationship between neutron tool response and limestone porosity. It was used to demonstrate the effectiveness of the tool: Devonian, Crossett Limestone, Texas (re-drawn from Archie 1950).

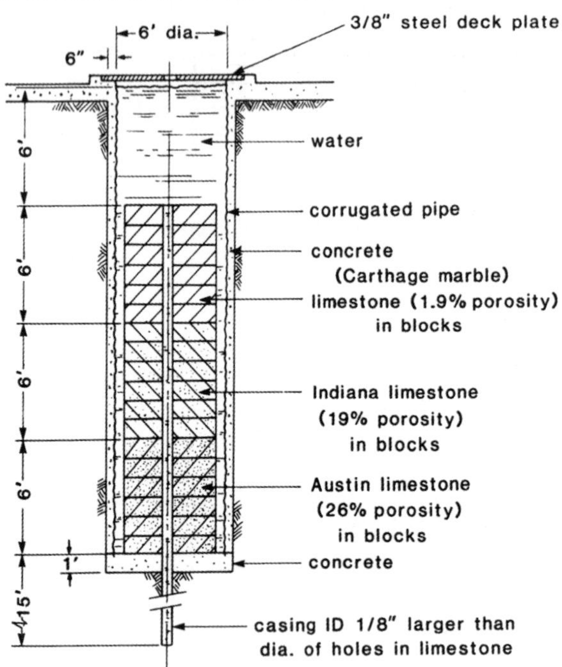

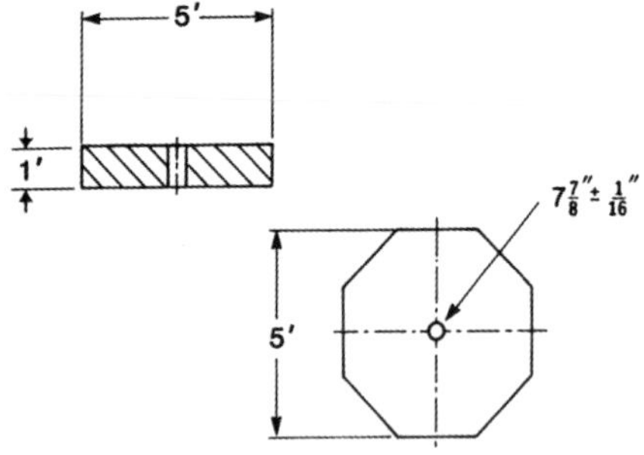

Figure 11.10 The API nuclear log calibration facility at the University of Houston, Texas, USA (from Belknap *et al.* 1959).

The formations used for the standards consist almost entirely of calcite and water with no neutron absorbing impurities. They were also chosen because porosity hardly varies from one block to another. Ideally, every neutron porosity tool would be calibrated and their readings standardised in this facility but, in practice, each major company has its own facility for doing this, and these play an analogous role to the secondary standards for SI units that are held in various laboratories around the world (Kimminau 1994). It has been suggested that a series of synthetic formations would offer a more reliable calibration standard than the complex natural ones (Butler and Clayton 1984). The standardisation and calibration of neutron tools is an important and sensitive matter.

Although modern tools use the neutron porosity unit there are, confusingly, several of them. Porosity measurements from thermal and epithermal sensors have different names: different processing routines are given different curve labels. Thus, for Schlumberger, the NPHI curve is from a thermal neutron porosity tool and derived from the ratio of near and far detector counts with the minimum of corrections. It is the curve found on the old (as well as some new) logs. The TNPH curve, thermal neutron porosity (equally from Schlumberger), can be from the same tool, but with corrections for hole size, mudcake thickness, salinity, mud weight, temperature and pressure. There are other additional corrections involved for the NPOR curve, the so-called alpha processing, which is considered to improve its vertical resolution (Luthi 2001). Geologists tend to use the NPHI and log analysts the TNPH. Epithermal neutron porosity is usually marked and is considered to be the best measurement of the Hydrogen Index (Section 11.1).

Log format

The neutron log is generally plotted across tracks 2 and 3 on an API format (**Figure 11.11**). The units, as discussed above, are neutron porosity units from empirical calibration. That is, neutron porosity units represent *real porosity* in clean, water-filled limestones but *only* in clean, water-filled limestones. The most common scale is from 45% (to the left) to –15% neutron porosity units (ØN). A fraction may be used instead of a % making these figures 0.45 to – 0.15 neutron porosity units. For high porosity formations, a scale of 60% to 0% is often used (or 0.6 to 0). This is common for unconsolidated clastics, which are the main target in deepwater plays.

Since the neutron is generally run combined with the density in one tool, a combined neutron-density log heading has become standard, and generally shows both logs plotted at chosen, compatible scales. This scale is usually for a limestone matrix, when the zero porosity is 2.7(1) g/cm^3. However, a sandstone matrix scale is also used, in which case zero porosity is 2.65 g/cm^3 (*see* Section 11.7, Neutron-density combination, for a full explanation). By tradition, with these formats, the density log is a solid line and the neutron log a dashed line (**Figure 11.11**).

11.4 Log characteristics

Depth of investigation

The depth of investigation of the neutron tool is generally shallow to moderate (although greater than the density) but varies with formation characteristics. In most normal formations logged it is of the order of 15–25 cm (6–10") (**Figure 11.12**). This varies with each tool but also varies as a function of the hydrogen index of the formation and therefore porosity. Maximum investigation is in low porosity materials (**Table 11.5**). As the table shows, the maximum penetration in a tight formation with a low hydrogen index is between 50 cm and 60 cm (20–24"). The pulsed neutron tool is said

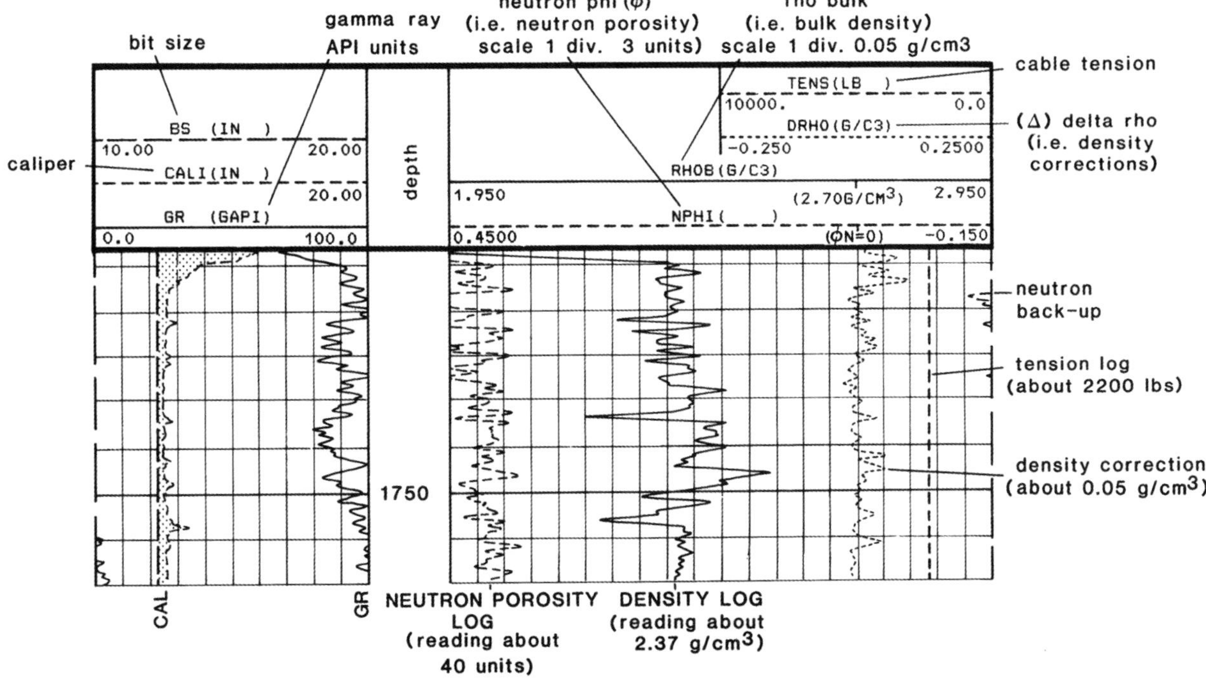

Figure 11.11 Typical log heading for an older neutron-density tool combination. This heading is of the type originally produced by the Schlumberger CSU unit. The neutron and density log scales are compatible for a clean limestone, ØN 0% = 2.70 g/cm³.

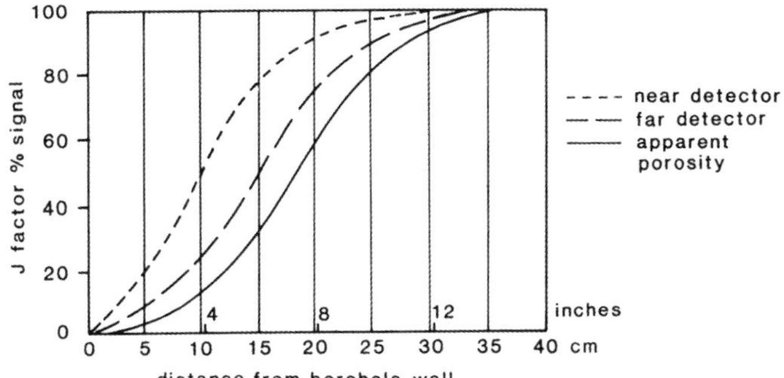

Figure 11.12 The moderate depth of investigation of the neutron tool illustrated by experimentally-derived, J-factor curves. These are for a thermal type, two-detector neutron tool and a 35% porosity, water-filled sand (from Sherman and Locke 1975).

to have a shallower penetration of between 15 cm and 25 cm (6″ and 10″) depending on which sensors are used (**Figure 11.7**) (Schlumberger 1993).

Since the neutron tool has a shallow depth of investigation, the reading generally comes mostly from the invaded zone. Gas, because it is highly mobile, is found in the invaded zone and will affect the neutron response. LWD measurements are known to be taken before significant invasion occurs and, for the neutron measurement, this is especially evident in gas reservoirs. The gas effect on while-drilling logs is more prominent than on later run wireline logs (*see* gas effects *below*). Another aspect is that thermal neutron tools read deeper than density tools, so the former often contributes more to the gas effect on the combination (discussed below). This can complicate quantitative analysis. Epithermal tools have a shallower depth of investigation, which is closer to the density tools.

Bed resolution

The moderate to shallow depth of investigation of the neutron tool is accompanied by moderate to good bed resolution. Wireline tools have a vertical resolution of about 43 cm (19″) and while-drilling tools about 30–34 cm (12–13.5″) (ODP document). With enhanced processing, it is said that the resolution of the wireline tools can be reduced to 30–38 cm (12–15″) (Smith 1990). However, in practice, true formation values can only be obtained on the log in beds with a thickness down to about 46–60 cm (18–24″) (Passey *et al.* 2006; Gilchrist 2008). The pulsed neutron tool is said to give

Table 11.5 Depth of investigation of the neutron tools as a function of porosity (from Serra 1979, after Schlumberger).

Porosity %	90% of signal
0	60 cm
10	34 cm
20	23 cm
30	16.5 cm

Table 11.6 Factors affecting neutron porosity logging, especially in the LWD environment. D.O.I. = depth of investigation (from Burnett *et al.* 1990).

Porosity method	Caving	Eccentered	Fm. Salinity	Boron	D.O.I	Count-rate
Epithermal sensors	most sensitive	most sensitive	least sensitive	least sensitive	shallower	lower
Thermal sensors	sensitive	sensitive	most sensitive	sensitive	deeper	higher

a bed resolution of between 20 cm and 35.5 cm (8" and 14") depending on the sensor combination (Schlumberger 1993b). The neutron log has a slightly lower resolution than the density log but is still a good bed boundary indicator.

Unwanted logging effects and environmental corrections

The Neutron Porosity measurement is strongly influenced by environmental factors (at least relative to other measurements). The changes these make are 'second order' in that they are not large enough to lead to an incorrect interpretation but they are large enough to produce a measurable difference in response and for accurate quantitative work they need to be accounted for.

Some of the environmental conditions which influence neutron detection are shown in **Table 11.6**. Many can be corrected using charts which are specific to the tool, assuming, of course, that the conditions in the borehole are known. The factors can be divided into two types: those determined by the borehole and those specific to the formation. The borehole factors, including temperature, hole size, mud composition and pressure, should be known and, in some cases, can be measured or calculated directly. Modern logging units can apply these corrections as the log is recorded. Formation specific factors include formation water salinity, general lithology and the concentrations of strongly neutron absorbing impurities. In general, these are not so easy to determine (although lithology and formation water salinity can be deduced from other log responses). The individual corrections normally amount to a few porosity units, and some are negative and some are positive. Therefore the net effect of adding all the corrections can be quite small and, occasionally, they all cancel each other out.

The use of epithermal neutrons reduces the influence of several environmental factors wich are mostly concerned with hole geometry and salinity characteristics, but also include thermal neutron absorber effects. Hole geometry is generally adequately compensated for by modern algorithms, provided the corrections are not excessive. Even though the effect of unwanted thermal neutron absorbers has been researched (Fertl 1979 1 & 2), there is no consensus as to their practical importance on logging measurements. It is worth noting that thermal neutron absorption can be a benefit in some circumstances. As will be seen below, the neutron porosity tends to be high in the presence of iron minerals, a direct result of iron having a strong affinity for thermal neutrons. A high neutron porosity is therefore a useful diagnostic tool for iron containing minerals. The influence of thermal neutron absorbers is obviously diminished when epithermal neutron detectors are used (Burnett *et al.* 1990).

11.5 Quantitative uses

Porosity

The neutron log is used to derive porosity. The tool, as indicated above, measures hydrogen abundance or hydrogen index. In clean, water-bearing formations, the only hydrogen present is in the formation water (H_2O). The neutron tool therefore responds to the volume of water filled pore space and gives a measure of the porosity (**Figure 11.13**). Expressed mathematically:

$$\text{Log}_{10}\, Ø = aN + B$$

where Ø is the true porosity, *a, B* are constants, and N is the neutron-tool count-rate.

However, calibration is necessary for the above calculation, as matrix materials have differing effects on the neutron log and change with porosity. In other words the constants a and B vary depending on the nature of the formation. A water-filled sandstone with 20% porosity gives a different neutron log reading to a water-filled limestone with 20% porosity (**Figure 11.14**).

In reality, as has been discussed, the neutron porosity is obtained from the ratio of count-rates from two detectors but the same basic principle applies, that different algorithms are required to convert the ratio to porosity in limestone, sandstone, dolomite, or something more exotic. These effects vary between tools so that porosity should only be taken from a chart (or algorithm) for that specific tool (Gilchrist 2008). Normally the tool is set-up so that neutron porosity is equal to the true porosity in water bearing limestone. In a typical water bearing sandstone, the neutron porosity will then be less than the true porosity (the difference is normally about 5% but the difference is not exactly constant over the whole porosity range). The conversion can be made using charts, and algorithms that do the same job will be included in any log analysis package.

Alternatively, the tool can actually be set-up to give the true porosity in water filled sandstone. This is commonly done in the Americas and/or for American opera-

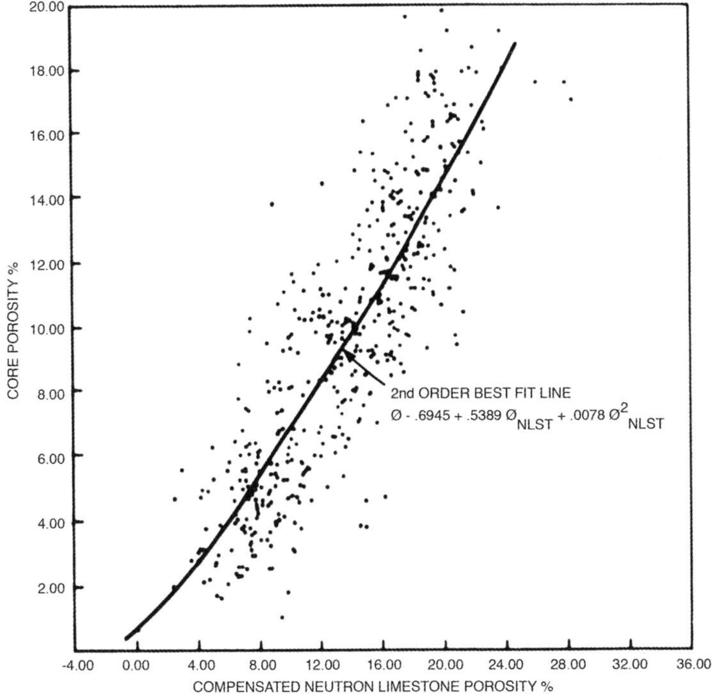

Figure 11.13 Compensated neutron log values plotted against core porosity values (points with grain densities between 2.84–2.88 g/cm³). 18, West Pembina D-2 Reef wells: *N* = 475 (from McFadzean 1983).

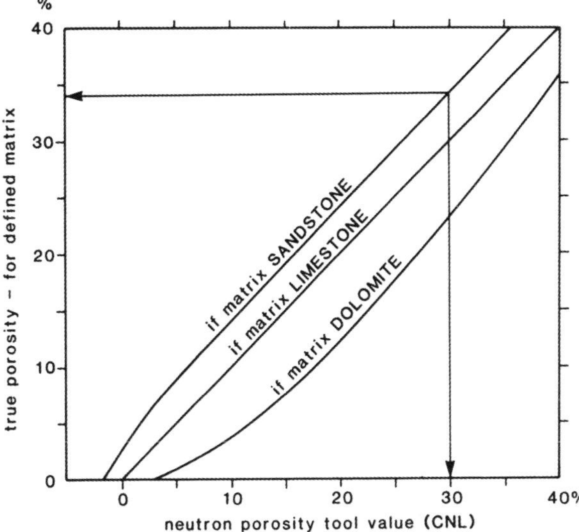

Figure 11.14 Graph for deriving the true porosity from values measured by a Schlumberger CNL tool and defined sandstone, limestone, and dolomite matrices. Note that only the limestone matrix gives a 1/1 relationship. Example: tool neutron porosity (ØN) = 30%, true porosity for sandstone matrix = 34% (from Schlumberger 1972).

tors. In limestone it will then read higher than the true porosity and if a tool set up for a sandstone matrix is going to be used to calculate porosity in limestone, a correction will need to be made. It is essential to check what matrix (lime or sand) the tool has been set up for in order to avoid erroneous interpretations. Unfortunately, the matrix that the tool is set up for is normally 'buried' deep within the log header.

In most parts of the world, tools are set up for limestone even if sandstone is the main reservoir lithology. This is partly because ultimately the tools are calibrated to limestone standards, but mainly because sandstones tend to be mineralogically more complex than limestone. Even within a single reservoir unit, sandstone composition can vary significantly and so the neutron porosity will only equal the true porosity at a few points. By using a limestone matrix, the user is implicitly acknowledging the tool is not measuring porosity but the end product of complex nuclear reactions.

Gas effects on neutron porosity

The rules governing the relationship between neutron log porosity and the true porosity in clean formations are valid for water filled porosity. They also often hold when oil is present (as many oils have essentially the same hydrogen index as water). However, gas, having a very low density, has a very low hydrogen index compared to water (**Table 11.7**). Therefore, in the presence of gas, the neutron porosity log will lead to the true porosity being under-estimated (**Figure 11.15**). Corrections for gas content can be made (Gaymard and Poupon 1968; Darling *et al.* 1997) but the best use of this phenomenon is still qualitative. Moreover, on the neutron-density combination (*see below*), gas stands out

Table 11.7 Hydrogen Index (HI) and neutron log values of some common lithologies (from Serra 1979; Edmundson and Raymer 1979).

	Limestone porosity units CNL	Hydrogen Index**
Water, fresh	100	1.0
Water, salt	60+	0.90
Quartz	−2	0.01
Sandstones*	−2 to 25	
Calcite	0	–
Limestones*	0 to 30	
Dolomite	1	–
Dolomites*	1 to 30	
Shales	25 to 75	0.09–0.37
Coal, lignite	52	0.66
Coal, anthracite	38	0.40
Oil	60+	
Methane	(20–50)	0.49

* Approximate ranges up to 30% porosity
**395°C, 482.6 bar (200°F, 7000 psi)

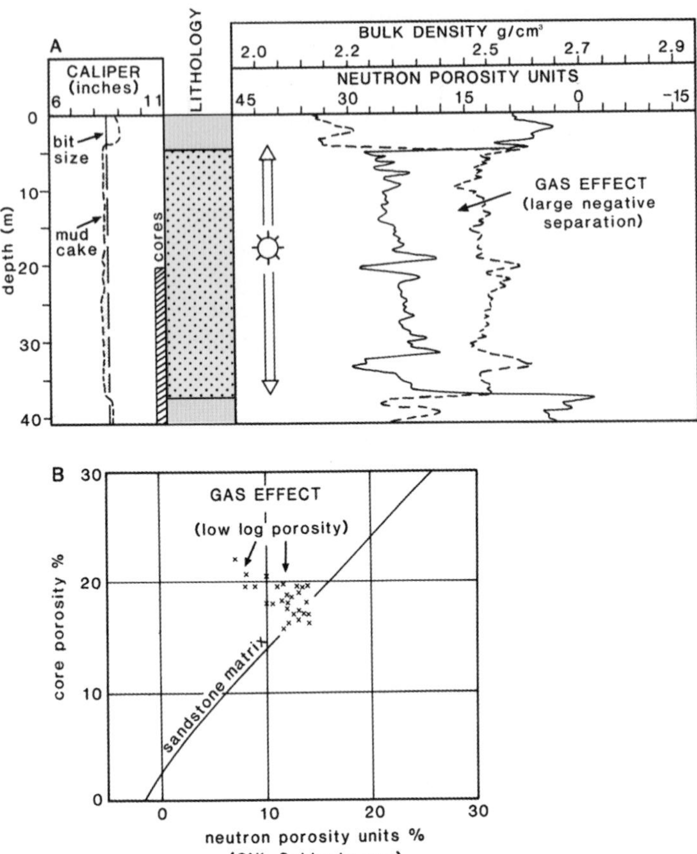

Figure 11.15 Logs (A) and cross-plot (B) showing the effect of gas on the neutron (and density) logs. The neutron values from A are used in the cross-plot B. The neutron porosity in gas zones reads too low.

very distinctly, giving a large negative separation (**Figure 11.15**). This separation is even more marked on LWD neutron-density logs since invasion has often not progressed as far as for normal wireline logging (**Figure 11.16**) and gas filled pores are directly detected by the neutrons (Benfield *et al.* 2004).

Heavy oil can also result in neutron porosity underestimating the true porosity, although the difference is normally smaller than for gas filled formations. The reason is that heavy oils contain a lot of unsaturated compounds and so contain less hydrogen than the alkanes, which are the main component of light oils. High GOR oils can also have a lower hydrogen index than water, and produce a similar change.

Shale effects on neutron derived porosity

Since the neutron log is sensitive to all hydrogen nuclei, it is sensitive to both free and bound water. Free water is formation water that occurs in shale pores, while bound water occurs either within the clay molecule or adsorbed between clay mineral layers (*see* Neutron log in shales, Section 11.6). However, shales are said to affect the neutron log in two additional ways. First is their density. As the density of most dry clay minerals is higher than the density of either limestone or sandstone for which the tools are calibrated, neutrons will be slowed or absorbed and sensors will register fewer counts. This will be translated into higher neutron porosity values. Secondly, thermal neutron absorbers are more common in shales than other lithologies. Again, this will cause lower counts and will be translated into higher neutron porosity values. As suggested, there is no consensus as to the importance of this contribution (*see* Unwanted logging effects).

There is another possible factor leading to the high neutron porosities in shales, and that depends on what precisely constitutes a water molecule. Strictly speaking, clay minerals contain a significant amount of hydrogen as part of their crystal structure (this is the only significant contributor to hydrogen in the sub-surface which is not a fluid). The hydrogen exists as hydroxyl groups (OH) that form the chemical structure of at least some of the sheets that make up the clay. This is not water, although it looks very much like it and it will certainly affect the neutron porosity in the same way as water. A lot of it is almost certainly erroneously included as 'clay-bound water' but, if it is removed from a clay, by extreme heat for example, there is no longer any clay! Disagreements over whether it should be included as water or not are probably the main reason why the values for clay neutron porosities vary so much between different references.

Slight admixtures of shale with reservoir matrix material therefore disrupt neutron porosity values and the true porosity cannot be calculated without corrections. The example (**Figure 11.17**) shows that the neutron log porosity stays constant while the true porosity varies considerably. A study of shaly sandstones showed that in quartz-clay mixtures, the hydrogen index of wet clay and of formation water can be similar (Heslop 1974). In other words, the neutron is incapable of separating wet clay from free, pore water. Cross-plotting gamma ray values (as a clay indicator) against neutron log values illustrates this. The gamma ray log shows diminishing clay volume but the neutron maintains nearly constant values (**Figure 11.18**). The neutron-derived porosity in shaly sands is therefore erroneous and, correspondingly, the neutron alone cannot be used to derive a clay volume.

In shaly formations the neutron porosity value should either not be used to derive porosity, or used with extreme care. If the neutron porosity is derived from epithermal detectors the shale influence is diminished (*but see* Neutron log in shales *below*).

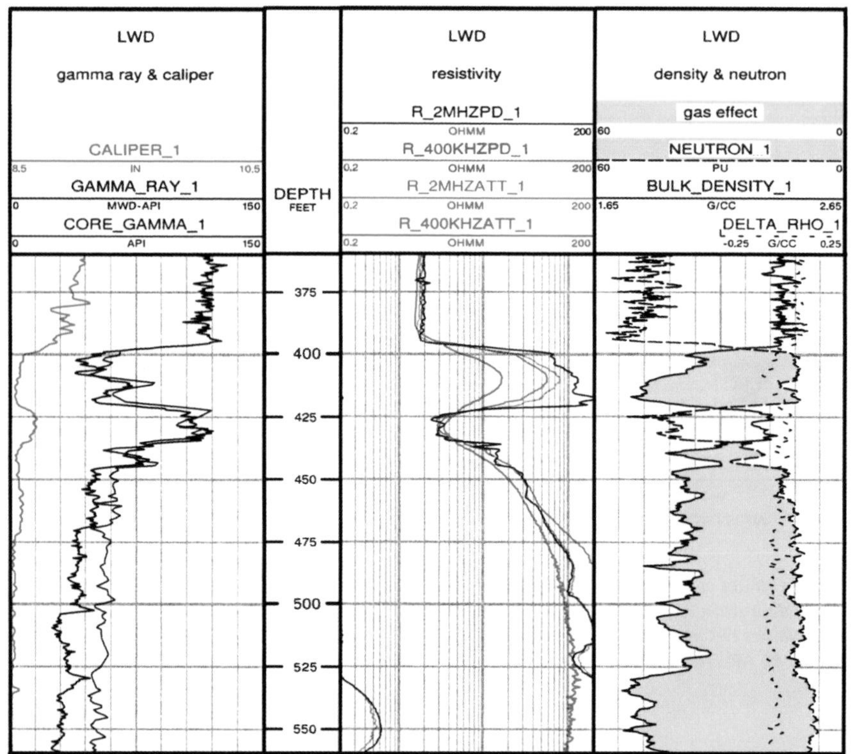

Figure 11.16 A marked 'gas effect' seen on LWD logs. The effect can be especially marked on LWD logs because significant invasion has not yet taken place. Neutron on sandstone matrix scale: 8.5″ hole, 1.7 g/cm³ (10.7 lb/gal) OBM mud and 50° deviation (from Benfield *et al.* SPWLA 2004).

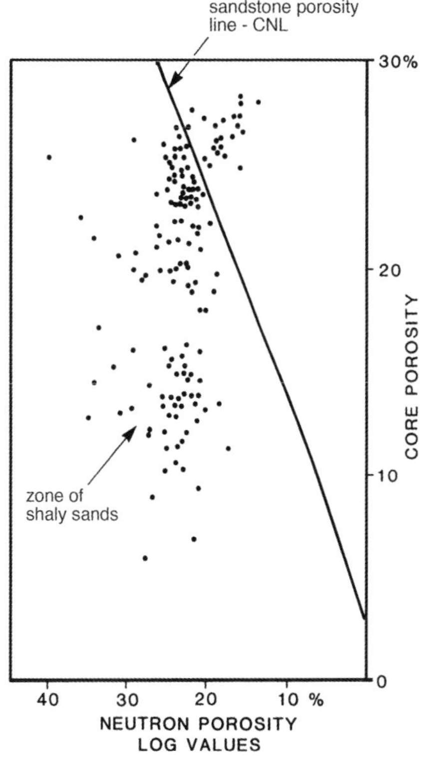

Figure 11.17 The effect of shale on neutron porosity values. The neutron log registers shale as porosity (water). The true porosities should fall along the diagonal line (compare Figure 10.13).

11.6 Qualitative uses

Lithology identification

The use of the neutron log to identify lithology depends on an understanding of the distribution of the hydrogen index in natural materials.

The hydrogen detected by the neutron tool occurs in two principal chemical combinations, the one between hydrogen and carbon (the hydrocarbons), and the other between hydrogen and oxygen (simply, water). Hydrocarbons occur as gases (methane, etc.), as liquids (oil, bitumen, etc.) or as solids (coal, organic matter, hydrates). Water occurs as free water (in pores), as adsorbed ions (in clay interlayer zones), as water of crystallization (in evaporites), or as combined water (in igneous rocks).

The lithologies in which these various forms of combined hydrogen are found have hydrogen indexes which cover almost the entire scale between 1 and 0 (**Tables 11.7, 11.8**). Probably only pure water can be recognized categorically by its hydrogen index, which is 1. However, the neutron log gives an extremely sensitive reflection of lithological

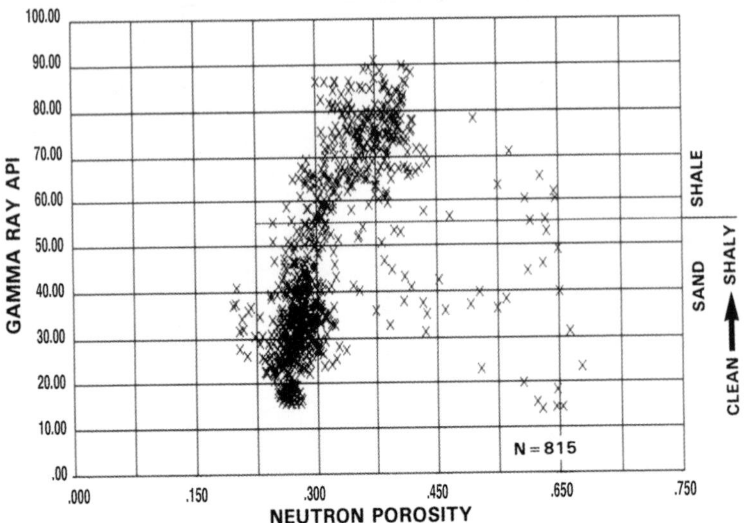

Figure 11.18 Neutron log values cross-plotted with gamma ray values in a shaly sand formation. The neutron log indicates the same porosity in shaly sands, with gamma ray values between 40–55 API, as in the clean sands with gamma ray values below 40 API. This is not the case in reality, porosities are lower in the shaly sands.

characteristics and changes and, combined with other log responses, the hydrogen index becomes diagnostic. This is examined below.

Neutron log in shales: porosity and compaction

The neutron log shows abnormally high 'porosities' in shale or clay intervals. Values vary between 75% ØN and 25% ØN but a typical shale has values around 40–50% ØN (**Figure 11.19**). Care must be taken with absolute numbers as the values vary between different tools from the same company and between tools from different companies. There is a large variation between logs from tools with thermal neutron sensors and logs from tools with epithermal sensors, between LWD logs and wireline logs. The figure (**Figure 11.20**) compares shale neutron porosity values from a wireline tool with a pulsed neutron source, a classic wireline neutron and an LWD neutron. The differences are large (Afonso de André 2004).

However, a typical neutron log will indicate probable shales (40–50% ØN) as opposed to sandstones (0–30% ØN) or limestone (0–35% ØN). The values in brackets are only 'typical', not exact. A shale with a neutron porosity value of 50% does not have a real porosity of this value. The hydrogen index is high because of the presence of both free and bound water and the density of the clay minerals **(Table 11.8)**. When a clay is deposited, up to 70% or more of its volume may be water. This diminishes very rapidly and, over geological depths typical of oil wells, is generally between 10% and 25% depending on the degree of compaction (cf. **Figure 10.23**).

As previously described (Section 11.5), clay water is divided into free pore-water, adsorbed water clinging to the clay but also lattice-water which forms part of the clay mineral structure. Clays with no lattice-water show a gradual elimination of both pore and adsorbed water by mechanical compaction (Mondol *et al.* 2007). A residuum of about 10% usually remains. Interstitial water is an important element of the smectites (**Table 11.8**) and complicates compaction since it is more or less stable up to an abrupt dehydration point. This point is largely temperature-controlled but, in oilfield work, is often related to depth. A clay rich in smectite above the dehydration point may contain up to 20–25% interlayer water: below it is rapidly eliminated. In depth terms this can be anywhere between 1500 m and 5000 m (4900 ft and 16500 ft) but is usually at about 2000 m (6500 ft) (Shaw 1980; Peltonen *et al.* 2009).

An attempt has been made to study the behaviour of the various clay waters using neutron-density cross-plot techniques (Honda and Magara 1982). Adsorbed and free water will be detected as porosity by both the density and the neutron tools. Interlayer water will, however, only be detected by the neutron. The line of equal density-neutron porosity indicates the limit of the interlayer water (**Figure 11.21**).

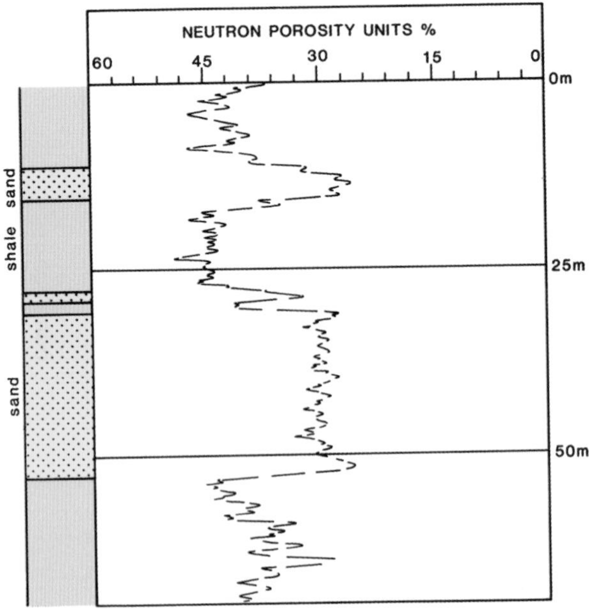

Figure 11.19 Typical neutron log responses in a sand-shale sequence. Shale gives high values, ØN 40–45%: sands give lower values, ØN 28–30%. ØN in shales is due to free, adsorbed and interlayer water, and does not give real porosity.

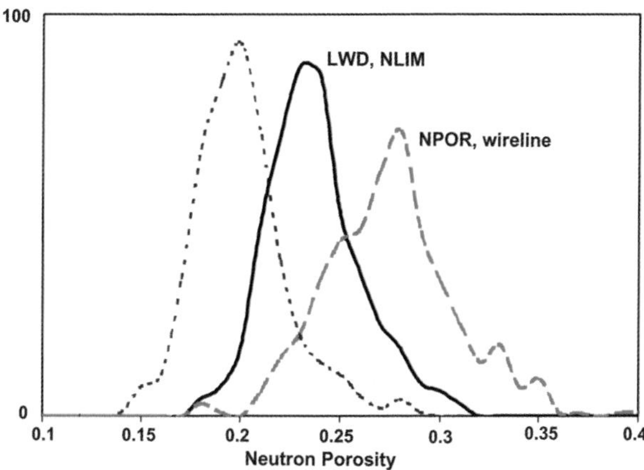

Figure 11.20 Shale neutron response differences due to equipment differences. The responses are from: a wireline tool with a pulsed neutron source (AP, wireline); an LWD tool with a chemical source (LWD, NLIM) (neutron on a limestone scale); and a wireline tool with a chemical source (NPOR, wireline). The corresponding density logs show no variations, indicating that the differences in neutron values are not caused by tool malfunction (from Alfonso de André SPWLA 2004).

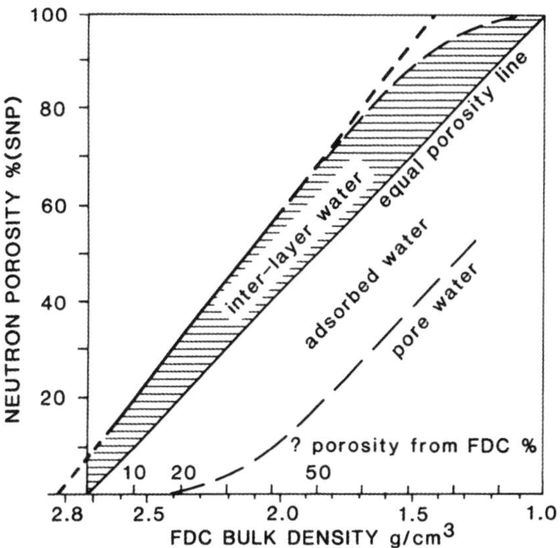

Figure 11.21 Indication of clay–water types on a density-neutron cross-plot. The outside (heavy) line has a slope of (ØSNP = 7.65 + 1.14 Ø FCD (re-drawn from Magara 1982).

Table 11.8 Combined water in clays (*Weaver *et al.* 1973; +Serra 1979; Alfonso de André 2004).

Clay type	% water* (av.)	Hydrogen Index+	Neutron porosity (CNL)
Illite	8	0.09	30
Kaolinite	13	0.37	37
Chlorite	14	0.32	52
Smectite	18–22	0.64	44

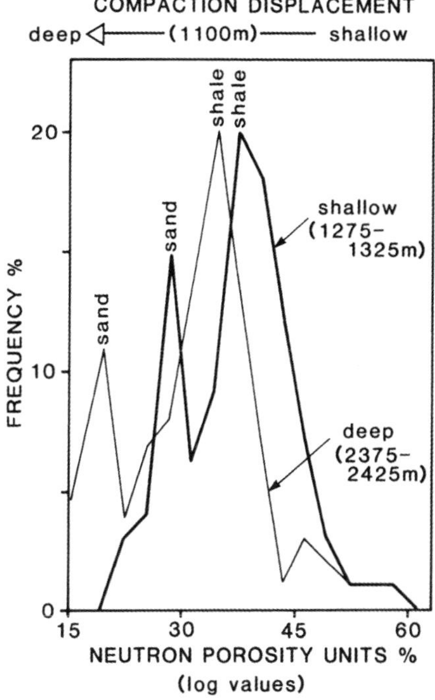

Figure 11.22 The effects of shale compaction on neutron log values in a sand-shale sequence. Histograms of the log values show the diminution in sand neutron porosity, but only a small change in the neutron porosity value of shales. cf. Fig. 11.23

This theoretical behaviour of water in clay formations (**Figure 11.21**) is difficult to understand on real neutron logs. In one, typical example well, over a depth of 3000 m there is a small, gradual diminution of the average neutron shale value (**Figure 11.22**). This is presumably the compaction effect yet it is surprisingly small when the theoretical diminution of water content with depth is considered. Frequently, when compaction is indicated on other logs (for example the sonic), the neutron log value remains constant (**Figure 11.23**).

In another example, through a shale interval with no major lithological changes (Peltonen *et al.* 2009), a gradual increase in shale RHOB density indicates a shale porosity decrease (**Figure 11.24**). It is not accompanied by a corresponding NPHI decrease as would be expected. In this figure, which shows X-ray diffraction analyses along with RHOB and NPHI plots, the lower part of the plot from 2200 m downwards, shows the expected behavior: as RHOB increases (porosity decreases), NPHI decreases (also porosity decreases). However, from 1800 m–2200 m, RHOB increases (porosity decreases) while NPHI *increases*, meaning that the hydrogen content (HI) of the shale increases. This NPHI response is clearly not due to the physical change associated with porosity diminution but the X-ray analyses do not offer an explanation either, although a diagenetic change can be suspected.

A verified explanation of these neutron phenomena has yet to be found. They indicate that the bulk water content of a clay, as seen by the neutron, is indepen-

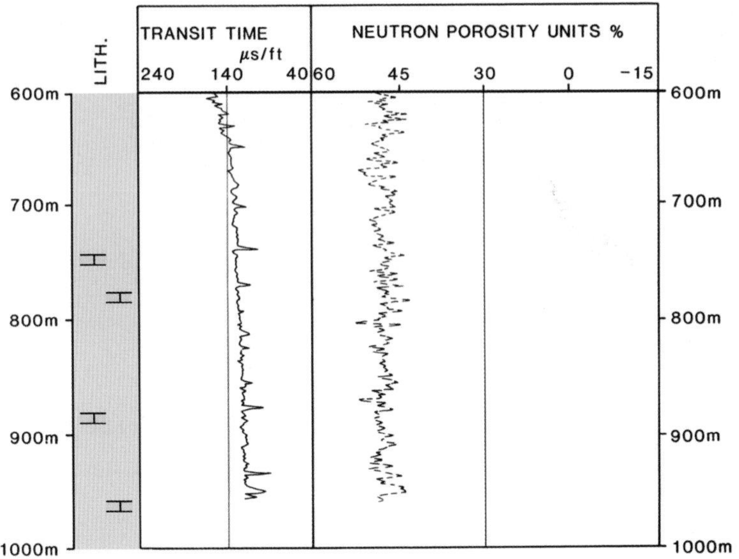

Figure 11.23 Compaction in a shale sequence shown by a decrease in interval transit time (increase in velocity) while the neutron log shows constant values.

dent of its distribution between pore-water, adsorbed water and interlayer water changes as reflected by shale porosity changes.

Neutron log in shales: composition

Even though there are differences in the amounts of combined water and neutron log value between the different clay mineral species (**Table 11.8**), variations in the proportions of these in natural shales seem to have little effect on the neutron log. Variations in non-clay minerals are much more noticeable and they dominate the neutron response. Rapid, or short-amplitude changes in the neutron log values in shales mostly result from changes in the amount of admixed quartz or carbonate and changes in organic-matter content.

Typical quartz-clay changes are seen on the neutron log in an example of a coarsening-up deltaic sequence (**Figure 11.25**). The upwards addition of increasing amounts of quartz, with a hydrogen index of 0.01, to clays with a high hydrogen index, acts as a effective dilutant, persistently lowering the neutron value (Heslop 1974). The same result is obtained on the admixture of any material with a very low hydrogen index with clays. This may be quartz, as above, calcium carbonate, dolomite or certain evaporites: the lower the clay volume, the lower the neutron log value. In addition, these added minerals may fill up the shale pore space, so decreasing the neutron but, at the same time, increasing the bulk density. Typically, the two curves 'track' each other, high density values corresponding to low neutron values and *vice versa* (**Figure 17.9**).

Entirely the opposite effect is caused by the admixture of organic matter with clays: it causes an increase in the hydrogen index. This is because organic matter has a higher hydrogen abundance per unit volume (hydrogen index around 0.66) than clay (**Table 11.8**) (**Figure 11.26**). The increase in neutron log values with organic matter is notable, especially when combined with the attendant decrease in bulk density (organic matter is light), and makes both coals and source rocks very distinctive (*see* **Figure 10.23**).

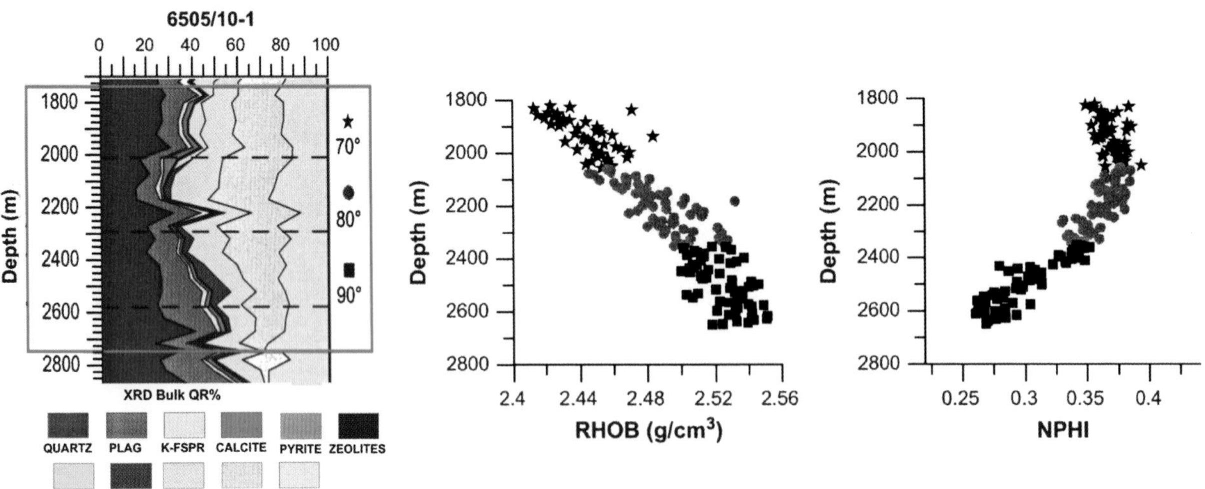

Figure 11.24 The neutron log over the shale interval 1800 m–2200 m does not show the decrease in shale porosity shown by the density log. The explanation is not known. Over the interval 2200 m–2600 m, both logs show diminishing porosity as expected. Mineral analyses from X-ray diffraction. Well 6505/10-1 from offshore Norway (from Peltonen *et al.* 2009).

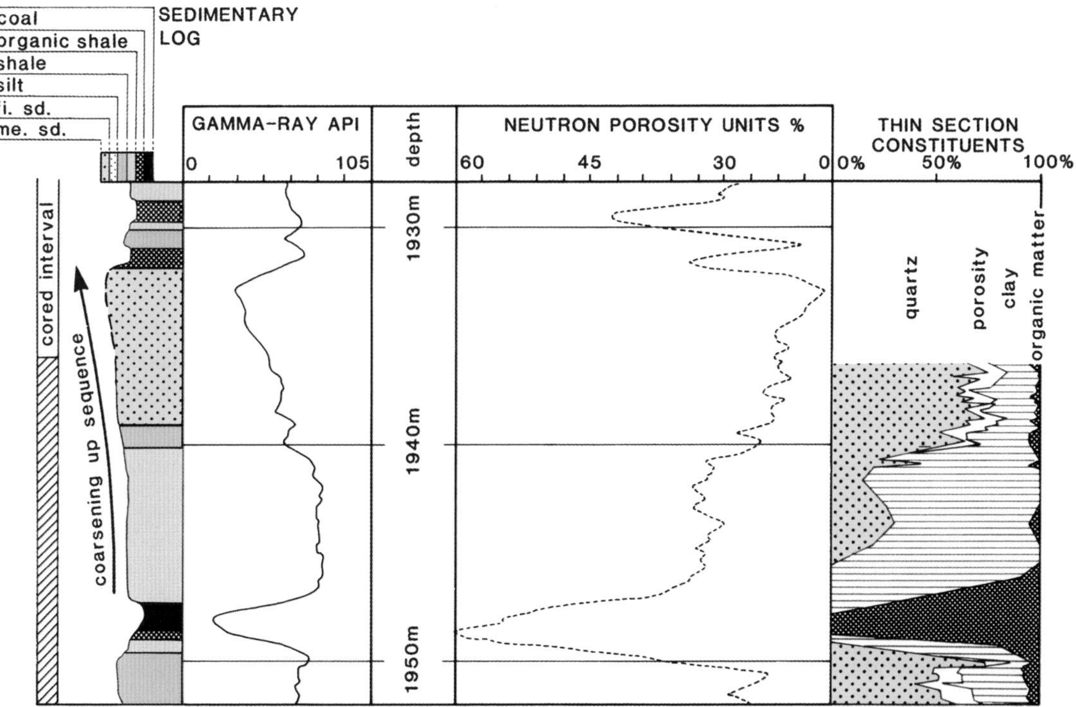

Figure 11.25 Changes in the neutron log corresponding to changes in quartz admixture. As the the shale (high HI) content decreases upwards and the quartz (low HI) content increases, so the overall neutron log value decreases. HI = hydrogen index.

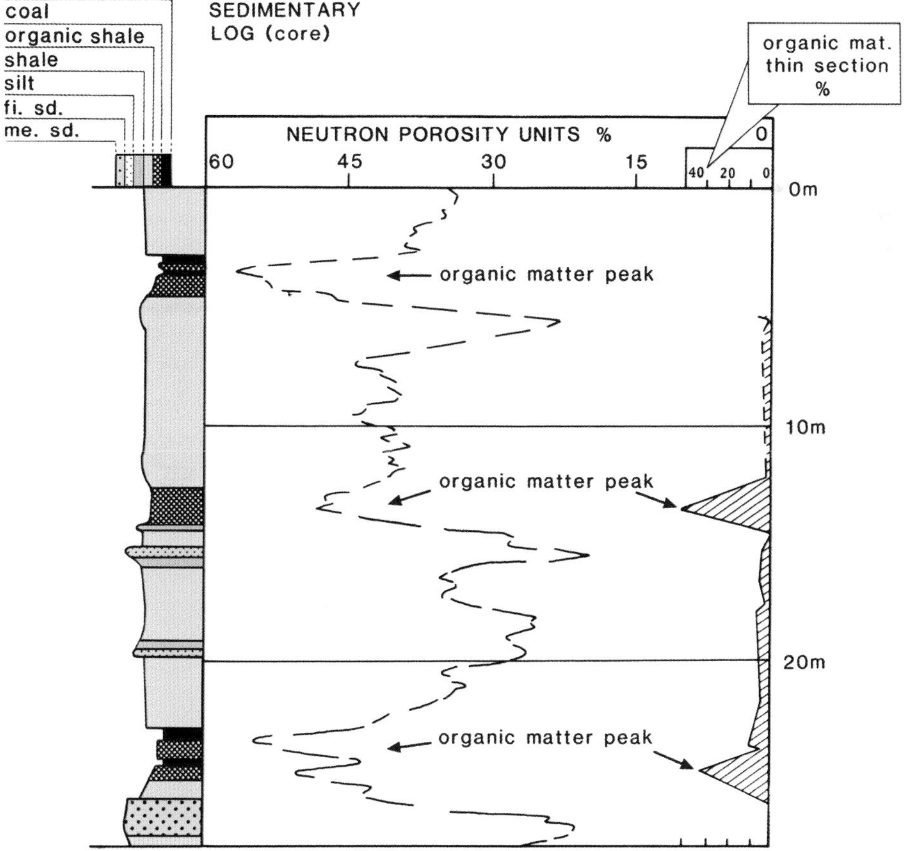

Figure 11.26 The effect of organic matter on the neutron log. Organic matter has a high hydrogen index (HI) and causes a moderate increase in the neutron log values.

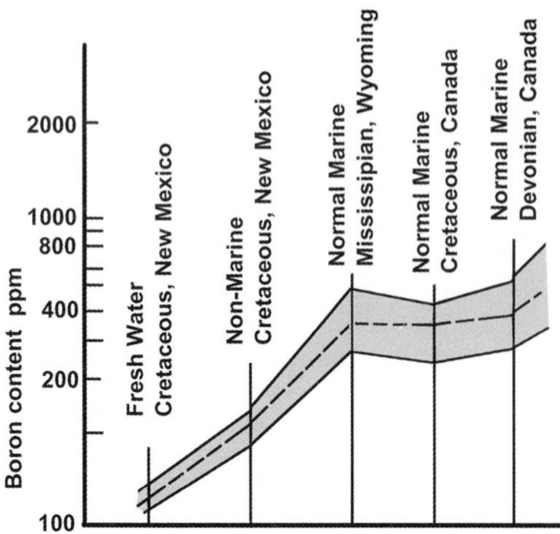

Figure 11.27 Boron content of illites in different environments. Boron concentration is higher in marine sediments than in non-marine (from Fertl SPWLA 1979b).

One aspect of the evaluation of shales with neutron tools, which still seems elusive, as has been mentioned, is the effect of thermal neutron absorbers. Capture and absorption in pore space liquids is mainly due to hydrogen (in water) but chlorine (in NaCl) can also have an effect. Chlorine is usually corrected for in tool response algorithms. Capture in the solid matrix is negligible unless it contains elements with unusually high capture cross-sections, such as boron or gadolinium (**Table 11.3**). Boron content has been examined in the Gulf Coast, USA, and is said have a noticeable effect in certain shales and shaly sands (Dunlap and Coates 1988), although the element is mainly present in the illites rather than other clay minerals (**Figure 11.27**) (Fertl 1979). The distribution of boron is said to be indicative of the salinity of the environment of deposition, low boron content in non-marine environments, higher content in saline environments, an effect seen in both coals and evaporites (Fertl 1979b *ibid*). To note, boron content is low in limestones and dolomites (<20 ppm) and also in clean sandstones, although this depends on tourmaline content. Boron can be present in altered oceanic basement. The geological significance of gadolinium is not known.

Table 11.9 Neutron log values of some evaporites (from Schlumberger 1985).

Mineral	Composition	Neutron log Value†	
Carnallite	$KClMgCl_2.6H_2O$	60†	High
Gypsum	$CaSO_4.2H_2O$	60†	
Kainite	$MgSO_4KCl.3H_2O$	60†	
Polyhalite	$K_2SO_4MgSO_4$ $2CaSO_4.2H_2O$	25	
Halite	NaCl	−3	Low
Anhydrite	$CaSO_4$	−2	
Sylvite	KCl	−3	

†ØCNL – apparent limestone porosity

Evaporites

The neutron log can be used to distinguish between evaporites on the basis of water of crystallization (**Table 11.9**). Of the evaporites with water of crystallization, gypsum ($CaSO_4.2H_2O$) is the most common. However, carnallite, polyhalite and kainite also contain the water molecule (**Table 11.9**). All these minerals have a high neutron-log value, which differentiates them from other evaporites such as salt (NaCl) or anhydrite ($CaSO_4$), which contain no water, and hence have a log value of zero (**Figure 11.28**).

Identification of hydrated minerals

Hydrated minerals (excluding evaporites) are not common. However, hydrated iron compounds may be sufficiently abundant to affect the logs. Thus, a zone of chamosite ($2SiO_2Al_2O_3$ $3FeO.nH_2O$) in the Liassic shales of the North Sea is sufficiently rich to be seen on the neutron log (**Figure 11.29**). The zone is characterized by an increase in the neutron log value associated with a corresponding increase in the bulk density (*see also* Section 11.7, Neutron-density combination).

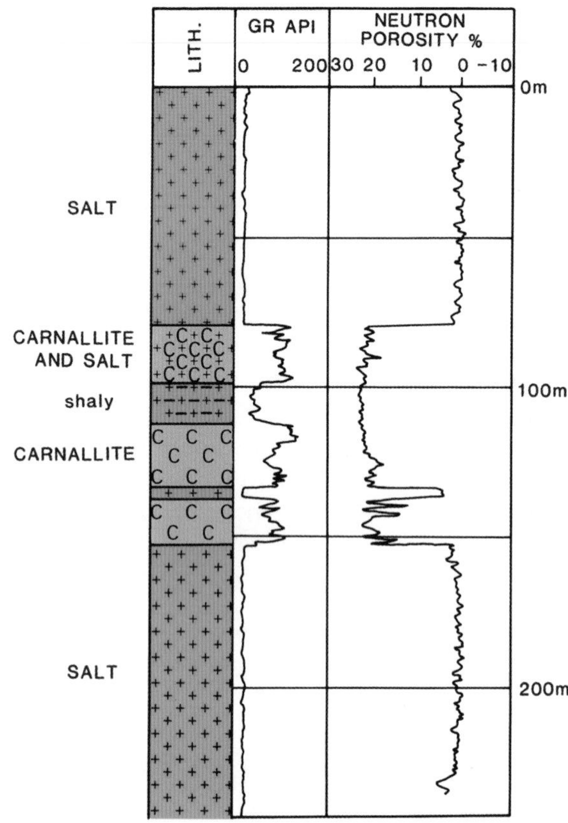

Figure 11.28 The hydrated evaporite carnallite ($KClMgCl_26H_2O$) identified on the neutron log by high values. The halite (salt) which accompanies the carnallite has a neutron value near zero.

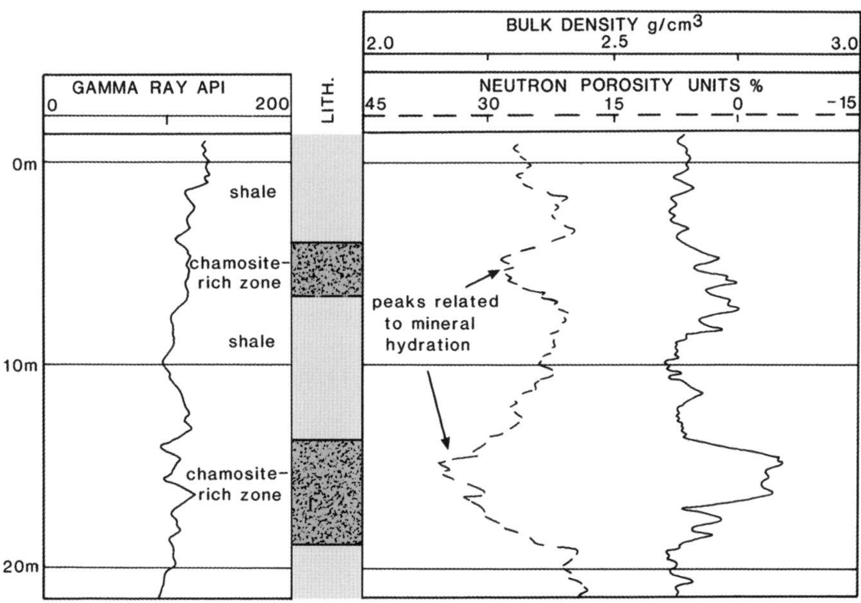

Figure 11.29 Chamosite, a hydrated iron mineral of formula $2SiO_2.Al_2O_33FeO.nH_2O$, causing high neutron values. Note the high density of the chamosite zone. Liassic, North Sea.

Volcanic and intrusive rocks

The neutron log is especially useful in the recognition of intrusive and volcanic rocks: most of these show high neutron log values and high densities (as in many shales) but are associated with low gamma ray values (unlike shales).

The high neutron log values in igneous rocks are due to their high content of chemically-bound water. The bound water may be original or associated with alteration products, mainly clay minerals, which result from the reaction of hydrothermal fluids with the original intruded rock. An example is shown of an altered diabase sill with no porosity (**Figure 11.30**). The neutron log is seen to be responding entirely to the bound water (1–4% by weight). The alteration products in this example are biotite, sericite, kaolinite, montmorillonite and chlorite, all of which themselves have varying amounts of water (**Table 11.8**) (Nelson and Glenn 1975; Millward *et al* 2002).

A series of basalt flows from the Middle Jurassic of the North Sea also show high neutron values, here diagnostically associated with low gamma ray readings and high densities (**Figure 11.31**). A characteristic profile of increasing values upwards is developed in the neutron log in each individual lava flow (**Figure 11.31**). The response appears to be typical of subaerial flows and is also seen in the Deccan traps of India (Buckley and Oliver, 1990). There are two possibilities. The first is that the log shape is related to alteration products, such as chlorite, which occur progressively towards the tops of the flows, and are formed during soil development and weathering, the water percolating downwards. The

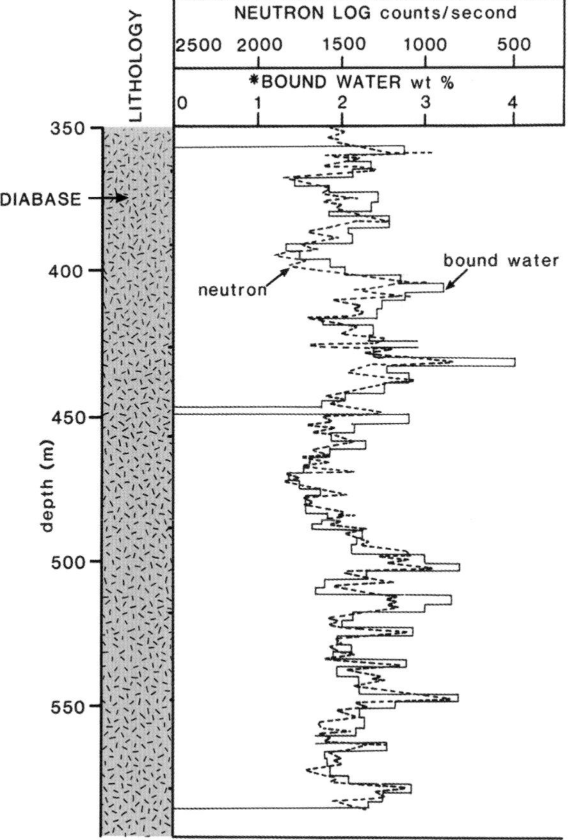

Figure 11.30 Neutron response to volcanic rocks with bound water: the example is of a diabase with 1–2% of sulphide mineralization. It has no porosity. *Bound water values from analyses of 10 ft (3 m) composites on pulp (re-drawn from Nelson and Glenn 1975).

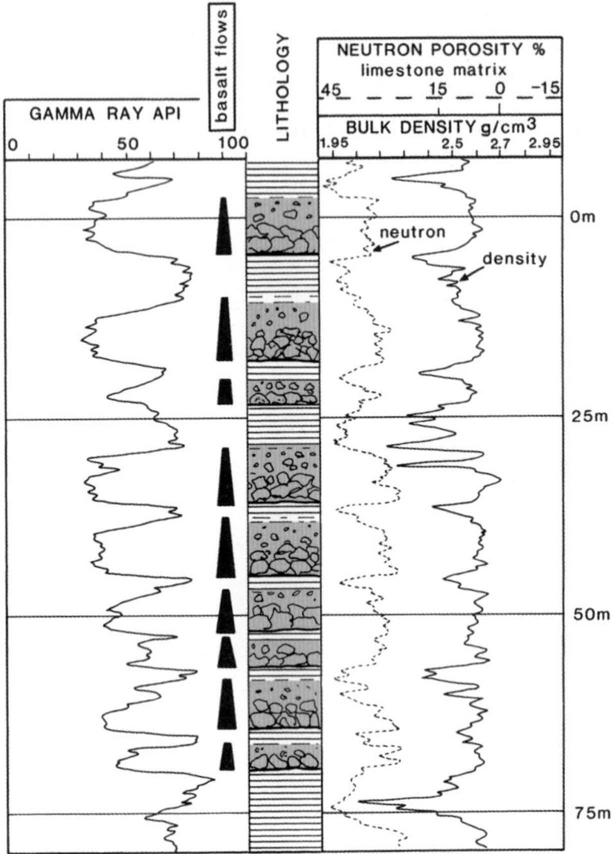

Figure 11.31 Neutron log response to basalt flows. The Jurassic age flows from the North Sea show low gamma ray and high neutron log values. The increasing-up neutron profile of each flow is characteristic. Flows are separated by soils.

second is that the shape is related to the increase in vesicles towards the top of a flow, either because the vesicles enclose water or water rich chemicals such as zeolites, derived from original fluids.

A more complex picture of the neutron log response in igneous rocks is seen in the work on oceanic basement basalts by the Ocean Drilling Project (ODP) (Brewer 2005). In this study, the neutron response is used to indicate the degree of alteration of the basalt by deriving porosity from the neutron response (similar to the case in **Figure 11.30**), but also exploring boron (B) and lithium (Li) concentration in the alteration products by calculating sigma (Σ) (**Figure 11.32**).

11.7 Neutron-density combination: lithology identification

Clean formations: matrix effects and porosity derivation

By themselves, both the neutron and the density log are difficult to use for gross lithology identification. However, once combined, they become probably the best available indicator for the reasons given below.

Both the neutron log and the density log should be showing the same formation parameter – porosity. Plotted on compatible porosity scales, they should give identical values and it should be possible to superimpose the two logs, as in the figure (**Figure 11.33**). In practice, this will only be the

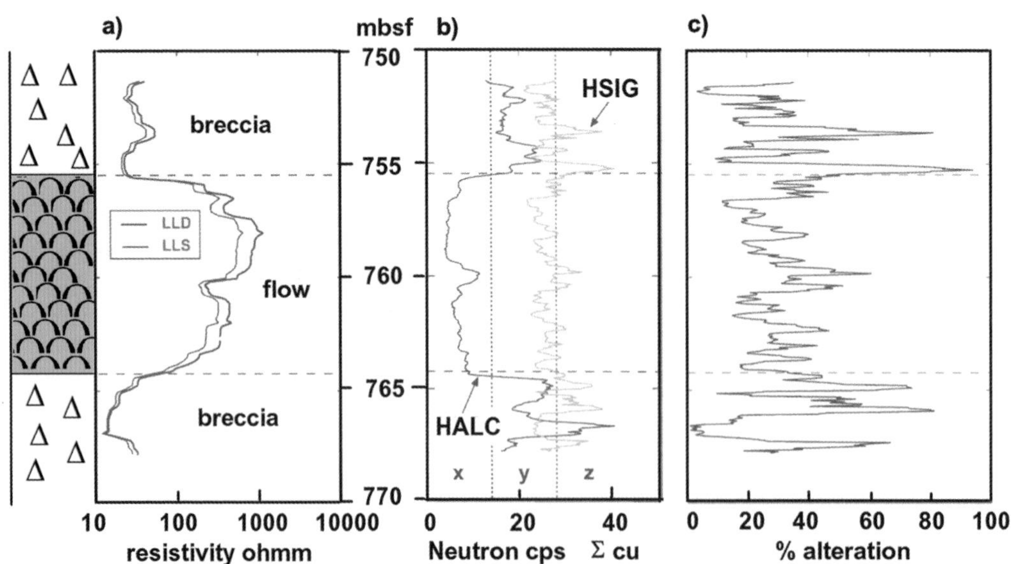

Figure 11.32 Oceanic basement explored using neutron log responses. HALC is the neutron response in counts per second. HSIG is sigma (Σ) in capture units. Alteration of the basalts is reflected in Σ as lithium and boron (both thermal neutron absorbers) become concentrated in alteration products (modified after Brewer *et al.* 2005).

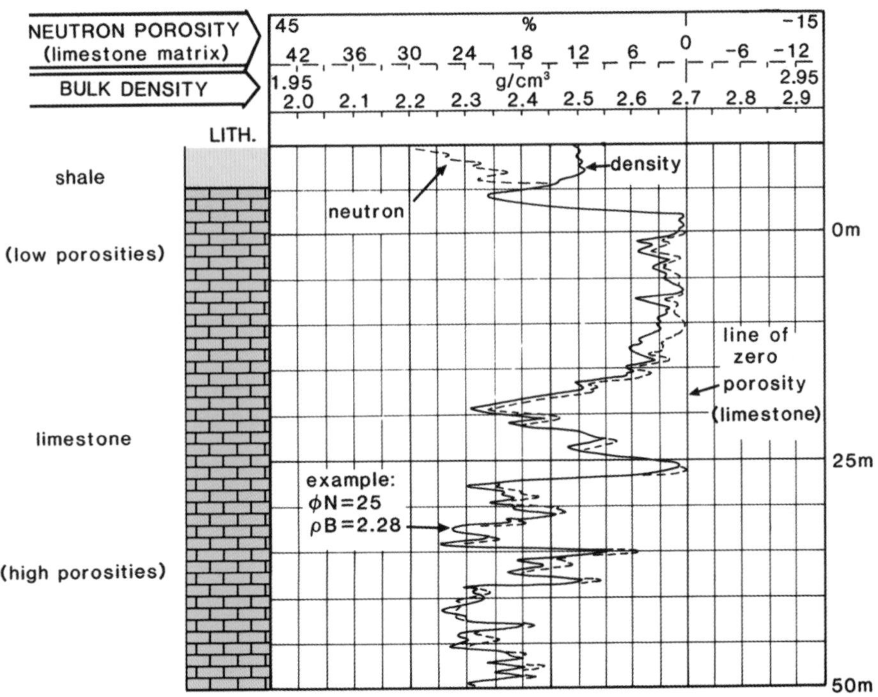

Figure 11.33 Neutron porosity log and bulk density log plotted on compatible scales. The neutron porosity is displayed with a scale for a limestone matrix (density matrix 2.70 g/cm³ = zero porosity). The two logs follow each other closely over the limestone interval. Example: ØN = 25%, Bulk density = 2.28 g/cm³ (*see* Figure 11.34 for cross-plot position).

case in clean, water-filled limestones, which give almost perfectly super-imposable logs, as shown (using limestone calibration, *see below*).

The explanations can be taken in two stages. Firstly, the scales of the two logs have been made compatible (in this case) on a clean limestone scale (i.e. limestone matrix). A neutron log value of zero (no porosity, 100% matrix) corresponds to a bulk density of 2.70 g/cm³ (the density of pure calcite is 2.71 g/cm³) and neutron value of 100 (100% fluid) corresponds to a density of 1.0 g/cm³ (the density of fresh water) (**Figure 11.33**). Using a cross-plot of density log values against neutron log values, instead of the log curves, the points from a clean limestone lithology (matrix) will plot on the straight, 'clean limestone' line (**Figure 11.34**). The position along the line corresponding to a particular limestone porosity.

The second stage of the explanation is that the straight line relationship only holds good for clean water-filled limestones, because matrix materials have variable effects on both logs. A sandstone is seen differently from a limestone on the density log because of a different matrix density (Chapter 10) and on the neutron log because of the different matrix effects. On the neutron-density cross-plot, the 'clean sandstone line' plots as shown on **Figure 11.34**. Again, a point on this line corresponds to a clean sandstone with a particular porosity. In the same way, a 'clean-dolomite line' may also be constructed (**Figure 11.34**). (These are actually lines of density, the 'sand line' being 2.65 g/cm³, the 'limestone line' 2.71 g/cm³ and the 'dolomite line' being 2.87 g/cm³).

Combining the neutron and density responses has for a long time been one of the principal and standard ways of deriving porosity. The rationale is that the two readings combined are better than just one. Even so, some operators prefer to use the density log alone, because the density tool response is more consistent and predictable than the response of the neutron tool, as well as having better vertical resolution than most neutron tools (Chapter 10).

Besides porosity, for logs plotted on compatible scales, variations in matrix translate into a separation of the curves. It is this that is used for lithology (matrix) identification (**Figure 11.35**). A clean limestone shows no curve separation, whatever the porosity. A clean sandstone shows a slightly negative curve separation of about 5% neutron porosity units (also called a cross-over), the density log plotting to the left of the neutron. A clean dolomite shows a positive separation so the density plots to the right of the neutron (**Figure 11.35**). For a constant matrix type, the absolute values will change with variations in porosity, but the separation will remain more or less constant (e.g. **Figure 11.34**).

These characteristic separations are a quick and generally reliable way of assigning matrix lithology. One needs to be wary, however, as (noted previously) some operators (especially in N. America) set the neu-

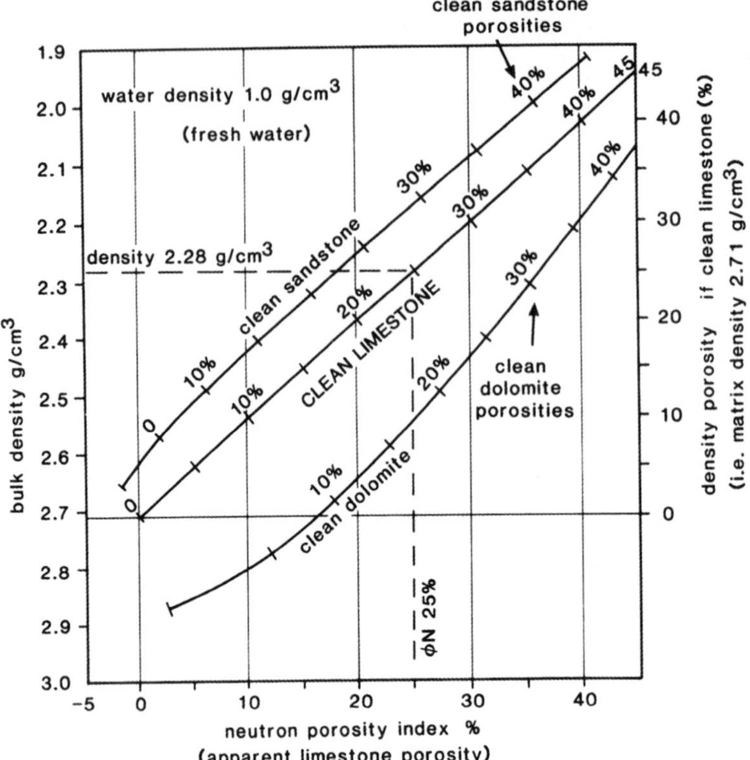

Figure 11.34 The density-neutron cross-plot. The plot is necessary to find real, clean formation porosities because of the differing effects of matrix type on the two logs (*see* text). Example: density 2.28 g/cm³, (ØN = 25%: real porosity 25%, lithology clean limestone cf. Figure 11.33). Cross-plot for Schlumberger FDC-CNL logs in fresh water-filled sandstone (plot from Schlumberger 1979).

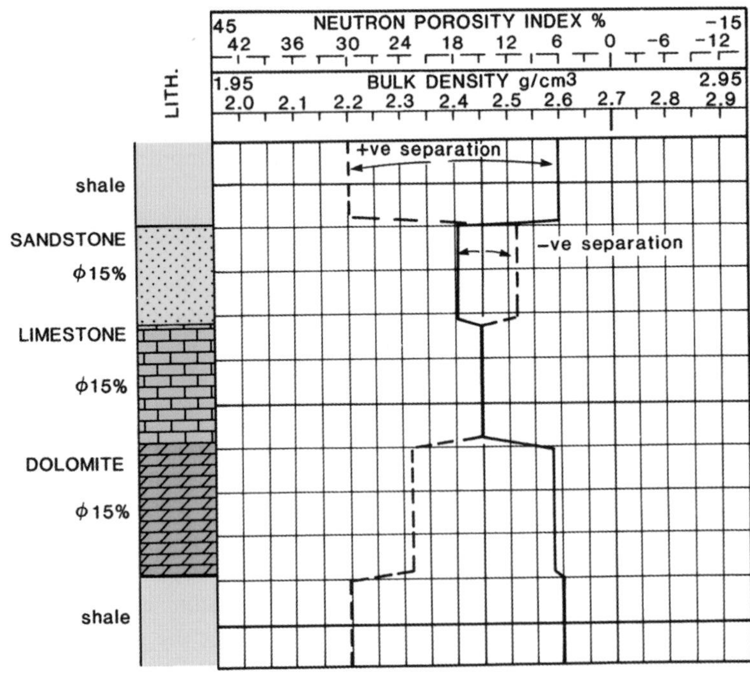

Figure 11.35 Idealised neutron-density log combination responses. The figure shows clean, sandstone, limestone and dolomite, all with 15% water-filled porosity. Limestone matrix scale.

tron tool up to read the true porosity in water bearing *sandstones* (with a matrix density of 2.65 g/cm³). If this has been done, the curves will overlay in clean, water bearing sandstones and use the default scale of 0% neutron porosity equivalent to 2.65 g/cm³ (quartz) density. Limestones will then have a characteristic response with the density plotting about 5% neutron porosity units to the left of the neutron curve.

Shale and shaly formations and shale volume derivation

Clean formations and the ideal reactions described above form the minority of cases. Shale is usually present. Pure shale is recognised on the neutron-density curve combination when the neutron value is high relative to the density value. It creates a large, positive separation on the logs, and the neutron plots well to the left of the density. This separation is typical and diagnostic (**Figure 11.35**) and is due to the high hydrogen index

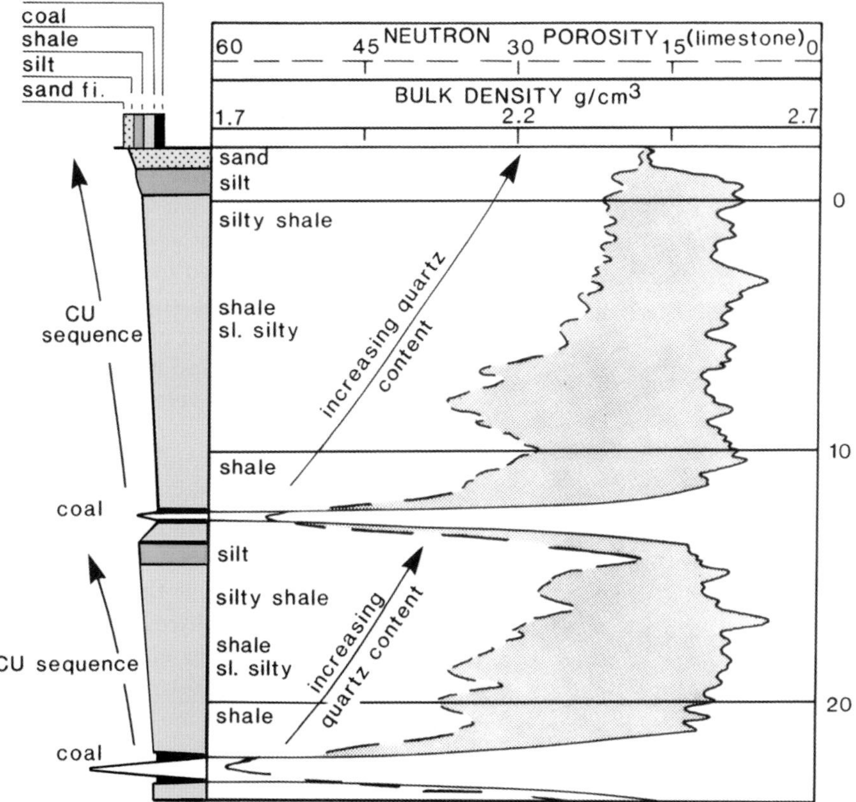

Figure 11.36 Changes in the neutron-density combination separation due to changes in quartz-clay admixture. In the two coarsening-up, deltaic sequences shown, the quartz content increases upwards relative to the shale. The separation changes are due mainly to the changes in neutron value (compare Figure 11.25).

of shale matrix material and high density of some clay minerals (*see* Neutron log in shales *above*).

If shale becomes diluted by matrix grains such as quartz or calcite with low hydrogen indexes (**Table 11.7**), the neutron log value decreases rapidly. Such a change is not seen so markedly on the density log since the matrix density of shales (2.65–2.7 g/cm^3) is similar to that of quartz and calcite (2.65–2.71 g/cm^3). On the neutron-density log combination, however, the result is a decrease in the log separation. The decrease continues until clean formation values are reached, as shown by the example of the two cleaning-up (coarsening-up) sand-shale sequences (**Figure 11.36**).

The change in response from pure shale to clean formation in the example is progressive, the volume of shale gradually decreasing. The relationship can be considered as roughly linear and means that, qualitatively, large or small separations can be considered to indicate more or less shale (**Figure 11.36**). That is, when the curves are widely separated, there is more shale and when they are close together, there is less shale. In practice, small separations indicating slightly shaly formations (or silt) tend to have low neutron values and a high density, while pure shales have high neutron values with moderate density and a large positive separation. The result is that cleaning-up (or coarsening-up) sequences form a typical 'hook' or 'crescent' shape on a neutron-density cross-plot **(Figures 12.18,19).**

The volume of shale may be derived quantitatively from the combined neutron and density measurements. The accepted technique is to identify a 'shale point' which corresponds to the readings of the two logs in a pure shale (**Figure 12.16**). The individual neutron and density values of the shale point are then used in algorithms, where end member values for constituents are required (Chapter 12, Section 12.6, Cross-plotting compatible logs). The other end members are typically, as a minimum, matrix and fluid. For quantification, therefore, a shaly rock is simplified down to three constituents, matrix, shale and fluid (porosity), the combined neutron-density response providing the shale value. As discussed, separating the neutron response to porosity from its response to shales in shaly formations can be very difficult (**Figure 11.18**) and prevents the neutron alone from being used for porosity in such cases. However, by combining the neutron and density values, there is the potential to separate the shale effect, and the method described above allows it to be quantified. However, because of the variable neutron response to shales, which depends on both neutron tool type and

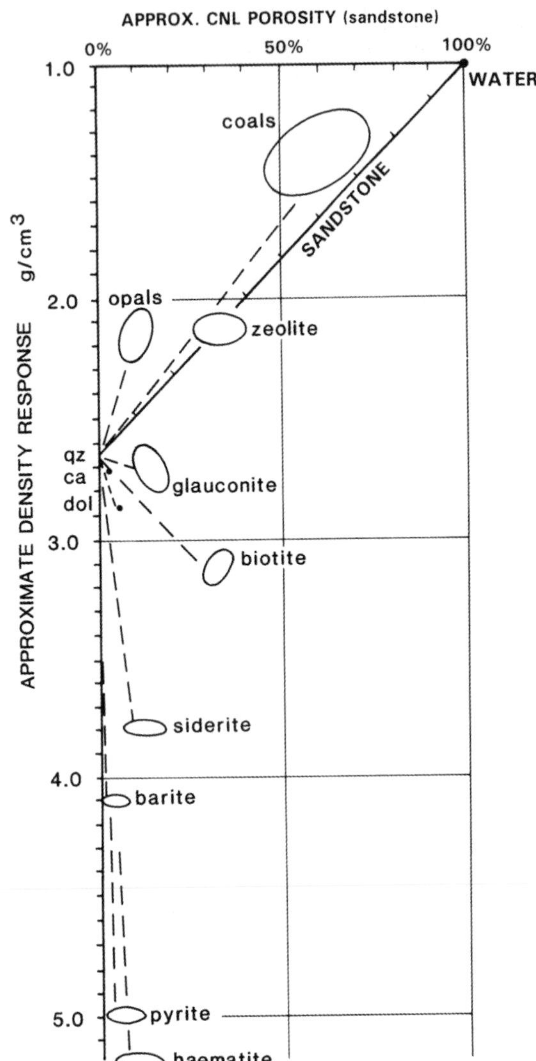

Figure 11.37 Neutron-density cross-plot with tentative locations of some zero-porosity, non-quartz materials (modified from Ransom 1977).

shale mineralogy, the quantitative method should be combined with other shale volume estimates, such as from the gamma ray, for verification.

Used properly, the neutron-density combination is a good log indicator of shale content. It gives another estimation, rather than just using the gamma ray log alone, and can be used to evaluate the degree of shaliness. The separation may even become a value itself, which is sometimes called the N-D log. Presented in this format, the N-D log can be used to indicate shaliness, and also reservoir quality in the clean zones. However, it should be noted that a particular separation between the two curves does not have a unique explanation. For example, curves that overlay may indicate a limestone, but may also indicate a shaly sandstone in which the shale volume is just sufficient to move curves until they are together. As always, supporting information from other logs or other data should be used.

Distinctive lithologies and minerals

Certain minerals and some less common lithologies have very distinctive neutron and density values and show unusual neutron-density separations on log plots. Some of these are shown graphically on the neutron-density cross-plot grid (**Figure 11.37**). This figure shows clearly that on log plots some of these responses will be very distinctive and can be diagnostic. Coals, for example, are easily recognised from their very marked neutron-density response of unusually low density combined with unusually high neutron values (**Figure 11.36**). Pyrite, haematite and to some extent siderite, are recognised as having very high density values with zero neutron response.

A further, interesting example underlines the use of the combined neutron-density response. On log plots, both the density and the neutron log generally 'track each other', a higher density corresponding to a lower neutron-log value. Both responses are reacting to porosity changes as discussed. When a very high density value corresponds to an even higher neutron log value, a simple porosity explanation is not possible. This is exactly the case with the chamosite beds common in the Liassic of the northern North Sea (**Figure 11.29**). The high neutron log values are caused by the chemically-bound water in the chamosite (an hydrated iron mineral), while the mineral itself has a high density (3.03 g/cm^3). The large positive separation, even larger than the surrounding shales, is very typical of the chamosite. Other log responses are not diagnostic.

Evaporites

Evaporites are distinctive from their neutron-density responses. Since their densities (Section 10.6, Mineral identification) and also their hydrogen indexes are diagnostic (*see above,* Evaporites), evaporites become very distinct on the combination of both logs. The absolute values of each log and the log separation all become indicative (**Figure 11.38**).

Gas hydrates

The hydrogen index of pure methane hydrate (CH_4.$(H_20)_6$, is 1.06 (Murray 2005) so there is no gas effect. Since the density of hydrate is close to that of water (0.91 gcm^3), it means that hydrates cannot be identified from their neutron and density characteristics (**Figure 11.39**). Hydrates are best identified using acoustic and resistivity properties (Chapter 9).

11.8 Gamma-Neutron Tools

All the tools discussed in this chapter bombard the formation with neutrons and then measure the count-rate(s) of neutrons that have been scattered back to the tool. The earliest neutron tools bombarded the formation with neutrons and counted the gamma rays that were produced when the neutrons were captured. The two types of measurement actually give similar results

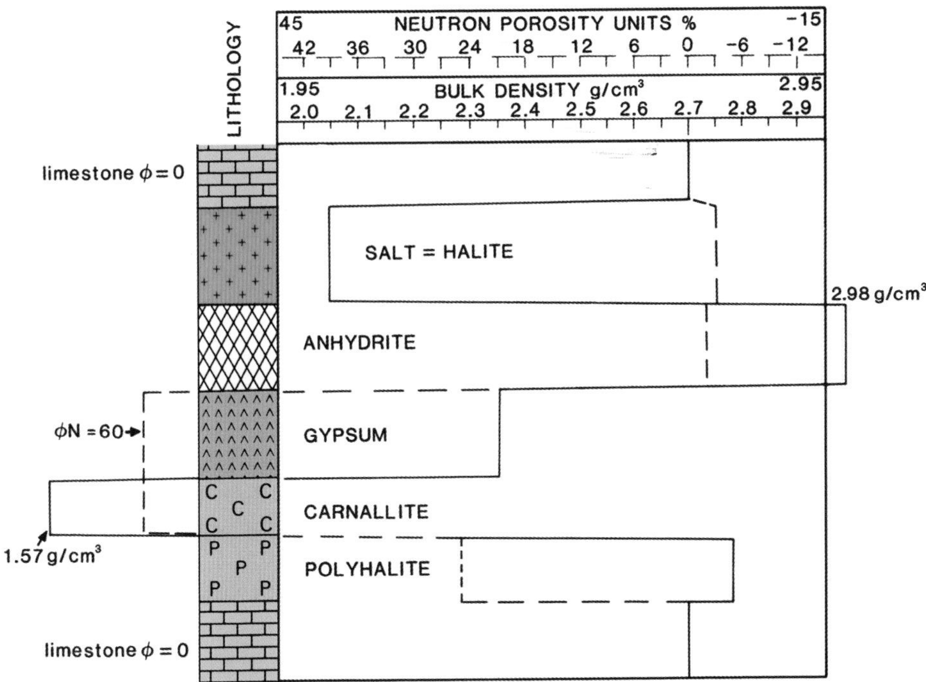

Figure 11.38 Idealized neutron-density log, combination responses in a series of pure evaporites (for FDC-CNL Schlumberger. Figures from Edmundson and Raymer 1979).

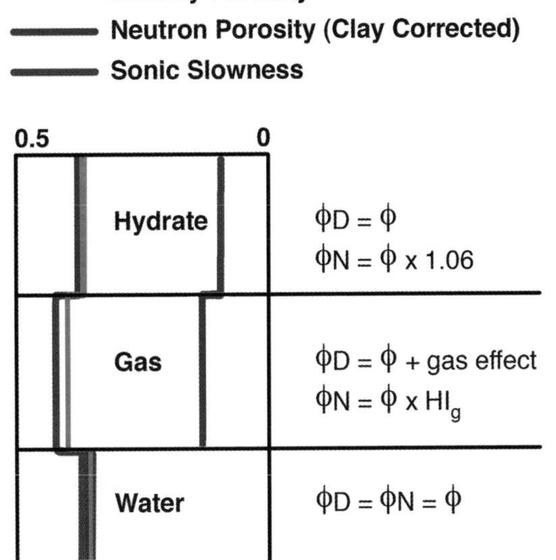

Figure 11.39 The characteristics of methane gas hydrate on neutron, density and sonic logs. HI_g = hydrogen index gas, Ø = porosity (modified after Murray *et al.* SPWLA 2005).

because the scattering and slowing down processes are the same for both types of tool. The simple gamma-neutron tools fell out of favour because the final neutron capture process was less reliable than simply counting neutrons. Nevertheless, they are still used as a relatively inexpensive tool for monitoring gas-water contact movement in producing wells (this application does not need an accurate measurement of hydrogen index, since a large change marks the position of the contact).

The gamma-neutron principle has evolved into two different types of tool, neither of which is intended to measure hydrogen index. These tools are:

– Gamma-Spectroscopy or Geochemical tools
– Neutron Lifetime Logs

The latter are designed primarily to measure water saturation behind casing, their principal application being to measure water movement in producing fields. Cased holes are not the subject of this book.

The geochemical tools basically perform a quantitative analysis of a number of key elements that are found in silicate and carbonate rocks and the fluids they contain. The current list of elements that can be determined by geochemical tools are: H, C, O, Si, S, Cl, Ca, Ti, Fe and Gd. If a natural spectral gamma-tool is run in combination, K, Th and U can be added to this list. The output from these tools is a set of elemental yields giving the relative amount of each type of element as a function of depth.

There are a few key elements missing from this list, which it would be nice to determine but, on the whole, it includes most of the elements that make up the Earth's crust. Knowing the elemental abundances that can be measured with these tools can be sufficient to determine the mineralogy at each depth. Even when this is not the case, geological insight can eliminate some combinations of minerals that mathematically fit the observed elemental abundances. Notable omissions from the list, however, are magnesium (Mg) and aluminium (Al), although recent improvements to the detectors means that Mg too can be analysed and, for example, limestone/dolomite ratios inferred. Aluminium is arguably the key omission since it is the defining constituent of the clay minerals. Although tools have been built that are sensitive to it, they rely on a Californium source, which is both expensive and relatively short lived. The geochemical tools are only briefly described.

All of the large logging contractors offer these types of tool, although there are many different types currently in service, which show major differences. The neutron source in some tools is the chemical type and in others it is a pulsed generator. There are pros and cons to both types of source, which are carefully listed on the contractors' web-sites (the reader is left to make up their own mind). The heart of the tool is a gamma ray detector which is very similar to that used in Natural Gamma Spectroscopy (NGS). In other words, the tool not only counts gamma rays but it measures their energy as well. At each depth a gamma ray spectrum is produced which is decomposed into the contributions from each element. This spectrum typically covers a range of energies from 1 to 8 MeV.

The first geochemical tools that appeared in the early 1980s were generally heavy, slow to run and not particularly accurate. Improvements in detectors and computing power, both downhole and at surface, have resulted in the present compact tools that can be combined with most other open hole logs.

There are a number of reactions between neutrons and the nuclei in the formation as described for the compensated neutron porosity tools. These fall into three classes: inelastic scattering; fast reactions; capture or thermal absorption (Section 11.2). To re-cap, inelastic scattering helps in the initial slowing down of fast neutrons, and thermal absorption is the process that ends most free neutrons' lives and was responsible for some of the problems caused by iron and other neutron absorbers. Fast reactions also result in the loss of free neutrons but as the name implies, they require high neutron energies to occur, and typically the target nucleus undergoes a significant change, such as the loss of an alpha particle. The interest in all these processes as the basis of a logging measurement is that they invariably result in a gamma ray with a very well defined energy. Sometimes the gamma ray is emitted almost instantaneously and sometimes a short period of time elapses before it is emitted.

Inelastic scattering reactions produce gamma rays almost instantaneously and the neutron collision excites the scattering nucleus which then returns to its ground state, emitting the characteristic gamma ray. The inelastic events are normally over within 50 μs of the neutrons entering the formation. The elements that can be determined using this process are C, O, Si, S, Ca and Fe.

Thermal absorption starts to occur as soon as the neutrons have been slowed down, but can continue as long as thermal neutrons are in the formation. So, if a pulsed neutron generator is used as the neutron source, gamma rays produced by thermal absorption can be distinguished by delaying the measurement of the spectrum. Elements that can be determined using thermal absorption are H, Si, S, Cl, Ca, Fe and Gd. Gadolinium (Gd) is a rare-earth element that is measured because it is such a strong absorber, rather than because it is a significant component of the crust. Since it can be accurately determined, a lot of research has been carried out to see if there are any consistent relationships with lithology or particular minerals.

Arguably the simplest of the geochemical tools is Schlumberger's Elemental Capture Sonde (ECS). This uses a chemical neutron source and has a single gamma ray detector, which is very similar to that used in the natural gamma spectroscopy tool. The tool uses thermal absorption of neutrons which have been slowed in exactly the same way(s) described for thermal neutron porosity tools. Because the source is continuously emitting neutrons, the tool cannot distinguish gamma rays produced by inelastic scattering and fast reactions from those produced by thermal absorption. Nevertheless it is quite capable of determining yields for Ca, Si, S, Fe, Ti, Gd (and possibly Mg).

More complex tools like the Baker Atlas FLEX™ tool and the Schlumberger RST use a pulsed neutron source and so can distinguish inelastic scattering from thermal absorption events. In particular they can quantify carbon and oxygen in the formation. This is of great interest because the carbon-oxygen ratio is related to the oil-water ratio. The precise relationship depends on the porosity and the lithology, because silicates contain oxygen and carbonates contain carbon and oxygen.

12 LITHOLOGY RECONSTRUCTION FROM LOGS

12.1 Introduction

There are two independent sources of lithology data available from oil wells, one set of data coming directly from the drilling and one set from geophysical logging, either LWD or/and wireline.

The drilling data consist of cuttings, cores and the recorded drilling parameters. The logging data consist of the LWD and wireline, geophysical log suites (Sidewall cores and pressure tests arguably fall between the two). For a reliable lithological reconstruction, both geophysical logs and the drill data are essential. As a result of the great sophistication of modern logs, the drill cuttings data are often neglected. This should never be the case: they provide the only continuous, physical sample of formation lithology.

This chapter describes ways of interpreting lithology from logs: by manual methods using log and drill data; by semi-automatic methods using mainly logs; and by fully automatic methods using only a computer manipulation of logs.

12.2 Subsurface lithology

Different lithologies

It is one of those odd facts that lithology, despite the apparent simplicity of the concept, means different things to different people, principally because their requirements are different. In general usage, lithology simply means the macroscopic physical character of a rock, which normally means the mineralogical composition of a rock but also includes texture and sedimentary make up. Sandstone, micaceous sandstone and shaly sandstone are all examples of lithology. So is coarse grained, poorly sorted sandstone. The petrophysicist wants the lithology in order to eliminate its effect on calculations; the geologist wants the lithology in order to interpret the depositional environment and help build a geological model. The petrophysicist needs a numerical representation of lithology and in considerable detail in order to use petrophysical formulae, but generally only over the reservoir sections; the geologist needs summary lithology, in moderate detail, to be able to identify sequences and formations but over the entire well; the stratigrapher and bio-stratigrapher also consider the entire well but in less detail; the seismic geophysicist requires only a summary, bulk lithology and the identification of critical surfaces. The needs are different; the lithologies are different. It is no good using a Formula 1 racing car to pull a plough: each lithology should be fit for purpose. A look at lithology for the geologist follows, but in no way forgets the petrophysicist.

Petrophysical (geophysical) lithology

The petrophysicist needs to put numbers on the volume and presence of hydrocarbons in the subsurface, the numbers on which investment decisions can be made: porosity and water saturation must be calculated. This is what logs were invented for and why they are especially sensitive to these particular rock properties. Evaluating lithology is incidental. One recent authoritative book refers to the effect of lithology on logs as a 'peturbation'! However, to properly evaluate the petrophysical properties from the logs, this 'peturbation', the lithological influence, must be evaluated.

To illustrate the point: the density log response is used to calculate porosity, but to get the required numbers, the petrophysicist must first quantify the formation (*i.e.* matrix) effect on the raw log value. That is, the lithology must be known. However, this is a numerical value, such as a matrix density of 2.68 gcm^3 (quartz) for a sandstone and not simply a geological lithology. Using figures such as this, the petrophysicist is able to calculate a formation represented by percentages of matrix and porosity. In this very simple case, for example, 80% is quartz, 20% is porosity (**Figure 12.26**). To the geologist such numbers do not represent a geological lithology.

Another limitation within which the petrophysicst works is that of logging tool bed resolution, a subject that has been mentioned frequently in previous pages. The petrophysicist will try to summarise geophysical properties down to the smallest bed that can reasonably be characterised and can be expected to contribute to hydrocarbon production. The effort is not to miss pay (**Figure 12.25**). Core is important, not for its lithological content but as a calibration for log calculations, to be able to physically measure, say, porosity and permeability, and then to compare these real, physical measurements to the log calculated numbers (**Figure 12.23**). This is why cores are taken. For the geologist, it is quite different.

Geological lithology

For a geologist, lithology is not defined by porosity and permeability. A sandstone is not 80% quartz, 20% porosity: it is a whole set of characteristics that can be seen at outcrop and in cores. A sandstone has grains of a certain size and shape, which are generally made of quartz but also of other minerals, organised in a certain texture, such as clay in the matrix or concentrated in layers, and has a characteristic internal structure. These allow the recognition of the mode of emplacement from which predictions can be made. In other words, it is composition, texture and sedimentary make up which form an entity (bed) distinct from that below and that above. For example, a sand deposited by a turbidity current will have (classically) a sharp base, internal grading (coarsest grains at the base, finest at the top) and a passage upwards into silt and shale above. The lithology and internal structure are related, and this is important for the geologist. The lithology is a consequence of the sedimentary make up.

The reality of a geological lithology, then, is not the same as a petrophysical lithology even though both start from the same basic concept. This chapter does not cover the 'lithological concerns' of the petrophysicist but instead covers methods of lithology interpretation for the geologist and casual log user. However, knowing the way a petrophysicist uses geophysical responses is essential and should influence their use by the geologist. The rest of this chapter, like the entire book, is written with the geologist in mind but with lessons taken from the petrophysical approach.

12.3 Lithology from drill data – the mud log

The mud log and the way in which it is made is described briefly below so that the data it represents can be used properly in log interpretation. As a geologist, I feel that data from the mud log is frequently under-utilised.

The mud log (a misnomer that has somehow stuck) is the geologist's record of the drilling of a well. Before wireline logging was invented, it was the only record that existed. On this log are recorded the lithology, the drilling rate, bit changes, gas record, dates, calcimetry, events and more (**Figure 12.1**). The drilled lithology description is based on a regular examination of *cuttings* – small chips broken off the formation as the drill advances. They are washed away in the stream of drilling mud flowing over the bit face and brought to the surface. They do not float in the mud but are entrained by friction and drag. At the surface, the drilling mud is

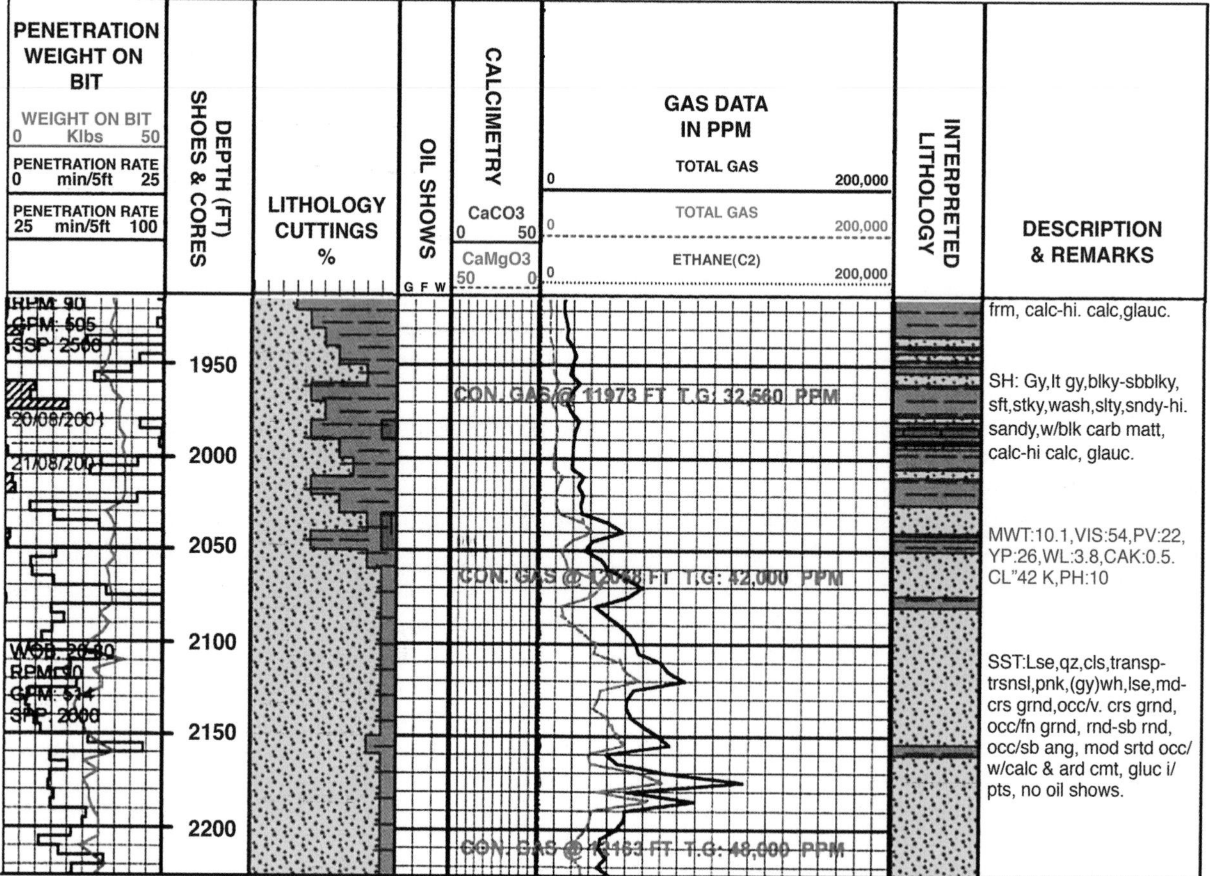

Figure 12.1 A typical mud log. The log is the well-site record of lithology (cuttings), selected drilling parameters and LWD logs (if run). In this example, there were no LWD logs and the lithology interpretation is based entirely on cuttings samples which were taken every 3.05 m (10 ft). Without logs, the detail of this interpretation is not reliable. Depths in feet.

passed through a large metal sieve, the 'shale shaker', and the cuttings are recovered. It is from the shale shaker that the geological cuttings sample is taken.

On the mud log, lithology is usually recorded as percentages of cuttings types in a particular sample, say, 10% sand and 90% brown shale. New samples are taken every 2 to 20 metres (6–60 ft), depending on the rate of drilling. Fast drilling rates of perhaps 1 minute per metre (3 ft/min) at the top of the hole allow only one sample to be taken every 20–25 m drilled (60–80 ft) (*i.e.* 1 sample per 20–25 minutes). At greater depths, rates of 30 minutes to drill 1 metre (3 ft) of formation are common, and a sample can be taken every 2 metres (6 ft) (i.e. 1 sample per hour) or even closer.

To construct the mud log as a depth (driller's) record, the time it takes a sample to reach the surface after being cut, the 'lag time', must be calculated. A sample drilled at 3000 m (10,000 ft) will take perhaps 1 hour and 10 minutes to reach the surface. It will be travelling at 43 metres per minute (140 ft/min) up the hole (about 2.6 km/h, 1.6 mi/hr), the exact rate depending on the rate at which the mud is 'circulated', that is, pumped through the mud system. The drilling rate is used as one of the basic curves on the mud log (**Figure 12.1**) and is presented as real depth. A metre drilled is instantly recorded, but the lithology corresponding only appears much later so that for the example above at 3000 m–3002 m, the sample will only be recovered at the surface, 1 hour and 10 minutes after it has been drilled.

The same principle of lag time is applied to gas readings and to 'shows' as to cuttings.

On mud logs, the geologist may record not only an analysis of the percentages of the cutting types present, but also what this means in terms of real subsurface lithology. For instance, if a sand-shale sequence is being drilled, these lithologies become 'smeared' while travelling to the surface. In the cuttings sample will be seen 50% shale, 40% sandstone and 10% calcareous shale. The geologist will then make a 'guess' (when there are no LWD logs) at the real lithological column using the drilling rate, knowing that shales will drill slowly, porous sandstones faster (**Figure 12.1**). When there are LWD logs, interpretation can be log based.

There are occasions when the drilling rate log is comparable to a subsequently run sonic log or a gamma ray log (**Figure 12.2**) and a good interpretation of bed boundaries can been made from it. However, in general, the drilling rate involves too many variables, such as weight on the bit, bit wear, pump rates and so on, for it to be an accurate bed boundary indicator. Lithological beds interpreted from only the mud log should not be used when LWD logs, or eventually wireline logs, are available.

It is important, then, to use the cuttings percentages in the right manner. As described previously, a rock cutting from 3000 m (10,000 ft) takes over one hour to reach the surface. During this time it becomes mixed with other cuttings from shallower depths but moving more slowly up the hole, mixed with chips washed from the well walls higher up the hole, so-called 'cavings', so that by the time it reaches the surface, the original cutting will be mixed with other cuttings not representative of the newly drilled formation (**Figure 12.1**). An experienced rig geologist will usually recognise cavings and eliminate them from his count. But there is always a mixture of cuttings from various lithologies, which is why percentages are recorded. All lithological boundaries have become very blurred.

When interpreting the cuttings logs, it is the *appearance* of a new lithology which is significant along with associated drilling parameters. For example, when drilling from a thick shale into a thick sandstone, as the sandstone bed is actually penetrated, only a small percentage of the cuttings will be the new (sand) lithology. This increases, but there may only be a recognisable percentage of sandstone cuttings some metres lower. Along with the first appearance of a new lithology, the drilling rate may change, a so-called 'drilling break', which marks the actual lithological change. A drilling break, of course, occurs before a cuttings sample is seen at the surface and even before LWD logs can make their measurements. Gas levels may also change.

Clearly, the difficulty of interpreting lithology while drilling was one of the reasons for developing LWD logs. These can be available to the geologist in a matter of minutes after drilling (Chapter 1) and geophysical log interpretation (Section 12.5) can begin immediately, so that some of the comments in this section 12.3 can be ignored.

Some pitfalls

Some types of drill-bit are especially designed to grind the rock rather than scour it. As a result, instead of producing cuttings, the rock is turned into an ultra fine-grained material called 'rock flour', from which very little lithology can be identified.

Certain lithologies are notorious for appearing on logs, but not in the cuttings samples. Such is the case for loose sands, silts and soluble evaporites such as salt.

The mesh of the shale shaker sieve is such that loose grains of sand or silt, even coarse sand, will pass through. If this is suspected, the mud may be diverted through de-sanders, where all small grains are extracted. However, de-sanding is not routine and there are many cases where unconsolidated sand reservoirs have been drilled and shale has been recorded on the mud log! Salt is a very similar case. Unless the drilling mud is salt-saturated, no cuttings will be found on the surface. Shale, mostly cavings, will be recorded. An experienced rig geologist, however, will note mud salinity changes along with drilling-rate indications which suggest the presence of salt.

The exact opposite situation exists where lithologies

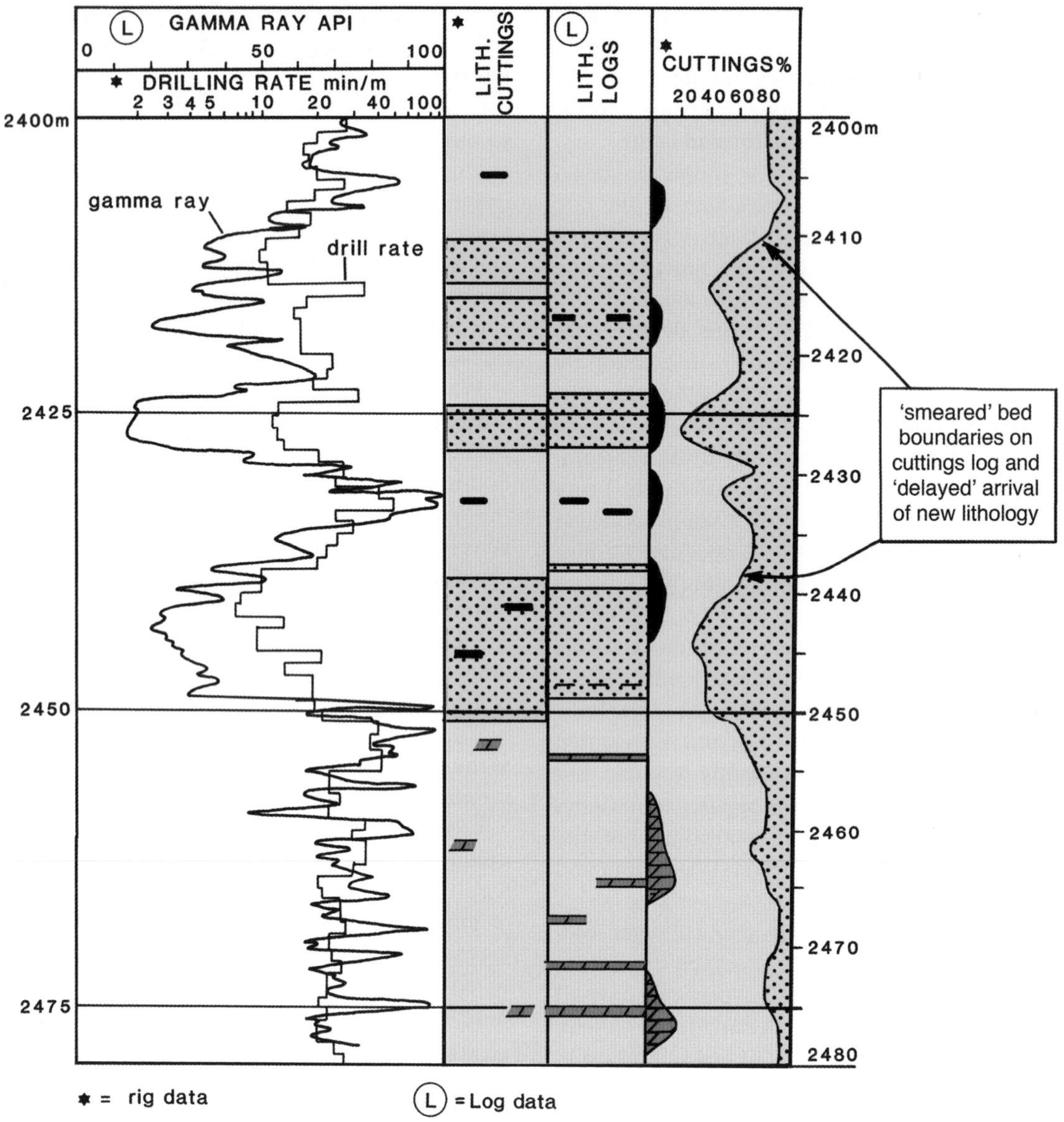

Figure 12.2 Comparison between rig-derived lithology interpretation and subsequent log interpretation. Note the effect of the arrival of a new lithology on the cuttings percentages. Without logs, the rig bed boundaries are only a 'good guess'.

which appear on the mud log do not actually occur in the formation. A typical case is when lignosulphonate, a mud additive which reduces water loss, is used over long shale sections. Lignosulphonate resembles lignite and is frequently interpreted as coal on the mud logs. Coal interpreted over pure shale sections is suspect since real coals mostly occur in zones where both sand and shale occur. If LWD logs are available these described difficulties will, of course, be avoided.

Even with LWD logs, though, the mud log is still important. As stated previously, it represents the only continuous physical record of formation lithology (except where cores exist: *see below)* and is essential to validate interpretations based on subsequent LWD or wireline geophysical logs (Sections 12.5–12.7).

12.4 Lithology from cores – direct physical sampling

Conventional cores are cut during drilling, when a continuous, cylindrical sample of the formation is recovered: it represents a significant volume of the borehole. But conventional cores are taken 'blind', that is, they are taken with no knowledge of the formation that will be recovered. Coring may start too late or end too soon. Post-drilling, once the hole exists, only very small cores may be taken from the borehole wall, although importantly their depths can now be chosen.

Cores cut during drilling (conventional cores)

During drilling and before wireline, or even LWD logging, when a complete record of lithology is required (for example, in a reservoir), a continuous sample is taken by conventional coring. The drill bit is replaced by a core barrel and the sample cut. The retrieved core, depending on the preceding hole size, will be a cylinder of rock 2–15 cm (0.75–6 in) in diameter and up to 60 m (200 ft) long (Blackbourn 1990, 2009). It is an actual physical sample of the formation.

Being the actual formation, a core appears to need no interpretation, especially of the lithology. In fact, the reverse is true: cores should be used as a reference lithology to compare with the lithology interpreted from the logs. Indeed, such comparisons are used frequently through this book: they are essential to a proper understanding of the capabilities of logs, even the image logs. Cores provide the geologist with the only record of real subsurface lithology, the so-called 'ground truth'.

But before they can be used to compare to logs, cores need processing, the primary problem being one of depth. Cores are cut during drilling so that they are referenced to driller's depth (**Figure 12.3**). Frequently these depths do not agree with the depths shown on subsequent wireline logs (that is logger's depths). A reference depth must be decided upon and for simplicity this may be from just one log, such as the wireline density. Core depths (driller's) must then be adjusted to log depths. These shifts, when wireline depths are chosen as a reference, are often around ±5 m (16 ft) but may be as much as ±15 m (45 ft).

Because of recovery problems, different depth shifts between contiguous cores are frequent and shifts are valid for only one core at a time. Different depth shifts are even seen within single cores when working with more detailed logs, such as the electrical image logs (Chapter 15). These are minor differences and are due to the core itself, where there may be losses in friable or broken zones, or to the wireline tool, where minor sticking and cable stretch can cause depth variations. A perfect match at fine scales is often very difficult to achieve.

Even with the core depths perfectly matched to the log depth, inconsistencies between the two may still arise. It is at this point that the capabilities of the logging tools emerge. The problems of bed definition (Chapter 2) become clear (**Figure 12.3**), as do those of depth of investigation (also Chapter 2) and what this implies in terms of the volume of rock sampled by the log (Passey *et al.* 2006). In extremely heterogeneous formations, for example, the directional tools such as the density may be difficult to calibrate because of changes across the small distance between the core and the borehole wall. These particular problems are discussed in the chapters on individual tools, especially the imaging tools (*see* Section 15.5).

For effective core to log comparisons and for a record that can be archived, core lithology needs to be captured digitally. There are three ways: by digital core drawing

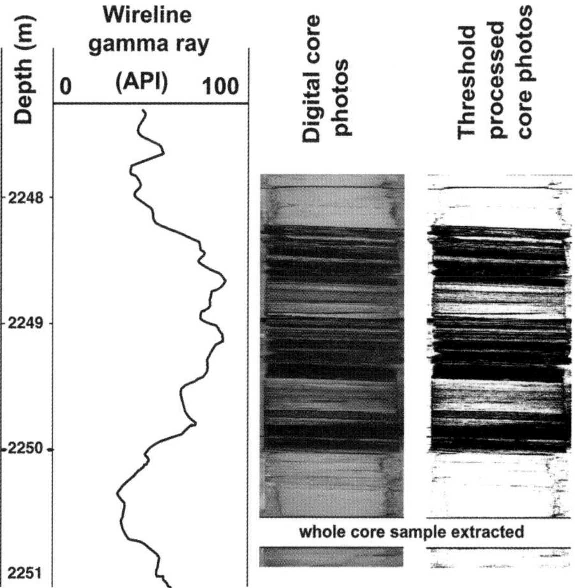

Figure 12.3 Digital core photos compared to a standard gamma ray. The example shows the limited bed resolution of the logs; they cannot show the fine detail. Even the simplification of the photos using a threshold format, where notionally white is sand and black is shale, is beyond the log.

methods, by scanning manual core descriptions or by using digital core photos. Additionally, current 'best practice' involves digitally coding the lithology and other descriptors which can be directly integrated with log data, and provides a powerful interpretation tool.

Digital drawing methods use software techniques from the outset: lithology is drawn on screen and furnished with digital symbols (and colour), digital grain size, digital structures and so on (**Figure 12.4**). The outcome can then be displayed at any scale at will and in any combination of detail. The more traditional, older method is to manually describe the core lithology, grain size and structures, and then scan this graphic log so that it can be integrated into the database and displayed at various scales (**Figure 12.4**). However, because this is a scanned image changing scale, especially when symbols are used, is not very successful, but it does allow the geologist to use any method he or she prefers.

The final method is to use the core photos. This does not replace a core description but it does allow examination of core and log at the same time. Although most core photos are digital and can be viewed on screen, a significant and very useful advance is the rendering of an entire core into a single strip of high quality digital photo image that can be digitally re-processed and then displayed alongside the logs themselves (**Figure 12.3**). Such photos are now publically available online (i.e. npd.no\)

The core-derived lithology is generally combined

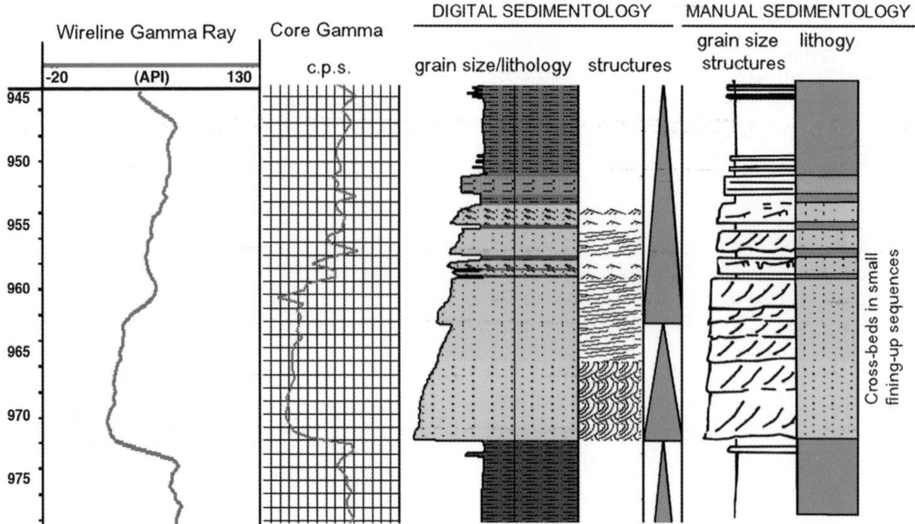

Figure 12.4 Digital drawing of core sedimentology compared to the traditional, manual method. The digital routine used WellCad software. The manual routine was simply scanned. Core Gamma c. p. s. = counts per second.

with the sedimentological record and should bring the natural detail of a core down to a manageable level for use. A scale of 1:50 is frequent or, if necessary, 1:20 (**Figures 12.4, 12.5**). Sedimentological, reservoir and calibration studies can be carried out at these scales and the natural lithological detail of the core maintained despite the 50% or 20% decrease in scale. However, the detail should not be 'mimicked' by a sedimentological log but be a stylised representation, an implied interpretation having been made, which is why digital photos still need an interpretation. Such sedimentological generalisation is a skill learned through experience and the result should be a clear, concise and accurate representation.These detailed core records can be used for reservoir studies and for comparisons to image logs. For general stratigraphical work, a much larger scale is used and a hardcopy completion log at a 1:500 scale is common. In this case core detail is discarded; 20 m (60 ft) of core is represented by only 4 cm (2") on a hardcopy 1:500 log, so that considerable lithological generalisation is

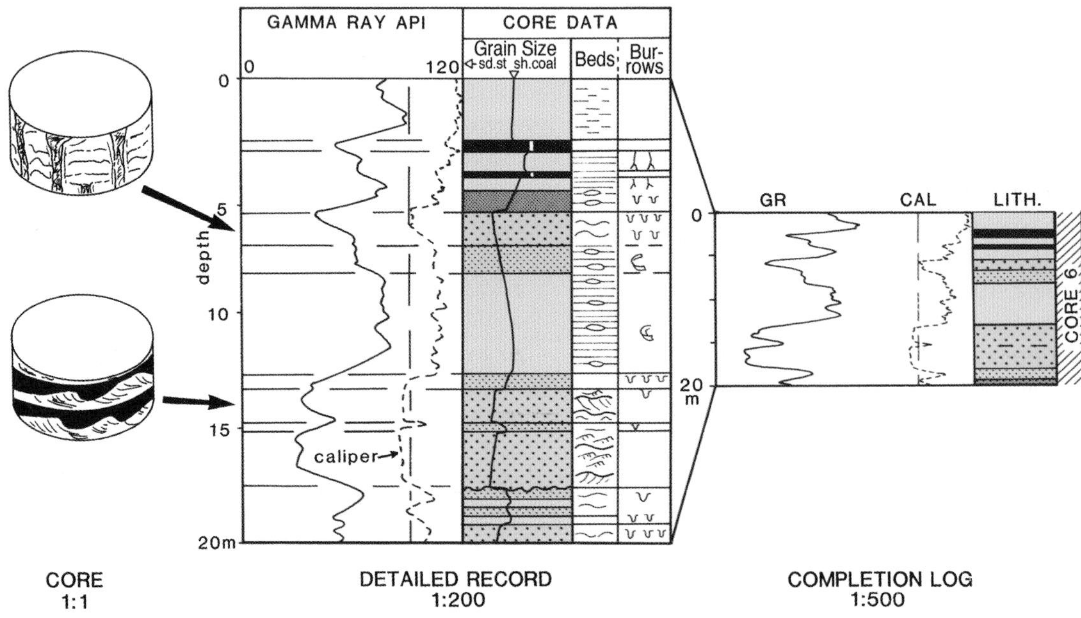

Figure 12.5 The lithological record of cores cut while drilling. The natural detail of a core is 'generalised' on the sedimentological log at 1:200, reservoir scale (c.f. Figure 12.3). This detail is generalised to summary lithology only at 1:500 final log scale.

Table 12.1 Wireline sidewall coring tools.

Tool type	Name	Acronym	Sample number	Company
Percussion tools	Chronological Sample Taker	CST	up to 50	Schlumberger
	Sidewall Coregun	SWC	25 (each gun)	Baker Hughes™
	Sidewall Coregun	SWC		Halliburton
Rotary tools	Mechanical Sidewall Coring Tool	MSCT	20 (up to 50)	Schlumberger
	Rotary Sidewall Coring	RCOR™	30	Baker Hughes™
	Rotary Sidewall Coring Tool	RSCT		Halliburton

necessary, the core being represented only by a more precise and accurate lithology (**Figure 12.5**) (Blackbourn 1990, 2009).

Cores cut after drilling (sidewall cores)

Two principal methods, percussion sidewall coring and rotary sidewall coring, are used to obtain very small, limited core samples once a hole has been drilled and logged. Both methods involve cutting into the borehole wall and both tools are wireline conveyed **(Table 12.1).**

Percussion sidewall coring is still used. A sidewall 'gun' is lowered into the hole on the logging cable: it consists of a series of hollow cylindrical 'bullets' 1.8 cm (0.7 in) in diameter and 2.0–3.0 cm (0.8–1.2 in) long (**Figure 12.6**). The 'bullets' are arranged in series along the sidewall tool and attached to it by retainer wires. There are typically 25 bullets per gun (**Table 12.1**). The tool is run to total depth, depth-calibrated with a gamma ray tool on the gun, and then pulled up the hole. The sampling points are decided in advance and are based on an inspection of the logs previously run. When a sampling point is reached, the sidewall tool is stopped at exactly the depth chosen and a 'bullet' is fired. A small directional charge shoots the hollow steel sidewall bullet into the formation wall, which it penetrates by force. As the tool is moved upwards to the next location, the retaining wires pull the bullet out of the formation. The sample that the sidewall gun recovers can be, as indicated, about 1.8 cm (0.7 in) in diameter and up to 3 cm (1.2 in) long. This sample is a reliable indicator of lithology (depending on the accuracy of the depth calibration) but, because of the sampling method, the rock is frequently shattered, meaning that petrophysical characteristics and texture are destroyed. Porosity measurements should not be made on percussion sidewall cores. They can be used in mineralogical analysis, biostratigraphic dating and source rock studies.

The rotary sidewall core tool actually drills into the borehole wall to take the sample. The drilled sample is approximately the same size as a conventional core plug, that is, 2.5 cm (1 in) diameter with a possible length of 4.5–5 cm (1.75–2 in). The tool can take 20 (MSCT Schlumberger) or 30 (RCOR™ Baker, RCST Halliburton) samples each trip **(Table 12.1)**. Rotary sidewall coring is most effective in hard formations and the samples can be analysed for porosity and permeability in the same way as conventional core plugs (Luthi 2001). The use of this tool is becoming more common and in certain jurisdictions is now largely replacing the older percussion method.

Sidewall coring as a method of lithology sampling should be used with care. As the sample is so small, interpretation problems can easily arise. For example, in thin-bedded turbidites when clean shale and clean sand are interlaminated (**Figure 12.3**), a sidewall core may fall entirely within a shale lamina and will not be representative of the zone as a whole. For this reason, in reservoirs, a closely-set series of samples is taken. The obvious advantage of a sidewall core, however, is that its wireline log depth is known and it can be taken in a specific, chosen lithology.

12.5 Manual lithology interpretation from logs (qualitative)

Display routines

Modern on-screen colour log displays can be used to aid qualitative lithological interpretations. A gamma ray curve, for example, can be plotted simply as a curve, shaded to a constant (i.e. cut-off), colour coded to the

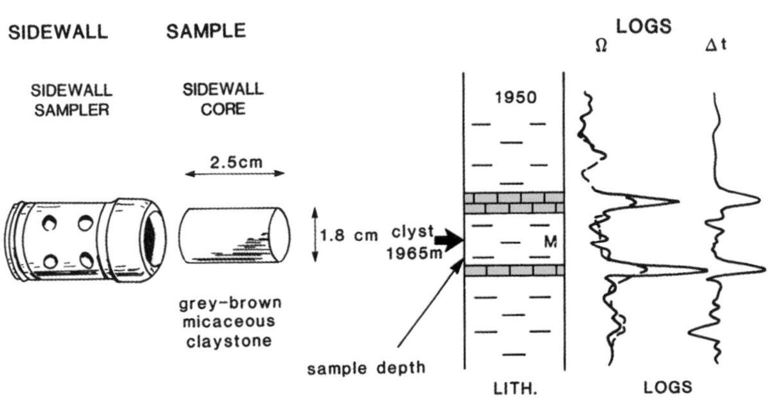

Figure 12.6 Sidewall core sample. Schematic illustration of a sidewall sampler, sidewall core and its record on a final lithological log.

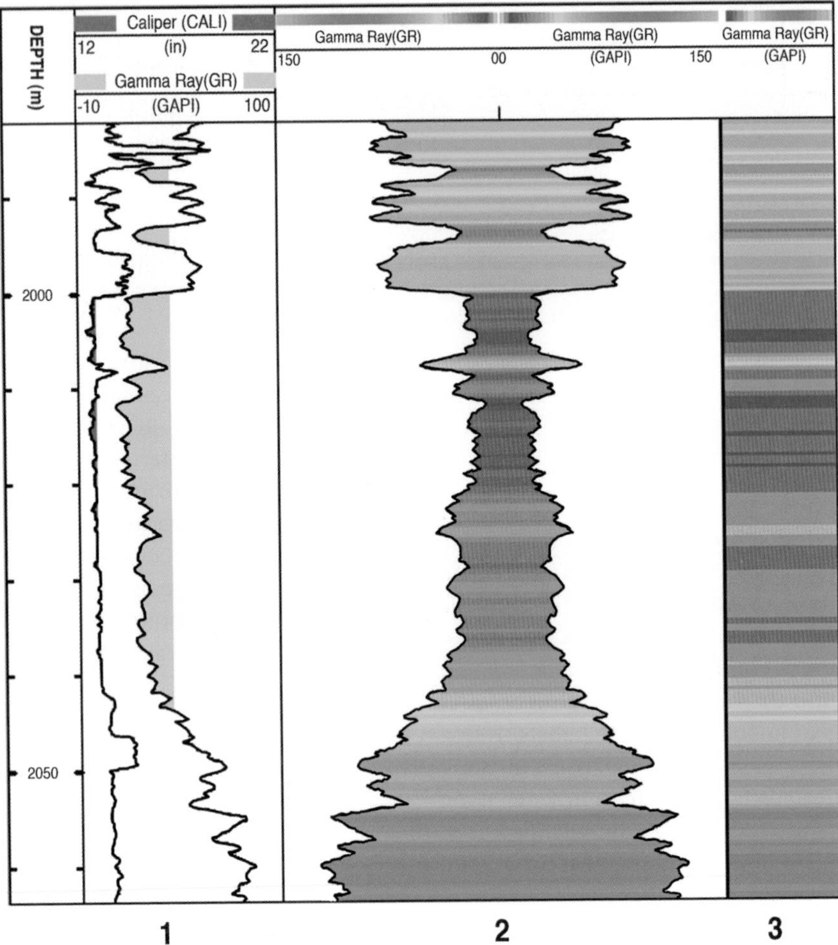

Figure 12.7 Ways of displaying the gamma ray. 1) using an arbitrary cut off and shading. 2) colour coded to a mirror, gamma ray log trace. 3) colour coded bar log of gamma ray values. (Note: the same interval is used for Figures 12.8, 26, 27 and 28).

curve itself, displayed as a mirror image or simply colour coded (**Figure 12.7**). These presentations still leave the curve to be interpreted but they help the eye to spot useful information.

(Nota: *In order to be able to compare several of the ways of interpreting lithology, the interval in this figure is the same as in Figures 12.8, 12.26, 12.27 and 12.28*).

More purposeful displays bring out a curve's relationship to a constant or to a targeted function. For example, a caliper can be shaded to a constant to bring out zones where it is smaller than the bit size and indicative of mud cake (**Figure 12.7**, column 1). The gamma ray may be shaded to indicate of V_{sh}, (shale volume) or plotted on an actual V_{sh} percentage scale. The neutron density combination can be shaded to bring out matrix type when the two logs are plotted on compatible scales (**Figure 12.8**) (Chapter 11).

The more complex plots are, in fact, part interpretation, part presentation, as is the case the the V_{sh} plot. A formula is used to derive the V_{sh} and not just a simple log value. This may be taken further and, for example, the density logs may be converted to porosity, the resistivity logs converted to saturation and so on. The raw logs are furnished with formulae and numbers, which allow a new property to be calculated and displayed. These are petrophysical routines, as will be described, but are very helpful to the geologist.

Even in the digital age, geologists like to have hard copy plots to work on, despite the fact that the final lithological interpretation will be carried out and captured on screen. Any hard-copy plot should comprise at least the basic log set and use the edited, depth matched versions taken from the database once drilling is completed. A normal log set will include calipers, gamma-ray, SP, resistivities, density, neutron and sonic. Specialist logs, such as images and the NMR, should be available but, importantly, also the mudlog and drilling parameters.

The final lithological interpretation prepared by the geologist is used for the completion log, or final log, so it must be digital. It is useful for this to be a summary interpretation so that it can be understood by log non-specialists such as stratigraphers, geophysicists or other occasional users.

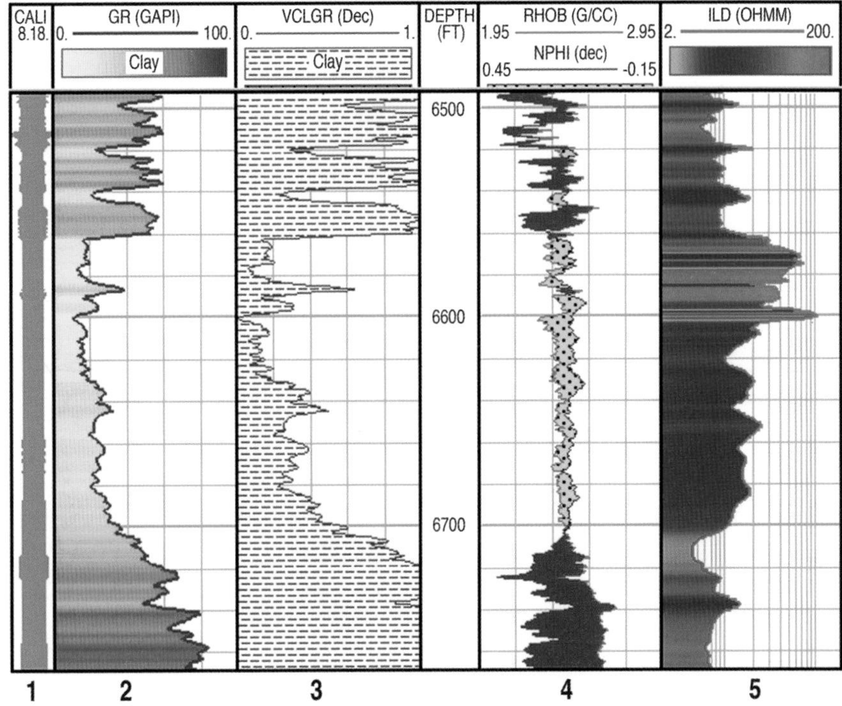

Figure 12.8 Log displays to help both interpretation and calculation. 1) mirror image caliper. 2) colour coded gamma ray and gamma ray curve, 3) shale volume (V_{sh}) from gamma ray calculation. 4) neutron and density plotted on limestone compatible scales 5) deep induction colour coded using the raw resistivity values. (Note: the same interval is used for Figures 12.7, 26, 27 and 28).

Horizontal routine

There are no simple rules for the quick manual interpretation of lithology from logs: if there were, this section would not be necessary. This book outlines the capabilities and characteristics of each of the openhole tools. To interpret lithology, these capabilities and characteristics must be known and used. A systematic approach is required. First, an iterative, horizontal routine.

The gross lithology, for example, is suggested by the mud log, this can then be corroborated and compared at the same depth, horizontally, to a simple log such as the gamma ray or the SP (**Figure 12.9,2**). The interpretation is then continued, again horizontally, through the other logs: resistivity, sonic and density-neutron. Log quality is checked: for example, the hole may be very caved, and one or more of the logs may be badly recorded. If there is corroboration, the lithology can be noted and then compared to sidewall cores or other samples (**Figure 12.9,3**). If the lithology is not corroborated, then there must be a 'feedback' from one log to the next.

For example, 60% sand and 40% shale are marked on the mud log. There are no sidewall cores. The gamma ray log reads persistently high suggesting a shale interval. The resistivity log and the sonic log are not diagnostic. The density-neutron combination is consistent with a sandstone: the curves have a cross-over (negative separation). A check with the SP indicates that these neutron-density intervals correspond to permeable zones and that they have a mudcake as shown by the caliper. A permeable sandstone interval can therefore be interpreted. The anomalous log is the gamma ray, perhaps because of feldspars, micas or other non-shale radioactive sand-sized grains. Through this iteration, the final interpretation is made compatible with all the log responses.

Vertical routine

Although the horizontal routine is the basis for any lithological interpretation, individual logs should also be examined vertically for consistent lithological values. For example, a shale may occur inter-bedded with a sand but maintain its characteristics vertically; sand beds may also be similar. These lithological consistencies will be seen in vertically consistent log responses and is, of course, the basis for the use of SP and gamma ray sand and shale lines (Chapters 6, 8). However, vertical consistency can occur on all the logs and should be examined (**Figure 12.10**). Software routines that colour code curves as described above will help these routines.

Absolute values and lithology

For some of the more difficult, uncommon lithologies, and for beds with very high or very low readings, absolute value tables can be useful. For example, evaporites are generally pure enough in the subsurface to have

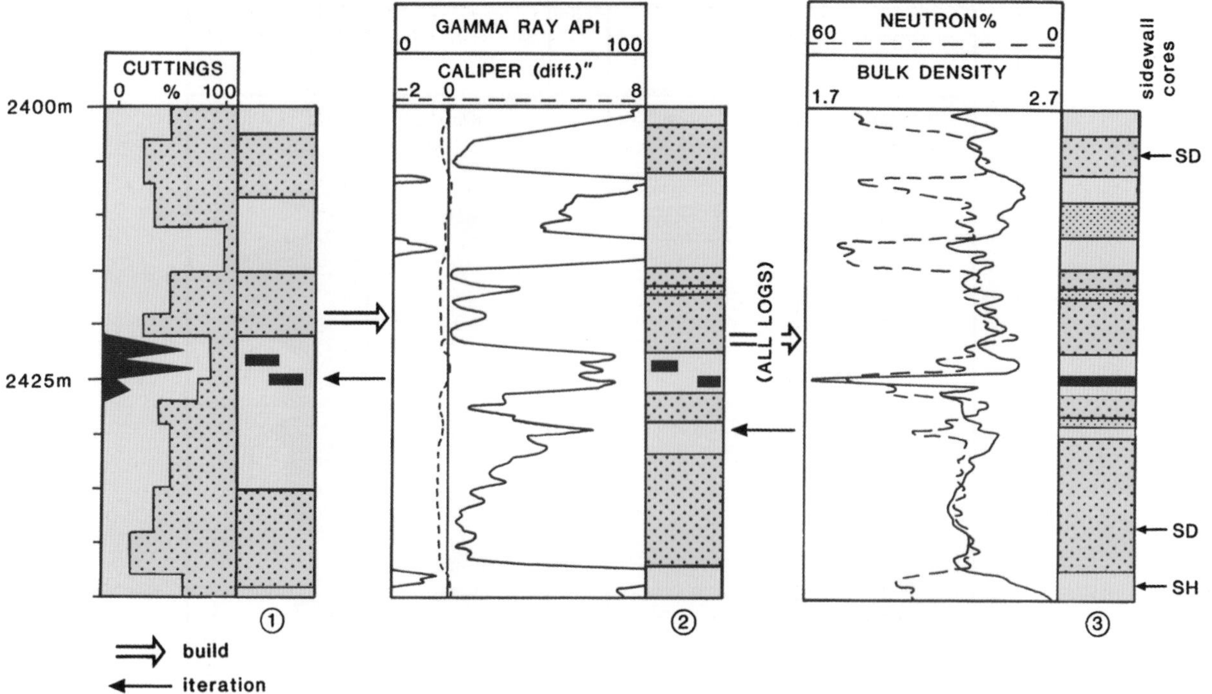

Figure 12.9 Horizontal routine, manual method. The stages for building up lithology: 1, rig data; 2, simple wireline log; 3, all logs and well samples (only neutron-density shown). The lithology is built up from 1 to 2 to 3, but with iteration. Note the increasing detail and precision.

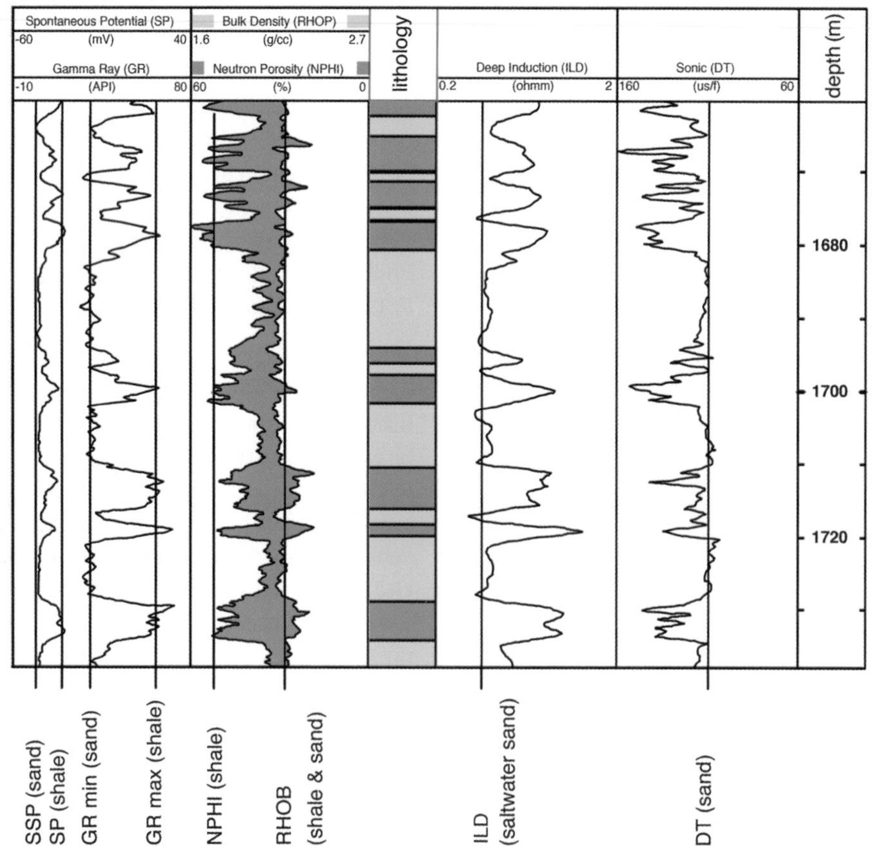

Figure 12.10 A composite log display to aid with vertical lithological interpretation routines. Any of the logs can show vertical consistency (base lines) and not just the gamma ray and SP.

Table 12.2 Logging-tool response values. All values are shown so that they cover the ranges found in the various sources, i.e. none of the sources has values outside those listed. From Serra 1972, 1979, 2003; Dresser Atlas 1983; Gearhart 1983; Schlumberger 1985, 1989a.

	Material	Resistivity (ohm m²/m)	Gamma Ray API [1]	Δtma (μs/ft) [2]	Density log [4] (g/cm³) (ma)	Neutron porosity units [3]	*Pe* [7] b/g
Common lithologies [6]	Sandstones	up to 1000	18–160	53–100	2.59–2.84	0–45	1.8–2.3
	Limestones	$80-6 \times 10^3$	18–100	47.6–53	2.66–2.74	0–30	5.0–5.2
	Dolomites	$1-7 \times 10^3$	12–100	38.5–45	2.8–2.99	0–30	4.5–4.7
	Shales	0.5–1000	24–1000	60–170	2.65–2.7	25–75	3.7–4.1
Matrix minerals	Quartz	10^4-10^{12}	0	51.2–56	2.64–2.66	−2	1.8
	Calcite	10^7-10^{12}	0	45.5–49	2.71	−1	5.08
	Dolomite	$1-7 \times 10^3$	0	38.5–45	2.85–2.88	1	3.16
Clay minerals	Illite		250–300		2.52–3.0	30	2.6–3.5
	Chlorite		180–250		2.6–3.22	52	˜6.3
	Kaolinite		80–130		2.4–2.69	37	1.6–1.8
	Smectite		150–200		2.0–3.0	44	1.6–2.3
Micas	Glauconite		75–90		2.2–2.8	38	4.8 (5.8–7.3)
	Muscovite	$10^{11}-10^{12}$	140–270	49	2.76–3.1	20	2.4
	Biotite	$10^{14}-10^{15}$	90–275	50.8–51	2.65–3.1	21	6.3
Fsp			220–280	45	2.53–2.57	−3	2.9
			220–280	69	2.52–2.63	−3	2.9
Coals	Antracite	$10^{-3}-5$	0	90–120	1.32–1.80	38	0.16
	Bituminous coal	$10-10^6$	0–18	100–140	1.15–1.7	60	0.17
	Lignite	4×10^3	6–24	140–180	0.5–1.5	52	0.2
Fluids / Gas	Gas (av.)	∞	0		.000886		
	Methane	∞	0	626	.00076		0.1
	Oil (40° API)	10^9-10^{16}	0.12–0.40	238	.85–.97	60	0.12
	Water (80°F)						
	pure	∞	0	189–207	1.00	100	0.36
	salt (33,000 ppm)	0.031 (var)	0	180	1.19	60	1.64
Metallic minerals	Pyrite	$10^{-1}-10^{14}$		39.2–39	4.8–5.17	−3	17
	Siderite	10^4-1000	0	47	3.0–3.89	12	14.7
Evaporites	Halite	$<10^4-10^{14}$	0	66.7–67	2.03–2.08	−3	4.7
	Anhydrite	10^4-10^{10}	0–12	50	2.89–3.05	−2	5.06
	Gypsum	1000	0	52–53	2.33–3.05	60	4.0
	Sylvite	$10^{14}-10^{15}$	500	74	1.86–1.99	−3	8.51
	Polyhalite		200	57.5–58	2.79	25	4.3
Crystalline rocks	Basalt	$8 \times 10^2-10^5$	12–24	45–57.5 [5]	2.7–3.2		5.36
	Granite	10^6	24–96	46.8–53.5	2.52–2.8		2.86
	Gneiss	10^2-10^4	24–48	48.8–51.6	2.6–3.04		4.45

(1) No hole conditions specified; will therefore vary. (2) Values for the matrix material, compressional wave. (3) For the CNL tool of Schlumberger. (4) Calibrated. (5) Pressure 1 kbar. (6) All values variable. (7) Barite has a *Pe* of 266.8 b/g.
Fsp = Felspar; ma = matrix; b/g = barns per gram

distinct densities and velocities: this is certainly the case with salt (Chapters 9, 10). Abrupt peaks, which may be important in stratigraphic interpretations or diagnostic of a particular interval, are often best interpreted using absolute-value tables. Coals, for example, will be distinct on logs, as will be pyrite and other mineralisations (cf. **Figure 10.18**).

Table 12.2 gives a resumé of some of the more useful absolute log values for lithology interpretation. Tables in the individual chapters can also be consulted.

Manual bed boundaries

Bed boundaries should be drawn precisely, and on-screen routines will normally require a set limit and a line to be drawn. The correct log should be chosen to position a limit. The best geophysical logs for bed boundary definition are those with a moderate depth of investigation (Chapter 2), generally the lateral type resistivity and the density logs (Chapters 7,10). The 'shoulder', where a log is responding to two different lithologies simultaneously (Chapter 2), is generally broader in logs with greater depth of investigation but thinner in shallow investigating logs. In the example used (**Figure 12.11**), the gamma ray (GR) has a greater depth of investigation than the micro-spherically focused log (MSFL) but has a broader shoulder effect. When mud cake is present, an accurate limit may be taken from the caliper because it gives a sharp mechanical response: there are no shoulder effects (**Figure 12.11**) (Chapter 5). Expanded scales should be used for on-screen positioning.

As a general rule, a manual bed boundary is drawn in the mid-point of the tangent to a shoulder (**Figure 12.11**). This may not always be the real position since both anisotropy and dip affect log responses (Chapter 2), but it is an identifiable method which can be applied consistently and corrected subsequently if necessary and is usually sufficient for geological needs.

A bed boundary will inevitably be represented on an interpreted log by a line and hence appear as sharp. It may or may not be sharp in reality and the interpretation is a simplification. However, this is justified since any significant change in log values is caused by a real formation change which, at log plot scales, effectively appears as sharp.

Presentation

The final geological lithology interpretation should be clear and concise. Accepted colours and stylised symbols for lithology and bed boundaries should be used *(see also* Chapter 16). Inevitably the interpretation will lose some of the details seen on the well logs. Nonetheless, it is the interpreter who has all the data for the interpretation at his or her disposal and who must decide the level of detail necessary. The resultant (digital) lithology should not be over-cluttered as this is an interpretation normally used for the Well Completion Log, the document used to summarise the drilling and geological data when a well is completed (variously called Final Log, Completion Log, Composite Log etc.). Along with the lithology, the Completion Log will be furnished with information on fluids, tests, cores, side-wall cores, stratigraphy and casings at a minimum (**Figure 12.12**) and is commonly used by non-specialists. The lithological interpretation may also be used as a database for stratigraphy, correlation, for making small scale, summary logs and geophysical callibration. Too much detail is a disadvantage. The scheme followed through this book illustrates the use of simplified symbols for lithology.

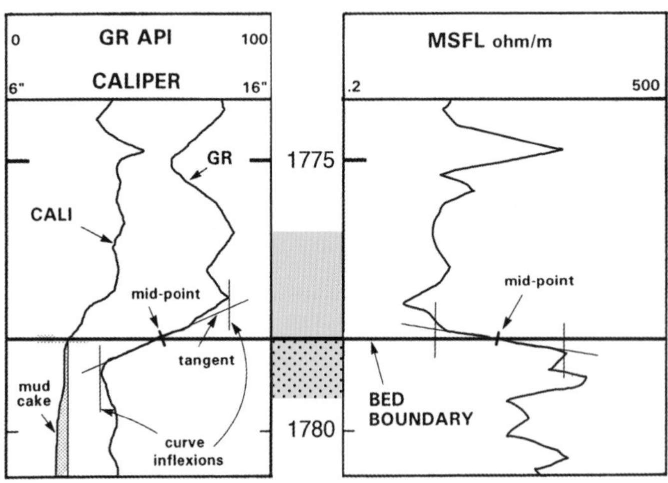

Figure 12.11 Positioning a bed boundary. The mid-point of the tangent to the log curve between inflection points (i.e. the shoulder interval) is taken. Note this is thinner on the MSFL compared to the gamma ray log, but the mid-point is the same. The caliper, being mechanical, shows an instantaneous response, in this case to mud cake limit.

12.6 Computer aids to manual lithology interpretation (semi-quantitative)

Between the purely manual and purely automatic software methods of lithology interpretation, there are semi-quantitative, mainly graphical aids. Some of these are described here. The methods take log curve data and re-display and compare them in different ways so as to bring out otherwise hidden characteristics and relationships. And these are quantitative. In fact, these graphical methods can be regarded as way stages of a purely automatic calculation, the plots giving an insight into the workings of the mathematical software routines.

Graphical quantification may be made at several levels of sophistication: one-log, two-log or multi-log. The most sophisticated multi-log quantifications lead eventually to an entirely computer-derived, log based interpretation. The semi-quantitative methods described here allow the geologist to do two things: to make decisions with more geophysical consistency than comes from purely manual methods; and to understand better the workings of purely automatic, mainly petrophysical routines.

Histograms – one-log quantification

The simplest way of grouping well-log values is by using a histogram, where the log value is simply plotted against frequency (**Figure 12.13**). The histogram has various uses. It can be used to define populations or average values and, for example, the 'shale' and 'sand' ranges of a gamma ray log may be presented in this manner (**Figure 12.13**). A second example shows a gamma ray histogram in a series of volcanic rocks with values forming distinct populations (**Figure 12.14**) (Sanyal *et al.* 1980). Used

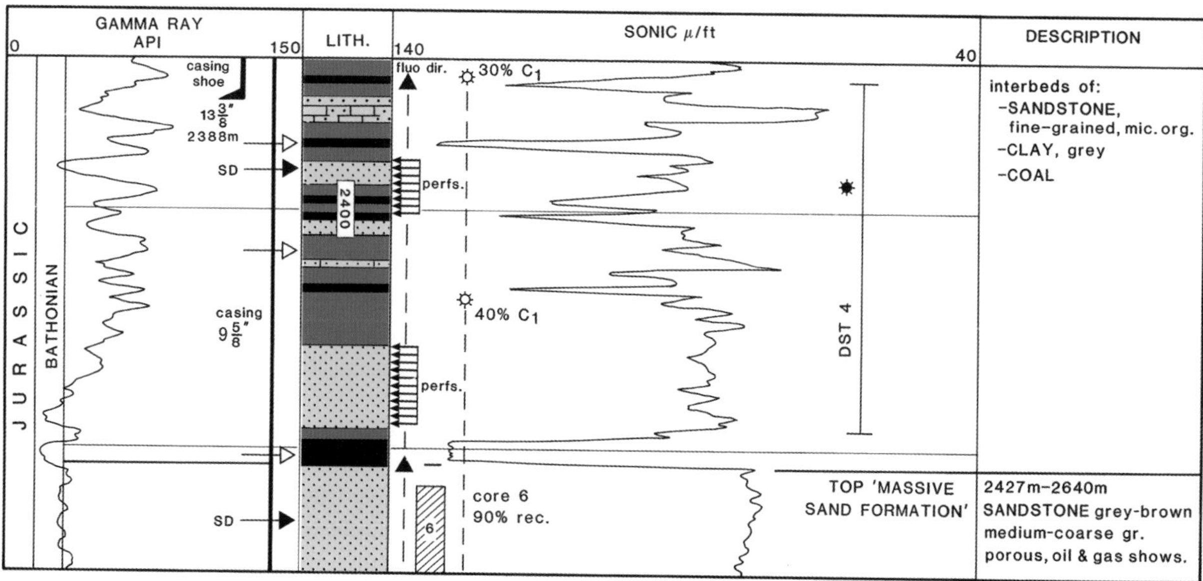

Figure 12.12 The completion log. An example of the log with interpreted lithology, stratigraphy, hydrocarbon shows, tests and drill data. It is the geologist's 'basic record' of a well. The lithology comes from an interpretation of the full log suite, cores and drilling data.

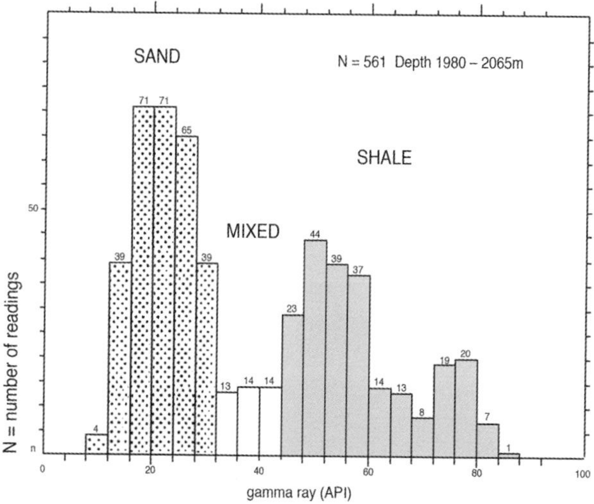

Figure 12.13 Gamma ray histogram of a sand-shale sequence. The lithology is a simple alternation of sand and shale but the two geophysical populations overlap in the 'mixed' zone.

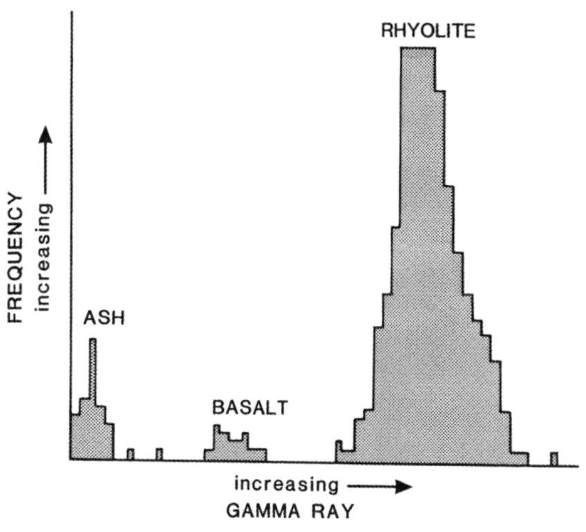

Figure 12.14 Histograms of gamma ray log values. Gamma ray values from a volcanic sequence showing distinct populations for various lithologies (re-drawn from Sanyal *et al.* 1980).

in this way, the histogram helps to define the log limits of lithology and average log values (Walters 1968), but just for the one log.

A second use is in the normalisation of particular logs. This is done by selecting a consistent stratigraphic interval where responses should be similar and then comparing the responses by comparing histograms of the log values (**Figure 12.15**) (Kowalchuk *et al.* 1974; Wylie and Wood 2005). This is done as much for petrophysical as for geological reasons. In this same manner, histograms of log values may be compared to histograms of laboratory values when the same character is being measured. In the petrophysical usage, logs and laboratory values are made consistent for reservoir calculations.

Finally, histograms have been used to make stratigraphic correlations when curve comparisons were inconclusive (Walters 1968). The method is difficult to apply, but does bring out the idea that a formation can be recognised be a certain data range which is stratigraphically and lithologically diagnostic.

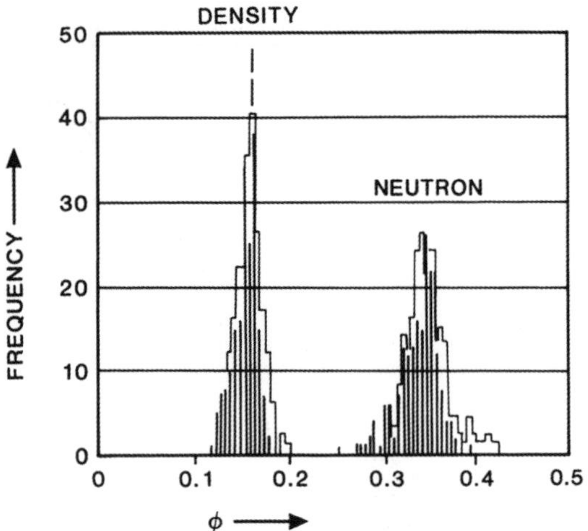

Figure 12.15 Comparison to a master histogram. Neutron and density log value histograms of one well, compared to master histograms (continuous line) of six wells from the First White Speckled Shale. Upper Cretaceous, Alberta, Canada (re-drawn from Kowalchuk *et al.* 1974).

Cross-plots – two-log quantification

When any two values are cross-plotted, the resulting series of points may be used either to define the relationship between the two variables, or to define fields using both x and y axis values to give the upper and lower limits of the variables. Both styles of output are used with logs.

Three types of well log cross-plot exist:

1. Cross-plots of compatible logs, that is those measuring the same parameter, for example, porosity logs such as the neutron and the density.
2. Cross-plots of incompatible logs, for example a plot of gamma ray against resistivity values: the logs do not measure the same parameter.
3. Cross-plots of laboratory or sample values against log values, for example porosity core values against neutron porosity values.

Cross-plotting compatible logs

Typical and illustrative of this type is the neutron-density cross-plot: the plot of neutron porosity values against bulk density values. The method has been explained previously (*see* Chapter 11, neutron-density combination). It was shown that cross-plotting neutron and density values can be used to identify pure matrix points and/or the related porosity. This is impossible using only the value from one of the logs. For example, a neutron log value of 25% may be a dolomite with 17% porosity, a limestone with 25% porosity or a sandstone with 29% porosity (**Figure 11.35**) but, when associated with a density of 2.28 g/cm^3, it has a unique attribution, a limestone with 25% porosity.

When there are only two variables, such as porosity and one matrix type (lithology) and no hydrocarbons, the neutron-density cross-plot allows a simple identification of lithology (actually matrix density). In effect, applying algebraic solutions to cross-plot type datasets are behind the lithology lines (**Figure 11.35**) (Doveton 1986). However, when there is a third variable (e.g. a second type of matrix or more usually shale), there are no longer unique solutions to the equations and new end-member values must be defined if they are to be used. For example, to find a solution for any point when shale is present, a shale end member with density and neutron values must be defined (Bhunan & Passey 1994; La Vigne *et al.* 1994). Typically, this 'shale point' is defined empirically. A great many lithologically unidentified points are plotted and the 'shale point' is chosen to correspond to a value at the edge but within the supposed shale population (**Figure 12.16**). Once the 'shale point' is defined, the cross-plot can be graphically solved by dividing it into a compositional triangle, the end-members being shale 100% (shale point), porosity 100% (fluid point) and matrix 100% (matrix point). The 'shale

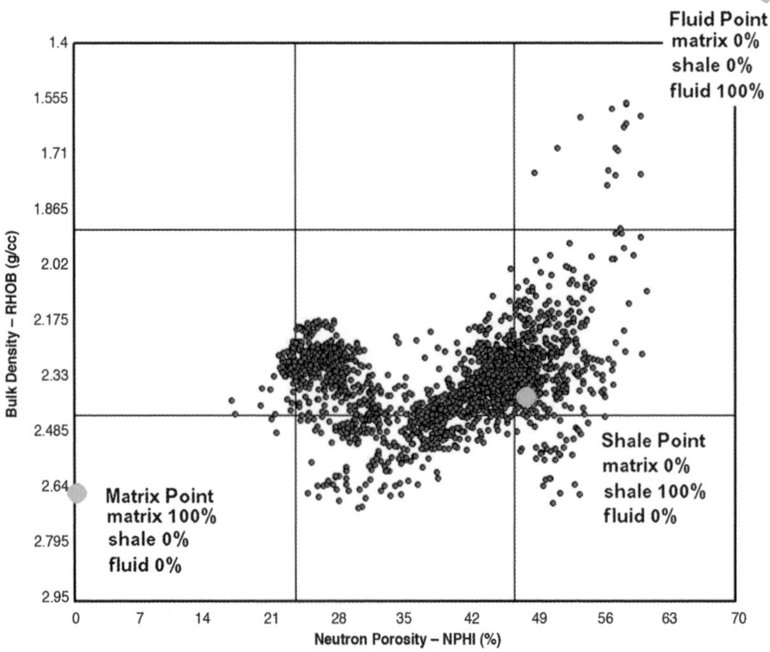

Figure 12.16 A shale point defined on a neutron-density cross-plot. Values from 290 m (953 ft) of a sand- shale formation. Note the arbitrary choice of one 'point' to represent shale. The matrix and fluid points are precise.

point' on this example is actually the 'wet shale point' (*WSh*) and consists of probably only 60% clay (minerals) and should be scaled to the 'dry clay point' (*DCly*) (Bhunan & Passey 1994 *op. cit.*). Any point on the plot now has a precise value of the three variables, quartz, water and clay: a numerical representation of a lithology (**Figure 12.17**, Although to note on this plot, the Y axis 'density porosity', which is not measured, would be better replaced by 'bulk density', which is measured).

This 'shale point' use in cross-plots has many drawbacks. Firstly, only one matrix can be considered at a time. A zone will be interpreted as only shaly sandstone or only shaly limestone, never both. But more importantly, it mixes definable with indefinable values. Shale is inevitably very variable, and the shale point therefore very imprecise (**Figure 12.16**), yet the matrix and liquid points are both quite precise (Doveton 1994). This mixing of precise and imprecise end-members is a general criticism.

A more realistic approach from a geological point of view is to define fields of values on this plot in which a particular lithology is likely to be plotted. The approach is empirical and the log limits of each lithological field will vary from well to well, and even within one well with depth (**Figure 12.18**). This is best achieved today by using software which allows the interactive exploration

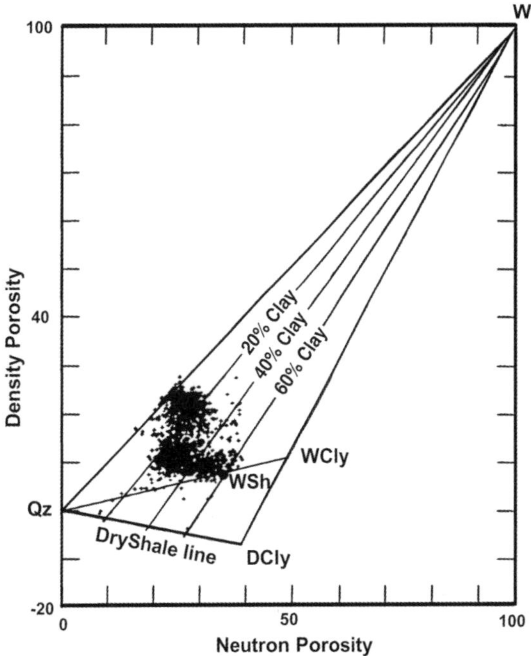

Figure 12.17 Neutron-density cross-plot furnished with wet shale (*WSh*), wet clay (*WCly*), and dry clay (*DCly*) points. It allows a proper clay (clay mineral) content to be assessed (Bhuyan & Passey SPWLA 1994).

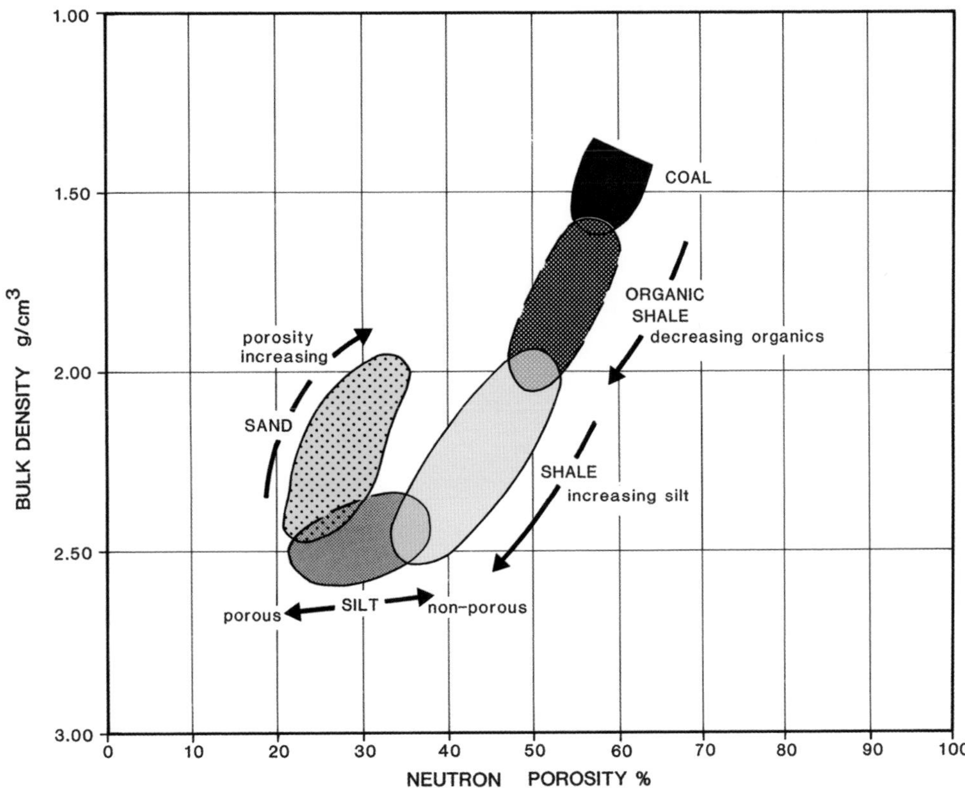

Figure 12.18 Lithological fields defined on a neutron-density cross-plot. Based on the values from a 500 m (1640 ft) interval in one well.

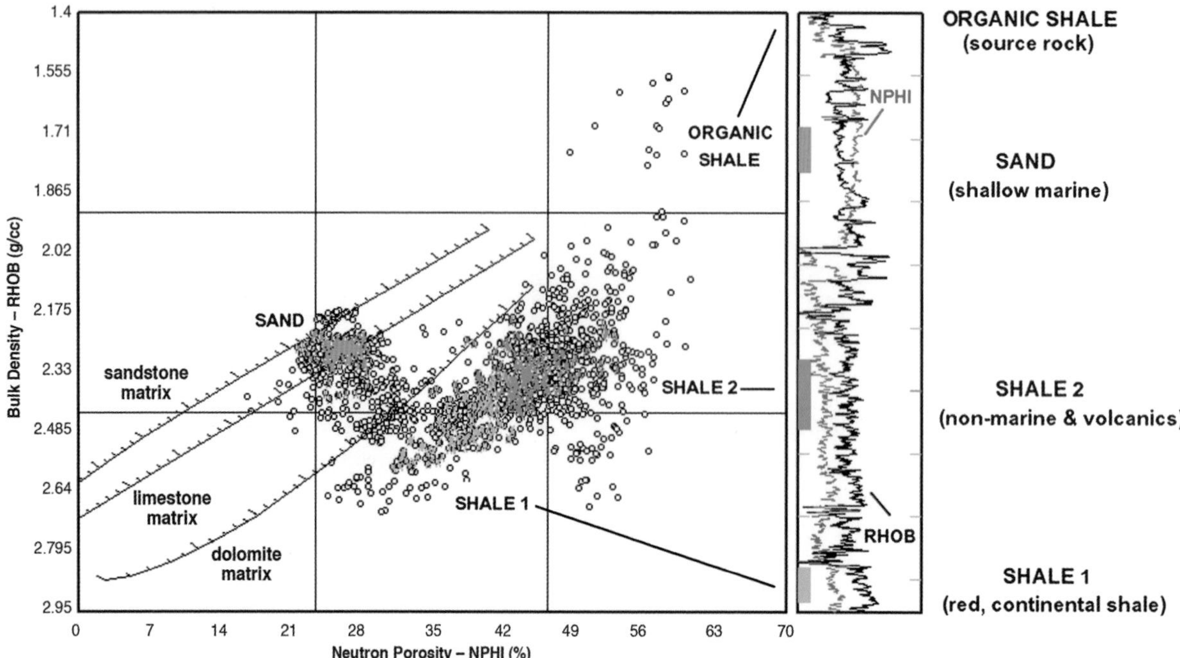

Figure 12.19 Interactive investigation of a neutron-density cross-plot in order to define lithology empirically but quantitatively. There are 2 shale populations (shale 1 blue, shale 2 green) an organic shale, source interval and a sand interval (orange). The intervals were selected on the logs and appeared automatically on the cross-plot. The same interval is shown in Figure 12.20 (routine from TerraStation).

between logs and their cross-plot, both of which are displayed simultaneously on the screen. That is, intervals selected on the log traces may be inter-actively matched to points on the cross-plot, or a set of points on the cross-plot identified in their depth position on the log traces. The example (**Figure 12.19**) is a standard neutron-density plot with the two curves on the right (labelled). The logs show one interval of sand (orange) and two different types of shale, shale 1 and shale 2 (green and light blue), picked on the logs and the cross-plot. Shale 1 is red and continental, shale 2 is non-marine and contains abundant volcanic material: they are geologically quite different types of shale. The cross-plot shows that they are also distinctive in terms of log responses. Using interactive routines such as this allows for a rigorous, graphical use of cross-plots and effectively a quantitative identification of lithology. An extremely useful geological tool.

A modern addition to the 2-D cross-plot is the on-screen 3-D plot which allows even greater exploration. The example (**Figure 12.20**) shows a standard neutron-density plot with a gamma ray added in the third dimension. This 3-D plot is of the same interval as the interactive 2-D plot (**Figure 12.19**).

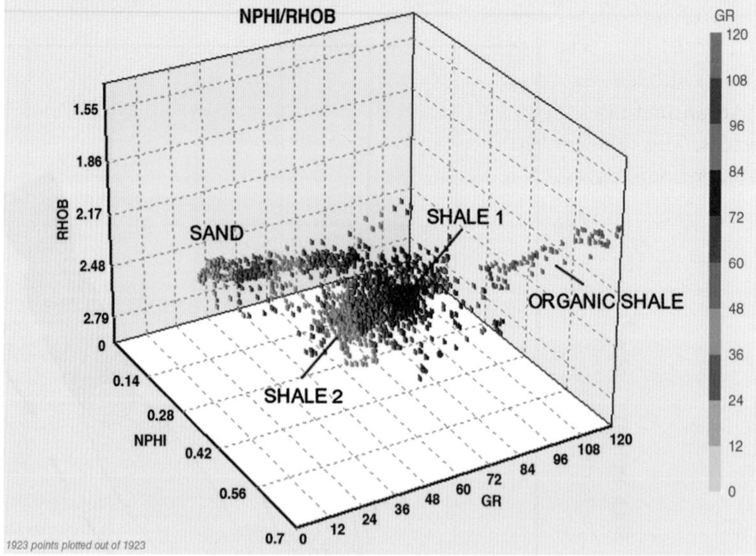

Figure 12.20 3-D display of a neutron-density cross-plot with the gamma ray on the Z axis. The interval is the same as in Figure 12.19 (routine from Interactive Petrophysics).

Cross-plotting incompatible logs

The cross-plotting of incompatible logs is usually done to quantify lithology. Incompatible logs are those which do not, in the first instance, measure or indicate the same parameter. Resistivity and gamma ray logs are incompatible, one gives the resistivity, the other natural radioactivity and, by inference, shale volume. However,

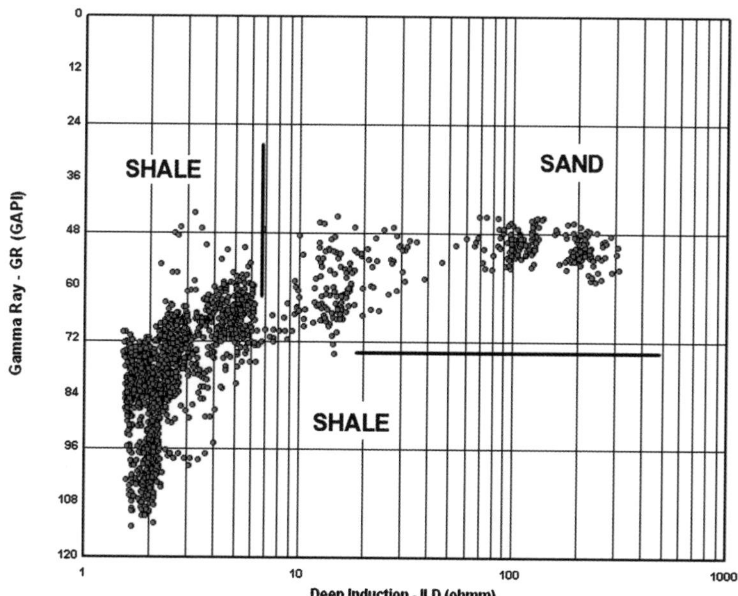

Figure 12.21 Cross-plot of 'incompatible' logs. Gamma ray and resistivity values cross-plotted to define lithology fields. Shales are seen with gamma ray values ranging from approximately 55–115 API but consistent resistivity values below 7.0 ohm/m. Sands show high resistivities (hydrocarbons) up to approximately 300 ohm/m and with low to moderate gamma ray values, between 40–70 API. Gamma ray values of the sands and shales overlap in the 55–70 API range but are separated by their resistivity values.

on cross-plotting a compatibility will become evident. The resistivity logs will show a consistent set of values in shales and a different set in hydrocarbon bearing sands. The gamma ray log equally shows shale and sand differences. The relationship between the two logs becomes evident on cross-plotting and allows lithological boundary values to be defined (**Figure 12.21**). In fact, almost all cross-plots show elements of a consistent relationship of some sort (cf. Heslop 1974) and often empirical relationships become evident, which would otherwise remain hidden.

Plotting the gamma ray log values against the neutron log values, for example (**Figure 12.22**), brings out several relationships (Rider *et al.* 1979). There is a consistent, straight-line relationship between the two where both the gamma ray and the neutron logs are reacting to a shale-sandstone mixture. Each log is showing the volume of shale in its own way. Through this straight-line region, changes in neutron porosity typically involve changes in shale content. However, in very clean sandstones there are variations in porosity which do not involve shale (i.e. the GR) and the relationship between the two logs changes. In the example (**Figure 12.22**), the sands are gas filled and the changes in porosity significantly affect the neutron while the gamma ray is unaffected. On the gamma ray curve alone, the changes between sand and shale are not evident: when the logs are plotted together the relationship becomes clear (cf. Heslop 1974).

On this same plot (**Figure 12. 22**), at higher gamma ray and neutron values, there is also a relationship break. This is due to organic matter. Since the neutron tool

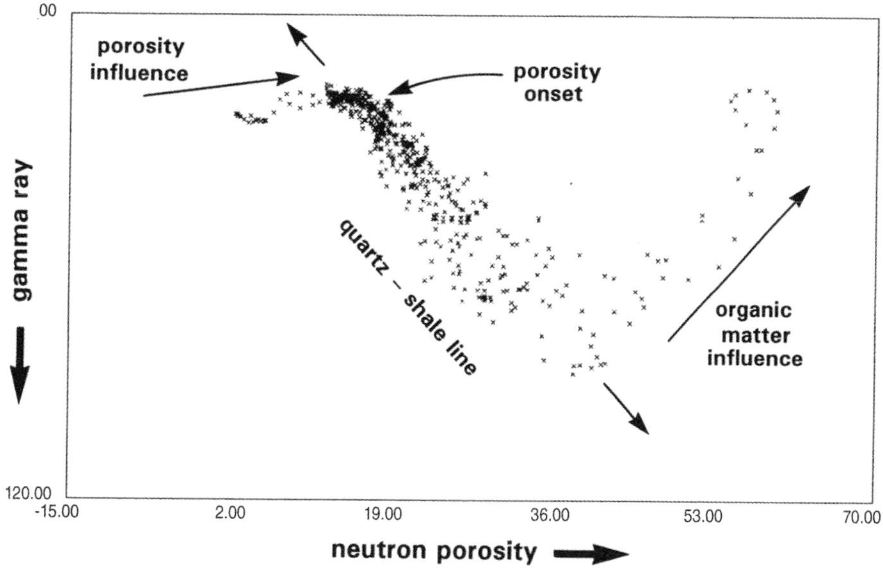

Figure 12.22 Cross-plot of gamma ray against neutron porosity. A constant relationship is seen over a wide range of values when only quartz and shale are involved (quartz-shale line). Where porosity begins, an inflection is seen. Where organic matter becomes abundant, an opposite inflection is seen.

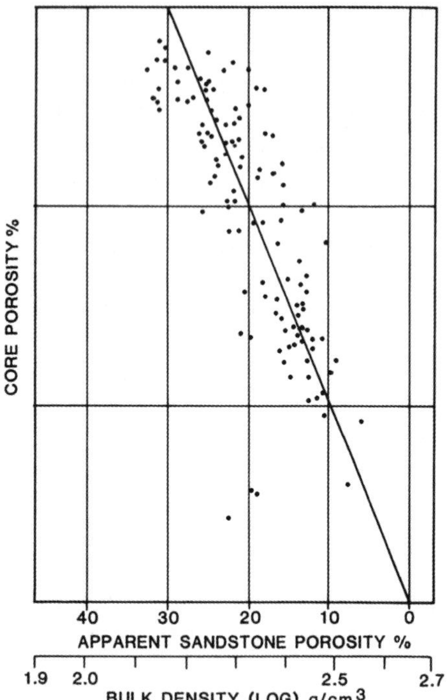

Figure 12.23 Cross-plot of log values (apparent density porosity) against sample values (core porosity). The plot shows the limits of accuracy to be expected from log values.

reacts to all hydrogen present (Chapter 11), it reacts to the hydrogen combined with carbon in organic matter (a solid hydrocarbon). In this example, the organic matter is mostly coal and lignite grains which have a low radioactivity. Thus, while the gamma ray values diminish as the organic matter replaces the shale, the neutron values increase or remain high (Rider *et al.* 1979 *op. cit.).* A quite different response will occur if the organic matter has a high gamma ray signature (as is usual, Chapter 8), when the gamma ray will increase more rapidly than the neutron (**Figure 17.23**).

Cross-plotting log values against sample values

Cross-plotting core and log values is commonly used to verify and calibrate log derived porosity against values from the laboratory (**Figure 12.23**). This, obviously, can only be done over cored intervals. But, once calibrated, the logs can be more confidently interpreted over the non-cored zones. The technique is essential to petrophysical log interpretation. However, it must always be remembered that measured values and log values are not *a priori* identical. Core porosities are measured on a small plug about 25 cm^3 in volume, porosity logs measure between 4000 cm^3 and 400,000 cm^3 of formation (*i.e.* up to over 16000 times the plug volume, **Figure 2.17**). In addition, core porosities are measured under atmospheric conditions, log porosities under reservoir conditions, notably of pressure and temperature. A persistent difference between log and core porosities of 1% or 2% will often indicate a difference in physical conditions, rather than badly-calibrated logs (Dahlberg and Fitz 1988). In order to more accurately use core porosities to calibrate logs, a compaction correction is applied to the core porosities.

Sample calibration may also extend to lithologies. For example, the validity of the gamma ray log as a shale indicator can be checked against laboratory measurements of clay percentages (Heslop 1975; Bhunan & Passey 1994) (**Figure 12.24**). Geochemical log results are necessarily compared to laboratory analyses (Herron and Herron 1996). The amount of ash in a coal can be deduced from its bulk density measured by logs (Lavers and Smits 1977). The technique of calibration for lithology is consistently useful for geological purposes.

Cross-plotting a log value against a laboratory value means that the depth position of the points used is lost. This is a statistical comparison, which is the advantage of the method: it compares averages. In order to re-introduce individual depth readings, depth identified points from a core can be plotted on a cross-plot with log values. Such a task is easily done with the interactive software described previously (cross-plotting compatible logs, **Figure 12.19**) and is a process once removed from plotting the laboratory values on a depth scale and comparing them with the logs themselves (cf. **Figure 10.13**).

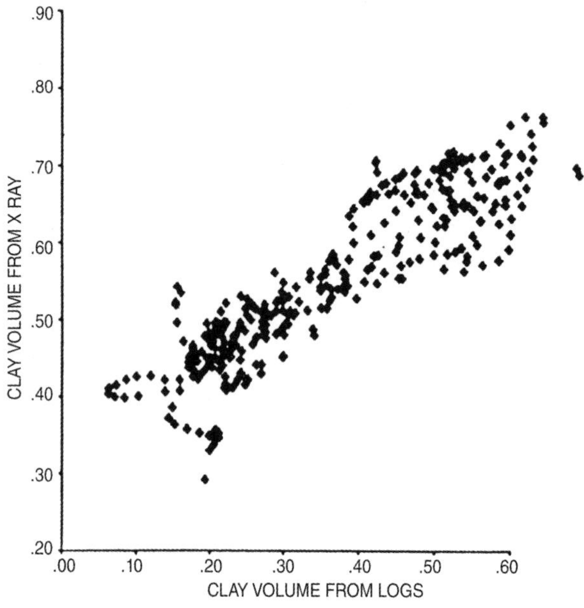

Figure 12.24 Cross-plot of laboratory values (of clay volume) against log values (of clay volume). The plot is a partial verification of the log derivation of shale volume (from Heslop 1975).

12.7 Software derived lithology from logs (quantitative)

Generalities

Software calculated 'lithology' is now standard. The routines are mostly petrophysical and therefore designed to evaluate porosity, water saturation and so on, numbers from which investment decisions can be made. Lithology, as already suggested in the introduction to this chapter, is incidental in these routines, something to be evaluated and eliminated. Nonetheless, it is still required.

The identification of lithology using well logs or its effect on the logs, is an exercise in classification, as is any identification of any lithology, not just using logs. A certain set or population of log responses, that is, a set of numbers, can be classified as indicating a certain lithology. The problem is therefore one of statistically analysing numbers from typically 6 or more logs to recognise multiple properties, one or some of which are relevant to lithology. This is typically a task for multivariate analysis, that is the simultaneous evaluation of several observations on sets of samples (Doveton 1994; Moss 1997). As will be briefly described below, there are a number of different ways of doing this but one of the major decisions is whether the method should be 'supervised' or 'un-supervised', that is whether the classification works to find pre-determined objects (supervised) or is allowed to find its own objects, which are subsequently determined (un-supervised). For lithological work, this means either defining mineralogical end members such as quartz or calcite (supervised), or observing a group which has values which can be allocated to, say, sandstone or limestone, but of which the limits are identified by the logs themselves (un-supervised). Methods are available which solve these problems sequentially (as happened with the cross-plots) or simultaneously.

The attempt, then, is to relate statistically defined populations to particular lithologies. The term 'electrofacies' has been used for such purely mathematically defined populations (i.e. Doveton 1994, *op. cit.*). In its original usage, electrofacies was applied in a broader sense as simply being defined by logs, and not purely mathematical (Serra and Abbott; 1980 Serra 2003). The broader sense, as will be discussed in Chapter 16, is used in this book. The qualifier, 'statistical electrofacies', is used for the purely mathematical sense here. A statistical electrofacies, then, is just numbers and, to gain geological significance, is assigned to, or shown to characterise, a particular lithology.

Examples follow in the text below.

Preparation

Prior to any multi-log calculation, raw logs must go through a series of preparations. They are in different units, have different sensitivities, different vertical resolutions and so on. They must be reduced to commonality.

The first requirement, it goes without saying, is for all logs to be depth matched. This is especially important when LWD and wireline logs are mixed. Although bulk shift depth matching is available (**Figure 2.25**), responses need to be checked and matched manually. Each log also needs to be environmentally corrected for any unwanted influences such as caves or thick mud cake. These corrections, specific to particular tools, are now generally routine.

In order to be able to compare and use logs numerically, scales should be made compatible. Neutron log values have a linear range from 0–80, while the resistivity values have a logarithmic scale from 0.1–2000. Rescaling is usually done by using the (Gaussian) standard deviation of a log's data and its mean. To re-scale, the mean is subtracted from the reading of interest and divided by the standard deviation so that the range of –1 to 1 is one standard deviation for all the logs. In this way the different log types may be used together.

The last item is squaring the logs (**Figure 12.25**). The micro-logs have a greater frequency content (change more frequently) than the induction logs, the micro-spherically focused log (MSFL) is more 'nervous' than the deep induction log (ILD). Using these two curves together will cause 'shoulder' effects, which are not indicative of the formation, only of the log response

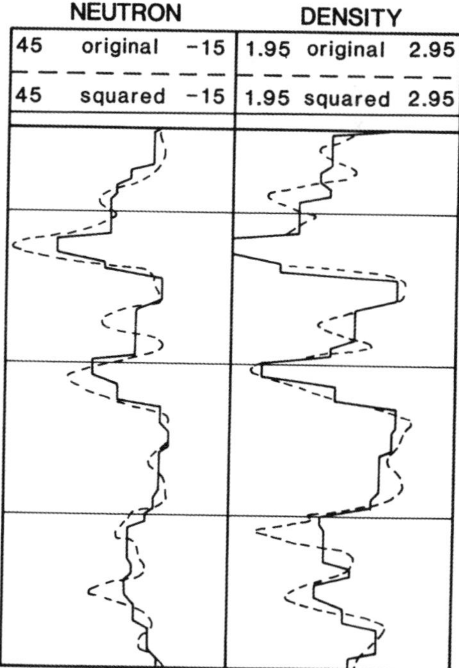

Figure 12.25 Squared logs made from statistical clustering. The example shows the clustered and squared values alongside the original values for a neutron log and a density log (re-drawn from Schlumberger 1982).

(**Figure 12.11**) (Serra 2003). They are therefore 'squared', that is, made more bed-like, and such variations as sample rate and response frequency are harmonised. In effect, a minimum (and similar) electro-bed thickness is chosen (**Figure 12.25**) (Serra 2003 *op. cit.*).

Supervised methods (multivariate analysis)

Supervised, multi-log quantification for petrophysical properties and 'lithology' begins with the numerical definition of all the variables: of the pure end-members of matrix minerals, minor minerals, fluids and so on. For example, pure quartz (i.e. sandstone matrix) will have a gamma ray value of 20 API, a density of 2.68 gcm^3, a hydrogen index of 10 NPHI, an interval transit time of 56 µs/ft and a resistivity of 20 ohmm. The mathematical process, then, is to identify the influence of the pure end members (such as quartz) on each and all of the log responses. This can be done by solving a number of linked algorithms for unknown volumes of the chosen minerals or matrices. Some of the end members such as quartz or calcite, substitute for a lithology (i.e. sandstone and limestone respectively). It is an 'inverse' approach in which components are defined in advance (i.e. Doveton 1986, 1994) and it effectively imitates the graphical methods discussed previously (Section 12.6). Problems arise, as already discussed, when some defined end-members have consistent physical properties (such as quartz) while others have quite variable properties (such as shale). Calculations are done in steps, sequentially, as was the case with the graphical techniques.

For example, in a basic routine a clay percentage may be first calculated from a gamma ray and an SP. The shalyness is then applied, perhaps as a simple cut-off, to neutron and density logs to derive mineral percentages including shale (a 'lithology'), which allows a porosity to be calculated. This porosity is then used with the resistivity logs to derive a saturation. The series of thresholds or filters is applied sequentially until the required values of mineral percentages, porosity, hydrocarbon percentage (water saturation) and hydrocarbon type are derived. This was the method when logs first began to be used quantitatively and was the one used by Archie (Chapter 7). It has simply progressed in sophistication as new signal types and new mathematical methods have been invented. As suggested, the previously illustrated cross-plots are 'snap shots' of this process under-way.

An alternative to the progressive solution is one in which all variables and all parameters are solved-for simultaneously in a classic, multivariate analysis. Pure end members (variables) of matrix, fluid (even elemental composition) etc. are defined for each log so as to identify *n* components (variables) as already discussed. As a minimum, *n-1* logs are required. With pure end members such as calcite (limestone), dolomite, quartz (sandstone) or even evaporite (e.g. gypsum), the method can work well since responses are generally known and linear. In the presence of shale, however, relationships are unpredictable and results are less satisfactory. Improvements are made by user intervention and iteration and there is also the possibility of using several models simultaneously (Quirein *et al.* 1986). However, perhaps it is best to use simple models in which user intervention can be more obviously applied (Marett and Kimminau 1990).

The output of the supervised methods is in volume per cent of the defined components, mainly minerals such as quartz or feldspar, but also shale and porosity, and the log frequently referred to as a CPI (computer processed interpretation) (**Figure 12.26**). Such supervised programmes are preferred by some log analysts. GLOBAL and ELAN, originally marketed by Schlumberger are illustrative, but there are now many examples (Serra 2003).

The outputs from the CPI programmes can be criticised from a geological point of view as being dependent on artificially-defined absolutes which have limited relationships to lithology in the usual, geological sense. A sandstone is not recognised just by its quartz percentage: it has compositional and textural characteristics. A silt may be 60% quartz, but this does not make it a sandstone. The output of these computer-defined 'lithologies' in percentage of constituents, therefore, does not represent geological lithology.

Un-supervised methods (cluster analysis, neural nets)

For a geologist, a more realistic 'lithology' is obtained using un-supervised classification methods where the data 'speaks for itself' (cf. Doveton 1994). Unclassified methods attempt to find populations in multi-dimensional space which have a mathematical significance (and hopefully a geological one as well). The dimensions will be the number of tool inputs. These are then used to define mathematical populations. In a very simple way, this can be illustrated graphically by a plot of neutron, density and gamma ray values. It shows populations in three dimensional space (**Figure 12.20**). A sandstone will occupy a certain volume defined by the three dimensions, a limestone another (and different) volume and so on. Multi-dimensional space cannot be illustrated graphically, but can be numerically described. In unsupervised methods, a multi-dimensional population will be identified but its significance not known: it is simply an *n*-dimensional object, *n* being defined by the number of logs or inputs.

There are a number of ways of working with populations in *n*-dimensional space to capture and classify them. Cluster analysis can be used as an illustration. Clustering tries to find small populations (or local modes) that can be represented by one number but without loss of information. Local modes can be grouped into larger clusters, reducting the data by the order of 10 to 1 (Wolff and Pelissier-Combescure 1982). In practical terms, a programme may be told to find, say, 50 clusters. The number of these initial groups, however,

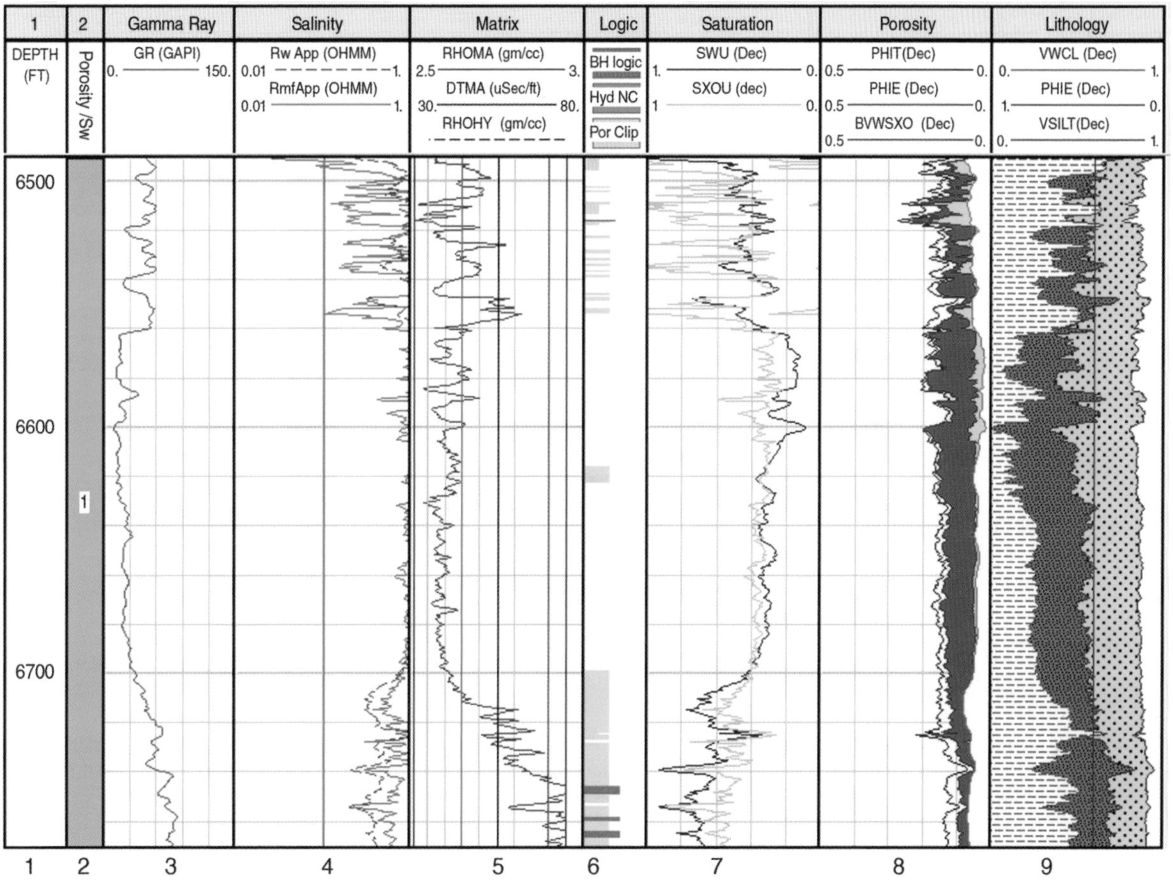

Figure 12.26 A typical computer processed interpretation (CPI) built from sequential solutions to petrophysical equations. The progressive calculations are represented by the derivative curves (tracks 4–8) and the final result (track 9, lithology) is expressed in constituent percentages, which in this example are wet clay volume (VWCL), silt volume (VSILT), sand (quartz) and porosity (PHIE). (Note: the same interval is used for Figures 12.7, 8, 27 and 28) (display from Interactive Petrophysics).

is still too many and a further reduction to, say, 6 (statistical) electrofacies is necessary. The reduction can be done in a number of mathematical ways, but one easy way to illustrate it graphically, is to use a dendrogram (**Figure 12.27**). The branching diagram shows the diminishing (mathematical) relationships of larger and larger groups. It can be cut at any level but the relationships between the original clusters and the final, smaller number of clusters, is retained. The eventual, very reduced number of clusters, allows a comparison with core or other geologically recognisable data.

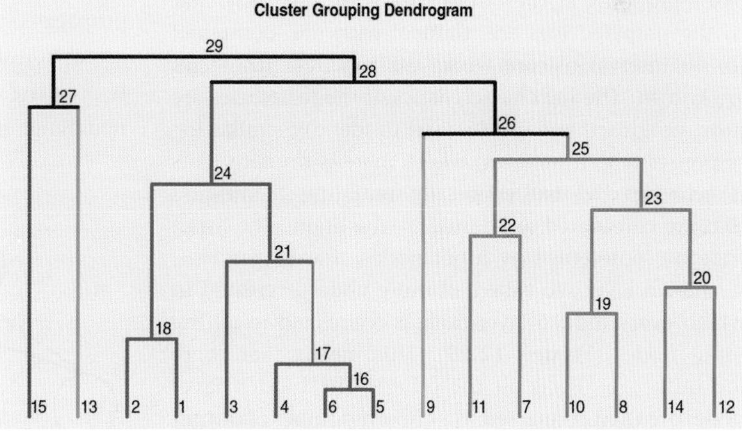

Figure 12.27 Dendrogram of the clusters represented by the 'all clusters' log (track 1) of Figure 12.28. (Note: the same interval is used for Figures 12.7, 8 and 26) (display from Interactive Petrophysics).

The illustration (**Figure 12.28**) shows the clusters derived from the dendrogram of **Figure 12.27**. The log column 1 (**Figure 12.28**) shows all the clusters from a preliminary grouping. The programme was then given the instruction to cut the dendrogram in order to leave only 6 clusters. The mathematical rule for this was to calculate the maximum (mathematical) distance between cluster objects. The result is the log in column 2 (**Figure 12.28**), which shows a much more understandable grouping in terms of real lithology. This type of approach was originally used for the Sch-

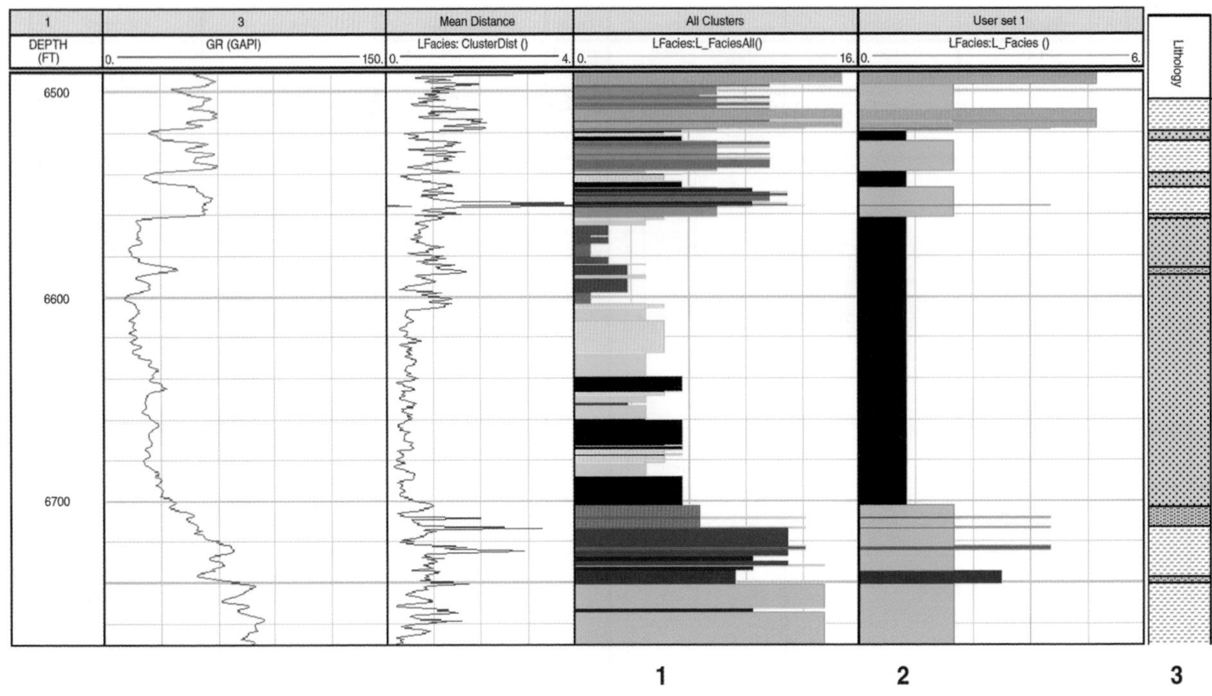

Figure 12.28 Logs produced by a cluster programme. The initial clusters are shown in column 1 and a much reduced set in column 2. Column 2 can be compared to a core derived, summary lithology in column 3. (Note: the same interval is used for Figures 12.7, 8, 26 and 27) (display from Interactive Petrophysics).

lumberger 'Faciolog' programme (Wolff and Pelissier-Combescure 1982) but, again, there are now quite a number of programmes.

A more interventionist (and in reality supervised) way of finding groups is to use neural nets. This technique is gaining in popularity as it establishes a realistic core based grouping at the outset (the ground truth). That is, the prepared logs are 'trained' with (i.e. compared to) an interval of core where the required lithofacies are known. The log characteristics of the lithofacies are now recognised and can be used to identify similar log responses (e.g. lithofacies) where there is no core. This is achieved by mathematically imitating techniques that are considered to be used by the brain. The input data are represented by input nodes, that is, the logs. A 'hidden layer', so called, of more nodes is created in which every hidden layer node is connected to all the input nodes (**Figure 12.29**). This means that every log influence affects all the others. The hidden layer nodes are then connected to a chosen number of output nodes, which are the lithofacies. Again, every hidden layer node is connected to every output node. When a neural net is shown, for example, lithofacies 'A', the hidden layer 'trains' itself to recognise that more from this log, less from that log and nothing from a third log, are the responses of lithofacies 'A', the multiple connections allowing this. From now on, this particular set of log values and log weightings will be recognised as lithofacies 'A' and all the logs are involved in the decision.

The example (**Figure 12.30**) shows the use of a back-propagation neural net to identify lithofacies. Back-propagation is a particular type of neural net design that works by comparing initial outputs from the neural net to a training set. The errors in the initial outputs, what the output should have shown, are then propagated backwards to the (in this case) single hidden layer. Adjusting the output error to give a minimum is how the system learns. In the example shown, the neural net used 7 inputs logs, a hidden layer of 11 nodes

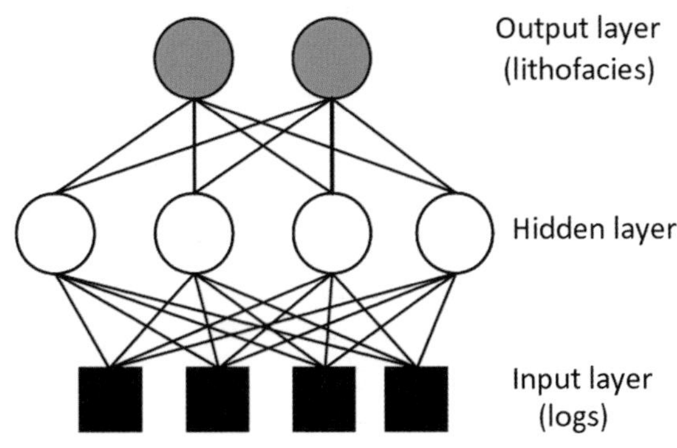

Figure 12.29 The design of a typical neural net for lithofacies recognition. Input nodes are the logs and output nodes the lithofacies.

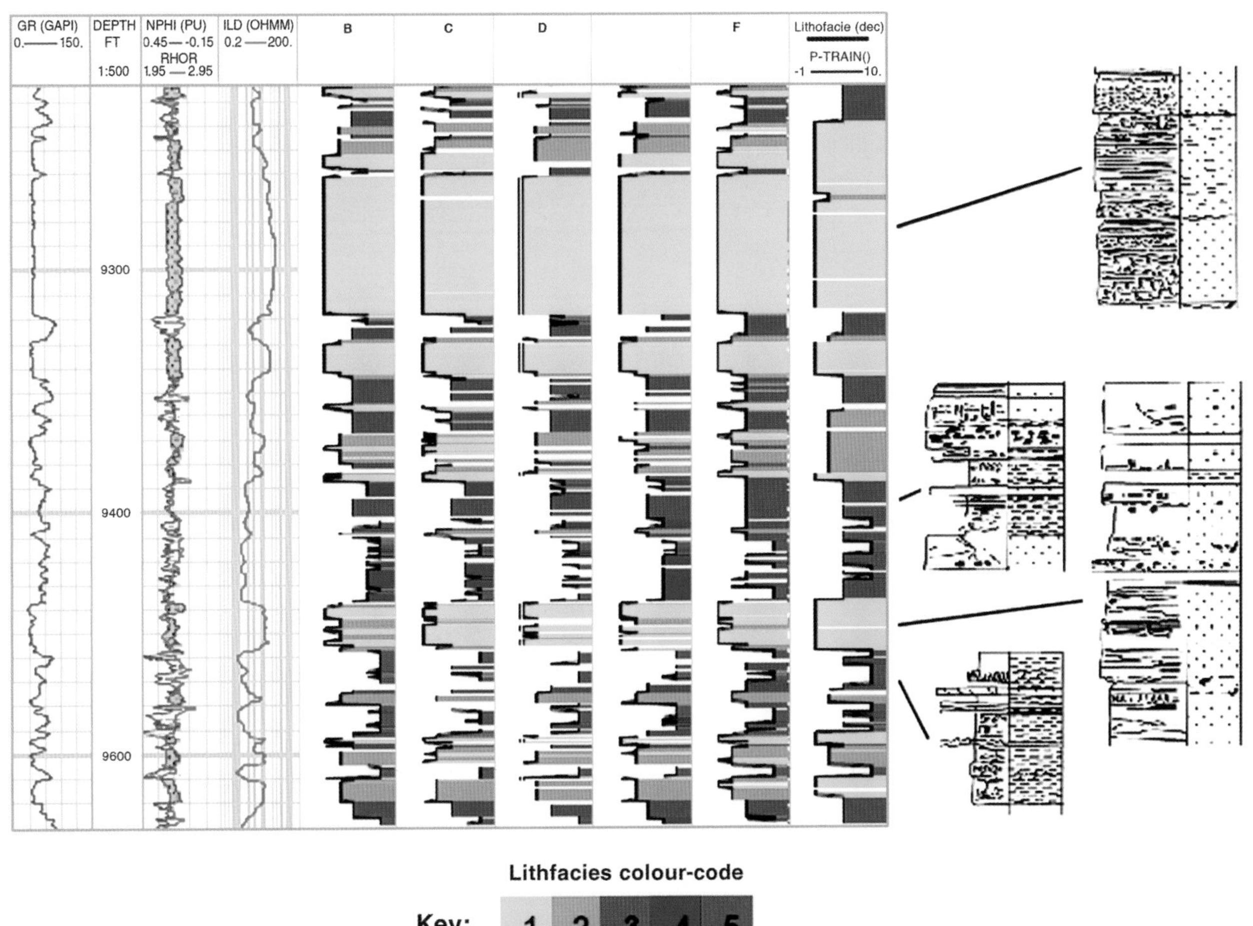

Figure 12.30 An example of a neural net prediction of lithofacies. Lithofacies types: 1 = homogeneous sand. 2 = slightly slumped sand. 3 = interbedded sand and shale, deformed. 4 = sand with thin interbeds. 5 = shale. B-F = differently trained neural nets. P = actual lithofacies (from Martin 2004).

and 5 outputs lithofacies (**Figure 12.30**). This system was found (by mathematical tests) to be successful approximately 70% of the time, although this is probably an underestimation of its real success (Martin 2004). In this respect, it was found that the core lithofacies of the learning set were not actually geologically consistent! Which underlines the need for geologists to use the full potential of the logs.

Some additional observations on this particular work are worth making. Certain lithofacies were more predictable than others, meaning that their log signatures were more marked. Also, the weights between the various inputs and the hidden layer were important, some lithofacies relying heavily on just a few inputs. For example, the influence of fluids on the resistivity response was a dominant factor in certain cases. Neural nets are only as good as their training sets and, in this work, the sets were found to be valid over a limited number of wells (Martin 2004 *op. cit.*). Such systems must be used with knowledge and care, but can be very powerful.

A mathematically simpler method, which is commonly used today in log analysis software, is fuzzy logic. This is an enhanced multidimensional clustering technique, which can be 'trained' in a similar fashion to neural nets. Such methods are used not only to define lithology, but also facies (Cuddy 1997; Fang and Chen 1997).

12.8 Conclusion

The advantage of statistical methods in general is that natural variability is reduced to a mathematical consistency. The geological recognition of a lithology is reduced to the classification of a series of geophysical numbers, a conceptually simple operation, albeit complex mathematically as described above. The geologist's lithology, formerly a qualitative concept, becomes numbers, easier to manipulate using a computer and more consistent. This brings huge advantages but is only a basis on which to build. As Moss states (Moss 1997) 'mathematical consistency is not a guarantee of geological accuracy'. Statistical electrofacies do not inherently correspond to geological lithologies. There are geological elements that are not captured in the numbers.

Using logs to investigate facies and sequences is described in the following chapters (Chapters 16, 17).

13 NUCLEAR MAGNETIC RESONANCE

13.1 Generalities

The log

The modern nuclear magnetic resonance tool was added to the commercial logging suite only in 1992, by the NUMAR Corp. (Coates *et al.* 1999), even though there were numerous earlier attempts and the physical principles used by the tool had been known since 1946 (Bloch *et al.* 1946). Nuclear magnetic resonance (NMR) is also known as magnetic resonance imaging (MRI) because it does not sound radioactive (which it isn't). It is a technique that observes the behaviour of protons (hydrogen nuclei) in a magnetic field. A similar technique is used in medical scanning and is known especially for investigations of the brain when the subject is surrounded by a scanner. The borehole tool turns this inside-out and it is the scanner that is surrounded by the subject, in logging terms, the formation. The first, historically introduced NMR logging tools were not successful as they required specially treated (doped) mud and could only be run

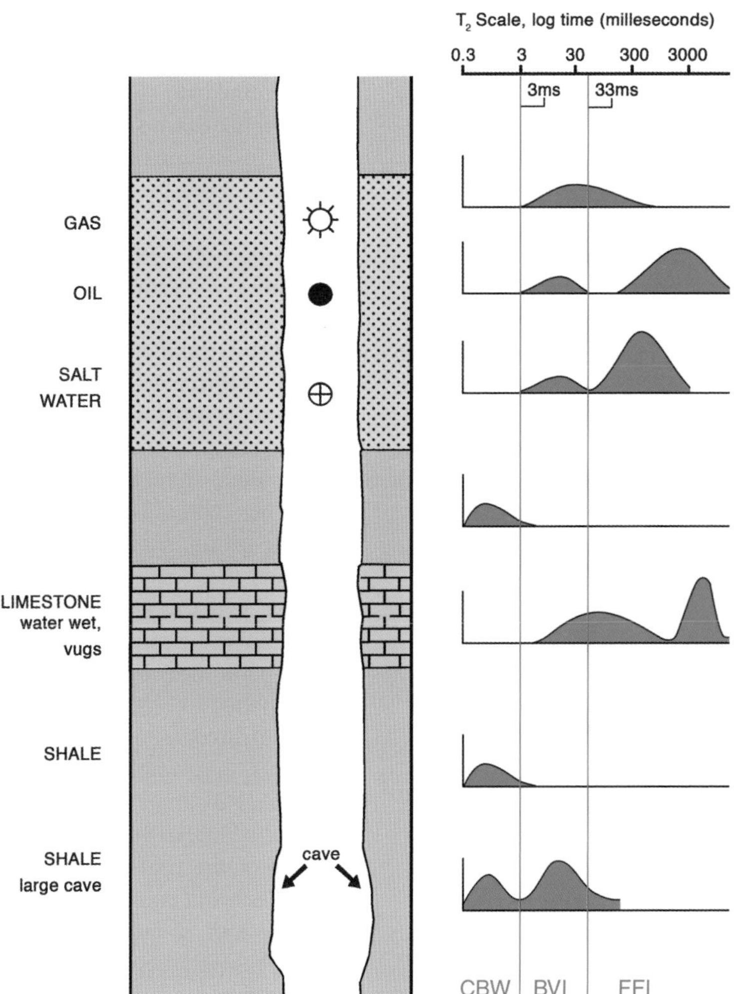

Figure 13.1 The Nuclear Magnetic Resonance (NMR) log: some typical T_2 distribution responses. The T_2 distribution has a vertical Y axis scale in porosity units (p.u.) and an X axis scale in log, time (milliseconds). The area under the curve is porosity. CBW = clay bound water, BVI = irreducible, capillary bound water, FFI = free fluid (index).

very slowly. However, techniques largely developed by NUMAR overcame these problems and today's tools (2011) do not need special treatment, may be logged at normal logging speeds and are now part of the standard logging suite, being routinely used in both the wireline and the while drilling environments.

Uses

The principal use of the NMR is to measure porosity and pore size distribution (**Figure 13.1**). It is the ability to estimate pore size that distinguishes NMR from the other porosity logs. NMR also has the highly desirable feature that it responds exclusively to protons, that is, hydrogen nuclei. Since most hydrogen in the subsurface is part of either a water molecule or a hydrocarbon molecule, the NMR measured hydrogen content can be related directly to porosity. The traditional porosity tools, like the density, neutron and sonic, only allow a total porosity to be calculated. Proton behaviour as observed by the NMR, however, allows the porosity to be divided into different pore size ranges. These are typically categorised as large pores associated with free fluids, pores in which the fluids are capillary-bound or irreducible, and clay-bound fluids (**Figure 13.1**). In addition, in order to calculate the porosity from the traditional porosity tools, the relevant rock matrix properties have to be known. Because the NMR measurement is only responding to protons, NMR porosity is almost independent of the matrix type. The accuracy of the NMR porosity measurement is considered to be better than one porosity unit (1%Ø) (Coates *et al.* 1999).

From the composite NMR porosity, a good estimate of permeability can often be calculated and most logging companies provide at least one permeability curve as a standard output. It is often the best, log-derived permeability estimate available. It is important to note, however, that permeability is not measured by the NMR tool and there are circumstances where the NMR derived permeability value is completely misleading.

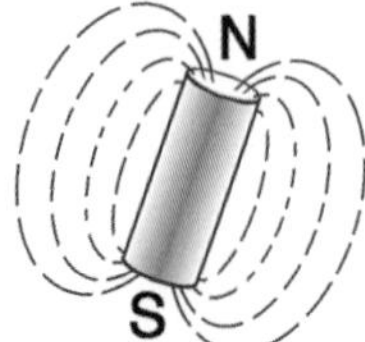

Figure 13.2 Schematic sketch of the magnetic moment of a proton and its notional similarity to a spinning bar magnet.

Modern NMR tools can also provide information on fluid type and properties such as the presence of oil (and gas), oil viscosity and an independent NMR water (hydrocarbon) saturation. These developments mean that the NMR could, in ideal cases, be the only logging tool necessary to provide the data needed for a petrophysical evaluation: porosity, permeability, saturation and hydrocarbon type. For operational reasons and in practice, however, the tool is used to complement the conventional logs, rather than replace them.

A DVD with many major NMR references is available from the SPWLA (NMR Reprint Collection, dated April 2006).

13.2 Principles of measurement

Physics

Quantum mechanics predicts that many nuclei, including the proton, have an intrinsic magnetic moment (field): they behave like spinning bar magnets (**Figure 13.2**). In the absence of any external magnetic field, their orientations are random but, when a steady, external magnetic field is applied, their moments become aligned. The process of alignment, called relaxation, is not immediate and will only be reached after a particular time. But because the protons are rotating, any change in alignment exerts a torque, and causes them to precess about the external magnetic field orientation (like a gyroscope in the gravity field).

Because only certain states are allowed in quantum mechanics, the proton magnetic moment will actually align with or against the external magnetic field (parallel or anti-parallel), the only two possible states for protons (**Figure 13.3**). These states are separated by a small energy difference and a slightly greater number of protons align parallel with the external field, the lower energy state, than align against it, the higher energy state. This slight imbalance results in a net (overall) macroscopic proton magnetisation parallel to the external field, and its strength is proportional to the number of protons. It is this that can be detected, allows proton behaviour to be monitored and is the theoretical basis for the NMR measurement.

As applied to logging tools (and core), an NMR measurement involves a series of proton manipulations to provide a measurable signal. Modern NMR tools have permanent magnets within the tool itself, which create an external magnetic field, and formation protons in the vicinity of the tool align with this field. They are described as being polarised. A short electromagnetic pulse from the tool, of precise frequency and duration, is applied to the polarised protons and it modifies their alignment and energy state. The protons absorb the energy of the pulse as it is applied but radiate it back again when the pulse ends. That is, they resonate (alternate absorption and loss of energy). This is because the protons try to revert to their original polarised state but, as they do

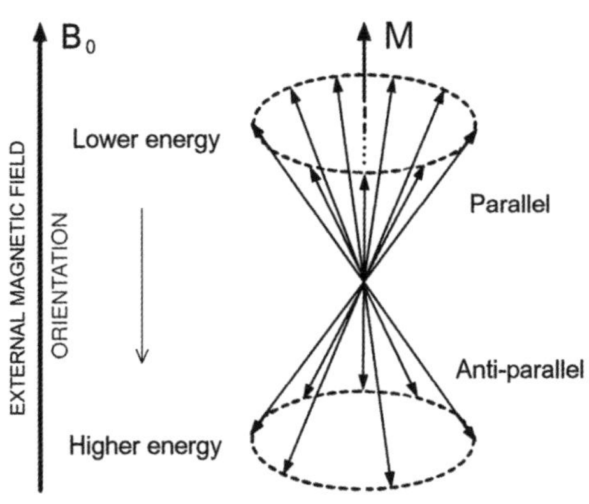

Figure 13.3 Representation of the equilibrium proton state in the external magnetic field B_0. The spins are parallel (lower energy) and anti-parallel (higher energy), but actually precess around B_0. The parallel, lower energy population is slightly greater and M is the bulk net magnetic vector. The cones represent the surface of precessing protons.

so, they release the originally absorbed energy. This is measured by the tool.

By selecting the tool's external magnetic field strength, and setting the frequency of the perturbing electromagnetic pulse, the latter can be tuned to act exclusively on protons. The frequency used is called the Larmor frequency and is proportional to the external magnetic field strength. The pulse with the chosen Larmor frequency, therefore, affects only protons, and only at the particular field strength of the tool. This explains why the NMR measurement is so highly selective and also explains why the word 'resonance' figures in the name of the effect.

Downhole measurement

To make a viable downhole measurement of the NMR effect requires some very clever and very sensitive instrumentation (the rigorous description of which is well beyond the scope of this book). At the heart of a tool are small but powerful permanent magnets creating the external magnetic field described above. Indeed, the ability to build powerful magnets, with the right field distribution and small enough to fit into a downhole tool, was one of the key technologies needed to produce a viable tool. Even so, a tool's magnetic fields give an equivalent energy difference that is so small that the number of protons aligned with and against the field, is almost identical: perhaps of every 100,000 anti-parallel, there are 100,006 parallel.

The pulse of electromagnetic radiation, which is applied to the formation to manipulate the protons, as explained, has to be at precisely the right Larmor frequency, and for modern downhole tools this turns out to be of the order of 1 MHz. Towards the end of this pulse, more protons have become aligned against the external field (high energy state) than with it (low energy state) but as soon the pulse finishes, the nuclei try to re-establish the equilibrium distribution within the external field with nearly identical numbers aligned with, and against it. In order to make this change of state, the protons have to emit photons (energy) at the same frequency that was used to excite them (i.e. about 1 MHz radio frequency). It is this small, resonance signal that can be detected by a sensitive antenna in the tool. The signal's amplitude is proportional to the total number of protons in the volume investigated by the tool and this number (i.e number of hydrogen nuclei) can be interpreted in terms of the water and hydrocarbon fluids in the formation and so, the porosity.

However, there is another property of the resonant signal, and that is the time it takes to die away following the perturbing pulse: the time it takes to decay. Not all proton signals decay at the same rate: it depends on the microscopic environment that the proton is in, and is quantified by a characteristic decay time named T_2, the so-called *spin-spin relaxation* (there is also a T_1, *see below*). As a general rule, the more tightly bound a proton is, the more rapidly the signal decays and the shorter the T_2 time. So protons attached to a water molecule that is bound tightly to a clay grain will decay far more quickly than liquid water in a large vug or fracture. The T_2 time for the clay bound water is short (a few ms) and the T_2 time for the liquid water is long (up to several seconds). Hydrogen that is in the solid state, such as that associated with the crystal structure of clay, is actually invisible to the particular type of measurement used for logging tools and core measurements (it can be detected in the laboratory using special techniques). This is actually an advantage as it means the hydrogen associated with the clay structure is not wrongly identified as clay bound water (contrast this with the neutron log). At the other extreme, a water molecule in the centre of a large pore is free to move around and will decay with T_2 values approaching 1000 ms. Between these two extremes are small pores associated with water that is bound to the surface of grains. So, by measuring how the NMR signal decays, the protons can be allocated to the different categories: clay-bound water, surface-bound (capillary) water and free water (or hydrocarbons).

The CPMG pulse sequence, measuring T_2

Measuring a viable T_2 signal in the subsurface requires not just a single pulse of Larmor frequency electromagnetic radiation to disturb the protons, but a whole sequence of pulses.

The length of time of the initial perturbing pulse is chosen so that the proton's magnetic moment rotates until it is at 90 degrees to the tool's external magnetic field (The external field is termed B_0 and is in the borehole axis or longitudinal direction, the field at 90 degrees is B_1 and is the transverse direction **Figure 13.4**). As soon as this perturbing pulse is removed, the protons, or strictly speaking their magnetic moments, will attempt to realign with the external field (B_0). But the rules of physics do not allow them to do this and instead they are forced to precess in a plain that lies at 90 degrees to the external field (i.e in B_1). The protons actually precess at the Larmor frequency and emit a similar frequency electromagnetic field as they do so. This is detected by the tool's antenna which is now functioning as a receiver.

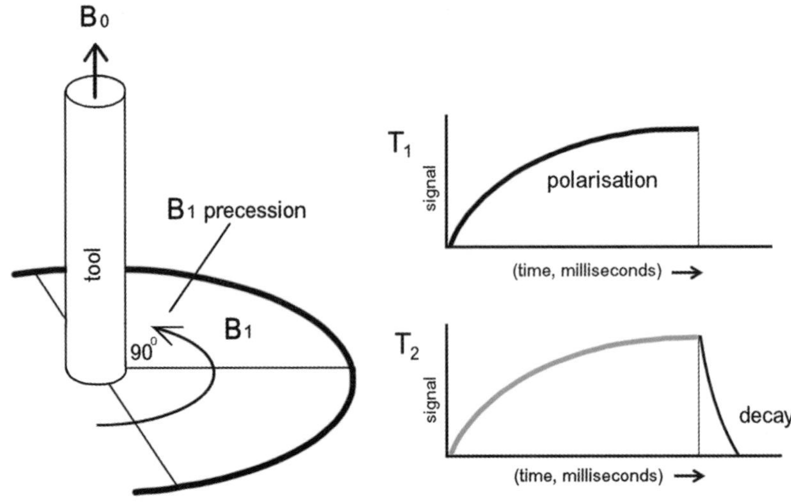

Figure 13.4 In NMR logging, the tool imposes a strong, axial (longitudinal) magnetic field (B_0) and this polarises the protons of the formation (T_1). To observe proton behavior, the tool tilts the aligned protons into an orientation transverse to the tool (B_1) and then observes their decay (T_2).

Ordinarily, this precessing proton signal decays quickly to zero. This is because the external magnetic field is never truly homogeneous and the individual protons are all in slightly different magnetic environments. The result is that they precess at slightly different rates and their individual contributions interfere destructively so that the signal disappears rapidly. To produce a signal that can form a viable log measurement, the proton signal has to be manipulated. Various ways of doing this have been proposed, but at present the technique all logging tools and core analysis instruments use is known as the CPMG spin-echo sequence (CPMG is named after the physicists and engineers that developed it: Carr, Purcell, Meiboom and Gill).

The CPMG spin-echo sequence involves imposing a series of pulses of Larmor frequency radiation on the formation, and not just one. Following the initial, single pulse that tips the protons 90°, a series of pulses is emitted that are twice as long in duration and are equally spaced at a characteristic time, which is programmed into the tool. These are universally known as the 'echo spacing' or TE (time echo) and the total number of pulses as NE (400 is a typical number). The period of the pulse train (TE × NE), is typically of the order of 0.5 seconds and the entire manipulation is the CPMG sequence (Coates *et al.* 1999). Because the pulses that make up the series are each twice as long as the original pulse, they reverse the precession direction. This means that the magnetic moments which had started to 'de-phase' at the end of the previous pulse are brought back into phase. When this occurs, the signal each proton emits will constructively interfere, and a signal, the 'echo', can be detected. (The commonest way this is illustrated is to imagine runners on a track being repeatedly told to change direction. The faster runners who were at the front of the pack then find themselves at the back. They will catch up with the slower runners when they have all returned to the start.)

However, after each pulse in the CPMG sequence, the amplitude of the echo declines. This is caused by three processes. The first is *surface relaxation* and occurs when protons lose their polarisation as a result of interacting with the surface of mineral grains. The second process is *bulk relaxation*, when protons lose their polarisation as a result of exchanging spins with other protons, and the third is *diffusion* whereby some molecules simply diffuse out of the tool's volume of investigation. These three different influences act together and are additive. The resulting decay of the echo amplitudes is exponential and is the characteristic decay time, T_2 (**Figure 13.4**).

In porous rocks T_2 decay time is related to the pore environment the molecule is in. For example, protons in pores will lose their alignment (decay) by surface relaxation as they collide with the solid, pore surface. Protons, or strictly speaking the molecules they form, are under permanent Brownian movement and, in their constant agitation, will frequently bounce off the pore wall (**Figure 13.5**). This causes them to lose alignment quickly. In large pores, collisions with the pore surface will be fewer and relaxation slower than in small pores.

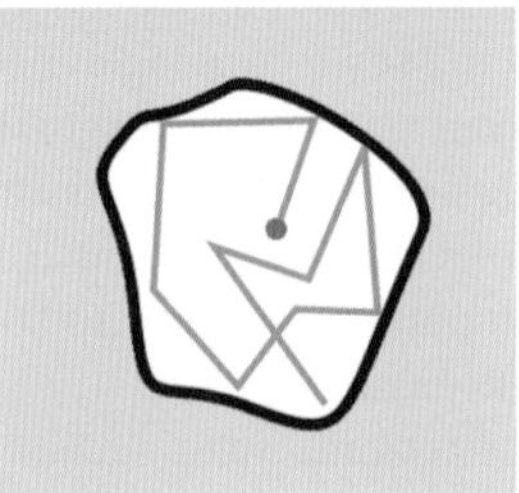

Figure 13.5 Schematic proton behaviour in a pore. In its permanent movement, the proton collides with the pore wall and loses alignment. The smaller the pore the more frequent these collisions and the quicker the alignment is lost.

Table 13.1 NMR fluid properties at reservoir conditions, 93°C, 310 bar (200°F, 4500 psi) (Akkurt *et al.* 1996; Prammer *et al.* 1999).

		*T1 (ms)	†T2 (ms)	HI	Viscosity (cp)	Diffusivity (cm²/s)
Brine		1–500	1–500	1	0.2–0.8	$1.8–7 \times 10^{-5}$
Oil		3000–4000	300–1000	1	0.2–1000	$0.0015–7.6 \times 10^{-5}$
	Light oil		609		2.7	(faster)
	Medium oil		40		35	
	Heavy oil		1.8		4304	(slower)
Gas		4000–5000	30–60	0.2–0.6	0.011–0.014 (methane)	$80–100 \times 10^{-5}$
OBM-filtrate		1500–2500	500–800?	1		$0.92–2 \times 10^{-5}$

*T1 = full polarisation time. †T2 = decay time. Brine = 120 ppm

That is, the larger the pore, the longer the decay time. For protons that are within the layer of water that adheres to the pore wall, however, or within the water that is associated with a clay sheet, or even the hydrogen atoms that form part of the clay structure, the decay time will be extremely rapid.

The environment of the proton also influences the other two effects. Bulk fluid relaxation, the effect that protons have on one another within the fluid, is effectively the upper limit on T_2. It increases with temperature and decreases with increasing viscosity. It only becomes important if pores are very large, or if hydrocarbons fill the pores and are non-wetting (as is usual) and do not come into contact with the pore surface. Fluids themselves tend to have long relaxation times (**Table 13.1**). Lastly, there is diffusion, which affects T_2 when protons are able to diffuse in a fluid across a magnetic gradient, that is, into, or out of, magnetic fields with different strengths, during the time of a CPMG experiment. Such changes cause an increase in relaxation time. Relaxation or decay times, therefore, reflect the distribution of pore sizes and location of the proton (**Figure 13.6**).

In summary, T_2 decay time can, at a minimum, be interpreted in terms of porosity, pore sizes and proton location. It is usually described in terms of *free fluid* that can move (it may be water or hydrocarbons), irreducible *bound water* that clings to grains and does not move (i.e. capillary water or, in rare cases, wetting hydrocarbons) and *clay-bound water*, that is, in the clay lattice or part of the clay structure (**Figure 13.7**). Free fluid is contained within larger pores while pores below a certain size only contain bound water that cannot move. Porosity is derived from the total number of protons.

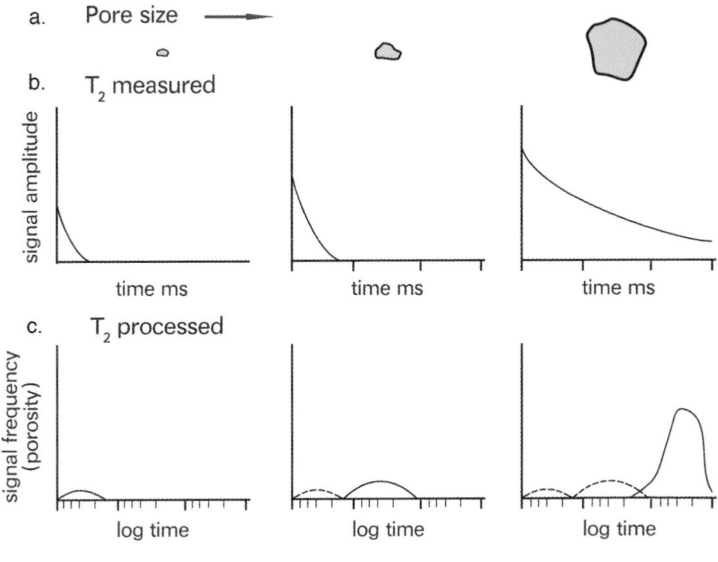

Figure 13.6 a. different pore sizes give rise to different T_2 signal amplitudes as observed by an NMR tool. b. The observed signal amplitudes as measured by the tool are processed to a porosity distribution. c. The porosity distribution from the processed T_2 signal allows fluid to be identified as being in: micro-pores (clay bound); small pores (capillary bound); and large pores (free to flow).

Polarisation and T_1

The other characteristic time in NMR logging is T_1, the so-called *spin-lattice relaxation time*. *Relaxation time* is a constant associated with the return of nuclear spins to their equilibrium positions after excitation. The T_1 relaxation time is the time it takes for protons to align with the (longitudinal) static external field, that is, the time taken to establish polarisation. Looked at a slightly different way, it means that longitudinal magnetisation builds up from zero to a maximum during T_1 (polarisation), whereas T_2, the transverse magnetisation, decays following the Larmor frequency pulse from a maximum to zero. Longitudinal align-

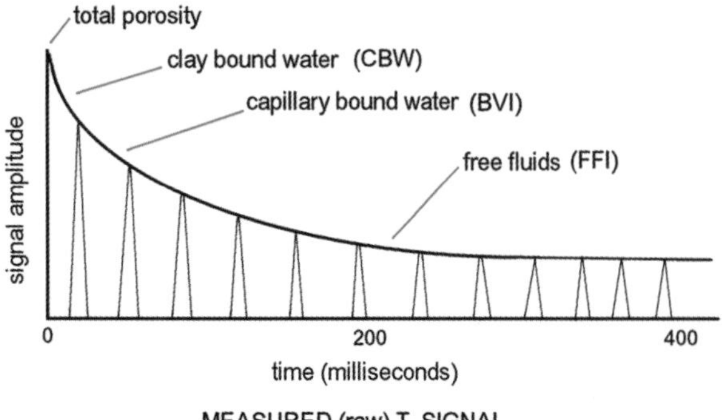

Figure 13.7 Representation of a measured T_2 signal from an NMR tool. The full amplitude represents the total porosity of the formation. The amplitude of the clay bound proton signal (CBW) decays very rapidly, while the capillary bound proton signal (BVI) is only slightly less rapid. The amplitude of the free fluid signal (FFI) decays at a slower and slower rate as pore size increases. (An actual T_2 measurement record is shown in Figure 13.10,a).

ment or polarisation is not instantaneous, and will only be achieved gradually and with a characteristic time (T_1) that depends on the microscopic environments of each proton. As a general rule, the more easily the molecule containing the proton can move, the longer is T_1. Under typical subsurface conditions T_1 can be as long as several seconds. However, because it is so long, it allows NMR to not only measure the fluid content of a rock, but also to categorise it as free, capillary or bound.

In order to measure porosity accurately, the CPMG experiment (sequence) can only be performed when all the formation's protons are 'fully' polarised, that is, aligned to the external magnetic field (B_0). Polarisation is slow, as indicated, with full polarisation typically three times T_1, so that it can be difficult to ensure while logging. The time used to polarise the formation is called TW (time wait). The time taken by a complete CPMG experiment is typically about 0.5 seconds, but TW can be 10–12 seconds (**Figure 13.8**). The total duration of polarisation and the CPMG experiment can therefore easily take 30 seconds, during which a wireline tool may move several metres. Furthermore, the signals that are being detected during an experiment are very small and have a poor signal to noise ratio. Several measurements may need to be stacked to get an acceptable result. The stacking amplifies the signal (which is coherent) but not the noise (which is random), a technique similar to seismic stacking.

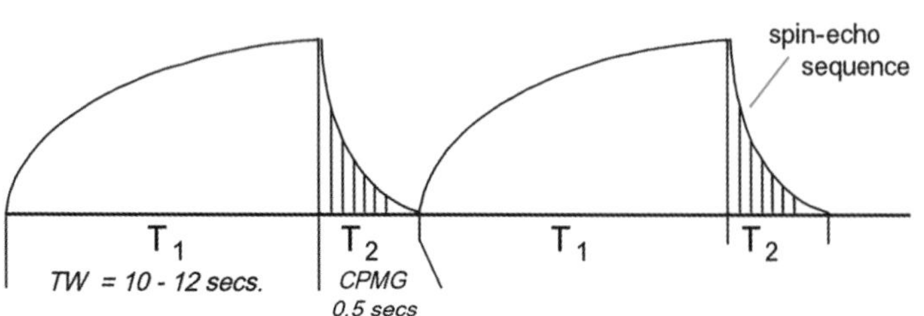

Figure 13.8 Wait time (TW) is much longer than time during which the CPMG spin-echo sequence is run. T_1 polarisation occurs during TW and T_2 is measured during the CPMG sequence.

In some measurement sequences, a full polarisation is purposely not always used. If a partially polarised formation is analysed by a CPMG echo-train, it will only be able to analyse the protons polarised up to that moment. For example, after a short polarisation time (TW) only clay bound and capillary bound water will be polarised, so that the corresponding T_2 will show only these elements (**Figure 13.9**). After a long TW and full polarisation, clay bound water, capillary bound water, free water and hydrocarbons will all be seen in the T_2 distribution (Mullen *et al.* 2005).

The CPMG sequences in modern tools are now programmable. Wait times (TW), inter-echo times (TE) and echo number (NE) can all be varied and different activating frequencies selected: according to the formation type, porosities to be expected, fluids (or gas) to be expected, and required logging speed. For example, long wait times (TW) may be chosen for high porosity formations and carbonates; short inter-echo times (TE) chosen for shale dominated horizons as they make short T_2 times easier to measure; and long echo trains chosen for hydrocarbon bearing reservoirs. For sensitive experiments, tools may be stationary to take these measurements.

Tool calibration

NMR tools are calibrated to water. For a master calibration, doped water containing NiCl is used and fills the area sensitised by the radio antenna. The doping reduces the full polarisation time to 50 ms and allows a wait time of 5 minutes to be used to measure a good signal (Freedman & Morriss 1995). The processed spin-echo signal of the calibration will represent 100 porosity units (p.u.). The signal amplitude measured during logging is compared to this tool master calibration, and scaled appropriately.

Tool output (displays)

T_2 decay, as observed by the CPMG spin-echo sequence is, in effect, a multi-exponential decay curve, that is, a combination of many, single exponent curves, one for each proton. Each single exponent curve is related to just one pore size or environment. In other words, the decay of each individual proton reflects its immediate environment. The raw, *measured* T_2 amplitudes can be inverted and re-plotted as a spectral T_2 distribution (**Figure 13.10**). It is this *processed* T_2 that is usually plotted as a wiggle trace on the logs (**Figure 13.11, track 5**). On the trace, incremental porosity is the y axis and the x axis is a log scale of time. A single trace is shown in **Figure**

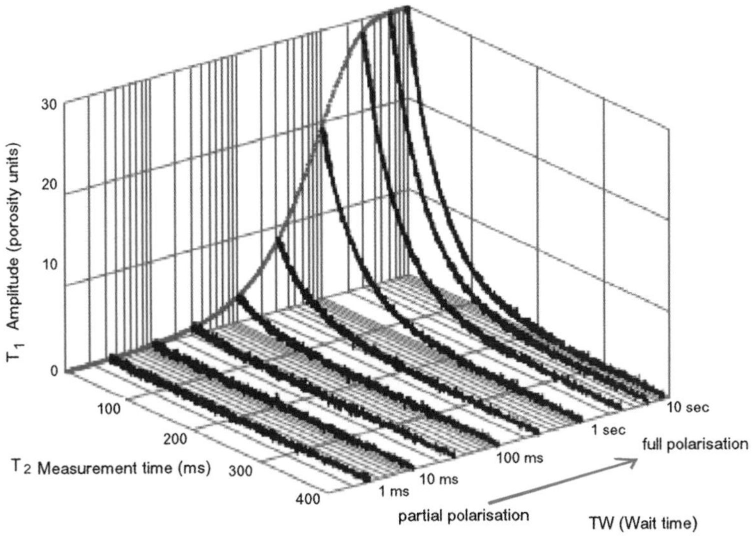

Figure 13.9 Partial polarisation can be used to selectively analyse elements of T_1. After a short TW, polarisation has only affected clay-bound and capillary bound water. The resulting T_2 will only be an analysis of these elements. Free water and hydrocarbons will only be analysed after a long TW and full polarisation (modified from Mullen *et al.* SPWLA 2005).

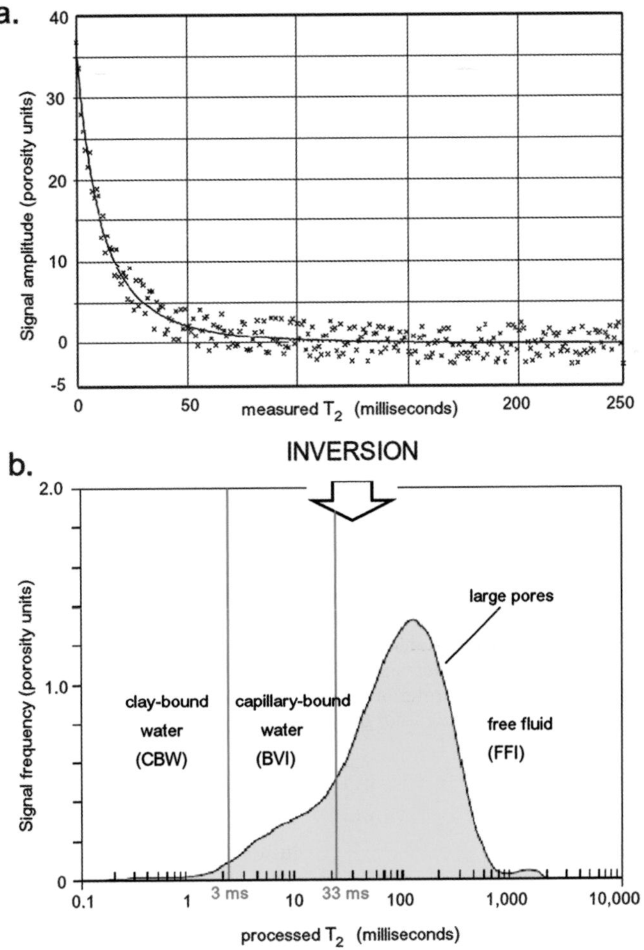

Figure 13.10 (a) measured T_2 record of signal amplitude and (b) the T_2 signal distribution derived from it by inversion. Tool calibration allows the signal distribution to be scaled in porosity units and the area under the curve gives actual porosity. The porosity is divided into clay-bound fluids (CBW), irreducible, capillary bound water (BVI bulk volume irreducible) and free fluids (FFI) (modified from Coates *et al.* 1999). *Halliburton © 1999. Reproduced with permission of the copyright holder. Further reproduction prohibited without permission.*

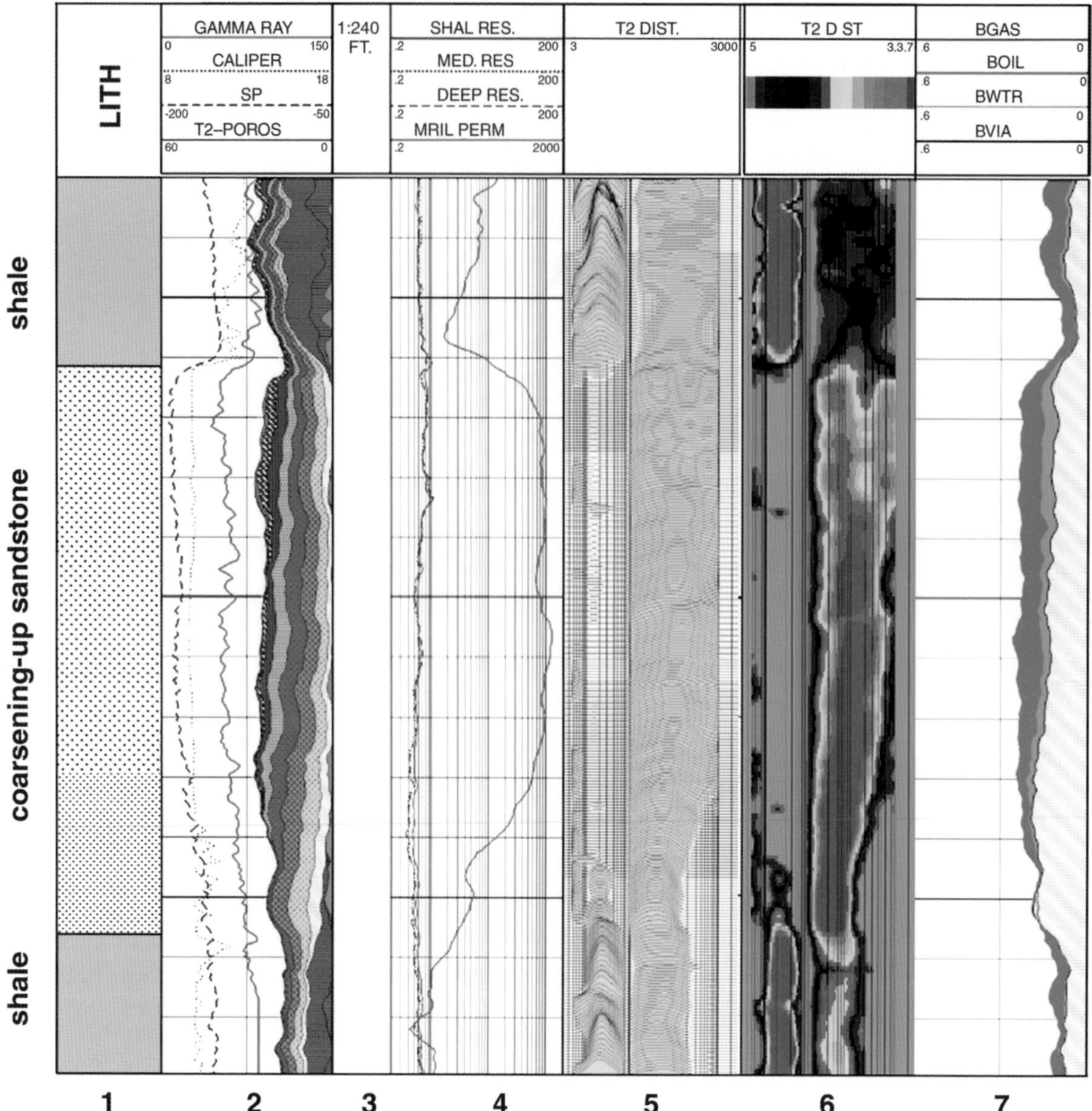

Figure 13.11 NMR log display. Track 1, interpreted lithology. Track 2, T_2 plotted using a series of time bins; the total porosity is the same as in tack 7. Track 3, depth in feet. Track 4, standard resistivity logs and NMR (MRIL) permeability. Track 5, stacked T_2 signal distribution wiggle traces, horizontal scale, log time in milliseconds, Y scale in porosity units. Track 6, same T_2 signal distribution as a 2-D amplitude map. Track 7, T_2 porosity. The total porosity is divided into porosity with oil (green) porosity with water (blue) and porosity with irreducible capillary water (grey). Note the capillary water (BVI) decreases upwards and the permeability increases because of the increasing sandstone grain size (coarsening-up). The sandstone produced 2000 bbl of light oil on test (from Coates *et al.* 1999, lithology interpretation added). *Halliburton © 1999. Reproduced with permission of the copyright holder. Further reproduction prohibited without permission.*

13.10,b and many of these are stacked to make the log display. The traces can also be plotted as a 2-D amplitude map (**Figure 13.11, track 6**).

The area under the processed T_2 distribution represents porosity (the total number of protons) and this can be plotted as a single value log of total porosity (**Figure 13.11, track 7**). On some displays this porosity is divided into T_2 time bins (**Figure 13.11, track 2**). However, more generally, within this porosity the pore sizes identified by the NMR measurements will be related to fluid behaviour as described, that is, whether they will flow or not. So the single, total porosity is usually divided into porosity occupied by capillary bound fluids and free fluids (**Figure 13.11, track 7**). The free fluid volume may be further sub-divided into the percentage occupied by water and by hydrocarbons, which is the saturation. These are all values derived from the NMR. On many plots the value between the producible fluids and the irreducible fluids is shown as a line (often red) with either a fixed value (based on laboratory comparisons) or the variable value of the log mean of the T_2 (T_{2LM}).

Although the edited, processed T_2 is generally

Table 13.2 NMR tools (only some) (Chen *et al.* 2003; Serra 2008)

Company	Wireline tool	frequencies	echos (NE)	TW (seconds)	TE (minimum)
Schlumberger	CMR		3000	6s	0.2 ms
	CMR-plus				
	MR Scanner	3			0.45 ms
Halliburton	MRIL				
	MRIL-prime	9	400	1 & 8s	0.6 & 1.2 ms
	MRIL-XL				
Baker Hughes™ (Atlas)	MR Explorer™ (MREX)	6	500–1000	4–6s	0.4 or 0.6 ms
	LWD tool				
Schlumberger	Pro-VISION		20,300,500		0.8 ms
Halliburton	MRIL-WD				0.5 ms
Baker Hughes™ INTEQ	MagTrak™	1 (500 kHz)		6s	0.4 or 0.6 ms

the basic value on plots, T_1 is also sometimes used (**Figure 13.25**). Other specialised plots exist and will be described. In addition, processed T_2 distributions will again be examined under petrophysical uses (Section 13.5).

A simple inspection of NMR displays, especially the T_2 distribution, can give great insights into the nature of a formation. They can be used by non-specialists. The interpretation of NMR data does not always need sophisticated log analysis software, a simple log plot is sufficient.

13.3 Tools

Modern wireline NMR logging tools are combinable with more traditional tools and, for a basic porosity measurement, can be run at standard speeds. For example, the Schlumberger Combinable Magnetic Resonance (CMR) tool can be run at 1000 m/hr (3600 ft/hr), while the Halliburton Magnetic Resonance Imaging Log (MRIL) can be acquired on a single run at 460 m/hr (1500 ft/hr) (Menger and Prammer 1998). As more information is required or greater accuracy demanded, the tool has to be run more slowly. This is because either more time is needed to polarise the protons or individual measurements have to be repeated multiple times to improve signal to noise ratio. For example, for fluid profiling with the MR Scanner (Schlumberger), the tool should be run at 75 m/hr (270 ft/hr).

The basic NMR technology developed for wireline tools has now been successfully transferred to the LWD environment although, as will be seen below, this required some significant changes to the hardware. LWD tools are available for at least 8½" holes. The LWD log is sometimes is called the LNMR (**Table 13.2**).

NMR wireline logging tools

All commercial NMR tools consists of permanent magnets, a radio antenna to transmit the CPMG pulses and measure the echos, and the supporting electronics. The exact design and arrangement of these components varies a lot between companies and present NMR tools can be said to differ more than any other generic tool type. The original NUMAR tool was borehole centred with a volume of investigation that was basically the curved surface of a cylinder centred on the borehole axis. The NUMAR tool subsequently became Halliburton's MRIL tool, which was also built under licence by Baker.

Schlumberger's NMR tool had a different design in which the magnets and antenna were incorporated in a pad that was pushed against the borehole wall. This resulted in a small volume of investigation located a few centimetres into the formation in front of the pad (so, like the density tool it is directional). Baker and Schlumberger have now introduced second generation tools. The new tools are similar and consist of a sonde that is pushed against the borehole wall, like the first Schlumberger tool. The volume of investigation is, however, larger and consists of part of the curved surface of a cylinder. The electronics have also been improved to give a series of concentric, partial cylinders and hence multiple depths of investigation. Since NMR is a relatively new measurement, it will undoubtedly undergo more evolution and probably several different tools will ultimately be available and, like resistivity tools, will be designed to emphasise different properties (e.g. depth of investigation or vertical resolution).

The MRIL, developed by NUMAR and now used by Halliburton, can be used as an example tool. The MRIL tool is run hole centred and has strong permanent magnets that orient (polarise) the formation's protons axially around the tool. The Earth's field has a flux density (strength) of 0.5 gauss while the tool's magnets produce a flux density of 175 gauss in the formation investigated. Since this is more than 350 times stronger than the Earth's field, the latter can be ignored. The magnets are oriented transverse to the tool's axis and produce static magnetic fields in the formation that are radial to the

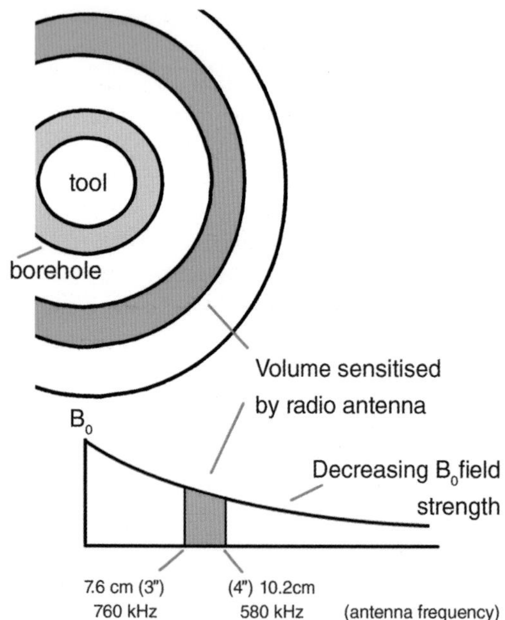

Figure 13.12 Sketch of the relationship of the imposed B_0 magnetic field and the B_1 volume sensitised by the radio antenna during a CPMG measurement. The B_0 field decreases in strength away from the tool so that the (Larmor) frequency of the antenna signal determines where the formation is sensitised. Numbers are only illustrative. See Table 13.3.

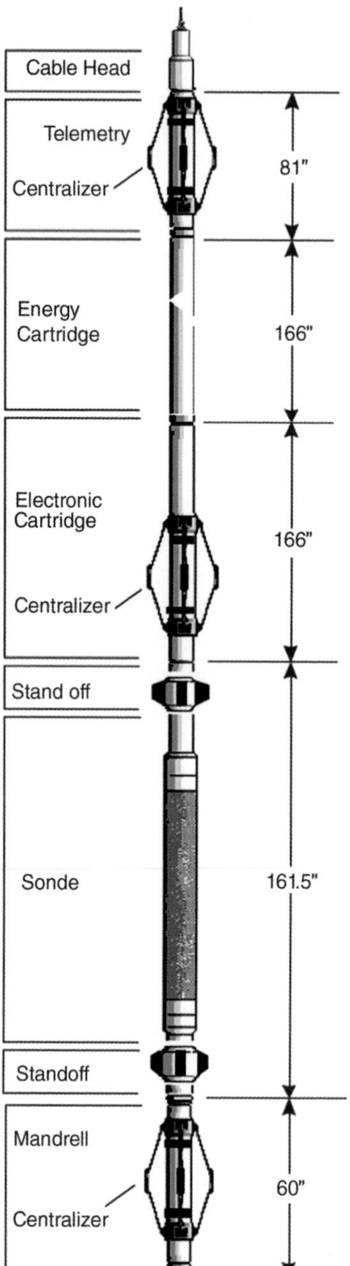

Figure 13.13 The Halliburton, NUMAR wireline MRIL tool. The tool is run hole-centred (from Coates *et al.* 1999, courtesy Halliburton).

tool. The flux density diminishes away from the tool so that there is only a narrow range of distances from the tool axis where the Larmor frequency of the tool's pulse matches the strength of its magnetic field (Coates *et al.* 1999) (**Figure 13.12**). This also means the tool's volume of investigation can be very precisely defined as the curved part of the surface of a cylinder with a diameter of 40 cm. Any protons lying inside or outside this shell, do not contribute to the measurement.

In the MRIL tool, the magnets are 0.6 m (2 ft) above and below the radio antenna (for up-logging and down-logging), the tool thus moving into the polarised region. The CPMG pulse sequence is transmitted from the radio antenna in the central 0.6 m (2 ft) of the sonde. The antenna also acts as the receiver. The Lamor frequency for the magnetic field used by the MRIL is approximately 750 kHz (in a 175 gauss field). The stand-alone tool is nearly 15 m (50 ft) long (**Figure 13.13**).

The latest version of the MRIL (the 'MRIL-Prime') and the Baker and Schlumberger Magnetic Explorers exploit the fact that, because the magnetic field strength diminishes into the formation, the Larmor frequency drops with distance from the tool axis. So, by operating at several different frequencies, these tools have multiple depths of investigation. The MRIL-Prime uses 9, 12 kHz frequency bands between a high of 760 kHz and a low of 580 kHz , to investigate a thin, cylindrical volume around the tool axis, with a diameter of 37 cm–42 cm (14.5"–16.5"). (Lower frequency signals investigate deeper than higher frequency signals, but deeper investigation requires greater power, and the signal to noise ratio becomes worse.) Using all frequencies, the sensitive volume is a cylinder about 2.5 cm (1") thick (**Figure 13.12**) (Prammer *et al.* 1999).

The pulse sequence in the MRIL is programmable (Prammer *et al.* 1999). Wait time (TW) may be between 1 and 12 secs, inter-echo time (TE) is 0.6–1.2 ms and the number of echos (NE) is 400. A special sequence of TW 0.02 secs, TE 0.6 ms, NE 10 and a repeat of 24 times, is used for short T_2 components such as bound water. Overall cycle repeat is every 14 secs. When logged at 300 m/hr (1000 ft/hr) or 5 m/min (16.7 ft/min), up to 2 samples a foot are provided. The readings are, however, time based in this tool. The programmable sequences are used for particular purposes (**Table 13.4**) and these numbers simply give an idea of what can be expected.

The equivalent figures are different for the Schlumberger Combinable Magnetic Resonance (CMR) tool since, as indicated, it is a skid type, eccentered device and magnetises only a small volume in front of the skid (**Figure 13.14**). The magnets are 76 cm (30") long with a 38 cm (15") pre-polarisation magnet above a 15 cm (6") radio antenna (Kenyon *et al.* 1995). The MR Scanner, equally from Schlumberger, a post CMR tool, uses a main antenna and two 'high resolution' antennae, with

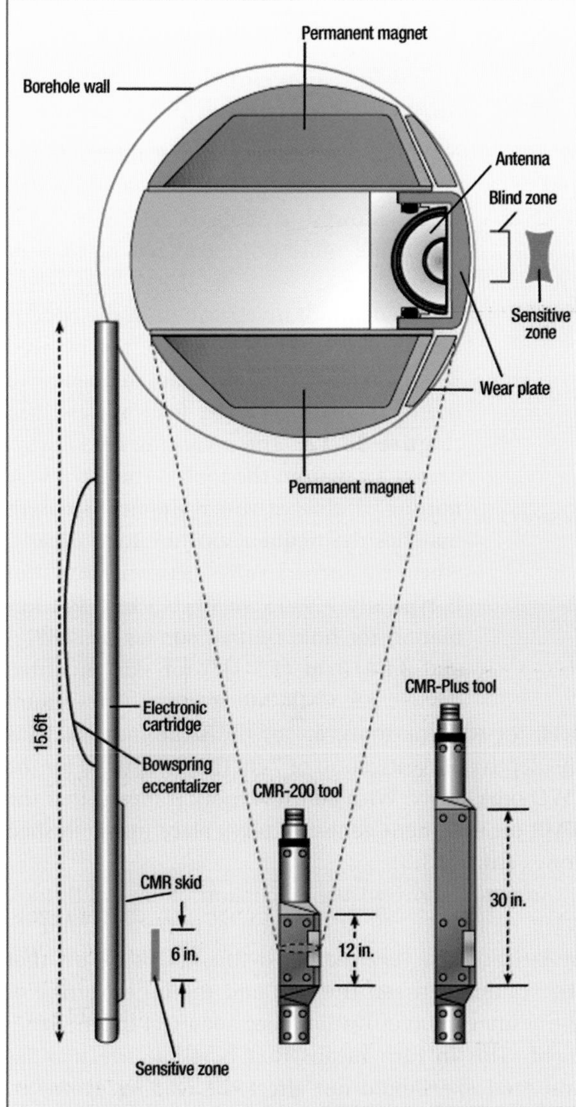

Figure 13.14 The Schlumberger wireline CMR, CMR-200 and CMR-plus tools. The tool is run eccentred with a skid against the borehole wall (from Allen *et al.* 2000). *Copyright Schlumberger Ltd. Used with permission.*

a range of pulse sequences to acquire standard NMR readings and diffusion readings used to detect hydrocarbon type and oil viscosity (Section 13.5, Hydrocarbons and oil viscosity). This tool has an investigation depth ranging from 3.8 cm–10 cm (1.5"–4") and a vertical resolution from 10–46 cm (4–18") but can still potentially be logged at 61–91 m/hr (200–300 ft/hr) (DePavia *et al.* 2003). All NMR tools are evolving quite rapidly, so that details, sizes and especially TW and TE pulse sequences are quite variable.

LWD NMR tools

NMR wireline technology has been transferred to the LWD domain and LWD NMR measurements are becoming more commonplace. This was not a simple matter of re-packaging wireline components in an LWD housing (as effectively happened with density and neutron tools). The NMR measurement takes several seconds and, in that time-scale, the typical vibration and lateral movements that occur in a drill string can move the excited part of the formation out of the volume of investigation of the receiver coil. Furthermore, the powerful magnets at the heart of the tool could interfere with the navigational components in the measurement while drilling (MWD) tools which are normally placed close to the bit. Of all the LWD tools, NMR arguably requires the closest co-operation between driller and logging engineer.

The current generation of LWD NMR tools have a cylindrical volume of investigation that is similar to the original NUMAR tool. The magnets are, however, designed to produce a low gradient field so that the thickness over which the resonant condition occurs is much thicker than in the wireline tool. This means that even if the receiver moves during the measurement it is still sampling excited nuclei. The tool itself is fitted with stabilisers to reduce lateral movement, and the movement of the string is continuously monitored by accelerometers so that, if it becomes excessive, a warning is generated (this serves as a warning that data quality has been compromised and also offers the chance to change drilling parameters to reduce lateral movement). Because of these motion effects on the NMR reading, some LWD tools, such as the MRIL-WD from NUMAR, measure T_1 rather than T_2 (Prammer *et al.* 2000). The T_1 measurement is not affected by lateral movement.

The Schlumberger proVISION tool can act as an example LWD tool (**Figure 13.15**) (Alvarado *et al.* 2003). It has two hollow, cylindrical, samarium-cobalt permanent magnets located above and below the antenna coil, which itself is a helix, co-axial with the tool axis. The magnets are stable up to 150°C (300°F) and 138 MPa (20,000 psi). They produce a field which decays relatively slowly with distance into the formation. The radio frequency field produces a shell with a diameter of 36 cm (14"), 10 mm (0.4") thick and a height of 15 cm (6") in the formation about the tool (**Figure 13.15**). The static magnetic field is about 60 gauss and the gradient

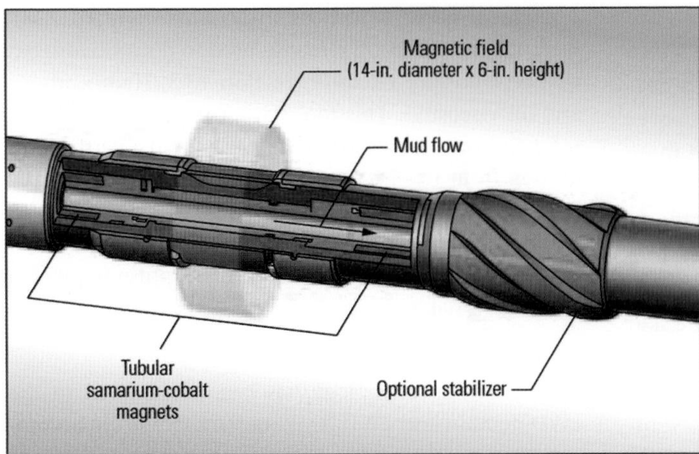

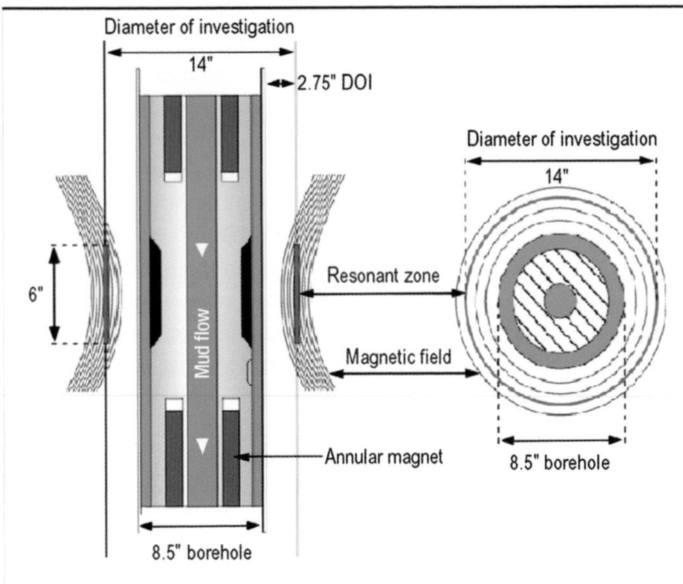

Figure 13.15 The LWD NMR pro-VISION tool from Schlumberger showing the magnetic field and the resonant zone giving a diameter of investigation of 14" (35.6 cm) (from Alvarado *et al.* 2003). *Copyright Schlumberger Ltd. Used with permission.*

3 gauss per cm. From the fact, as indicated, that permanent magnets in the borehole can affect the directional magnetic surveys used in geosteering and imaging tools, a 12 m (40 ft) separation from steering sondes has been suggested (Prammer *et al.* 2000). The tool is 11.3 m long (37 ft).

This tool operates in cycles rather than continuously, that is, a polarisation and wait time mode and then the oscillating antenna mode of CPMG signals. Each CPMG is collected in pairs of different phase, which are then combined in an effort to improve the signal to noise ratio. The tool measures both T_1 and T_2 although T_2 provides the principal results. The tool measurement sequence can be modified to function when the drill is rotating, sliding or stationary.

Because of the limitations in the volume of data that can be up-loaded in the LWD environment, not all the measured LWD NMR values are available in real-time. The T_2 inversion is done downhole, which means that the T_2 spectral distribution is available in real-time, although uploaded only as single values of an NMR porosity, BFV (irreducible water volume), FFV (free fluid volume), a logarithmic T_2 mean and a quality indicator. With these numbers, an NMR permeability can be calculated and is therefore available in real-time. The complete measurement cycle information is stored in tool memory and can be retrieved when it is brought up to the rig floor. For data transfer there is a limitation of dogleg severity of 8°/30 m (8°/100 ft) during rotation, or 16°/30 m (16°/100 ft) during sliding, as is usual.

13.4 Log Characteristics

Depth of investigation and vertical resolution

NMR is a shallow reading measurement and, in fact, some NMR tools are amongst the shallowest reading of all tools. This fact alone must be considered when they are used.

The depth of investigation of the NMR is determined by the strength of the induced B_0 polarising field and the frequency of the B_1 oscillating CPMG field as described (**Figure 13.12**). The polarising field always decays away from the tool so there is a very narrow window at which the field strength matches the frequency of the tool. Clearly, where this occurs varies between tools, but is typically 7.5–15 cm (3–6") into the formation for hole centred sondes (i.e. MRIL) and 3.8–10 cm (1.5–4") for skid mounted devices (i.e. CMR, MR Scanner). These numbers, for wireline tools, are of the same magnitude as the depth of investigation of 7 cm (2.75") quoted for the LWD proVISION. With all these tools, it means that the NMR measurement generally takes place in the flushed zone (**Table 13.3**).

As noted above in the discussion of the MRIL tool, NMR tools have the distinction that their volume of investigation is very sharply defined. This means that the volume between the tool and the inner surface of the volume of investigation does not affect the measurement. This in turn means that borehole irregularities and mudcake should not affect the reading. However, if the magnetically sensitised volume impinges into the mud, it will increase the total porosity (high hydrogen index) but depress the long T_2 values (they relax quickly). The measurements will be un-usable and there are no borehole corrections (**Figure 13.1**) (Coates *et al.*

Table 13.3 Depth of investigation (DOI) and vertical resolution of some NMR tools (Akbar *et al.* 1995; Prammer *et al.* 1999; Prammer *et al.* 2000; DePavia *et al.* 2003; Chen *et al.* 2003; Serra 2008; Schlumberger (website 2010)).

Company	Type	Tool	DOI	vertical res.	precision
Schlumberger	eccentred	CMR	2.8 cm (1.1″)	15 cm (6″)	
	″	CMR-Plus	3.8 cm (1.5″)	15, 23, 61 cm (6, 9, 24″)	±0.5 p.u.
	″	MR Scanner	3.8–10.2 cm (1.5-4″)		±0.5 p.u.
			3.2 cm (1.25″) hi res.	10.2 cm (4″), 45.7 cm (18″)	
			6.9, 10.2 cm (3.8, 5.8″) main		
Halliburton	centred	MRIL			
	″	MRIL-prime	7.6–10.2 cm (3-4″)	61 cm (24″)	±1.0 p.u.
	″	MRIL-XL			
Baker Hughes™ (Atlas)	eccentred	MR Explorer™ (MREX)	6.3–11.4 cm (2.5-4.5″)	61 cm (24″)	
Schlumberger	LWD	Pro-VISION	7 cm (2.75″)	114 cm (45″)	
Halliburton	LWD	MRWD	17.1 cm (6.75″)	152.5 cm (60″)	
Baker Hughes™ INTEQ	LWD	MagTrak™	5.1 cm (2″)	123 cm (48″)	±1.0 p.u.

1999, Mardon *et al.* 2000).

The vertical resolution of the NMR depends on the size of the radio antennae that send the CPMG echo train. Clearly, each tool is different (**Table 13.3**). In the MRIL it is 61 cm (24″), while for the CMR and CMRplus it is 15, 23 or 61 cm (6″, 9″ or 24″). With a moving wireline tool, the vertical resolution will also depend on the speed of logging, the tool moving out of a polarised formation into a new region of the formation during one measurement cycle. The faster the logging the greater the effect. Vertical resolution will also be affected by signal averaging during processing. Logging speed and averaging both tend to make the vertical resolution larger (Coates *et al.* 1999).

In LWD tools also, vertical resolution will generally depend on the antenna length, for instance, 6″ in the Schlumberger proVISION and 24″ in the Halliburton MRIL-WD. The eventual resolution, however, will depend on subsequent averaging, as several depth readings are usually combined to improve the signal to noise ratio. This will have the effect (as with the wireline tools) of making the vertical resolution greater. For the Schlumberger proVISION, at a drilling rate of 15 m/hr (50 ft/hr) the vertical resolution, for example, is 0.9–1.2 m (3–4 ft) (Alvarado *et al.* 2003).

Unwanted logging effects

Mud type

Because NMR tools rely on transmitting and receiving high frequency electromagnetic radiation they are influenced by the size of the borehole and the resistivity of the mud (for the same reason that induction and propagation resistivity tools are influenced by these). A large hole filled with a conductive, saline, water-based mud will lead to the NMR signal being attenuated and hence signal to noise ratio is degraded. This will be more detrimental in low porosity formations (or more generally formations with a low hydrogen index). Signal to noise ratio can be improved by stacking more than one signal, which, in practice, means multiple passes or more likely slower logging speeds.

It is tempting to believe that the ideal environment for NMR logging is non-conductive oil-based mud. But in fact this is not necessarily true. The problem with oil-based mud is that the radio frequency signals can propagate a long way without significant attenuation. They can then be influenced by parts of the tool string a long way from the antenna. With wireline tools this can be overcome by running the NMR tools as stand-alone devices (at the cost of increased rig-time). With LWD tools, of course, this is not an option as they are part of the drill string.

Muds that contain paramagnetic or ferromagnetic materials will definitely affect NMR tools (e.g. haematite). The magnetic material's influence is on the tool's magnetic field rather than the propagation of the radio signals. In general, the field strength in the formation will be reduced and hence the Larmor frequency will change. All commercial tools actually have to cope with changes in the permanent magnetic field anyway, so providing the change is not too drastic, the tool can cope.

Temperature

Magnetisation is temperature dependent, which means that the strength of a tool's magnetic fields will be affected, higher temperatures being associated with lower field strengths (B_0). This means that the Larmor frequency will actually change with time and depth. In order to account for this, the tool is constantly re-tuned downhole. Very high temperatures require additional data averaging (Coates *et al.* 1999). NMR tools have temperature sensors.

Magnetic junk

The permanent magnets of the tool attract metallic objects, so that any junk in the hole risks sticking to the tool and affecting measurements. Junk is quite common and unfortunately occurs mainly as iron filings that are worn away from the drill string. The filings affect the tool's magnetic field but their most serious affect is attenuating the radio frequency signals to and from the formation. In this respect, they act like an extremely conductive mud and will certainly adversely affect log quality and can render the log useless. The best way to avoid the problem is to use ditch magnets in the mud system to remove the filings as they form.

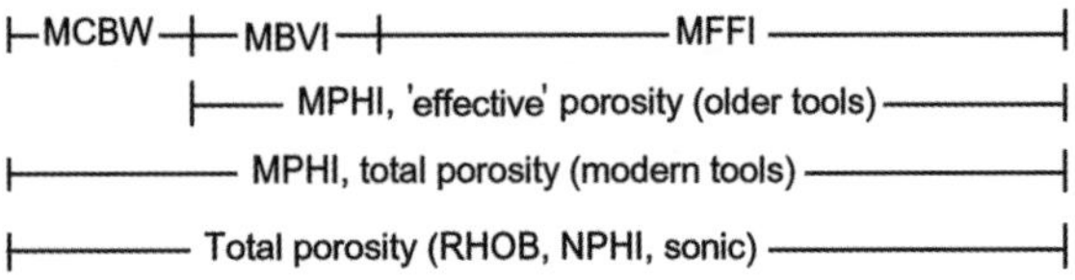

MCBW — MBVI — MFFI
MPHI, 'effective' porosity (older tools)
MPHI, total porosity (modern tools)
Total porosity (RHOB, NPHI, sonic)

matrix	CBW	BVI	FFI		
			water	oil	gas
NO EFFECT	clay -bound water	capillary -bound water	free water	free oil	free gas
T_1	v. SHORT	SHORT	med. LONG	LONG	LONG
T_2	v. SHORT	SHORT	med. LONG	LONG	SHORT
D	SLOW	SLOW	MEDIUM	MEDIUM (variable)	v. FAST

Figure 13.16 The various porosities derived from NMR measurements, their comparison with standard wireline porosity and their T_1, T_2 and diffusion characteristics. MPHI = porosity from T_2; MCBW, MBVI, MFFI = CBW, BVI, FFI from T_2. D = diffusion.

13.5 Petrophysical uses

Porosity and pore size distribution (CBW, BVI, FFI)

The two distinguishing features of the NMR log as a quantitative tool are:

A T_2 distribution at each depth level, which allows the porosity to be sub-divided into pore size ranges (**Figure 13.10**).

A porosity that is largely free of matrix effects (unlike the traditional density, neutron or sonic porosities).

Of these two features, it is the ability to determine pore sizes that is truly unique to the NMR. The fluids within a rock can be classified as fluids that will flow and can be produced or FFI (Free Fluid Index), capillary bound fluids or BVI (Bulk Volume Irreducible), which cannot be produced, and clay bound fluids (CBW) (**Figure 13.16**). These concepts have already been introduced but will now be discussed from a petrophysical view.

The important separation of producible fluids from irreducible fluids is based on T_2 thresholds. Reliable default values have been established to use in the absence of any other information, but values can be set by the interpreter. Ideally, such cut-offs are based on NMR measurements made in the laboratory on core plugs. Laboratory instruments that work on the same principles are available 'off the shelf' and use similar field strengths, as the downhole tools. Most core analysis laboratories possess at least one of these and some can operate at borehole temperatures and pressures. In the simplest experiment, a T_2 distribution is recorded for a plug saturated with brine. The plug is then drained until irreducible water saturation is established, and the T_2 distribution is again measured (**Figure 13.17**). The difference between the two distributions is assumed to represent the free fluid which, of course, is characterised by the longer T_2 times, and an appropriate cut-off time can be found by inspection.

The T_2 distributions measured on core plugs can also be directly compared to pore-throat values via capillary pressure curves. Mercury is injected into the sample in steps of increasing pressure and capillary curves constructed (The mercury intrusion capillary pressure method, MICP). At each increasing pressure step, smaller and smaller pore throats are used. These measurements are quick to perform but provide a large number of points so that the pore size distribution can be quite detailed. They also only require small samples. However, they can be transformed to provide a direct comparison to the NMR T_2 distribution (Ausbrooks *et al.* 1999). These are not routine measurements, but they do show that the NMR T_2 spectrum does indeed reflect pore-throat size as well as pore size distribution (**Figure 13.18**).

Sandstone porosity

For sandstones, a relatively consistent cut-off in time on the T_2 distribution between producible and irreducible fluids (FFI-BVI) is between 20–50 ms, with 33 ms generally being taken as the default (White 2000). This value is often plotted in red as a constant value line on plots of the T_2 distribution so that the user can see if it is appropriate to use it or not (**Figure 13.19**).

This default 33 ms cut-off value for sandstones is not applicable to limestones or more exotic reservoir rocks. There are two reasons for this:

- The mineralogy of the rock *does* actually influence the T_2 values.
- There are a wider variety of pore types found in some limestones.

In order to understand how mineralogy influences T_2, one needs to understand how precisely the equilibrium spin population is restored. A proton which is aligned against the magnetic field will only change its state if

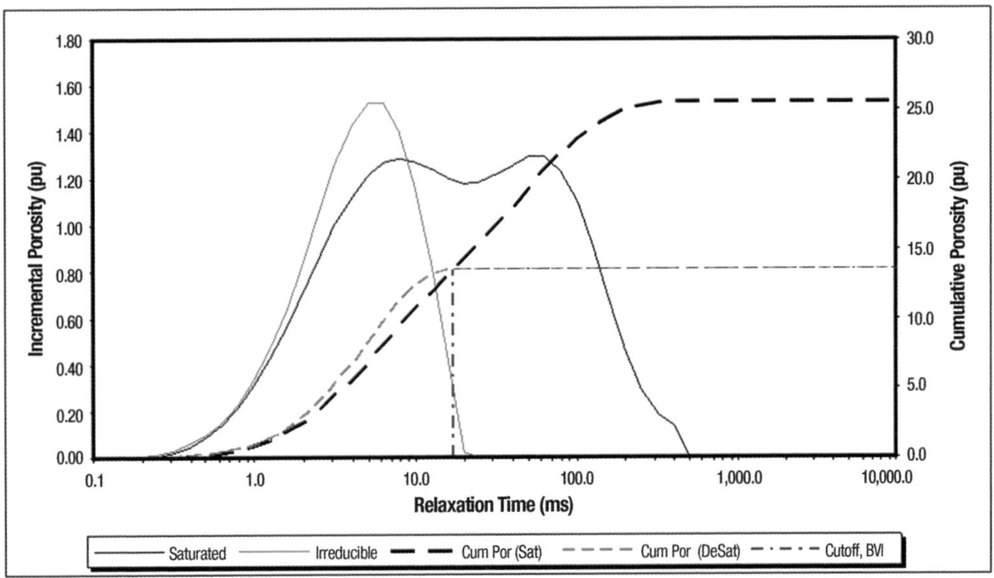

Figure 13.17 Example of a T_2 distribution derived from routine laboratory measurements. The irreducible volume (BVI) is measured (red) and this allows a cut-off for pores that contain movable fluids to be defined. BVI = bulk volume irreducible.

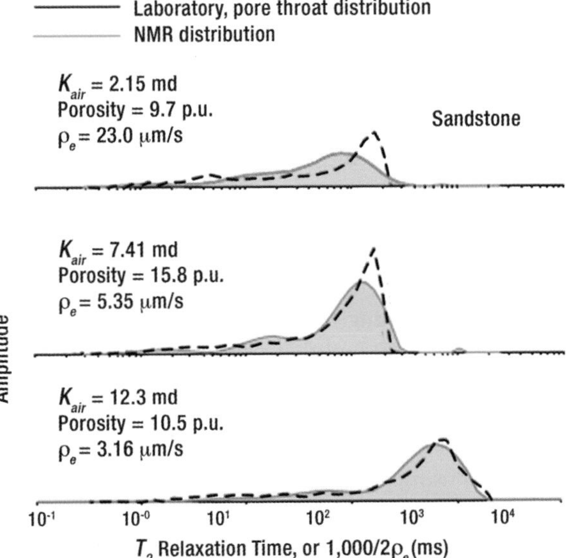

Figure 13.18 NMR measured T_2 distributions compared to mercury injection pore throat size distribution (MCIP). This is a specialised laboratory measurement (from Coates *et al.* 1999, courtesy Halliburton).

it is perturbed in some way. As explained previously (Section 13.2), two ways this can happen are by interacting with other protons (for example in a neighbouring water molecule) and by interacting with the surface of a mineral grain. It is the latter which produces the mineralogical over-print on the T_2 distribution. It is suggested that sandstone pores are 'rough' and about 3 times more efficient in relaxation than smooth crystalline carbonate pores (Kenyon & Gubelin 1995). This arguably means that even NMR cannot provide a truly lithology (matrix) independent porosity.

In addition, the presence of heavy, metal atoms at mineral surfaces, particularly iron, can considerably reduce T_2 times. Iron is a relatively common impurity in sand grains, so for the average sandstone, T_2 values are expected to be shorter than the average T_2 values for a carbonate. A default value of 100 ms for limestones is not unreasonable although some, such as ferroan dolomites, contain a lot of iron and can have T_2 cut-offs shorter than the 33 ms default for sandstones. As already noted, ideally a T_2 cut-off needs to be established for each different reservoir by core measurement.

Carbonate porosity

The 100 ms default T_2 cut-off between FFI and BVI for limestones has been indicated. Carbonates differ from clastic rocks (most) in the variety of pore systems they can host. Not only is there a greater variety of porosity types, but often two or more can co-exist at the same point in a reservoir. For example, large isolated vugs can be located in a background matrix of limestone grains so that the vugs can exchange water molecules (diffusion) with inter-granular pores on a timescale that is comparable to the NMR measurement cycle. The tool will then record a T_2 distribution, which is the average pore type rather than a reflection of the different types of pore and their abundances.

Another aspect is that the size of limestone pores frequently does not reflect whether the fluids they contain will be produced or not. The situation is extreme in the case of vugs (defined as pores with a size greater than adjacent grains, Ausbrooks *et al.* 1999), where large volume vugs may in fact be isolated and with no or only small connecting throats.

The result is that limestones can show a broad, single T_2 peak, where no cut-off is clear (**Figure 13.20**), or

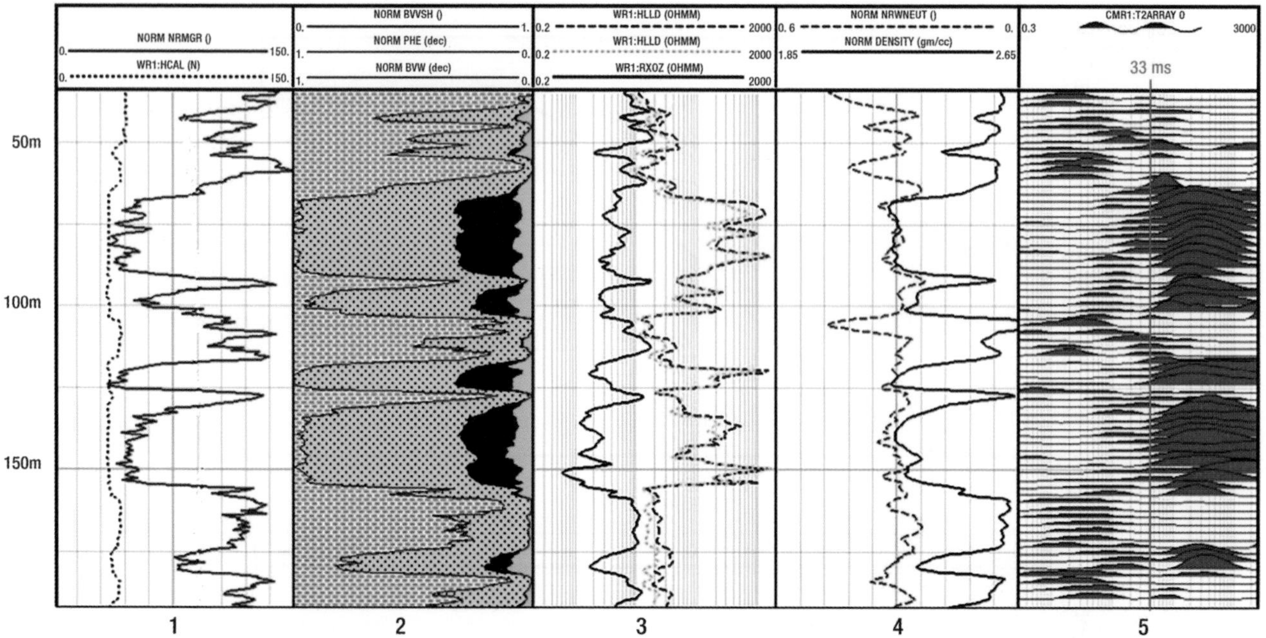

Figure 13.19 A typical NMR log though an oil bearing sand-shale sequence. The red vertical line in track 5 is 33 ms, the default value between producible and irreducible fluids. Track 1, Gamma ray and caliper; Track 2, shale = green, sand = yellow, black = porosity with oil, blue = porosity with water; Track 3, deep and shallow resistivities; Track 4, density-neutron; Track 5, NMR T_2 with red line indicating the default cut-off for sandstones (33 ms).

pore sizes that do not relate to the capacity of fluids to be produced. And although 100 ms is the default cut-off for limestones, the only way to validate the actual value is by comparing it with core measurements (Chang *et al.* 1997).

Hydrocarbon saturation

From NMR measurements, a hydrocarbon saturation can be derived. It is quite independent and does not require a resistivity measurement or knowledge of the Archie '*n*' and '*m*'. On the T_2 distribution (**Figure 13.10,b**), the area under the curve is the total porosity. Any part of the area taken up by hydrocarbons on this plot represents the porosity they occupy. Expressed as a percentage, this is the saturation. In normal operation, the NMR tool cannot distinguish oil and water, so the tool can only put an upper limit on the oil saturation. That limit is basically the ratio of the free fluid to the total porosity. This is because, in a water wet rock, the hydrocarbons are always free fluids, but this complete replacement of free water will only occur above the transition zone. Below the transition zone (that is, below the free water level, FWL) all the free fluid is water. Therefore, over the transition zone itself, generally some additional information is needed to obtain a saturation from a T_2 distribution

Permeability

An important use of the NMR T_2 porosity distribution is in inferring permeability, although it is important to note that NMR tools do not currently measure it.

Often there is a better correspondence between permeability based on the T_2 porosity distribution than other log based permeability methods. This is because account can be taken of irreducible fluid porosity which, as explained below, is indirectly related to grain size. However, as discussed, the T_2 porosity curve is a distribution of *pore* sizes, while permeability, the actual measure of fluid flow through a rock, is based on pore *throat* sizes. However, pore throat sizes measured by the mercury intrusion capillary pressure (MICP), as described (**Figure 13.18**), suggest that pore size distribution can be indicative of pore throat sizes and that a permeability calculated using pore sizes will be valid.

Mathematically, the transform from NMR T_2 to permeability is invariably based on a function of porosity and irreducible water saturation. A large number of these functions have been published over the years and some date to the 1940s. Most were not developed specifically for use with NMR data but, as will be seen below, they are particularly well suited to it. They all predict that permeability will increase with porosity and decrease with irreducible water saturation (or the relative bound water volume). The different equations are distinguished simply by the precise functional relationships with porosity and S_{wir} (irreducible water saturation). For a particular rock type, permeability is expected to increase with porosity because more pathways through the rock are created the more pores there are. But permeability will fall with an increase in irreducible water saturation. This requires more explanation.

Irreducible water is a film of water that adheres to the surface of the mineral grains. In a fine-grained sand the

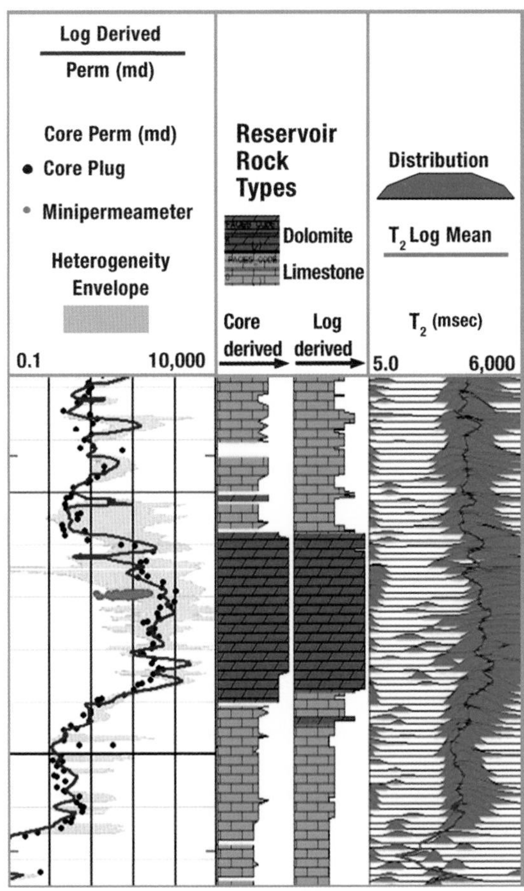

Figure 13.20 A typical NMR log through a water bearing limestone showing no short T_2 values but quite a broad T_2 distribution, straddling the cut-off value (Ramamoorthy *et al.* SPWLA 2008).

surface area of the grains will be larger than in a coarse grained sand of the same porosity, so the volume of irreducible water will be greater in the former. Permeability is expected to be lower in the fine grained sand because, on average, pore throats will be smaller. The net effect is that permeability and irreducible water saturation are inversely related; the higher the permeability the lower the irreducible water and *vice vesa*. By including irreducible water saturation in the formula the effect of changing grain size can be accounted for.

These relations are general, and all that is needed to apply them are estimates of porosity and irreducible water saturation. These are available above the transition zone using conventional log analysis because, by definition, above the transition zone the water saturation is at irreducible. In the transition zone and the water leg however, these equations cannot generally be applied because there is no way to find S_{wir}. NMR logs, however, can distinguish bound water from free fluids even in the water leg, and so can provide the estimate of S_{wir} (it is normally described as capillary bound water). In water and oil sands the NMR log will also provide the porosity estimate, which means that a permeability curve can be calculated as the log is recorded.

Two particular relationships to estimate permeability are commonly applied to NMR data. They are described in more detail below but both assume permeability increases as the fourth power of porosity. When applied to NMR data neither is written explicitly in terms of irreducible water saturation but, in fact, they are basically inverse square functions of this. The first is the Timur/Coates relationship. To use this, the cut-off between movable and irreducible fluids must be identified and the ratio of the free fluid (FFI) to bound fluid values (BVI) from the T_2 spectrum is considered to give an indication of pore throat dimensions. The second is the Schlumberger-Doll Research (SDR) method, which uses a logarithmic mean of T_2 as representative of pore throat dimensions and there is no cut-off identified (Allen *et al.* 2000). The two formulae are (there are others):

Timur/Coates $Kmd=\alpha.\text{Ø}^4.\ (FFI/BVI)^2$ (Coates *et al.* 1991) 1

SDR $Kmd=\alpha.\text{Ø}^4.\ T_{2LM}^{\ 2}$ (Kenyon *et al.* 1988) 2

Where Kmd = permeability, α = constant, Ø = porosity, FFI = Free Fluid Index, BVI = Bulk Volume Irreducible, T_{2LM} = T_2 logarithmic mean

These algorithms can be adjusted for local conditions and ideally should be matched to core measured permeability. In addition any one of the other porosity/S_{wir}. relationships may actually produce a better match (see the Baker Hughes™ (Atlas) chart book for other examples). The Timur/Coates formula (1) is said to be best when there are multiple fluids but the two are similar (Sigal 2002). However it must be noted that permeability prediction from logs is always problematical because permeability is highly scale dependent and it is not always clear exactly what is being predicted (e.g. single phase gas permeability or effective permeability to the reservoir fluid).

Sandstone permeability

In sandstones, the relatively consistent relationship between pore-throat size and pore size, means that NMR permeability is often a good approximation to laboratory measurements (**Figure 13.21**). In fact, it is an implicit assumption in the NMR permeability equations that pore size *is* a good indicator of pore throat size. If pore size is not a good indicator of the pore throat sizes, then NMR permeability equations will not give a reliable estimate of the true permeability. For example, in low porosity sandstones where diagenetic cement is preferentially deposited in pore throats, the NMR permeability will over-estimate the true value (White 2000). The opposite problem occurs in sandstones where clay or shale contributes to the total porosity but does not block the pore throats. Examples include sandstones with so-called ‘structural shale’ in which some of the

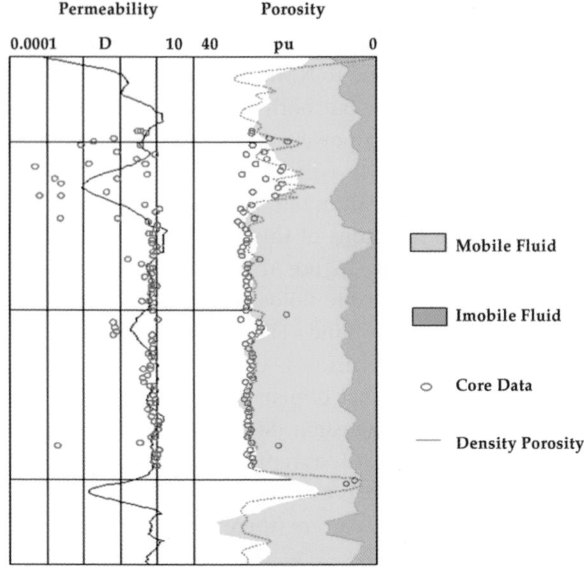

Figure 13.21 Comparison between NMR measured porosity with derived permeability, and core measured values. In this sandstone the match, even between the permeabilities, is very good (from Fletcher *et al.* SPWLA 2008).

grains are actually shale clasts. These will contribute a significant volume of clay-bound water which, when put into the permeability equation, will result in a low value. Glauconite commonly introduces significant volumes of clay-bound water by this mechanism. In these cases, therefore, the permeability estimate will be too low (White 2000, *ibid*). A similar problem occurs in sands with grains coated in chlorite. The chlorite causes these sands to have high irreducible water saturations, which again will be interpreted by the NMR as a low permeability. In reality, however, these sands often have very high permeabilities because the chlorite inhibits compaction. It should also be pointed out that in sandstones in general, NMR permeability is a horizontal permeability: the vertical value is not assessed by the tool (Lowden 2003).

Carbonate permeability

As noted several times above, the NMR permeability relations are based on the implicit assumption that pore size is a good indicator of pore throat diameter. In limestones, as has been discussed (*see porosity*), there are many porosity types in which pore size bears no relationship to pore throat size and so NMR cannot be used to predict permeability. For example, in a typical vuggy carbonate, the pore system could be described as a few large pores (the vugs) connected by a few narrow paths. The NMR will respond mainly to the vugs which have a very low irreducible water volume (essentially just a film of water coating their surfaces). The NMR permeability equations will therefore predict a high value but, in reality, the permeability is controlled by the few narrow pathways and will be low. Furthermore, it is common to find limestones which have a bi-modal porosity system but do not exhibit a bi-modal T_2 distribution. This is a result of the relatively long time scale which is needed to measure T_2 distribution, which is sufficiently long for water molecules to diffuse between the different sized pores. The result is that what started as a proton in a small pore ends up as a proton in a large pore, and the T_2 distribution becomes just a broad, single peak; the bound fluids and free fluids cannot be separated (Allen *et al.* 2000). A practical recommendation in this case is to remove the very large pores from the T_2 distribution (i.e. long times) before deriving permeability (White 2000).

Even in carbonates that do satisfy the assumption that pore size is closely correlated with pore throat size, such as carbonate sands (grainstones), the T_2 cut-off defining what is irreducible and what is free fluid is likely to be different from the default 33 ms value found in siliciclastic sandstones. In other words, NMR may be able to provide a good estimate of permeability in certain limestones, but the parameters in the equations will probably have to be adjusted to achieve this.

In addition, because the NMR does not evaluate pore throat size, the measurement cannot identify fracture porosity or permeability.

Hydrocarbons and oil viscosity

Hydrocarbons can be detected by NMR measurements because water, oil and gas have different combinations of T_1, T_2 and diffusion responses (**Figure 13.16**). A measurable difference exists between water T_1 and oil and gas T_1. The important T_2 difference is between gas and liquids (water and oil) (**Table 13.4**). In the same T_2 distribution, oils of different viscosities have a wide range of times and diffusivities and these can be used for their recognition.

Table 13.4 Variable wait time and echo spacing settings and their uses. Refer also to Figures 13.21 & 13.22 and Table 13.1 (compiled from Akkurt *et al.* 1996; Coates *et al.* 1999; Freedman and Heaton 2004).

	TW	TE	Identification	
A.	Long	Short	water + oil + gas	
B.	Short	Short	water	
A minus B (Figure 13.21)			= oil + gas	
C.	Long	Short		
D.	Long	Long		
C to D (Table 13.1) (Figure 13.22)			Small difference Medium difference Large difference Larger difference	= heavy oil = oil = water = gas

In terms of logging techniques, there are two methods for hydrocarbon typing: multiple wait time (TW) and multiple echo time (TE) manipulations (Akkurt *et al.* 1996; Coates *et al.* 1999; Freedman and Heaton 2004). The wait time, TW, method uses the T_1 contrast between water and light hydrocarbons. The echo spacing, TE, method uses the difference between the diffusivity of water and oil (even different oil viscosities) and between liquid (water or oil) and gas.

In the TW method used by the MRIL, there are two wait times, a long and a shorter (Coates *et al.* 1999). After the shorter TW, all water will be polarised, but only a fraction of the hydrocarbon because it has long polarisation times: after the long-TW, the water and the hydrocarbons will both be polarised (**Figure 13.9**). The CPMG echo train after the shorter TW will only identify water: the same echo train after a long TW will detect water and oil. Subtracting the shorter TW from the long TW will thus leave only the response of the hydrocarbons (**Figure 13.22**). If hydrocarbons can be identified, then the volume of the NMR porosity that they occupy can be calculated, and this is the (NMR) hydrocarbon saturation (*see porosity*).

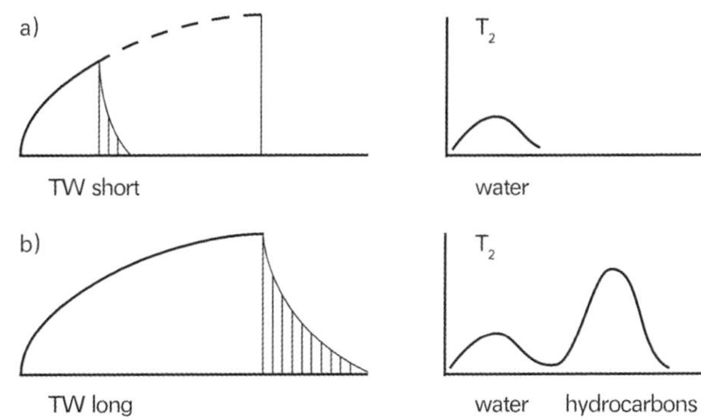

Figure 13.22 The variable TW method used to detect hydrocarbons. Subtracting the T_2 result of a short TW from a long TW brings out fluids that take longer to polarise, that is, liquid hydrocarbons.

The TE method is used to bring out diffusivity contrasts and two or more echo spacings are used. A long spaced echo train will allow more time for diffusion between echos, so that, when long and short echo train results are compared, relatively rapidly diffusing water will show a larger difference than slower diffusing oil (**Figure 13.23**). With multiple echo spacings it is even possible to construct a map of diffusivity against T_2 in which gas, oil and water have different locations (**Figure 13.24**). In addition, oil viscosities are a function of diffusion, light oils diffusing more rapidly than heavy oils (**Table 13.1**) so that, by using the different echo spacings, oil viscosities can also be derived (Freedman and Heaton 2004). If the different fluids can be distinguished on a diffusion–T_2 map, then their various saturations can be calculated. However, knowing that oil viscosity covers a large range from faster diffusing light oil to slower diffusing heavy oil, some oils will have similar diffusion rates to water, in which case oil and water will not be able to be separated.

NMR fluid typing is very delicate and measurements must be of the highest quality if the methodology is going to work (c.f. Zittel *et al.* 2006). This is especially the case as the NMR tools have a shallow depth of investigation and normally detect the fluids in the flushed zone where there will be mixing of mud-filtrate (which may be oil-based or water-based) and native fluids. In addition, oils may change in viscosity from the bottom to the top of the reservoir, which leads to changes in the NMR oil signal. Because of these complications, if necessary, the wireline tool can take stationary measurements and the LWD tool can be logged after drilling (MAD). Developments in fluid-typing techniques are evolving and will almost certainly improve.

Gas

Gas creates similar problems for NMR logs as for neutron logs (Chapter 11). The low hydrogen index means that the basic porosity measurement will under-estimate the true value. In fact the situation is even worse with NMR because the high diffusivity of gas creates additional problems. In principle, these can be solved if the properties of the gas are known and the tool is set up properly, but often a virtue is made of necessity and the problems are turned into a way of identifying gas.

Although gas has a low hydrogen index (HI, Chapter 11), generally between 0.2–0.6 at typical reservoir pres-

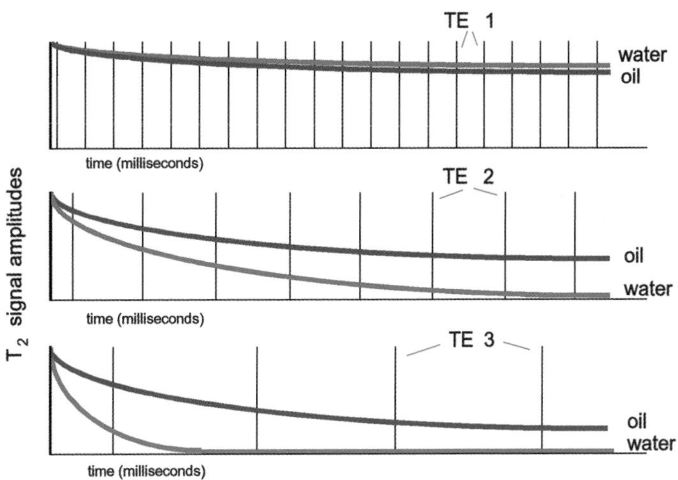

Figure 13.23 The effects of variable TE on the water and oil T_2 signal. The graphs show that the water (brine) diffuses much more rapidly than the intermediate viscosity oil. Refer to Table 13.1 for values (modified after Freedman and Heaton SPWLA 2004).

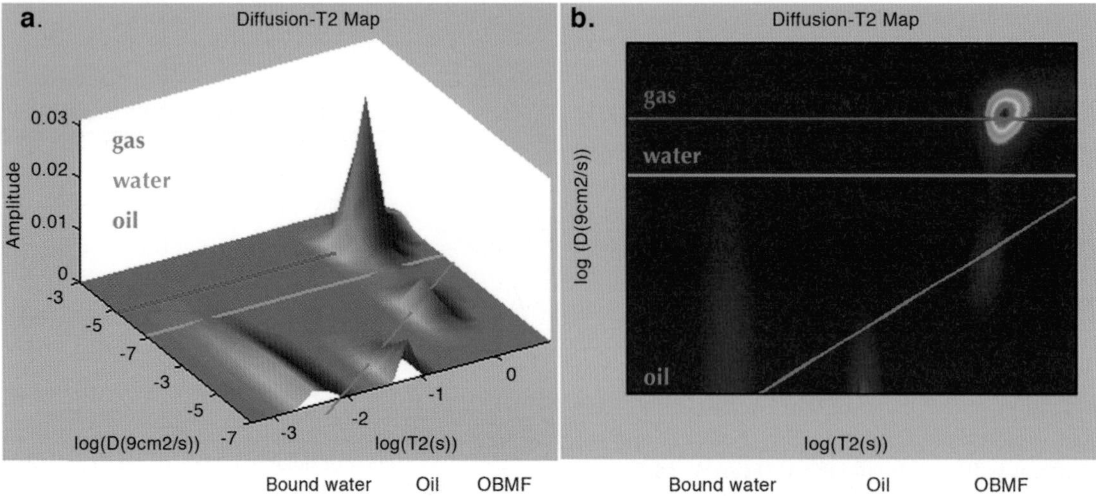

Figure 13.24 The T2-diffusion map. a. 3-D representation. b. 2-D map plot showing oil, water and gas overlay. This example shows gas with minor oil, oil-based mud filtrate and bound water (from Minh *et al.* 2003). © 2003 SPE. OBMF = oil-based mud filtrate. *Reproduced with permission of the copyright owner. Further reproduction prohibited without permission.*

sures, it is still sufficiently high for it to be detected in NMR measurements and for gas to be identified on the T_2–diffusion map (described above). However, gas, because of its rapid T_2 relaxation times and low hydrogen index (HI), when standard CPMG sequences are used, has the effect of reducing the NMR T_2 porosity and will be seen in the irreducible fluid times (BVI) (Akkurt *et al.* 1996). As a result, the T_2 porosity through a gas zone is lower than a density porosity (The fact can be used to identify gas sands). Equally, if T_1 distributions are available, they will show a contrast to T_2, as T_1 is not affected by diffusion (**Figure 13.25**).

When gas is present, since the T_2 porosities will be underestimated, the NMR numbers will obviously need to be corrected if, for example, they are going to be used in permeability estimates. However, if corrections are applied to the NMR numbers, then a reasonable porosity can be found and gas saturation can be calculated. In cases where oil-based muds are used, in theory, gas can still be identified and accounted for (**Figure 13.24**).

13.6 Geological uses

The geological uses of the NMR are at the moment limited. Part of the reason for this is that the rock matrix is generally considered to have such a limited effect on the measurement. In addition, NMR is still often regarded as a specialist petrophysical device and so many geologists have been deterred from using it for qualitative analysis. This is a pity, as the T_2 distribution provides the best information on the nature of the pore system and the distribution of shale, outside a whole core. All that is needed to interpret this information is a log print with the T_2 distributions included. In the future, as the tool becomes more familiar, and it is realised that there are elements of lithology that can affect the NMR, the geological uses will increase (Djafarov *et al.* 2004).

Four studies can be used as examples. The first is based on the observation that some limestone facies can be identified by their porosity distribution characteristics; the second uses the relationship between grain size and T_2 distribution; the third tries to characterise clay minerals from their proton distribution; and the fourth investigates the paramagnetic influences of certain iron-containing minerals.

Limestone facies

If a limestone facies can be characterised by its porosity distribution, then the NMR log can be used for this. A study in a horizontal Middle Eastern well, used LWD NMR and standard LWD logs to differentiate between 3 limestone facies (Rose *et al.* 2003). The well encountered a coarse crystalline, bioclastic facies, without micrite and very little bound water; a second facies with common micrite but some skeletal material and a moderate bound water volume; and a third facies containing mainly fine, pelletal material with a high bound water content (**Table 13.5**). Since this was a horizontal well and vertical resolution was not so important, the quality of the LWD NMR measurements were improved

Table 13.5 Differentiation of limestone facies using LWD NMR measurements (Rose *et al.* 2003).

Facies	DPHI	LNMRØ	BFV	FFI	FFI/BFV	T_{2lm}
Facies 1	27.6%	27.6%	7.8%	19.8%	2.54	232.8
Facies 2	28.8%	28.7%	10.7%	18.0%	1.68	167.5
Facies 3	31.2%	28.0%	15.6%	12.4%	0.79	90.8

DPHI = density log porosity, LNMRØ = LWD NMR total porosity, BFV = bound fluid volume, FFI = free fluid index, T_{21m} = T_2 logarithmic mean

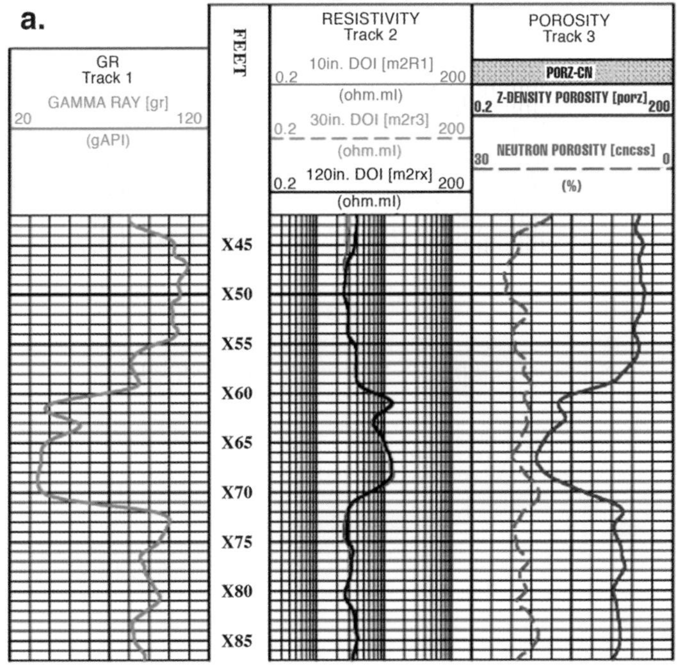

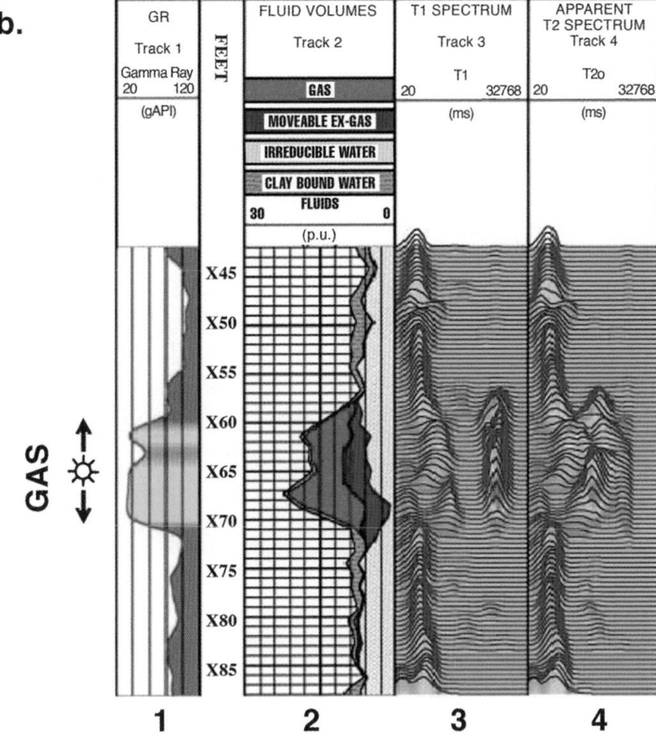

Figure 13.25 The effect of gas on T_1 and T_2. a. standard log suite of gamma ray, resistivities, neutron-density porosity. The gas effect on the neutron-density is not obvious. b. NMR logs. Comparing tracks 3 (T_1) and 4 (T_2), it is clear that the long T_2 signal has been reduced: a result caused by gas. For b. Track 1, value shaded gamma ray. Depth in feet; Track 2, NMR porosity with gas filled volume (red), water filled volume (dark blue) and capillary water (light blue); Track 3, T_1 distribution; Track 4, T_2 distribution (uncorrected for gas) (modified from Hursan *et al.* SPWLA 2005).

by stacking 31, 6″ measurement levels, meaning that 4.7 m (15.5 ft) of formation were averaged. The resulting quality of the processed T_2 log allowed the 3 facies to be identified. Although, in this case, identifications were verified by memory data and wireline logs, the numbers available during drilling would have been sufficient.

Grain size

NMR T_2 distribution is directly proportional to the grain volume to surface ratio, which, in turn, is related to the mean grain size (Gladkikh *et al.* 2008). This is the same relationship that is used to derive permeability from the NMR (Section 13.5). The example (**Figure 13.26**) shows an apparent coarsening-up sequence in which the gamma ray and clay volume decrease regularly upwards. The NMR, however, shows that the pore volume suddenly increases at 27.5 m and that the base of the topmost sandstone is more likely to be associated with a distinct sedimentary break. This topmost, hydrocarbon bearing sandstone, based on the NMR pore distribution, can be interpreted as coarser-grained than the interval below and does not appear to coarsen-up. These interpretations are confirmed by the core, which indeed shows that there is no simple, overall coarsening-up. The lower sand body is, in fact, finer-grained and bioturbated, explaining the lack of porosity (and permeability). The upper sand shows a sharp base and several thin, fining-up bed forms while the topmost interval is finer-grained (**Figure 13.26**). Interpreted grain size trends are quite general in this example as the vertical resolution of the NMR tool used, is over 50 cm.

Clay mineral identification

Early NMR tools did not 'see' clays (actually clay-bound water) as their relaxation time is very fast (Prammer *et al.* 1996). Perhaps for this reason, very little work seems to have been done on using the NMR to characterise downhole shales. One laboratory study used an inter-echo spacing, TE 240 μs, 8192 echos and a very high degree of stacking (all of which are impossible to duplicate downhole) to study laboratory samples. The intention was to find if the various clay water sites, such as surface, inter-layer and mesopore, would be differentiated in the T_2 distribution (Clennell *et al.* 2006). The results showed that most mudrocks are uni-modal (**Figure 13.27**) but that bi-modal results are encountered. The possible reason is that protons are in such proximity in mudrocks that there is diffusion between the different sites, so they cannot be differentiated and this leads to the single T_2 distribution. However, there is a suggestion that if there is a high enough

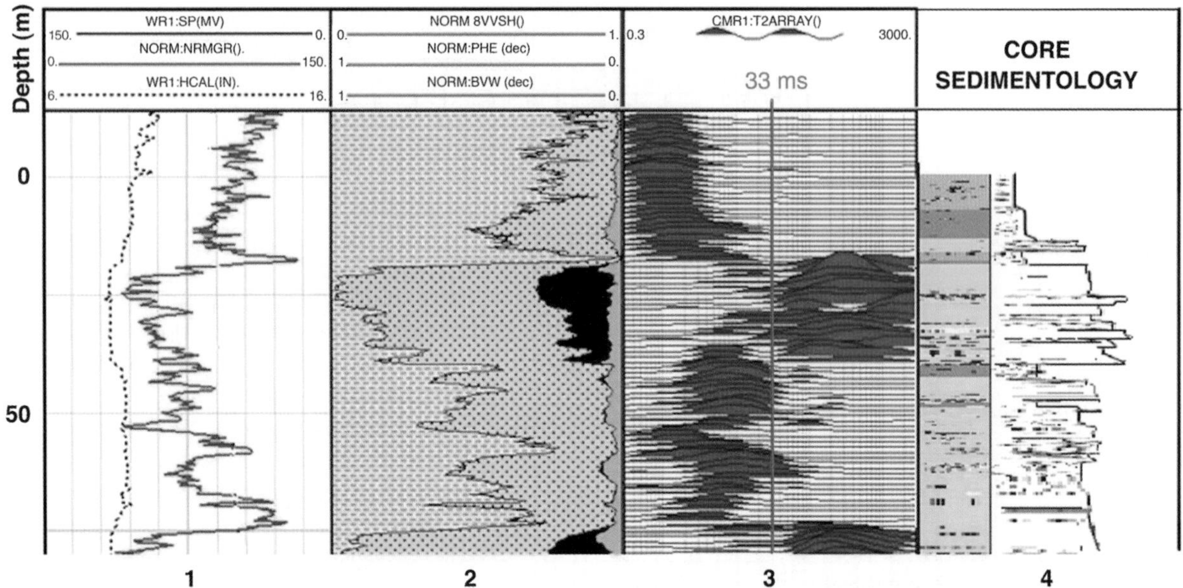

Figure 13.26 Grain size interpreted from the NMR T_2 distribution. The standard logs suggest a simple coarsening-up (cleaning-up) sequence but the NMR suggests an upper, separate sand body, with a marked grain size change. Core confirms that there is no simple coarsening-up sequence. Track 1, caliper, gamma ray; Track 2, shale = green, quartz (sand) = yellow, porosity with hydrocarbons = black, with water = blue; Track 3, T_2 signal distribution; Track 4, core sedimentology.

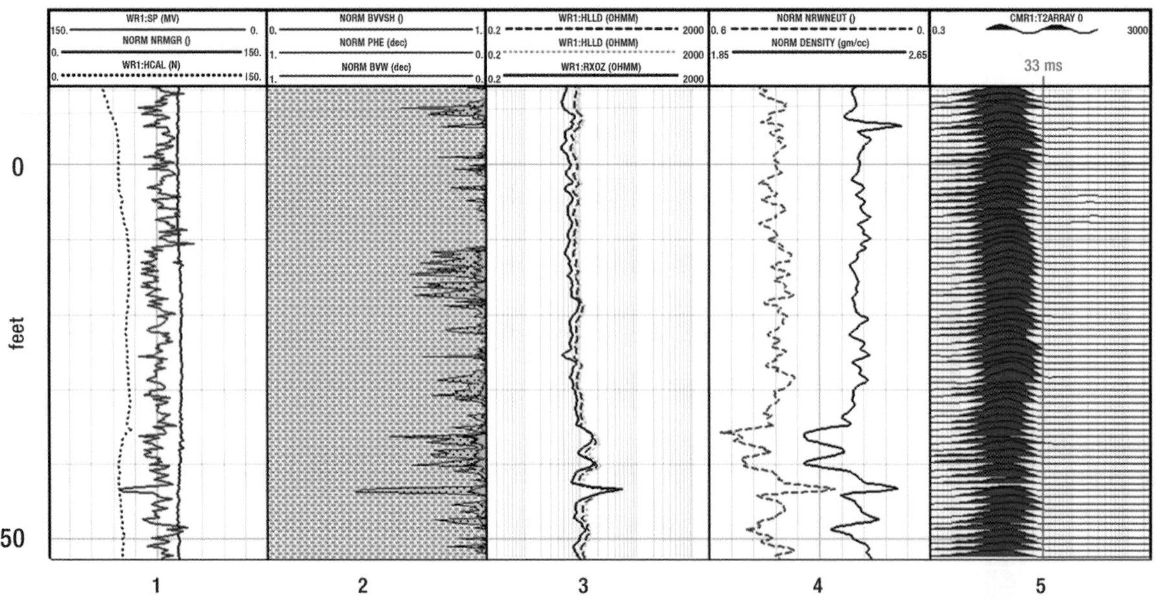

Figure 13.27 A typical NMR log through a shale interval. The uni-modal T_2 signal (track 5) is below 33 milliseconds. Track 1, gamma ray and caliper; Track 2, shale = green, quartz (sand) = yellow; Track 3, resistivities; Track 4, neutron-density; Track 5, NMR T_2 signal distribution.

concentration of a swelling clay such as montmorillanite, the interlayer peak can be distinct.

How these observations can be used geologically is not clear at the moment.

Paramagnetic material

The presence of iron in minerals such as pyrite, chlorite and glauconite (the latter both clay minerals containing iron) create a secondary magnetic effect in the external magnetic field used by the NMR tool. They cause irregularities in the field gradient, which affects diffusion. The result is a decrease in relaxation times which can mask free fluids (Djafarov *et al.* 2004). Some studies have suggested that the amount of iron rich material (chlorite in this case) can be quantified (Hürlimann *et al.* 2003). However, the case is not proven and it is only mentioned by way of example.

14
THE DIPMETER

This chapter has been left largely unchanged from the 1996 second edition. Image logs (Chapter 15), have now all but replaced the dipmeter as a means of deriving dip and azimuth, but ideas, attitudes and difficulties apparent from earlier dipmeter interpretation, are relevant to image interpretation today. This chapter is something of a time capsule from the mid-1990s, but hopefully the more useful because of that.

14.1 Generalities

The log

The dipmeter log provides a continuous record of formation dip and direction of dip, or *azimuth. It comes from a two stage process: acquisition of the data followed by data processing. The tool acquires, typically, four microresistivity curves from orthogonal positions around the borehole – the first stage. By correlating the curves across the borehole, the computer can provide a dip and an azimuth – the second stage (**Figure 14.1**).

Dipmeter tools consist not only of the logging sonde for the microresistivity curves, but also a positioning sonde, so that tool orientation, inclination and speed are known, all essential information to the computation of the dip and azimuth. Moreover, the dipmeter microresistivity curves are sampled 30 to 60 times more densely than ordinary logs (**Figure 14.4**).

Early dipmeter processing required a mainframe or workstation. When it was eventually able to be done quickly on a personal computer or laptop, attitudes changed and processing developed into an interpretation tool, often using interactive software.

*Azimuth is used to mean the direction, relative to true north, of dip or any other orientation measurement.

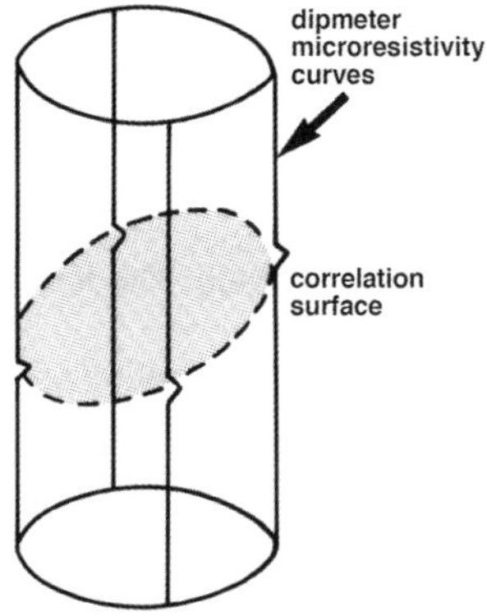

Figure 14.1 The principle of the dipmeter. Detailed resistivity curves are measured from (typically) orthogonal positions around the borehole and then correlated to give a surface which has dip and azimuth. It is a two-stage process (from Cameron *et al.* 1993).

It should be remembered that at the time this chapter was written (1995), logs were provided as hardcopy. Also, some of the remarks on the knowledge of dip and azimuth characteristics of sedimentary structures or tectonic features are now much better known than in the mid-1990s, thanks to image logs. This is certainly the case for turbidites and drilling induced mechanical effects.

Principal uses

Clearly, the principal use of the dipmeter is to provide dips! But there is more to the meaning of dip than is implied in the preceding sentence. The dipmeter provides data for two rather different domains: structural geology and sedimentary geology (**Table 14.1**). In structural geology, it provides information on struc-

Table 14.1 Uses of the dipmeter log.

Discipline	Feature	Comments
General	Hole position Hole size and shape Breakouts	gives continuous deviation and TVD gives shape with orientation derive stress field orientation
Sedimentary geology	Sedimentary structure (bedform) orientation Palaeocurrent analysis Reservoir (sand-body) orientation Facies characterisation	from foresets, dunes, HCS etc. using statistical analysis from compaction drapes, slumps etc. thin bed analysis possible
Structural geology	Structural dip Unconformities Faults Folds Fractures	seismic section overlays can be used vector analysis plots used stereographic analysis used graphic analysis used (images now used)

Table 14.2 Dipmeter logging tools.

Company	Tool	Names	Pads	Electrodes/pad	Comments
Schlumberger	HDT	High Resolution Dipmeter Tool	4	1	older tool
	SHDT	Stratigraphic High Resolution Dipmeter	4	2	2.5mm samples
	OBDT	Oil Based Dipmeter Tool	4	1	oil based mud tool
Atlas Wireline	Diplog	Diplog	4	1	5mm samples
(now Baker Hughes™)	HDIP	Hexdip Log	6	1	independent arms
Halliburton	HEDT	High Resolution Dipmeter Tool	4	1	
	SED	Six Arm Dipmeter	6	1	independent arms

tural dip, unconformities, faults and folds. Structural dips from the dipmeter can be compared to dips on seismic sections or used in log correlation. In sedimentary geology, the dipmeter can provide facies information, bedform orientation and palaeocurrent directions.

Prior to 1967, a dipmeter tool could be expected to provide one dip and azimuth per 2m (6ft). Between 1967 and 1984 this increased to 3–4 dips per metre: an eight-fold increase. But modern tools can provide 40 times more information than the original tools, that is, up to 20 dips per metre: this means that there may be 20,000 individual dip points measured over 1000m of logged open hole. This is a huge mass of data to interpret - and understandably discourages and confuses most geologists. Dip is a familiar geological concept and yet the data from the dipmeter are unfamiliar. Clearly, this is a fundamental problem that must be tackled.

About this chapter

In the past, too many expensive dipmeter logs were simply put in a geologist's drawer and forgotten about (Is this now true of image logs?). The high sampling rate of the raw dipmeter data meant that it was not integrated with the other open hole logs, even in computer software. Additionally, the fact that it needed processing, and that its presentation was unique, added more barriers. The dipmeter also suffered from poor credibility, not because of tool design or reliability, or even processing - all excellent, but from very poor interpretation.

Historically, much dipmeter interpretation was based on the recognition of dip patterns. Three patterns were standard: *red* = decreasing dip upwards, *blue* = increasing dip upwards, and *green* = constant dip (Gilreath *et al.* 1969). These patterns were given a meaning: *blue* = foreset beds, *red* = channel fill, *green* = structural dip. The associations between the dip patterns and directional features were expanded from their original inception and enshrined in interpretation procedures. The technique being that if a blue pattern or a red pattern was identified, then an interpretation was assured. This methodology blocked creative thinking about the dipmeter for a long time. *It will not be discussed and will not be used in this chapter.* A strong bias is put on one of the author's (Rider) own views on dipmeter interpretation. It will be shown how processing and interpretation interact and how outcrop models can (and must) help interpretation.

Many of the ideas in the chapter owe a great deal to the work of colleagues.

14.2 Dipmeter tools

Generalities

As indicated, the dipmeter tool measures dip by comparing the displacements of features on microresistivity curves from opposing sides of the borehole wall (**Figure 14.1**). Typically four pads are used, but tools exist with 3, 4, and 6 pads (three being the minimum number of points to define a planar surface) (**Table 14.2**). Moreover, although a single electrode on each pad is usual, the SHDT of Schlumberger has two on each pad (**Figure 14.5**).

Since the electrodes of the dipmeter tools register resistivity or conductivity, it is necessary for the borehole mud to be water based, allowing an electrical contact between the tool and the formation. In oil based muds this is not possible, and specialist tools using induction principles are run (**Table 14.2**). Alternatively, in some cases, a compromise in oil based muds is to use a standard resistivity dipmeter tool with 'scratcher blades', upstanding blade-like electrodes attached to the pads to give a direct contact with the formation. The results using this configuration are variable (often poor).

Tool mechanics

The standard four arm dipmeter tool has four pads held at 90°, generally configured as two pairs, so that opposite pads move the same amount and the tool is automatically centred (**Figure 14.2**). The arms can be so engineered that, as hole size varies, the pad pairs move in a plane normal to the tool axis, but they generally move in a shallow arc and in six arm dipmeters, each arm moving independently and also in an arc. The pads are held against the borehole wall hydraulically. In deviated boreholes, this is a difficulty as the weight of the tool presses on the down-directed pad and the top pad 'floats', or becomes disconnected from the formation. The weight of the tool on the pads may be reduced using a flexi-joint and stand-offs (guards to keep the tool away from the borehole wall). Tools can function in holes from about 50 cm–15 cm (20″–6″) in diameter but are best in holes in the 30 cm–20 cm (12″–8″) range.

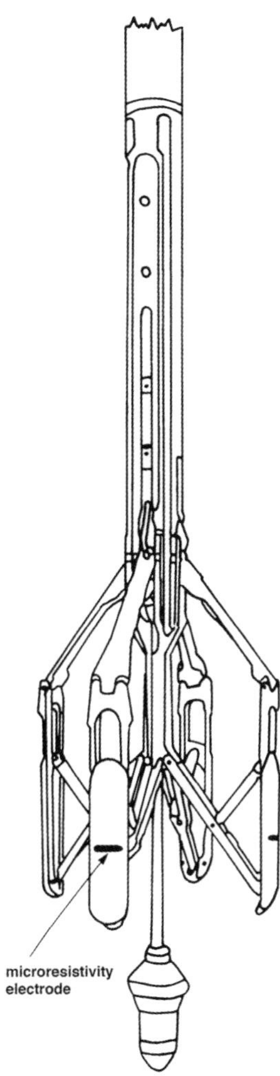

Figure 14.2 A typical dipmeter tool: the HDT (high resolution dipmeter) of Schlumberger. The four arms are at 90° and acquire four, micro-resistivity curves (modified from Bell 1990).

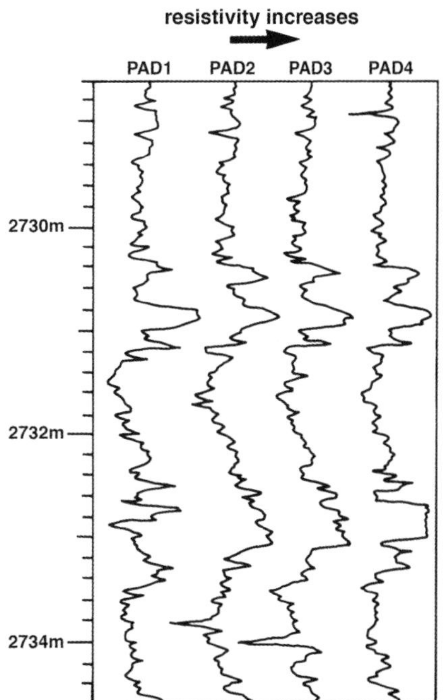

Figure 14.3 Raw dipmeter data from a Western Atlas Diplog, sampled every 5mm (0.2").

Resistivity curve characteristics

A dipmeter tool measures a microresistivity curve (or curves) from each pad (**Figure 14.3**). The essential for these curves is to register small variations in resistivity or conductivity, and not absolute values. Consequently, a tool will typically use a 'floating zero'. The Schlumberger SHDT dipmeter, for example, emits a current from the entire lower section of the tool (the EMEX current). The pads themselves are conductive, but only a small part of the overall current actually flows through the measuring button electrodes, the major part being used to focus the current from the buttons. Buttons, pads and sonde body are kept at the same potential, so that button current will vary with the conductivity of the formation in front of it. Since the EMEX current is constantly varied, depending on the average formation resistivity, button resistivity (conductivity) variations are recorded in both generally high resistivity and low resistivity formations. For example, in both hydrocarbon and salt water zones (**Figure 14.4**). The dipmeter microresistivity curves do

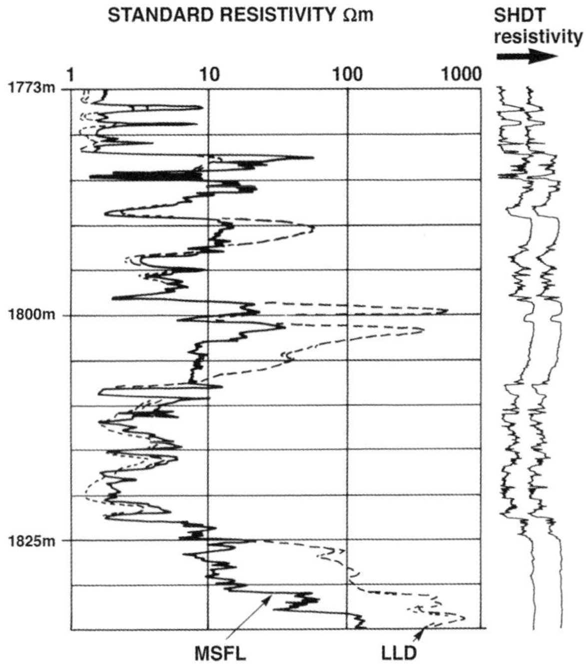

Figure 14.4 Standard resistivity logs compared to SHDT dipmeter resistivity curves. The SHDT curves are sampled every 2.5 mm (0.1") and are very detailed while the standard logs are sampled every 15 cm (6"). However, the SHDT curves give only relative resistivity values, as base resistivity (EMEX) varies depending on formation resistivity. In this way, detail is measured in both the absolute low and high resistivity intervals (hydrocarbon bearing in this example). SHDT = Stratigraphic High Resolution Dipmeter of Schlumberger.

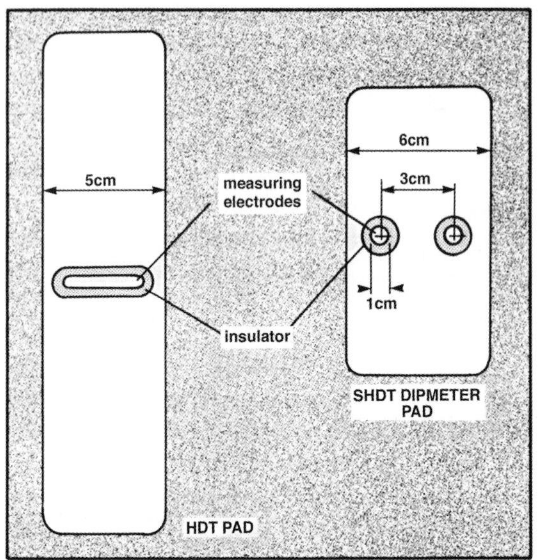

Figure 14.5 Dipmeter pads. The single electrode HDT (High Resolution Dipmeter) pre-1985 and the two electrode SHDT (Stratigraphic High Resolution Dipmeter) with a shorter pad for better formation contact (re-drawn from Schlumberger 1986).

not, therefore, give a standard resistivity: this can only be calculated by accounting for the base current variations.

The dipmeter microresistivity curves are sampled very densely, every 5mm (64 per foot) in the Western Atlas Diplog, and at twice this rate, every 2.5 mm (0.1") in the Schlumberger SHDT, as opposed to the usual 15cm (6") in other open hole logs (**Figure 14.6**). Dipmeter microresistivity data are handled in the so-called 'fast channel' while the navigation data and calipers are handled in the 'slow channels'. The high dipmeter curve sampling rate is associated with very small pad electrode, or button (i.e. small electrode) size, in the region of 1cm, so that features as small as 1cm–2cm (0.4"–0.8") are registered and depth of penetration varies around 2cm (0.9") (which must be added to the hole size to calculate dip). The SHDT, for example, has two electrodes 1cm (0.4") in diameter 3cm (1.2") apart (**Figure 14.5**). The microresistivity pads themselves vary between tools but tend to be short and wide (5–6cm) to maximise formation contact and to avoid sticking (Bigelow 1985).

Orientation and other measurements

To calculate the resistivity curve displacement across the borehole, clearly, the borehole size must be known. To this end, the two pairs of arms measure two independent calipers, giving two orthogonal hole size measurements. This allows a dip to be calculated from the displacement. However, for this plane to represent the true dip, in other words, not just any plane but referenced to north, other orientations must be measured by the tool. These are: the orientation of the tool in relation to north (pad 1 acts as the tool reference = pad 1 azimuth); the deviation of the axis of the tool from the vertical (= the deviation of the borehole); the direction of this deviation relative to north (= azimuth of hole deviation, sometimes called drift). The latter orientation is calculated, not measured, from the 'relative bearing', which is the clockwise angle

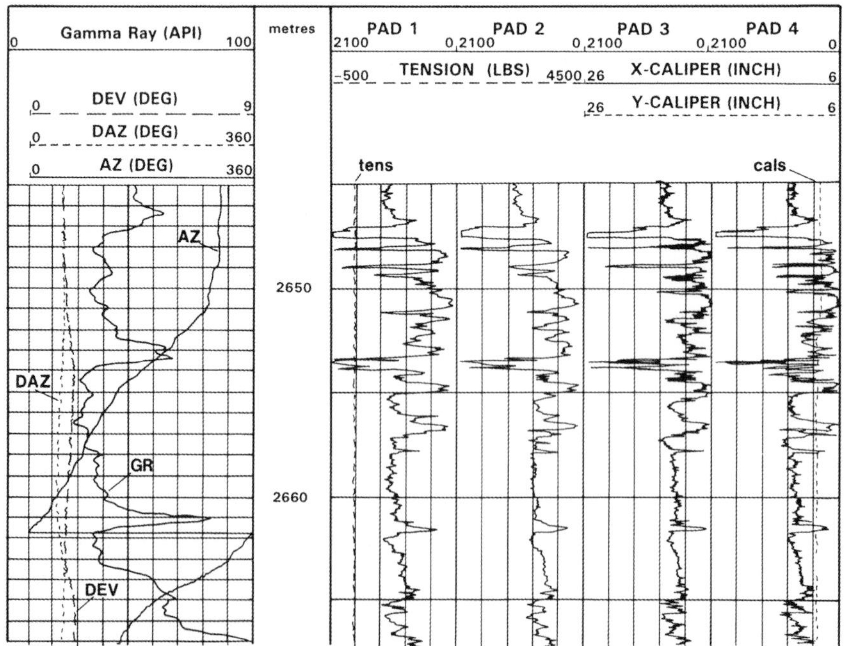

Figure 14.6 Standard log presentation of raw dipmeter data. The dipmeter curves are sampled every 0.5cm (0.2") while the standard logs are sampled every 15cm (6") (Western Atlas Diplog). DEV = hole deviation from the vertical; DAZ = azimuth of hole deviation; AZ = azimuth of pad 1; PAD 1-4 = pad conductivity curves.

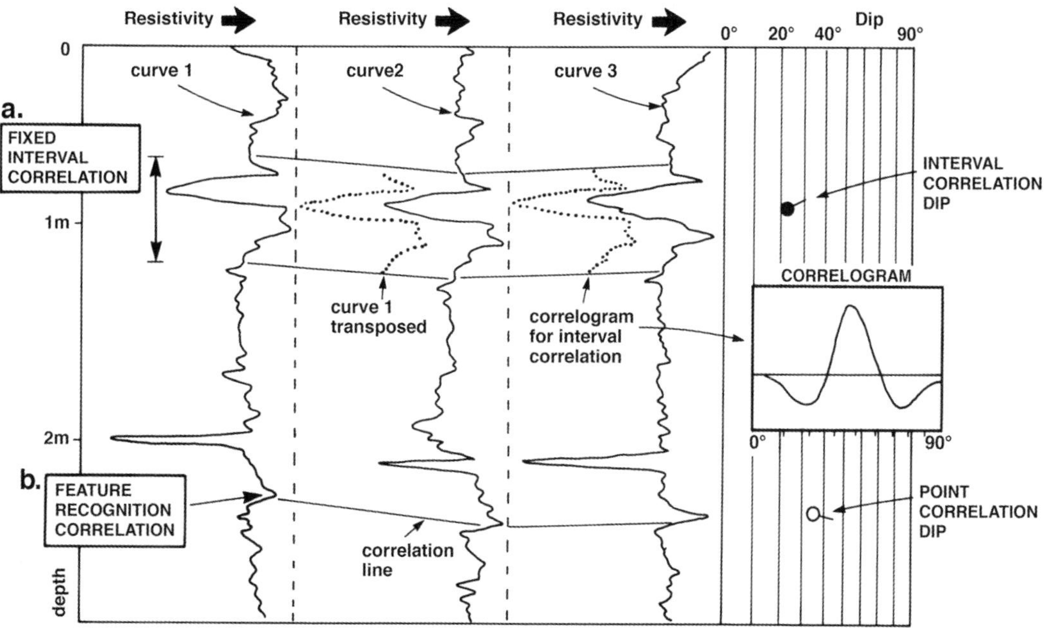

Figure 14.7 Correlation methods for deriving dip and azimuth from dipmeter resistivity curves. a) Fixed interval correlation: one dip is produced representing the entire selected interval; b) feature recognition correlation: a dip is produced representing the correlation of a recognizable feature. Fixed interval correlation methods are the most common: feature recognition imitates the way the eye correlates. Example taken from interactive screen routines in QLOG.

between pad 1 azimuth and the high side of the tool (this is the same as the hole deviation azimuth orientation). Pad 1 azimuth minus relative bearing azimuth (+360°) = hole deviation azimuth. Speed variations may also be measured. This can be done directly by using accelerometers or by using a speed electrode. The latter is a duplicate electrode on one or two of the pads, several centimetres vertically above the main electrode, which should duplicate the main measurement. When there are large speed differences, the speed electrode and main electrode readings will differ and corrections can be made.

Two types of dipmeter log are produced. The first is a field log, a plot of the raw data acquisition curves; the second presents the processed data - the actual dips derived by the computer. The field logs will be described in this paragraph, the logs showing dips are described in Section 14.4.

A typical dipmeter field log will show not only the raw microresistivity curves, but also most of the orientation and caliper data. The example chosen is from a Western Atlas, 4-arm (pad) Diplog (**Figure 14.6**). In track 1 are the deviation of the borehole from the vertical (DEV) and azimuth (DAZ), the azimuth (AZ) of the reference pad (pad 1) and a gamma ray curve from a sonde attached to the dipmeter tool. The gamma ray allows the dipmeter to be matched to the standard log runs (note the great difference in detail between the gamma ray and the dipmeter curves). In tracks 2 and 3 are the raw acquisition curves, the tension and the two calipers. The tension curve is useful in identifying zones of tool sticking although these are usually evident on the caliper and the raw curves themselves. The format of the raw dipmeter data varies between companies although the basic information included is similar. The logs are plotted at a 1:200 scale.

14.3 Dipmeter processing

Generalities

Deriving a dip direction and azimuth from the raw, tool produced resistivity curves needs computer processing. The requirement is to correlate the curves around the borehole so as to identify the various displacements, which then define a surface across the hole. There are two principal methods: *fixed interval correlation* and *feature recognition*. Fixed interval correlation is the most common method used and simplest for the computer, but feature recognition imitates the way the human eye works. Processing is normally done automatically by the computer, but a modern development is the possibility of correlating the curves and producing dips interactively on the computer screen (**Figure 14.7**). Interactive methods are only for detailed work.

It is essential to understand the general principles of dipmeter processing: proper interpretation depends on it. This will be demonstrated subsequently. It is not necessary to know the details of the computer programmes, which vary between companies, but the basic, consistently used principles must be understood. The essentials of the two methods (fixed interval and feature recognition) will be described separately below.

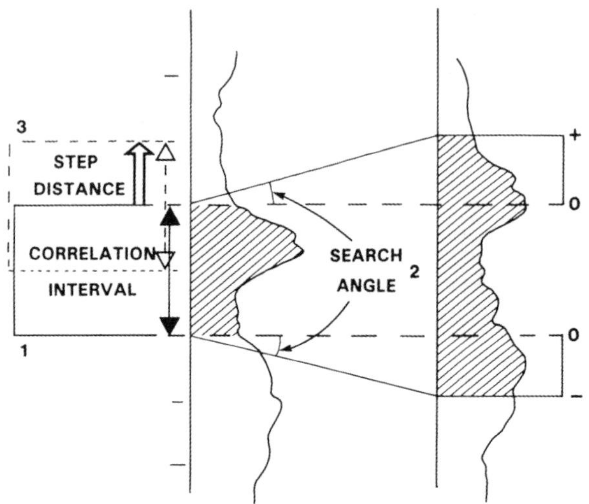

Figure 14.8 The features which must be defined for a fixed interval correlation processing. 1. correlation interval = length of curve used; 2. search angle = length of new curve to be searched, defined in terms of dip angle; 3. step distance = depth increment change for next correlation (always above).

Fixed interval correlation

Fixed interval correlation methods are the most commonly used. Dip computation is based on a comparison and correlation of the microresistivity curves over short, fixed vertical intervals or depths (**Figure 14.7**). The calculated correlation gives a curve displacement from which, with a minimum of three displacements around the borehole, a dip and azimuth can be derived. Several parameters are varied by the computer operator and are chosen depending on the perceived interpretation requirements. The three principal parameters to choose are the *correlation interval,* the *search angle* and the *step distance* (**Figure 14.8**). The correlation interval is the fixed depth interval or, more properly, the length of microresistivity curve used for correlation, usually between 0.1m (10 cm) and 2 m (4"–6 ft). The search angle defines the length of curve over which a correlation is searched for on a second curve, typically sufficient to give up to 70° of dip in the borehole's frame of reference. (Schlumberger often quote a search angle of 35° × 2, which means that the computer will search up to 35° on the first pass but, if it finds nothing, will eventually search another 35°. This is a technique to save computer time). The third parameter, the step distance, is the length of curve moved between one level of correlation and the next above (computation is always from the bottom upwards). Typically this amount is half (50%) of the correlation interval or a step ratio of 0.5 (**Figure 14.8**).

In more detail, the fixed interval method works as follows. The length of microresistivity curve *one* to be used is defined by the correlation interval, say, 1 metre. This length of curve *one* is compared to microresistivity curve *two,* using cross-multiplication *(see below)* by moving curve *one* in increments along curve *two.* The length of curve *two* which is used is defined by the search angle. For instance, if a search angle of 50° is chosen, curve *two* will be searched along a length sufficient to give 50° dips and no higher (the actual length varies with size of borehole). Such correlations are made on all possible combinations, being 6 with 4 microresistivity curves, 15 with 6 curves, 28 with 8 curves. The displacements derived from the correlations are then used to define a plane – the dip. The entire process is begun again in the interval above according to the step distance. Typically, this next interval will re-use the top 50% of the previous correlation interval. That is, if the correlation interval is 1 metre, the step distance will be 50cm and the overlap will be 50% (**Figure 14.8**).

It is helpful to general understanding to examine the actual process of curve correlation. The system is one of cross-multiplication. A graphic representation of this, called a *correlogram,* shows that when the two curves are most similar, there is a maximum cross-multiplication product (**Figure 14.9**). That is, when the two curves are most similar, the correlogram has a marked peak, which is the correlation point, and is taken as the curve displacement for dip calculation. When there is no peak, the two curves show no similarity. Mathematical tests for the quality of the computed dip can be made, for example, by using the shape of the correlogram. Most dipmeter programmes give a quality rating scale to each dip and azimuth value of say 0 –1 or 1–10. A simplified quality is usually indicated on the final dip and azimuth plots, or else quality cut-offs are applied, below which the computed dips are simply not plotted (Section 14.5).

Fixed interval parameter variation

The result of a fixed interval correlation programme is a *regular* series of dip and azimuth readings with a depth at the centre point of every correlation interval and sepa-

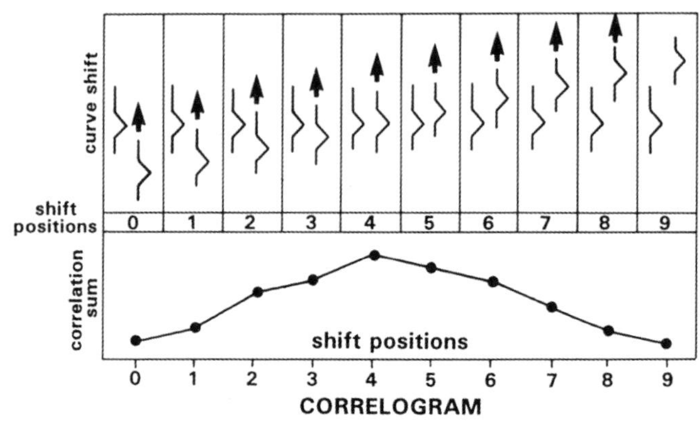

Figure 14.9 Schematic representation of the construction of a correlogram used in automatic, fixed interval correlation routines (from Cameron *et al.* 1993) (*see also* Figure 14.7).

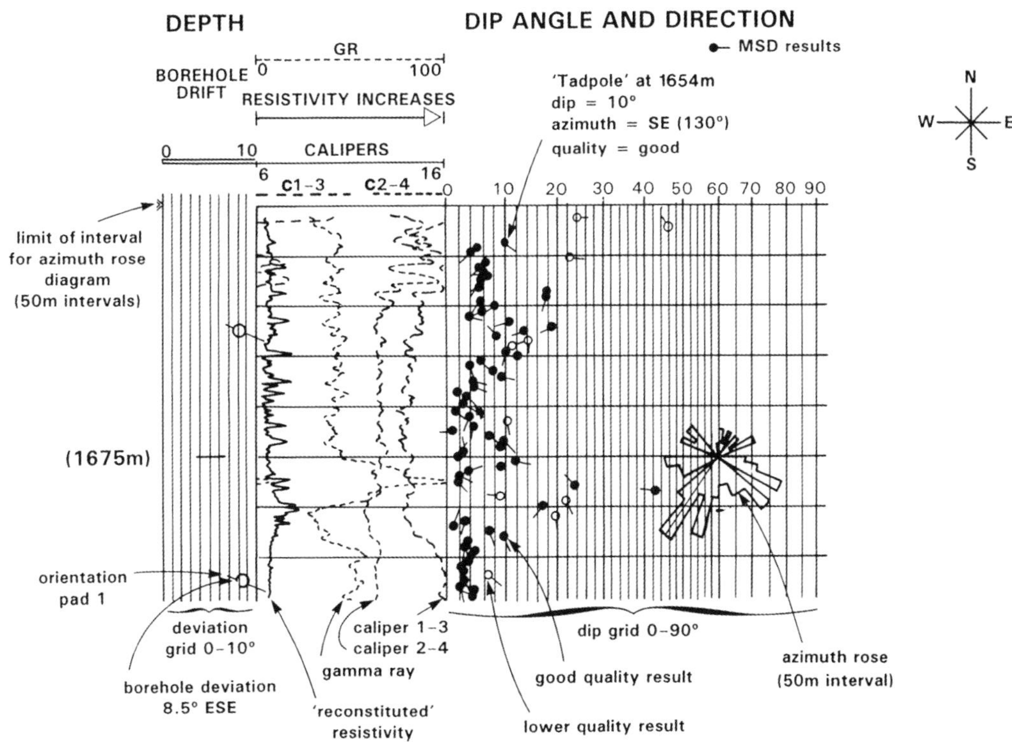

Figure 14.10 A standard, processed dipmeter tadpole plot and log header. The example is of an MSD (Mean Square Dip, a fixed interval method) processing from a Schlumberger SHDT tool (see text for explanations).

rated vertically by the step distance increment. However, with a single set of raw dipmeter data, a whole series of processed dipmeter logs can be produced by varying the processing parameters.

For example, correlation interval, step distance and search angle must all be defined by the operator and therefore can be varied at will. A typical set of parameters will be 1.0 m correlation interval, 0.5 m step distance (4ft correlation, 2ft step are the foot equivalents) and a 50° search angle. A dip and azimuth value will be given every 50 cm (the step distance) but representing a 1 m interval. This is a relatively coarse set of parameters and is used for defining 'structural' dip (section 14.7): fine features will not be measured. The correlation interval may be set, however, at a much smaller value, even down to 10cm (4") on very good quality SHDT logs, which means using only 40 microresistivity curve sample values (i.e. made every 2.5 mm) for each correlation. An example of a single set of raw dipmeter data processed with gradually varying parameters is shown in **Figure 14.18** and discussed in Section 14.6.

Feature recognition

Microresistivity curve correlation by feature recognition tries to imitate the way the eye correlates. When correlating, the eye picks out a remarkable feature and searches for a similar feature on the curves to be compared. For instance, the peak at 2.3m (**Figure 14.7**) is picked out easily on all the curves and leads to a visual correlation. Programmes for feature recognition imitate this method. Geodip, a Schlumberger programme, mathematically defines a number of curve features such as large peaks, small peaks, large troughs, etc, and then correlates to similar features in the other curves (Vincent *et al.* 1977). Interactive correlation programmes now allow this to be done by eye on the screen (**Figure 14.7**).

Feature correlation is made at a defined level, an identifiable curve feature being used. This gives an irregular series of dip and azimuth results: where curve features are good, results are dense; where curves are featureless there are no results. This clearly has geological implications as will be discussed below (Section 14.7). But feature correlation methods are not often used and are certainly not standard.

14.4 Processed log presentations

Although the 'tadpole plot' (*see below*) is standard for the processed dipmeter log, a number of additional presentations are also available, especially as more dipmeter processing software programmes become available. Some presentations are general, others unique to one service company or one software programme. Some of these are shown below but the list is not exhaustive.

Simple standard presentation: the 'tadpole plot'

The standard dipmeter presentation is a 'tadpole plot' (**Figure 14.10**). The basis for the plot is a standard grid

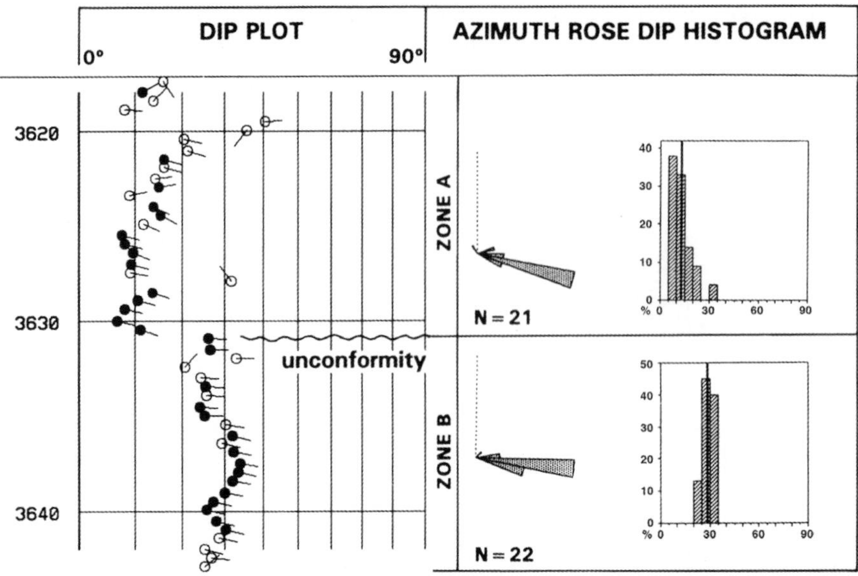

Figure 14.11 Standard tadpole plot with associated azimuth rose diagram and dip histogram presentations of zoned data. The zones are above and below an unconformity. Such data zoning allows the overall dip and azimuth characteristics of intervals to be quickly assessed.

in which the vertical scale is depth and the horizontal, variably spaced scale, is dip from 0°–90°. On this grid, the dip is plotted as a large black dot (the tadpole head) whose position has the co-ordinates of depth (from the vertical scale) and dip (from the horizontal scale). The azimuth is then given by a small, straight line (the tadpole tail) plotted from the centre of the dot with an orientation relative to the vertical grid lines, which represent true north. On the example log (**Figure 14.10**), the 'tadpole' at 1654 m (arrowed) has a dip of 10° with an azimuth to the SE of 130°. The tadpole is often varied from the standard black dot. Square or triangular shapes may be used and sizes varied. Quality, discussed below (Section 14.5), is frequently indicated by infilled or open shapes, good quality infilled (i.e. solid tadpole 'head'), poor quality left open. When colour is used, dip types may be classified or a range of qualities indicated by different colours. The use of the various symbols or colours should be indicated on each log head.

Accompanying log data

On standard dipmeter logs processed by service companies, other information from the tool is plotted besides the dip grid with dip and azimuth values. Typically, this will include the two caliper results, a plot of hole azimuth and drift and a reference log, such as a gamma ray or resistivity, which allows correlation to the other open hole logs. These latter, however, are derived from the dipmeter tool itself, the gamma ray, for example, being from the gamma ray unit fixed to the dipmeter tool (Section 14.2, **Figures 14.6, 14.10**). Unfortunately, logging service companies seldom present dipmeter results along with the standard open hole logs. This is symptomatic of the 'isolation' of dipmeter data. Integration with the standard open hole logs is essential for proper interpretation, an integration from the level of computer format upwards.

Acquisition curves

It is a common and useful practice to plot the dipmeter microresistivity curves alongside the dipmeter grid and processed results. The plotted curves are usually edited and simplified from the raw data but are excellent for quality control, to indicate textural characteristics and for facies identification (**Figures 14.24, 14.29**).

The acquisition curves are normally plotted on feature recognition processed results logs, such as Geodip and Locdip from Schlumberger, so that the level of each correlation from which a dip is derived may be shown. A quick glance at a Geodip log shows that it has an important geological content, especially useful in examining sedimentary features (Delhomme and Serra 1984).

Additional plots on standard presentations

– Azimuth rose plot

Frequently on standard dipmeter tadpole plots, azimuth data are grouped over certain intervals. Typically, on a 1:500 scale dipmeter log, azimuth data are grouped over 50 m intervals and plotted as a frequency rose diagram (**Figure 14.10**). The azimuth rose is useful in indicating unconformities, structural dip direction and faulting. Plotting azimuth roses on pre-determined intervals (i.e. each 50m) however, should be refined by plotting over intervals with meaningful stratigraphic or sedimentary limits (**Figure 14.11**). Standard azimuth plots often fail to show important surfaces such as unconformities or faults, which have different azimuths, because the predetermined zone straddles the feature (Cameron 1992).

– Dip histogram

A useful addition to the rose diagram is a dip histogram plot in which dip angle, on the X axis, is plotted against frequency on the Y axis. A histogram is integral to some software programmes (**Figure 14.11**). The plot is useful in showing a separation of structural and sedimentary dip and in showing high angle noise dips (Section 14.5).

– Separate azimuth plot

By using a standard dip grid and a 360° grid side by side, dip may be plotted on the first, and azimuth values alone, as dots, on the second. The second grid brings out the variations in azimuth, which are generally masked on the standard plot (**Figure 14.12**). The separated azimuth plot is a powerful aid in structural dip interpretation.

A specialised structural interpretation technique called SCAT (Bengtson 1981; 1982) uses a variation of this plot. It will be discussed under structural dip interpretation (Section 14.8).

Some stand alone plots and manipulations

– Stereographic polar plot

Much used by structural geologists to analyse complex geometry, stereographic polar plots are also a useful tool in dipmeter analysis, especially for structural geometry. Special polar grids (Wulff net or Schmidt net) are used on which planes are plotted as their poles (normal axis) and three dimensional geometry can be analysed graphically (cf. **Figure 14.14**). Stereographic plots of dipmeter data are generally made for selected intervals and for specific, usually structural problems. They require careful analysis. This is not the place to describe the use of stereograms, the classic text of Phillips should be consulted (Phillips 1971).

– Stick plot

A stick plot represents dip as a line. Because no azimuth can be indicated, stick plots are usually presented in two (sometimes more) sections, one at 90° to the other: typically a north-south and an east-west set. The sticks represent the apparent dip in the orientation indicated (**Figure 14.12**). The plots are most effective using broad interval averages and small vertical scales to illustrate an entire well. Stick plots can be useful when added to correlation diagrams.

The conversion of dipmeter records to a time scale (as opposed to depth) is a very useful development. Time scale data are normally presented in the form of a stick plot, so as to be exactly compatible with seismic sections. This presentation is especially useful for structural interpretation (**Figure 14.32**).

– Azimuth vector plot

Azimuth vector plots are constructed by plotting dip azimuth values sequentially in their true orientation but without any depth scale. Thus, a sequence with a dip to

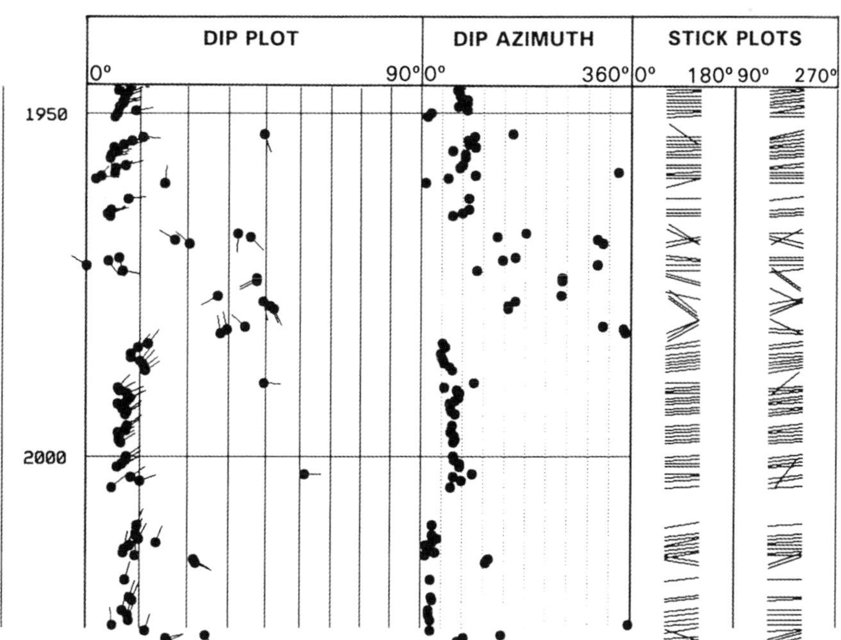

Figure 14.12 Standard dipmeter tadpole plot (left) with corresponding dip azimuth against depth plot (centre) and two, orthogonal orientations of stick plot (right). The azimuth plot is especially useful in structural analysis. The stick plot is used on correlation cross-sections and for seismic comparisons.

the west will create an east-west line, one to the northwest, a line to the northwest and so on (**Figure 14.13**). At an unconformity, where dip azimuth changes, the line orientation will change. Faults will also cause orientation changes but they will be more variable than at unconformities.

This plot is useful where small azimuth changes occur, such as at disconformities. Azimuth vector plot data must be combined with the standard open hole logs to be interpreted. Variations to this type of plot have been proposed (Hurley 1994).

– Structural dip rotation

An essential routine in dipmeter work is to be able to change the structural dip (see Section 14.8 for a definition of structural dip). When, for example, palaeocurrent directions are obtained from sedimentary cross-bed orientations, if there is structural dip, the palaeocurrent orientation will be structurally distorted. To obtain the true palaeocurrent direction the structural dip must be 'rotated out'. In other words the structural dip must be returned to zero (**Figure 14.14**). Very little effect is seen in dips below 5° but, as the dip increases, so the rotation effect increases, as would be expected.

Structural dip rotation should be available both as a bulk facility and as a zone facility. The sedimentary effect described above only requires the zone with cross-beds to be rotated. If an unconformity comes in the middle of a well and the well is structurally tilted, it is useful to be able to rotate out the structural dips above and below the unconformity separately. Or to be able to structurally rotate separate fault blocks. That is, it should be possible to rotate one dip and azimuth value from an entire well, or one small zone.

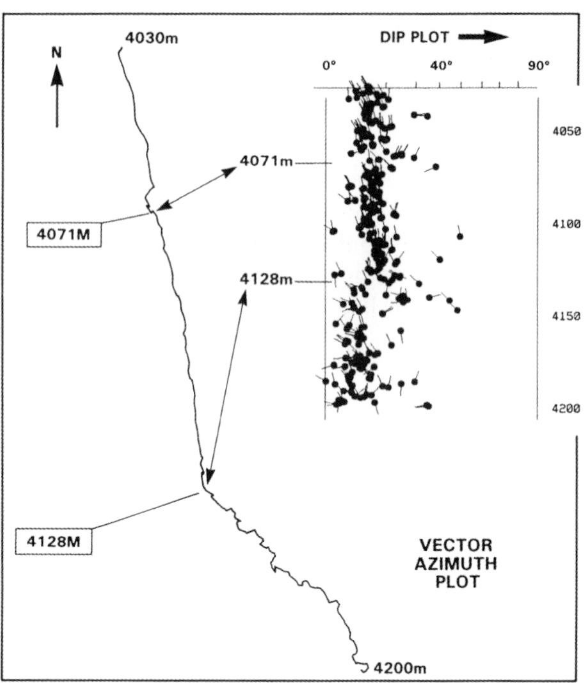

Figure 14.13 An azimuth vector plot and the corresponding standard tadpole plot of the same interval. The azimuth vector plot shows the nature of the structural break at 4128m much more clearly than the tadpole plot. The plot is used in the analysis of unconformities and faults.

– Summary scale logs

An extremely useful facility in dipmeter analysis, indeed the analysis of any log, is to be able to change scales. Compressed scale, summary dipmeter logs of 1:2000 to 1:5000 do two things. Firstly they allow a bulky document at standard 1:500 or 1:200 scales to be presented

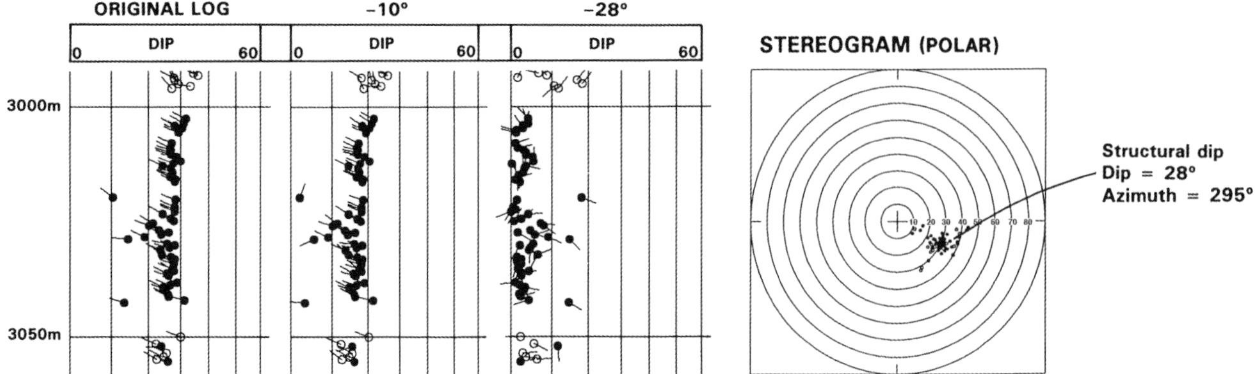

Figure 14.14 The effect of structural dip rotation. The original dipmeter log shows a structural dip of 28°, azimuth 295°, seen on the stereographic representation. Subtracting this dip and azimuth from the original log removes all structural dip (log on the right) while subtracting only 10° at 295° still leaves a substantial structural element. This routine is used, for example, in sedimentary palaeocurrent analysis.

on one A4 page, and secondly, they bring out large scale structural trends.

Frequently, structural dip varies gradually but consistently through a well (**Figure 14.30**). For example, a typical normal fault block shows slowly increasing dips over several hundred metres, as the fault is approached. Drape of shale sequences over reefs or fault blocks will equally show only gradual changes. Such changes are brought out clearly in summary scale logs. Indeed, a structural interpretation indicated on a summary scale dipmeter log should be a standard document in any well file: it will ensure that the dipmeter is used and that it contributes to routine analysis.

14.5 Dipmeter quality assessment

The assessment of the quality of a processed dipmeter log is essential: it affects the possibilities, but especially the credibility, of an interpretation. In very poor datasets, there is often a high noise content. Noise dips have no meaning and are a result of the computation method (Cameron 1992). Even on properly processed and filtered logs, core to log comparisons show that noise dips are still present. However, interpretation routines are designed to accommodate this and, along with careful raw data examination, noise effects on a final interpretation can be minimised. Quality assessment is essential.

Borehole conditions, data acquisition and data processing should all be assessed for quality: all affect an interpretation and are considered below.

Borehole quality

Poor borehole conditions affect the dipmeter probably more than the other standard open hole tools. Hole ovality causes pads to 'float', especially in deviated wells. A floating pad loses contact with the formation and shorts out into the mud. Caving may also cause pads to float and is often the cause of a tool sticking.

A good method of judging hole quality is to plot compressed scale dipmeter calipers (e.g. 1:5000) along with the dipmeter tool orientation data. When this is done, intervals where data may be poor are quickly seen (**Figure 14.15**). Frequently borehole wear can be seen on these plots, the nearer the hole to TD, the better the condition, the lower parts having been less exposed to drilling wear. Alternatively, detailed 1:20 or 1:50 scale plots are found to be useful in indicating where dipmeter curves mimic the calipers, as occurs in small scale riffling (R.Trice, pers. comm.). Although calipers are normally plotted with the processed dipmeter results, prior examination helps the processing itself.

Data acquisition

Quality assessment at the acquisition stage concerns tool performance during logging and tool calibration. Tool rotation, sticking and curve activity are indicative of performance. A tool should not rotate more frequently than one turn per 15m (50ft), as this can affect pro-

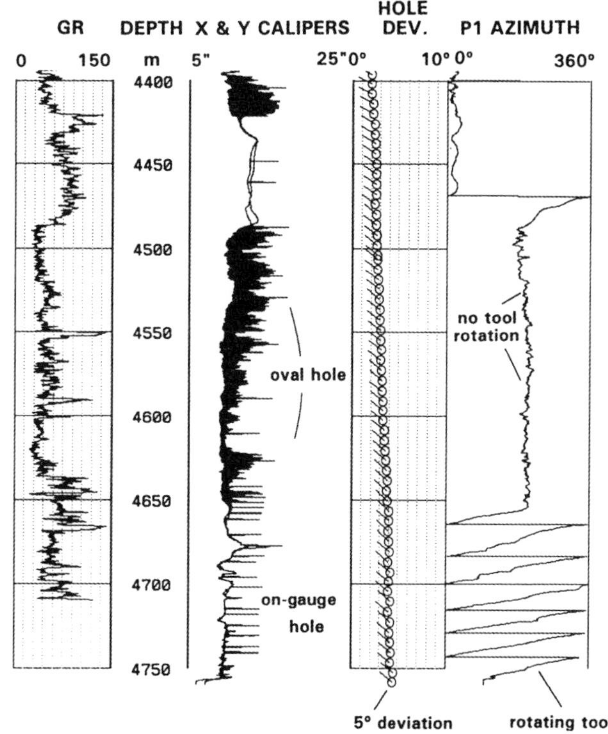

Figure 14.15 Compressed scale logs of factors which affect dipmeter acquisition. From logs such as these the quality of a processed dipmeter can be assessed. Note the tool rotation (indicated by pad 1 azimuth) over the interval of on-gauge hole. Over the section of oval hole there is no tool rotation as one set of calipers becomes fixed in the long axis of the hole, which in this case has a constant orientation.

cessing (Waid 1987) and dips can be seen to vary with rotation. Orientation data are averaged over a correlation interval in fixed interval routines (section 14.3), so that rapid tool rotation affects especially high dips and logs processed with broader parameters rather than small ones (it does not affect manual picking). Tool rotation is quickly judged from the compressed scale logs (**Figure 14.15**).

Sticking in poor borehole is serious for the dipmeter. Although the tool contains accelerometers, and speed changes can be accounted for, serious sticking generally does not allow valid data to be collected. A tool which sticks (stops moving) while the cable runs several metres and then jerks free will be noticed on both the tension and the featureless curves gained during the stuck period (**Figure 14.16**). Speed correction will attempt to discount the data when the tool is stuck and expand the data collected as the tool jerks free. However, when sticking is serious, there will be no valid data.

As a check on the orientation calibration of the dipmeter tool, which can cause problems, it is useful to compare dipmeter derived hole deviation with the quite independent directional surveys measured during drilling.

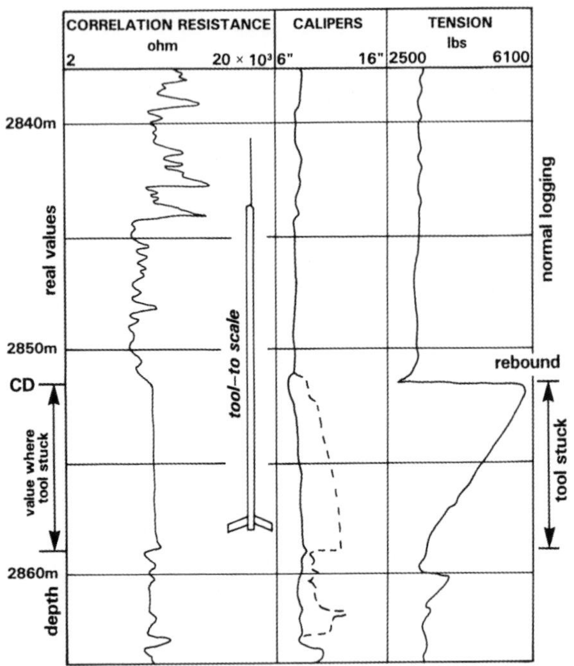

Figure 14.16 The effect of a dipmeter tool sticking. The cable continues to be reeled in, even though the tool is stuck. The cable tension increases continually until the tool breaks free (it may then rebound or yo-yo as in this example). When the tool breaks free a 'flat' set of data are produced. CD = compressed data

Processing quality

Most processing software has built-in quality indicators. That is, tadpoles are plotted with filled or open heads representing good or bad data. This assessment is generally statistical. However, the limit between good and bad data, as printed on the log, can generally be varied at will.

The example shows the effect of quality rating with a dataset using a scale of 0–1 (0 = poorest, 1 = best) and a cut-off from open dips to closed dips at 0.5 (**Figure 14.17**). With all the data, two lines of dip are evident, at 10° and at 60°. The search angle for this data is 60° and the poorest data are concentrated at about the search angle, that is the high angle line of dips. If the data with 0 to 0.2 quality rating are discarded, most of the data at the search angle disappear, but there is still a considerable scatter. Showing only data with a quality rating between 0.5 and 1.0, that is, only the filled-in dips, the log has a much 'cleaner' look and is much more interpretable. The quality filters are based entirely on correlation statistics.

Processing quality can depend very much on choosing the right parameters, especially correlation interval, to suit the data. Very good quality logs may be processed with small correlation intervals but, with too small parameters, many logs will become meaningless. Comparisons with core show that datasets can be processed with 10cm–15cm (4"–6") correlation intervals and still retain meaningful results. When a dataset breaks down, noise dips and poor data will appear close to the search angle as described (**Figure 14.17**).

When borehole conditions are very bad, noise on the dipmeter traces will tend to cause anomalous spikes simultaneously on all the curves. These will be in a plane perpendicular to the hole axis (i.e. tool axis) and all at the same depth. On the processed log they will be seen as dips of apparently good quality, but will have a dip angle equal to the borehole deviation (i.e. tool tilt) and with an azimuth exactly opposite. These are historically termed mirror image dips.

14.6 Dipmeter interpretation: the basic principles

The problem

A correctly processed dipmeter log is not immediately intelligible; it requires a great deal of interpretation. To most geologists who have tried to use dipmeter logs, this is a truism, and the preceding sentence is quite unnecessary! But to persist. The reason it requires interpretation is that the dipmeter log presents a data set quite unlike any which a geologist working at outcrop will collect. It is beyond normal geological experience. When dip and azimuth or palaeocurrent data are required, a geologist chooses where he will make a measurement: his data points have been very strongly selected. Dipmeter results show no selectivity: everything is mechanically measured. Herein lies the philosophical problem. The dipmeter is like a radio receiver that accepts all wavebands simultaneously and produces a nonsensical cacophany. The data must be filtered, must be selected. The difference between the geologist at outcrop and the dipmeter in the subsurface is:

Outcrop	*geologist - choice - dips*
Subsurface	*dipmeter - dips - choice*

This is a simple but important concept (Cameron 1992). It shows that the dipmeter interpretation problem is one of how to 'choose' dip data.

The solution

More than with the other open hole logs, the dipmeter requires manipulation (in effect computer manipulation), before interpretation is possible. The manipulation is effectively a progressive series of choices which, in themselves, are already part of the interpretation process. Three principal choices are involved: choice of *processing parameters;* choice of *post-processing data grouping;* choice of *processed data format.* What these choices imply is briefly explained immediately below, while their effect on the data is illustrated in the examples throughout the text.

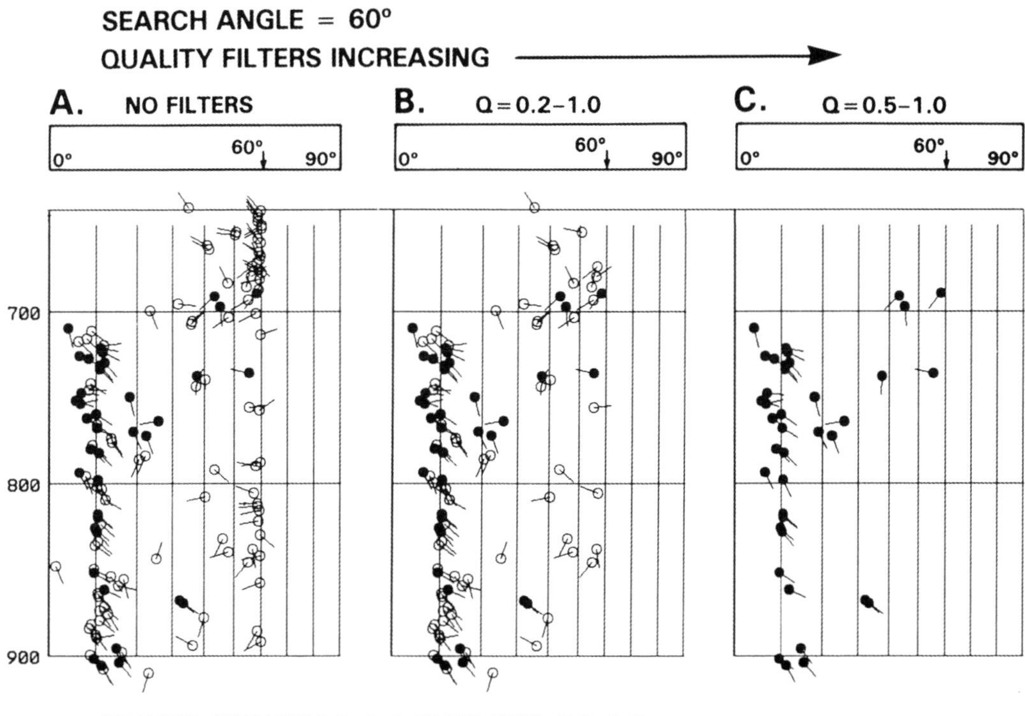

Figure 14.17 Dip correlation quality characteristics. Dip quality is based on the statistical values of the correlation which in this example have a scale of 0–1.0 (0 = poor, 1.0 = excellent: open dips = 0–0.4, filled dips 0.5–1.0). The poorest dips tend to plot at the correlation angle (log A) and are removed by not plotting qualities below Q = 0.2 (log B). Only plotting quality above Q = 0.5 (log C) gives a much 'cleaner' looking result.

The division of dipmeter interpretation into the sedimentary and structural fields has been mentioned. The choice of *processing parameters* underlines this division. A sedimentary interpretation requires a detailed, small scale processing, while structural interpretation, using the same raw data, needs a broader scale (**Figure 14.18**). In other words, it must be known whether a structural or a sedimentary interpretation is required before processing parameters are chosen. A 'structural' processing cannot replace a 'sedimentary' processing and *vice versa*. For the dipmeter interpreter, this choice is similar to the selection, by a field geologist, of a site for dip measurement: it gives an intentional bias to the data.

The choice of *processed data format* can also be regarded as an interpretation tool. The children's game of joining numbered dots to make a picture involves a choice of format: simply adding a line makes the data understandable. Similarly, with dipmeter data, varying the format or the way in which the data are presented helps interpretation. The reason for this is that, for most people, a series of 'tadpoles' on a dipmeter grid does not suggest the geometric form that created them. A fold or fault is not recognisable from a line of dips. Choice of format includes the scale of display, the separation of dip and azimuth and the choice of a format that attempts to actually reconstruct the geometry of the feature measured by the dipmeter.

Post-processing data grouping is carried out on logs already processed and provides a means of enhancing useful data. As discussed, comparison with cores shows that poor dipmeter logs contain noise. Individual noise dips cannot be identified or eliminated in a subsurface data set, but their effects may be significantly lessened by grouping processed results: it allows valid data to dominate (Cameron 1986; 1992). For instance, for a structural interpretation, all data over a 200 m interval may be grouped to give a dip and azimuth mean which, if there is data scatter, will not be clear on a standard plot. In a sedimentary analysis, grouping data from a single channel allows palaeocurrent data to be extracted. Clearly, the choice of data to group together must be geologically biased.

The results of using these three choices on dipmeter data are illustrated in the examples below.

14.7 Sedimentary dipmeter interpretation

Sedimentary dip: definition and processing

By *sedimentary dip*, in the dipmeter context, is intended *the dip of any sedimentary structure which is inherited during deposition, or soon after.* It is a loose definition and includes sedimentary structures such as laminations, cross-beds, bioturbations, slumps and drapes. The prin-

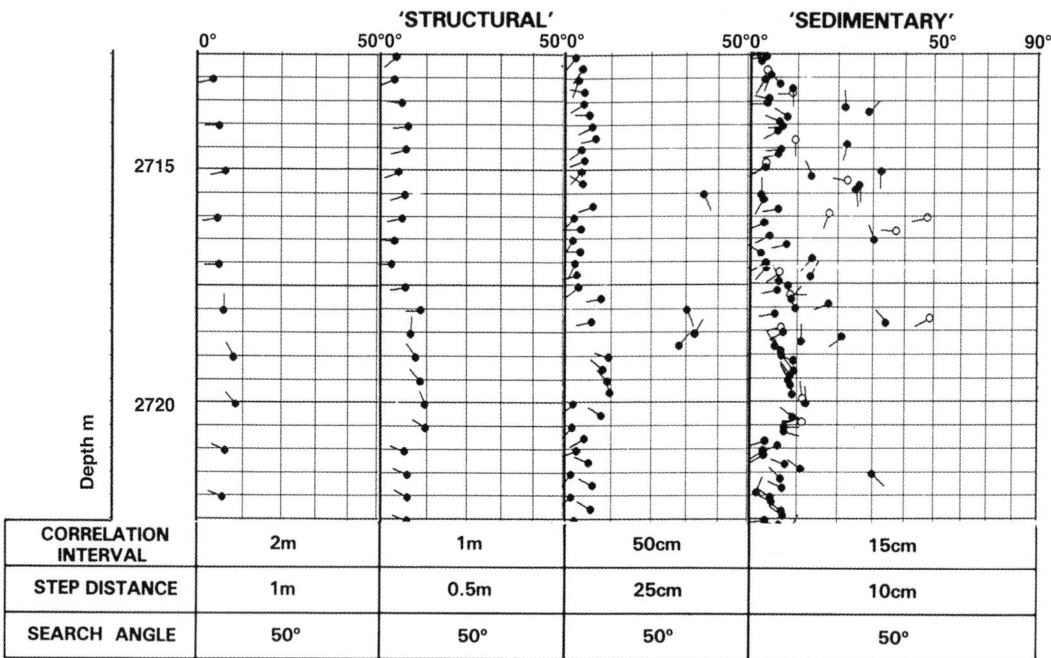

Figure 14.18 The effect of varying fixed interval processing parameters using the same raw, dipmeter data. The logs processed with broader correlation intervals such as 2 m or 1 m (6ft or 3ft) are used for structural (tectonic) interpretations. Processing with small scale correlation intervals such as 15cm (6"), produce logs used for sedimentary structure analysis and palaeocurrent interpretation.

cipal objective of sedimentary dipmeter interpretation is to find the orientation of reservoirs and reservoir parameters. This can be based on the orientation of internal features such as cross-beds, and hence palaeocurrents, or external features such as compaction drapes. The characterisation of facies is another objective (**Table 14.1**). For some unknown reason, some service companies refer to this use of dipmeter as 'stratigraphic'.

Dipmeter data must be specifically processed for sedimentary interpretation. The effects of changing the correlation interval in fixed interval correlation processing have already been illustrated (**Figure 14.18**). Smaller correlation intervals are necessary for sedimentary studies. If the dip of the internal laminae of sedimentary structures is being looked for, then the length of the correlation interval is critical. For example, the typical thickness of cross-bedded structures is less than 1m (Hocker *et al.* 1990). If the raw data are processed with a correlation interval of 1 m, no internal lamination dips will be measured (**Figure 14.19,a**). This is because the set boundaries have the greatest textural contrast and cause the largest resistivity peak. This peak will be preferentially correlated (Rider 1978). It is only when small correlation intervals are used that the internal features stand the chance of being measured (**Figure 14.19,b**). Typically, the dipmeter processed for a sedimentary interpretation will have a correlation interval of 15cm–20cm (6"–10") and a step distance of 7cm–10cm (3"–5"). However, these parameters will depend on the size of the sedimentary features being looked for and the quality of the data. Interpretation begins with the choice of processing parameters (see especially cross-beds and palaeocurrents below).

Scale

When the dipmeter is used as a sedimentological tool, as described above, the question of scale arises immediately. What is the optimum size of sedimentary feature 'seen' by the dipmeter (i.e. the dip measured) and what is the minimum size? The minimum resolution of the dipmeter tool sensors is between 1.0cm – 0.5 cm (0.4" – 0.2"): a bed of this approximate thickness will cause dipmeter curve variation. A bed of 1.3 cm (0.5") will be fully resolved (Sallee and Wood 1984). Tool resolution is not the limiting factor.

The minimum size of sedimentary structure with internal dips which can be resolved by the dipmeter is in the region of 30 cm (1ft). Ripples, for example, will not be seen (**Figure 14.20**). *The limiting factor is processing resolution.* To show how the dipmeter derives its dip, take this book to any outcrop with sedimentary structures and lay it on the rock surface. Now interpret the structure with the part behind the book covered. This is what the dipmeter does. It assumes that, if there is a correlation in the curves, it is due to a planar surface crossing the entire borehole (**Figure 14.19**).

To have the potential for being resolved, a structure must be present, and consistent along bedding, for at

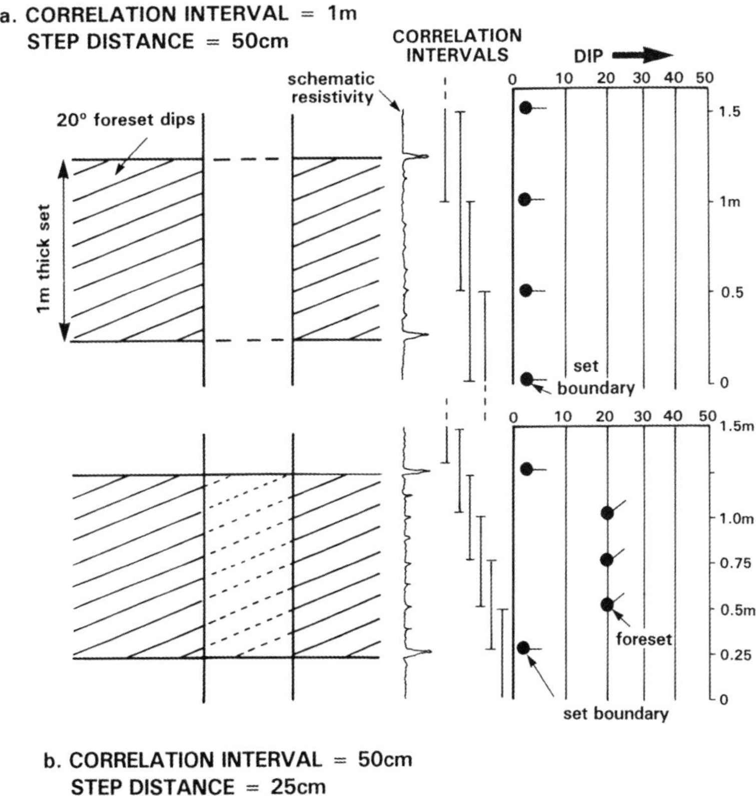

Figure 14.19 Fixed interval dipmeter processing parameters in relation to size (thickness) of sediment structure. With a cross-bed set 1m thick, a dipmeter log processed using a correlation interval of 1m (example a), will not show the dips of the cross-bed laminae. A dipmeter log processed with a 50 cm (2ft) correlation interval (example b), can show several cross-bed lamina dips from one set. The choice of processing parameters is therefore crucial for cross-bed interpretation.

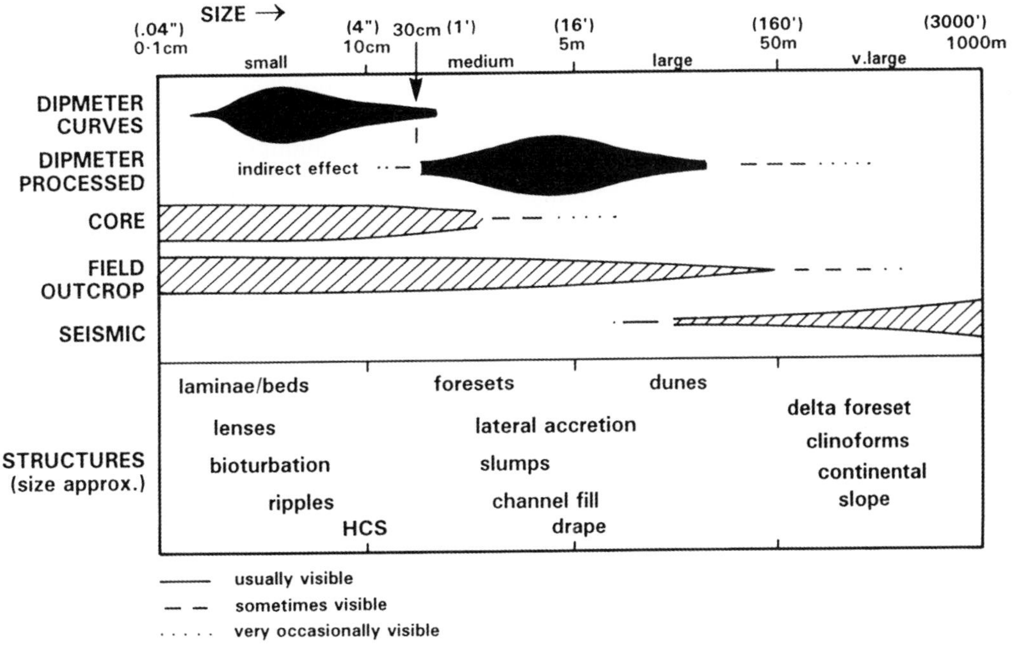

Figure 14.20 Dipmeter resolution of sedimentary structures. Very small scale features can be detected (not identified) by the dipmeter curves. Processed dipmeter logs are quite different. Sedimentary structures with vertical thicknesses from about 30cm–50m (1ft–160ft) can be measured and recognised. The minimum depends on processing parameters, the maximum on presentation format. HCS = hummocky cross-stratification.

Table 14.3 Across hole displacements of dipping surfaces.

Hole size	6″	8.5″	12.25″	17.5″
Dip 10°	2.7cm (1.1″)	3.8cm (1.5″)	5.5 cm (2.2″)	7.8 cm (3.1″)
Dip 20°	5.5cm (2.2″)	7.9cm (3.1″)	11.3 cm (4.5″)	16.2 cm (6.4″)
Dip 30°	8.8cm (3.5″)	12.4cm (4.9″)	18.0 cm (7.1″)	25.7 cm (10.1″)
Dip 40°	12.8cm (5.0″)	18.1cm (7.1″)	26.1 cm (10.3″)	37.3 cm (14.7″)

least the across-hole displacement of internally dipping surfaces. For foresets, the cross-bedding structure must be quite large (i.e. thick in dipmeter terms). A foreset with a 25° dip (bedding horizontal) has an across borehole displacement of 10 cm (4″) in an 8.5″ borehole and 14.5cm (5.7″) in a 12.25″ borehole (**Table 14.3**). For the foreset laminae to be measurable, they must be present over the vertical thickness required for at least two separate, processed measurements (fixed interval processing). For example, a minimum thickness of 40 cm (16″) with a 20 cm (8″) correlation interval (10 cm (4″) step) is required (**Table 14.3**). From theoretical considerations and empirical observations, cross-bed foreset structures (subaqueous only) exist with heights between 10 cm and 10 m (4″ and 33 ft) (aeolian go up to 100 m, 330 ft) with typical values being (subaqueous) between 10 cm (4″) and 2 m (6′). At the smaller scale, the structures will not generally be seen (**Figure 14.20**).

If the minimum size of structure resolved is dictated by processing, the maximum size is dictated by the structure itself. Generally, structures which have a vertical thickness of around 50 m (160 ft) (provided they cause a recognisable anomaly) are clear on the logs. Partly this is a question of display format. Compressed scale logs (**Figure 14.30**) can show much larger scale structures than normal 1:500 scale logs. However, in most large scale structures, such as drapes and sedimentary depositional slopes, the angles involved are very small, 2°–1°, and will not be differentiated from random, background spread, which is typically around 5°. As a rule of thumb, the optimum size of sedimentary structure resolvable by the dipmeter (including internal structures), assuming a correct and appropriate processing, is 30 cm to 50 m (1–160 ft) (**Figure 14.20**). There are exceptions.

Cross-beds and palaeocurrents

Dipmeter response to cross-bedding is central to sedimentary dipmeter interpretation. All the basic principles are involved. Response depends on textural (electrical) contrast, size of structure and processing parameters. Moreover, interpretation of cross-beds requires a knowledge of the sedimentology of bed-forms and an understanding of the manipulation of grouped dip and azimuth data. These principles will be illustrated using dipmeter-type logs (dip-logs) measured at outcrop as well as subsurface examples.

The outcrop example (**Figure 14.21**) is from a deltaic sequence in which both tabular and trough cross-bedded structures are present (Cameron *et al.* 1993). Bed-set thicknesses are generally 1 m (3ft) or less. That is, one bedform with a consistent set of cross-beds is normally less than 1 m in thickness. This is a typical size (thickness) and has implications for the choice of processing parameters as discussed above. Only logs with small correlation intervals, in this example 20cm (simulated), will contain foreset data. When the correlation interval is too large, the set boundaries, which have a high textural contrast and hence create a strong resistivity anomaly, will dominate the correlations (**Figure 14.19**). A correlation interval of *no more than half the bedform thickness* is needed to bring out the internal structure.

With a correct correlation interval, the outcrop work demonstrates that a typical cross-bed interval shows dip groupings or 'clumps' related to the cross-bed dips (**Figure 14.21**). The actual style of the clumps depends on the bed form: tabular sets give regular clumps with low angle set boundary dips; trough sets give less regular dips with higher angle set boundaries (**Figure 14.21**). Each of the two bedforms gives a distinctive dip histogram and azimuth rose diagram. The tabular sets give a tight azimuth rose and two populations of dip, a higher angle one between 10°–30°, which are the foresets, and a very low angle one, which are the bed-set boundary dips (**Figure 14.21,a**). The trough-set bedform gives a more variable rose azimuth diagram and a single dip population with a maximum around 15°–20°. In trough sets, the set bounding surfaces themselves are dipping, albeit at a wide angle to the cross-beds, but set-boundary and cross-bed dips are indistinguishable (**Figure 14.21,b).**

To derive a palaeocurrent from such dipmeter data it is essential to try to eliminate the effects of set boundaries as much as possible (Williams and Soek 1992). This is especially true if trough cross-beds are involved. These, as shown above, have set boundary dips at high angles to the palaeocurrent (**Figure 14.21,b**). The outcrop example shows that dominant cross-bed dips are between 10° and 30° (Cameron *et al.* 1993). Thus, if only dips in this range are accepted as possible foreset indicators, set boundary effects will be minimised. Filtering the data in the outcrop example in this way yielded palaeocurrent directions essentially identical to directions previously measured by classical means (Bristow and Myers 1989).

The techniques learned from outcrop can be applied to the subsurface. The example (**Figure 14.22**) shows that the degree of data filtering leading to the interpretation is considerable. Firstly, the dipmeter is plotted with, at very minimum, a gamma ray log so as to be sure of lithology, in this case, a sand interval. The consistent azimuth and high dip angles through the sands suggest foresets: such dips are limited to the sands. With this diagnosis, the low angle dips are discarded and an azimuth rose constructed using only the dips between 15° and 30°. These data indicate the palaeocurrent orientation (**Figure 14.22**).

The next stage in the study of orientations is to analyse a number of wells through the same sandbody and prepare a palaeocurrent map. This may be presented using the azimuth rose diagrams (**Figure 14.23,a**), or the orientations may be analysed statistically. There are a limited number of ways of analysing circular data. The vector mean azimuth simply gives the mean orientation, but the resultant length, with a value between 0 and 1 gives an indication of the narrowness of the population about the vector mean. The higher the value the narrower the population. However, these tests are designed for uni-modal distributions. Generally in sedimentary dipmeter work there is a large spread of data. An additional statistic, the Rayleigh test, may be applied to rate the significance of a preferred orientation (Davis 1986): it gives a measure of the probability that a given azimuth sample comes from a uniform (i.e. random) population. The smaller the test value the more likely it is that the sample comes from a population with a clear uni-modal distribution. It can be used as a measure of the value of the vector mean azimuth. In this way a large dataset of dipmeter results can be distilled to a single azimuth with a value rating (**Figure 14.23,b**).

Occasionally the interpretation of foresets from the dipmeter is possible without the filtering just discussed. When structures are very large and very consistent, such as in aeolian dunes or tidal sandwaves, dipmeter patterns are self-obvious, and even toe-sets are seen (**Figure 14.24**). But it should be stressed that these cases are not

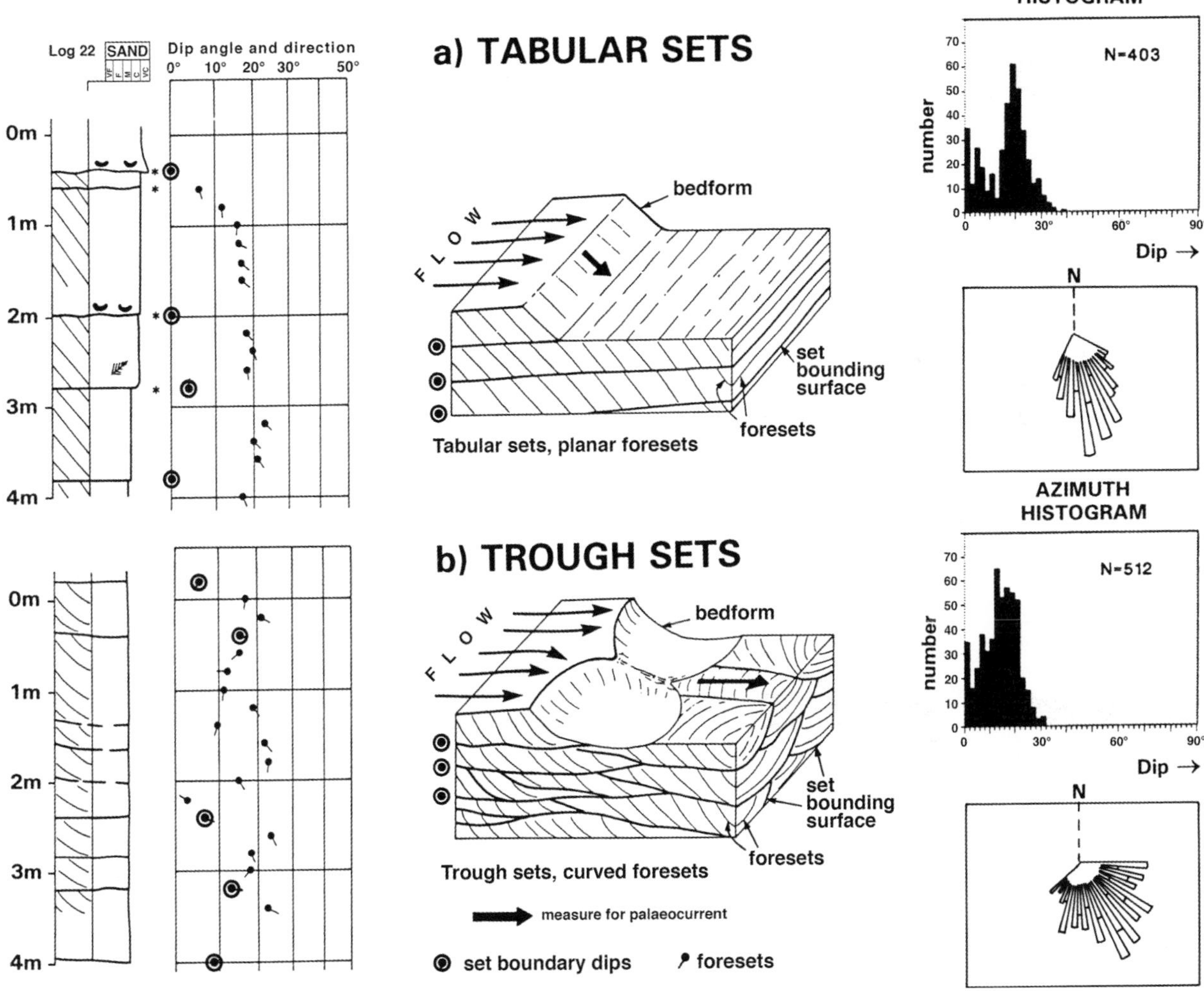

Figure 14.21 Dipmeter cross-bed characteristics illustrated by outcrop measured diplogs. a) Tabular sets show a bi-modal dip histogram (set boundaries and cross-beds) and tight azimuth rose; b) trough sets show a uni-modal dip histogram (set boundaries and cross-beds combined) and a broad azimuth rose. Simulated 20cm correlation interval (from Cameron *et al.* 1993).

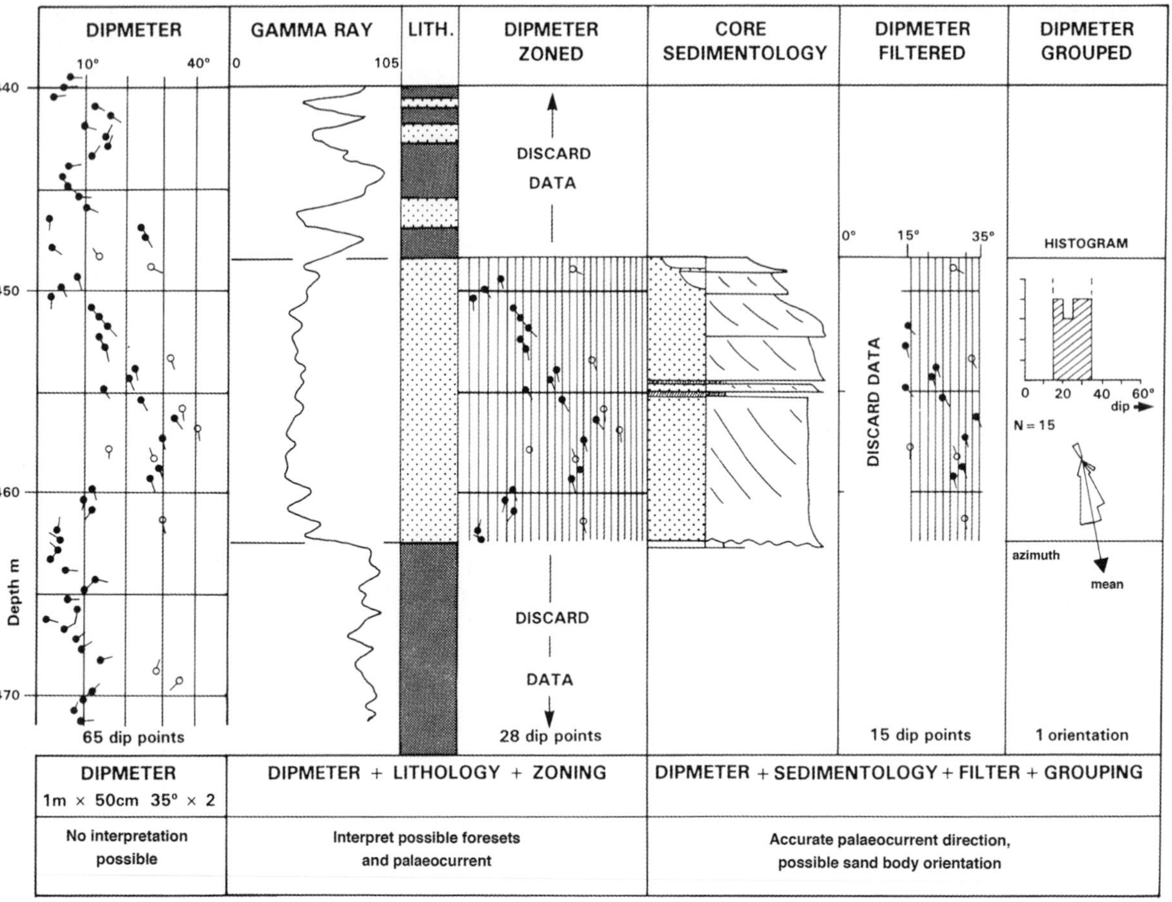

DIPMETER	GAMMA RAY	LITH.	DIPMETER ZONED	CORE SEDIMENTOLOGY	DIPMETER FILTERED	DIPMETER GROUPED
10° 40°	0 105		DISCARD DATA		0° 15° 35° DISCARD DATA	HISTOGRAM 0 20 40 60° dip N = 15 azimuth mean
65 dip points			28 dip points		15 dip points	1 orientation
DIPMETER 1m × 50cm 35° × 2	DIPMETER + LITHOLOGY + ZONING			DIPMETER + SEDIMENTOLOGY + FILTER + GROUPING		
No interpretation possible	Interpret possible foresets and palaeocurrent			Accurate palaeocurrent direction, possible sand body orientation		

Depth m: 2440, 2450, 2460, 2470

Figure 14.22 Analysing a subsurface interval for cross-bed orientations. The dipmeter data are strongly filtered for lithology and dip characteristics to reduce the 65 dip data points to 1 measurement of mean azimuth. The mean azimuth can be interpreted in terms of palaeocurrent (*see text*). NB structural dip = <1°.

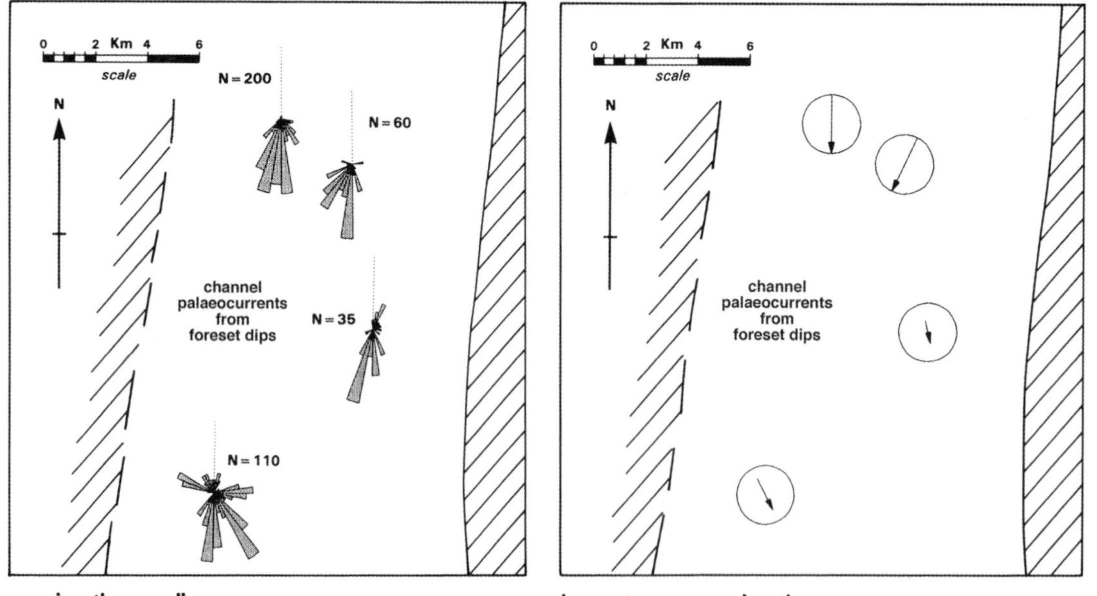

Figure 14.23 Palaeocurrent analysis from subsurface dipmeter. Carefully filtered dipmeter logs give an indication of cross-bed orientations and palaeocurrents. Only dips in sands and with dip values from 15°–40° have been retained. Map a) shows the data plotted as azimuth roses; map b) shows the mean azimuth orientations of the same data, the length of the arrow being related to the Rayleigh test value (*see text*).

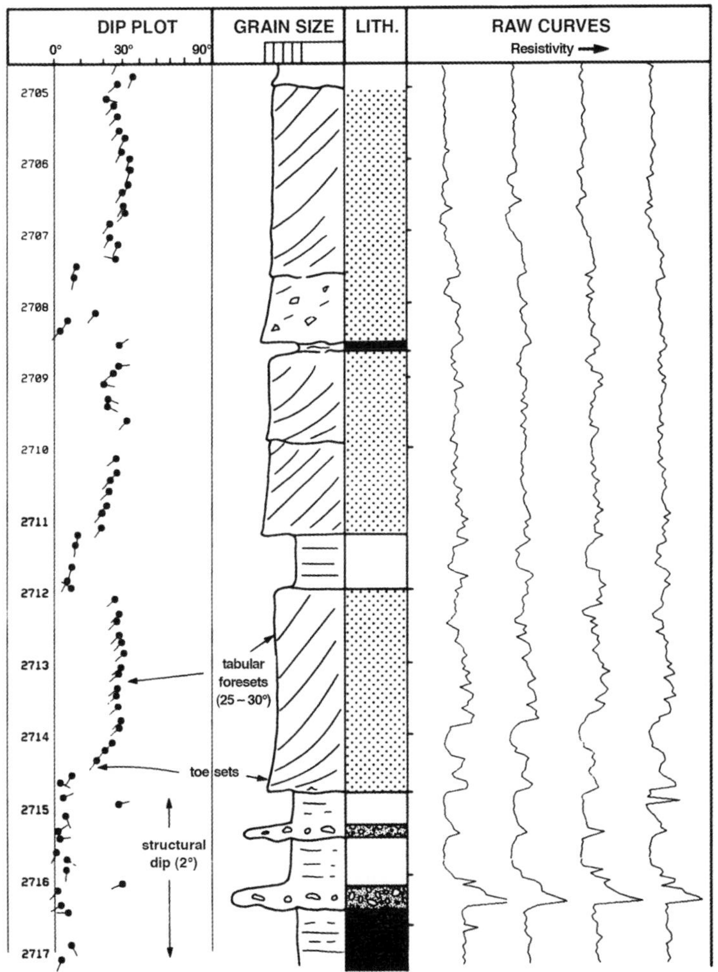

Figure 14.24 Very large, shallow marine cross-bed structures (sand waves) and characteristic dipmeter plot. The consistently oriented dips at 30° indicate cross-bed orientation. Tangential laminae (toe-sets) are seen between 2714m–2715m. Structural dip is below 3°. The acquisition curves are plotted to help refine correlation to core. Such large scale sedimentary structures and clear dipmeter patterns are not common.

frequent and the structures involved are unusually large.

A geologically meaningful grouping of data is generally the key to interpreting cross-beds and palaeocurrents from dipmeter. The complex routines used in the example (**Figure 14.22**) were quite simply carried out with interactive software. One complication, which has not been brought up here, is that of structural dip rotation. When sedimentary, especially palaeocutrent, information is required, all structural dip must be 'rotated out' before applying filters as discussed above. That is, the structural dip must be put back to zero first. Only when this is done will the sedimentary dips have their true, original orientation and magnitude (**Figure 14.14**).

Depositional surface dips

The dip of most depositional surfaces is very close to the horizontal. For instance, in delta mouth-bar areas, or in alluvial levees, depositional surfaces have dips of less than 2°. Since dipmeter dip accuracy is within this amount, dipmeter studies cannot indicate the dip of depositional surfaces – despite many authors proposing models to the contrary. Also, depositional surfaces seen on the seismic, such as clinoforms, have very low absolute dips and are only seen because the horizontal scale of the seismic sections is very compressed. The vertical exaggeration is some 13–30 times and real dips are in the region of 2–6° (slumping begins at 4°). It is unlikely that these would be recognised on a typical dipmeter log: local, small scale variations dominate.

The dip characteristics of depositional surfaces which do have significant dips, other than those associated with cross-beds and dunes, are not well-known. Accretion surfaces which infill channels show lower angles of repose than typical cross-beds and, importantly, their dip azimuth is at 90° to the depositing current and channel orientation (**Figure 14.25**) (Herweijer *et al.*1990). 'Classic' channel fill with compaction drape, which features in many dipmeter manuals, is reserved for the very large scale and is rare *(see* **Figure 14.27**). More typical, in fact, are compaction features above or below channels, although the orientation of these in respect to the channel axis is generally difficult to be certain of.

Some other structures

Many features detected by the dipmeter which are shown to have a marked preferred orientation have no sedimentological model applicable to dipmeter interpretation. For example, HCS (hummocky cross-stratification) often gives good, slightly irregular dip with vertically consistent orientations (**Figure 14.26**). HCS is generally not thought of as showing a depositional orientation: the dipmeter suggests otherwise. Recently, it has been suggested that, in rare cases, preferred orientations may exist (Duke *et al.* 1995). The dipmeter suggests that, in fact, it is quite common. However, whether this orientation is parallel to the coastline, facing the offshore or the onshore (most probable) is not yet known (cf. Williams and Soek 1992).

The dipmeter characteristics of turbidite sequences are generally uncertain. One example, however, shows some characteristics which may be expected. In this example (**Figure 14.27**), a large (30m × 1km) (100ft × 3300ft), previously eroded channel is filled essentially by shale but with several episodes of turbidite sand channels (Phillips 1987). The western margin of the channel is picked out on the dipmeter as a result of draping from

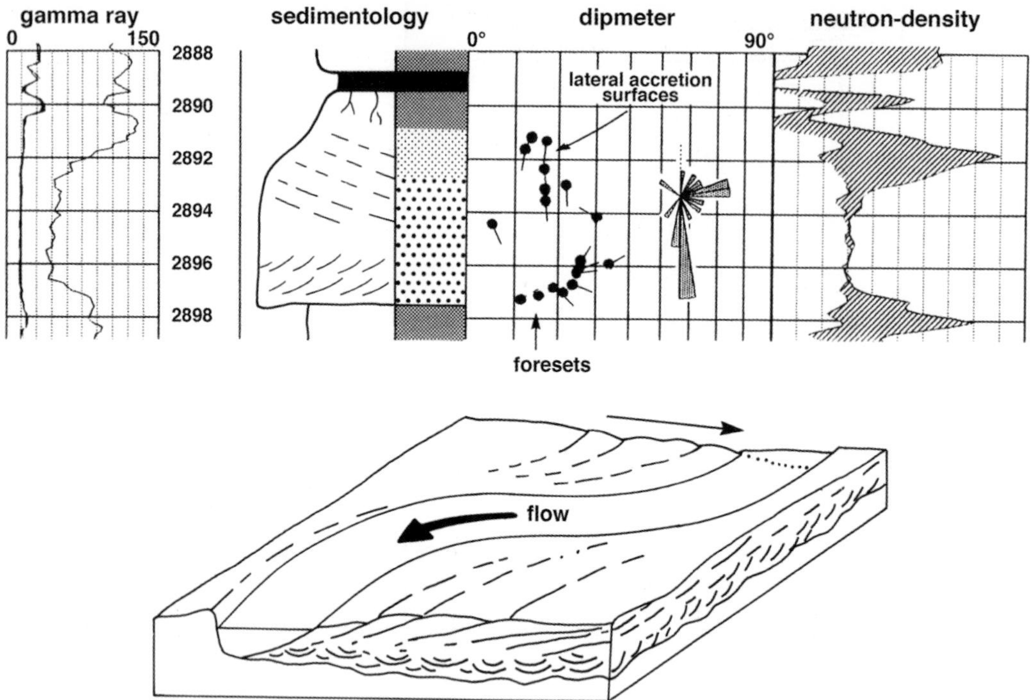

Figure 14.25 Complex dipmeter from a deltaic channel. The lower interval shows higher angle dips to the east (cross-beds). The upper interval shows lower dips to the south - which are lateral accretion surfaces. Cored interval.

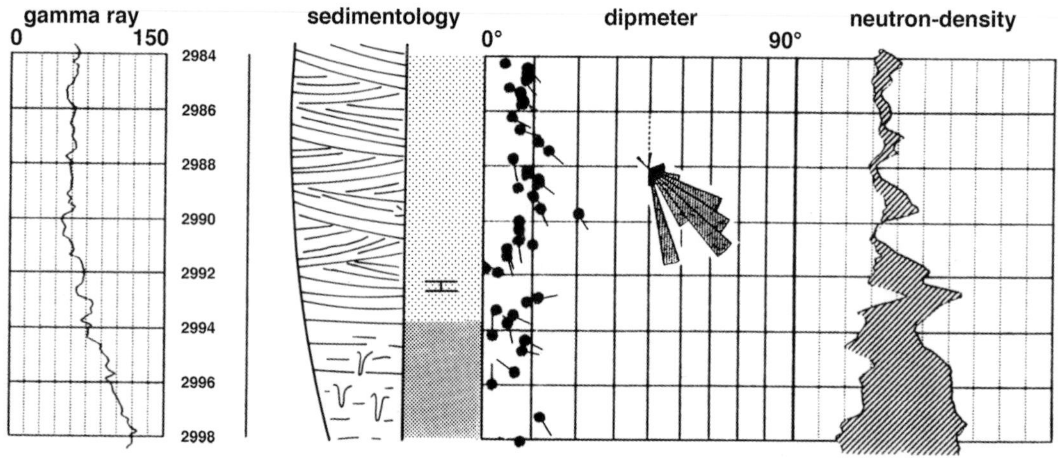

Figure 14.26 Dipmeter characteristics of HCS (hummocky cross-stratification) in a coarsening-up, marine sequence. Low angle dips with consistent orientations occur in HCS quite frequently. Cored interval.

the covering sediments (**Figure 14.27**, AU19). Slumping is also interpreted, essentially as small normal faults (**Figure 14.27**, AU23). As far as the turbidite sands themselves are concerned, they show no internal dipmeter characteristics and are considered massive. Their orientation, however, is indicated by drape (**Figure 14.27**, AU 15), generally assumed to be normal to the depositing currents.

These seem, in fact, to be the more typical features of turbidite sequences. Regular dips occur in the thicker shale intervals, but these change from one shale section to the next, the overlying shales giving drape orientations (**Fig 14.28**). Whether these are channel margin or lobe margin orientations depends on the type of turbidites present. In the example (**Figure 14.28**) a lobe deposition is suggested, and sand thickness is predicted to increase to the southwest.

Texture and facies

Dipmeter microresistivity curves are acquired to bring out small scale resistivity variations and are therefore

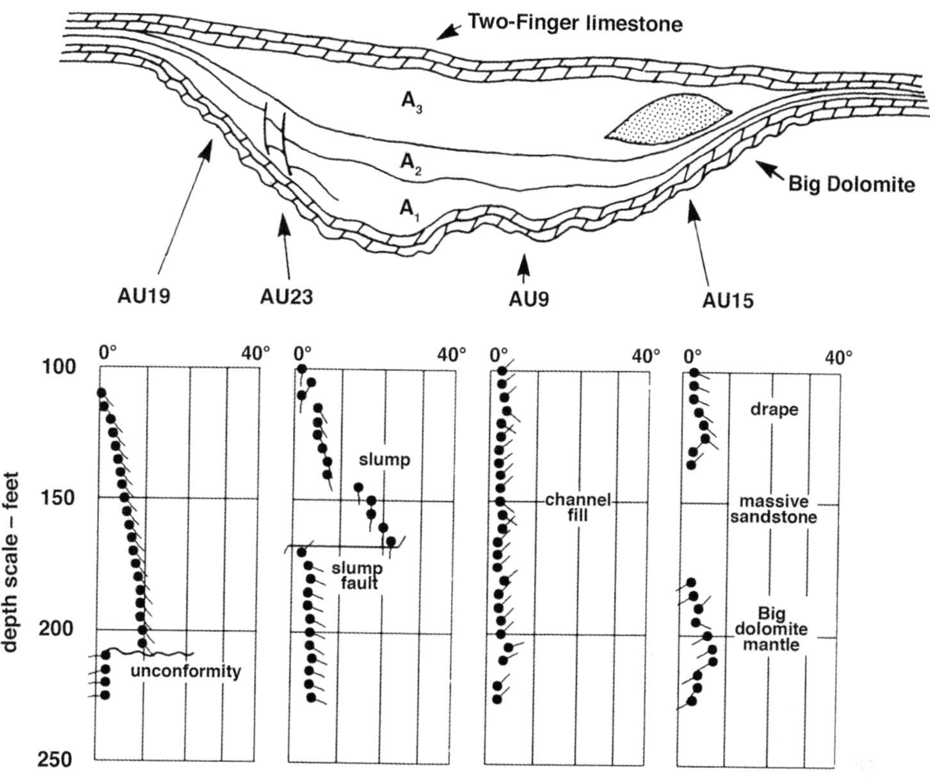

Figure 14.27 Dipmeter characteristics of a valley-fill sequence. The previously eroded channel was filled by shales and some turbidite sands. On the dipmeter the sands are featureless but the shales show compaction (AU 19), slumping (AU23) and draping over sand-bodies (AU I5) (re-drawn and re-plotted, after Phillips 1987).

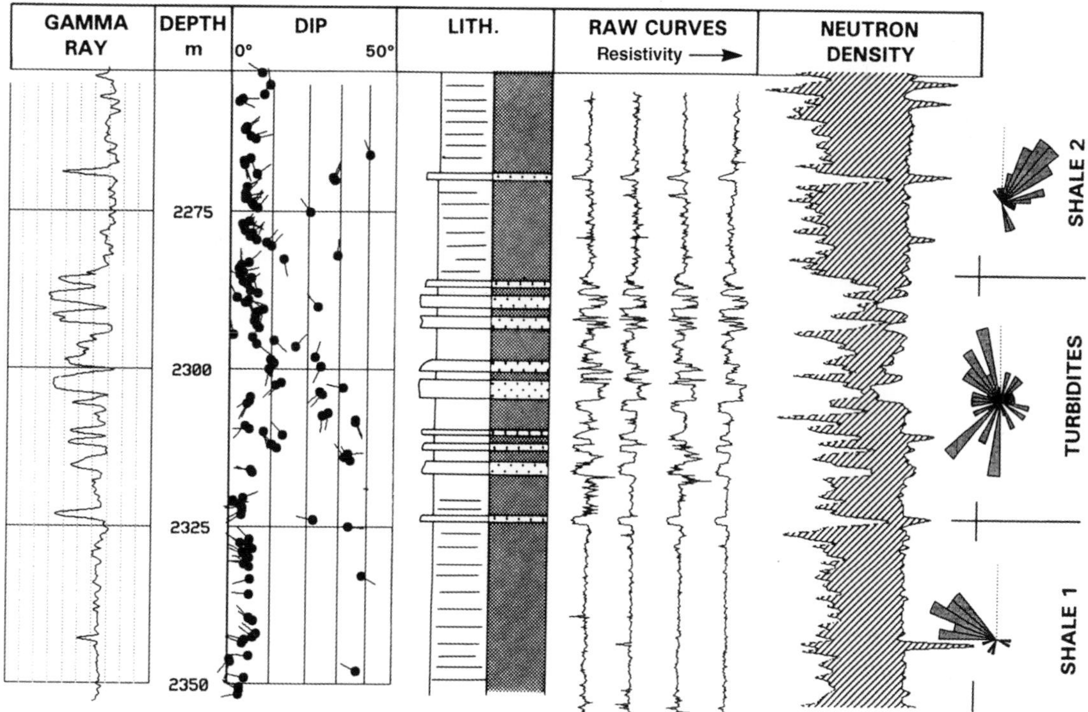

Figure 14.28 Typical dipmeter response in a turbidite sequence. The turbidite sands show scattered dips with no preferred orientation. The shale sections show regional dip (shale 1) and drape over very subdued submarine topography, in this case a lobe (shale 2). The acquisition curves are essential to fine lithological interpretations in such (thin-bed) sequences.

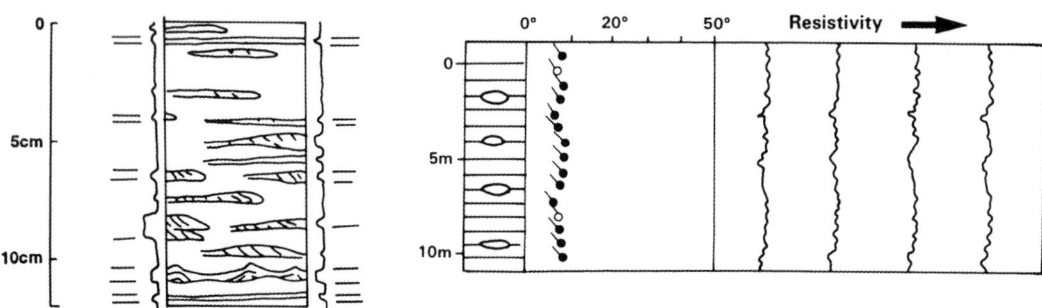

A. LAMINATED silty shale

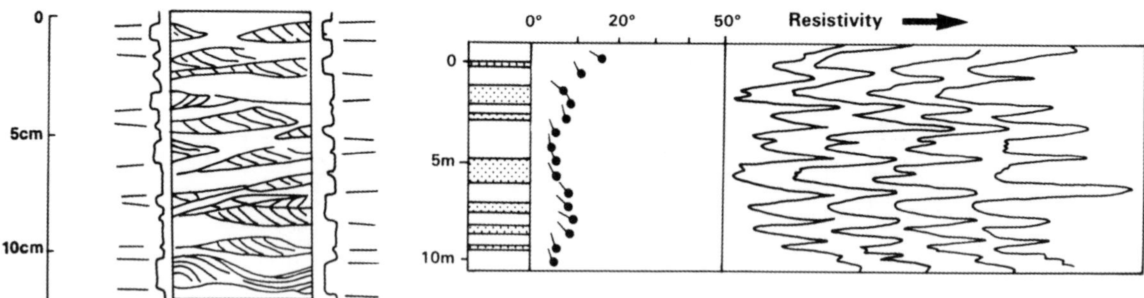

B. FLASER-LINSEN sands and shales

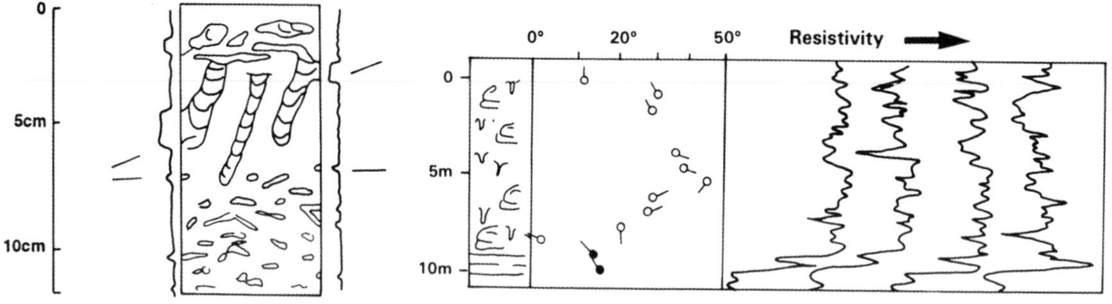

C. BIOTURBATED sandy shale

Figure 14.29 Texture and facies indicated by dipmeter acquisition curves and dipmeter plots. A. Laminated silty shales give regular dips but little acquisition curve character; B. flaser and linsen give excellent curve character but irregular, variable dips; C. bioturbation can give good curve character which is, however, irregular and produces poor quality, scattered dips (the so-called bag-of-nails).

sensitive to small scale variations in lithology and texture (**Figure 14.19**). In the simplest case, the curves can be used to identify thin beds, beds down to 1cm (0.4") rather than 15cm (6") typical of the standard logs (cf. Serra *et al.* 1993). However, from a geological perspective, the fine scale of the dipmeter curves may be used as facies indicators (Cameron 1992). Three typical siliciclastic facies are illustrated along with schematic dipmeter microresistivity curves (**Figure 14.29,a-c**). Each facies shows distinct microresistivity curve characteristics illustrated by the real, core controlled, subsurface examples alongside (**Figure 14.29**). For example, facies *b,* flaser and linsen, shows strong electrical contrast between the discrete, clean sand and clean shale layers. In facies *a,* laminated shale, electrical contrasts are much less pronounced.

Although it is principally the microresistivity curve characteristics that bring out facies information, the processed dipmeter results themselves are indirectly affected. For example, although a bioturbated sandy shale may show good electrical contrasts in the curves, there is no curve similarity and the processed dips are poor, inconsistent and scattered (**Figure 14.29,c**). Equally, the other two facies illustrated show the effects that the curve characteristics have on the computed results, although it is only when the curves are plotted alongside the results that it is possible to make a facies interpretation.

14.8 Structural dipmeter interpretation

Structural dip: definition, processing and identification

By *structural dip* is meant the *'general attitude of beds'*. It is the dip that would be measured at outcrop. It is usually the dip seen on seismic reflectors, themselves a generalisation. It avoids any sedimentary structures of any size and is generally considered to represent the depositional surface, which also is considered to be horizontal. There are, of course, many exceptions where the depositional surface is not horizontal (**Figure 17.22**).

A dipmeter log is processed for structural dip with a relatively broad correlation interval, typically lm (3ft or 4ft) (**Figure 14.18**) (Bigelow 1985). Step distance, expressed as a percentage, is normally 50%, although 25% sometimes gives better results. The search angle may be set reasonably low if the general dip is known. Programmes that generalise and 'clean up' dipmeter logs can be used for structural work. Cluster, a Schlumberger programme (Hepp and Dumestre 1975), attempts to diminish inconsistent dips so bringing out structural trends in the more consistent data. However, programmes which group and do not modify the original data are probably better (*see* next section).

On the log itself, structural dip should be measured over fine grained (shale) intervals where bedding is more likely to be planar and regular (**Figure 14.30**). Thick shale intervals are clearly best since thinner shales in

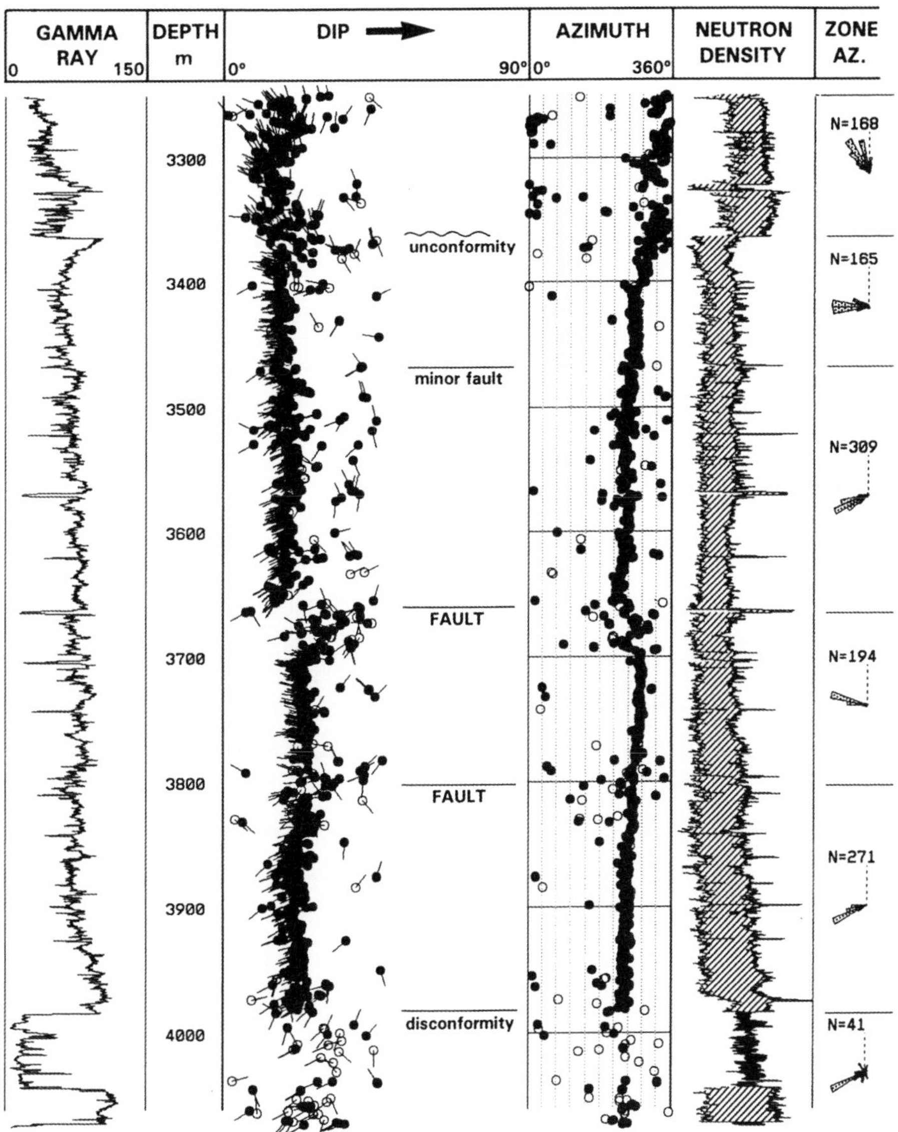

Figure 14.30 Structural dip seen on a summary scale dipmeter log. Dips are generally to the west at between 10°–15° through this essentially shale section, but as the zoned azimuth plot and the azimuth log indicate, there are subtle variations caused by faulting and unconformities. Such changes are not picked out effectively on standard scale plots.

sand-shale sequences often show distortion inherited during compaction. Structural dip may be measured either on the log itself, when it is relatively constant and there is little scatter, or from a stereographic polar plot, where it will be chosen as the most common orientation (**Figure 14.14**). Statistical tests may also be applied to derive a value. In the case of structure, simple two dimensional statistics are usually not acceptable and it is necessary to apply eigen vector analysis (Davis 1986).

A reliable identification of structural dip is essential, as most recognisable structural features are a distortion of it. The structural interpretation of dipmeter data, like structural geology, is about geometry and geometrical consistency or inconsistency.

Structural dip: correlation, mapping and seismic sections

The most straightforward use of the structural dipmeter is in simple structural situations. For example, on structural cross-sections or correlation sections which are drawn to scale, dipmeter stick plots in the line of the section (i.e. show the apparent dip in the line of the section) can be very helpful. Secondly, seismic maps can be checked against the dipmeter. The contours of a typical, depth converted (isobath) seismic map contain an implied amount of dip and orientation. Map and dipmeter can be checked against each other (**Figure 14.31**).

An extremely practical and useful aid to structural dipmeter interpretation is being able to directly compare dipmeter results with seismic sections. This involves

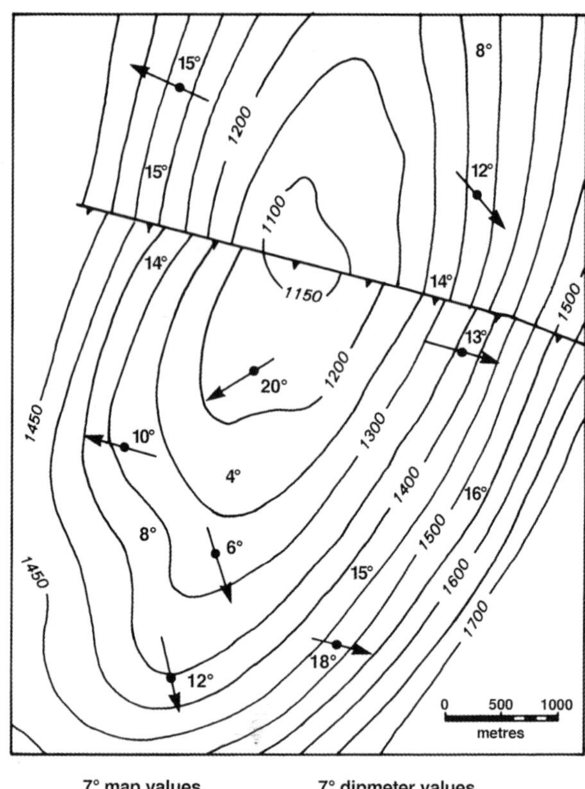

Figure 14.31 Structural dipmeter results plotted on an isobath map produced from the seismic. Dip angles derived from the map are shown: the azimuth is indicated by the map contours. Dipmeter and map data should correspond.

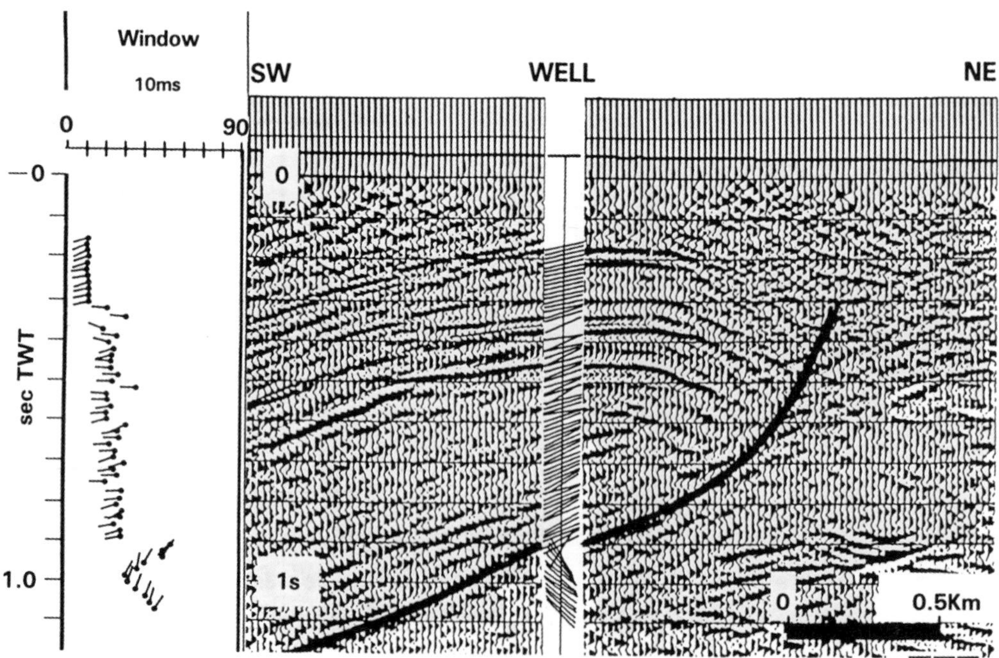

Figure 14.32 Dipmeter data plotted on a time scale and converted to the scales and orientation of a seismic line for direct overlay. A stick plot is used for this. The example shows a listric fault with rollover (from Werner *et al.* 1987).

quite complex conversions such as plotting the dipmeter on a time scale rather than depth scale, correcting for interval velocity, plotting the dip results in the plane of the seismic section (i.e. with apparent dip) and with a compressed horizontal scale. The results are best presented in the form of a stick plot. Necessarily, this conversion is achieved by computer. The example (**Figure 14.32**) shows a listric fault, with a marked rollover, crossing the well just above TD (Werner *et al.* 1987). The fact that it is a listric fault is clear on the seismic but not on the dipmeter, although the location of the fault is clear on the dipmeter but difficult to pick on the seismic. The integration of both sets of data, dipmeter and seismic, gives confidence in an interpretation beyond either set individually. In areas, for example, of difficult multiples, side-swipe or complex tectonics, the seismic dipmeter plots are very useful.

Unconformities and disconformities

One of the most frequently perceived uses of the structural dipmeter is in the identification of unconformities. However, for an unconformity to be seen on the dipmeter, it must be angular: disconformities or paraconformities will not be seen. The first example (**Figure 14.33**) shows a strong, angular unconformity, the beds above being nearly horizontal, those below dipping at approximately 22° to the west. The example also shows, which is very typical, that the dipmeter cannot be used to pinpoint the actual unconformity level: the dips are too scattered due to burrowing, weathering or diagenesis.

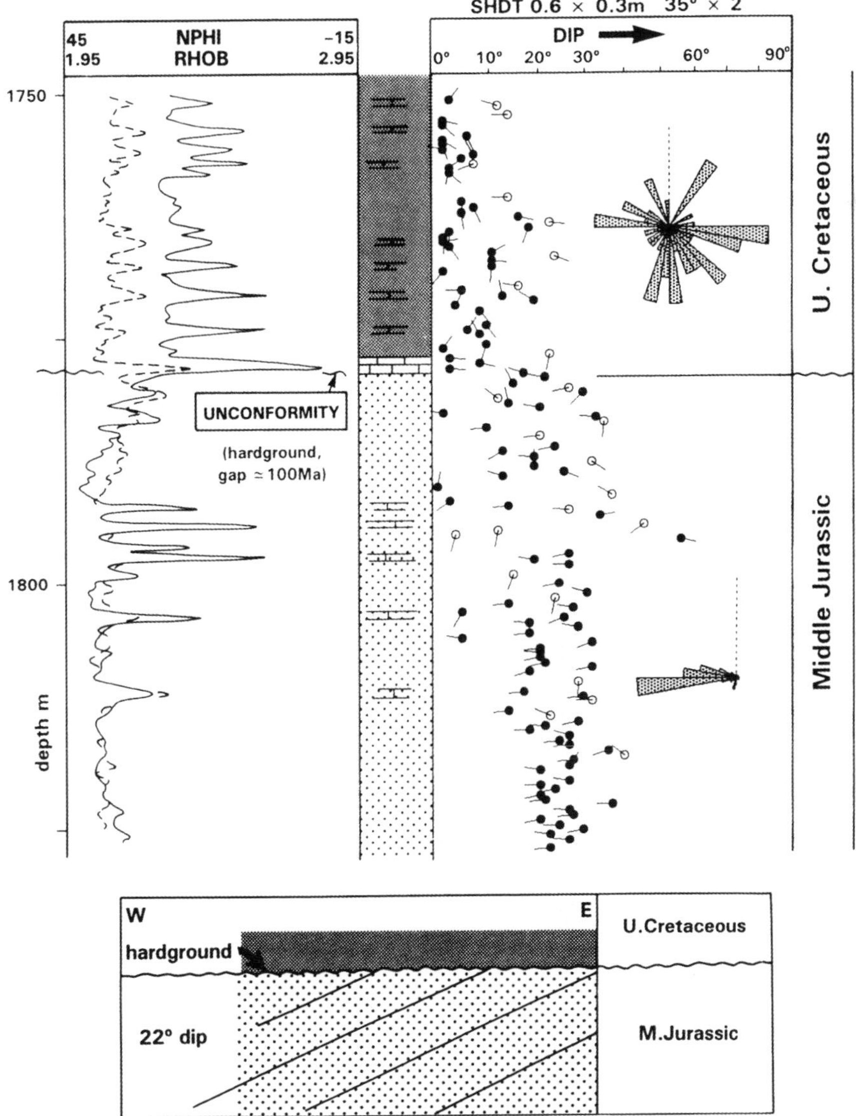

Figure 14.33 An angular unconformity on the dipmeter. Jurassic sands dip at approximately 22° to the west and are overlain by horizontal, Upper Cretaceous shales. The unconformity is picked from the standard logs and a hardground is interpreted from the density log at the unconformity level. It is the dipmeter, however, that shows that the unconformity is angular.

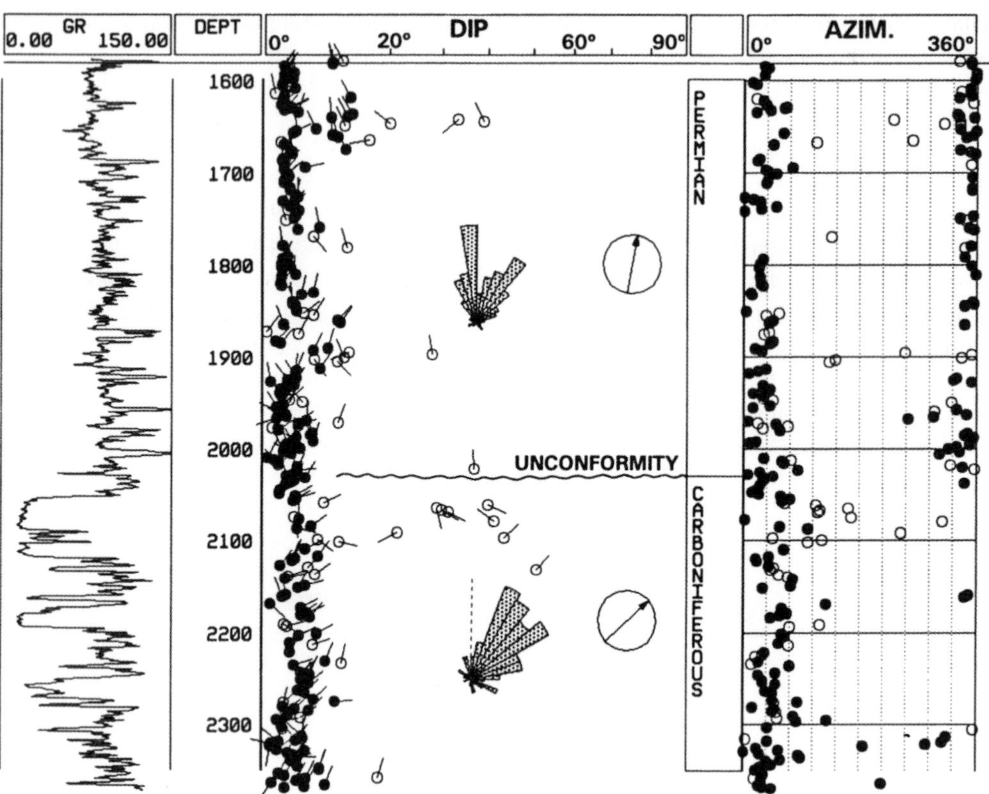

Figure 14.34 A slight angular unconformity indicated by zoned dipmeter data. Only when the unconformity is picked on the standard logs and the dipmeter data are zoned, do the differences in azimuth become apparent. This type of unconformity is typical.

Using the neutron-density logs allows the precise level to be located at a probable hardground (**Figure 14.33**), but it is only the dipmeter that indicates the angularity of the break. The second example (**Figure 14.34**) shows a more typical unconformity, where the angular change is very small and the break is indicated by a moderate azimuth change, not a dip change. For such subtle breaks to be brought out, it is necessary to use a compressed scale log (1:2000 to 1:5000) and to zone the dipmeter data carefully, the actual break being selected on the standard logs rather than the dipmeter itself. The necessity for combining the dipmeter with other open hole logs is clear.

Faults

Faults are identified on the dipmeter through geometrical distortion; that is, changes of dip or changes of azimuth, or both (**Figure 14.30**). If there is no distortion, no fault will be seen. In reality, there are two types of distortion with a potential to be identified on the dipmeter: distortion about the fault plane itself and distortion, or geometrical change, from one fault block to another. Interpreters often confuse the two, but the scale is quite different as illustrated below.

A second confusion is that the dipmeter can seldom give a conclusive indication of fault plane dip, or of whether the fault is normal or reversed. If distortion about a fault is cylindrical, a fault plane strike can be given, but not the dip of the fault plane. The following examples show this.

– distortion at the fault plane, fault drag

It is generally assumed that faults can be recognised on the dipmeter by *tectonic drag*. Drag forms as beds are pulled along a fault zone like a wet rag, as movement progresses (**Figure 14.35,a**). This movement is considered cylindrical, so that beds are rotated (dragged) progressively into the plane of the fault as the fault itself is approached. A dipmeter through a zone of drag will show a cusp pattern on the log (**Figure 14.35,a**) while the dips in the cusp, when plotted on a stereogram, will fall on a great circle (i.e. form a cylinder). There are cases when this is true, but personal field experience suggests that drag zones are very limited and often not seen on a structurally processed log, or the style of drag is not the classical cylinder (**Figure 14.37**).

It is sometimes suggested that drag, when it occurs, can indicate the amount of throw on a fault. That is, the vertical extent of the drag zone corresponds to the amount of throw. It is possible to use the drag zone as a minimum, but not as an absolute indication of the throw. An interesting case described recently suggests that drag characteristics may be indicative of whether a fault seals or not (Berg and Avery 1995).

– distortion between fault blocks, tectonic rollover and reverse drag

Frequently, what is considered as, or at least called drag, is in fact *tectonic rollover or reverse drag*. Rollover and reverse drag occur on a much larger scale than drag and are related to the distorting effects that faulting has on the entire rock mass, not the distortion just around the fault itself. Moreover, rollover and reverse drag cause beds to dip *into* a fault, not to parallel it (**Figure 14.35,b**). (Although rollover is shown in the example (**Figure 14.35,b**) as restricted to the hanging wall, this is not always the case. It is the case in listric faults - *see below*). If a cusp pattern is identified on the dipmeter, it is essential to know whether it is drag and parallel to the fault, or rollover/reverse drag and contrary to the fault. This dilemma is beautifully expressed by an example from Nigeria (Adams *et al.* 1992). An obvious tectonic cusp pattern is seen in the dipmeter over 60m (200ft) of borehole, the dip consistently increasing downwards from 10° to 50°, then dropping back to 10° (**Figure 14.36**). A computer programme was used to model this dip pattern. Three equally valid cases satisfy the dipmeter results: a normal fault with drag, a reverse fault with drag and a listric fault with rollover. The computer programme very effectively provides a model for the eye that a line of dips cannot (cf. Etchecopar and Dubas 1992). Indications from the seismic suggest that it is a normal fault with drag. However, the example illustrates perfectly the difficulties in interpreting faults from the dipmeter and that, even though a fault may be identified from the dipmeter alone, it is generally not possible

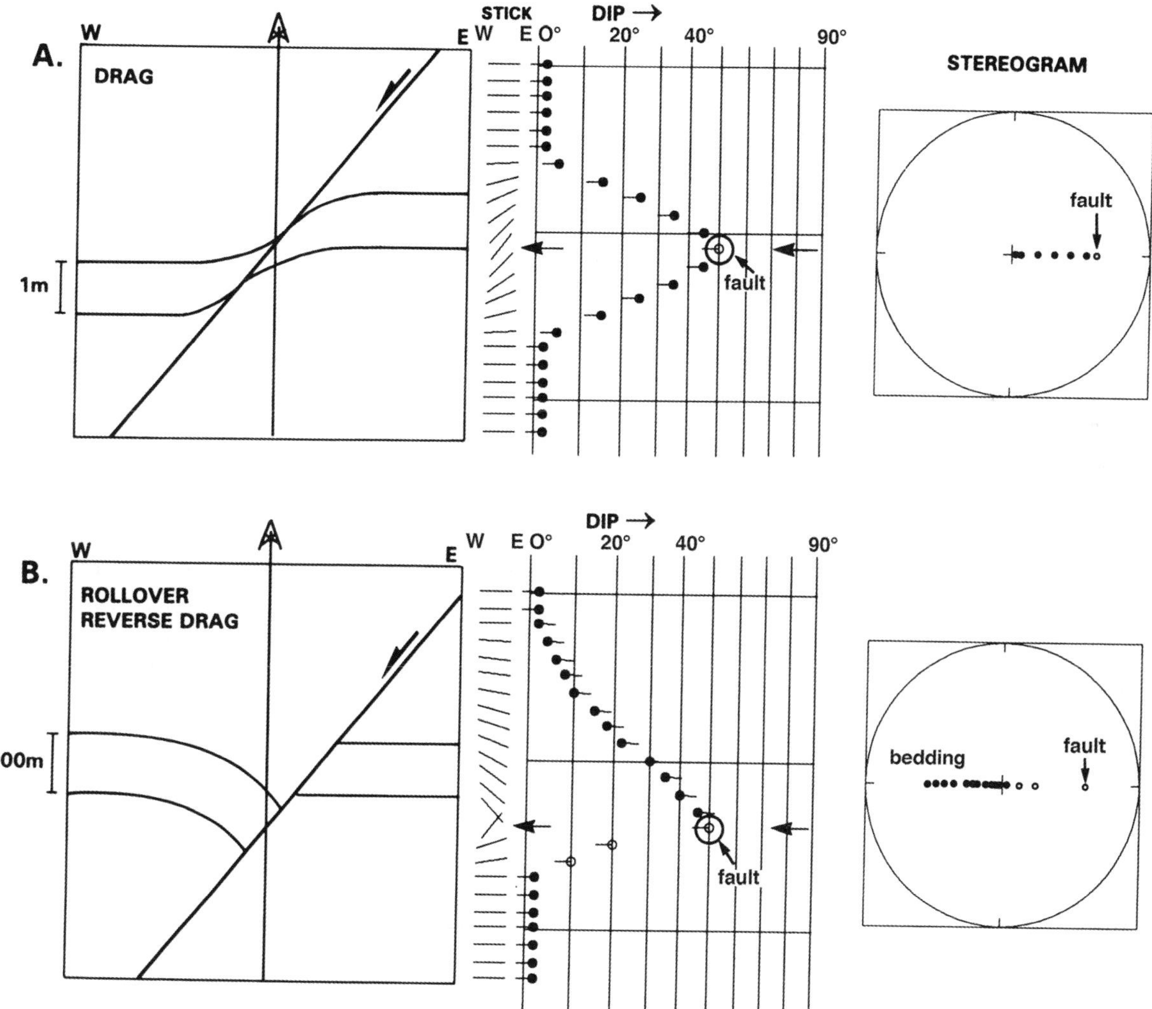

Figure 14.35 Fault characteristics on the dipmeter illustrated by a sketch, log and stereogram (Schmidt). A. drag, typically at a small scale around the fault plane itself. The stereogram shows cylindrical distortion with the highest dip close to the dip and orientation of the fault plane. B. rollover or reverse drag, a large scale effect. The stereogram shows cylindrical distortion with the dip of the fault plane opposite to bedding dip.

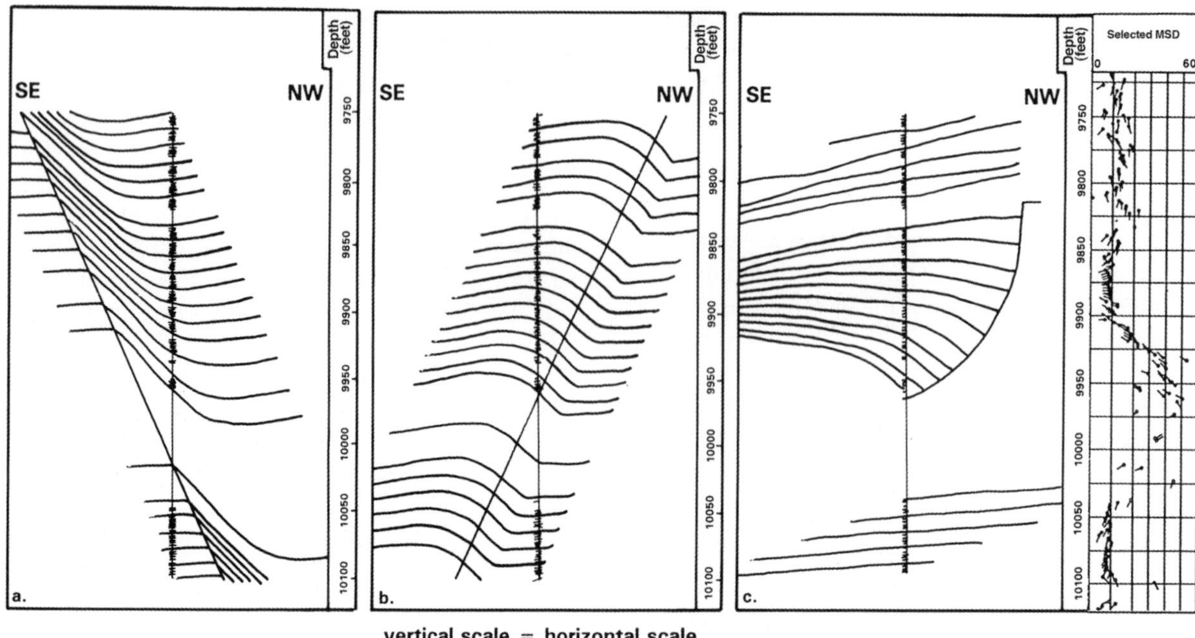

Figure 14.36 Fault geometry interpreted from the dipmeter. Three interpretations are possible from the one dipmeter dataset (shown on the right): a) normal fault with drag (correct interpretation) ; b) reverse fault with drag; c) listric fault. Computer generated profiles (from Adams *et al.* 1992).

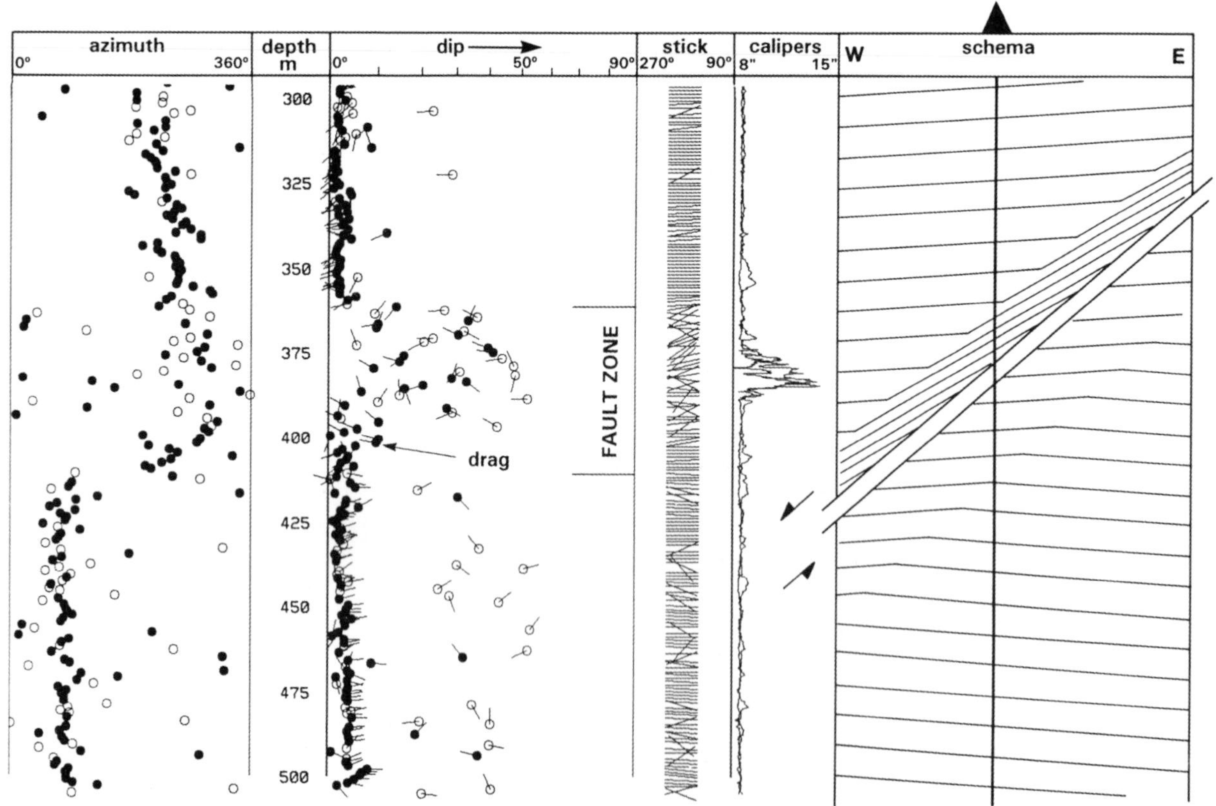

Figure 14.37 Dipmeter example of a large normal fault (300 m throw (980ft), seismically visible, westerly dipping). There is no clear dip change and the fault is best recognized from the azimuth plot (far left): dip azimuth is east below the fault, west above. There is no typical drag but a zone of about 50 m (160ft) has high dips which parallel the fault dip. The position of the fault plane (if there is just one) can be proposed at the site of caving indicated on the calipers. The entire section is shale.

to interpret the type of fault or the direction of displacement on it. The fault strike is, however, generally clear, being orthogonal to the distorted bedding dip.

– subsurface example

The reality of fault identification using the dipmeter is more prosaic and practical than most dipmeter handbooks would suggest. The first necessity is to identify a break as a fault. The next necessity is to describe the geometry. Usually the dipmeter responses are not classic in the least. The example (**Figure 14.37**) shows the dipmeter response to a large normal fault through a shale sequence. The presence of a fault is obvious. The upper section (300m–360m) dips at low angles to the west: the lower section (390m–500m) at low angles to the east. There is a distinct azimuth change although no change in dip angle, a feature common in subsurface faults. Between the two sections is a zone of high, poor quality, confused dips which is the fault zone. In this case, a normal fault has been identified on the seismic dipping to the west. The dipmeter then shows the exact location of the fault, that the dominant dips in the fault zone are westerly and parallel to the fault plane. There is very minor drag just below the fault seen as a dip reversal. Clearly, there is an absolute need for combining the carefully analysed dipmeter with seismic interpretation. This can be refined by using the time scale dipmeter plots in direct overlays as illustrated previously (**Figure 14.32**).

– outcrop example

The final example is of field measured diplog profiles across a small normal fault which outcrops over a wide, wave-cut platform and through an associated vertical cliff. The illustration shows the fault as it is seen in the cliff, dipping to the north (**Figure 14.38,a**). The two diplog profiles are measured at different points on this fault as it crosses the wave-cut platform. The first diplog, 130m (425ft) from the cliff, shows the fault more or less as it is in the cliff section (**Figure 14.38,b**). The diplog registers the fault as a change in azimuth and not a change in dip, which tends to be a more diagnostic feature for the eye in vertical slices through faults. The second profile (**Figure 14.38,c**) 230m from the cliff, crosses the same fault where there is neither a dip nor an azimuth change: no fault would be identified in the subsurface. There is clear character change along fault strike.

This example is used to stress two things: the dipmeter is just one more tool in fault identification to be used in conjunction with others, and there is a great need for outcrop study of fault detail in terms of dipmeter response.

Folds

Folds are not often seen in hydrocarbon wells in their entirety. Slump folds are the obvious exception. However, it is instructive to look at dipmeter patterns of small scale folds to illustrate the problems of interpretation of large scale folds as they are encountered in wells.

The figures (**Figure 14.39**), are all taken from photos rendered as line drawings. The dipmeter profiles alongside the drawings are measured partly in the field, partly from the photos and are therefore somewhat schematic. Case A is a tight anticline sampled from one limb. The picture is relatively simple. Case B is a box fold with vertical beds in one limb. The dipmeter in this case would be extremely difficult to interpret and may be confused with a fault, or simply missed. The last case, C, is of a simple anticline with the well passing across the crest. The line of the section is north-south so that, as the fold crest is crossed, dips swing abruptly from south to north across a low dipping section. The dipmeter profile is reasonably interpretable, especially if a sterographic projection is used. If, however, the fold plunges, the dip pattern becomes more complex and interpretation more difficult. In this case stereographic analysis is obligatory. The obvious feature of these examples is the extreme difficulty in recognising the fold geometry from the dipmeter profile. To analyse and identify fold geometry, stereograms may be used as in classical structural geology (Ramsey 1967) but this destroys the depth information in the original dipmeter data. A more effective solution is to present the dip and azimuth data separately or as SCAT plots (Bengtston 1980; 1981; 1982). Details of the SCAT (Statistical Curvature Analysis Technique) plot technique cannot be given here, but it allows folds to be identified and also the level at which the well crosses certain unique positions such as the fold axis and axial plane. An effective description of the structure being drilled can be made. In some exploration areas, even today, seismic is very poor and wells are drilled on surface outcrop structure, just as they were in early days. SCAT techniques allow the integration of the surface data and the well data. The example shows the fold of Figure 14.39,c in SCAT format (**Figure 14.40**).

Fractures

Fracture identification with the dipmeter is notoriously difficult. Dip tadpoles themselves will not normally indicate fractures since they have dips much higher than the associated bedding. When a dip is calculated, the lowest angle of dip is taken, and two dips cannot be calculated at the same level. Hence, even when marked fractures are present, the dipmeter dip will be that of the bedding. This is nicely illustrated by an image log analysis of the Monterey Formation of California. Manual image log analysis identifies high dipping fractures and low dipping bedding planes while dipmeter processing of the same data shows only the bedding planes (Sullivan and Schepel 1995).

The technique for fracture identification which has been marketed uses the dipmeter curves, not the processed dip results. When an open fracture is present it

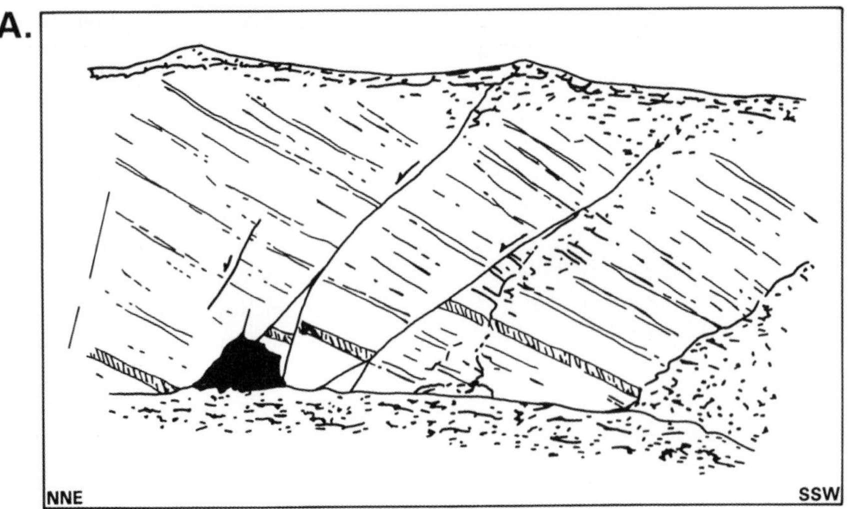

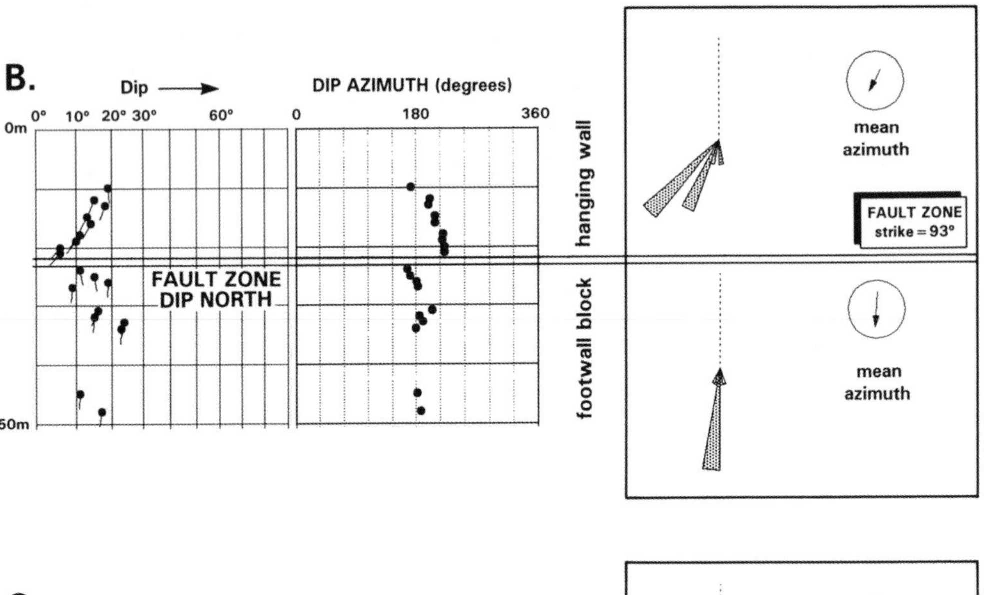

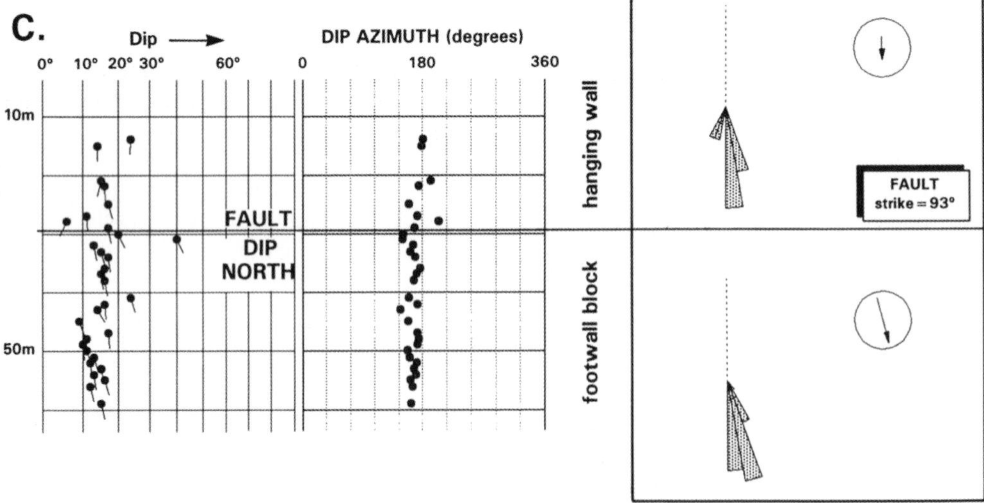

Figure 14.38 Outcrop example of a small normal fault. A. cliff profile. The diplogs were measured through the fault across a wave-cut platform in front of the cliff. B. 130 m (420ft) from the cliff, showing a well-defined fault and azimuth change. C. 230 m (750ft) from the cliff showing no dipmeter changes across the fault. The example illustrates that character may change along the same fault and that a fault may not be detected by the dipmeter when there is no geometrical change (measurements by C. Townsend and R. Sutherland).

A. Tight Anticline

B. Complex Box Fold

C. Anticline (no plunge)

D. Plunging at 20°W

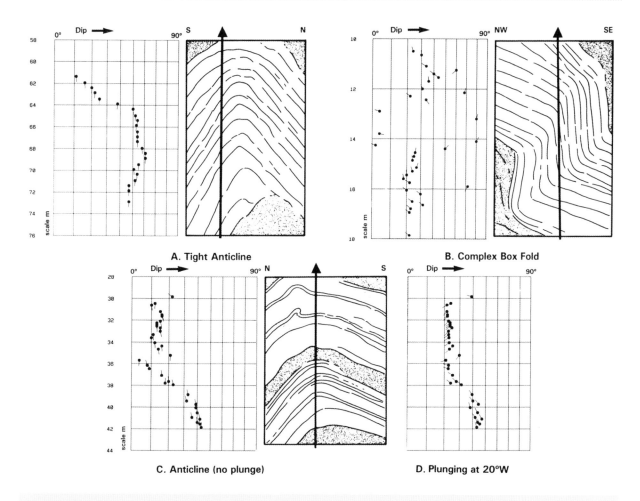

Figure 14.39 Folds on the dipmeter. Outcrop measured diplogs with line diagrams of the corresponding fold. The well symbol indicates the line of measurement. a) tight anticline, one limb measured; b) complex box fold; c) anticline with well crossing the fold axis (dip section, oriented N-S); d) same with a 20° plunge to the west (measurements by G. Cameron).

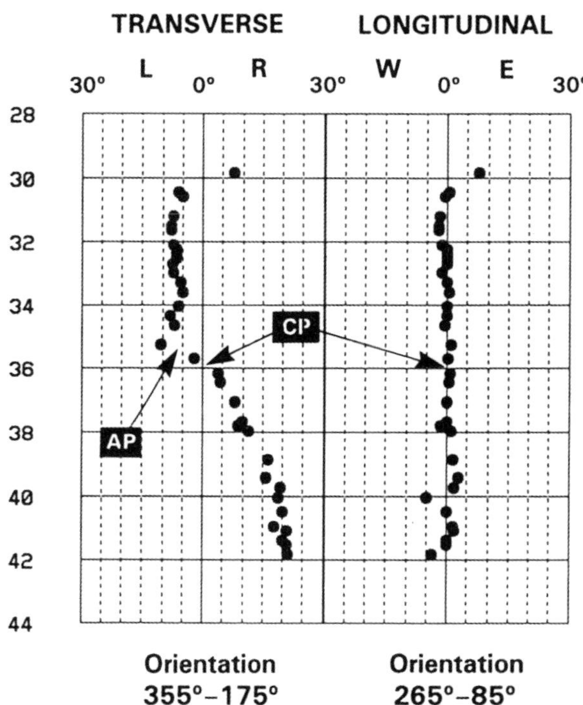

will be seen on a dipmeter microresistivity curve as a conductive anomaly, caused by the invasion of the drilling mud. Normally, this anomaly will only be seen on one (at most two) of the curves. Thus, comparing the normal resistivity at any level allows conductive anomalies to be detected. These are attributed to fractures and may be given an orientation since the dipmeter pad bearings are known. Although this was an interesting idea, its application was full of problems from floating pads, poor hole etc. and the results never certain. Borehole imaging tools now offer an excellent and better way of detecting fractures (Chapter 15).

Figure 14.40 SCAT (Statistical Curvature Analysis Technique) plot of the fold of Figure 39, C. The transverse plot shows the amount of dip in the transverse (or dip) orientation while the longitudinal plot shows the amount of dip in the longitudinal (or strike) orientation. Special points are the CP or crestal plane (the present structural top) and the AP or axial plane, which is the point of maximum dip change. Such plots are used to identify geometry, especially of folds, from dipmeter plots.

14.9 Conclusion

This chapter on dipmeter requires an up to date conclusion.

Image logs (next Chapter) have largely replaced the dipmeter for orientation evaluation. Image derived dip and azimuth are much more reliable than dipmeter dip and azimuth. However, some of the present problems of image log interpretation are similar to the problems described above that were encountered with dipmeter interpretation: problems such as the need for outcrop models and integration with other data, the standard logs at the very minimum but also with sedimentology, structural geology and the seismic. Dipmeter 'experts' had a tendency to over interpret dipmeter data, generally in isolation. The same is now true of image 'experts'. They over interpret image logs in isolation.

Looking back at the mistakes made with dipmeter data can help guide the use of image logs, which is why this chapter has been left largely unchanged from the 1996 edition. The dipmeter was an excellent tool, it was its interpretation that failed it.

15
IMAGE LOGS

15.1 Generalities

Description and history

A fundamental new concept was introduced into logging in the 1980s with the advent of the modern imaging tools. The formation is now no longer sampled by a single sensor to create a single log, it is sampled many times horizontally, and at a high rate vertically, to form a matrix of measurements from which an image is created. This is not a picture like a core photo made in visible light: it is a computer created image based on geophysical measurements such as electrical conductivity, acoustic reflectivity or formation density and displayed in false colour. Standard interpretation techniques no longer apply: with the new tools, new attitudes are needed.

Since its invention, there has been an explosive development in imaging technology, principally in terms of tools, but also in terms of producing the image. The progress has been linked with the availability of downhole processing of signals and the possibility of transmitting large data volumes in real time. Where the standard logs are sampled every 15 cm (6"), image logs may sample every 2.5 mm (0.1"); where the standard logs have one measurement per depth point, image logs may have 250. This makes for very large data volumes, some wireline imaging tools transmitting in the region of 200 kilobits per second up the cable to achieve a collection rate of 60,000 samples per metre (3 ft) of borehole. More recently, imaging technologies have been transferred to the Logging While Drilling domain so that images are now available in real time.

This chapter is written with two objectives in mind, first to describe the imaging tools and how they work, and second to show something of the practicalities of image log use and interpretation. It is intended for generalists who will look at logs interpreted by specialists, and not for the specialists themselves.

Types of imaging tool

Images can be produced from electrical, acoustic, density, photoelectric, gamma ray and caliper measurements, and tools may be wireline or LWD conveyed. The highest resolution comes from wireline imaging tools, which are either electrical with pad type sensors (highest resolution) or acoustic. LWD devices, which use the rotation of the drill string to achieve full borehole coverage, produce lower resolution images. Specialist tools, such as a deep-looking, LWD resistivity used for geosteering, can produce far field images.

The high resolution images produced by the wireline electrical tools, are mostly used for detailed, post-drilling geological interpretation, while the slightly lower resolution wireline acoustic images, are mostly acquired for borehole geometry and fracture studies. Lower resolution LWD images are used for geosteering and other decisions taken during drilling, although their use in post-drilling studies as well, is developing. These are the traditional ways in which images are used but, as this chapter will describe, interpretation techniques are evolving.

The specialist, high resolution, wireline electrical imaging tools are mostly multi-pad (4 – 8) type devices with arrays of small electrodes, and are available for both conductive and non-conductive (oil-based) muds (**Table 15.1**). They can produce excellent detailed, oriented images. However, pad type devices only produce an image over the extent of the pad: there are therefore normally gaps in their coverage of the borehole wall.

Specialist, relatively high resolution, wireline acoustic tools, sometimes called the borehole televiewer (BHTV), use a rapidly rotating transducer, which sends and receives ultrasonic pulses to and from the borehole wall. It sweeps the entire borehole circumference several times a second, making 200 or so paired measurements of amplitude and travel time during each revolution. A very dense dataset is created and used to build the acoustic images which provide a full, oriented borehole coverage. The tools function in holes filled with any type of liquid, be it fresh water, water-based barite mud or, importantly, oil-based mud (**Table 15.1**). Wireline imaging tools, both acoustic and electrical, are described in Section 15.2

In the directional while drilling (LWD) environment, any measurement can be converted to an image as long as the sensor is rotating. In practice, resistivity, density, *Pe* and gamma-ray are all routinely used to generate images. The tools make multiple, oriented measurements as they rotate and these can be processed into a map of the property around the borehole. However, probably the commonest while drilling (LWD) images are produced from density tools. The Schlumberger LWD density tool (adnVISION), for example, can acquire data from 16 oriented segments over each half foot (or less) of hole drilled.

Normally LWD images have a lower resolution than the purpose built wireline imagers (**Figure 15.26**). This is because the sensors have an inherently poorer vertical resolution: they are, after all, designed primarily to measure formation properties. Nonetheless, the images are often quite good enough to identify and characterise

Table 15.1 Wireline electrical imaging tools. Most are pad-type devices, only the ARI and HALS are hole centred.

Tool	Description	Company	Pads	*Res/Electrodes
Water-based (pad type tools)				
FMS	Formation MicroScanner (old)	Schlumberger	4	96 (4 × 24)
FMI	Fullbore Formation MicroImager	Schlumberger	8	192 (8 × 24)
STAR™	Simultaneous Acoustic and Resistivity Imager	Baker Hughes™	6	144 (6 × 24)
EMI	Electrical Micro Imager	Halliburton	6	150 (6 × 25)
XRMI	X-tended Range Micro Imager	Halliburton	6	150 (6 × 25)
HMI	High resolution Micro Imager	Weatherford	6	150 (6 × 25)
Oil-based (pad type tools)				
OBMI	Oil Based Micro Imager	Schlumberger	4	20 (4 × 5)
OBMI-2	Oil Based Micro Imager-2	Schlumberger	8	40 (8 × 5)
EI™	Earth Imager	Baker Hughes™	6	48 (6 × 8)
OMRI	Oil Mud Resistivity Imager	Halliburton	6	36 (6 × 6)
OMI	Oil Based Microimager	Weatherford	6	[1]48 (6 × 10)
Macro-imagers (hole centred tools)				
ARI	Azimuthal Resistivity Imager	Schlumberger	–	12
HALS	High def. Azimuthal Laterolog Sonde	Schlumberger	–	12

Useful sources: Paillet *et al.* 1990 ; Hurley, In Asquith & Krygowski 2004 ; Serra 2008 ; Lagrabda *et al.* 2010.
*Res = resistivity measurements. [1] = derived resistivities.

fault planes and bed boundaries. Some tools are specifically designed to acquire LWD images, however, tools such as the Baker Hughes™ STARTRAK electrical imager, and they have a vertical resolution similar to a wireline imager. LWD imaging tools are described in Section 15.3

Creating an image

To create an image from a single log curve it is simply necessary to assign a grey tone or a colour to a particular range of values. For example, 0– 10 may be green, 10–20 light green, 20–30 light yellow and so on. With this technique the single curve can be plotted as a 1-D colour image, in effect, a coloured bar code (**Figure 15.1,a**).

An additional technique is used for the output from image logging tools. These tools provide multiple readings at any one depth. The FMI, for example, provides 192 electrical readings at any one depth: in other words, there are 192 curves, not just one. To create an image from such a dataset, all the logs are sampled with a vertical increment, which is the same as the spacing between

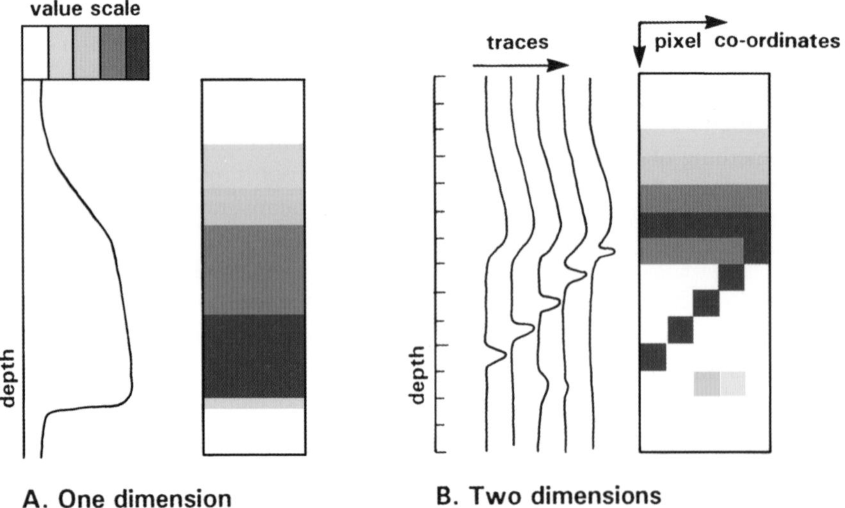

Figure 15.1 Producing an image from log responses. (A) One dimensional method in which a defined range of log values is represented by a particular grey shade or colour. A banded column is produced. (B) Two dimensional method used with multiple log traces. Each trace is sampled at regular vertical increments so that, with multiple logs, a pixel matrix is achieved. False colours or grey scales still represent defined ranges of log values.

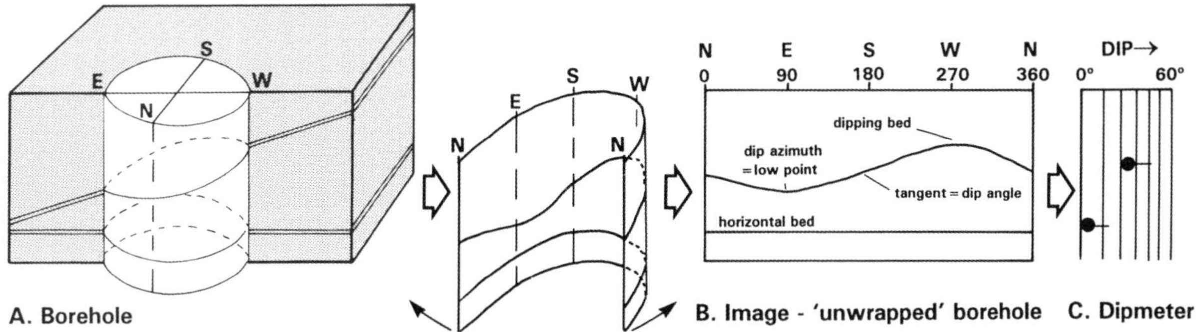

Figure 15.2 Representation of borehole wall images on a flat surface. (A) The images derived from the cylindrical borehole are presented on a flat surface (screen or hard copy log plot) by 'unwrapping' onto a vertical depth grid and horizontal grid of compass bearings. (B) In this format, horizontal and vertical surfaces are unchanged but dipping surfaces become represented by a sinusoid. (C) Dip and azimuth results may be plotted on a standard dipmeter tadpole grid.

the curves, namely 2.5 mm (0.1") for the FMI. When the borehole is sampled like this with regular vertical and horizontal data points, a patchwork is created with vertical and horizontal co-ordinates: in other words a pixel (picture element) matrix. Each pixel is assigned a false colour from the associated log value. If the pixels are small enough, a 2-D image will be perceived (**Figure 15.1,b**).

Because some image pixels are rather large, especially from the LWD tools, images can appear as a series of coloured boxes: for instance, the raw image from an 8 sector LWD density looks like 8 separate rectangles rather than a continuous image. Using processing techniques the problem can be resolved, and the boundary between contiguous pixels is interpolated to create a 'smoother', more realistic image (Meyer *et al.* 2005).

Image presentation

The standard presentation for image logs is the 'unwrapped borehole' format. The cylindrical borehole surface image is unzipped at the north azimuth and unrolled to a flat strip (**Figure 15.2**). The compass points form the horizontal, X axis co-ordinates so that 'south' plots in the centre of the image, north at the right and left margins. In horizontal wells, the centre of the image is the down-facing orientation (bottom), the up-facing orientation (top) being at the left and right margins. In both plots, the vertical Y axis is depth. In this way, a continuous representation can be made of the borehole either on screen or as a hardcopy plot (when horizontal wells are plotted horizontal, the depth generally increases from left to right). The system is effective for any vertical, deviated or horizontal well. Other, especially 3-D, formats exist for on-screen display but the unwrapped borehole presentation has become the standard for general use and hardcopy.

With the unwrapped borehole format, like any projection of a curved surface on a flat one, there is inevitable distortion. Real horizontal features will be seen on the image log format as horizontal and real vertical features as vertical (in a vertical well). But real dipping surfaces will appear on the plot (log) as a sine wave (**Figure 15.2,b**): the steeper the dip, the greater the wave amplitude. The actual dip of a bed can be accurately measured from the sine wave. The crest of the curve is the high point of the surface as it intersects the borehole, and the trough is the low point as it leaves, the displacement between the points gives the dip and their direction, the dip azimuth (**Figure 15.2**). Modern interpretation software allows a sine wave to be fitted to the signature of a dipping bed and computes its dip and dip azimuth. The software will also account for the deviation of the well so that the dip is relative to the horizontal. This is described in more detail below (Section 15.5).

In horizontal wells, bedding (usually nearly horizontal) tends to be encountered in almost the same orientation as the borehole itself and creates extreme patterns on the image log. If a horizontal well encounters a bed boundary dipping at a small angle away from the advancing bit, it will see the boundary first in the up direction (edges of the image). The boundary will then move progressively towards the centre of the image, so making a very extended sine shape (**Figure 15.3**, left side). If the boundary is dipping towards the advancing bit, the reverse pattern is seen and it will move from the image centre to the margins (**Figure 15.3**, right side). These are the so called smile and frown patterns. They can be used for steering wells.

Colour convention

The accepted colour scale for image logs is black-brown-orange-yellow-white, the so-called 'heated object' scale. The lighter colours are electrically more resistive (less conductive), acoustically more reflective and have a higher density, higher *Pe* and higher gamma ray (**Table 15.4**). The colour scale can be distributed into any number of divisions chosen by an operator, say 64 or 128. This scale may then be allocated to a fixed range of

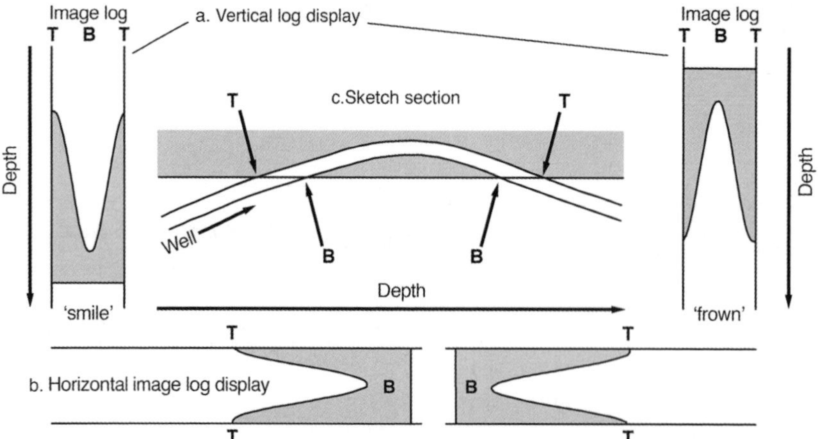

Figure 15.3 The extreme sine curves seen on borehole images from a horizontal well when the borehole trajectory and the stratigraphic layers are nearly parallel. The diagram illustrates the so called 'smile' and 'frown' patterns. a. vertical log display; b. horizontal log display; c. sketch section. T = top; B = base.

data, say between 1 and 10, 10 and 20, and so on (equal bins), or a set number of data points, say 50, for each number shade (equal increments). Colour can also be manipulated manually to achieve the best result. It is generally not an absolute scale. That is, a certain colour does not represent a set data range. Colour allocation is further discussed under *electrical image processing* and *acoustic image processing,* since the different data types require different processing routines.

This standard colour scale means that hydrocarbons will appear on an electrical image as light colours because of their high resistivity (and coals will appear white!). Carbonates, with a high density and a high resistivity, will have a light electrical image, and a light density image as well (high density = light colours). Shales, on the other hand, will tend to have darker colours on the electrical, acoustic and density images, being less resistive, less acoustically reflective and less dense respectively, although they will have a light gamma ray image because of their higher radioactivity (**Table 15.4**). Colour, however, is only a guide to lithology or fluids, and interpretation should never be based on colour alone. Having a colour convention, though, does help in the use of images produced by different companies and different tools. The images in this book follow the convention.

15.2 Wireline imaging tools (Tables 15.1, 15.2)

Electrical, high resolution, water-based mud, micro-imaging tools

In the mid 1980s, Schlumberger introduced their first electrical imaging tool, the Formation MicroScanner (FMS), as an evolution of their SHDT dipmeter (Chapter 14). The first tools only provided an image of 20% of an 8.5" borehole, using just two pads. However, the

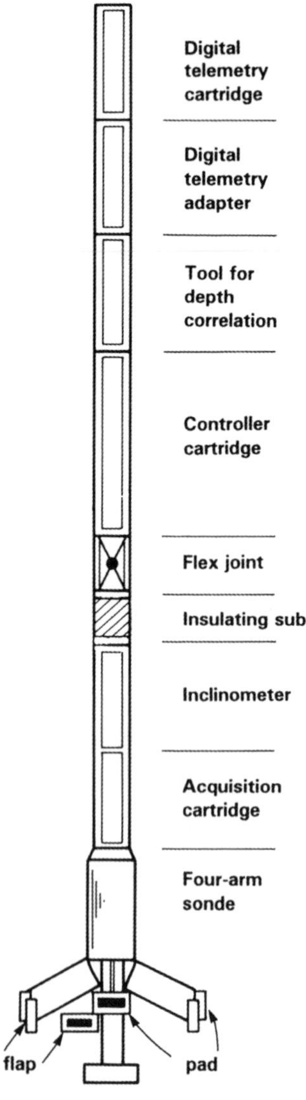

Figure 15.4 The FMI (Fullbore Formation MicroImager) tool of Schlumberger (re-drawn from Schlumberger 1994).

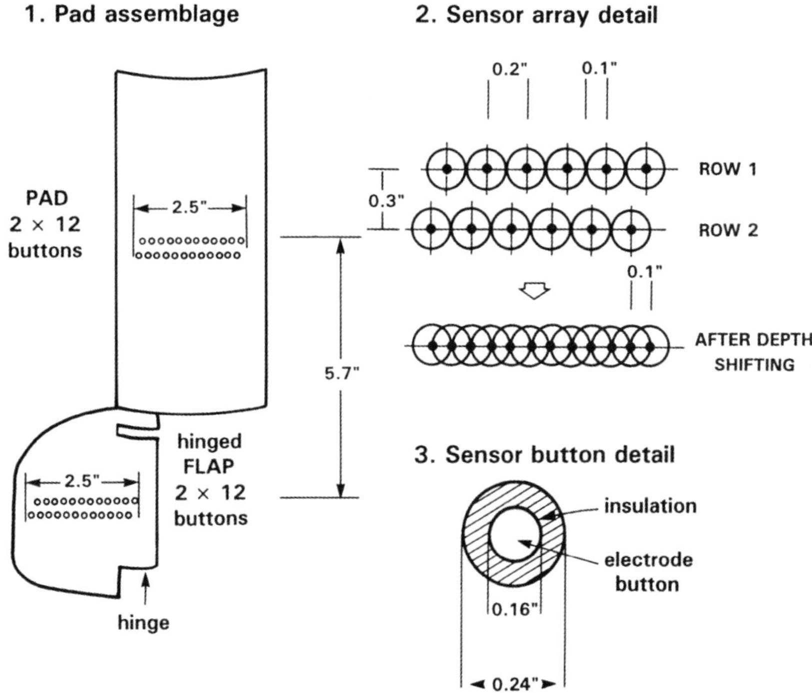

Figure 15.5 Pad assemblage and sensor detail from the Schlumberger FMI tool (re-drawn from Ekstrom *et al.* 1987; Schlumberger 1994).

tool signalled a sea-change in logging thinking so that now (2011) imaging has become mainstream. The direct descendent of the early tools is the Fullbore Formation MicroImager (FMI). It provides nearly 80% coverage in an 8.5″ diameter borehole, with water-based mud (in a smaller hole, the coverage can exceed 100% thanks to a clever 'pad and flap' arrangement – *see below*). Very high quality images are produced, but water-based mud in necessary. Since this is the current Schlumberger tool for these conditions, it will be used for description (information from Schlumberger 1994, unless otherwise indicated). Other companies have equivalent tools: Baker Hughes™ (Atlas) have the Simultaneous Acoustic and Resistivity Imager™ (STAR™) tool; Halliburton the Electrical Micro Imager (EMI); and Weatherford the High resolution Micro Imager (HMI) (**Table 15.1**).

Example tool: Fullbore MicroImager (FMI)

The Schlumberger FMI consists of four pads on two orthogonal arms and, in this respect, is like a four arm dipmeter (**Figure 15.4**) but, in the imaging tool, the four pads each have a hinged flap so as to extend the area of electrical contact (**Figure 15.5**). Pad faces are curved to match borehole size (curvature) and are approximately 8 cm (3.2″) wide and 18 cm (7″) long; flaps are 8 cm (3.2″) wide but only 6 cm (2.5″) long. Both pad and flap have arrays of 24 button electrodes (described below). In order that the pads and flaps maintain contact with the formation, they are free to tilt independently of the tool body. Thus, when the tool is not parallel to the borehole wall, as frequently occurs in horizontal and highly deviated wells, the pads still remain in contact. In addition, the tool uses hydraulic self-centring to improve pad contact, especially in horizontal wells where the usual pad leaf springs are not adequate to support the weight of the tool.

As well as the tool circuitry, the body of the FMI tool houses the inclinometry (as in the dipmeter) and a digital telemetry sub (**Figure 15.4**). The upper part of the tool is insulated from the lower part and this forces the current to return some distance above the sensor section (see *below*). The FMI and its equivalents can be combined with most other tools, and normally at least a gamma ray tool would be added into the string to assist with depth matching.

The FMI pad and flap are both conductive and have inset, 24 individually insulated button electrodes, arranged in two rows of 12. Dimensions are given in the figure (**Figure 15.5**). When the tool is used with the flaps, 192 (8 × 24) button samples are recorded at every depth sample point (actually at 4 different depths: pad, top and bottom row; flap, top and bottom row). Each button emits a pencil shaped beam of current into the formation, and it is the resistance that this current encounters that builds the image.

The button electrodes are 0.4 cm (0.16″) in diameter but, with surrounding insulation, this increases to 0.6 cm (0.24″) (**Figure 15.5**). With this arrangement, it is considered that the electrodes have a resolution of 0.5 cm (0.2″). However, because the electrodes are

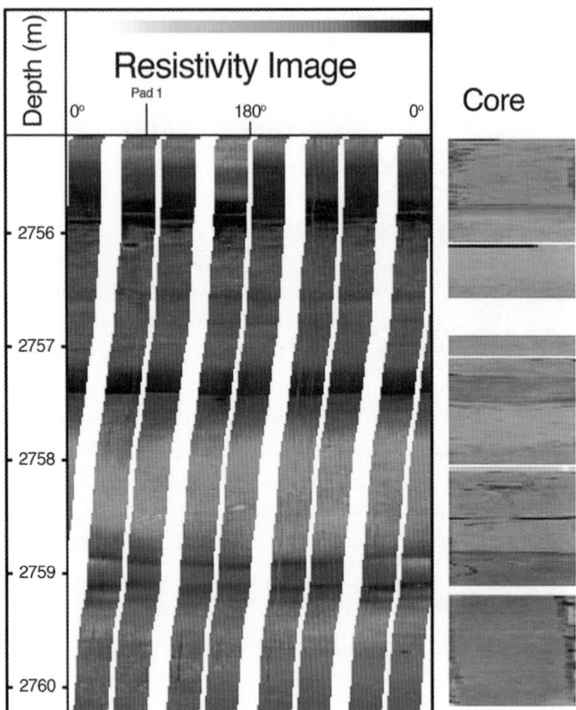

Figure 15.6 Digital core photographs compared to the log image from an FMI (Fullbore Formation MicroImager) 4 pad & flap tool. Dark colours (conductive) are thin shale beds, while the yellow/orange/white colours (resistive) are irregularly invaded, hydrocarbon bearing sandstones. Dynamic image, reference true north.

offset vertically, the formation is sampled horizontally across the electrode array at half this distance, that is, every 0.25 cm (0.1") (**Figure 15.5**). At a recommended logging speed of 475 m/hr (1500 ft/hr), button currents are sampled in time at every 0.02 sec. which, when processed translates into vertically every 0.25 cm (0.1") (Passey *et al.* 2006). The tool, therefore, acquires a data matrix of 0.1" both vertically and horizontally in front of the pads and flaps (calipers, magnetometers and accelerometers are sampled every 3.8 cm or 1.5"). With the pad and flap configuration, the FMI acquires 8 image strips along the borehole representing the formation (**Figure 15.6**).

In terms of electrical circuitry, the imaging tools are similar to the dipmeter tool in that a slowly varying, 'low frequency' EMEX signal (emitter exciter), which is modulated for formation resistivity changes, is used to focus a rapidly changing, 'high frequency' signal from the pads themselves (**Figure 15.7**). In practice, each conductive pad face is an equi-potential surface, held at a constant potential relative to the return electrode, which is the upper section of the tool (Ekstrom *et al.* 1987). The pad injects current into the formation and the current density across the pad is sampled by the button array (**Figure 15.7**). Changes in current density across the pads are caused by local formation resistivity variations. Button array resolution is discussed below.

Electrical, high resolution, oil based mud, micro-imaging tools

A serious limitation of the FMI type tools was that they could not be used with non-conductive muds. Since their introduction coincided with an industry-wide shift to the use of oil-based muds, this was a severe limitation. The logging companies responded by producing tools that could produce images in non-conductive muds. Ironically, these tools began to appear at a time when improvements in water based mud technology and concerns about the environmental impact of oil based muds resulted in a shift back to the widespread use of conductive muds! Nevertheless, oil-based muds are still commonly used for development wells and in environments where unconsolidated sands are expected, so oil-based mud imaging tools are still in great demand. The images from these tools are not as good as those from the water-based mud tools. The reason for this is that, with the non-contact methods used, the individual electrical sensors cannot be made as small as the electrodes on conductive mud devices. The images, therefore, have to be based on fewer and larger individual measurements, but can still be used for geological work.

Example tool, Earth Imager™

The Baker Hughes™ Earth Imager™ is an example of an oil-based mud imaging tool (Wang *et al.* 2004). It has eight electrodes per pad and six, small, 9 cm × 8 cm

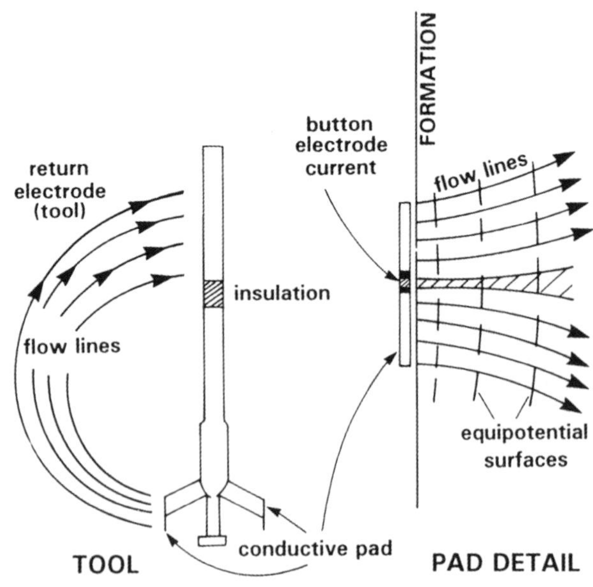

Figure 15.7 Current flow characteristics of an electrical imaging tool (based on the FMI of Schlumberger). A low frequency current controls the pad output, while the high frequency button electrodes provide the image (re-drawn and modified from Ekstrom *et al.* 1987; Schlumberger 1994).

Figure 15.8 The pad configuration of the Earth Imager™, the Baker Hughes™ (Atlas) oil-based mud, wireline electrical imaging tool (from Lofts *et al.* SPWLA 2002).

(3.5″ × 3.1″) pads on separate arms (**Figure 15.8**). The equivalent tool for water based mud has the same arrangement of pads but each pad has 24 button electrodes (like the FMI these are arranged in two rows of twelve). The six arms are all independently articulated and can reach a hole size (diameter) of 53.5 cm (21″). They are kept centralised by an independent, six-arm, powered stand-off (Lofts *et al.* 2002).

The tool works on the same basic principles as the water based FMI described above in that a current exists between the six conductive pads and the conductive, return part of the tool. However, the Earth Imager uses a high frequency, 1 MHz current, which is electrically forced from the conductive pad into the conductive formation across the non-conductive mud. This is achieved by so-called 'capacitive coupling' in which an AC current can pass between two capacitors (tool and formation) in spite of being separated by a medium (oil-based mud) non-conductive to a DC current (Wang *et al.* 2004).

The tool is sampled 120 times per foot (2.5 mm, 0.1″) for the 48 electrodes with an 8.5 mm (0.31″) spacing, giving a 65% coverage in an 8″ hole (Lofts *et al.* 2002 *op. cit.*). The depth of investigation is said to be about 2.5 cm (1″), but varies with bed thickness and resistivity, while the electrical diameter (the effective diameter for dip calculation) is about 5.0 mm (0.2″) larger than the borehole diameter (**Figure 15.24**). Vertical resolution is about 3.0 mm (0.12″), which translates into a theoretical ability to recognise the true thickness of beds as thin as 7.6 mm (0.3″). These figures come from a combination of laboratory calculations and some case studies (Wang *et al.* 2004) but may not translate into actual operating conditions.

Electrical, low resolution water-based mud, macro-imaging tools

In parallel with the high resolution electrical imaging tools, much lower resolution but deeper looking, sectorised tools without pads have been developed. The Schlumberger tools, based on the laterolog principle, are the Azimuthal Resistivity Imager (ARI) (described in Chapter 7 simply as a resistivity tool, **Figure 7.25**) and the High Resolution Azimuthal Laterolog Sonde (HALS) (Smits *et al.* 1995). Both tools use the laterolog principle but in the central section there are 12 azimuthal electrodes. The current from the azimuthal electrodes is effectively focused by the non-directional body electrodes (**Figure 7.25**).

In the ARI the vertical resolution is around 20 cm (8″) while for the HALS tool it is either 20 cm (8″) or 40 cm (16″) depending on either a deep or a shallow mode of operation. The tool has software focusing. The depth of investigation is said to be similar to the deep laterolog (White 1993). In imaging mode, the tools are sampled every 1.3 cm (0.5″) vertically. While the lateral sample covers a 30° angle of the borehole, it is said to have a 60° resolution (Schlumberger 1993). The image produced has a much lower resolution than the FMI (**Figure 15.26**) but is useful in horizontal or highly deviated, water-based mud wells.

Acoustic, high resolution, imaging tools

An acoustic imaging tool was first developed by Mobil in the 1960s (Zemanek *et al.* 1969; 1970). The idea was further developed and improved by the oil companies, Amoco and Shell and, later, ARCO, before eventually being taken on by the service companies in the late 1980s (Broding 1982; Faraguna *et al.* 1989). The tool uses a rotating piezoelectric transducer as both a source and a receiver of pulses of high frequency sound (**Figure 15.9**). As the tool is pulled up the borehole, the transducer rotates and the sound pulses describe a helical path around the borehole wall. The rate at which the transducer pulses results in a very dense matrix of digital data points. This is the raw data that is processed into an image (Pasternack and Goodwill 1983). The modern service company tool will be illustrated by the Circumferential Borehole Imaging Tool (Log) (CBIL) of Baker Hughes™ (Faraguna *et al.* 1989; Atlas Wireline 1992) although all major companies have acoustic imaging tools which work on the same principle (**Table 15.2**).

Example tool: Circumferential Borehole Imaging Tool (Log) CBIL

The CBIL consists of a tool string approximately 12 m (40 ft) long with the rotating transducer housed in a mandrel at the bottom. Like other image tools, it can be combined with other services but it normally has

Table 15.2 Wireline acoustic imaging tools.

Tool	Description	Company	Samples,	*rps	¹Logging speed
UBI	Ultarsonic Borehole Imager	Schlumberger	180–250/500	7.5	120–250 m/hr (400–800 ft/hr)
CBIL™	Circumpherential Borehole Imaging Log	Baker Hughes™	125–250	6	730 m/hr (2400 ft/hr)
STAR™	Simultaneous Acoustic and Resistivity Imager	Baker Hughes™	250	12	180–365 m/hr (600–1200 ft/hr)
CAST	Circumpherential Acoustic Scanning Tool	Halliburton	100–200	6–18	275–365 m/hr (900–1200 ft/hr)
UMI	Ultrasonic Micro-Imager	Weatherford	240	18	549 m/hr (1800 ft/hr)

Useful sources: Paillet *et al.* 1990 ; Hurley, In Asquith & Krygowski 2004 ; Serra 2008 ; Lagrabda *et al.* 2010.
*rps = revolutions per second. ¹Logging speeds indicative only.

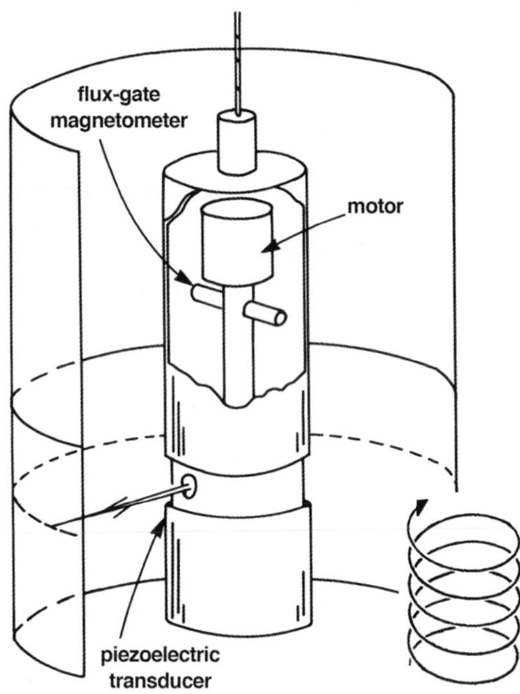

Figure 15.9 The borehole televiewer tool (BHTV), schematic representation. A piezoelectric sonic transducer in transmit-receive mode, spins rapidly as the tool is pulled up the borehole (re-drawn from Zemanek *et al.* 1969).

Figure 15.10 The head of the Ultrasonic Borehole Imager (UBI), a Schlumberger acoustic imaging tool. The head contains the piezoelectric transducer which rotates at 7.5 rps. while it acquires 180–250 readings of amplitude and time of flight (Table 15.2) (from Schlumberger 1993). *Courtesy of Schlumberger.*

to be located at the bottom of the tool string, and the transducer has to be well centred in the borehole. This is achieved by using strong bowsprings. Above the transducer there is an inclinometer and the electronics to control the tool and transmit data to the surface. When the tool is logging, the transducer, in pulse-echo mode, turns at 6 revolutions per second, taking 250, digitised samples on each revolution, or every 1.44°. It thus acquires a tight spiral of data points from around the entire borehole wall. For an image to be produced, one rotation must occur during the vertical sampling distance. When logged at a typical logging speed of 3 m (10 ft) per minute, the tool makes one complete scan of the borehole circumference each 0.83 cm (0.33″) of depth, thus acquiring a matrix of 30,000 sample points of paired data readings (30,000 readings of amplitude and 30,000 of time of flight, as explained below) for each metre of borehole logged.

Transducers in the acoustic imaging tools are piezoelectric, that is, activated by an electric pulse. They are normally made from a thin circular disc 1″– 2″ in diameter (**Figure 15.10**). In CBIL™, the transducer is hemispherical and has a concave surface facing outwards, which has the effect of collimating (focusing) the sound pulse (**Figure 15.11**). Pulse beams can only hold an optimum focus over a short distance, so that CBIL allows the choice of two different transducers with different diameters and different focal lengths for use in different sized holes. One has a diameter of 3.8 cm (1.5″) for small holes, the other a diameter of 5.1 cm (2″) for use in larger holes. The smaller 1.5″ transducer is focused to a 0.76 cm (0.3″) diameter beam from 15 cm to 20 cm (6″ to 8″); the larger 2″ transducer has a similar beam from 20 cm to 30 cm (8″ to 12″) (Faraguna *et al.* 1989).

The tool is considered suitable for use in holes between 13 cm– and 46 cm (5″–18″) in diameter (depend-

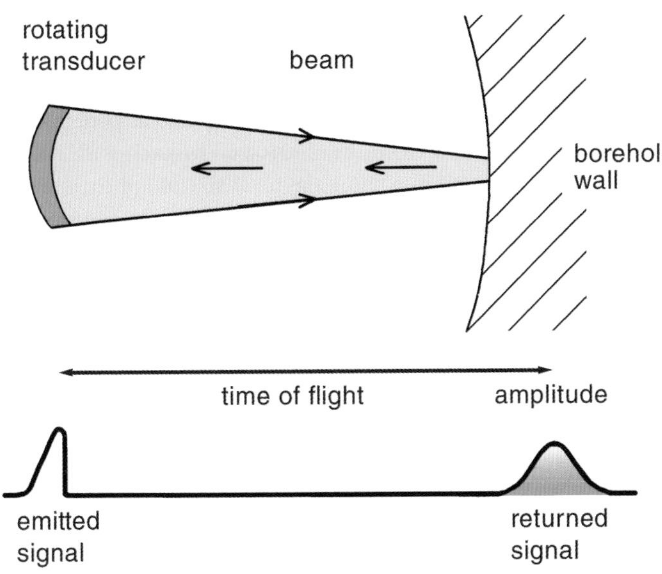

Figure 15.11 Schematic acoustic televiewer signal characteristics. (a) The transducer signal focused on the curved borehole wall. (b) The two measurements taken from one signal pulse, the amplitude of the returned pulse and the return travel time (time of flight) (re-drawn, modified after Luthi 2000).

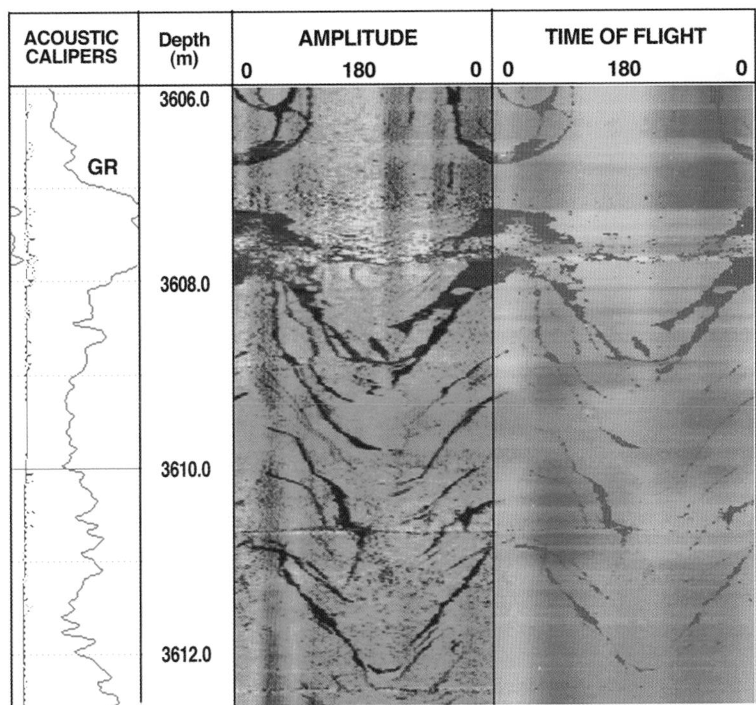

Figure 15.12 Typical acoustic image presentation. The left-hand track shows the amplitude image and the right hand track the time of flight (blue is used here to bring out the difference). The images show open, steeply dipping, natural fractures (dark colours) in a carbonate. There is a near horizontal shale parting just above 3608 m. On the extreme left-hand track are an E-W and a N-S pair of acoustic callipers, and a gamma ray.

ing on mud weight). Piezoelectric materials can produce (or detect) a signal with very little 'ringing' and may therefore be pulsed very rapidly. In the CBIL tool, the transducer produces an ultrasonic pulse 1500 times per second with a frequency of 250 kHz, giving it good penetration. The original Mobil design used a 2 MHz signal and the Amoco design a 1.3 MHz, so that the lower frequency CBIL™ signal has a distinct penetration advantage (in other words it is less attenuated by mud).

At each sample point, as indicated, the acoustic tool acquires 2 different measurements, *time of flight* (or travel time) and *reflected amplitude* (**Figure 15.11**). The time of flight is simply the time between emission, reflection off the borehole wall and detection back at the transducer: this gives a detailed profile of the borehole. The reflected amplitude is the strength of the reflected sound pulse and depends on the shape and roughness of the borehole wall and its acoustic properties. The transducer converts the received pulse back into an electric signal so that the amplitude is actually the magnitude of this electric signal (**Figure 15.11**). In a typical screen presentation or hardcopy plot, both acoustic readings, the amplitude and the time of flight, will be shown (**Figure 15.12**).

Acoustic imaging tools can function in a hole filled with any fluid: water, water-based mud or oil-based mud. Muds attenuate the signal quite strongly, however, so that the best images are obtained in wells filled with a single-phase fluid like brine or diesel oil. Most commercial tools, like the CBIL™, have a choice of different diameter transducer assemblies for different hole sizes. This allows good quality images to be acquired even in large diameter holes filled with heavy mud. As already noted, the transducers are also designed to operate at a frequency where attenuation is reduced. Together, these features allow images to be obtained in large holes filled with heavy muds (up to 1.7 – 1.9 g/cm^3 or 15 – 16 lbs/gal) (**Table 13.6**).

15.3 LWD imaging tools (Table 15.3)

LWD tools are able to provide an image because the sensors they use rotate. The common use of rotary, steerable downhole motors, with a high rotation rate, helps with LWD imaging. When a rotating sensor is linked with an orientation sonde, the measurements can be allocated to oriented sectors. The early LWD technology designed for horizontal wells used only 4 sectors: up, down, left and right. However, modern tools now routinely capture 16 sectors (a 22.5° arc) for nuclear tools and rates of up to 120 samples per revolution for electrical tools. Even so, not only are there generally fewer measurements radially around the borehole but the vertical resolution of the measurements is considerably lower than the electrodes or ultrasonic pulses used by purpose built imaging tools (*see* resolution *below*).

LWD images represent a considerable volume of data so that, as long as mud pulses are used to transfer data while drilling (Chapter 2), real time images will only be sub-sets of the full dataset stored in memory downhole. Real time images are used for geosteering. Detailed memory images will only be downloaded when the LWD tool is brought back to the surface. These aspects are considered below.

LWD electrical, water-based mud images

Images while drilling can be produced by LWD electrical tools in water-based muds (**Table 15.3**). An example of this type of tool is the Resistivity at Bit (RAB) tool from Schlumberger (the now improved tool is called GeoVISION). It has already been described (Chapter 7, **Figure 7.27**). The images are produced by three button electrodes, each with a 1.0″ diameter, which make a focused measurement. Each electrode is sampled 56 times per rotation and about 2.5–5 cm (1–2″) vertically (it varies with rate of penetration, ROP). The electrodes are said to have a vertical resolution of 2″ to 4″ (5–10 cm) and a depth of investigation of 1″, 3″ and 5″ (2.5 cm, 7.6 cm and 12.7 cm) (**Figure 15.13**). They have an azimuthal resolution of about 15° (Luthi 2000). When drilling, the scan rate is once every 5 seconds, with a suggested drilling rotation rate of at least 30 rpm and a penetration rate of less than 61 m/hr (200 ft/hr) (Bargach *et al.* 2000). The tool produces an image pixel size of approximately 2.5 cm × 1.27 cm (1″ × 0.5″) vertical and horizontal respectively (**Figure 15.26**). A lower resolution image can be produced while drilling and the higher resolution image recovered from the tool's memory. Since this type of tool is most effectively used for geosteering, it is important to have the images while drilling even though they are of lower resolution.

A significant aspect of this tool is its variable depth of investigation from 2.5 cm to 7.6 cm to 12.7 cm) (1″, 3″ and 5″). It means that the images from the memory data, available when there is time to study them, can be used to separate near borehole effects, which are often drilling related, from deeper formation effects beyond the drill bit influence. For instance, the shallow image in a reservoir may show invasion while the deeper images will show more of the original fluids. The example (**Figure 15.13**) shows a 4.5 m (15 ft) shale bed separating two, metre thick sands with hydrocarbons. The shallow image shows only invasion (water-based mud), the medium image some streaks of invasion and the deep image (5″, 12.7 cm) shows the full hydrocarbon charge.

One of the present Baker Hughes™ INTEQ LWD water-based imaging tools is StarTrak™ and is different from the previous tool example in that it is designed

Table 15.3 LWD tools from which an image is produced. Coverage of the borehole wall is 360° for all tools.

Tool	Description	Company	Type	Sectors
Resistivity (GR)				
RAB	Resistivity at Bit	Schlumberger	Electrical	4, 56 samples
GeoVISION (GVR)	newer tool	Schlumberger	Electrical, GR	16, 4
StarTrak™		Baker Hughes™	Electrical	
InSite AFR	Azimuthal Resistivity	Halliburton	Electrical	
Density (*Pe*) (GR)				
adnVISION (ADN)	Azimuthal Density Neutron	Schlumberger	Density, *Pe*	16, 4
ALD	Azimuthal LithoDensity	Halliburton	Density, *Pe*	16
LithoTrak™		Baker Hughes™	Density, GR	16
On Trak™		Baker Hughes™	Density	
AZD	Azimuthal Density	Weatherford	Density	16
iFinder		Pathfinder	Density	32 memory 16 real time
Gamma Ray				
Stellar (DGR)	Dual Gamma Ray	Halliburton	GR	6
SAGR	Spectral Azimuthal Gamma Ray	Weatherford	GR Spectral	
HAGR	High temperature Azimuthal Gamma Ray Tool	Weatherford	GR	4

Useful sources: Paillet *et al.* 1990 ; Hurley, In Asquith and Krygowski 2004 ; Serra 2008 ; Lagrabda *et al.* 2010.

to acquire high quality images while drilling. It has a single, rotating imaging electrode that samples 120 sectors of the borehole. The tool has a maximum drilling rate of 55 m/hr (180 ft/hr) and RPM limited to 200–130 rpm in good conditions. The images produced have a pixel size of 0.5″×0.5″ (1.27×1.27 cm)(Ritter *et al.* 2004) with pixel resolution calculated at 0.25″ (6.4 mm) (Lofts *et al.* 2005). The single depth of investigation is considered to be about 20 mm (0.8″) and an electrical diameter for dip picking of 1 cm (0.4″). The images produced by this tool can be used for geological investigations (Lofts *et al.* 2005). In addition, when compared to wireline electrical images, they can be used to identify drilling induced features that disappear before the wireline images are acquired (Lindsay *et al.* 2007).

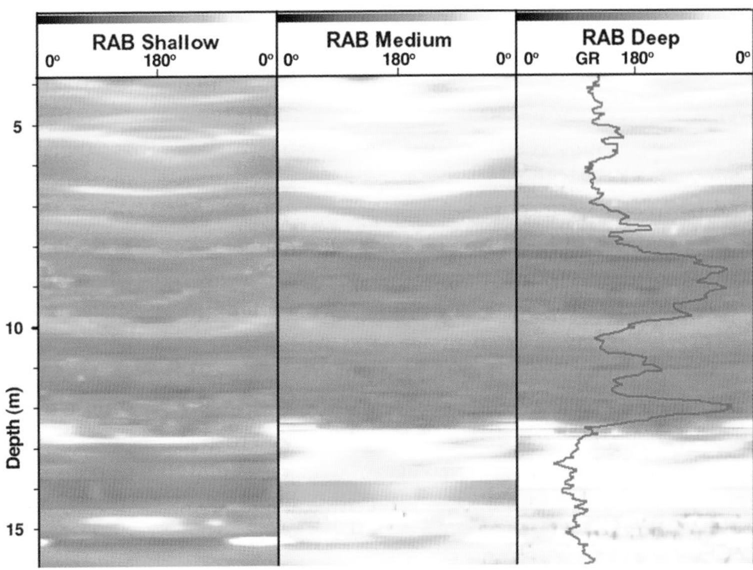

Figure 15.13 Schlumberger LWD, Resistivity at Bit (RAB) images of sandstones containing hydrocarbons (light colours) separated by laminated shales (dark colours). A gamma ray is added to the right-hand track (red curve). The shallow image (1″ or 2.5 cm investigation) shows the sandstones invaded with conductive mud filtrate. The medium image (3″ or 7.6 cm investigation) shows minor invasion and brings out the difference between the sand and the shale. The deep image (5″ or 12.7 cm investigation) shows that the formation has not been invaded to this depth. Near vertical well. (the RAB tool is now replaced by the improved GeoVISION tool).

LWD density, photoelectric and caliper images

The primary application of density images is in geo-steering, so that the density tool is normally placed as close to the bit as possible and images are transmitted in real time. These tools now routinely produce images of both density and photoelectric factor (*Pe* or PEF) measurements (Meyer *et al.* 2005) (**Figure 10.10**). Far detector density, near detector density and corrected density may be plotted separately (**Figure 15.14**). These three plots are sometimes called shallow, medium and deep density but this is misleading: they should be labelled for what they are, near detector (shallowest), far detector (medium) and corrected far detector (the deepest sometimes).

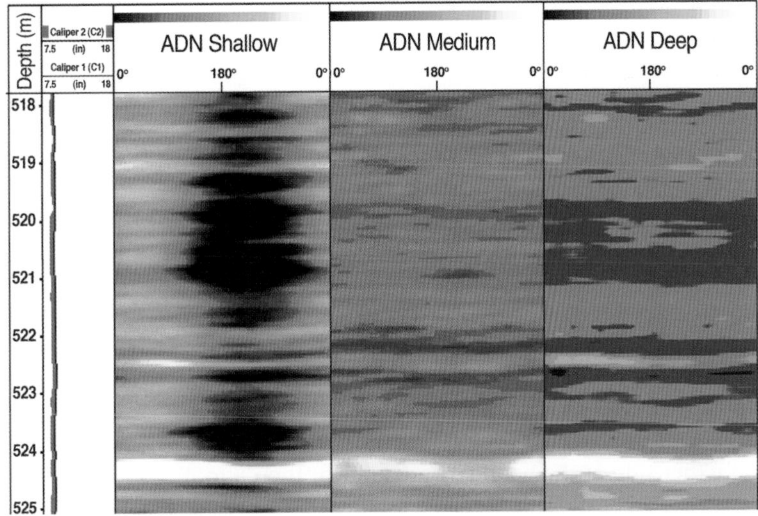

Figure 15.14 Density images from the Schlumberger adnVISION, LWD tool. The 'shallow' image is from the near receiver, the 'medium' from the far receiver and the 'deep' from the compensated density. The near receiver image shows the hole effect (black is greater standoff) while the compensated image is more responsive to bedding. The darker layers (lower density) are shale, lighter layers sandstone and the white layer, cemented sandstone. Vertical well.

The LWD version of the density tool has been described previously (Chapter 10, **Figure 10.5**). These tools use the same technique of counting back-scattered gamma rays from a tool-born source as the wireline tools. However, in the LWD version, as the tool rotates, the back-scattered gamma ray counts are allocated to individual bins or angular sectors, usually every 22.5° or 16 sectors per revolution. For example, in the Schlumberger adnVISION tool, counts are allocated to each of 16 sectors on each revolution for a period of about 10 seconds (Radtke *et al.* 2003). That is, during 10 seconds, every rotation adds to each individual bin count. At the end of this period bin counts are 'emptied' and a new 10 second counting sequence begun. Individual bin counts, when processed, provide the numbers for the image pixels. The resulting pixel size is around 15.25 × 2.5 cm (6″×1″).

The sensitivity of density tools to stand-off has been discussed (Chapter 10) and it is especially important in LWD tools. For example, while drilling in horizontal wells, the LWD tool may rest on the bottom of the borehole, which results in a good down-facing density but a poor up-facing reading because of the stand-off (separation between toolface and borehole wall). Poor density readings may also be caused by borehole enlargement such as when breakout occurs (*see* below). However, these poor data regions will become clear when the density is displayed as an image, and will appear as dark strips (low values) (**Figure 15.14**). Efforts are generally made to reduce stand-off effects using processing (Radtke *et al.* 2003), but they may equally be used to give an estimate of borehole geometry from which 3-D plots of hole conditions can be produced (Meyer *et al.* 2005) (**Figure.5.3**).

LWD gamma ray images

Under the right circumstances, a rotating scintillator crystal in an LWD gamma ray tool can be used to produce an image (**Figure 8.8**). Very little has been published on the design of these tools. In general terms, two opposing, rugedised, scintillator sensors, heavily shielded by tungsten, are allowed to receive radiations from only a limited orientation, through a focusing slit (Jan and Harrell 1987). The counts of received radiations are sectorised and oriented as the tool turns, in the same way as for the density tool (*above*). Depending on the tool, 16 sectors (Schlumberger GeoVISION) or 8 sectors (Baker Hughes™ INTEQ) are used to create an image with a nominal pixel size (Baker) of 15 cm (6") (Meyer *et al.* 2005). They are used primarily for geosteering, so are normally placed as close to the bit as possible and the images transmitted in real time.

LWD deep resistivity images

When geosteering, it is a distinct advantage to be able to 'see' several metres to the side of the bottom hole assembly (BHA). In this way the directional driller gets an early indication that the bit is approaching the top or base of the reservoir (or a contact). If the resistivities on either side of the boundary are known, then a tool response can be modelled for any distance to the boundary. In this way, the tool response can be converted to a distance to the boundary. As a general rule, the greater the contrast in resistivity, the further from the tool a boundary can be detected. It is also useful to have some look-ahead capability, particularly if faults are known to exist in the reservoir.

Any deep reading resistivity tool will respond to a bed boundary within its depth of investigation but it cannot tell which direction the boundary is in (assuming a resistivity contrast across the boundary). This is not a problem providing the driller is certain which boundary the tool is responding to (for example top reservoir). But if the direction of the boundary could also be determined, the bit could always be confidently steered away from it. This is now possible using a new generation of propagation devices that have a directional capability. This is achieved by orienting some of the receiver coils at 90 degrees to the tool axis. The output of the tool is presented as a borehole image normally oriented to the top of the hole (since geosteering normally involves very high deviations). In a typical application, for example, where the well path is to be kept a few metres below a shale that forms the top of the reservoir, the resistivity will be lowest on the high side of the hole.

A typical work-flow involves modelling the tool response for the desired well path (relative to top and base reservoir). This is then compared with the actual tool response, and the well is steered to keep the differences to a minimum. If this cannot be achieved, it is likely that the model is not reflecting the true situation and it will have to be modified. The actual tool response can be used to do this.

It is also useful to have some look-ahead or at least near-bit capability, particularly if faults are known to exist in the reservoir. Because the near bit tools have a shallow depth of investigation, they cannot prevent a fault being penetrated, but the images they produce can give the orientation of the fault plane and hence whether the drill has entered an up-thrown or down-thrown block.

Geosteering is a highly specialised activity which relies on good planning and preparation for success. There is a strong cost incentive to place long, high angle wells in the reservoir without having to resort to trial and error. It is certain that even deeper reading tools specifically designed to aid this will be developed.

15.4 Image processing: electrical and acoustic

Electrical image processing

This section describes the processing of the high resolution FMI data. The routines will be similar for other high resolution electrical tools.

The raw data acquired by the FMI tool, as described, comes from 192 microresistivity measurements, which are made every 0.1". These need to be processed in order to create an image. The first necessity is to correct for variations in EMEX (the slowly varying background current) and to equalise the curves to the same gain and offset (Harker *et al.* 1990). That is, the curves must be equalised to give them all the same sensitivity range (Ekstrom *et al.* 1987). This occurs before they are written to the digital storage medium but further refinement is generally necessary to produce a useable image (**Figure 15.15**).

Next, the depth differences between the rows of buttons must be corrected. As explained, the 192 resistivities are acquired at 4 different actual depths, a 0.75 cm (0.3") difference for the two button rows on a pad or flap

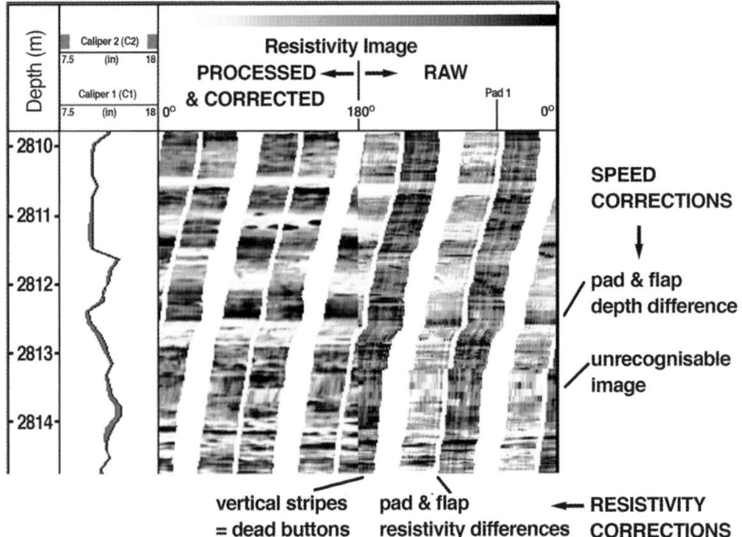

Figure 15.15 Raw and processed FMI electrical images. Processing involves speed correction to rectify depth differences (shown to the right) and relative resistivity corrections (shown at the bottom) to make a balanced image.

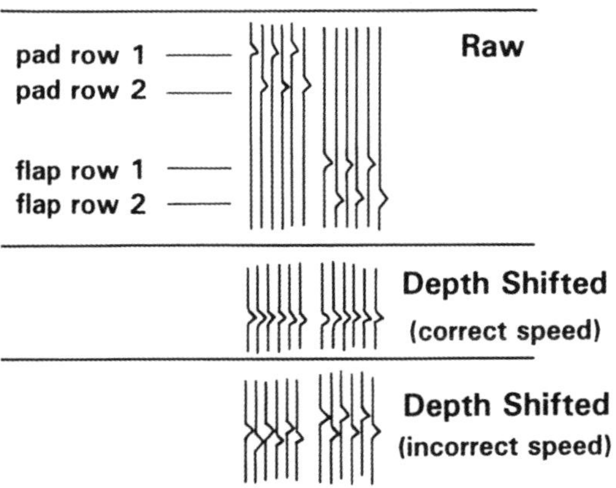

Figure 15.16 The effect of speed correction and depth shift on the raw image traces. The effect this has on an image is shown in Figure 15.15 (modified from Serra 1989; Schlumberger 1994).

and a 14.5 cm (5.7″) difference between the pads and flaps themselves. These different acquisition depths are simple to correct if the tool speed is constant (**Figure 15.16**). However, if the tool does not run smoothly and jumps or sticks, a simple depth correction leaves differences, especially between pad and flap measurements (**Figure 15.16**). In these cases, to achieve a proper depth alignment, a speed correction is necessary, using the accelerometers included in the tool. Whilst the speed correction is relatively easy to describe, it is notoriously difficult to compute. This is partly because the depth measured by the computer is based on the cable movement at surface, and this is not necessarily the same as the tool movement.

At some point in the processing chain, a few other steps are also made. These include converting the contractors' names for the raw data channels to a name recognised by the software, possibly re-normalising the raw data and almost certainly rotating the tool azimuth from magnetic to true north.

With the equalised, depth corrected dataset, images can be produced. In the FMI tool, the spacing between the curves (i.e. between electrode buttons) is 2.5 mm (0.1″) and the sampling rate is also 2.5 mm (0.1″), so that a datapoint exists every 2.5 mm (0.1″), both vertically and horizontally: a single log measurement represents a 2.5 mm square pixel. Individual log values are colour coded using the methods and scales previously described (Section 15.1) (**Figure 15.1**). Having set the scales, each pixel is now represented by a colour, and the matrix forms an image with 2.5 mm square pixels at natural scale. For interpretation, the image is usually scaled down to 1:10 or, more usually, 1:20 and the vertical and horizontal ratio can be maintained.

Processed data can now be examined on-screen in the 'unwrapped' format previously described (**Figure 15.6**). It is at this stage that the orientation of the image becomes important. Deriving dip orientation from the images is an essential task, as described below. During logging, tool position and orientation are taken from the X,Y,Z magnetometers and the X,Y,Z accelerometers inside the tool. Plots of the X-Y co-ordinates of both of these will confirm that they are working properly and that the orientation and positions derived from them are accurate (**Figure 15.17**). When accelerometer readings do not conform to the expected patterns, dip derivation from the images may be wrong. When the magnetometers do not conform, the tool may be self-magnetised and cause serious errors. It is also known that volcanic rocks can be magnetised by the NMR and cause difficulties with the inclinometer.

If all the orientations are correct, it is possible at this stage to refine the processing in terms of speed correction and button correction to 'sharpen up' and 'tidy up' the images. Various quality checks are possible on the raw data. For example, in a vertical well, a histogram of the Z axis accelerometer readings should have a peak at about 9.8 m/sec^2 (32 ft/sec^2) (**Figure 15.17**). Logs which indicate image acquisition quality, such as the calipers and tension log, should be included on the basic interpretation screen format. Standard open hole logs should also be included, and not just the gamma ray (which may be part of the image tool string). Additional screen

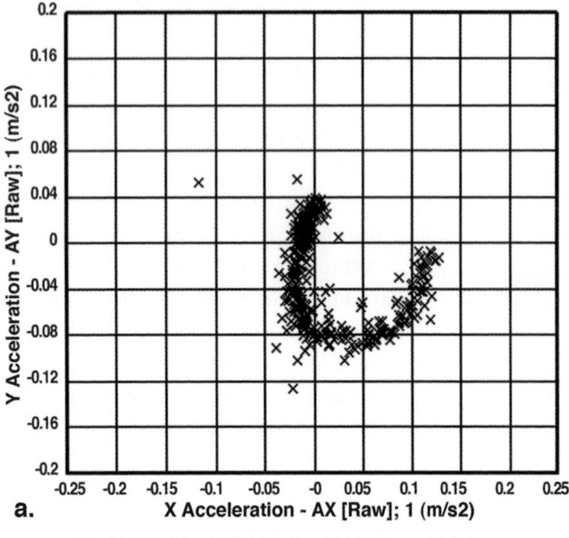

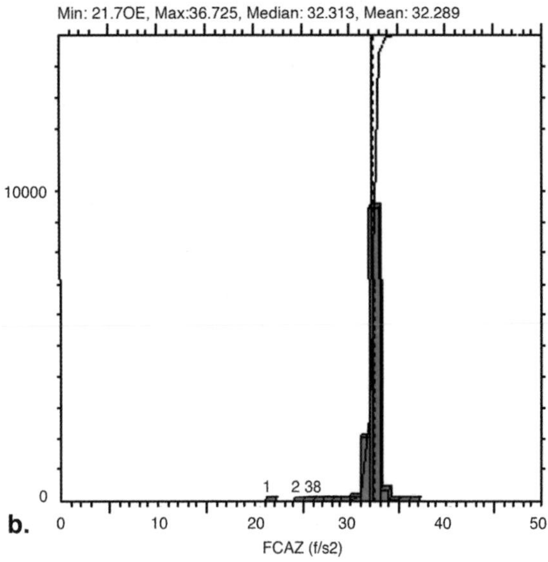

Figure 15.17 Electrical image quality control plots. (a) X–Y accelerator plot indicating tool rotation. This example shows the positions of the tool around the borehole that can be expected in a borehole with a slight deviation. (b) The vertical, Z accelerator should centre on the acceleration due to gravity, 32 ft/sec^2, as it does in this case.

space may be taken up with a dipmeter grid or core photograph images as interpretation requires.

Static and dynamic electrical images

Two types of colour image have become standard, one in which the colour range is allocated to the entire data population from one log run, called *static normalisation,* and one in which the population sample is only a limited 'window' (a screenful, or similar very restricted quantity) of data values, when it is called *dynamic normalisation* (**Figure 15.18**).

Using static normalisation, intervals (formations) with similar electrical properties will give similar colours throughout the log. Amongst other things this means water bearing sands will look similar everywhere and water and gas sands will have a significantly different colour (fluid contacts will appear as a change in colour). However, much detail will be lost, especially in zones of very high values such as in hydrocarbon bearing reservoirs or carbonates. Dynamic normalisation, on the contrary, enhances small scale contrast. So, for example, a high resistivity gas sand that would give a uniform pale colour on a static image will show plenty of character on a dynamic image because of the small variations in resistivity, which will now be seen (**Figure 15.19**). Unfortunately, this does mean that, with a dynamic normalisation, similar lithologies can have different image colours through the one log run. The two processings are therefore complementary. Dynamic normalisation is generally best for detailed on-screen interpretation; static normalisation is conveniently used for whole well analysis, and whole well hardcopy, especially at compressed vertical scales when detail is inevitably lost.

Artefacts and factors affecting electrical image log quality

The electrical image logs are more susceptible to quality difficulties than standard logs. They are affected, at the acquisition stage, by the borehole condition and the logging tool's functions, at the processing stage, where parameter manipulation is important, and during in-

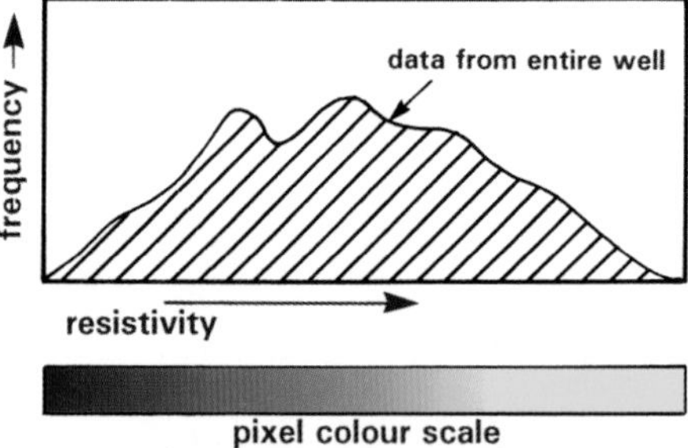

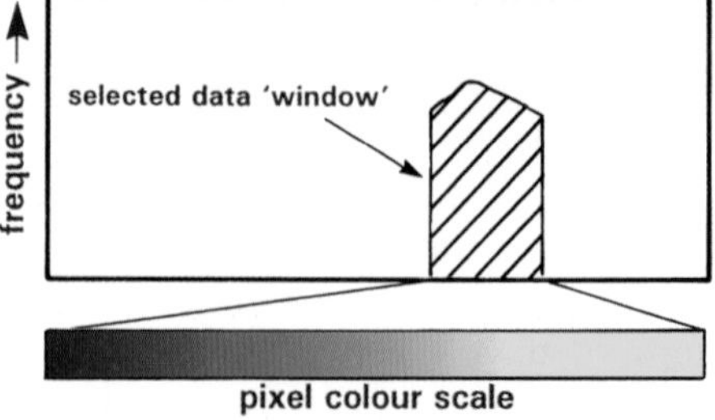

Figure 15.18 The principle of static and dynamic normalisation. (1) Static normalisation can be used to compare images over an entire well. (2) Dynamic normalisation is used to bring out local detail. The full colour scale is used for a limited data range or 'window' which can be from any chosen interval such as a bed of interest, a screenful or a pre-set, small depth range. The two different processings are illustrated in Figure 15.19.

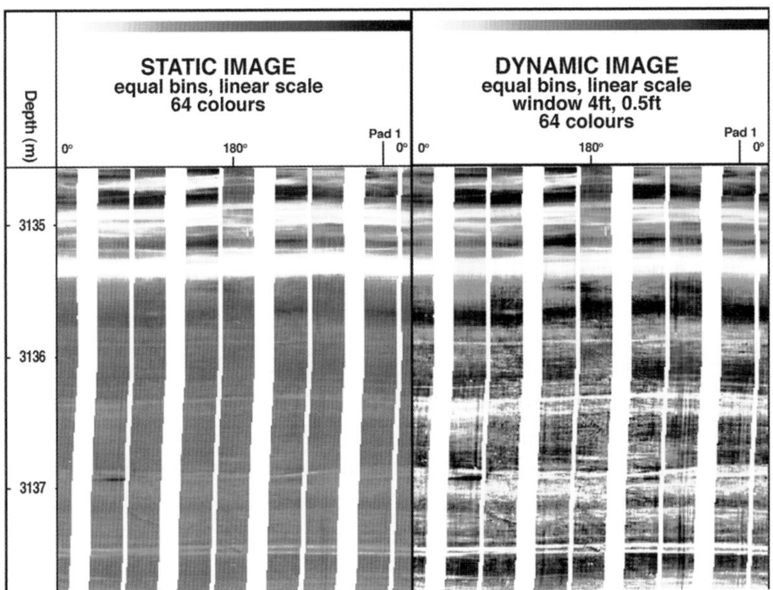

Figure 15.19 Electrical, FMI images showing the effects of static and dynamic processing. Both images were processed using equal bins and a linear, 64 colour scale. The dynamic image was made using a window for the colour scale of 4 ft (1.2 m) and a step of 0.5 ft (15 cm). TerraStation software routines.

terpretation, where artefacts may be confused with real features. Some problems are now described.

– mud weight

Mud conditions are important for good electrical image acquisition. The mud to formation resistivity ratio should be less than 20,000 and the maximum mud resistivity 50 ohm/m (for the FMI, Schlumberger 1994).

– borehole condition

Borehole rugosity and caving, clearly, have a great effect since the electrical image log is produced by a pad tool and images are essentially of the very near borehole. As a minimum, in caved formations, pads (some or all) will 'float', that is loose contact with the formation and a flat series of low, mud values will be recorded. In irregular holes, tool acquisition speed will often vary. In the worst case, the tool will stick, and a flat series of values will be recorded on all curves as the cable continues to be reeled in but the tool remains stationary (cf. **Figure 12.29**). Such poor acquisition parameters will be recognised on the logs, but slight sticking and speed variation may not. This is when speed correction is necessary. Some of the oil-based electrical Imaging tools were extremely sensitive to rugosity and mudcake and often produced un-interpretable logs. This was a direct result of their shallow depth of investigation. Although the tools have improved in this regard, they still require a good quality hole to produce useful information.

– tool function

Malfunctioning of buttons can occur during acquisition. Selective electrodes may become clogged with mud and fall dead, or individual buttons can fail when the insulation between the electrode and the pad breaks down. A black vertical trace is left on the log where no data are acquired. The effect of losing a single button on the image can be corrected by replacing its output with the average of the two adjacent ones. More difficult to cope with are pads that collect cuttings or lumps of detatched formation and drag them along while logging (Bourke 1989). Fuzzy images and poor data zones running more or less vertically up the image are created.

– artefacts

Artefacts in processed images may result from the original acquisition of the data. For example, in intervals where mud cake is thick (over 1.2 cm, 0.47"), images may come from the mudcake or irregularities in the mudcake. This is especially true where a previous tool has left pad traces in the cake, or logging cable rub has made a groove. Generally, these features will be recognised as they continue vertically for some distance or spiral up the images.

'Shadows' are another common artefact and are created when formations with very different resistivities are in contact. Current is sucked into the low resistivity layer and repulsed from the high resistivity. Because the current density is measured across the pad face, the low resistivity zone becomes very dark at the contact and the high resistivity becomes abnormally light (**Figure 15.20**) Cheung 1999). This also results in conductive spots such as vugs appearing to be larger on the image than they really are. Conversely resistive nodules will appear smaller than they should be.

Detailed discussions of artefacts are found in published literature (*i.e.* Bourke 1989; Serra 1989, Lofts and Bourke 1999).

Acoustic image processing

The raw acoustic image data consists of approximately 200 measurements of both amplitude and time of flight recorded during each revolution. The raw data are generally processed to standard colour images; one for time of flight and one for amplitude. The time of flight data can also be displayed as a continuous acoustic caliper or, more interestingly, in various 2-D or 3-D formats. The image type presentations will be discussed first.

The dense matrix of both amplitude and travel time data acquired by the acoustic imaging tools is processed into standard colour images covering the entire borehole wall (Pasternack and Goodwill 1983). The two measurement images are plotted side by side so that they can be

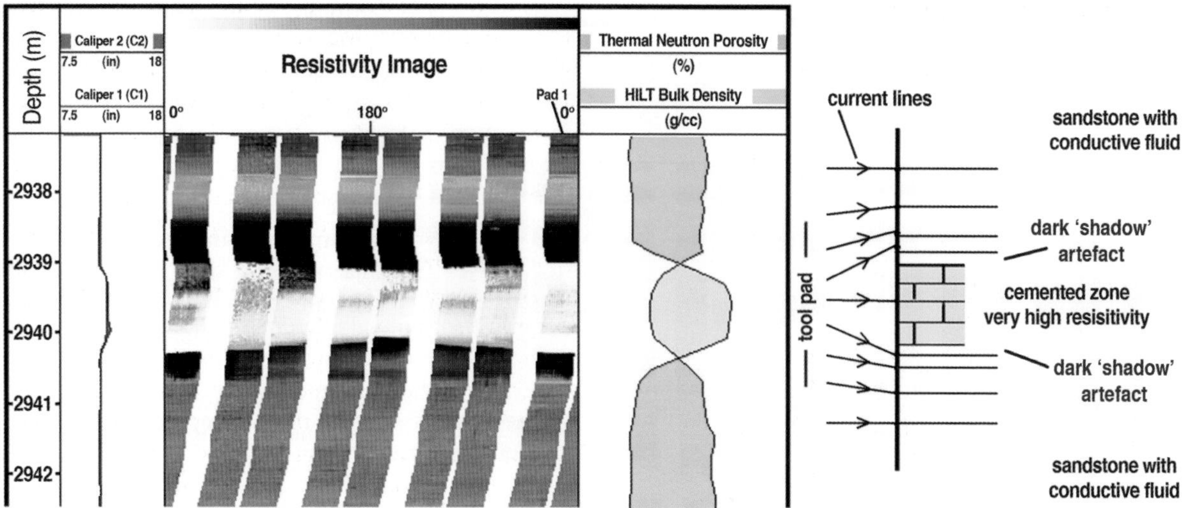

Figure 15.20 Dark 'shadows', an electrical image artefact, created when two formations with sharply different resistivities are in contact. The electrical current, in this example, is sucked into the low resistivity (salt-water bearing) sandstones and repulsed by the very high resistivity, impermeable, calcium carbonate cemented zone. FMI resistivity image, dynamic processing.

Table 15.4 Colour scale conventions for different image types.

Image Type	Image shows	Colour Scale Light (yellow-white)	Colour Scale Dark (brown-black)
Electric	resistivity	high	low
	Conductivity	low	high
Acoustic			
Amplitude	reflectance	high	low
Time of flight	time/distance	short	long
Density	bulk density	high	low
Photoelectric	*Pe* (atomic absorption)	high	low
Gamma ray	natural radioactivity	high	low
Acoustic caliper	time/distance	short	long

Useful sources: Paillet *et al.* 1990 ; Hurley, In Asquith & Krygowski 2004 ; Serra 2008 ; Lagrabda *et al.* 2010.

used together (**Figure 15.12**). The yellow-brown colour scale is generally used. On the amplitude plot, lighter colours indicate a higher amplitude (better reflectance); on the time of flight plot, lighter colours indicate a shorter time (smaller hole) (**Table 15.4**).

Production of the colour image is the major step in both amplitude and travel time image processing. However, because of a number of unwanted acquisition effects, explained below, improvements are often made to the images themselves (of both measurements) by a second layer of processing. This includes filtering, equalisation, edge detection and other techniques of image processing (Wong *et al.* 1989). The improvements can be operator applied to screen displays (**Figure 15.22**).

The time of flight measurements can be presented in an additional format, usually called an acoustic caliper. That is, the time of flight is converted into a distance by accounting for the mud velocity (which is monitored continuously by the tool in a special sensor). This produces 200 or so tool to borehole distance measurements around the full circumference of the borehole (contrast this with a conventional caliper) and is a sufficiently large number to build a detailed 3D depiction of the borehole. It is commonly viewed externally (**Figure 15.23**). This data may also be displayed as a polar plot (that is, viewed looking down the hole from the inside), or as a 'travelling polar plot', which lets the operator move up or down the hole like a tool, observing the caliper changes while doing so.

Amplitude versus time of flight acoustic images

Using the two acoustic image logs, the reflected amplitude and the time of flight, plotted together, aids interpretation. Of the two readings, the amplitude is generally the one that is the more sensitive and contains more information about the formation (**Figure 15.12**). It is this amplitude image which is usefully compared to the electrical images. The time of flight image is more sensitive to borehole geometry and therefore gives information on hole condition.

The amplitude log is an indication of both formation acoustic impedance contrast and physical borehole wall roughness. It will provide lithological information if one or both of these factors is related to rock type. For ex-

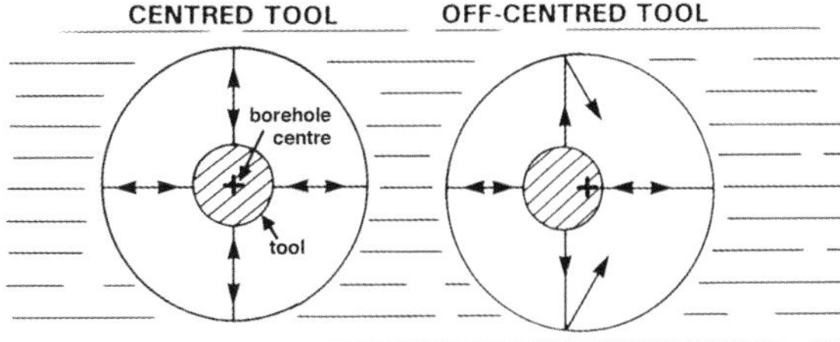

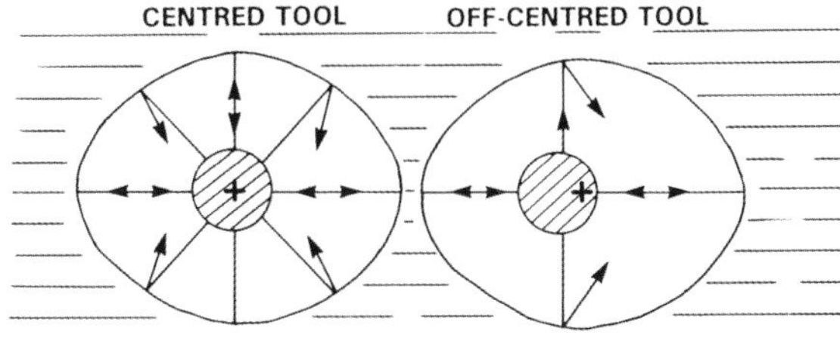

Figure 15.21 Unwanted geometrical factors which can affect acoustic images (re-drawn from Georgi 1985).

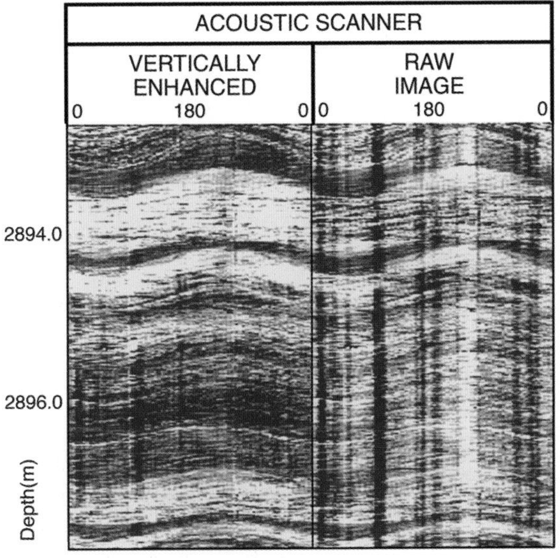

Figure 15.22 Acoustic images 'improved' by adding a second layer of processing to take out vertically consistent features caused by geometrical or mudcake artefacts. Refer to Figure 15.21 for an explanation.

ample, a dense carbonate can present a smooth borehole wall, and returns a high amplitude signal, while coals can have low reflectance and return a low amplitude signal. However, this is not always the case and sometimes the amplitude image can be very bland even though the formation is known to be highly variable. Unfortunately, these formation acoustic impedance variations may be dampened by the acoustic impedance contrast between the borehole wall and the mud. The best signals come from intervals where the mud to formation contrast is the largest.

Time of flight response is clearly quite different from the amplitude response. Time of flight records borehole geometry. It can therefore identify drilling induced artefacts such as spiral or oval holes as well as stress related features such as breakouts and tensile fractures (**Section 13.9**). However, it will also be affected by voids on the borehole wall such as open fractures, which will return no signal (**Figure 15.12**). Lithological effects will be much less obvious.

The complementary nature of the two presentations helps in their mutual interpretation. For example, comparison between amplitude and time of flight logs can indicate whether a fracture is open or closed. An open fracture gives a response on the amplitude log through loss of signal, and also on the time of flight log as no signal is returned. A filled fracture may provide an image on the amplitude log (depending on acoustic impedances) but no image on the time of flight log (Taylor 1991). Fracture characterisation is even more powerful if an electrical image log is also available.

Factors affecting acoustic image acquisition and quality

There are a number of factors which affect acoustic tool acquisition in general and have an influence on quality and hence interpretation. These are briefly described below.

– borehole geometry and tool position

Because the transducer pulse is highly collimated (focused), it will only be reflected back to the transducer from a surface that is normal to the beam (Georgi 1985). With angles even slightly away from 90°, little or no energy will be returned to the transducer. This means that hole ovality and tool tilt or non-centring will affect the sampling (**Figure 15.21**). The result will be dark or light stripes running up the image. Controls such as AGC (automatic gain control) help to diminish these effects so that they are generally (but not always) contained (**Figure 15.22**). This allows real geometric hole effects such as spiralling and breakouts, still to be seen, especially in the time of flight plot (**Figure 15.23**).

– mud weight

Although acoustic imaging tools need a fluid in the borehole to function, mud causes attenuation. The pulse energy is absorbed and scattered by the mud particles and the beam is spread. This means that the acoustic tools will not function in heavy muds. All mud causes some loss of signal and it is suggested that quality is poor in 8.5″ holes with weights above 1.62 g/cm^3 (13.5 lbs/gal) and 1.25 g/cm^3 (10.5 lbs/gal) in 12.25″ holes. However, such strict limits are not indicative as much depends on the acoustic impedance between the mud and the formation (*see* below). It is certain that the tool should generally not be used in mud weights above 1.7 g/cm^3–1.9 g/cm^3 (15–16 lbs/gal), even with CBIL, which has lower operating frequencies, as discussed.

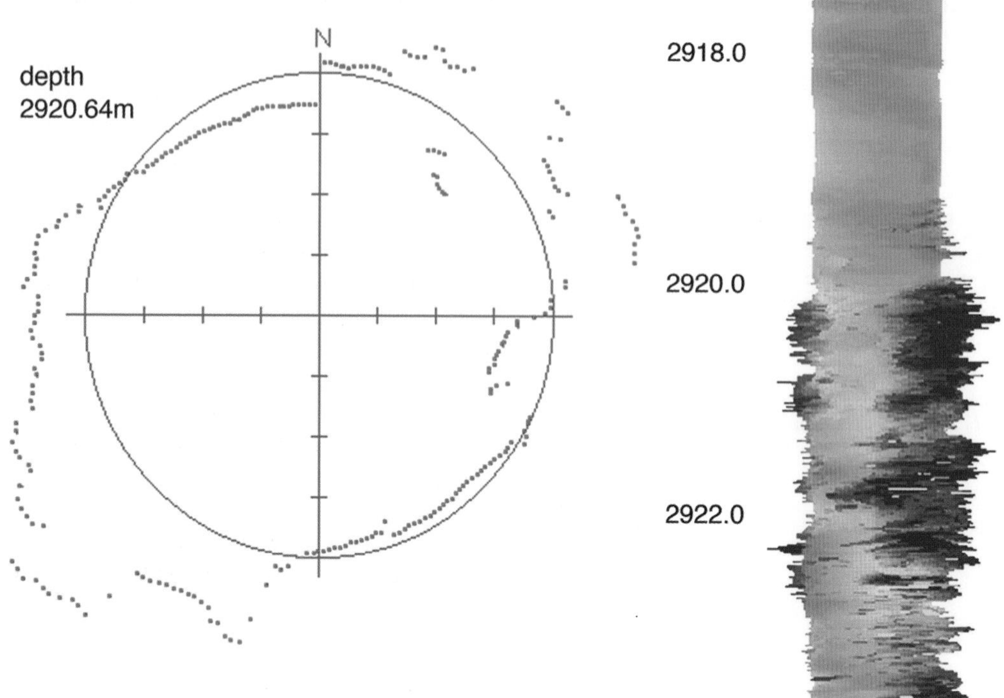

Figure 15.23 Polar plot and 3-D image from acoustic, time of flight measurements. The dots on the polar plot represent measurement stations (200) at 2920.64 m. The 3-D picture shows a round hole above about 2920 m but considerable caving (breakouts) below. The upper interval is a sandstone with mudcake, the lower interval is shale.

Logging companies should be consulted about this and how it applies to their particular tool.

– acoustic impedance contrast

For there to be a significant reflection of pulse energy at the borehole wall, there must be an acoustic impedance contrast between the mud and the formation. For this reason, the acoustic imaging tools are traditionally used in 'hard' formations such as limestones or older rocks (and crystalline rocks for the non-hydrocarbon industries). However, it is equally true that strong acoustic impedance between *formations* produces viable images (**Figure 15.30**). This is well illustrated by the use of the tools in the coal industry, coal having big impedance contrasts with other lithologies (Rubel *et al.* 1986).

– borehole surface

In the same way that borehole geometry affects the strongly focused acoustic beam, so also does the reflectivity, the topography of the actual surface of the borehole wall. That is, good reflection will come from a smooth surface, and any roughness will cause scatter and reduce the energy of the reflected signal. Thus, acoustic images show scratches left by the bit on the borehole wall, or zones of wall breakage (spalling). Such effects may dominate an image. However, usefully, fractures and other natural features such as breakouts will also be seen for the same reason (Section 15.7).

15.5 Some basic practicalities for interpretation

On-screen dip and azimuth measurement from images

Because the electrical image logs evolved from the dipmeter, they were originally used mainly to derive dip and azimuth. This is still one of their main functions. With the image data displayed on screen in the unwrapped borehole format, as has been explained, dipping surfaces appear as a sine wave, the amplitude of the wave indicating the dip, the position of the wave's low point indicating the dip azimuth (**Figure 15.2**). In a typical on-screen routine, a computer generated sine wave is fitted to a surface on the screen-displayed image and the true dip and azimuth of the surface automatically given. The fitting may be done either by interactively choosing three or more points along the surface and letting the computer choose the sine wave that fits best, or by using a pre-set, but interactively adjustable sine wave, which is permanently on the screen and is fitted by eye to the surface to be measured. These interactive measuring routines are simple and accurate but, being manual, take considerable time.

The dip and azimuth calculated from an interactive sine curve will typically use either a fixed borehole size or the actual, variable caliper measurements. That is, to calculate a dip, the sine fit must have a diameter mea-

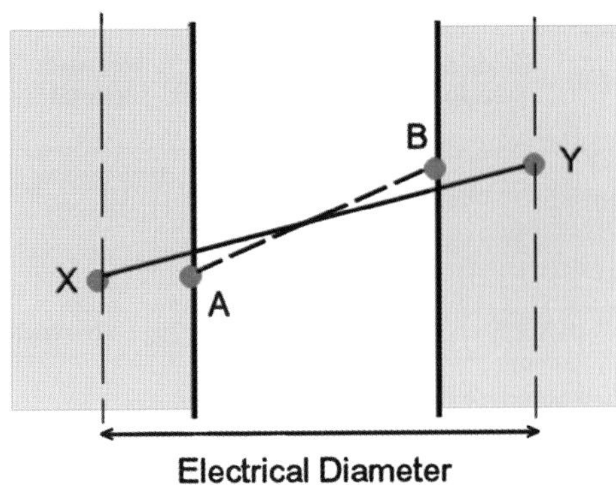

Figure 15.24 Illustration of the notion of 'electrical diameter' for dip picking. The electrical image signal is considered to come from points X and Y within the formation and not from the borehole wall at points A and B. Density, gamma ray and *Pe* images are also affected by this effect (see Table 15.5) (modified and re-drawn after Hansen and Parkinson 1999).

surement (Perkins *et al.* 2009). It has become clear that it is not the physical size of the borehole that should be used but the *electrical diameter*, or equivalent depth to which other geophysical image signals penetrate the formation, as illustrated by the LWD density discussed below. For example, the average electrical diameter of the EARTH Imager™ of Baker Hughes™ is given as 0.5 cm (0.2″) but varies with resistivity values and dip of the bed in question (Wang *et al.* 2004). The electrical diameter for dip picking is not the same as the depth of investigation (DOI), which is usually 50% of the theoretical total response, namely 0.5 of the J factor (Bittar *et al.* 2008). The diameter for dip picking is the effective location of the dominant image in relation to the borehole wall (**Figure 15.24**) and must be added to the hole size. It varies between tool types, but some approximate values are 1.27 cm (0.5″) for the LWD resistivity, 4.6 cm (1.8″) for the LWD density (compensated) and 0.5 cm (0.2″) for the wireline electrical tools (**Table 15.5**) (Perkins *et al.* 2009).

Acoustic images will generally have only a small correction, the signal being reflected from the borehole wall itself (Hansen and Parkinson 1999). One recent paper suggests that errors of around 3° in dip, and rather more in dip azimuth, can result from errors in effective image diameter, but that the error varies with the geometrical relationship between the picked dip, true dip and the borehole axis (Perkins *et al.* 2009). More importantly, however, error varies with the geophysical characteristics of the formation itself and, for example, using electrical images carbonate levels (high resistivity) often show higher dips than background shales (low resistivity). In other words, electrical diameter is less in high resistivity formations than in low resistivity ones.

For the dip and azimuth measurements to be effective in subsequent analysis, every measured surface should be classified according to the feature it represents. For example, if fractures are being measured, interpretation should allow coding of the several types able to be identified: open fractures, cemented fractures, drilling induced fractures and so on. If sedimentary features are being analysed, the classification may include foreset bedding, shale bedding, concretions, in fact, any feature necessary. Sine curve fitting to features provides excellent quality orientation information, but there is often a huge amount, and it needs subsequent filtering and interpretation. This is possible when each dip is separately classified. For example, open fractures and cemented fractures may be extracted and studied separately: foreset orientations can be extracted to study palaeocurrent directions.

Core to image comparison

It is quickly discovered that image logs do not, in the first instance, replace cores: the two datasets are complementary. Although the vertical resolution of image logs is impressive, they still cannot resolve features smaller than about 1 cm. A core can be viewed at microscopic scales if desired. Comparison between core and log image is similar to the comparison between a picture of the body itself and an X-ray. The log images are a geophysical representation and, although they provide much information, do not give anything like the detail or certainty of a visual record and an actual physical sample.

Some large features seen on core, such as a fracture or a conglomerate, may be recognisably resolved by the images, but this is not common (see below, *image log resolution*). More typical is a 'look' to the image, sometimes called an *image facies*, where the underlying cause is not known but the appearance is distinct. In such cases, cores must be used to ground truth the images, in

Table 15.5 Some suggested approximate electrical diameters or actual diameters for dip picking (cf. Figure 15.24).

Tool	Signal location	Diameter for picking (add to hole size)
Micro-resistivity (wireline)	flushed zone	5.0 cm (2″)
Macro-resistivity (wireline)	flushed zone & beyond	varies with sensor 2.5 cm, 5 cm, 12.7 cm (1″, 2″, 5″)
LWD resistivity	formation before flushing	1.27 cm (0.5″)
LWD density	flushed zone (& beyond)	4.6 cm (1.8″)
Acoustic (wireline)	mudcake/borehole wall	hole size
Gamma ray	formation	no information

other words, explain the 'image facies' and allow calibration. For example, bioturbation is usually not resolved as separate burrows but, when common and abundant, can cause a typical image facies. If this image facies can be calibrated to core, it can then be used to identify bioturbation over non-cored intervals. Such comparisons are best made with digital core photos displayed alongside the images, sedimentological logs and standard logs (*cf.* **Figures 15.30–33**).

Although it is a good technique, care needs to be taken with core comparisons because similar image responses may have different causes. For example, a cemented sand may be confused with a carbonate as both have light colours (high resistivity, good reflectance). Alternatively, similar lithologies may show different responses, and on an electrical image, a hydrocarbon bearing sand will appear different (lighter) to the same sand with salt water. And, of course, dynamic normalisation causes images to vary. When images are of a very high quality, it is easy to forget that they are still geophysical responses and not simple pictures.

Comparing image detail to core detail also involves coping with physical differences of depth and to some extent spatial position (Adams *et al.* 1990). When working with cores it becomes quickly clear that there are real depth calibration difficulties at the centimetre scale of the image logs (**Figure 15.25**). Modern software routines now enable both bulk and manual point shifts between image logs, standard logs and even core photos. However, even this produces problems as it is not clear which depth to take as a master. The image? There may be cable stretch, irregular tool movement or other difficulties. The core? There may be pieces missing, pieces in the wrong order, and depth shifts are common. Orientation is no help as the orientation of a core slab is quite likely to change from core piece to core piece. A conscious decision must be made to choose the source of the master depth, and this should be noted in any report. In the end, the master depth may be from the image log itself.

Image log resolution

General comments

In subjective terms, image resolution is often thought of as expressing how small an object can be seen, and how sharp it is. In more scientific terms, there are two aspects: *resolution* and *detection*. *Detection* is the ability to recognise that there is an object; *resolution* implies that the object can be recognised and that its parameters can be determined. For instance, the Baker Hughes™ Earth Imager™ is said to be able to *detect* resistive beds (in a conductive background) down to 7.6 mm (0.3") and conductive beds (in a resistive background) down to 2.5 mm (0.1"). However, the tool can only *resolve* actual resistivity in beds (conductive or resistive) that are thicker than 18 mm (0.7"). These are figures from

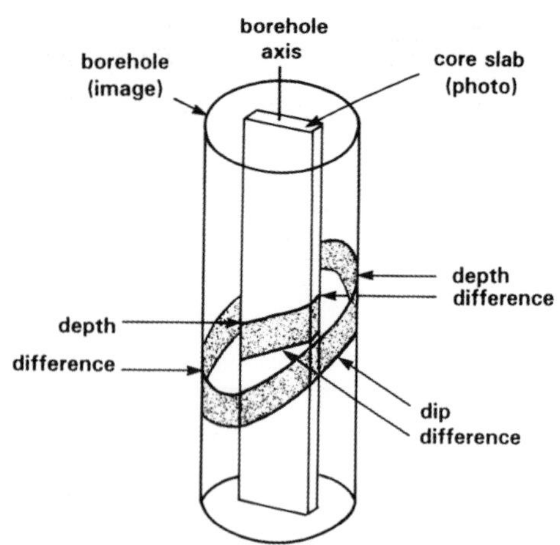

Figure 15.25 Illustration of the difficulties of depth matching core photos to borehole images.

numerical simulation (Wang *et al.* 2004).

With borehole images there can be a theoretical difference between vertical and horizontal resolution (Lagraba *et al.* 2010): it can depend on the tool but also on logging conditions, especially speed. However, when images are being used, it will also vary with the shape of the feature being examined (irregular features are less easy to recognise than continuous horizontal features); with geophysical contrasts; with image processing – and so on. Resolution is, in fact very hard to be precise about.

However, resolution is also often discussed in terms of pixel size, the implication being that the smaller the pixel, the better the presumed resolution. On this basis, the highest resolution images are from the wireline electrical, water based tools which have the smallest pixel size (a function of electrode button size), namely 2.5 mm × 2.5 mm (0.1" × 0.1"), while the LWD density and gamma ray images have amongst the largest 15.25 cm × 2.54 cm (6" × 1") (Meyer *et al.* 2005) (**Figure 15.26**).

In pad type imaging tools, which means essentially the wireline electrical imaging tools, pixel size remains constant in various borehole sizes: hole coverage, however, changes. In centralised tools, such as the acoustic wireline tool and all the LWD tools, coverage is always 360°, while horizontal pixel size depends on azimuthal sampling rate (tool design) and hole size or stand-off. The bigger the hole size, the larger the area (horizontal distance) of the borehole wall represented by a single pixel (**Figure 15.27**).

Resolution will be discussed below with these general characteristics in mind although in this book the term is used subjectively, despite the attempted definitions in the previous paragraphs.

Electrical image resolution

The following paragraph uses figures from the Schlumberger FMI as an example. The vertical resolution of in-

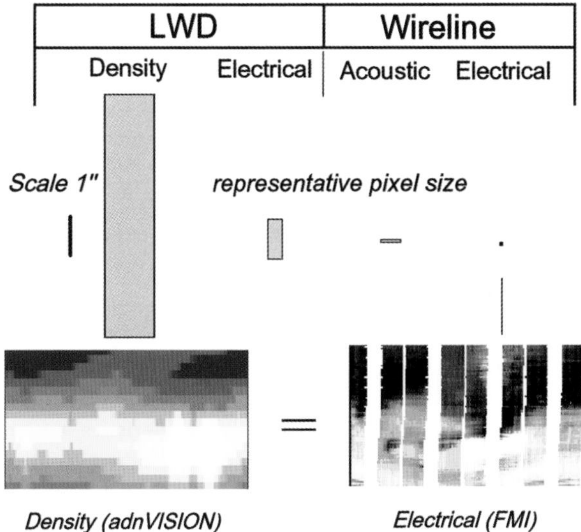

Figure 15.26 Image pixel size differences between image types and tools. Pixel size gives an indication of the potential resolution of an image. The example images used here are of the same bed imaged by the LWD adnVISION and FMI of Schlumberger. Pixel sizes are approximate: ADN 15.25 cm × 2.5 cm (6″ × 1″) (near detector), LWD electrical 2.5 cm × 1.75 cm (1″ × 0.5″), acoustic 1.46 cm × 0.833 cm (0.58″ × 0.33″), FMI 2.5 mm × 2.5 mm (0.1″ × 0.1″) (diagram much modified after Bargach *et al.* 2000).

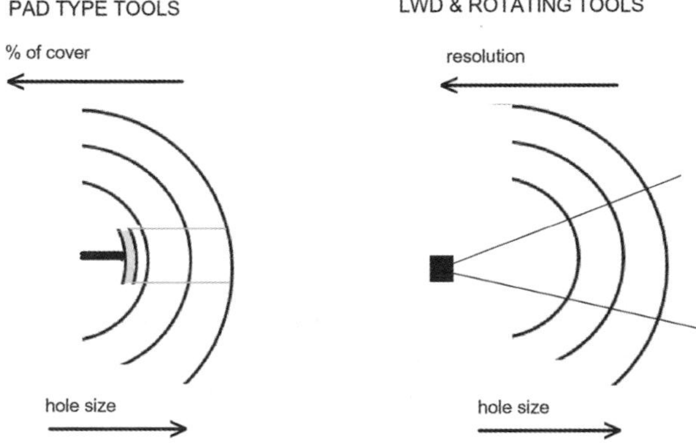

Figure 15.27 With increasing borehole size, the % of the borehole wall circumference covered by the pad type tools diminishes, resolution stays the same. For hole centred, rotating tools, the area of the borehole wall represented by a single pixel increases with borehole size, and resolution decreases.

dividual FMI buttons is indicated at 0.5 cm (0.2″) which is also the effective electrode size (Schlumberger 1994). Signal penetration is around 1.4 cm (0.55") but varies (Bourke 1993). However, in terms of the images produced, the formation is sampled horizontally and vertically every 0.25 cm (0.1″) (Section 15.2, **Figure 15.5**). The 0.25 cm × 0.25 cm (0.1″ × 0.1″) pixel matrix used for image creation is half the individual electrode resolution (2 samples per button resolution distance). Features the size of a pixel will not be resolved, i.e., will not be separated. Features smaller than a pixel will appear pixel sized. But what does this mean in practical terms?

Some notion can be gained from work on bed detection, which shows that shoulder effects (**Figure 2.10**) are important. Schlumberger (Trouiller *et al.* 1989) found that the FMS tool would resolve the thickness of sand beds (resistive) in a sand/shale turbidite sequence down to 5 cm accurately. For sand beds thinner than this, interpretation of the electrical image gave an exaggerated thickness (**Figure 15.28**) and a corresponding underestimate of (conductive) shale bed thickness. However, thin turbidite sands have been recognised down to 2.5 cm (Pezzard *et al.* 1992) and fine detail resolution is evident in outcrop comparisons (Slatt and Davis 2010). At an even finer scale, below tool and image resolution (resolution cannot be smaller than sensor size), fine lamination will be recognised, but in a general sense only rather than each lamina being identified (ie. detection finer than resolution).

For irregular features, at very small scales, shoulder effects are likely to merge and dominate and render identification difficult or impossible. For example, an individual burrow (bioturbation) is seldom identifiable, although together, because they affect texture and permeability, burrows will affect the image in a general way, and often produce a blotchy effect (**Figure 15.33**). However, because of the marked resistivity contrast, conglomerates and breccias can be more easily resolved (**Figure 15.34**).

The eventual identification of features near the limit

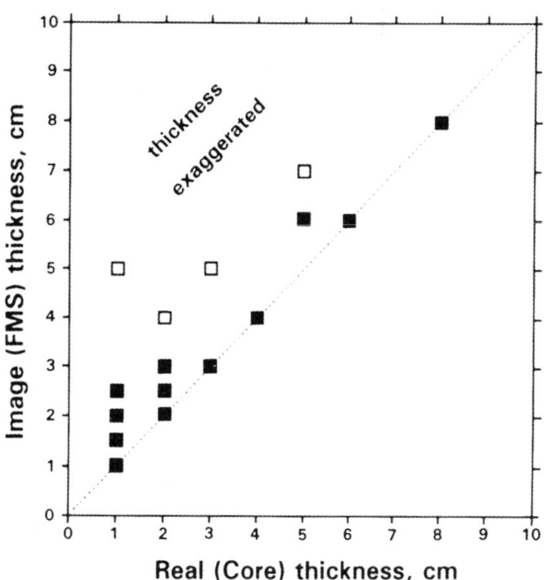

Figure 15.28 Comparison of real thin bed thickness from core, and estimated bed thickness from (wireline) electrical images. Sands were relatively more resistive than shales (from Trouiller *et al.* 1989).

of image resolution will depend both on their geometry and electrical contrast, linear features of any orientation being easier to identify, irregular features of limited extent the most difficult. The smallest linear features to be identified are probably fractures; the smallest irregular objects are probably conglomerate or breccia pebbles, where objects down to 1.3 cm (0.5") with good electrical contrast have been recognised (Harker *et al.* 1990) (**Figure 15.29**).

In summary, high definition, water based electrical images are sufficiently sharp to provide interpretable information down to about 2 cm–3 cm (0.75"–1.2"). Although there are some examples at even smaller scales, confidence is low.

Oil based, wireline electrical imaging tools have an inferior resolution than the water based versions. For example, the EarthImager™ of Baker Hughes™ has a vertical resolution of 7 mm (0.3") while the OBMI of Schlumberger and the OMRI of Halliburton both have resolutions of 1.0 cm (0.4"). These numbers are about twice those for the water based tools. Pixel sizes are correspondingly larger.

Generally, it is the small scale limit of detection which preoccupies interpreters. There is, however, an upper limit also. This is hard to define but, depending on the interpretation techniques used, it is around 2 m – 3 m (6' – 10') and almost certainly below 10 m (30'). That is, features above 10 m will generally not be recognised (**Figure 15.29**).

Acoustic image resolution

The pixel matrix of the acoustic images is built up from around 200 horizontal samples from the full borehole circumference and a very small depth sampling. In an 8.5" hole, logged at 3 m (10 ft) per minute with 250 samples per revolution and 6 revolutions per second (CBIL™ tool), each sample will represent an area of approximately 1.46 cm on the X (horizontal) axis by 0.833 cm on the Y (vertical, depth) axis (0.58" × 0.33") but, in a 12.25" borehole, the equivalent area will be 3.04 cm X axis by 0.833 cm Y axis (1.2" × 0.33"). With the tool operating from the centre of the borehole, as suggested above, the actual area of borehole wall represented by a pixel will depend on borehole size (**Figure 15.27**). However, the image is essentially from the borehole wall and penetration is minimal.

With acoustic images, in addition, feature resolution is controlled by transducer beam characteristics, which in turn are a function of transducer size and tool electronics (Georgi 1985). Using experimental models, under ideal conditions the Baker Hughes™ CBIL™ acoustic tool is indicated to *detect* a fracture aperture with a width of 0.025 mm (0.001") (Lincecum 1993), much smaller than the resolution of the transducer. Resolution is equal to the radius of the pulse beam (or the transducer size in unfocused beams). Detection, in this case, is the ability to recognise a single object while resolution is the ability to separate two objects. The experiments show clearly that the acoustic tools can detect features below their resolution, but that all features up to the resolution resemble each other. Under conditions of good acoustic impedance contrasts, acoustic tool resolution can be good (**Figure 15.30**).

Laboratory based figures are somewhat modified by subsurface experience. For example, an in-house tool used by Shell (Dudley 1993) was able to detect, in the subsurface, fractures 1 mm (0.04") or greater in width and to resolve fractures 8 mm (0.3") apart. Other studies

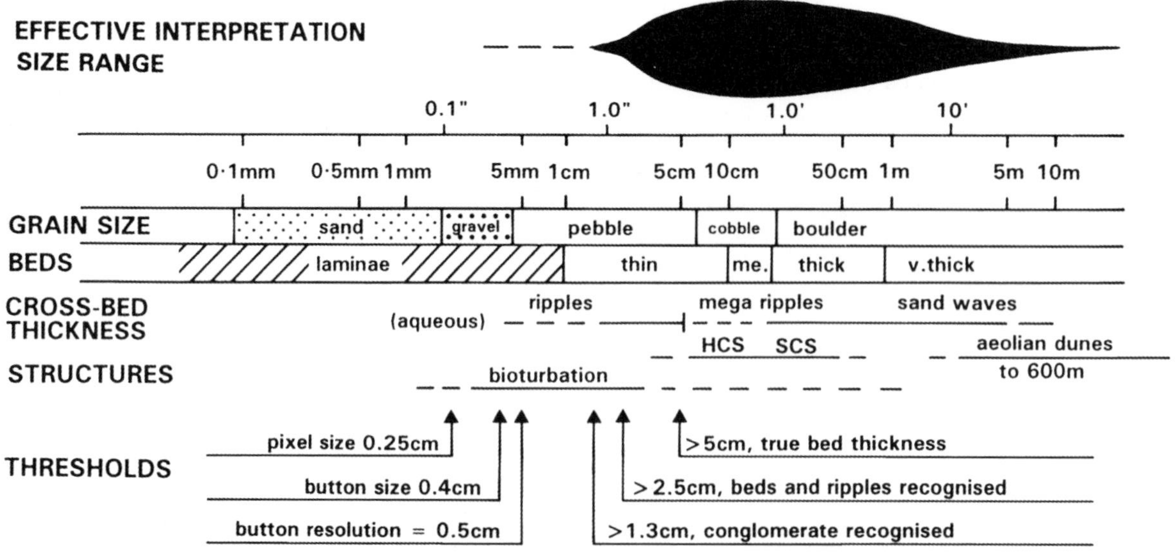

Figure 15.29 Recognition and resolution of wireline electrical images in relation to grain size, bedding and common sedimentary structures. HCS = hummocky cross-stratificaion. SCS = swaley cross-stratification.

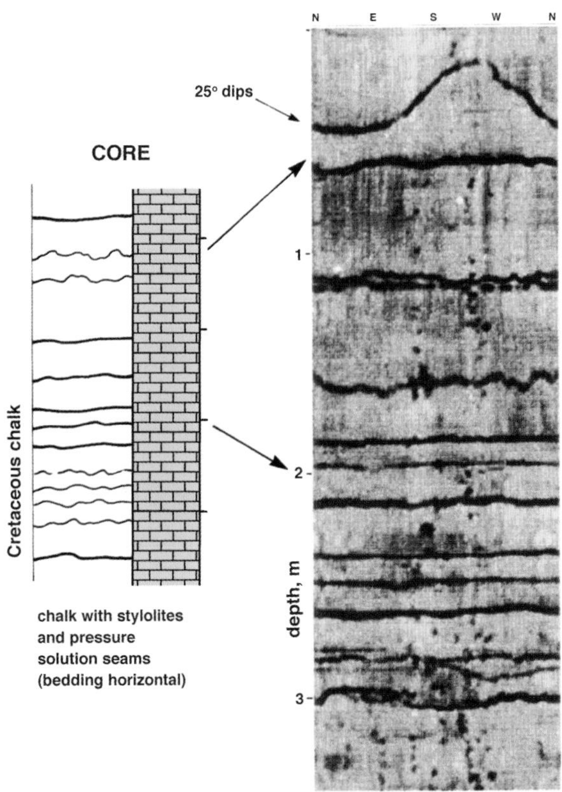

Figure 15.30 Chalk with stylolites and pressure solution seams well characterised by wireline acoustic images. Acoustic amplitude plot from Western Atlas CBIL. Core sedimentology from D. Mackertich Amerada Hess. Data published by permission of Amerada Hess (UK) Ltd. and Western Atlas (now Baker Hughes™).

have found that acoustic tools can detect fractures only with apertures greater than 0.5 mm (0.02") (Laubach *et al.* 1988). Clearly, there are variations between tools and local conditions which affect the operation.

In more general terms, CBIL™ is indicated to have a vertical resolution of approximately 1.3 cm (0.5") (Verdure 1991). This figure is indicative of the resolution to expect when examining sedimentary features. However, figures indicative from subsurface analysis are often much larger than this and an early study found that features 15 cm (6") thick were not recognised (Laubach *et al.* 1988). Experience shows that recognising especially smaller scale sedimentary structures using the acoustic tools is difficult and that putting numbers on a practical acoustic tool resolution is not possible.

LWD images

The LWD, water based, electrical images now available can approach the quality of water based wireline tools and a pixel size of 0.63 cm × 0.63 (0.25" × 0.25") is quoted (Lofts and Morris 2010). However, if these images are required in real time, they will be degraded compared to the memory images downloaded when the tool is brought to surface. Other LWD electrical imaging tools, such as the GeoVISION of Schlumberger, are not designed for high resolution.

The same is true of the other tools whose responses can be imaged, namely the density, *Pe,* and gamma ray: their resolution is much lower (**Figure 15.26**).

Electrical versus acoustic images

There is a tendency to compare acoustic images with electric images, not just because they are both images but also because of commercial competition. Of course the two should be compared, not in a competitive sense, but to find out which tool to use for a particular set of circumstances. After all, the tools are responsive to different geophysical properties. The following comments concern questions of resolution and generalities. The sections on interpretation indicate the type of image on which particular features are best seen.

There are two obvious differences between the acoustic and the electric imaging tools *per se.* The acoustic tools give a full 360° coverage while the pad type, electrical tools give only partial coverage, from 20% – 90%. The acoustic tools can be used in any fluid including oil-based muds; the highest resolution electrical tools cannot. The claimed resolution and detection are similar for both tools although, in practice, the electrical images are generally far more detailed.

From experience it is found that the acoustic tools have a good sensitivity to fractures of any type, both natural and drilling related. The full 360° coverage is essential to study fractures as they are often irregular, branching and non-planar (Laubach *et al.* 1988). The acoustic logs are also good in the study of drilling-induced fractures, breakouts and borehole geometry because they essentially image the borehole wall (Davatzes and Hickman 2010) (**Figure 15.23**) but, because acoustic impedance differences are generally small, definition of sedimentary features and lithological boundaries is generally poor to moderate (although not always **Figure 15.30**).

Because, in general, sedimentary features have a horizontal (bedding related) consistency, full 360° image coverage is less important for their recognition. In addition, the features exist in the body of the formation, where the electrical images are derived, and not just on the borehole wall. Also, that they show small and rapid contrasts in resistivity is a clear advantage for the electrical images. This is seen in practice, for example, where thin beds, cross-beds and course textures are all clearly interpretable from the electrical images. Features such as breakouts which are especially related to the borehole wall and borehole geometry are less well imaged.

In summary, from a resolution point of view, electrical and acoustic images are indicated as similar. However, because of the nature of the geophysical signal (acoustic impedance/geometry against resistivity differences) and the physical borehole wall coverage, acoustic images are more effective for fracture and borehole geometry studies or where oil-based mud is used; the electrical images

Table 15.6 Grades of interpretation based on images from wireline electrical, high resolution imaging tools (modified from Serra 1989; Salimulla and Stow 1992).

Grade	Tectonic	Sedimentary	Diagenetic
Grade 1 **SELF EVIDENT**	structural dip fractures folds	bedding surfaces, laminations cross-bedding, grading erosional surfaces deformation features i.e. slumps lithology changes	stylolites (high amplitude peaks)
Grade 2 **AMBIGUOUS**	faults	cobbles, pebbles, breccias shale clasts ripples, bioturbation grain size textures	nodular concretions chert vugs, caverns sulphide/sulphate crystals
Grade 3 **NEEDS CORE**	small fractures bed-parallel fractures	bioturbation, thin lamination limestone textures	stylolites (low amplitude peaks)

are more effective in the analysis of sedimentary features and where water-based muds are used (highest definition). But these are only underlying generalities, which may be altered by specific operational conditions.

15.6 Sedimentary interpretation of images, some concepts and examples

From a sedimentary and sedimentological point of view, high resolution wireline electrical and (under good conditions) LWD electrical images are used to identify sedimentary structures and features, measure sedimentary orientation and give detailed information on lithology, texture, sedimentary facies, sequences and sequence stratigraphic surfaces. Acoustic images are less used for sedimentary analyses so, unless stated otherwise, this section refers to the use of high resolution electrical images (mostly wireline).

The sedimentary interpretation of high resolution electrical images tends to follow routines similar to those used in a purely sedimentological analysis, that is, building up through lithology, texture and sedimentary structures to facies, sequences and sequence stratigraphic interpretations. With the image logs, this tends to consist of: feature identification; dip and azimuth measurement with classification; refinements to lithological interpretations; recognition of image facies and sequences; interpretation of sequence stratigraphic surfaces. In sedimentary work, the images are being used as a descriptive tool although inevitably a lot of interpretation is required.

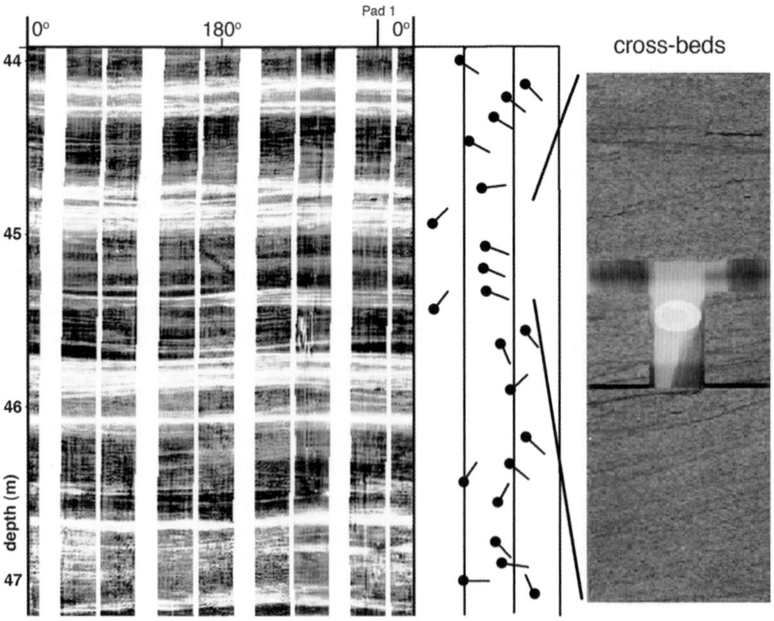

Figure 15.31 Cross-beds and cross-bed set boundaries seen on wireline, Schlumberger FMI, electrical images. The cross-beds give measureable palaeocurrent dip and azimuth, while the set boundaries show low, near structural dips (dynamic processing).

Sedimentary structure identification and orientation measurement

In sedimentary image log interpretation, some features are instantly identifiable, some require additional log information and most require calibration with core to be recognised (**Table 15.6**) (Serra 1989; Salimullah and Stowe 1992). For example, cross-bedding can usually be recognised from image characteristics alone, and both the cross-beds and set boundaries identified (**Figure 15.31**). Reliable palaeocurrents can be derived from the cross-bed, sedimentary dips (**Figure 15.38**). Ripples are too small to be resolved by the images although, when abundant, they create a recognisable 'image facies' which, once calibrated to core, may be recognised outside cored intervals (**Figure 15.32**). Abundant bioturbation can also create a distinc-

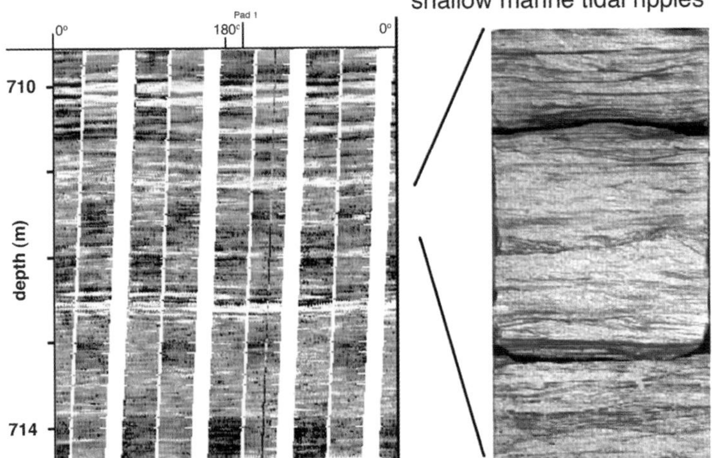

Figure 15.32 Ripple bedding showing an 'image facies'. Ripples are too small to be resolved individually by the images but are distinctive on this wireline, Schlumberger FMI, electrical image (dynamic processing).

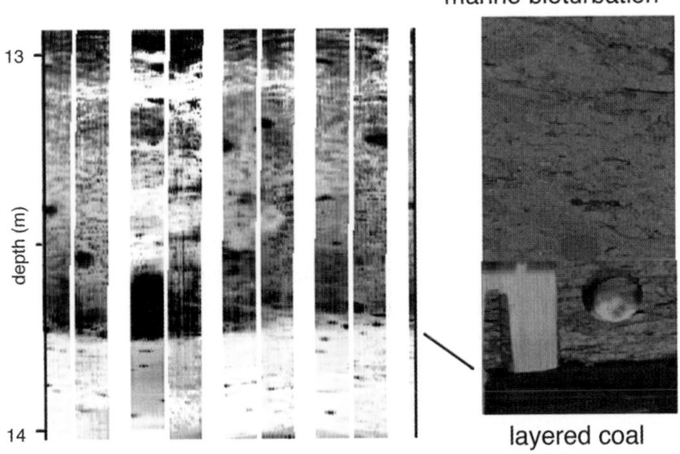

Figure 15.33 The typical image facies of abundant marine bioturbation on a wireline, Schlumberger FMI, electrical image. The bioturbation is not resolved but creates a typical speckled effect on the image. However, similar effects can be caused by small pebbles, mud clasts and concretions (*see* text). The light coloured, layered beds at the base of the image are from a laminated coal (high resistivity) (static image).

tive image facies although the individual burrows are unlikely to be resolved (**Figure 15.33**). Care must be taken with these sorts of feature because the same image log response can be produced by several different objects. For example, it has been shown that small pebbles, mud clasts, concretions and bioturbation can all have a similar image expression (Salimullah and Stowe 1992). Core calibration is therefore essential for identifying fabrics, and indeed is highly desirable for all sedimentary feature identification (Weissenberger *et al.* 2006).

Beyond simple sedimentary feature identification, images are used to measure sedimentary orientations, as suggested in the cross-bed example above. To be effective for this task, the feature being measured should be identified, as far as possible, and the dip and azimuth data classified. For example, sedimentary classifications will include structures such as shale laminae, sand beds, sand bases, cross-beds, hummocky cross stratification (HCS) and so on. This classification will be used for subsequent filtering and, for example, cross-beds can be extracted to provide palaeocurrent directions (**Figure 15.31**). However, any classification must be sufficiently robust to account for surfaces positively recognised, such as cross-beds, those vaguely recognised, such as ripple bedding, and unrecognised features. A numerical quality rating may be included from certain to doubtful.

As image interpretation work progresses, so a more and more detailed picture is built up. For example, orientation data may allow an interval to be identified as deposited in just one, consistently oriented channel, or mottled images identified as bioturbation and so on. This progressive building is implied in the following text.

Lithology and texture

Electrical images are not *a priori* primary lithology indicators (Chapter 12). Lithological information must come from other sources such as the neutron-density or gamma ray logs or drill cuttings. However, image logs can do two things to help with lithology interpretation: recognise very thin beds, because they have a have a much higher vertical resolution than the standard logs and identify irregular features such as vugs (**Figure 17.33**) or conglomerates (**Figure 15.34**), equally beyond the capability of standard logs. That is, image logs can provide a very detailed bedding and coarse textural input to lithological interpretation.

An example of this ability is shown in the thin bedding example subsequently discussed (**Figure 15.52**). Fine, centimetric interlaminations of clean sand and clean shale are not resolvable on the standard logs. However, the thin bedding is well characterised on the image logs and the constituent lithologies can be separated. In deep-sea turbidites, this ability to detect thin shale beds allows a much more meaningful facies analysis than with the standard logs (Pezard *et al.* 1992; Passey *et al.* 2006).

The ability to detect coarse, irregular, textural features is especially significant in the analysis of carbonates (Wang *et al.* 2008). Carbonates are generally character-

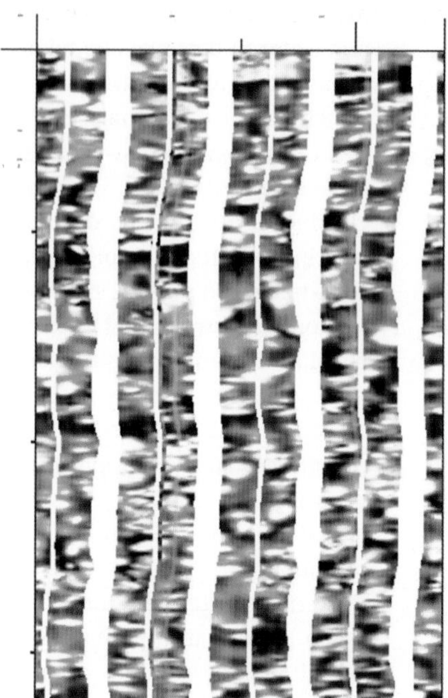

Figure 15.34 A conglomerate seen on electrical images. The conglomerate consists of rounded, indurated shale clasts and pebbles in a more conductive shale matrix. Schlumberger FMI electrical images (dynamic processing).

ised not just by lithology but also by texture. In fact, texture is generally more important in determining their reservoir properties, which means standard logs are of limited use in characterising them (Rupel and Jones 2006; Ramamoorthy *et al.* 2008). To be detected, textural features must be of a significant size and have distinct electrical characteristics. For example, large vugs in a carbonate will have a significant permeability and porosity meaning that, in the flushed zone, they will be filled with drilling mud. If water-based mud is used, then the mud will show as dark, conductive patches (the mud-filled vugs) within a light backgound (the higher resistivity carbonate matrix). (**Figure 17.33**). In such work, calibration with core is essential as there are other sedimentary features that can produce dark patches (e.g. filled burrows).

Image facies, sequences and sequence stratigraphy

An *image facies* can be considered as an image with sufficient characteristics to be able to be recognised in itself and to be able to be separated from other image facies. An image facies will not necessarily correspond to a geological facies. Geological facies from core will be more detailed and need to be upscaled and simplified for image work (Wang *et al.* 2008). The term has already been used in discussing the recognition of sedimentary structures, and it was implied that such facies are generally qualitative, the same as sedimentological or geological facies. Indeed, it is found that, although some image facies appear to be common and recognisable (**Figures 15.32,33**), others are typical of just one log or one field. This is exactly what is found with sedimentological facies.

Image facies need to be calibrated to core in order to have a geological significance (**Figure 15.35**) (Onu *et al.* 2008). For example, bioturbation as discussed, is generally below image resolution, and rarely identified individually, but imparts a general 'look' or facies to the images. Once calibrated, this same facies can be identified with confidence even where there is no core. The same technique may be used with types of laminae (**Figure 15.35**). Image facies interpretation also requires lithological information, which usually comes from the standard logs. Fine scale laminations on a dynamically

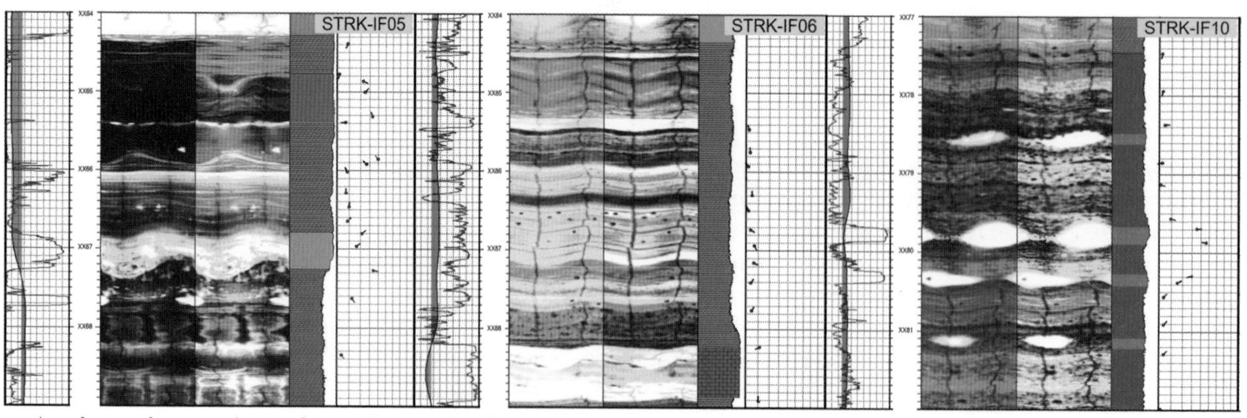

Figure 15.35 'Image facies' interpreted from LWD electrical images (and standard logs) from fluvial and littoral environments. Output from Baker Hughes™ StarTrak™, High-definition LWD, electrical imaging tool. Track 1, gamma ray, mean image resistivity; Track 2, depth in meters; Track 3 StarTrak image static normalisation; Track 4, StarTrak image dynamic normalisation; Track 5, image facies; Track 6, dip (from Onu *et al.* SPWLA 2008).

processed image look similar in shale, sand and argillaceous carbonate: it is the small electrical contrasts which dominate. Only lithological information will allow them to be separated.

Individual image facies can be combined into sequences in much the same way that a sedimentological analysis will lead to a description in terms of facies and then sequences. It is at this stage that any additional information is incorporated. For example, sands with foreset laminae and 'cleaning-up' gamma ray trends can be recognised as forming channels. A finely laminated clay may be interpreted as a plug deposited within an abandoned channel (**Figure 15.36**).

Beyond sequences, it is also possible to use images to investigate key, sequence stratigraphic surfaces. For example, the abrupt contact between the Fife Sandstones and the Kimmeridge Clay (Jurassic, North Sea) are very well shown, even on acoustic logs (**Figure 15.37**). The use of images in sequence stratigraphy is further developed in Chapter 17.

Final data synthesis

A great deal of detailed information is produced during the sedimentary analysis of image logs: it must be distilled down to a manageable level for the average user, in the same way that sedimentological detail has to be distilled. This can be achieved with a quasi-sedimentological presentation even if the information is mostly based on image interpretation (ie. **Figure 15.36**). Ultimately, it serves the same purpose of enabling the data to be integrated into more general work. Sadly, often the summarising step is not done and an excellent interpretation is never used because it is far too detailed for the end-user.

For example, there is a huge amount of dip and azimuth data that can be derived from an image log analysis, but it must be distilled if it is to be useful. Reservoir models only take one orientation per sandbody. Software allows orientations to be filtered from image analysis and analysed by feature and by facies. Cross-bed orientation data, for example, can be extracted and pooled to create a rose diagram and mean orientation for each separate sandbody. It may suggest a particular body is multi-storey and with variable orientations, or just one, thick channel with consistent orientations, but such distilled information can at least be integrated into the reservoir model. Although analysed separately, orientation data are most effective when first pooled and then re-integrated with the overall sedimentary image analysis (**Figure 15.38**).

It is good practice to produce a pdf plot (or other, often company specific format) of the sedimentary interpretation at both a detailed reservoir scale and a summary scale, say 1:200 and 1:1000. This is because, regrettably, many companies do not have the image interpretation

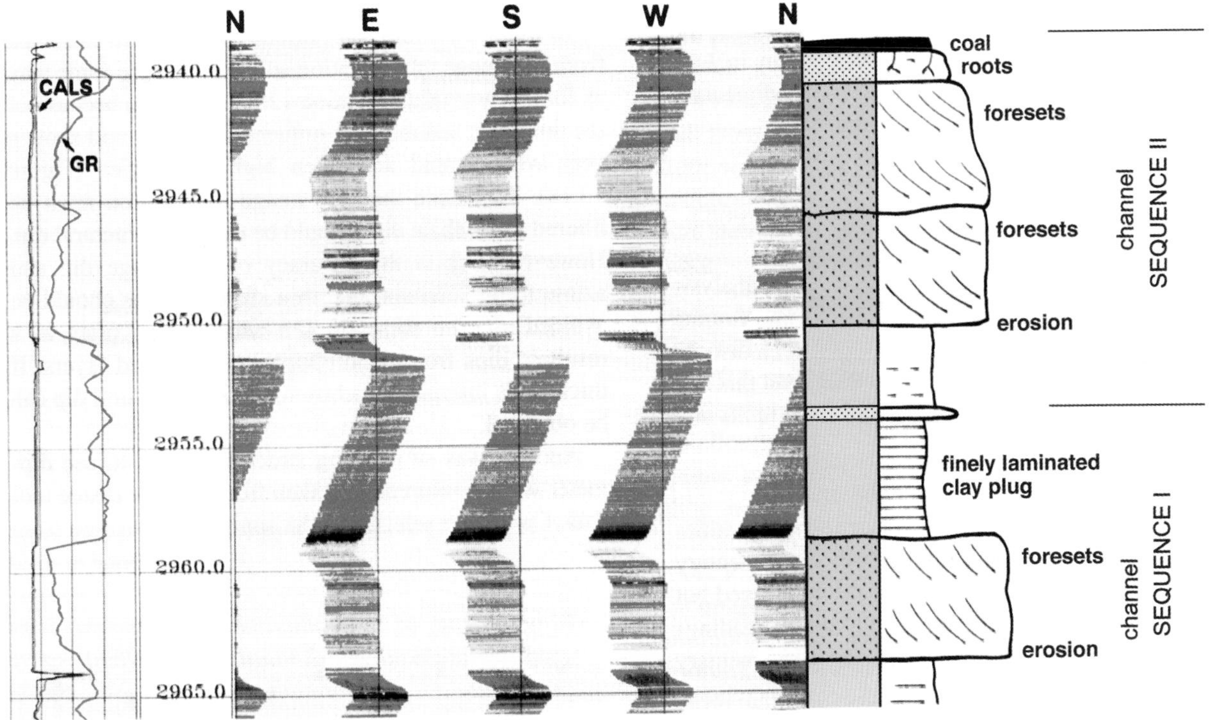

Figure 15.36 The interpretation of two fluvial sequences from electrical images and standard logs. The sequences were built up by examining 'image facies' and the interpretations are represented by a standard, sedimentological profile. The interval was not cored. Output from Schlumberger wireline, 4 pad FMI.

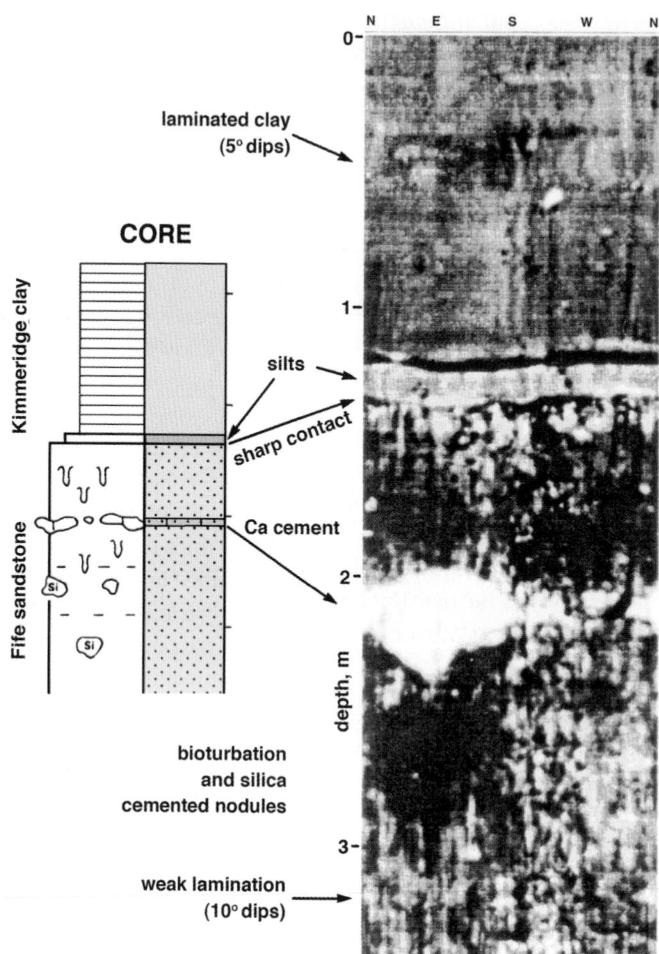

Figure 15.37 A key sequence stratigraphic surface and sedimentary features on acoustic images. Burrowed, fine grained Fife Sands with carbonate layers and silica cemented nodules, abruptly overlain by laminated Kimmeridge Clay (Jurassic, North Sea). Acoustic amplitude plots from Western Atlas CBIL. Core sedimentology from D. Mackertich Amerada Hess. Data published by permission of Amerada Hess (UK) Ltd. and Western Atlas (now Baker Hughes™).

software which would allow them to investigate the data live. Displays of the results are the next best thing and at least allow an interpretation to be examined on screen, in detail and understood.

15.7 Structural interpretation of images, some examples

The first, simple and most basic objective of a structural analysis of images is to recognise and measure an accurate structural dip and to recognise unconformities, even disconformities. But objectives can go far beyond this, to the recognition and measurement of fractures *in situ* (both natural and drill-induced), breakouts, faults and even slumps.

Structural dip and unconformities

Dip and azimuth can be measured from most images even at the lowest resolution. However, the low resolution images allow only a few measurements while the highest resolution can provide many more dips per metre. In fact, more dips could be picked than are actually used but this does allow a statistical analysis of the dips to be made so that, for example, error bars can be defined. In addition, low resolution image dips tend to be less scattered than those from high resolution images, the latter being affected by small scale sedimentary features such as concretions, which stand out geophysically and are invariably picked, but which do not represent a reliable background (structural) dip and azimuth (cf. Hurley 1994).

To derive a structural dip from image interpretation the data are normally pooled using the methods suggested for dipmeter data (Section 14.8). Data are plotted on a stereogram or rose diagram, probably zoned stratigraphically, and statistics extracted. Best results are obtained from high resolution data when dips from shale intervals only are used. That is, during picking, a category 'shale dip' is set up and then extracted for the structural dip statistics. Thick shale intervals will provide the best results and, if sufficient dips are picked,

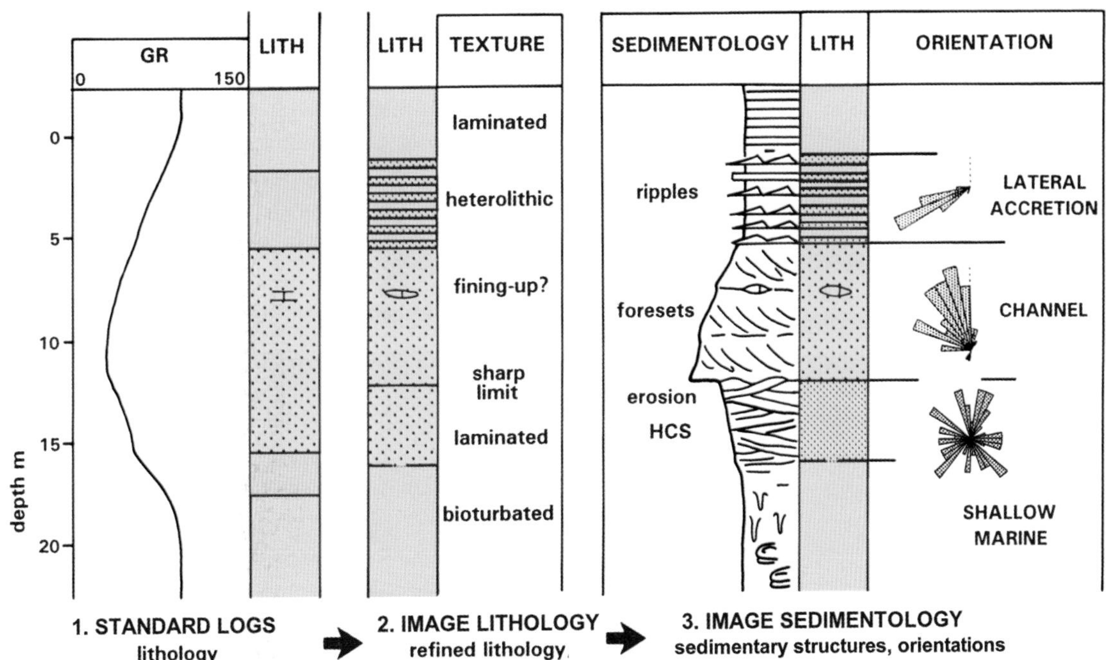

Figure 15.38 Technique for interpreting an image derived lithology, sedimentology and orientation using both the standard logs and the electrical image logs. (1) Lithology interpreted from the standard logs. (2) Lithological boundaries and thin beds refined using the images. (3) Sedimentary structures, orientations and a sedimentological profile built up and interpreted from image characteristics.

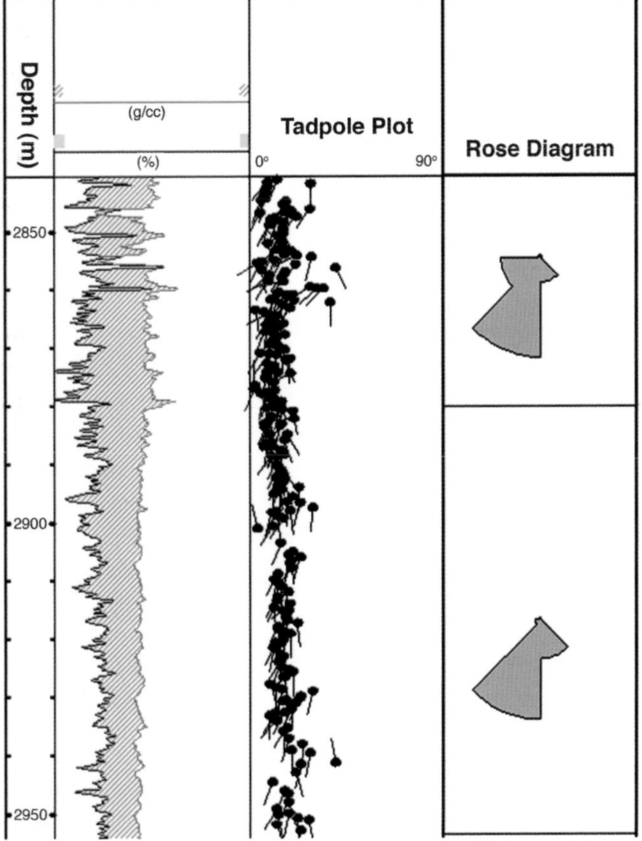

Figure 15.39 Structural dip plot. Structural dip measured manually on wireline electrical images through a thick shale section. The individual measurements are pooled over stratigraphic intervals to produce the rose diagrams. This pooled structural dip should be comparable to seismically derived dip.

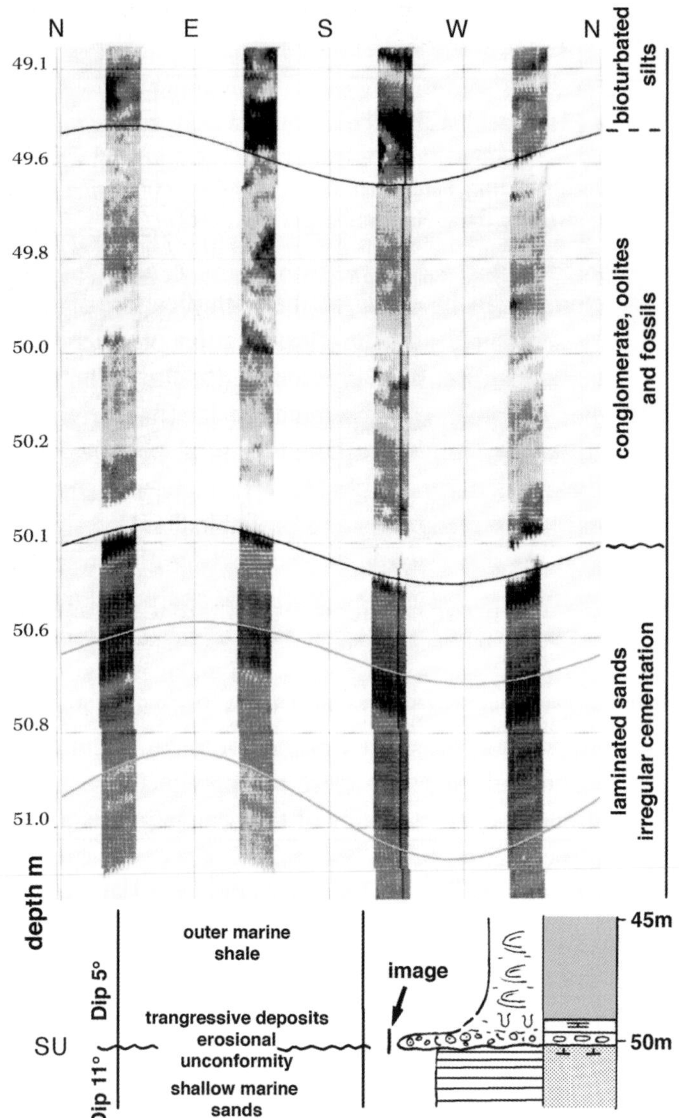

Figure 15.40 Electrical image of an unconformity surface and covering transgressive lag. The unconformity is seen on the image as a sharp surface separating an angular dip change (11° to 5°). The covering lag shows cementation at the contact (light colours) and a speckled image (cored interval, Schlumberger FMI tool).

local irregularities lose importance (**Figure 15.39**). The pooled image derived dips will be comparable to seismically derived dips.

A unique element of image interpretation is that, if an unconformity or other structural break is suspected, then the actual surface itself can be examined. The level may show diagenetic effects, abrupt changes in image facies and biological activity. The details of the angular change can also be explored (**Figure 15.40**). Such details are helpful in a sequence stratigraphic analysis since image features around key stratigraphic surfaces are often very distinctive (Chapter 17).

Drilling-induced and natural fractures

The detection of fractures, and eventually faults, is an important objective of the image logs, traditionally more so for the acoustic images, as discussed, than for the electrical images, especially in the non-hydrocarbon industries (water, geothermal etc.) (Paillet *et al.* 1990). Fractures are never satisfactorily cored and are inevitably under-sampled by them, so that to be able to see fractures *in situ* using the image logs and to measure their characteristics accurately is invaluable. Although acoustic images are often preferred for fracture work, wireline electrical and especially LWD electrical images are now being used more frequently (Stamm *et al.* 2007; Davatzes and Hickman 2010). Though the detection of a fracture and its orientation measurement in the subsurface is a major step, 'just to find a fracture is not enough' (Nelson 1985). There is a need to identify its character, that is, to distinguish natural from drilling induced fractures and to distinguish open fractures from closed. Image logging

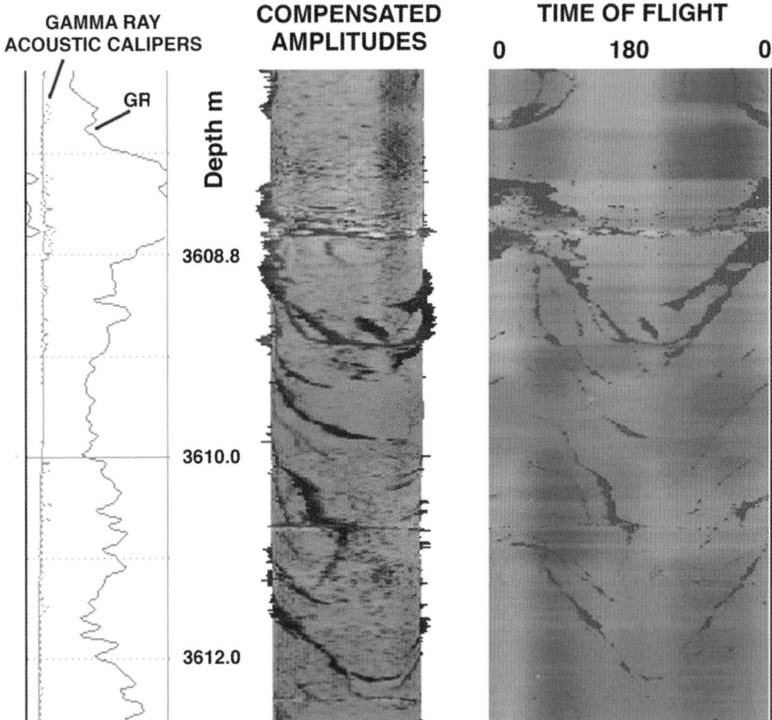

Figure 15.41 Naturally fractured carbonates seen on acoustic images. The fractures are irregular, seen on both plot types, penetrate the full wellbore and show physical breakage at the exit and entry points (cf. Figure 15.54), all characteristics of natural fractures. 3-D image of amplitudes (open fractures, dark colours = low amplitude) and blue colour plot of the time of flight (red and dark colours = long times).

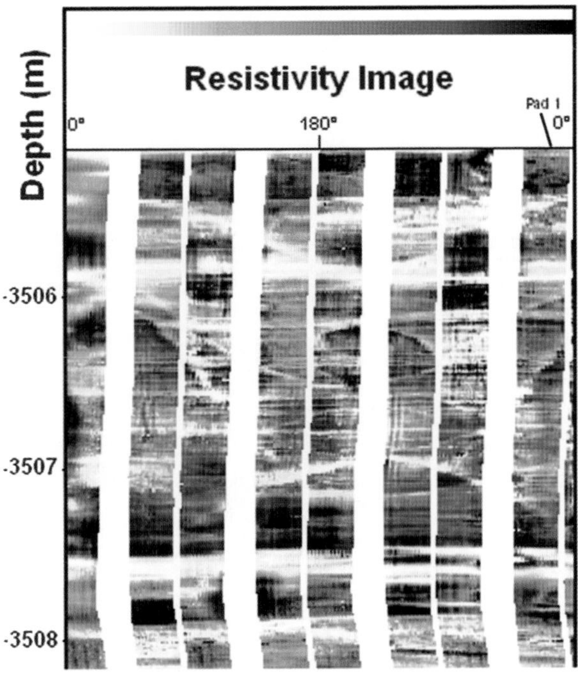

Figure 15.42 Natural fractures in silty sandstones seen on Schlumberger, wireline, FMI electrical images. The fractures are interpreted as mainly cemented because of the light colours (resistive) along the traces. Fractures dip at 55°–75°, while bedding dip is around 5° (dynamic processing).

technology has evolved in parallel with a better understanding of how rocks fracture and it is increasingly clear that drilling-induced fractures are very common, if not ubiquitous (Lincecum *et al.* 1993). They must be distinguished from natural fractures if a fractured reservoir is to be properly understood. The study of drilling-induced fractures is now a study in itself and is important for designing high angled wells, sand control and fracture stimulation (Barton and Zoback 2002).

Open fractures of any kind will be seen on most images. The acoustic images reveal open fractures as a low amplitude return and long time of flight (**Figure 15.41**). The response of an electrical imager depends on whether the well was drilled with water or oil based mud (and hence the type of tool used). In a water based mud, open fractures will be highly conductive relative to the background matrix (will appear dark on the image). At reservoir conditions, the mud will typically have a resistivity between 0.01 ohmm and 0.1 ohmm and the background will have a resistivity of at least a few ohmm and possibly hundreds of ohmm. In oil based mud, the situation is the opposite and open fractures can be more resistive than the background (will appear light on the image). .

Fractures that are mineralised will generally be resistive and show light colours along the facture trace on electrical images (**Figure 15.42**) while comparison between acoustic amplitude and time of flight images can

Table 15.7 Some common differences between natural fractures and drilling-induced fractures

Natural Fractures	Drilling-induced Fractures
Cross the entire borehole	Tensile fractures only exist in the section of the borehole wall under tension
Often highly irregular	Generally regular
Penetrate the entire formation	Only exist near the borehole wall
Geometrically unrelated to the borehole and do not run along it	Geometrically related to the borehole and may run continuously along the borehole
Unrelated to present day stresses (no relationship to breakout if present)	Oriented in relation to the present day stress field (and breakout if present)
Do not change with time	Change with time (may heal, may increase)
Exist in core	Do not exist in core
Can be cemented	Never cemented, always open
Can produce flow (in or out)	Never flow into the well (can cause mud-loss, ie. flow out)

suggest an open, as opposed to a mineralised, fracture. Open fractures will have an image on both acoustic logs (**Figures 15.41**). Mineralised fractures, however, may only appear on the amplitude image, mineralisation generally having a high acoustic impedance (Taylor 1991), while on the time of flight, being closed, they will not be seen (**Table 15.7**). However, according to comparisons with core, only a limited percentage of fractures are seen on the images. In one comparison between core and acoustic images, the logs detected perhaps only 25% of all fractures, although possibly 50% of the larger, more important ones with apertures above 0.5 mm (0.02") (Dudley 1993). Another study, equally with acoustic images, found undersampling of fractures less than 1.0 mm (0.3") thick and the logs showing two to six times fewer fractures than the cores (Genter *et al.* 1997). These numbers should be kept in mind as, on top of this, cores are too small in volume and orientation to capture a representative sample of a fracture population.

Most interpreters will provide themselves with a set of characteristics for fracture classification, such as simply either mineralised or open, their subsequent (orientation) analysis depending on it. However, it is the initial separation of natural from drilling-induced fractures that is important and being able to identify and classify these two classes early in a study is essential. As always, it is good practice to begin with cored intervals (keeping in mind the previous paragraph) and compare fractures seen on core with the images since only natural fractures will occur on both image and core (**Figure 15.43**). Coring-induced fractures exist (Kulander *et al.*1990) but they are geometrically related to the core and will not be seen on the images. A fracture which runs along a core's length is most likely coring-induced. Drilling-induced fractures are related to borehole geometry, as explained below, and will not be seen in core (**Table 15.7**) (Lincecum *et al.* 1993).

Natural fractures exist before drilling takes place and therefore have no *a priori* geometrical relationship to the borehole. They will normally continue fully across the entire borehole circumference, will penetrate the formation and are often very irregular (i.e. **Figure 15.41**). Drilling-induced fractures, on the contrary, *do*

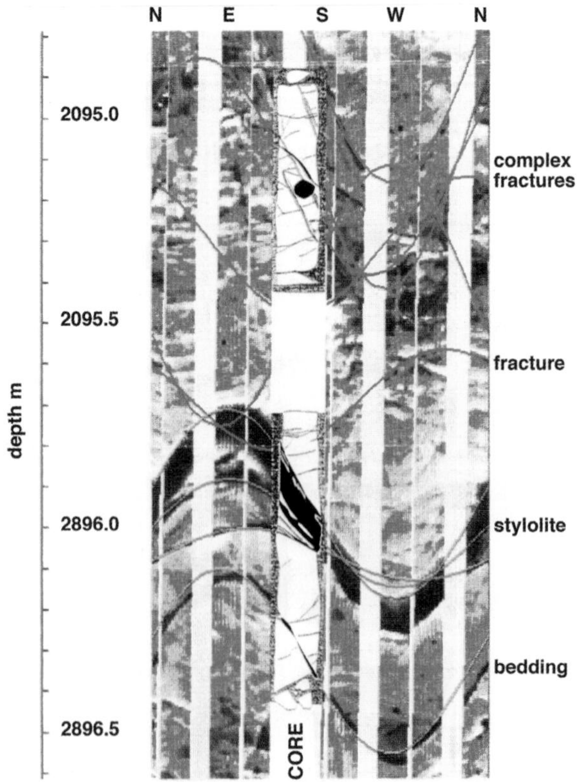

Figure 15.43 A naturally fractured chalk with stylolites seen on electrical images and in core. The many natural fractures are seen on both the core and the image: a diagnostic of natural features. 4 pad Schlumberger FMS tool, two passes.

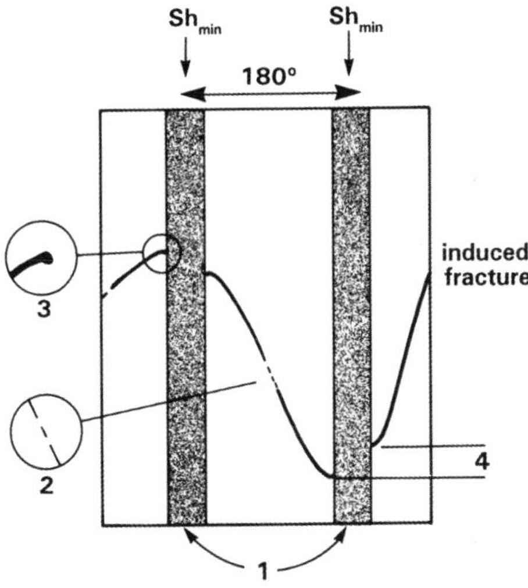

Figure 15.44 Illustration of drill-induced fracture chacteristics on acoustic images. The sinusoid represents an open, induced fracture and the dark grey, vertical stripes are breakouts. (1) Breakouts indicating the orientation of Sh_{min}. (2) Fracture strike parallel to Sh_{max}. (3) Spalling at breakout margin. (4) Offset across breakout (modified from Lincecum *et al.* 1993).

have a geometrical relationship to the borehole and also to the existing stress directions (**Table 15.7**). That is, induced, tensile fractures form parallel to the maximum horizontal stress direction (Sh_{max}) and normal to breakouts, which form in the minimum horizontal stress orientation (Sh_{min}) (*see* breakouts *below*) (**Figure 15.44**). Also, drilling-induced fractures often do not cross the entire wellbore and may only appear on a limited circumference of the borehole wall or along the borehole axis. This is because high angle, drilling-induced tensile fractures can only form where the borehole wall is in tension (**Figure 15.45**). (If natural fractures have the right orientation, they may be 'drilling-enhanced' and appear very like drilling-induced tensile fractures (Barton and Zoback 2002): they are probably natural if they fit a sinusoid). Drilling-induced fractures are never mineralised, do not penetrate the formation and do not cause bedding offset.

Modern imaging tools are able to add both a time and a spatial dimension to the investigation of fractures. The time dimension is given by the LWD images, which may be acquired during drilling and then at subsequent, later, times, and then compared to wireline images run much later. The example shows tension fractures on LWD images acquired while drilling, which are no longer there and have healed by the time the electrical wireline images were run (**Figure 15.46**). Such images show that drilling induced fractures change over time: some heal (close) (Lindsay *et al.* 2007); others get worse (Wilson *et al.* 2007). Also, the spatial distribution of fractures can be investigated with the images from a multiple depth of investigation tool such as the Schlumberger GeoVISION (Chapter 7). The images from this tool are said to be from 1″, 3″ and 5″ (2.5 cm, 7.6 cm and 12.7 cm) into the formation. Natural fractures will cross this entire field and occur on all three images, while drilling induced fractures are likely to disappear on the deeper ones.

Fracture studies with images can be combined with wireline or LWD pressure measurements, flowmeter measurements (Paillet *et al.* 1987; Paillet 1991; Paillet *et al.* 1992), temperature measurements (Davatzes and Hickman 2010) and information from production tests. It is well known in aquifer studies that most of the flow is contributed by just a few fractures. Integrating image logs with flow profiles from production logs allows the in-flow from a fracture to be related to its orientation and aperture (cf. Barton and Zoback 2002). Fractures are further considered under Section 15.8, Quantification.

Borehole breakouts

The study of images makes an important contribution to understanding reservoir geomechanics (Barton *et al.* 2009). Software now exists to model wellbore integrity from images and other data before a well is drilled, but it can also be assessed as a well is drilling. Understanding breakouts is essential to this.

Breakouts were discussed with caliper measurements (Chapter 5) but they are more thoroughly investigated using borehole images. The acoustic images are particularly useful because of their sensitivity to borehole geometry, which means they can be used to distinguish

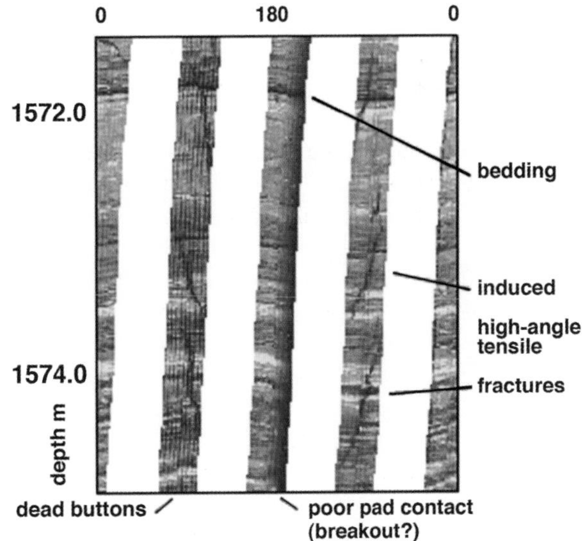

Figure 15.45 Drilling-induced tension fractures on Schlumberger FMI, wireline, electrical images. The fractures only form on the borehole wall where it is under tension and do not cross the entire circumference. The bedding is not displaced by these fractures, a characteristic of induced features (cf. Figure 15.44). Breakout is suggested by the poor images at around180°, but this may also be simply poor flap contact (*see* text).

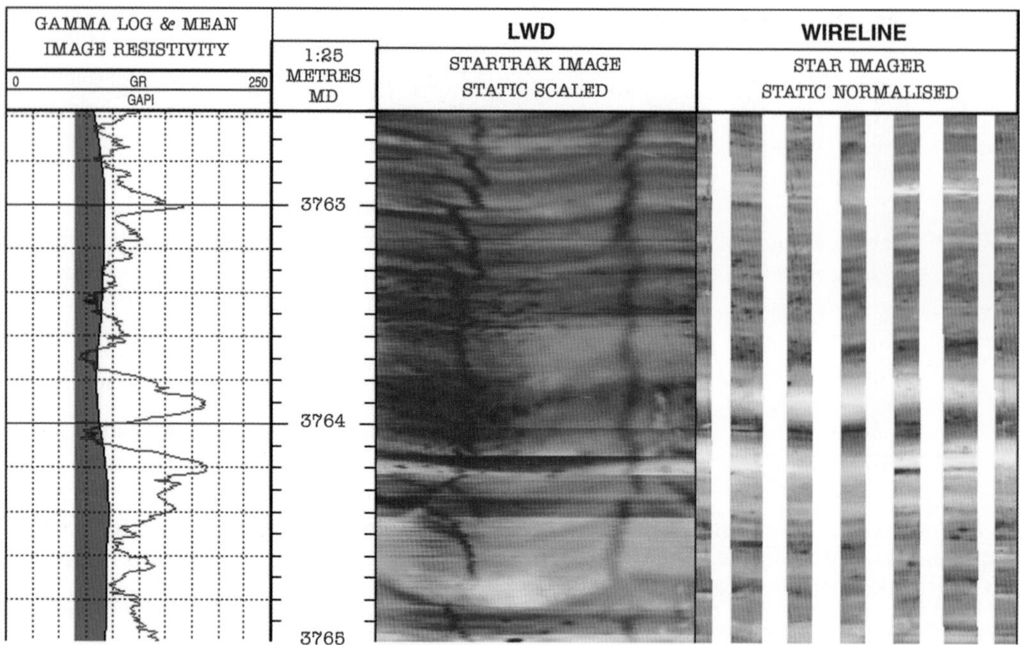

Figure 15.46 Vertical, tensile, drilling-induced fractures seen on LWD electrical images but not on subsequently run, wireline electrical images. The tensional features have 'healed' by the time the wireline images are made. Vertical well, output from Baker Hughes™ StarTrak (LWD) and Star (wireline) tools (from Lindsay *et al.* 2007).© *2007 SPE. Reproduced with permission of the copyright owner. Further reproduction prohibited without permission.*

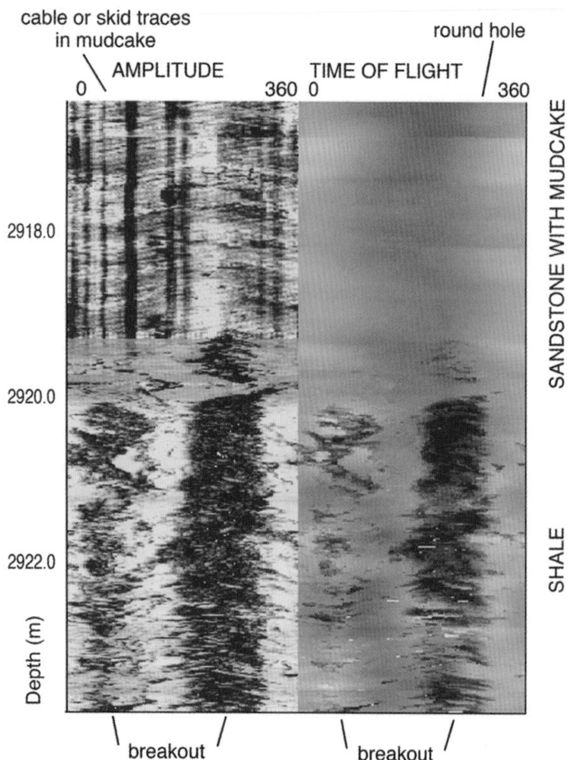

Figure 15.47 Acoustic images showing a (lower) shale interval with serious breakout and an (upper) sandstone interval with mudcake and a round borehole. The mudcake is marked by cable or tool traces. This is the same interval illustrated on the 3-D time of flight plot in Figure 15.23.

true breakout from a well that is simply ovalised. High resolution electrical images can also normally be used to recognise breakout, as can LWD density images. Breakouts are seen as hole enlargements in the minimum horizontal stress (Sh_{min}) direction and, on images, appear as vertically orientated stripes that strike in a consistent direction (**Figure 15.44**). There are always two such stripes, 180 degrees apart. On the acoustic log, the stripes (breakouts) have poor reflectivity and long travel times (**Figure 15.47**). On the electrical images, they are more subtle and appear as fuzzy, poor, more conductive images caused by the enlarged hole and poor electrical contact (**Figure 15.45**). Additionally, breakouts can be investigated in three dimensions with the acoustic or caliper images (**Figure 15.23**).

Under the caliper heading (Chapter 5), the relationship was discussed between breakouts, borehole conditions and the present day stress field. That is, breakouts develop because of limited formation rock strength: the borehole breaks under compression, breakouts forming with the direction where the compressive stress is highest, that is in the minimum far-field stress direction, Sh_{min}. These conditions tend to occur when too low a mud weight is used and in extreme situations the borehole will collapse. This is the opposite of using too high a mud weight, when the borehole dilates, tensile fractures develop and eventually there is lost circulation (**Figures 15.45, 48**). Breakout orientation, therefore, gives the far-field stress orientations but, in addition, breakout severity gives an indication of rock strength. Because of this, by using image logs (and other data), it is possible to observe the relationship between breakouts, tensile fractures and mud weight, and so assess wellbore stability and the best direction in which to drill a deviated well (**Figure 15.49**) (Barton *et al.* 2009).

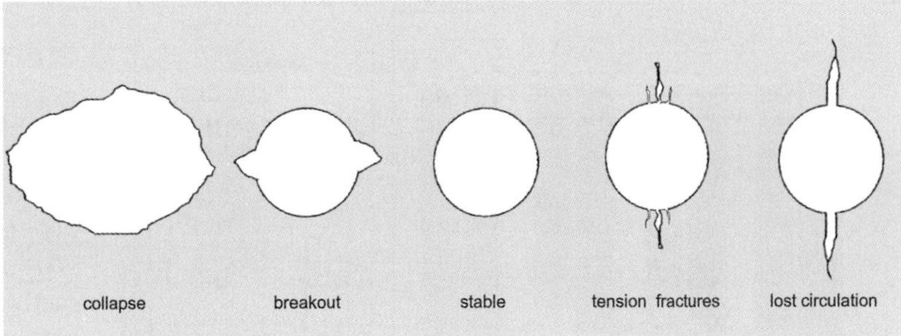

Figure 15.48 Schematic representation of modes of wellbore failure. Rocks will fail when stress is greater than strength. Mud weight can be adjusted to avoid the extreme situations which is why using LWD images to monitor wellbore behaviour is important (modified and re-drawn after Zhang *et al.* 2008).

In a vertical well, as discussed, breakouts develop in the minimum far-field stress direction (Sh_{min}). As the deviation of the well increases, this relationship is modified and, in horizontal wells, stress is dominated by gravity. In these cases breakout develops normal to gravity, along the horizontal, while tensile fractures develop vertically along the top and bottom of the borehole (cf. **Figure 15.48**).

The field of geomechanics and borehole images has now become quite sophisticated and specialist papers should be referred to (i.e. Zoback 2007).

Faults

Image logs are generally too detailed to allow the identification of faults and certainly too limited in the volume that they represent to be able to observe displacement. *Fault* is used to indicate a plane across which there is displacement whereas across a *fracture* there is none. Faults and fractures on images often cannot be separated using this criterion. The example shows three, steeply dipping surfaces which are interpreted as faults cutting low dipping shale beds even though no displacement is seen (**Figure 15.50**). The evidence for faulting is that the image 'texture' changes between the top surface (3241.5 m) and the lower surfaces (3242.5 m) and that bedding dip between the surfaces appears to change. The surfaces themselves are conductive (dark) and do not appear to be cemented or mineralised. The fault evidence is therefore indirect and illustrates the general difficulty in separating faults from fractures when actual surfaces are imaged.

Examination of any outcrop shows that actual fault planes are more chaotic the closer you get. Stand away from a fault and it is obvious; stand close (as with an image) and order disappears. Details in fault zones are very variable. Certain faults are associated with an increase in fracture intensity (Koestler and Ehrmann 1991) although, more frequently, there is a change in texture (Knott 1994) and, within faults with considerable throw, textures tend towards shear fabrics or chaotic breccias (Hurley 1994; Berg and Avery 1995). Image logs tend to be very difficult to interpret in such zones especially if several lithologies are involved (Grace *et al.* 1999). Moreover, there is a tendency for fault zones to cave (**Figure 14.37**) so that images are of poor quality.

One aid to fault investigation is to use the techniques developed for the dipmeter (Chapter 14). This involves taking frequent dip (structural) measurements and then examining dip patterns related to actual images looking for rollover or drag (Chapter 14). It is only by examining quite large formation volumes (thicknesses) that a fault may be indicated. Seismic indications of faulting can help, although faults need a significant throw to affect the seismic response and there can be a considerable depth imprecision on seismically imaged faults. In

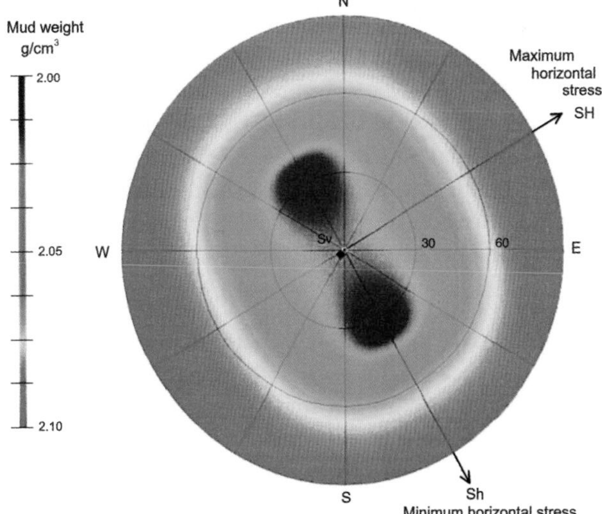

Figure 15.49 Wellbore stability behaviour predicted relative to mud weight and formation stress orientations. A vertical well falls in the centre of the circular plot, deviated wells at the various angles indicated and a horizontal well on the periphery. The required mud weight is less for a deviated well in the Sh_{min} orientation than in the SH_{max} direction but the same for any orientation of horizontal well (in this case).

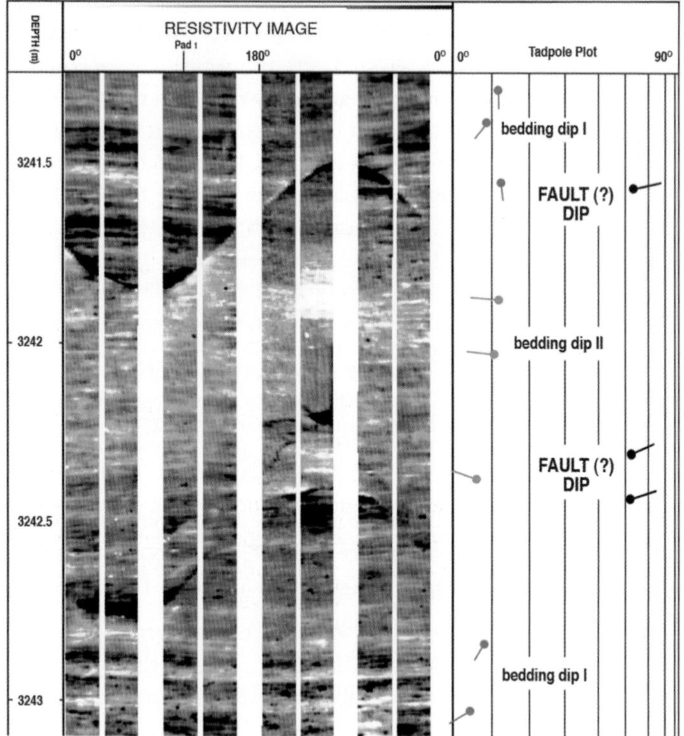

Figure 15.50 Possible minor fault on wireline, Schlumberger FMI, electrical images. A fault is suspected because image 'texture' changes across the highly dipping planes, and the bedding dip changes between the upper and lower planes. Vertical well through silt/shale lithology (dynamic image).

this respect one study, which unfortunately cannot be published, involved excellent images and a good 3-D seismic dataset. Faults had been convincingly identified on the image logs and looked fairly obvious on the 3-D seismic. The two data sets, however, did not compare at all. Definite seismic faults could not be found on the images and image log faults were not identified on the seismic. Depth uncertainties between the two datasets were not the cause and no explanation could be found (*see also* Grace *et al.* 1999).

Slumps

If definitions are to be followed strictly, then slumps are a sedimentary feature. However, following a definition for the definition's sake is an Anglo-Saxon failing. Slumps are considered here as showing a structural aspect on the images and, indirectly, the behaviour of non-linear features in general. The example (**Figure 15.51**) shows shale beds generally dipping at about 8° east, enclosing an interpreted slumped interval with picked dips of 20°–40°. However, these dips do not indicate the real structure of this slump and the feature at 2753.5m suggests there is an isoclinal hinge at this level. Dip picking on images generally assumes a planar surface across the borehole and non-planar features, as in this slump, are difficult to characterise.

15.8 Quantitative uses of electrical images: thin beds, permeability, fractures and facies

Much of the interpretation of image logs is qualitative, as has been described. But there is a need, and the possibility for quantitative methods (Serra *et al.* 1993; Sullivan and Schepel 1995; Kraaijveld and Epping 2000). There is an ongoing effort to characterise quantitatively, especially, thin beds, heterogeneous porosity, image facies, and fractures.

Quantification of these parameters often seems simply to use the multiple log nature of the image data, that is, the parameters are quantified as a series of many independent curves, and not as a 2-D image: the relationship between each curve is ignored, meaning the data are analysed as independent points and not as a pixel matrix. However, there are more interesting methods that do use the two-dimensional aspects of the data and try to analyse the images themselves. The following is only an overview and the specialist papers referenced should be consulted for algorithms and mathematical details.

Thin beds

Electrical images can be used to quantify thin beds (Trouiller *et al.* 1989; Kraaijveld and Epping 2000; Knect *et al.* 2004). The fine resolution of the electrical images allows beds down to at least 5 cm (2") to be accurately evaluated and, although they can be detected down to 1.0 cm (0.4") or so, thinner than 2.5 cm (1"), bed thicknesses are exaggerated (figures for the FMI, Pezard *et al.* 1992). Quantitative evaluation is typically in terms of just two lithologies, generally sand and shale, or reservoir and non-reservoir (the rest), and a conductivity threshold is used to identify one lithology or the other (Luthi 2000). The approach needs calibration to core and is aided by UV light photos (Passey *et al.* 2006). Thin-bedded turbidites lend themselves to analysis by this method since they are dominantly just the two lithologies, either sand (reservoir) or shale (non-reservoir). If core is available, reservoir can be estimated from UV photographs: if it fluoresces, it contains hydrocarbons and is reservoir. So, with this technique, what is reservoir is sand and what is not is shale. Threshold processing, even when the threshold is varied, makes it relatively easy to quantify the vertical thickness of each lithology (or reservoir and non-reservoir), above or below the (variable) threshold (Knecht *et al.* 2004) and the reservoir geologist can be given an image-based net to gross (N/G) (**Figure 15.52**) (Passey *et al.* 2006). Clearly, this method only works so long as image colours (i.e. the threshold) in a reservoir are constant. Changes

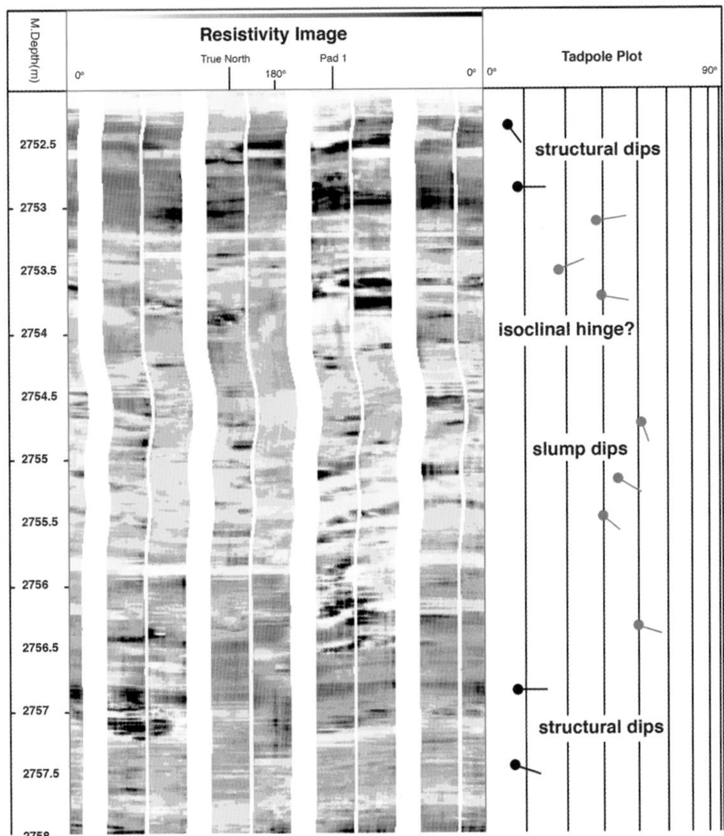

Figure 15.51 Slump or bedding disturbance in marly shales. The beds picked show moderate to high dips (red) but the structure is not properly described by these dips and its exact geometry is not clear. Beds above and below the slump have normal dips (black). Schlumberger wireline, electrical FMI images (static image).

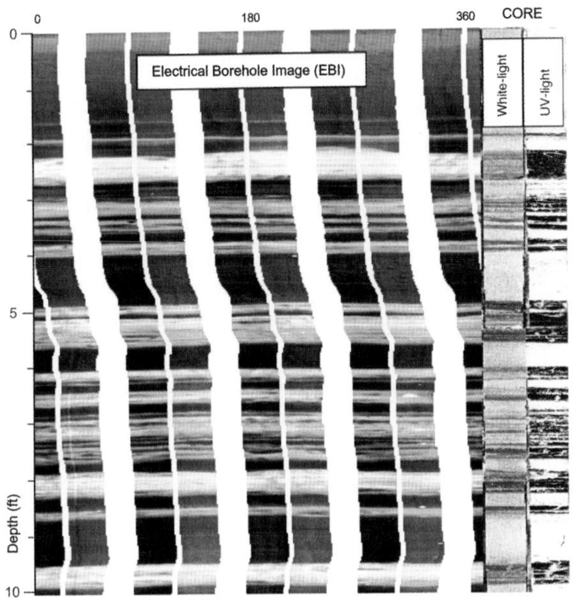

Figure 15.52 Thin beds from wireline electrical images compared to threshold plotted core photographs. From such plots a detailed net to gross can be calculated (from Passey *et al.* 2006). AAPG© (2006) *reprinted by permission of the AAPG whose permission is required for further use.*

in water saturation or changes in lithology will affect it. Moreover the tendency for current to be drawn into the more conductive beds and away from the resistive ones, will result in sand-shale ratios being distorted (*see* Section 15.4, Artefacts). The error will increase as the average bed thickness falls (**Figure 15.28**). Net to gross numbers (N/G) based on electrical image logs should not be considered as reliable unless they have been calibrated with a lot of core.

Porosity and permeability

Heterogeneous, vuggy carbonates have dual porosity systems (vug porosity and matrix porosity), which cannot be evaluated by standard density and neutron porosity logs which make a single trace,1-D representation of the formation. Wireline electrical image logs, however, have 2-D coverage and can capture the heterogeneity seen on the surface of the borehole wall.

One quantitative technique used to capture this porosity heterogeneity assumes that vugs (large pores) will be filled with mud-filtrate (water based) and therefore be conductive and have a dark image. All dark anomalies are then assumed to be vugs. Extracting the number of dark coloured, conductive pixels will thus be indicative of vug area in the borehole wall and by extrapolation, secondary porosity. Identification of the conductive pixels (actually curve values) can be achieved by a thresholding technique, when high conductivity values are extracted from each calibrated image curve (calibrated to flushed zone saturation) and graphed to represent porosity and eventually permeability (Newberry *et al.* 1996; Amer *et al.* 2009; Chitale *et al.* 2010). But note that the same problem occurs with vugs as was discussed above for thin beds. The vugs will typically appear larger than their true size because they attract the current. The calibration of image colour is based on the relationship of porosity to the ratio of mud filtrate resistivity to flushed zone resistivity (i.e. R_{mf}/R_{xo}), and requires a number of assumptions (Newberry *et al.* 1996 *op. cit.*). The method does not use the 2-D shape of the vugs although, in some cases, gives better results than attempted 2-D methods (Xu 2010).

An approach which does respect the two-dimensional character of the image logs is used by Delhomme (Delhomme 1992). Conductive, dark patches (vugs) are identified, digitally outlined on the images and extracted as 2-D objects. The statistics of these objects (vugs), such as area percentage, size distribution and so on, can then be extracted and eventually related to porosity. Interestingly, the methodology can be applied to core photos as well as log images. There are many difficulties with this method from resolution to calibration (Delhomme 1992 *op. cit.*) but it is significant that it uses the unique, 2-D characteristics of the log images. Recognition of image objects, familiar in any image processing, is also recommended by Hall (Hall *et al.* 1996) although there does not seem to have been a practical outcome.

These methods of 2-D analysis, like those using 1-D thresholds, rely quite heavily on there being only two colour objects: objects being characterised and everything else. For instance, only vugs can be dark in the method described and any conductive objects, such as a shale clast or pyrite nodule, will be mis-identified as a vug. The two methods described are effectively 1-D and 2-D thresholding. However, 2-D analysis leading to predictions in 3-D is the direction image quantification should take.

Attempts have also been made to quantify permeability from electrical images, generally by using a transform from image based porosity derived as just described. Empirical comparisons between core measured permeability and images show that, under the right circumstances, permeability can potentially be estimated from the electrical images. A comparison using mini-permeameter measurements on a core slab produced identifiable images (Bourke *et al.* 1993). Electrical images of core slabs seemed to show the same thing (Jackson *et al.* 1992). However, attempts to derive a quantitative permeability from images does not yet seem to have gained general support, even though it is frequently tried (Newberry *et al.* 1996, Amer *et al.* 2009; Chitale *et al.* 2010; Xu 2010).

Fractures

Fractures are ultimately discrete features, but two quantities that can be used to describe them are number per unit depth (density) and aperture. Together these determine their flow potential. However, it has become increasingly evident that the most reliable indicator of fracture permeability and potential flow is their orientation relative to the stress field. This has a bigger influence than either abundance or even size.

One of the easiest fracture characteristics to measure is their number along a certain depth/length of well (fracture density) (Standen *et al.* 1993). Core studies suggest that acoustic image fracture density (number) is a lot less than core density (Dudley 1993; Davatzes and Hickman 2010) although studies in the Monterey Formation (California) showed that fracture counts (density) on electrical images correlated well with indications of flow (Sullivan and Schepel 1995). Recent work in the Barnett Shale of Texas shows that joints and fractures

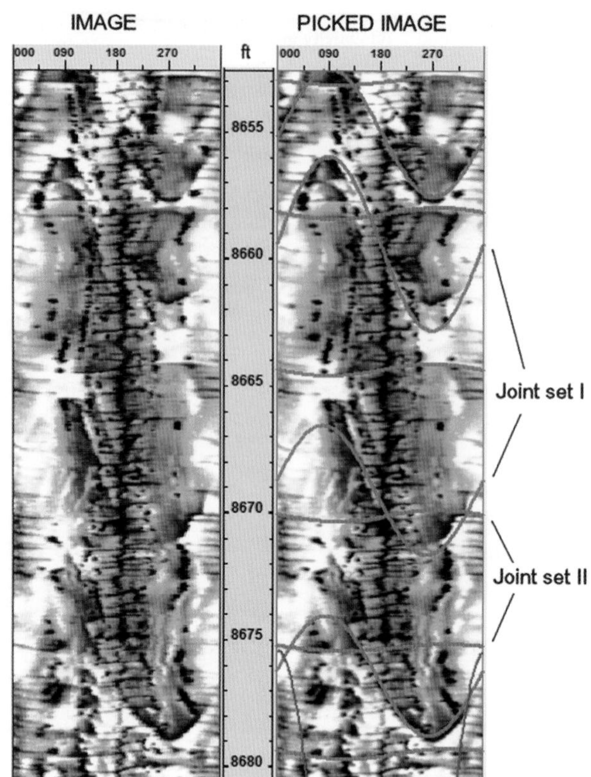

Figure 15.53 Barnett Shale, high angle fractures/joints seen in a horizontal well by LWD electrical images from the Baker Hughes™ INTEQ, StarTrak™ tool. Both fracture/joint sets are high angle but with different strikes, hence the different sinusoids in the horizontal well path image (from Stamm *et al.* SPWLA 2007).

are well characterised on electrical images, both wireline and LWD (**Figure 15.53**), but that fracture frequency is a function of well orientation relative to fracture orientation (Stamm *et al.* 2007). For example, a vertical well will consistently under-estimate vertical joints and fractures, while a horizontal well will under-estimate vertical fractures approximately parallel to the well path. Fracture counts, therefore, can depend more on well orientation than imaging tool capabilities. Moreover, fracture number is not now considered critical to fracture permeability.

Determining the open fracture width or aperture of a fracture has been attempted using acoustic images (Paillet *et al.* 1985) or electrical images (Luthi and Souhaité 1990). The results have been mixed, and electrical and acoustic results often not in agreement, either for reasons of tool design or, more generally, differences in what is being measured geophysically (Davatzes and Hickman 2010). Apart from these problems, fracture apertures tend to get enlarged during drilling, and their aspect at the borehole wall is not indicative of their behaviour deeper into the formation. This is because physical breaking by the bit and erosion by circulating mud occur. For example, highly dipping surfaces are often broken at the high and low borehole crossing points (**Figure 15.54**) (Paillet *et al.* 1985; Barton and Zoback 2002). Such breaks can be seen on the fractured carbonate example shown earlier (**Figure 15.41**). Similarly, fracture infill in the immediate vicinity of the borehole wall may be plucked out during mud circulation, so enlarging the aperture and suggesting that the fracture is open rather than cement filled. These physical changes must be kept in mind when assessing any borehole image fracture aperture study (Hornby *et al.* 1992; Luthi 2000; Davatzes and Hickman 2010).

Geomechanical studies suggest that it is the orientation of fractures in the stress field that is most indicative of flow potential (Barton and Zoback 2002; Barton *et al.* 2009). It is often assumed that all fractures are extensile (i.e. joints), are mostly vertical (to bedding) and are parallel to SH_{max} and so indicate the present stress state. However, it is found that fractures which are permeable (*i.e.* will flow), are more likely to be critically stressed, or with a potential to slip (fail in shear), and are probably sub-parallel to SH_{max} (Barton *et al.* 2009 *op. cit.*). In order to characterise and assess fractures, therefore, it is important to quantify fracture orientation but it is also essential to know the orientation and magnitudes of the present day stresses. Images can provide accurate numbers for all of these attributes.

Facies

The concept of 'image texture' is behind the attempt to quantify images in terms of rock facies (Linek *et al.* 2007). It requires image log attributes to be quantified, and methods for doing this are actively being developed. To be effective, these methods must address the revolutionary way in which image logs sample the formation: in great detail and in two dimensions. Extensions or refinements of methods used in standard, 1-D log analysis, will not do justice to the data.

To honour the two dimensional content of image data, various methods are used to quantify the relationship of the pixels to each other. For example, a scale-space technique has been used by Shell (Kraaijveld and Epping 2000), the Ocean Drilling Project uses Haralick texture features (Linek *et al.* 2006) and Schlumberger have used 'textural energy' to zone on bedding (Luthi 1993) as well as heterogeneous object delineation to identify facies in carbonates (Wang *et al.* 2008).

Core information can be used as input to these methods at various levels, generally quite early on in the processing, to ensure that they are meaningful. If the method is supervised, for instance, a cored interval is identified as belonging to 'facies x'. The image log is then sampled over 'facies x' and image attributes extracted (cf. Linek *et al.* 2006). 'Facies a, b....' etc are then subjected to the same process. The image has now been reduced to a series of reproducible, digital attributes, any number of which may be used to identify the corresponding core defined facies. The effort, therefore, is to distil the huge amount of image data down to a few, reproducible and geologically meaningful divisions, automatically and these will be digitally image defined facies.

Modern image processing concepts adapt themselves well to analysing borehole images and some of the concepts mentioned above come from such work. However, the particular format of borehole images, especially wireline electrical images which have many vertical strips without data, means that typical image processing routines must be adapted for the subsurface. A recent effort has been made by Thomas (Thomas 2011) who found that facies could be identified using a programme designed originally for medical work. Facies are first identified on core. The images from two or more small areas of each core defined facies are then chosen for 'seeding', and characterised by user defined, object oriented, mathematically defined attributes, such as colour, shape, relatedness, homogeneity and so on. The mathematically defined 'seeds' from the small areas are then propagated through larger core calibrated image areas to confirm that they are indeed discriminating the intended facies. From this calibration, a protocol can be constructed and applied to the entire image, cored and un-cored, for an automatic, mathematically based, repeatable facies identification (**Figure 15.55**). With this method, the initial identification of facies by an expert can be mathematically

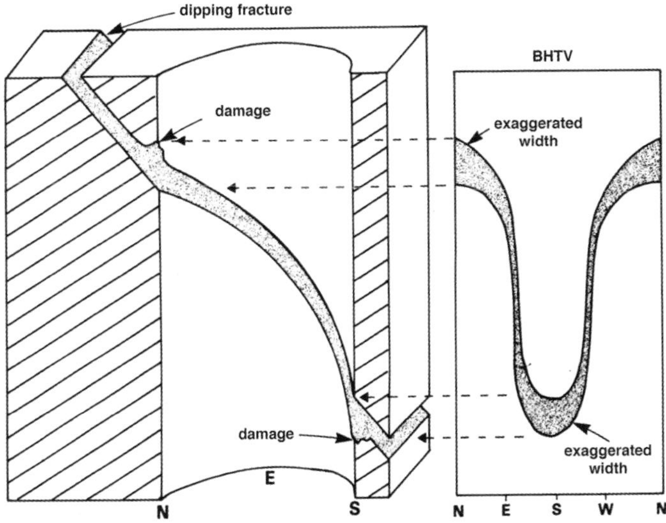

Figure 15.54 Typical characteristics of an open fracture seen on an acoustic image log. The fracture width becomes exaggerated at certain points around the borehole wall (entry and exit points) as a result of breakage and drilling damage (re-drawn from Paillet *et al.* 1985) (cf.Figure 15.41).

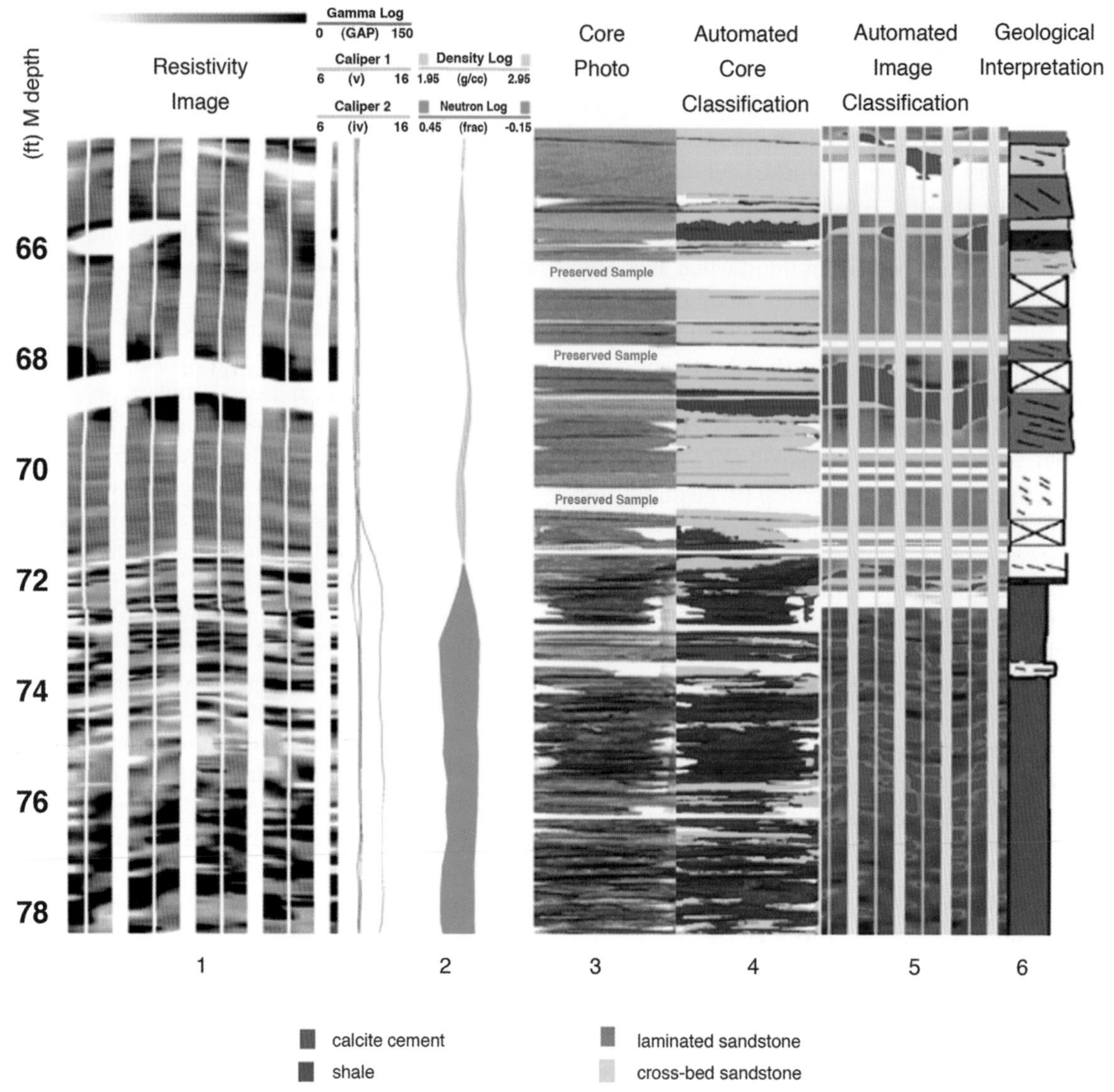

Figure 15.55 Illustration of automated image facies classification. Track 1, FMI image: Track 2, gamma ray, density and neutron wireline logs: Track 3, digital core photos: Track 4, automated core photo classification: Track 5, automated image facies classification: Track 6, geological interpretation of core (from Thomas 2011).

captured and objectively and rapidly applied to large volumes of images. Manual methods are expensive, long and expert intensive.

15.9 What next?

Using image logs of all types is routine, and they are now run for reasons as various as geosteering, pressure test location, fracture analysis and sedimentary characterisation of the reservoir. This means that image interpretation is required while the well is drilling (geosteering), while it is being completed (to choose pressure points) and post-drilling (fracture analysis and sedimentology).

Apart from the inevitable improvement in tool technology, which competition ensures is ongoing, there is a significant need for geologists to become more familiar with the characteristics and uses and limitations of image logs, and for the experts to develop better analysis techniques. Familiarisation is clearly necessary when one reservoir engineer asked "If it is yellow, does that mean it is sand?". And cheap, automatic interpretation routines need to be developed that are quick and moderately accurate, in order to cope with the great volume of LWD images being acquired. Post-drilling work can still be done manually by experts who can devote time to the work, but their results need to be able to be integrated with a wider data set and be produced on a timescale that allows them to have some influence. Einstein's quote that 'everything should be reduced to its simplest form and no further' applies as much to image log interpretation as cosmology!

16 FACIES, SEQUENCES AND DEPOSITIONAL ENVIRONMENTS FROM LOGS

16.1 Introduction

Geological disciplines do not use the full potential of geophysical logs. If logs are considered as surrogate outcrops, the amount of data in oil company records and government agency archives is absolutely enormous. It has a global reach, and much of it is available at the touch of a computer button. This chapter hopes to show how logs can be used in analysing for facies, environments, sequences and other geological tasks. Chapter 12 describes the use of logs to construct lithology. This chapter takes that geology a step further.

Siliciclastic sediments are at the origin of the methods discussed here in some detail. Their application to carbonate sediments cannot be applied wholeheartedly.

16.2 Facies

Gamma ray log shapes

A basic scheme to classify sand bodies in the Gulf Coast area of the USA, apparently developed by Shell (cf. Serra and Sulpice 1975), was based on the shape of the SP log along with its mirror image (sometimes), the resistivity log. The principal shapes observed were the bell, the funnel and the cylinder (**Figure 16.1**). The scheme was intended to give a classification of log shapes in order to aid correlation: it was essentially a geometrical approach. However, rather than just recognising and classifying shapes, an attempt should be made to understand why the shapes exist.

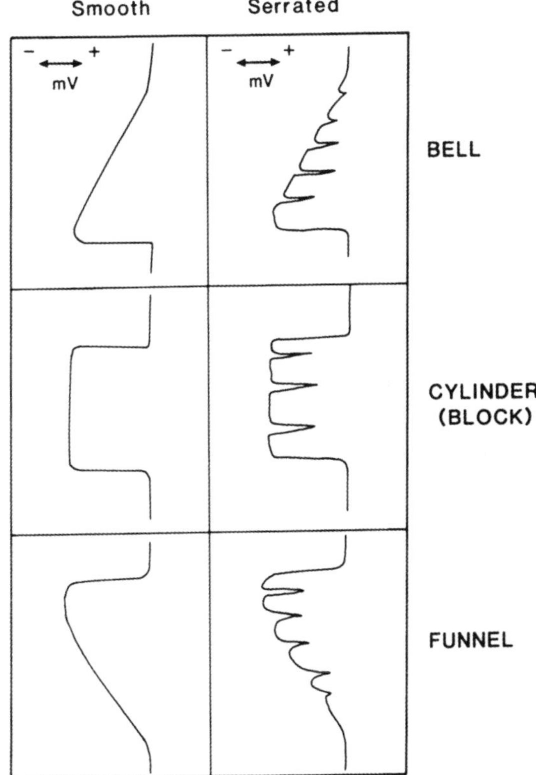

Figure 16.1 Log shape classification. The basic geometrical shapes and description used to analyse SP and gamma ray log shapes.

Although the SP was at the origin of the interest in log shapes, it is the gamma ray log that is generally used today: the curve gives a greater variety of shapes, shows greater definition and has more 'character'. To explain a log shape, the log response itself must be understood. Since the gamma ray log is *frequently* an indicator of clay (mineral) content (but by no means always – *see* Chapter 8, *and below*), gamma ray log shapes can be explained in terms of variations in clay (mineral) content. A bell-shaped log (**Figure 16.1**), where the gamma ray value increases regularly upwards from a minimum value, should indicate increasing clay content; a funnel shape, with the log value decreasing regularly upwards, should show the reverse, a decrease in clay content.

A core cut through a Triassic fluviatile sand body in the Sahara (**Figure 16.2**) shows a typical bell shape on the gamma ray log response (Serra and Sulpice 1975). The increase in gamma radiation corresponds to an increase in clay (mineral) content regularly upwards. The increase in clay content is correlated to a decrease in the grain size. A sedimentological analysis of the core shows a set of sedimentary structures typical of fluviatile point bar deposits (Serra and Sulpice 1975 *op. cit.). The* bell shape, therefore, can be interpreted as indicative of a fining-upwards, channel sandstone (in this case). A second example shows gamma ray funnel shapes with the corresponding, core-derived sedimentology (**Figure 16.3**). Each funnel shape represents a siliciclastic succession which coarsens upwards from bioturbated, offshore muds to silts to bioturbated, shallow marine sands capped by root beds and coals. The successions are

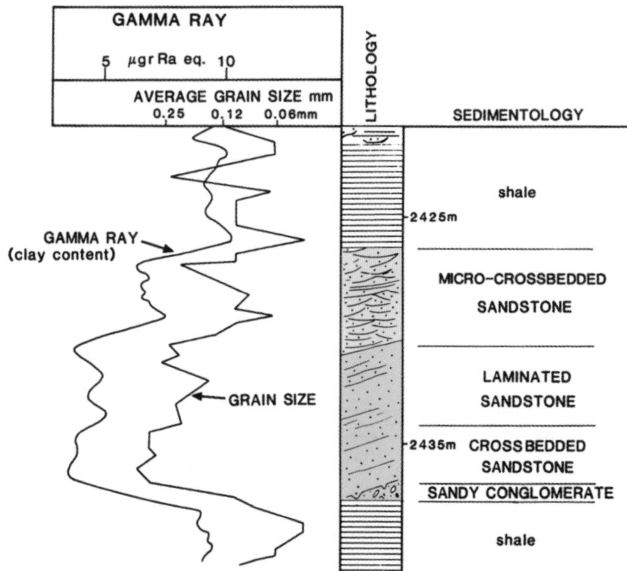

Figure 16.2 Sedimentology of a bell shape. A core cut through a sand body, with a typical bell shape on the gamma ray log, shows it to be a fluviatile channel. Note the close correspondence between the gamma ray (giving clay content) and grain size. Triassic, Sahara (re-drawn from Serra and Sulpice 1975).

interpreted to have been deposited in prograding, estuarine shorelines. The funnel shape is therefore indicative of coarsening-up, prograding siliciclastic successions (in this case).

These examples show the close relationship possible between the gamma ray log and grain size in siliciclastic sediments. Shapes on the gamma ray log can be interpreted as grain size trends and, by sedimentological association, as facies successions. A decrease in gamma ray values will indicate an increase in grain size: fine grain sizes will correspond to higher gamma ray values (**Figure 16.4**). The sedimentological implication of this relationship leads to a direct correlation between facies and log shape, not just for the bell shape and funnel shape as described above, but for a whole variety of shapes.

Numerous publications show the log shapes expected or found in various siliciclalstic facies (Krueger 1968; Galloway 1968; Fisher 1969; Forts 1969; Pirson 1970; Goetz *et al.* 1977; Coleman and Prior 1982; Galloway and Hobday 1983; Vail and Wornardt 1990; Van Wagoner *et* al. 1990; Cant 1992). They all depend on the relationship between log shape and grain-size trends in sandstone bodies. A bell shape indicates a fining-up succession, which may be an alluvial/fluvial channel but also a transgressive shelf sand. A funnel shape is a coarsening-up succession which may be a deltaic progradation or a shallow marine progradation (**Figure 16.5**). The analogies may even be extended to deep sea deposits. In these cases, the log shapes are those of overall successions rather than individual bodies (Parker 1977; Richards and Bowman 1998). The shapes come from the diminution in bed thickness associated with diminution in grain size, rather than the direct change in grain size itself. However, the principles are similar (**Figure 16.5**).

Once established, the log shape system can be used in a number of ways. Maps made of the geographical distribution of log shapes are effectively both facies distribution and palaeogeographic maps (Saitta and Visher 1968; Doveton 1986; Finley and Tyler 1986; Cant 1992). Once an interval is reliably identified, then the variations in log shape within that interval give an indication of facies variations and hence, an indication of palaeogeography (**Figure 16.6**). More recently, log shapes have been used as a tool for sequence stratigraphy (Van Wagoner *et al.* 1990), with variations in log shape (generally gamma ray), indicating parasequences (**Figure 16.7**) and parasequence stacking patterns at a very minimum (*see* Chapter 17). Indeed, often a heavy reliance is put upon log shapes.

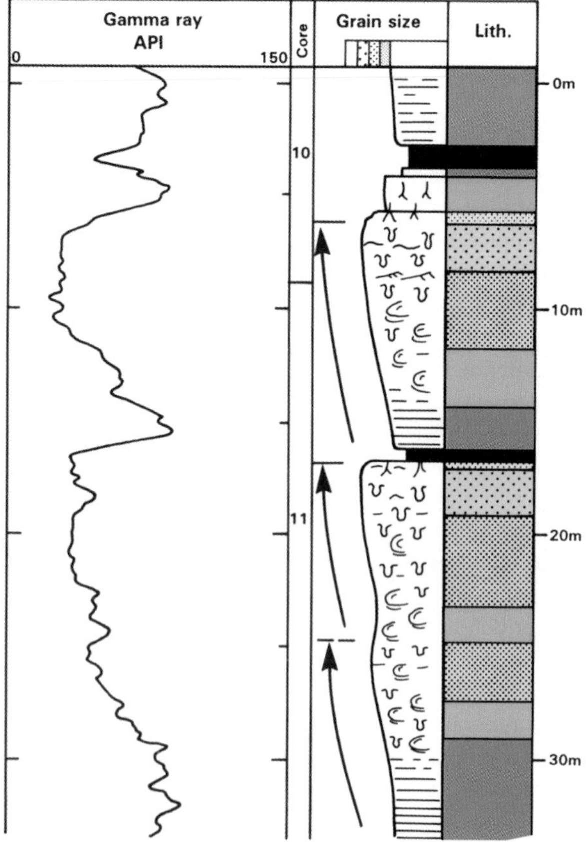

Figure 16.3 Funnel shapes on the gamma ray log corresponding to coarsening-upwards sequences, interpreted to have been deposited in prograding, estuarine shorelines. The gamma ray shapes in this example are characteristic.

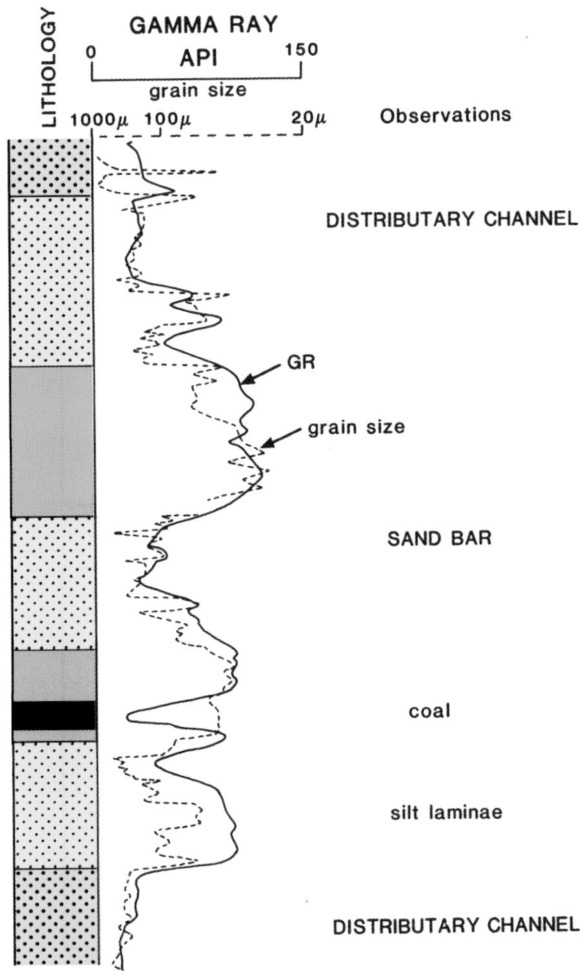

Figure 16.4 Grain size – gamma ray correlation: a very close relationship is possible between the two (modified from Simon-Brygoo 1980).

However, from a sedimentological viewpoint, relating a particular log shape to a particular facies, even in siliciclastic sediments, should not be done (Cant 1992): there are too many overlaps of different facies giving similar shapes. But the questions which arise from a logging view are more fundamental. Is there a consistent reason why log shapes exist and do they signify what is claimed of them? The reliability of using log shapes as an indication of grain size and, ultimately, facies information is examined below.

The gamma ray - grain size relationship: a critical examination

The gamma ray log does not vary because of changes in grain size: it varies (often) because of changes in clay (mineral) content (the same is true for the SP). However, sedimentological interpretations based on gamma ray log shapes require the log to vary with grain size. This involves undeclared assumptions: gamma ray variations are related to clay volume changes; clay volume changes are related to grain size differences. These two assumed relationships will be examined.

First of all, the gamma ray relationship to clay volume. This has been discussed previously (Sections 8.6, 8.8). It was pointed out that care must be taken in using the gamma ray to indicate clay volume because clay (rock) radioactivity is not constant and depends on the clay mineral and other mineral mix. More importantly, there are naturally radioactive minerals in the sand-sized grain fraction in siliciclastic sediments (Rider 1990). For example, in terms of clay formations, radioactivity varies significantly with stratigraphy (**Figure 12.19**), especially if organic matter is involved. In the coarser fraction, sands which contain potassium feldspars have a natural (potassium) radioactivity. Clean, heavy mineral bearing sands show a high radioactivity (**Figure 8.26**) and the gamma ray log variations reflect the distribution of heavy minerals, not clay. Other radioactive grains include micas, glauconite, feldspars and rock fragments in general, all of which will disturb gamma ray log shape interpretation. These variations in grain type are normal and are the basis of the often used classification of sands devised by Folk (1954), which shows quartz (nonradioactive), feldspars (radioactive) and rock fragments (frequently radioactive), as the compositional elements, which vary independently against clay content which gives the textural element (**Figure 16.8**).

Secondly, the relationship between clay volume and grain size. There is no doubt that in siliciclastic sediments, a grain size/clay content relationship exists (i.e. **Figures 16.2, 16.3**). However, it is by no means a constant one. The textural analysis in the example (**Figure 16.9**) is of two sandstones, one an alluvial molasse showing a consistent relationship between grain size and clay content, and the other a well-winnowed, marine sandstone with no relationship at all (Pettijohn *et al.* 1972). Using the gamma ray log itself, and comparing it to grain size fractions over cored intervals, brings out similar relationships (**Figure 16.10**): in sandstones where clay content varies with grain size, so do the gamma ray values (**Figure 16.10,b**); in others, there is no relationship (**Figure 16.10,a**). A good grain size to clay relationship is frequently seen in deltaic and fluvial environments, where deposition is largely controlled by flowing current energy. In open marine environments, changes in grain size often do not involve changes in clay content, at least changes that are significant enough to affect the gamma ray (**Figure 16.11**). In turbidites, grain size variations are seldom seen on the gamma ray (e.g. Shanmugam *et al.* 1995), only bed thickness changes and, as beautifully demonstrated by Slatt in outcrop studies (Slatt *et al.* 1992), interpreting the gamma ray response in terms of bed thickness/grain size trends can be very misleading (**Figure 16.12**). The clay volume-grain size relationship, therefore, is sufficiently common in siliciclastic sediments to be thought universal, but when detailed data are available, the evidence shows this is

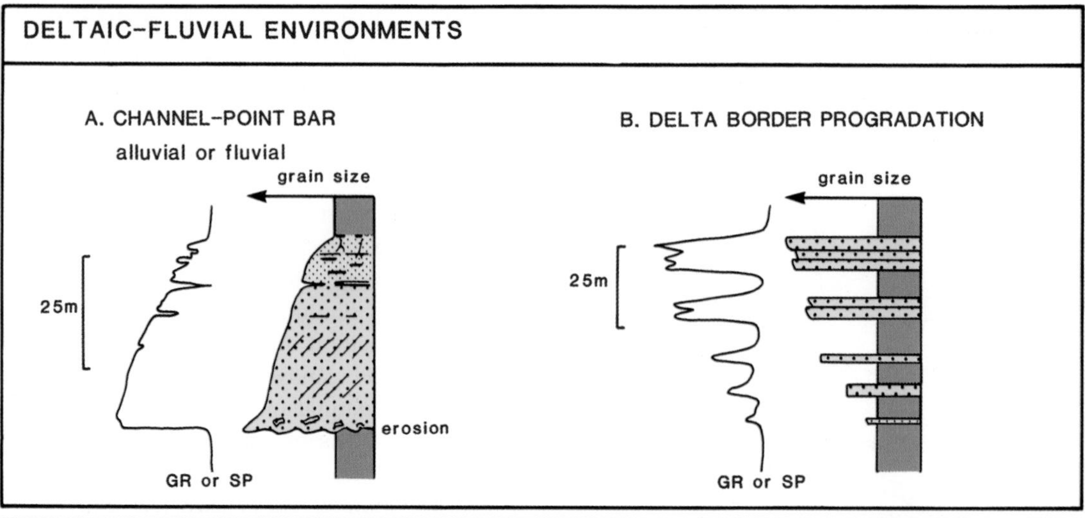

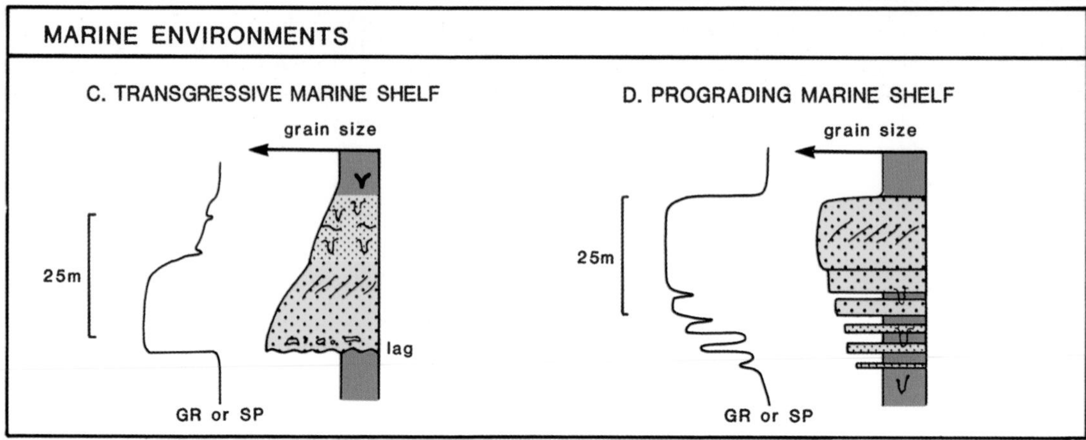

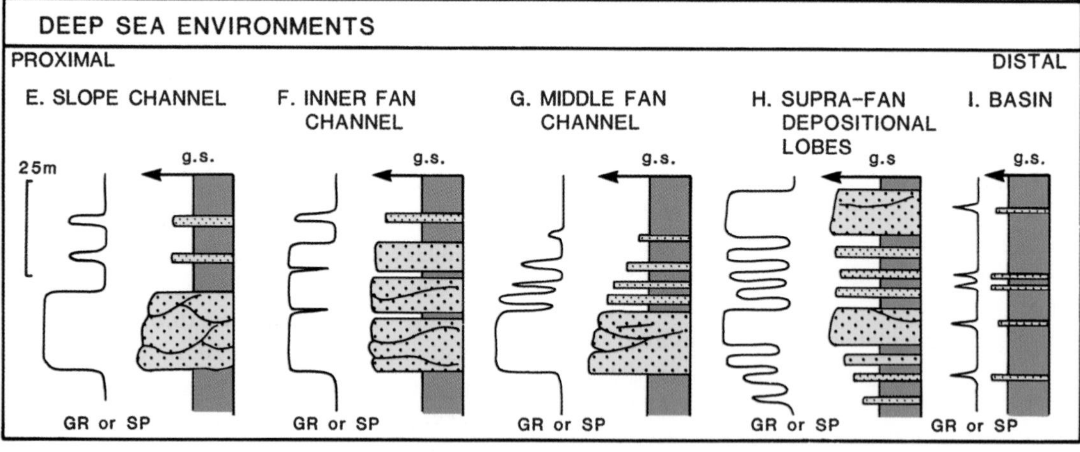

Figure 16.5 Facies indications from gamma ray (or SP) log shapes. These are idealized examples both of log shape and sedimentologic facies (modified from Serra 1972; Parker 1977; Galloway and Hobday 1983).

not the case. In carbonate sediments, facies and gamma ray log do not generally correspond, as will be described (Section 16.4).

In conclusion, the attractive idea that log shapes indicate depositional environments is too simplistic. Neither the relationship between gamma ray value and clay volume, nor the relationship between clay volume and grain size are consistent, as they should be if the shape of the gamma ray log is to be used as a universally applicable grain size indicator. However, core to log comparisons indicate that these relationships are *frequently* consistent enough in siliciclastics for log shapes to be useful grain size indicators, although care must be taken using them. The next section describes a quite different, more thoughtful and very effective way of geologically analysing logs, principally in siliciclastic sediments.

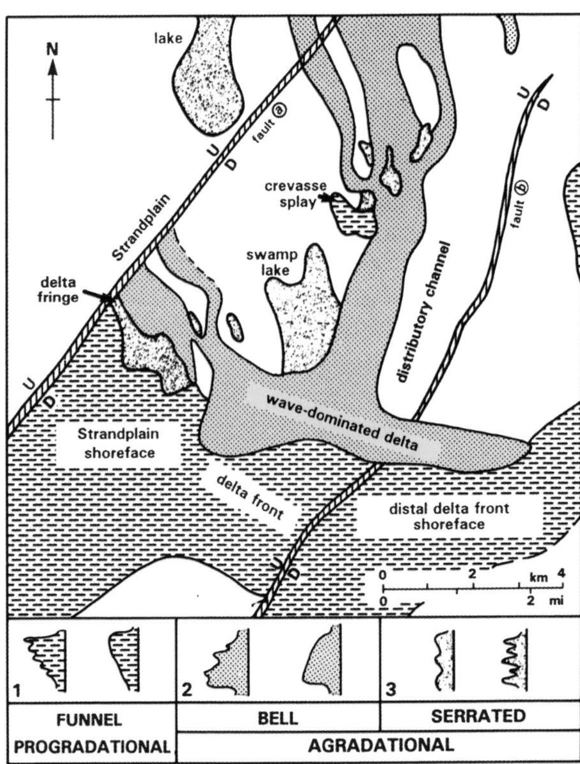

Figure 16.6 A palaeogeographic reconstruction based on SP log shapes in a deltaic environment, the Cayce sandstone (modified from Finley and Tyler 1986).

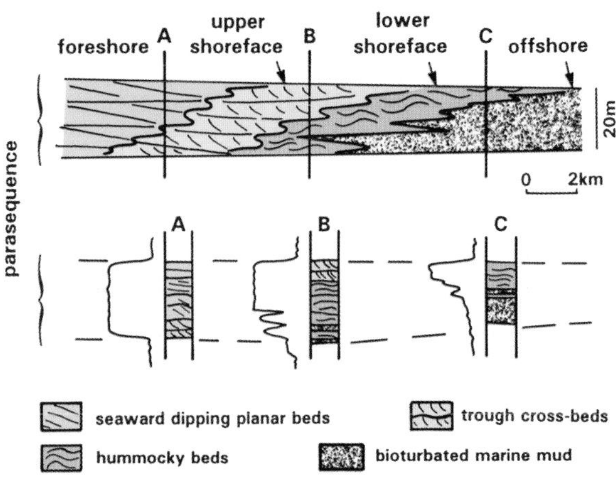

Figure 16.7 The gamma ray log used to show facies differences in a sequence stratigraphic analysis (from Van Wagoner *et al.* 1990).

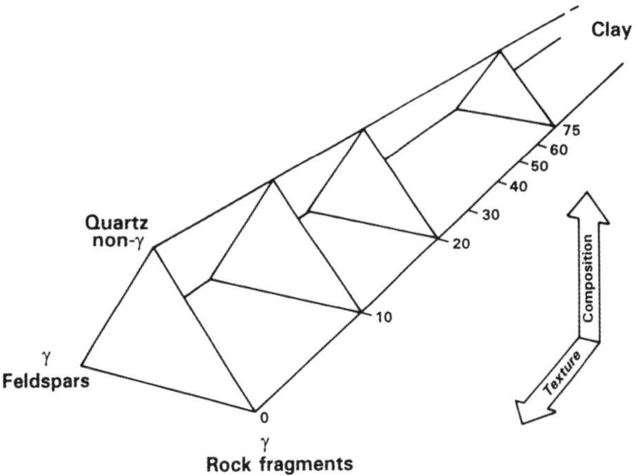

Figure 16.8 The Folk classification of sedimentary rocks. It is based on separate variations in composition and texture. Composition is defined by quartz (nonradioactive), feldspar (radioactive) and rock fragments (often radioactive). Texture concerns the variation between the elements of composition and clay (after Folk, 1954).

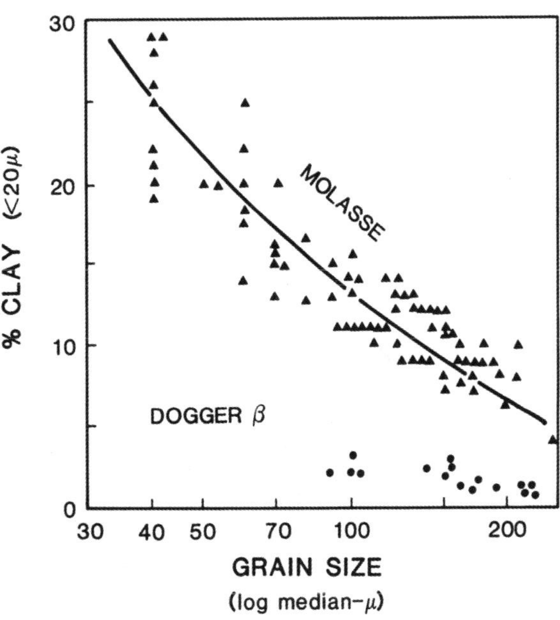

Figure 16.9 Textural analysis of the clay – grain size relationship. Clay content compared to grain size for an alluvial sandstone (the Molasse) and a marine sandstone (Dogger ß) (From Pettijohn *et al.* 1972, modified from Fuchtbauer 1964).

16.3 'Log-based sequence (Electrosequence) analysis': a tool for sedimentological and stratigraphic interpretation

The concept

This section describes a system for the identification and analysis of log-based sequences or electrosequences. (Rider 1986). An electrosequence is: *an interval defined on wireline logs, through which there are consistent or consistently changing log responses and characteristics, sufficiently distinctive to separate it from other electrosequences.* It will typically be tens of metres thick and corresponds to the sedimentologically identified succession of facies (i.e. a cycle). The objective of an electrosequence analysis is to extract from the logs as much geological information as possible, by identifying vertically continuous,

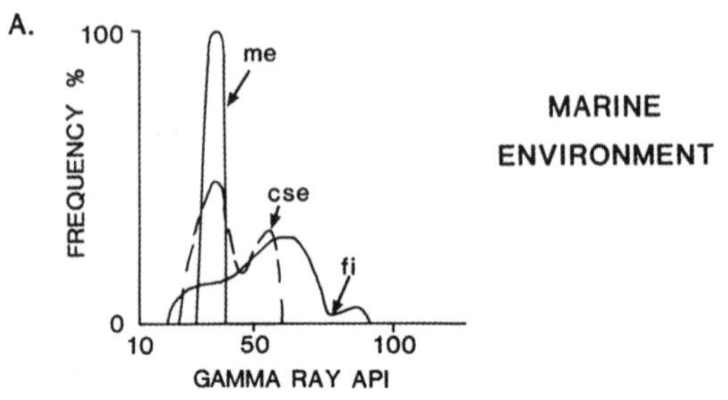

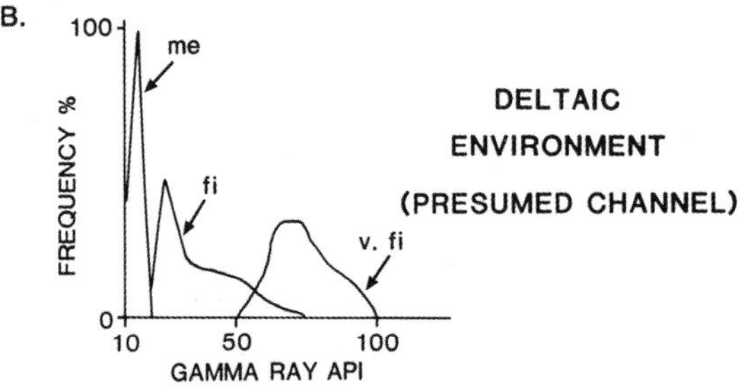

Figure 16.10 Gamma ray value correlated with grain-size classes. A. The marine sandstone shows similar gamma ray API values for different grain size classes, i.e. there is overlap. B. The deltaic sandstone shows excellent separation of classes. Average grain sizes from thin sections: cse = coarse, me = medium, fi = fine, v.fi = very fine (from Simon-Brygoo 1980).

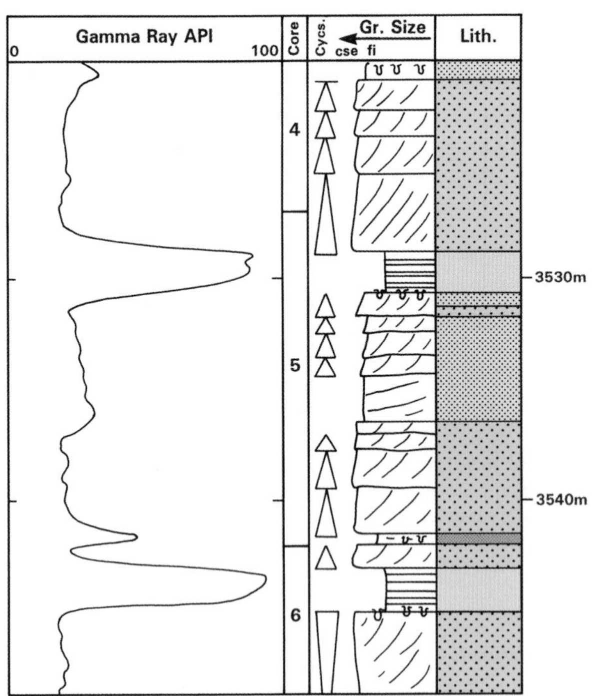

Figure 16.11 Gamma ray *not* showing grain size variations. Core analysis shows considerable variation from fine to coarse grain sizes within the sands. Because clay is not involved, grain size changes are not seen on the gamma ray. Cross-bedded sands from an open marine environment.

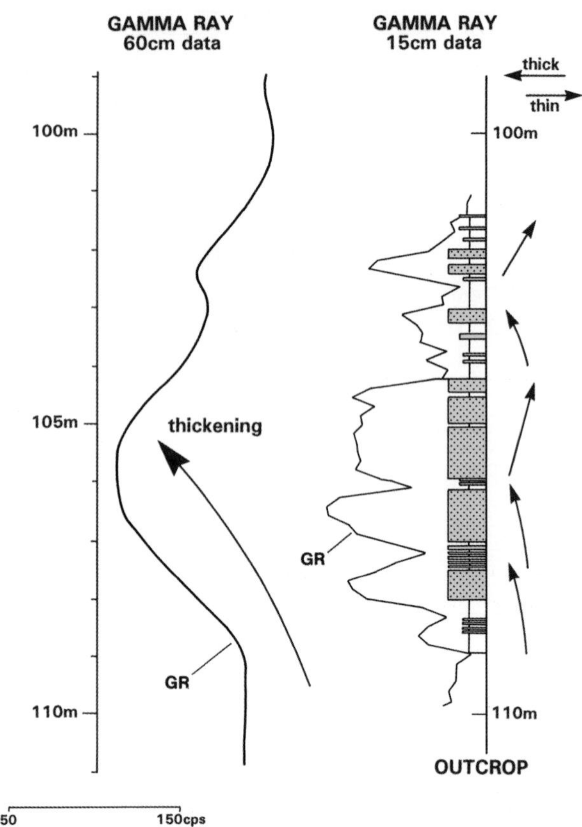

Figure 16.12 Outcrop analysis showing errors that may be made by interpreting grain size trends using the gamma ray log. The thickening-up trend interpretable from the 60 cm gamma ray data (typical of subsurface sensitivity), in reality corresponds to a complex series of smaller scale sequences, to some extent shown by the 15 cm data (modified from Slatt *et al.* 1992).

depositional, stratigraphic and eventually sequence stratigraphic units.

The study of log shapes described in the previous section has two major shortcomings: only one log is considered, and only sand bodies are involved. 'Electrosequence Analysis', by contrast, avoids these shortcomings and uses *all* the available logs, much other data, and covers *all* the well, not just the sand bodies and reservoirs. It is, above all, a *systematic* approach to log sequence interpretation, and was developed by Elf in France (Serra 1972, 1973; Serra and Sulpice 1975). The senior author has subsequently simplified the system and modified some of the sedimentological and stratigraphic principles to suit modern attitudes. These modifications have come out of both practice and discussions with oil industry colleagues and feed-back from many industrial courses. Throughout, the system has shown itself to be simple to apply, adaptable and capable of bringing out a great deal of geologically significant information. It also forms a base for an eventual sequence stratigraphic analysis (Chapter 17).

The first principle of the system is that reservoirs and

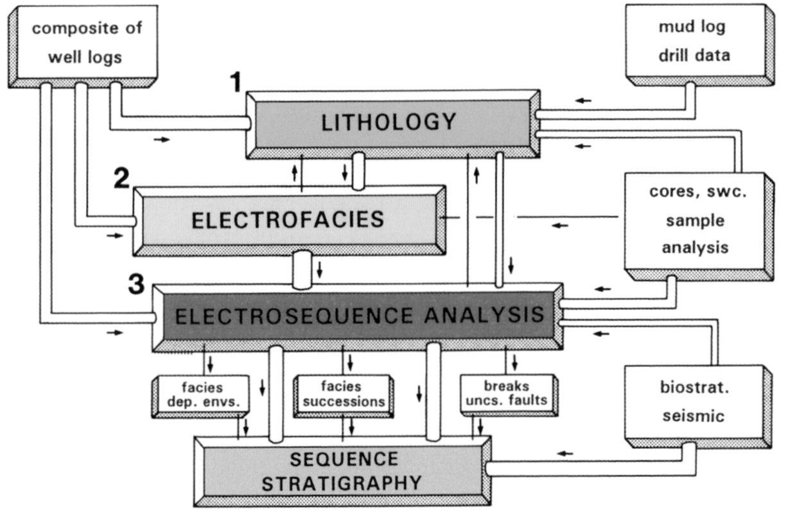

Figure 16.13 Flow chart for an electrosequence analysis. Numbers refer to interpretation steps discussed in the text.

non-reservoirs are equally important: geology is not restricted to reservoirs. In a sand-shale sequence, for example, the environmental information contained in the fine-grained, non-reservoir intervals equals, or even exceeds, that in the reservoir zones. The second principle is that no one log can characterise a formation: each logging tool examines the same formation but from different aspects, and all are equally characteristic (**Figure 16.13**).

The essential steps for a proper electrosequence analysis are laid out below in moderate detail. A house is built from the foundations upwards: the roof comes last. Electrosequence analysis must follow a route of construction. An interpretation for facies, depositional environment or sequence stratigraphy comes last: a lithological interpretation comes first (**Figure 16.13**).

Step 1: Interpretation of lithology

The electrosequence analysis is undertaken using all the standard well logs. The document on which the actual annotation is done will be a hardcopy at a summary scale (1:500) since no software exists for the moment for on-screen annotation. The log set used will be the same as that used for the manual lithological interpretation, namely calipers, gamma ray, SP, resistivity, density, neutron and sonic taken from the final, edited database. This dataset should include the detailed lithological interpretation, using the methods previously discussed in Chapter 12. This lithological interpretation will have come from an examination of both log- and drill-derived data (**Figure 16.13**) and is an essential and fundamental first step.

Step 2: Electrofacies definition and annotation

Once the lithology is established, the logs can be examined for characteristics seen on the traces which may or may not have geological significance. These characteristics, *baselines, trends, shapes, abrupt breaks and anomalies,* will be discussed individually below. Together, they make up what is called (*in this book at least) an 'electrofacies', which can be defined as: *a suite of wireline log responses and characteristics sufficiently distinctive to be able to be separated from other electrofacies.* Facies, and lithofacies in the usual geological sense have a similar significance, but are generally not identical to electrofacies.

The principal objective of an electrofacies annotation is to prepare the log set for an eventual interpretation for whatever geological information can be obtained, such as log sequence, depositional environment or facies. For example, an interval may be interpreted lithologically as entirely shale: an electrofacies annotation will bring out the fact that there are two distinct types of shale within this interval and that biostratigraphy indicates that they are, in fact, separated by an unconformity. There is much more in the logs than just lithological information, and the electrofacies annotation will show this.

The annotation should be done in a somewhat 'unthinking' manner. That is, an immediate explanation should not be sought for the annotations that are being marked: the explanation, if one is possible, is intended to be extracted in the final interpretation when all the information has been amassed. Also, because the annotation is on a hardcopy, it is a job for coloured pencils: dashes, dots and symbols are not enough. Although this is a 'low tech' approach, it is highly effective. Chapter 17 describes the use of more 'high tech' methods.

The annotations that should be marked on the logs are described below in a logical order of simple first to more and more complex.

Baselines. A baseline is a vertically constant log value. It has both lithological and stratigraphic significance. The name may perhaps be misleading as baseline in the present context is considered rather as a 'base value', or even 'average' value, which is constant vertically for at least some tens of metres but possibly up to hun-

**Electrofacies* is sometimes used to mean a purely numerical set of log responses which characterise a formation (Luthi 2001). In this book the meaning is broadened beyond the purely numerical but is still only based on log characteristics. It is considered to have a similar significance (but is not identical) to facies and lithofacies.

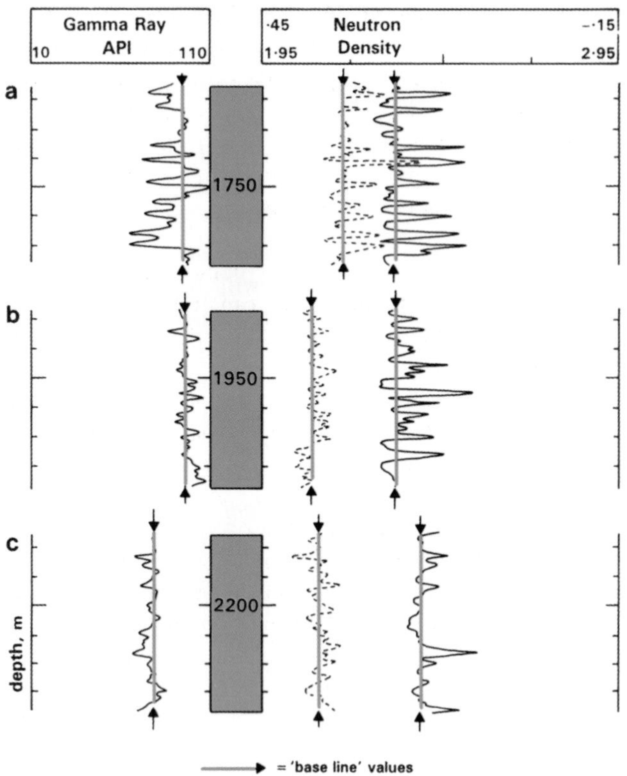

Figure 16.14 Baselines on the gamma ray, neutron and density logs in three shale sections of the same well. The baseline values of each log are indicated by the arrows. Some values are similar between sections but, in combination, the intervals are clearly different; the shales have different composition and texture.

dreds of metres. Gamma ray baselines are described in Chapter 8 as an aid to lithological interpretation (**Figure 8.19**), high average values (high baseline) indicating clean shale and low baseline values indicating clean sand (i.e. the sand and shale lines). However, this technique implies and requires that neither the shales nor the sands change characteristics vertically. In stratigraphic terms, the consistent log responses indicate that they are from the same formation. When the formation changes, baselines change.

Baselines, or base values, can be used with all logs, not just the gamma ray, so that if any log shows vertically constant values, it suggests that either the lithologies are constant and/or there is no change of formation. The example shows sections of three shale intervals from one well, each over 50 m thick (**Figure 16.14**). Although some baselines are similar from one interval to the next, for instance, the gamma ray baseline is similar in the top and middle intervals, the *combination* of baseline values for each interval is quite distinct. Each shale has a different composition and texture, which may affect one log more than another. In short, each comes from a different stratigraphic formation; each has a different electrofacies.

A baseline is marked on a log with a ruler as a constant value – for as long as it is constant. In the analysis for log based sequences, it is the changes which become significant: they will require a geological explanation. Baselines are marked in green.

Trend lines. A log trend is a persistent change in a log value over a certain thickness, either increase or decrease. Trends may be over one metre, when they are related to beds and bed junctions, tens of metres, when they are most likely to be related to cycles or sequences, or over hundreds of metres when they are related to large structures, compaction or basin filling. Trends over small thicknesses may occur within longer trends as higher frequency variations (**Figure 16.15**).

The trends that are chosen to be marked will vary in scale. Each change in log value over a few metres may be considered as a trend, but there is generally no geological significance in them at this scale. Trends over greater thicknesses may, however, indicate persistent changes in sedimentation, such as coarsening-up or fining-up successions. It is these that should be brought out.

In most non-systematic analyses it is trends, the movement of values vertically, that catch the eye. It was, in effect, trends that were discussed in the previous section under gamma ray log shapes. Examining any log set, it is quickly very evident that trends are not limited to the gamma ray log and occur, with varying significance, on all the logs.

Trends should be marked on each log with separate colours indicating decrease or increase *upwards* (e.g. red = increase; blue = decrease). Do not use one colour for changes to the right or left of the log grid as this will cause confusion during interpretation. For example, an increase in neutron values marked in red (indicating increase in shaliness?) deviates to the left, while an increase in gamma ray values marked in red (also indicating increase in shaliness?) deviates to the right.

Shapes. A log shape is a recognisable, but complex log pattern. Log shapes in sandstones have already been discussed (Section 16.2), such as increasing gamma ray in a fining-up sequence. However, shapes may occur in any lithology, on any log, in any form and at many scales. The form, as it exists, should be marked on the log in a distinct colour (distinct from the baseline and trend colours – say purple). It is difficult to define what is and what is not a shape to be marked. This will possibly only become evident after examining a large number of logs in the same area. Some shapes will simply be facies indicators, such as the bell and funnel shapes mentioned above. However, a selected shape should not be geometrically simple: it will probably occur in a fine-grained interval, could represent some distinct event and may

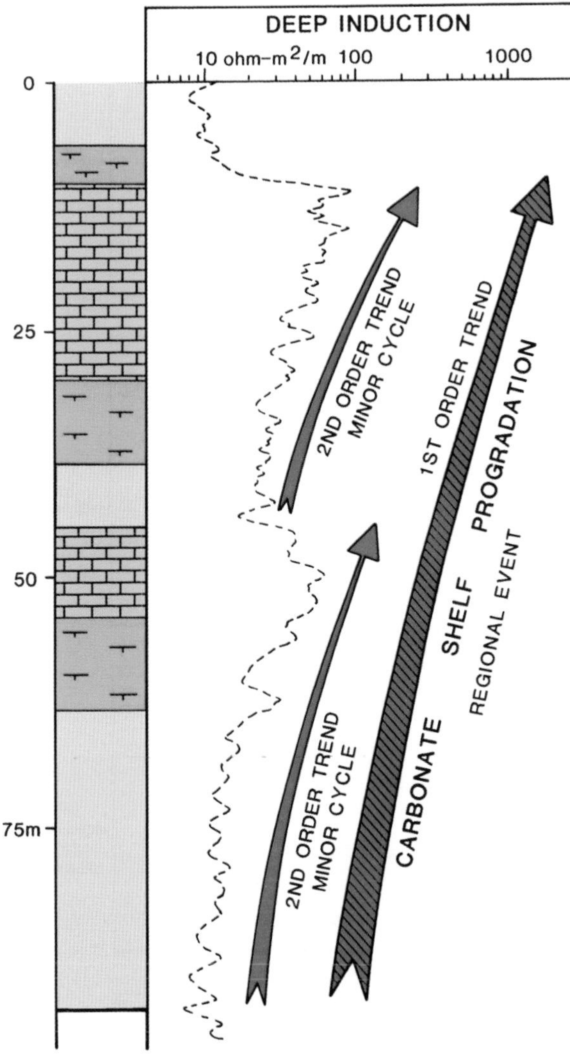

Figure 16.15 Trend lines. Large-scale, first-order log trends (on a deep induction), enclosing smaller, second-order trends, in a prograding carbonate shelf complex. Trends that increase-up in log value are coloured red. Lithology from log analysis and drill cuttings.

have basin-wide significance. The explanation for a particular shape may not be immediately evident. The example shows a complex shape on gamma ray logs, repeated in wells 30 km apart (**Figure 16.16**). It can, in fact, be recognised over a very large region and is caused by an interval of several hundred tuff beds, which record the opening of the North Atlantic.

Abrupt breaks. The recognition of abrupt breaks in a log sequence is important. They can indicate changes in lithology, structural breaks, changes in fluids or, importantly, they may indicate a break in 'depositional logic', that is, a break in the vertical 'flow' of related facies. The vertical persistence, for example, that causes a decreasing gamma ray trend (coarsening-up sequence?) implies a lateral continuity. The lateral gradation of mud to silt to sand (indicating shallowing? water) is implied from a vertically encountered decreasing gamma ray trend and continuous depositional logic. An abrupt break can interrupt this vertical sequence. In this sense, abrupt breaks are especially important in sedimentological reconstructions and sequence stratigraphic analysis.

In electrosequence analysis, an abrupt break applies to any sudden and significant change in log values. Obviously, the suddenness or rate of change will vary between tools but will normally be within the diameter of the depth of investigation of the tool concerned (Serra and Sulpice 1975). An abrupt change on the density log (vertical resolution 15–20 cm, alpha processed) will be sharper than that of the gamma ray (vertical resolution about 40 cm) (**Table 2.3**). A baseline shift may also indicate an abrupt break. Breaks can be effectively investigated using image logs when they are available, especially the more detailed electrical and acoustic images (**Figure 16.18**). Abrupt breaks may fit logically into a lithological (and depositional) pattern, such as the erosional base of a sandstone bed over shale, or they may be entirely unrelated to the lithological sequence, such as a fault or an unconformity.

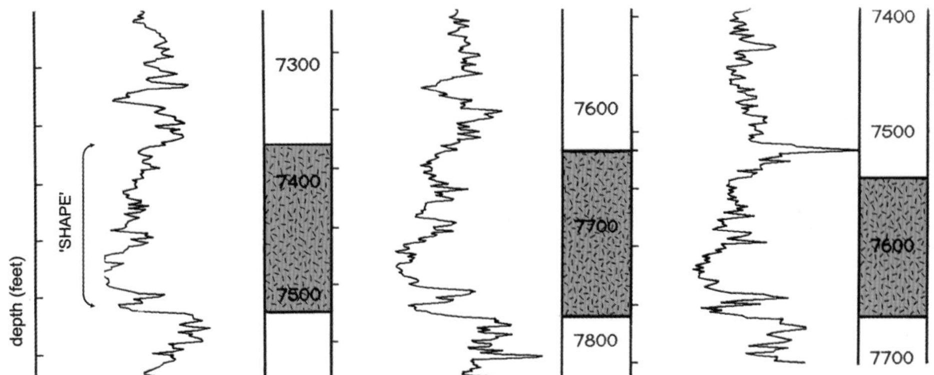

Figure 16.16 A distinctive 'shape' on gamma ray logs from wells 30 km apart. A similar 'shape' can be found over a very large area and represents a regional event. It is caused by an interval of several hundred, graded, tuff beds, deposited is deep water. They are a record of the opening of the North Atlantic. Violet = tuff zone with characteristic 'shape'.

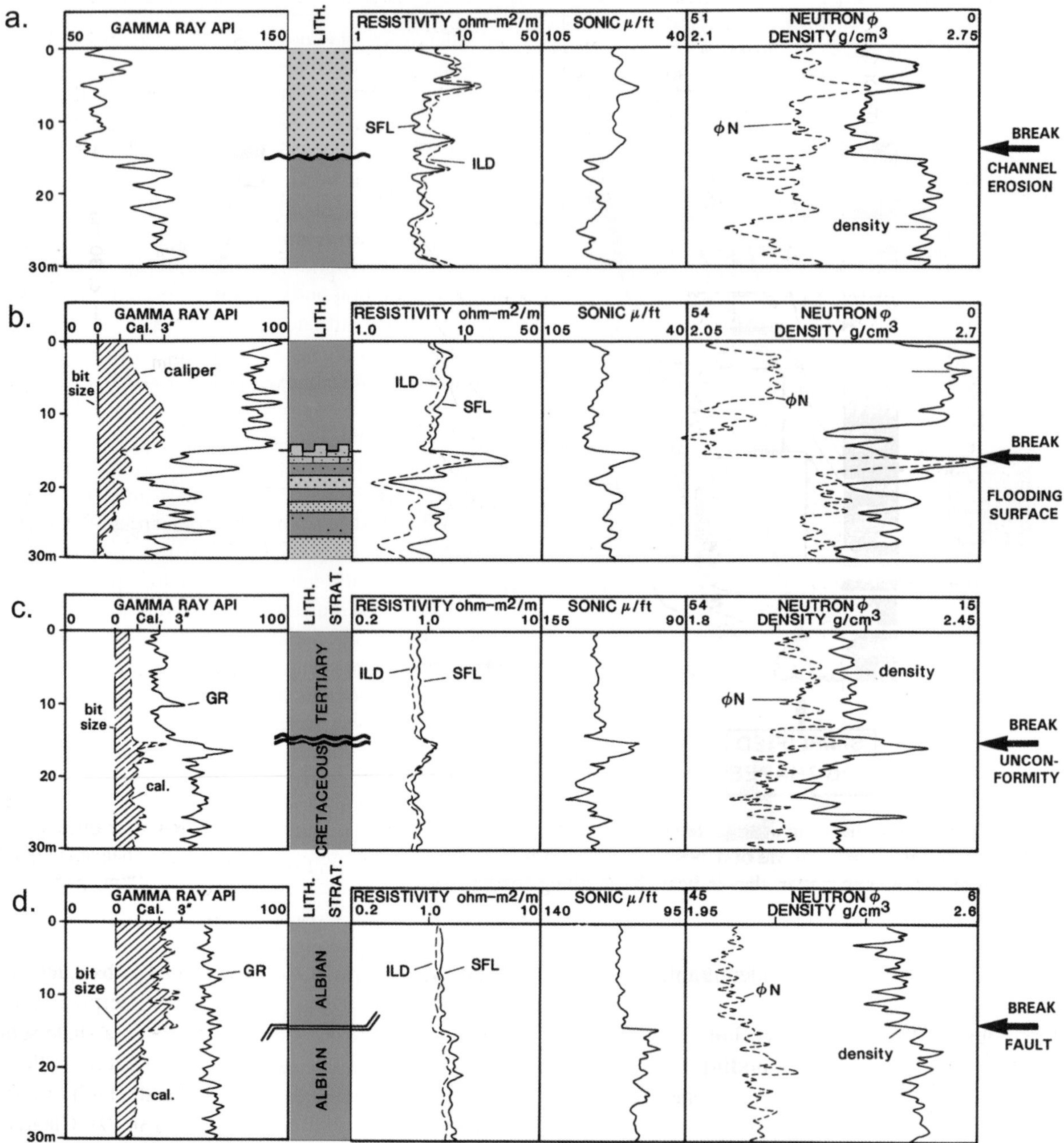

Figure 16.17 Examples of abrupt breaks. a. channel erosion, sand overlying shale; b. flooding surface, shale overlying sand; c. unconformity, shale on shale; d. fault, shale on shale.

The following abrupt breaks are identifiable:

Lithologically related breaks	*Erosion* *Flooding* (catastrophe)
Non-lithological breaks	*Unconformity* *Fault* (diagenetic change) fluids change)

(The items in brackets should be eliminated from the analysis as soon as possible as they do not contribute directly to the eventual geological interpretation).

All abrupt breaks should be marked (in pencil) on the side of the lithological interpretation, initially by a thick horizontal line. Next, an attempt is made to annotate the break by examining it with a 'geological logic'. For instance, if the abrupt log break separates a sandstone above from a shale below, this *may* be an erosional contact and can be annotated as such on the log using the appropriate symbol (**Figure 16.17,a**). If, on the contrary, the abrupt break shows a shale resting sharply on a sandstone, then erosion is unlikely and a flooding event can be proposed, again by inserting the appropriate symbol

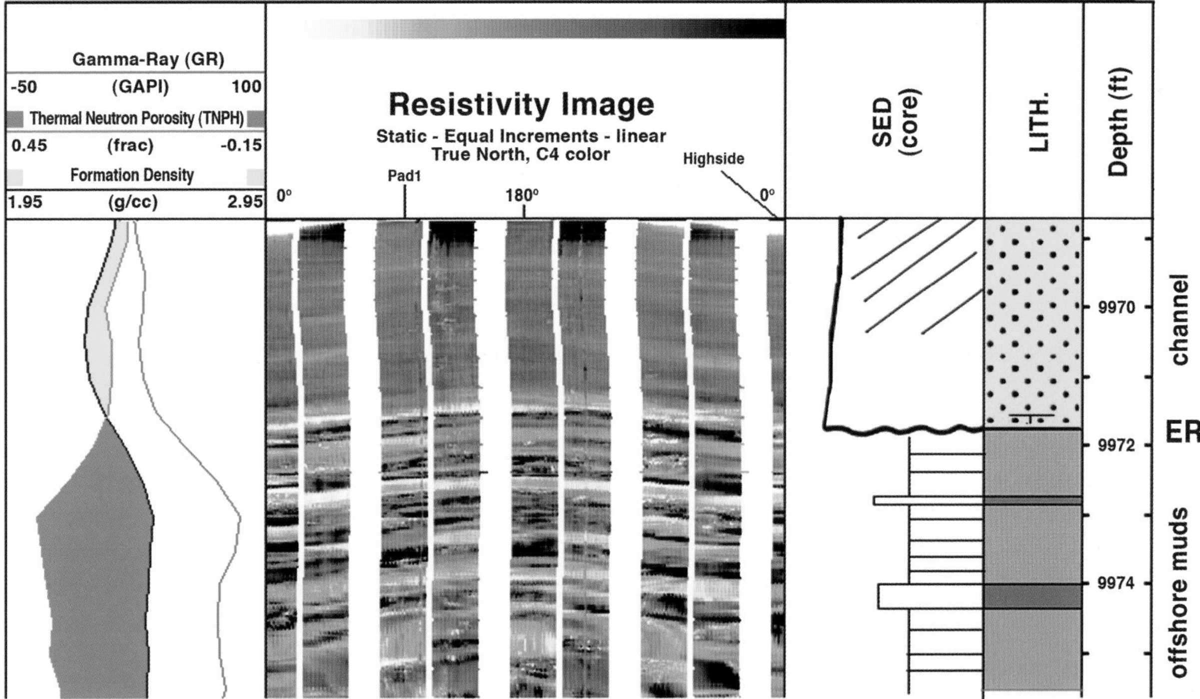

Figure 16.18 An electrical image log showing the abrupt , probably erosive, base of a channel sand, overlying offshore muds. The gamma ray, neutron and density logs are included for comparison (left track). Core based sedimentology. ER = erosion.

(**Figure 16.17,b**). These are only *reasonable propositions* and will need to be substantiated subsequently using additional data. If the lithological interpretation shows that the abrupt break is entirely within a shale sequence, shale resting on shale, then neither erosion nor flooding is an appropriate initial proposition and a fault or unconformity can be suspected (**Figure 16.17,c,d**). Clearly, more data are required to differentiate a fault from an unconformity: dipmeter and seismic possibly to substantiate the fault hypothesis; dipmeter, seismic and faunal dating to identify an unconformity. A symbol is used to indicate the possibility selected.

Many abrupt breaks will have a banal explanation and should be eliminated – simply rubbed out (hence the pencil). For instance, the limits of most coal beds are sharp, as are some diagenetic contacts. Other breaks may be more subtle and kept in for further thought, as is the case with shale on shale contacts. During the interpretation phase, the important abrupt breaks will normally come to stand out. It should, of course, be added here that, when a sequence stratigraphic interpretation is attempted, the breaks that have been marked will take on a new and quite specific significance (Chapter 17).

Anomalies. Anomalous log values are important – excessively high or excessively low peaks (values) often have important stratigraphic significance. The concentration of unusual minerals at unconformities or in hardgrounds, for instance, can create a large gamma ray peak (**Figure 16.19**), a high density value and so on. Anomalous log values are often either ignored, not identified as anomalous, or attributed with the wrong lithology. The bed involved is often thin, the unusual minerals in small quantities and the resulting lithology very complex, as indeed is the case with most hardgrounds. The example (**Figure 16.19**) shows an unconformity which spans a gap of approximately 15 Ma marked by an anomalously high gamma ray peak. The mineralogical concentrations at the unconformity are not known but quite probably include a high concentration of uranium possibly associated with phosphatic nodules (Chapter 8).

Anomalies should be annotated with an asterisk by the side of the anomalous log response.

Step 3: Analysis for log-based sequences (electrosequences) and implied facies and depositional environments

Having established a lithology and built up an annotation of electrofacies, the only remaining preparation before undertaking the final, grand interpretation is to add to the document all other relevant data such as faunal analyses and stratigraphic ages, core sedimentology, thin section information, image and/or dipmeter interpretations and so on (**Figure 16.13**). Frequently, an enormous amount of data is available which is not exploited: all should be added to the composite, annotated document.

The entire suite, lithology interpretation, electrofacies annotation, sample analyses, can now be subjected to the 'Electrosequence Analysis' from the base of the

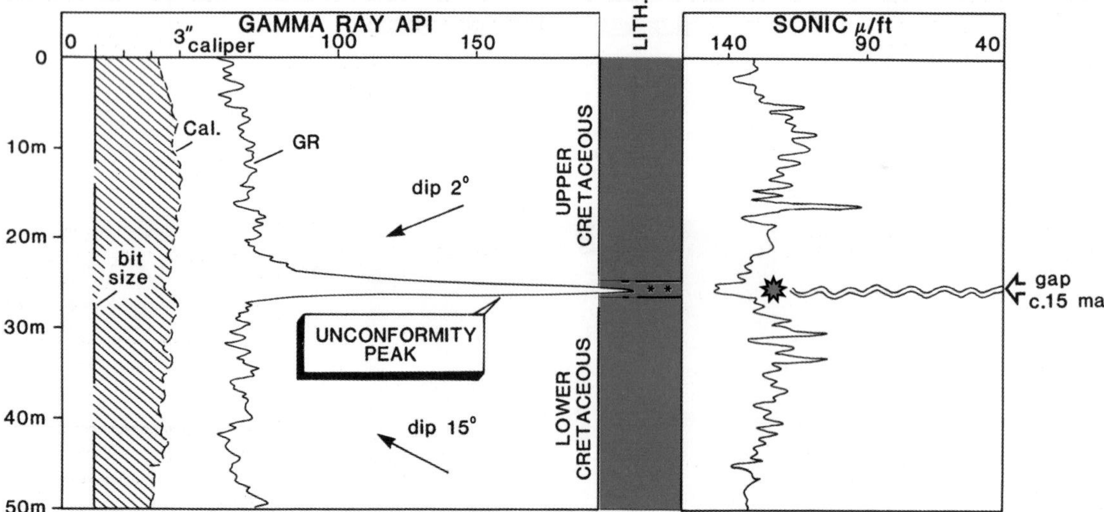

Figure 16.19 Anomalous gamma ray peak at an unconformity. The peak corresponds to gap of 15 Ma: its stratigraphic importance is evident. The radioactivity is probably due to uranium concentrated in phosphatic nodules.

well upwards. All the data are used (**Figure 16.20**). In this step, the objective is to build the succession of electrofacies into a vertical succession of log-based electrosequences, which can be interpreted in terms of *possible* depositional environments, facies, facies successions and stratigraphic breaks, faults and unconformities. These results can then be used as a database for a sequence stratigraphic analysis (Chapter 17). At this stage, some of the electrosequences could be expected to be sufficiently thick to be identifiable on the seismic.

The evidence for the construction comes from each preceding step. In the example used (**Figure 16.20**), the lithology analysis indicates a moderately thick, mainly shaly sand interval with thick shale intervals above and below. The top of the shaly sand interval is the cleanest.

The electrofacies annotation indicates log trends which show the shaly sand to have a gradational base and to be part of a typical cleaning-up succession. The top, cleanest part of the shaly sand interval appears to fine up (?) and is separated from the overlying thick shale by a major abrupt break, probably indicative of flooding and transgression. The overall cleaning-up succession can be divided into 5 smaller, equally cleaning-up successions based on smaller log trends and separated from each other by minor flooding surfaces. In general, the minor electrosequences become progressively cleaner upwards. Near or at the tops of these minor electrosequences are anomalous log responses interpreted as thin, dense, carbonate cemented horizons. One anomalous interval at the base of the section has very low density, high neutron, high interval transit time and low resistivity log values, suggesting the presence of elevated amounts of organic matter. Organic matter is confirmed by sidewall cores.

The analysis, therefore, indicates a major cleaning-up electrosequence built up from a series of smaller (minor) cleaning-up electrosequences, each separated from the next by an abrupt break and interpreted flooding surface. The minor sequences get thinner but cleaner upwards. The base of the entire electrosequence is an interval of organic rich shale, possibly a condensed sequence.

Biostratigraphic analysis of sidewall cores in the shale sections shows the presence of marine fauna throughout. The image log indicates good lamination and no large sedimentary structures. The evidence for a shallow marine, possibly tidal, prograding succession of facies and subsequent marine flooding is building up. Does this fit with the interpretation of the preceding and following electrosequences? Can an interval be identified on the seismic with a series of clinoforms?

The final interpretation should cover the entire well, although the amount of detail will vary from interval to interval, depending on both information and interest. It should propose a succession of sedimentologically coherent facies and depositional environments. The principal electrosequences and breaks should be marked and the environmental interpretations added. Depending on the significance of the breaks, the environmental logic may only continue between the major breaks, not through them. The document will now show the distinctive log-based electrosequences, stratigraphic breaks (disconformities, unconformities) and structural breaks (faults) (**Figure 16.20**). It is impossible to give details of all the reasoning that goes into constructing a document of this sort. Many geological disciplines are involved. This section simply describes the system, here called electrosequence analysis, and shows how the body of data is built up to form the interpretation tool. To use the tool, one needs not just the information from this book but experience in quite a number of other disciplines of geology and geophysics.

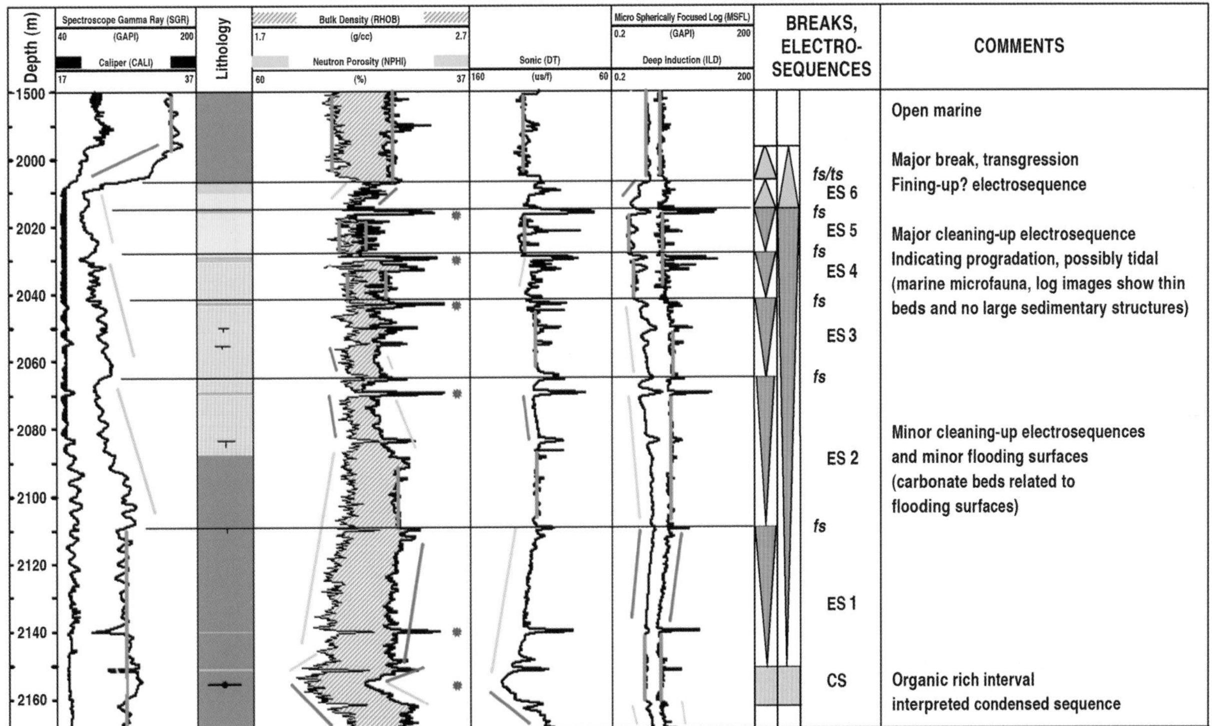

Figure 16.20 An electrosequence annotation and interpretation of a well in shallow marine, siliciclastic, probably tidal sediments. It shows a major, cleaning-up electrosequence made up of five, smaller electrosequences, which become thinner and cleaner upwards. A major break and probable transgressive event is above the major electrosequence. At its base, is an organic rich, probable condensed section. fs = flooding surface, ts = transgressive surface, ES = electrosequence CS = condensed sequence. yellow = sands, brown = silt/fine sand, green = shale. Red trend = increase-up, blue trend = decrease-up. star = anomaly.

16.4 Carbonates sediments

As suggested in Chapter 8 (gamma ray), there is often no link between the gamma ray log and carbonate facies. This is also true of other logs. This is because carbonate depositional facies are defined by their texture and this may not be linked to an unambiguous set of geophysical responses on the standard logs. That is, different carbonate textures and depositional structures can have similar standard log responses (Wang *et al.* 2008). This means that the ideas behind siliciclastic electrosequence analysis cannot be applied wholeheartedly to carbonates.

It is not the case, however, when carbonate sediments are mixed with detrital muds. In such mixtures, log responses to the detrital clay minerals will be the same as those in entirely siliciclastic sediments and a higher gamma ray will mean a higher detrital clay content (**Figure 8.19**). An upwards decreasing gamma ray trend will indicate a gradual reduction in detrital clay in favour of carbonate material. This type of succession (cleaning-up) normally indicates a decreasing water depth and increasing carbonate production, the shallow water being associated with the production of carbonate (carbonate factory) rather than a higher energy, as in siliciclastic successions (Padwellek and Aigner 2003, Borkhataria *et al.* 2006). To recognise such successions in carbonates (as in siliciclatics), the output from the spectral gamma ray tool, the CGR (Computed Gamma Ray) can be used, it being the most reliable clay indicator (Fiet and Gorin 2000, Ruppel and Jones 2006). The SGR (Standard Gamma Ray) includes uranium (as does the simple gamma ray), and the uranium content of carbonates is not a useful clay indicator (Raddadi *et al.* 2005).

Work on carbonate ramp deposits in Germany, using a combination of core, well logs, outcrop and outcrop gamma ray logs, brings out the relationships between gamma ray response and depositional facies (Aigner *et al.* 1995, Padwellek and Aigner 2003, Ruf *et al.* 2005). This work shows that the position on the ramp (that is water depth), and ultimately the facies, especially the deeper water more distal facies, is related to the ratio of carbonate content as opposed to detrital clay content, a relationship brought out by the gamma ray log (**Figure 16.21**). The higher amounts of carbonate are interpreted to indicate a greater input from where the carbonate originates in shallow water, and greater amounts of shale, which have a higher marine microfaunal content, are interpreted to indicate deeper water (Padwellek and Aigner 2003, *op. cit.*). A diminishing gamma ray trend (cleaning-up), therefore, indicates a shallowing water trend (**Figure 16.21**). The sediments in this example are considered to form symmetrical, shallowing-up and

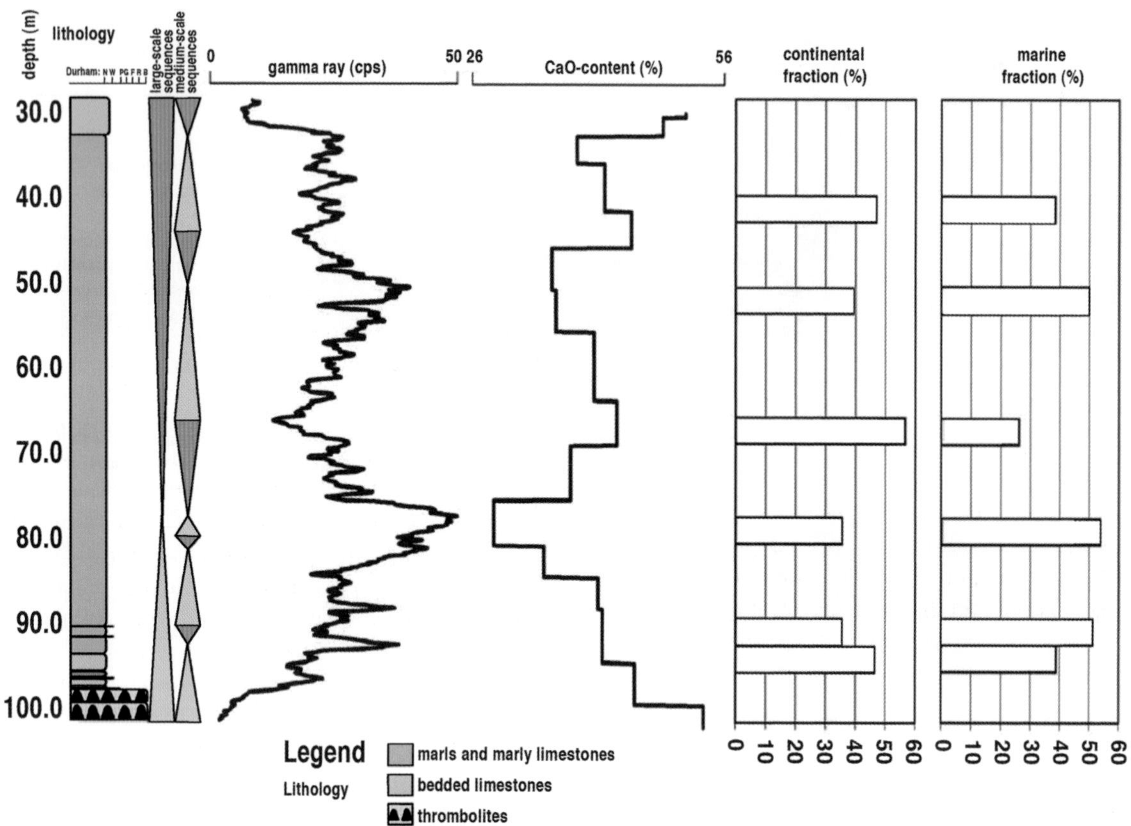

Figure 16.21 Shallowing and deepening upwards half-cycles in Upper Jurassic, ramp carbonates, shown by the gamma ray. Low gamma ray readings correspond to: high carbonate content; high continental fraction; low marine fraction; and low clay content (all indicative of shallow water). High gamma ray is the opposite and indicates a high clay content, high marine fraction, and a deeper water environment. Data from outcrop, SW Germany (modified from Padwellek and Aigner 2003).

deepening-up half cycles, each being identified by a combination of features (sedimentology, microfaunal content, log response etc.) and not limited by flooding surfaces as in the Exxon model. Limits between half-cycles are gradual, the gamma ray logs, therefore, show deepening trends (increasing values) or shallowing trends (decreasing values), separated by a 'turnaround' where values change.

Such predictable relationships do not exist when all the sediments are either carbonate or dolomite and, as suggested, there is often no relationship between log response and original depositional facies or environment of deposition. A consistent relationship between log responses and depositional facies is clearly required for an electrosequence analysis. In addition, carbonates are prone to early diagenesis when original depositional textures can be completely modified. Diagenesis can continue into the subsurface during burial, again either destroying depositional features or heavily modifying them. For example, if hypersaline fluids are available, as is often the case with arid climate carbonates, dolomitisation can take place and even the rock type can be modified (e.g. Collins *et al.* 2006, Lindsay *et al.* 2006). A lack of correlation between the original carbonate depositional features and the logs is understandable and common.

The use of logs in carbonate sequence stratigraphic analysis is taken up in the next chapter (Chapter 17) when the nature of carbonate deposition is described in more detail. The logs *can* be used for carbonate facies analysis, especially using image logs, but an understanding of the limitations of the logs and the behaviour of carbonates is required. This is best considered in the context of sequence stratigraphy.

16.6 Conclusion

Previously, the geological document produced from the electrosequence analysis would have been considered sufficient as a basis for reservoir studies, for stratigraphic correlation, for integration with the seismic and for understanding basin development. This is no longer the case: the data must now be subjected to a sequence stratigraphic analysis and considered in a geological time context. This is the main subject of the next chapter.

17 SEQUENCE STRATIGRAPHY AND STRATIGRAPHY

17.1 Introduction

Using well logs to correlate in the subsurface is obvious. So too is using logs to create a subsurface stratigraphic framework. But, because of the huge advances in logging technology over the last decade or so, their potential as a tool for use in sequence stratigraphy has not been sufficiently developed. In the 30 years since sequence stratigraphy was proposed, it has caused a conceptual revolution in stratigraphic practice and correlation. Oil Industry exploration techniques have become more sophisticated and more successful, and much has been learned from experience. The use of logs must keep up.

The object of the sequence stratigraphic part of this chapter is to describe how geophysical logs can be used to establish information that can be combined with a range of other data, from seismic, core, outcrop and so on, and used for a sequence stratigraphic analysis. Logs will be treated essentially as a tool for description. The techniques laid down in Chapter 16 will be extended and used in a sequence stratigraphic approach to analysis, correlation and stratigraphy. Methods discussed are both manual and software driven.

Sequence stratigraphy was first developed and refined using siliciclastic sediments but carbonate sediments are also included. However, as studies have progressed, it has become evident that there are some fundamental differences between the two and, for this reason, siliciclastic and carbonate sediments are considered separately, siliciclastics first.

The chapter ends with a description of logs used in classic correlation and stratigraphy. These come last since the concepts of sequence stratigraphy have caused such a revolution that earlier ideas can never be seen in the same light again.

7.2 High resolution siliciclastic sequence stratigraphy using well logs

Principles and generalities

Sequence stratigraphy can be broadly defined as: *'the study of genetically related facies within a framework of chronostratigraphically significant surfaces'* (Van Wagoner *et al. 1990*). A 'sequence', in the sequence stratigraphic context, is *'a relatively conformable succession of genetically related strata bounded by unconformities or their correlative conformities'* (Mitchum 1977). That is, sequence stratigraphy is the study of the surviving sediments deposited between identifiable geological surfaces, which are (as far as possible) time lines (chronostratigraphic surfaces). The overall objective is to link sediments that accumulated during the same time period whatever their environment, continental, fluvial, shallow marine or deep marine which, in addition, are related to changes in sea level.

Sequence stratigraphy was originally established as seismic stratigraphy using seismic sections, mainly by Exxon (Payton 1977), and further developed by them as high resolution siliciclastic sequence stratigraphy using outcrop, core and well logs. Exxon used the Book Cliffs in Utah and Colorado, USA to illustrate this high resolution siliciclastic sequence stratigraphy, which is particularly relevant to the use of well logs (Van Wagoner *et al.*1990). The original Exxon work was very model-driven and so stimulated other workers to propose alternative models (see below) and, since each model used its own terminology, confusion arose: it is still there. This is the reason for the present effort to bring some order into the subject (Catuneanu *et al.* 2009, 2010) even though there are still fundamental concepts to be resolved.

Sequence stratigraphy, as originally expounded by Exxon, was linked to eustatic (i.e. global) sea-level changes, a sequence being the product of one cycle of sea-level rise and fall, so that, potentially, sequences would be able to be recognised globally. Most workers accept that, prior to sequence stratigraphy, the influence of externally controlled sea-level changes on sedimentation was badly underestimated but the belief that all sequences develop only in response to global (eustatic) sea level changes is not accepted. Sedimentation rate, tectonics and subsidence, at a minimum, must be considered. However, the reaction by some workers against global sea level influence was overdone and the eustatic influence on sedimentation, which has important implications for the oil industry, is not being evaluated. For instance, IODP teams use Milankovitch frequency influences on sedimentation to fine-tune palaeontological age dates in deep-sea sediments, indicating that eustatic sea-level changes really do exist (Billups & Schrag 2002).

Important concepts developed over the last few years include that of accommodation space and the fact that sea-level change and shoreline trajectory change (advance or retreat) are decoupled. Accommodation

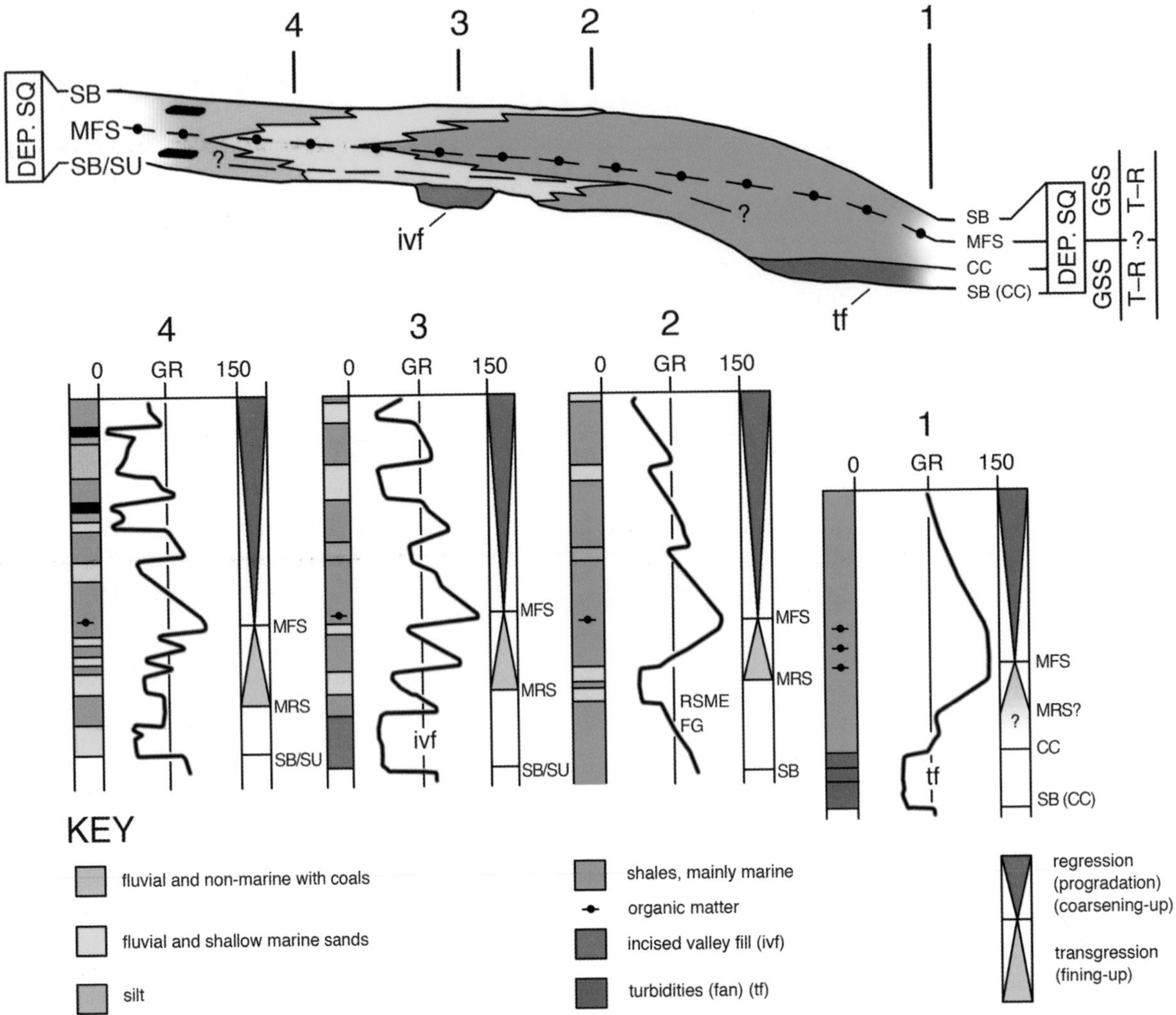

Figure 17.1 The three, principal sequence stratigraphic models compared and illustrated by schematic gamma ray logs and a simplified lithofacies cross section. Abbreviations: DEP SQ = depositional sequence; GSS = genetic stratigraphic sequence; T-R = transgressive regressive sequence; GR = gamma ray; SB = sequence boundary; SU = subaerial erosion; MFS = maximum flooding surface; MRS = maximum regressive surface; RSME = regressive surface of marine erosion; FG = forced regression; CC = correlative conformity; ivf. = incised valley fill; tf. = turbidite fan.

space is the space available for sediments to accumulate, which, in the marine environment is the space between sea-level (base level) and the surface of sediment accumulation. (Base level is (usually) the level to which a river erodes at its mouth and is approximately at, but lower, than sea-level. In this book, sea-level is used as a simplification). Shoreline advance (regression) and shoreline retreat (transgression) are decoupled from sea-level falls and rises because of the interplay between sedimentation, subsidence and sea-level. For example, transgression, that is, shoreline retreat, occurs when accommodation (i.e. space) is created more rapidly than it is filled by sediment or when subsidence outpaces deposition. Regression, that is, shoreline advance, occurs either when sea-level falls irrespective of sediment supply (forced regression) or when sedimentation rates outpace low rates of sea-level rise (normal regression).

In this chapter, an attempt will be made to present the subject from a well log point of view, using real examples (this is very important), in such a way that the information can be used without prejudice. This is a book about well logs, not the semantics of sequence stratigraphy, so the chapter will try to show logs being used for descriptive purposes in the same way that cores are, with examples of key surfaces, parasequences and the other building blocks of sequence stratigraphy.

Siliciclastic models and systems tracts

Three principal sequence stratigraphic models exist, each apparently applicable under certain circumstances, but all describing the effects on sedimentation of one cycle of sea-level rise and fall. The models are 1. *Depositional Sequence* (Mitchum 1977 – now modified) 2. *Genetic Stratigraphic Sequence* (Galloway 1989) and 3. *Transgressive-Regressive Sequence* (Embry & Johannessen 1992). The difference between the models lies in the key surface (or surfaces) used to delimit the sequence. The Depositional Sequence model uses the subaerial unconformity (SU); the Genetic Stratigraphic Sequence relies on the maximum flooding surface (MFS); and the Transgressive-Regressive Sequence model uses, for the most part, the maximum regressive surface (MRS) (**Figure 17.1**).

The original sequence stratigraphic model, the Depositional Sequence, developed by Exxon, used unconformities as bounding surfaces based on the logic that above and below unconformities, facies are unrelated; co-evil, time equivalent facies will not cross an unconformity. One problem with this model is practical in that unconformities (and equivalent conformities, so called 'correlative conformities') are difficult to recognise, especially in well logs. Much more recognisable are maximum flooding surfaces which are used to limit the Genetic Stratigraphic Sequence. They (often) appear on well logs as a gamma ray spike (and much more, as the following examples will show) and usually contain an abundant pelagic fauna, which can be dated. They are the most recognisable sequence stratigraphic surfaces on well logs. The Transgressive-Regressive model is also more easily applied in the subsurface but, from a conceptual point of view, uses complex, hybrid surfaces as sequence limits.

A sequence is made up from individual systems tracts, which can be defined as *'a linkage of contemporaneous depositional systems forming the subdivisions of a sequence'* (Brown & Fisher 1977). A systems tract is deposited during a particular phase of the sea-level fall and rise cycle and will be bounded by key surfaces. The lowstand systems tract (LST) is deposited during a relative sea-level fall and the transgressive and highstand system tracts (TST and HST) are deposited during a relative sea-level rise (**Table 17.1**). It

Table 17.1 Sequence stratigraphic systems tracts and their definitions in different models . Depositional Sequence 1 (Possamentier and Allen 1999), Depositional Sequence 2 (Hunt and Tucker 1995), Genetic Sequence (Galloway 1989), Transgressive-regressive sequence (Embry and Johannessen 1992). Depositional Sequence 1 uses the subaerial unconformity as a sequence boundary. Depositional Sequence 2 uses the top of the forced regression (top of the Falling Stage Systems Tract) as a sequence boundary. The Genetic Sequence uses the maximum flooding surface as a sequence boundary. The Transgressive-regressive sequence uses the maximum regressive sequence as a sequence boundary. HST = Highstand Systems Tract, TST = Transgressive Systems Tract, LST = Lowstand Systems Tract, FSST = Falling Stage Systems Tract, RST = Regressive Systems Tract, MFS = maximum flooding surface, MRS = maximum regressive surface, SB = sequence boundary, SU = subaerial unconformity.

Relative sea-level	DEPOSITIONAL SEQUENCE 1	DEPOSITIONAL SEQUENCE 2	GENETIC SEQUENCE	TRANSGRESSIVE-REGRESSIVE (T-R) SEQUENCE
Highest relative sea-level REGRESSION End of transgression	HST	HST	HST	RST
TRANSGRESSION End of regression	TST	TST	TST	TST
REGRESSION Lowest relative sea-level	Late (wedge) LST	LST	Late (wedge) LST	RST
Highest relative sea-level	Early (wedge)	FSST (forced regression)	Early (wedge)	

From Posamentier and Allen 1999, Catuneanu *et al.* 2009, 2010 and references given above.

Key surfaces		Attributes	Notes	non-marine	shallow	deep
MFS	maximum flooding surface	mapable	end of transgression	Present	Present	Present
TRS	transgressive ravinement surface		formed during transgression	Absent	Present	Absent
MRS	maximum regressive surface	cryptic	end of regression	Present	Present	Present
CC**	correlative conformity	mapable	end of forced regression	Absent	Present	Present
RSME	regressive surface of marine erosion		formed during forced regression	Absent	Present	Absent
SU	subaerial unconformity		formed during forced regression	Present	Present	Absent
CC*	correlative conformity	mapable	onset of forced regression	Absent	Present	Present

CC* *sensu* Possamentier & Allen, CC** *sensu* Hunt & Tucker.

seems to be generally agreed that the lowstand should be divided into a Falling Stage (Forced Regressive) and a Late Falling Stage (Normal Regressive) systems tract. The actual name given to a systems tract can depend on the model used. Exxon names are used here.

Systems tracts themselves are (mostly) made up of parasequences (i.e. sedimentary cycles). These are usually the smallest scale of sequence stratigraphic building block used and, on well logs, are recognised as log trends metres or tens of metres thick (Chapter 16). Modern work seems to suggest that, rather than being hierarchical, stratigraphy is, in fact, fractal by nature, meaning that small scale repetitions (for example parasequences) are similar to large scale repetitions (for example sequences) and that any classification is arbitrary (Catuneaunu *et al.* 2010). A hierarchical view will be taken here, and examples of parasequences, systems tracts and sequences, and the surfaces bounding each of them, will be described in a hierarchical manner. It is easier to consider time as broken into hours and minutes rather than the smooth continuum that it really is. So it is in stratigraphy.

Parasequence definition

As originally defined by Van Wagoner *et al.* (1990), the parasequence was a *'relatively conformable, genetically related succession of beds or bed-sets bounded by... flooding surfaces...'* (**Figure 17.2**). The use of the term has been expanded by many authors and now seems to mean any sedimentary cycle. This has taken the original parasequence well beyond its original meaning.

A parasequence should (following the definition) be identified as limited by a flooding surface, which is a surface across which there is evidence for an abrupt increase in water depth but where there is no, or only minor, erosion. The clean shale representing the flooding event will abruptly overlie the coarsest sediment below (or coals, as in **Figure 17.2**). In shallow marine environments, coarsening-up parasequences are common (identified on well logs as *trends,* Chapter 16) and indicate the filling-up of the available accommodation space in relatively shallow water. They are capped by a flooding surface, which can often be correlated over longish distances (kms.). Fining-up parasequences also occur but are generally less well marked, or only represent a single sediment body such as a channel (**Figure 17.4**).

The common use of the term parasequence for environments beyond the shallow marine has brought problems of definition. Posamentier and Allen (1999) and others point out that flooding in deep marine environments has no sense and they also dispute the use of the term 'flooding', insisting that it implies an initially dry surface. Because of these problems, an attempt was made in the text of this book to replace parasequence by the less tightly defined term, sedimentary cycle, or simply cycle, and only use parasequence when flooding surfaces could be identified, especially as the parasequence has recently been described differently as *'..an upward-shallowing succession of facies bounded by ...flooding surfaces'* (Catuneanu *et al.* 2010). Unfortunately, this effort created a very cumbersome text and made it difficult to understand. As a compromise, parasequence is used (rather loosely) with a qualification added in brackets when necessary. The scale of what may be called a parasequence is thus quite variable. Parasequences are described below (Section 17.4).

Work flow

This chapter will advocate some basic techniques and a work flow to use when interpreting sequence stratigraphy from well logs. In their excellent book on sequence stratigraphy, Posamentier and Allen (1999) suggest that sequence stratigraphic analysis should start by identifying 'log motifs' and 'electrofacies associations', move on to identifying maximum flooding surfaces and sequence boundaries and then, finally, stacking patterns. Chris Kendall, on his equally excellent web site (http://strata.geol.sc.edu/), suggests, however, that a study should start with the identification and correlation of maximum flooding surfaces and transgressive surfaces This then allows (candidate?) sequence boundaries to be detected before a full analysis is made. Both these methods have their advantages.

The approach advocated in this chapter, although it takes elements of both these published methods, follows a logical path for log analysis and builds on the results of the electrosequence analysis technique of the previous chapter. That is, it takes the geometrical log patterns (base lines, trends etc), abrupt surfaces (breaks), anomalies and lithological interpretation (Chapter 16) to begin a sequence stratigraphic analysis (**Figure 16.20**). Using this dataset, there are then 4 steps to a sequence stratigraphic analysis. The first is to attempt to classify all the breaks in sequence stratigraphic terms where possible (**Figure 17.3**). The second is to add maximum flooding surfaces if they can be identified. The third is to then propose candidate sequence boundaries. The fourth is to build up the complete sequence stratigraphic interpretation, from the base of a well upwards, attempting to recognise systems tracts and sequences themselves (**Figure 17.3**). In this way, the trends, breaks, flooding surfaces and sequence boundaries will have a time order on the log, as well as a depth one. The process uses one well at a time but allows construction of a library of wells in the knowledge that new wells may affect the interpretation of previous wells. All the wells, therefore, will be fully integrated.

This first three steps of this sequence stratigraphic work flow rely on the identification of key sequence stratigraphic surfaces. A succession of sediments cannot be put into sequence stratigraphic context without having identified these surfaces (Baum and Vail, 1988)

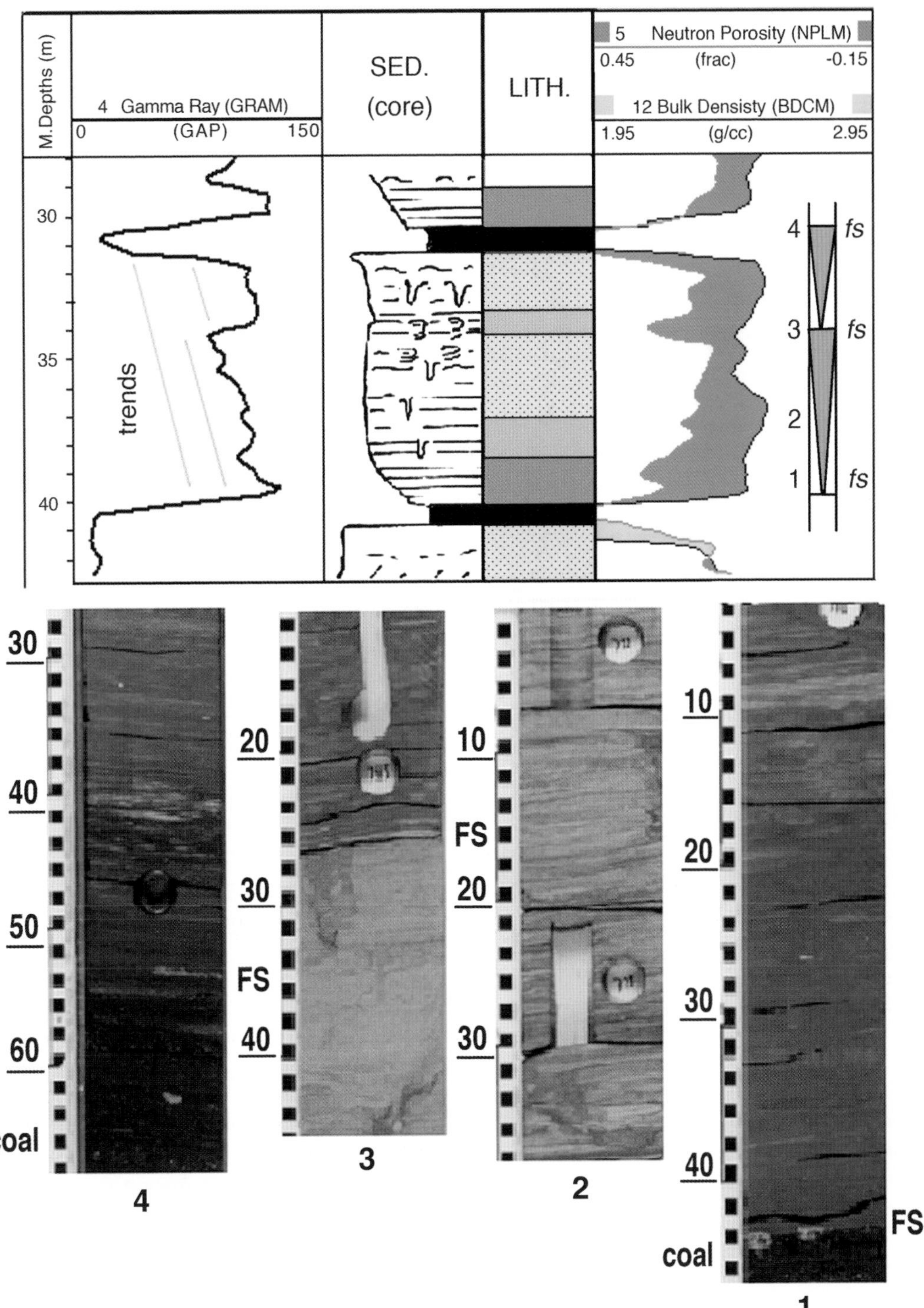

Figure 17.2 A typical coarsening-up, shallow marine parasequence. The complex parasequence contains a 'within sequence' minor flooding surface (photo 3). Flooding events (photos 1 & 4) define the parasequence boundaries. The parasequence is formed from rippled and bioturbated marine sandstones (Photos 2 & 3). FS = flooding surface.

(**Figure 17.1**). From a log point of view, these surfaces can be looked on as hierarchical in their importance. At the lowest level, surfaces (breaks), based only on logs as outlined in the electrosequence analysis (Chapter 16), are simply abrupt lithological changes (fluids and other causes eliminated). At a higher level, these same lithological breaks may be identified as separating facies across a potentially erosive surface or potential flooding surface. Such breaks may be only 'within trend' surfaces (explained below), and used to recognise facies limits, but they may equally limit parasequences. Slightly higher in importance are surfaces that bound sets of

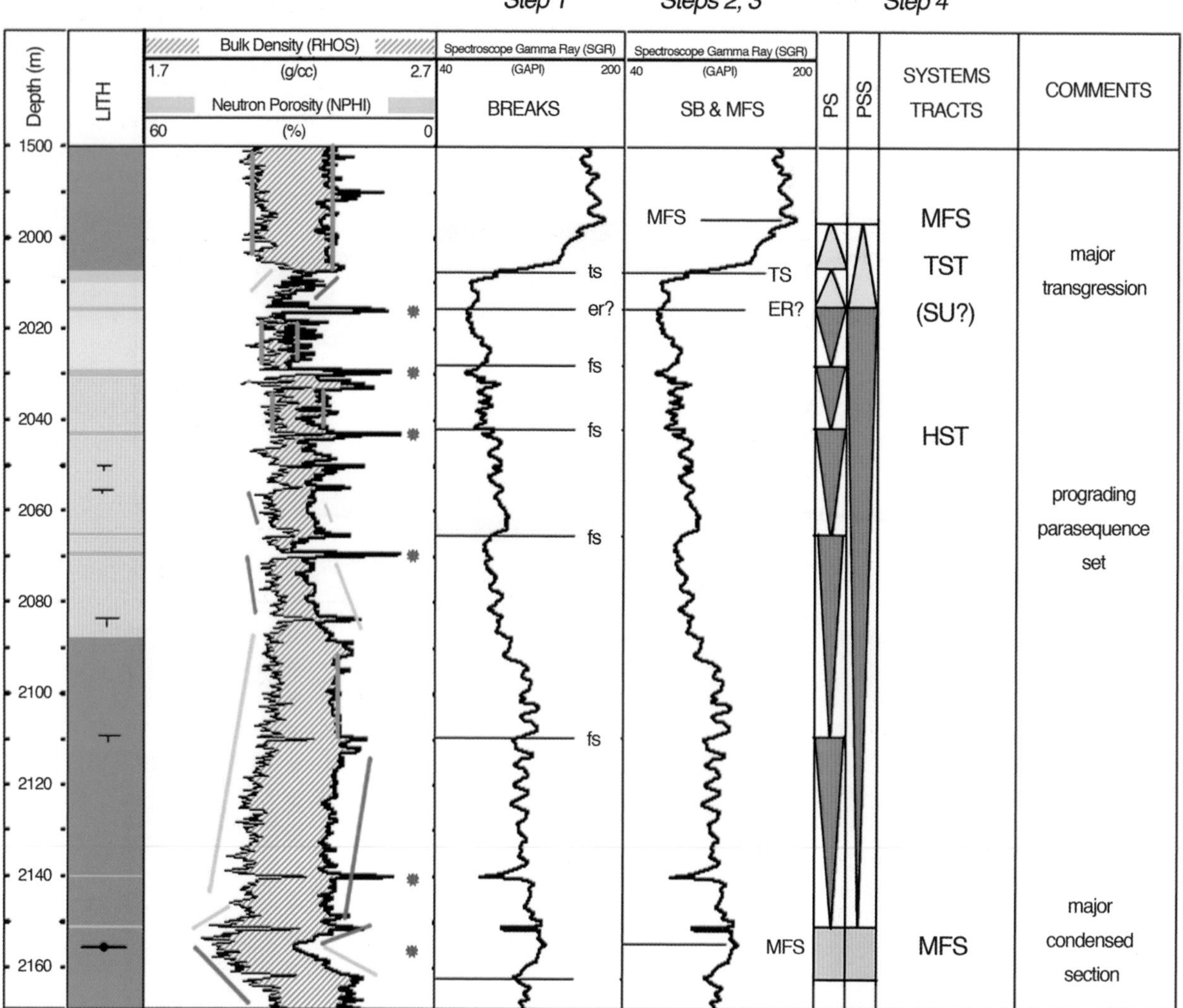

Figure 17.3 A suggested work flow for a sequence stratigraphic interpretation using logs building on a previous log-based electrosequence analysis. For details of steps 1 – 4, see text. PS = parasequence. PSS = parasequence set. For other abbreviations see Table 17.2.

repeated parasequences, or parasequence sets.

The most important surfaces, and highest in the hierarchy, are those that define systems tracts and sequences, that is, 'key sequence stratigraphic surfaces'. According to a recent review paper by a considerable number of eminent workers in the subject (Catuneanu *et al.* 2009), there are just seven such surfaces: *onset of forced regression; regressive surface of marine erosion; subaerial unconformity; end of forced regression; maximum regressive surface; transgressive ravinement surface; maximum flooding surface* (**Table 17.2**). Some of these are described below.

On the first attempt, the interpretation of surfaces (*steps 1–3*) in a well will be provisional: probably this, possibly that. With the surfaces (provisionally) labelled, the next step (*step four*) is to recognise the sediment characteristics between the surfaces, that is, the type of sedimentary cycle, facies, stacking pattern and so on. At this stage a great deal of information is added to the dataset: micropalaeontological, geochemical, sedimentological, in fact, whatever is available. The log information forms only part of the jigsaw. There is no limit to the type of information that can be used for a sequence stratigraphic analysis. A work flow is shown in **Figure 17.3**.

This text

Because recognising sequence stratigraphic surfaces is so important, the text now describes examples of typical log responses to some of these. The first described surfaces are the least important and lowest in the hierarchy and show either erosion or flooding. Some of these can be used as parasequence limits. They are followed by some of the key surfaces that allow systems tracts and sequences to be identified, and appear in the text in a rather arbitrary order related to the ease with which they can be identified on logs. These surfaces are illustrated by actual examples.

Many publications illustrate the use of well logs in

Table 17.2 Key stratigraphic surfaces and some of their attributes. Ordered as in the text. NR = normal regressive, FR = forced regressive, T = transgression, c-u = coarsening-up, f-u = fining-up

Key surface	contact type	facies below	facies above	depositional trends below	depositional trends above	notes
ER Erosion Surface	erosion	variable	coarse grained			local? Erosion **Figs 17.4,16.18**
FS Flooding Surface	conformable or erosion	coarse grained	fine grained			local? transgression **Figs 17.5,6,7,8**
TS Transgressive Surface (wave or tidal ravinement)	erosion	variable (if marine, c-u)	marine f-u or estuarine	NR, T	T	formed during transgression (diachronous) **Fig 17.9**
MFS Maximum Flooding Surface	comfortable or scoured	variable (marine f-u)	variable (marine c-u)	T	NR	end of transgression (mapable) **Figs 17.10,11,12,13**
SU Subaerial Unconformity	erosion or bypass	variable (if marine, c-u)	non-marine	NR, FR	NR, T	formed during forced regression **Figs 17.14,15, 15.39**
RSME Regressive Surface of Marine Erosion	erosion	shelf c-u	shoreface c-u	NR, FR	FR, NR	formed during forced regression (diachronous) **Fig 17.16**
MRS Maximum Regressive Surface	conformable	variable	variable (if marine, c-u)	NR	T	end of (normal) regression (can be cryptic) **Figs 17.17,18**
CC Correlative Conformity (Possamentier & Allen 1999)	conformable or erosion c-u on shelf	marine, c-u	marine c-u	NR	FR	onset of forced regression (mapable)
CC Correlative Conformity (Hunt & Tucker 1992)	conformable	marine c-u	marine	FR	NR	end of forced regression (mapable)

Modified after Catuneanu 2006, Catuneanu *et al.* 2009, 2010.

sequence stratigraphy by showing a simple log trace, generally just the gamma ray, and usually without even a scale. This is equivalent to using a violin with one string. It does not make music. Full log suites must be interpreted before logs can be useful in an analysis and, if a single curve is to be used for illustration, it should at least be accompanied by a lithological interpretation based on that full suite. The interpretations illustrated in this book come from such full log suite analyses, core descriptions and electrosequence analyses (Chapter 16).

17.3 Log examples of sequence stratigraphic surfaces

Sequence stratigraphic surfaces

Sequence stratigraphic surfaces are significant because they represent long periods of time: many time lines come together in a thin deposit or converge in a single surface. For example, a condensed section (which contains the maximum flooding surface) will be thin but represents a long time; an erosional unconformity represents the time taken to deposit the removed sediments and the period of their removal. Since the object of sequence stratigraphy is to reconstruct chronostratigraphically linked sedimentary systems, the ideal surface to find is a time line because it will give an indication of a basin's characteristics at the time. The idea that seismic reflectors are time lines is behind this concept.

Surfaces can be amalgamated, so that more than one event may be represented by the one, physical surface. The subaerial unconformity over an exposed shelf during lowstand may also become a surface of erosion during subsequent sea-level rise and transgression: the subaerial erosion surface and the transgressive surface become combined. In addition, some surfaces, by their very nature, are diachronous. For example, transgressive ravinement surfaces are diachronous, younger basinward, older marginward.

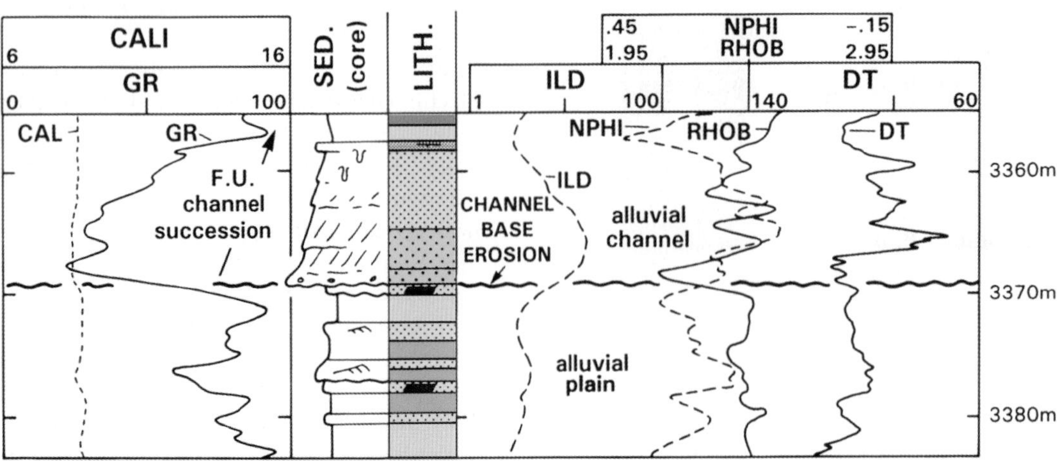

Figure 17.4 Channel base erosion log example. The erosion occurs at the base of a fining-up sequence, cuts into alluvial plain sediments and is interpreted as an alluvial channel. The reservoir contains hydrocarbons.

As will be illustrated, surfaces may have only local significance and be used as limits to facies or parasequences (sedimentary cycles), or they may be major (key) surfaces and used as boundaries to systems tracts and sequences. Some surfaces are seismically mappable; some are not; some have a physical reality; some are cryptic. In fact, sequence stratigraphic surfaces tend to be present at basin margins but selectively absent away from the margin, either in non-marine environments or in the basin (Catuneanu *et al.* 2010). For example, there are no erosional unconformities or transgressive surfaces in deep water environments.

Each example in the following text is discussed in terms of log responses and possible sequence stratigraphic significance.

Facies limiting surfaces (within-trend surfaces)

Channel base erosion (ER)

The commonest example of an erosion surface is the sharp base to a coarse channel deposit cutting into the sediments below. It is local and limited to the extent of the channel itself. On the logs, this type of erosion surface is characterised by an abrupt, upward change from any type of deposit, that is, any lithology, to coarse sand, and will be identified in an electrosequence analysis because of the physical, lithological change (**Figure 16.17,a**). The overlying channel deposit will be seen as a fining-up log trend (increase in shaliness) associated with an upwards decrease in porosity. The core calibrated log example (**Figure 17.4**) shows a series of thin, interbedded, non-marine silts, sands and shales, abruptly overlain by a 12 m thick, fining-up, fluvial sand with medium scale cross-beds. On the logs, erosion is indicated by the abrupt changes at the base of the sand. The fact that this is a local, channel base erosion surface can be suspected by its association with an overlying fining-up set of log responses (trends) and non-marine alluvial deposits below. Channel base erosion is often very clear on electrical image logs because of the strong resistivity changes involved in the lithology change (**Figure 16.18**).

The currents which erode and create this surface are also responsible for the transport of the sediments which immediately overlie it. Such surfaces are to be differentiated from those showing erosion and truncation but on which the overlying sediments are not related to the principal erosion (**Figure 17.14**).

In sequence stratigraphic terms, channel base erosion can be just local and the base of a single channel (either fluvial or submarine) or can represent the subaerial unconformity and indicate a major drop in sea (base) level. In the latter case, the channel deposits will always be non-marine (**Table 17.2**).

*Flooding surface (FS)

Coarsening-up parasequences are defined as bounded by flooding surfaces across which the abrupt shift from sandstone facies to shale facies is interpreted as indicating an increase in water depth (or a decrease in sediment supply). In an electrosequence analysis of siliciclastics, a flooding surface will be picked out, as described in Chapter 16, as an abrupt break between sand below and shale above (**Figure 16.17,b**).

The first example of a flooding surface is illustrated by

***Flooding surface** definition. Posamentier and Allen (1990) have pointed out that 'flooding' should take place over an originally dry surface and suggest that drowning would be a better term. Perhaps. But they are right in pointing out that neither term is applicable in the deep marine environment. There are still, however, rapid changes from coarse to fine deposition even in the deep sea. An effective term has not been proposed.

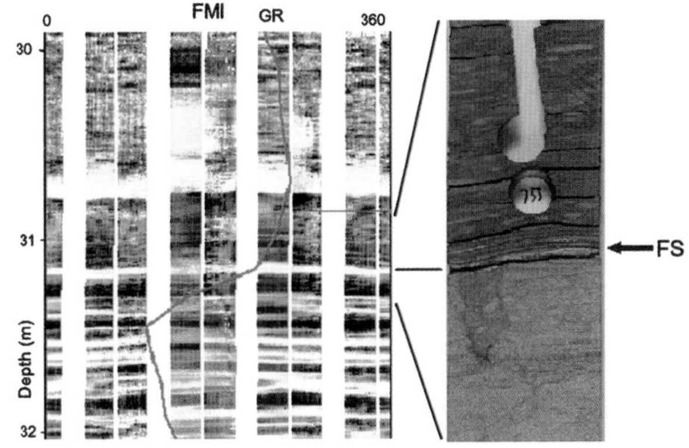

Figure 17.5 A flooding surface seen on an FMI, wireline electrical image, gamma ray (red line) and core. Laminated, clean shales lie abruptly on medium to fine grained, ripple bedded and bioturbated marine sandstones. There is no apparent erosion at the flooding surface. FS = flooding surface.

an FMI log, gamma ray and corresponding core (**Figure 17.5**). The core shows a medium grained, irregularly laminated, rippled sandstone, covered abruptly by a laminated shale, which grades upwards into a bioturbated, more silty shale. A large, vertical burrow descends into the sandstone from the flooding surface itself, indicating colonisation and the possible development of a *Glossifungites* surface (Gingras *et al.* 2001). This would suggest a firmground developed, although there is no other indication of exposure. The contact with the shale is extremely abrupt and there is no obvious indication of erosion at the flooding surface, despite the clear implication of transgression and water deepening above it. Based on correlation, this surface appears to be quite local.

The previous image shows the abrupt flooding surface contact in considerable detail, the electrical characteristics of the shale and the sandstone being sufficiently different. The image also shows the change from irregular bedding in the sandstone to fine bedding in the shale. However, neither the ripples in the sandstone nor the vertical burrow are resolved. The gamma ray (red curve) simply shows an abrupt change, as do the other logs (not shown). This surface would be classed as a 'break' in the electrofacies analysis and classed as a potential flooding surface on lithological grounds. Comparison with nearby wells is the only way to confirm that this surface only has local significance. It is a facies limiting, within-trend surface.

The second example (**Figure 17.6**) shows the coarsest, topmost part of a shallow marine, coarsening-up (probably tidal) succession covered abruptly by an interval of highly burrowed silt, itself covered by shale with deep water characteristics. The bioturbated silt is separated from the rippled, mainly clean sand below by a sharp surface (marine flooding) with no apparent erosion and with escape burrows. The highly bioturbated interval is 2.5 m (8 ft) thick and formed of silty sand with scattered, coarse sand grains. It shows as a subdued high on the density log (low porosity), but a high neutron value indicating a high shale content and, in this case, common chamosite oolites (Chapter 11). The gamma ray shows a rapid (but not abrupt) upwards increase from the sand through the bioturbated bed, into the shale. Correlation shows that this surface has a moderately wide extent.

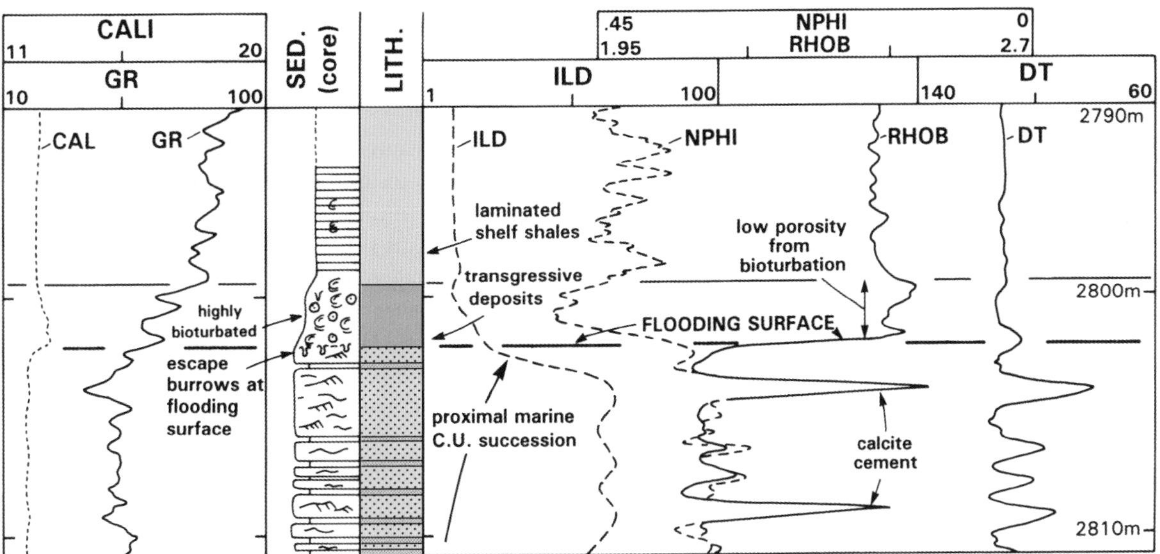

Figure 17.6 Log example of a flooding surface and transgressive deposits. The coarsening-up, sandy, proximal marine succession is covered by a highly bioturbated silty, transgressive deposit giving characteristic responses on the neutron and density logs. The base of the transgressive deposits is sharp, shows escape burrows and represents the flooding event: there is no evident erosion. The calcite cement in the marine sands is secondary, but probably early.

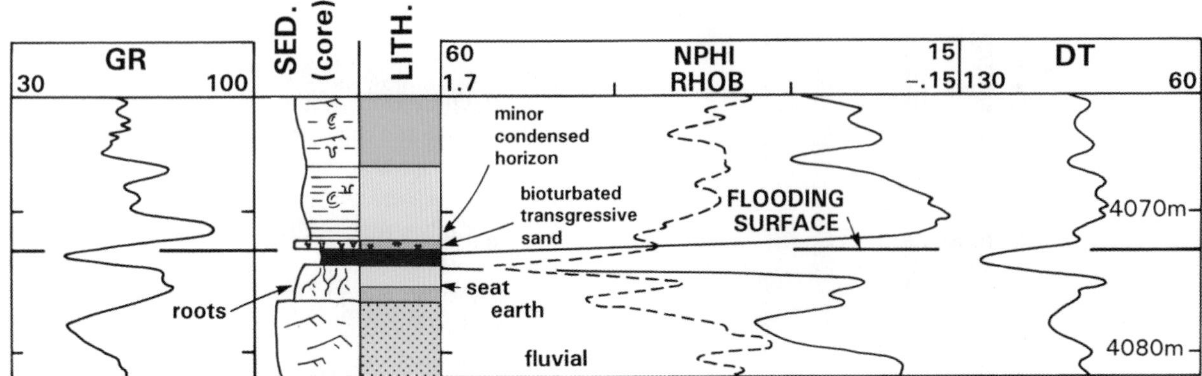

Figure 17.7 Coal followed by a flooding surface. There appears to be no erosion associated with the flooding event (marked by a very thin, bioturbated, heterogeneous sand, too thin to be seen on the logs). Open marine, deeper water, organic rich shales of a minor condensed sequence follow the flooding.

It is clear that the bioturbated interval of this example represents significant transgression. Below are the shallow water, rippled sands of the shallowing-up (coarsening-up) sequence and above are deep water marine shales, which continue for some thickness above the illustrated section. The transgression began at the surface on which there is flooding and escape burrows, and can therefore be called a flooding surface, but it also marks the beginning of the transgression and so is a transgressive surface even though there is no evidence for erosion (see below). Such bioturbated intervals are common and said to be diagnostic of low wave, low tide energy environments (Posamentier & Allen 1999), which would be consistent, in this example, with the lack of erosion. On the logs alone, the transgression would be clear from the lithological change and wide correlation. A transgressive surface would be (correctly) interpreted. The dense, bioturbated interval could be suggested, based on the typical neutron and density responses (*see also* **Figure 17.9**). This is, therefore, a flooding surface across which there is important transgression.

The final example (**Figure 17.7**) shows another expression of a flooding surface, this time immediately following coal deposition. Coal represents slow accumulation at sea-level with little detrital sediment input and is frequently associated with transgression (Milton *et al.* 1990). In this example, the core shows the coal to have a seat earth and so be *in situ.* Deposited over the coal is 30 cm of dark, organic-rich, laminated shale with pyrite representing a significant deepening of the environment of deposition. On the logs, this succession is seen as an obvious coal (low density, high neutron *cf.* **Figure 10.28**), followed abruptly by a shale with high gamma ray and very high neutron responses, (indicating the high organic content, *cf.* **Figure 10.20**). The organic shale is interpreted as a minor condensed sequence and grades upwards into shales with normal log responses which the core shows to be bioturbated silty shales.

The detail of the core shows that, in fact, immediately over the coal is a 2.0 cm burrowed, transgressive sand, not resolved by the logs (masked by the coal), which has a few scattered, very coarse sand grains and coal fragments. The flooding surface is at its base. As far as the logs are concerned, and in the absence of core, it is the high gamma ray and high neutron responses (condensed sequence) immediately following the coal which are very typical and suggestive of the flooding event. A previous example (**Figure 17.2**) shows that flooding events following coals are common and the detailed example shows that the electrical images have the capacity to resolve some of the details (**Figure 17.8**). This and similar intervals have good correlation potential.

Systems tract and sequence bounding surfaces

Transgressive Surface (may have wave or tidal erosion) (TS)

In the previous examples of flooding (**Figures 17.5,6,7,8**), erosion was insignificant or minor and there was no indication of truncation at the level of the surface. This is generally the case for flooding surfaces (Van Wagoner *et al.* 1990). With transgressive surfaces, however, there is evidence for erosion such as the presence of a lag, mineral concentrations (especially galuconite) and cementation of the underlying surface (Baum and Vail, 1988). A transgressive surface is created as sea-level rises, accommodation outpaces sedimentation and the shoreline moves landwards, that is, there is transgression. As the sea advances landward, so the sediments over which it passes are eroded by waves and tides (cause ravinement). This transgressive surface may cover either highstand or lowstand regressive deposits and is diachronous in that, at the seaward limit, it follows maximum regression and, at the landward limit, is co-incident with maximum flooding (Catuneanu *et al.*

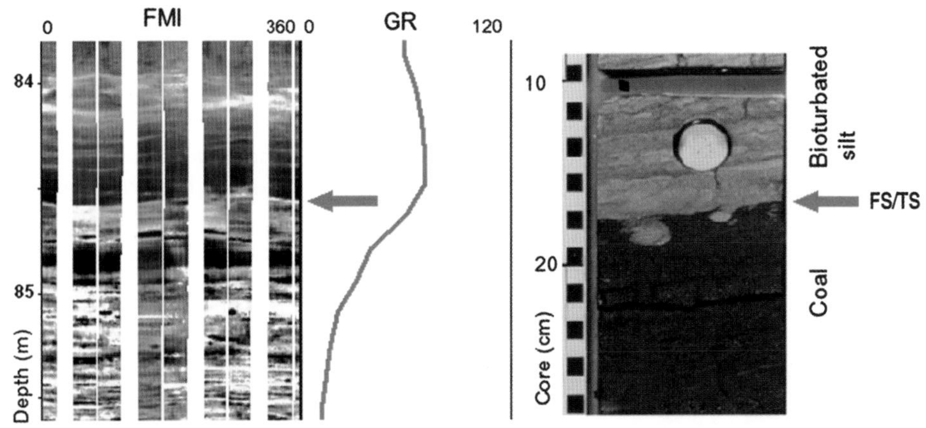

Figure 17.8 A transgressive surface (red arrow) on FMI, wireline electrical images and in core. A bioturbated silt lies sharply on a coal with burrowing and loading. Erosion is hard to judge. FS/TS = flooding surface/transgressive surface.

2008) (**Figure 17.1**). It is variously called the transgressive ravinement surface, or the transgressive surface of marine erosion (Nummedal and Swift 1987; Posamentier and Allen 1999).

The example (**Figure 17.9**) shows a medium grained, cross-bedded sandstone with thin carbonate cemented zones and no bioturbation, covered abruptly by a thick shale. Core detail shows the topmost surface of the sandstone to be a truncated bedform, which is very abruptly covered by a 20 cm, intensely bioturbated bed with occasional coarse grains. On the logs, the abrupt upper surface of the sandstone is evident. The bioturbated bed shows as high gamma ray and neutron shale-type values combined, but with high density and low interval transit time (high velocity), indicating a low porosity (**Figure 17.9**). The clean, laminated, moderately organic-rich shale interval rapidly follows the bioturbated bed. At the base of this shale there is a gamma ray high, a neutron high, density low and sonic high (velocity low) indicating organic content. This is interpreted as a condensed section. As detrital content increases, so the logs pass upwards into shale with normal responses (**Figure 17.9**).

The identification of this as a key transgressive surface, rather than a local, facies limiting flooding surface depends on two things: the abrupt log responses and the position in the vertical sequence. The abruptness is clearly suggestive of an erosional break. However, it is the position which gives the most significant clues. Most local, facies limiting flooding surfaces occur at the top of coarsening-up (shallowing-up) successions representing progradation. Transgressive surfaces need not. They

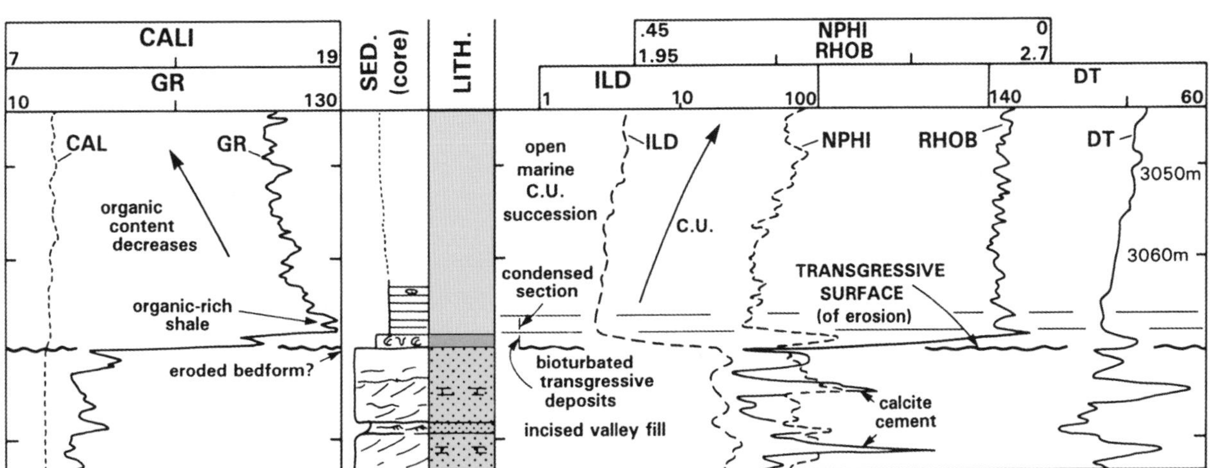

Figure 17.9 Log example of a transgressive surface of erosion. The underlying sand sequence of estuarine deposits, shows eroded bedforms at the top. The erosion surface is covered by thin, bioturbated shaly sands: the transgressive deposits. These are followed by well laminated, open marine, organic rich shales of a condensed section, which form the base of a shallow marine, coarsening-up, prograding sequence. CU = coarsening-up.

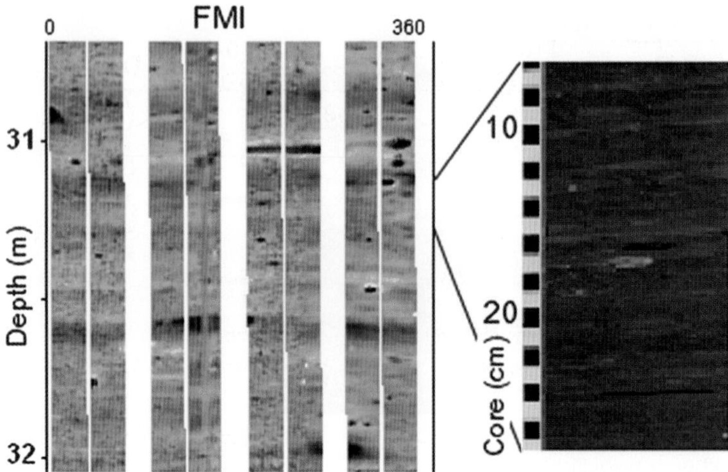

Figure 17.10 Finely laminated, black, organic rich shale on FMI, wireline electrical images and in core. The environment of these shales is anoxic (no oxygen) to preserve the organic matter and not be colonised by bottom dwellers, hence the lack of biotubation. It has the physical characteristics of a condensed sequence.

will cut into valley fill sediments and cut with a lag into the interfluves (i.e. ravinement). This example (**Figure 17.9**) is a case of erosion into valley fill. In other cases, however, the only record of transgressive erosion may be a coarse lag a centimetre or two thick and beyond log resolution (except image logs), although erosion is more evident when the transgressive surface is amalgamated with the subaerial erosion surface, as is often the case (**Figures 15.37,40**).

Maximum Flooding Surface (MFS)

In sequence stratigraphic theory and parlance, the maximum flooding surface represents the maximum retreat of the shoreline: below it, there was transgression and above, regression. The surface is called the downlap surface when it is prograded over by highstand clinoforms, and easily identified on seismic (**Figure 17.1**). The maximum flooding surface falls within a condensed section, which is what makes it significant in log interpretation. As explained below, a condensed section can be recognised by its distinctive log responses. The actual maximum flooding surface can be a bored, cemented starvation surface or hardground, and may separate the condensed section into two parts (Baum and Vail 1988).

A condensed section represents a long period of time during which land derived detrital input is small and most of the sediment deposited comes from pelagic or hemipelagic sources, which suggests deeper water conditions. Such a section is typically rich in pelagic fauna and microfauna, is finely laminated, has a low quartz content and is a black shale enriched in marine organic matter. It has a distinctive electrical image (**Figure 17.10**). It also contains exotic elements such as sulphides, pelletised glauconite, phosphates and iridium and can have a stable isotope fingerprint (Loutit *et al.*, 1988) (**Figure 17.11**).

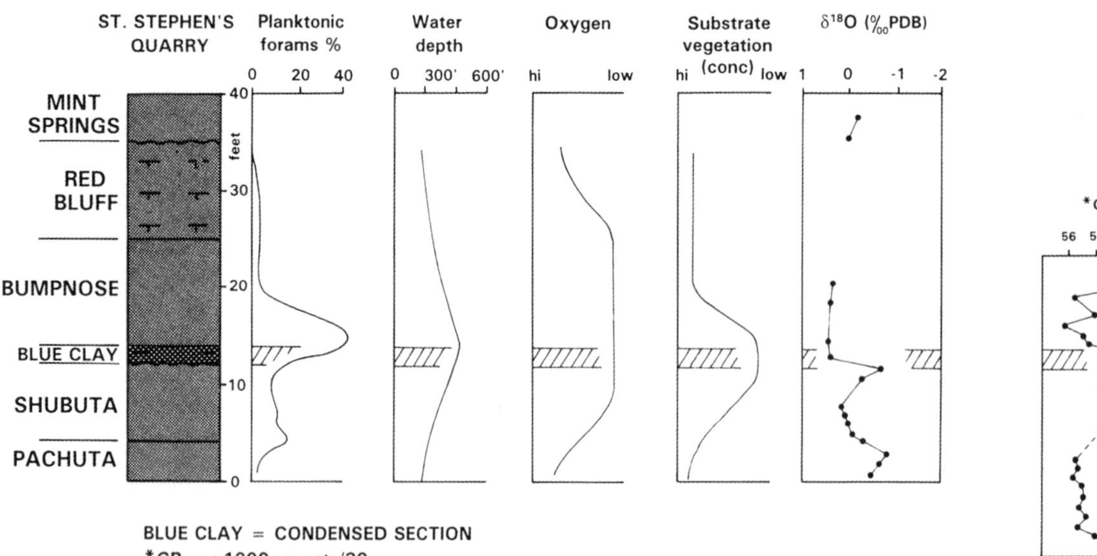

Figure 17.11 Characteristics of a condensed section, the Blue Clay, showing faunal, chemical, water depth and gamma ray signatures (re-drawn from Loutit *et al.* 1988).

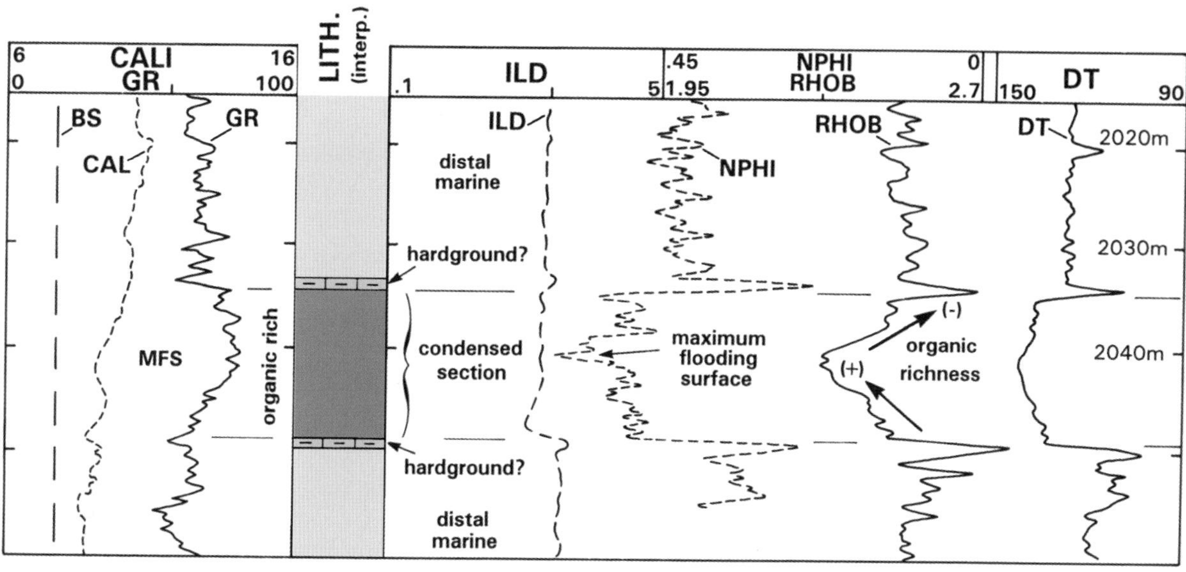

Figure 17.12 Log example of a maximum flooding surface (MFS). The MFS is interpreted within a broader condensed section characterized by high gamma ray and neutron values, low density and low velocity. The MFS itself is interpreted where the neutron log is highest and the density lowest. The thin carbonate rich bands may be hardgrounds or a later diagenetic effect.

However, variation exists in all these characteristics and there can be strong bioturbation and mineralisation, and even marine scouring.

On the logs, the identification of the maximum flooding surface depends especially on the high, mainly marine, organic matter content associated with condensation (Creaney and Passey 1993). Marine organic matter contains uranium (Chapter 8) so that condensed sediments have a high gamma ray value and a gamma ray 'spike' has become the diagnostic feature, often being considered synonymous with the maximum flooding surface. This may (or may not) be so. Obviously, if a gamma spike is caused by uranium enrichment, it should be identified as such on the spectral gamma ray log (**Figure 8.41**). However, the presence of organic matter and the unique texture of condensed shales (**Figure 17.10**) affects *all* the log responses, as described below.

The example of standard log responses through a condensed section and maximum flooding surface is from marine, shelf deposits. The condensed shales show only a slightly higher gamma ray value (**Figure 17.12**) but their organic richness is indicated by high neutron values (Chapter 11), low density (Chapter 10) and low velocity (high interval transit times) on the sonic (Chapter 9). The fine laminations, a frequent feature of these slowly accumulating shales (lack of bottom dwellers), amplify the low sonic velocity and generally also show a low resistivity (Chapter 7) (Creaney and Passey 1993). In fact, most of the log responses will be such that, in the electrosequence analysis (Chapter 16), condensed sections will be picked out as 'anomalous', having unusually high or low values (**Figure 16.20**). An organic rich condensed section, therefore, has a whole suite of log responses, which are generally more diagnostic and reliable than the simple gamma ray 'spike' alone (**Figure 17.12**). The interpretation of a condensed section as containing or being a maximum flooding surface, however, it is just that: an interpretation.

In proximal environments, the traces remaining of maximum flooding are much more subtle than in the open marine environment. The example (**Figure 17.13**) shows high depositional energy, shoreface sands, in which there is an interval of finer grained, highly bioturbated sand which is interpreted, both from the core sedimentology and from correlation with other wells, as a low depositional energy, condensed section and maximum flooding surface. The shale mixed with the fine sand causes the high gamma ray: the other logs do not give notable responses. Clearly, in this example, core is essential for the sequence stratigraphic interpretation and logs alone would not be adequate.

The identification of condensed sections is fundamental in any subsurface sequence stratigraphic analysis using logs, regardless of the theoretical sequence stratigraphic model preferred. In deeper marine environments and even some shallow, near coastal environments, the increased organic content and laminated texture of the sections gives the distinctive set of log responses which will be generally identified in an electrosequence analysis as anomalous (as described). These distinctive responses make the maximum flooding surface a correlatable event on the logs which can potentially be followed from the deeper to shallower depositional environments, from the basin centre to the shoreline, and even into the dominantly non-marine areas. In addition, since these horizons often contain abundant pelagic fauna, they are a microfaunally recognisable and

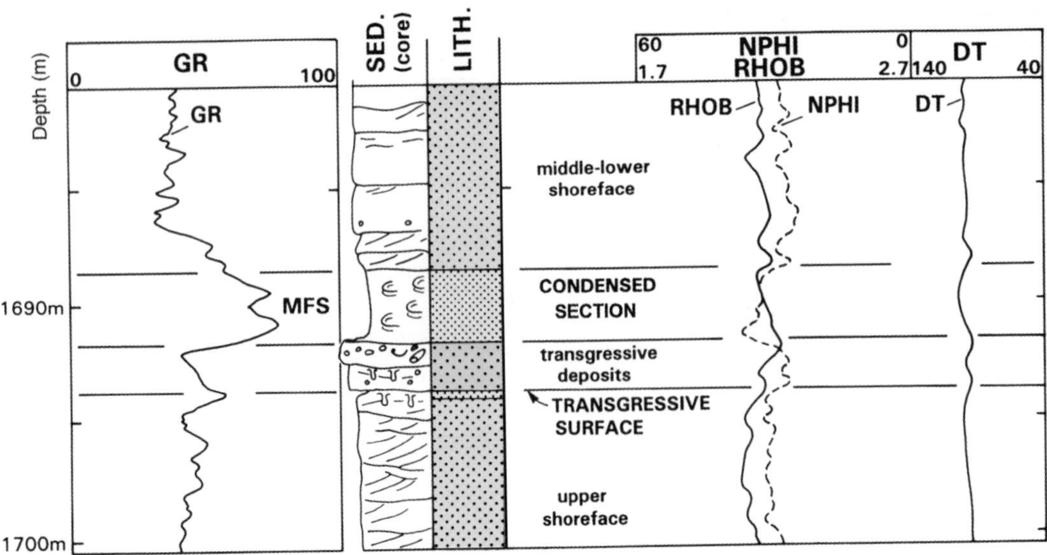

Figure 17.13 A maximum flooding surface (MFS) in a shoreline (proximal) environment. High energy in general, even during maximum flooding, makes for subdued log responses. Without core, such an interpretation would be extremely difficult if not impossible.

datable event. Condensed sections can be treated essentially as chronostratigraphic markers and are used as the limits to genetic stratigraphic sequences (Galloway 1989). Recognising maximum flooding surfaces is the *second step* in the interpretation work flow.

Subaerial Unconformity (SU) (Exxon sequence boundary)

Subaerial unconformity identification is often difficult in cores, even at outcrop, and is very difficult with logs. There are no consistent lithological characteristics and the surface may be marked by large lithological and facies changes, or hardly any at all.

The core in the first example shows clean, distal marine shales overlain by very coarse, nearshore marine, possibly estuarine, sands which can be interpreted as representing valley-fill deposits (**Figure 17.14**) (the North Sea, Middle Jurassic, Oseberg Formation, resting on Lower Jurassic shales). The coarse sands have large scale bedforms (Graue *et al.* 1987) and a coarse lag at the base (immediately overlying the erosional surface), is full of heavy minerals. The neutron-density log combination

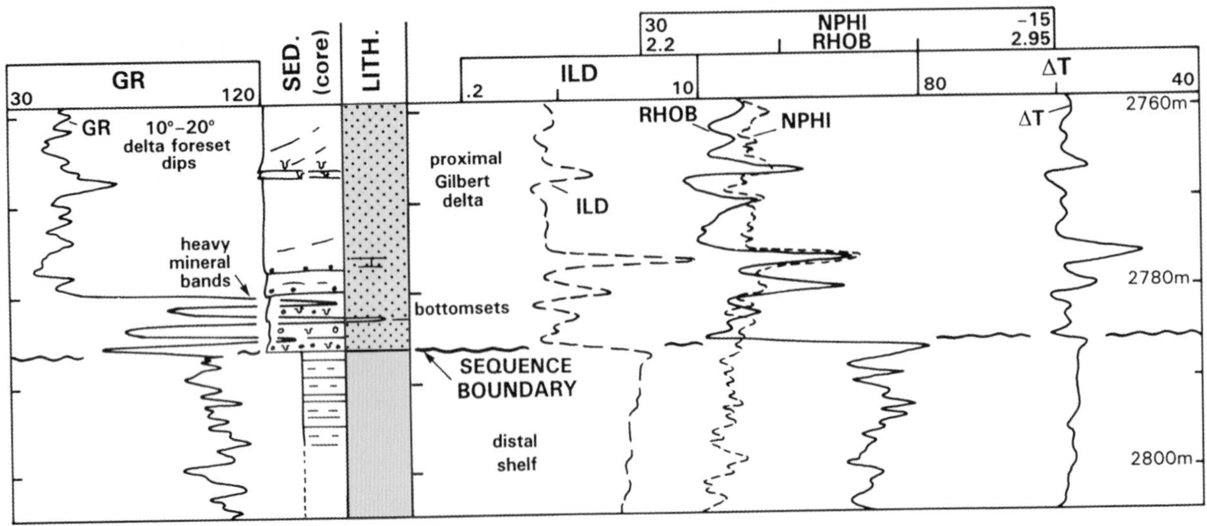

Figure 17.14 Sequence boundary log example. The boundary is abrupt and known to be erosional. A Gilbert type delta with coarse sands overlies distal shelf shale. The basinward shift in facies is very marked (see text).

shows the abrupt change from clean shale to coarse sand very well. The gamma ray, however, shows very high, spikey values just above this contact, which is not a shale response but is due to the heavy minerals noted in the core (**Figure 17.14**). Although erosion is strongly suggested by the abrupt log responses in this one well, it is only correlation on a basin-wide scale that makes evident both the extent of the surface and the truncation associated with it. This surface is the mid-Cimmerian unconformity which covers a large area and represents a significant lowering in (relative) sea level (Rawson & Riley 1982; Evans *et al.* 2004). In this evaluation, core is essential.

A clue to recognising such an unconformity and major erosion surface as a key stratigraphic surface is its position in the sedimentary succession and its effect on the facies succession. For instance, in the present example, a major jump is seen in the facies succession from clean, distal marine shales to shallow marine sands and bioturbated silts (**Figure 17.14**). This jump represents the 'basinward shift in facies' interpreted as caused by a major lowering of sea (base) level, and used by Exxon to identify their unconformity defined sequence boundary. As is typical in many such examples, the actual erosion surface is complex and possibly an amalgam of surfaces. In the example shown, the erosion surface as it is now preserved, does not appear to be associated with the immediately overlying sediments, which have interbedded, bioturbated layers indicating periods of low energy, despite the coarseness of the sands. The major erosion would have preceded their deposition.

The second example has been used previously to illustrate the detail visible in electrical (FMI) images. It also shows an interpreted sequence boundary (**Figure 15.40**). The core shows shallow marine sands eroded by a conglomeratic oolite with marine fauna. The image is remarkable in that it shows these features clearly: the erosion surface itself is sharp, the conglomerate is defined, and a change in dip angle across the surface identifies it as an unconformity. The interpretation of this as a sequence boundary, however, is only confirmed by regional studies. In fact, in this example, a sequence boundary is combined with a transgressive surface since the shallow marine sediments are covered by outer marine deposits (**Figure 15.40**).

The final example (**Figure 17.15**) is taken from the literature (Possamentier and Allen 1999, their Figure 4.36), and shows a sequence boundary in a set of fluvial-coastal plain environments. The boundary itself occurs at a notable change in lithology. Coarse, fluvial sands deposited by low sinuosity rivers erode into finer grained, coastal plain sediments deposited by high sinuosity rivers. The surface separating the two is described as an unconformity and interpreted as a sequence boundary (Possamentier and Allen 1999 *op. cit.*). However, the gamma ray does not show the obvious grain size changes seen on the core and indicates the practical difficulties in identifying sequence boundaries. Moreover, although the standard logs across all the interpreted sequence boundaries in the examples used here show the unconformity surface with a strong lithological expression, such a character is neither necessary nor diagnostic.

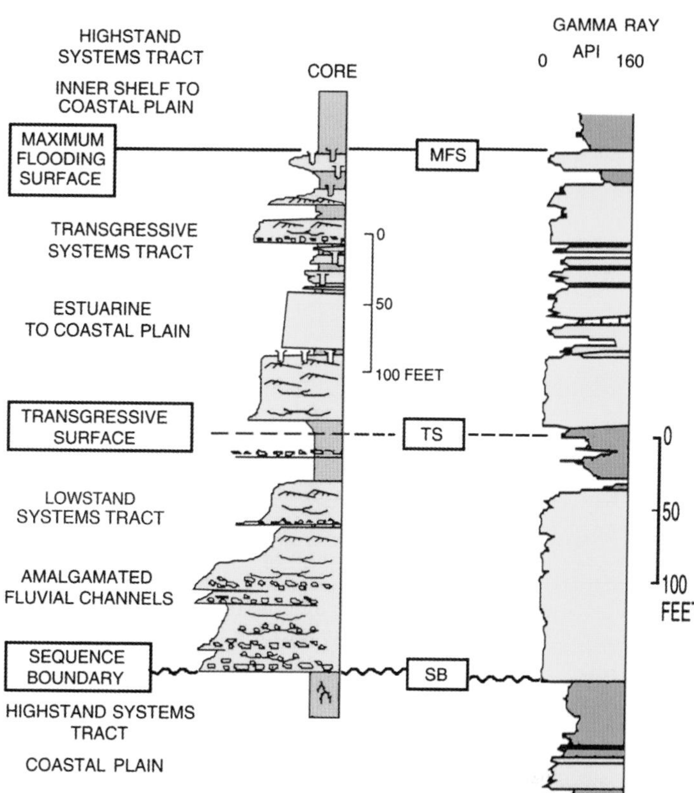

Figure 17.15 A sequence boundary (and other key sequence stratigraphic surfaces) in fluvial sediments. The sequence boundary marks the base of the lowstand systems tract where coarse grained, fluvial channels rest unconformably on a surface showing erosion into highstand systems tract, coastal plain deposits (modified from Posamentier and Allen 1999).

Regressive Surface of Marine Erosion (RSME) (base of forced regression)

When sea-level falls faster than accommodation space is created, the shoreline retreats towards the basin in so-called 'forced regression'. Previously deposited sediments will be exposed to wave and tidal erosion and a complex, diachronous set of erosion surfaces may be left in the sediment record.

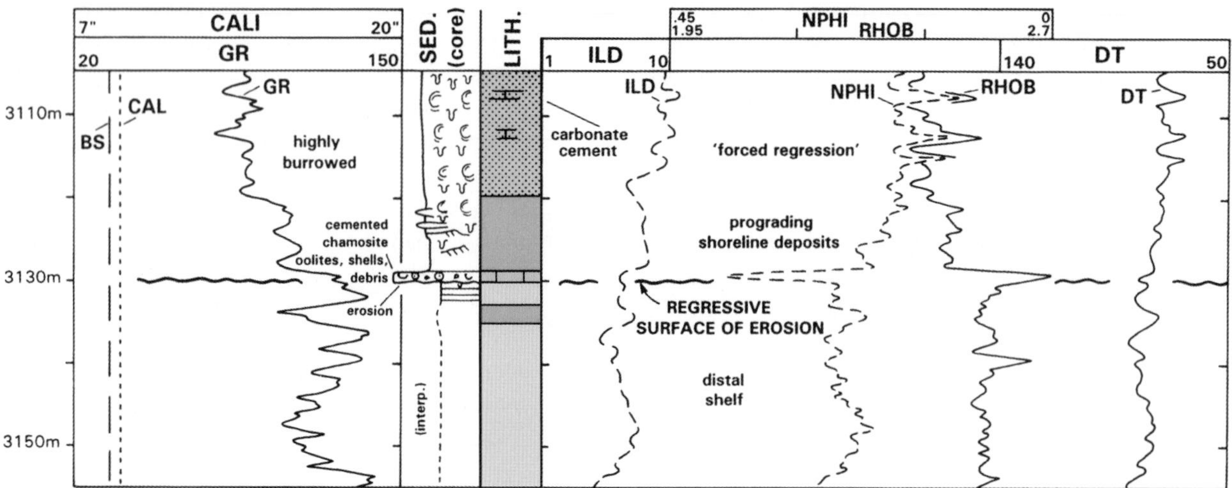

Figure 17.16 Regressive surface of erosion log example. The interpreted environments of prograding shoreline deposits overlying distal shelf shales, indicate a 'basinward shift of facies' and shallowing water. However, the erosion surface is succeeded by progradation, indicating a forced regression. The surface itself is covered by chamosite oolites, the chamosite being indicated on the neutron-density response.

In the example used here, the core shows an abrupt, upward change from a very clean, distal marine shale to a sequence of shallow marine, bioturbated, deposits, coarsening-upwards from very silty shale at the base to fine sand with carbonate stringers (**Figure 17.16**). The clean shale and the bioturbated silt are separated by a thin horizon with reworked chamosite oolites, shell debris and occasional, small, phosphate pebbles. The base of the bed is interpreted to show erosion, and is sharp. Regional correlation shows this bed is quite widespread and is interpreted as a regressive surface of marine erosion (Plint 1988).

The neutron-density logs of this example show well the abrupt boundary between the clean shales and the silty, coarsening-up (shaling-up) succession above (**Figure 17.16**). At the boundary itself, this log combination shows very unusual responses, the density increasing as the neutron also increases. Strange log responses, as previously proposed, are typical of key surfaces and used for their identification in an electrosequence analysis (Chapter 16). In this example, the unusual neutron-density response is caused by the hydrated iron mineral, chamosite (cf. **Figure 10.22**), and marks the winnowed, erosion surface seen on the core.

In sequence stratigraphic terms, this example is explained by proposing that the underlying, distal marine shelf shales have been eroded because of lowered sea (base) level in so called 'forced regression'. The coarsening-up sequence that developed over the erosion surface shows that a new shoreline developed but basinward of any previous shoreline. There is a 'basinward shift in facies' from the marine shelf below to the shallow shoreface above, a break in the normal sequence of facies.

Log responses alone are insufficient to recognise this surface as a regressive surface of (marine) erosion and it is only with core, micropalaeontological information, and correlation with other wells, that this diagnosis becomes credible. Some workers (Possamentier and Allen 1988, 1999) call this erosion surface a sequence boundary (onset of forced regression); others (Hunt and Tucker 1992) put the sequence boundary above the coarsening-up sequence (end of forced regression).

Maximum Regressive Surface (MRS)

Certain surfaces in sequence stratigraphy are more idea than physical presence. They are cryptic. They logically exist in a particular model and are typically extensions of actual physical surfaces. Their use in sequence stratigraphy can be likened to the use of zero in mathematical constructions. Zero does not exist, but, without it, mathematical constructions would not exist either. Without cryptic surfaces, sequence stratigraphy would be incomplete.

The maximum regressive surface is partly such a cryptic surface in that it represents the notional moment when maximum regression is reached, that is, the maximum advance of the shoreline into the basin. It is therefore the opposite of the maximum flooding surface and separates regression (progradation) below from transgression above. It can be recognised as a surface of maximum regression from changes in stacking patterns (explained below), changes in some log patterns and subtle changes in lithology. For example, within the basin there can be a tendency for shales to become more silty during regression as the sediment source (nonetheless distant) comes closer, but the reverse, less silty during transgression as the source retreats. The example shows the effect of the 'turnaround' on a set of sonic

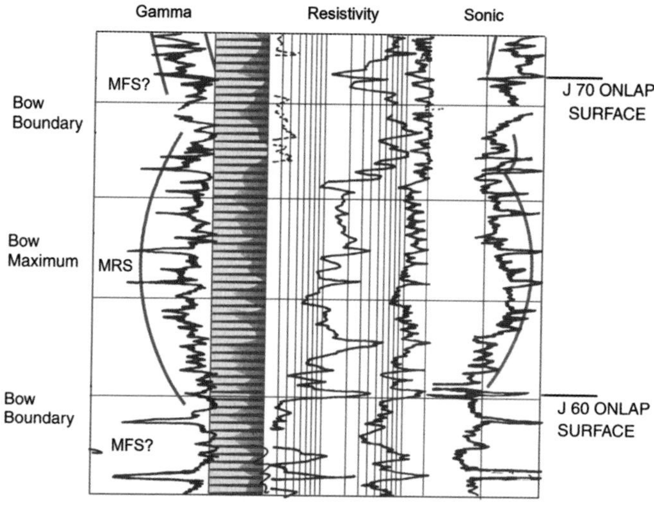

Figure 17.17 Maximum regression in fine grained, deeper water shales marked by a 'bow' in the gamma ray and sonic log responses. The maximum regressive surface (MRS) is taken at the lowest value of the gamma ray bow (the most silty) and minimum sonic (highest velocity) (modified fom Emery and Myers 1996).

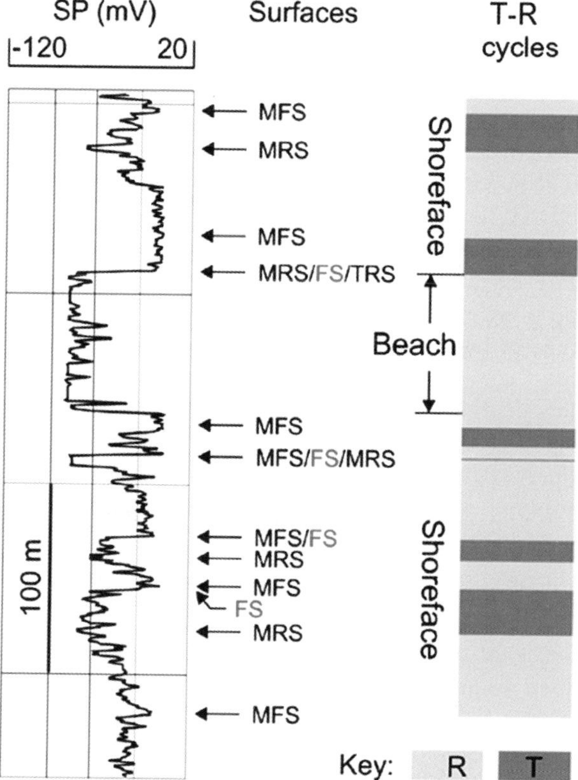

Figure 17.18 High frequency maximum regressive (MRS), maximum flooding (MFS) and flooding surfaces (red FS) in an upstepping series of parasequences. T-R sequences are defined by the maximum regressive surfaces (MRS). Genetic stratigraphic sequences are defined by the maximum flooding surfaces (MFS). Parasequences are defined by the flooding surfaces (FS). T = transgression: R = normal regression (modified from Catuneanu *et al.* 2010).

and resistivity logs (**Figure 17.17**).

The maximum regressive surface is used as the sequence limit in the transgressive-regressive (T-R cycle) model (Embry and Johanessen 1992). In certain environments, both maximum regressive and maximum flooding surfaces can be used as high frequency surfaces to denote where transgression changes to regression (MFS), and regression changes to transgression (MRS) (**Figure 17.18**). This theoretically allows any interval to be divided into transgressive-regressive (T-R) sequences but puts a heavy reliance on lithological changes, which may not be warranted.

17.4 Sequence stratigraphy: the building blocks

Sequence stratigraphy is often treated as hierarchical in that the events that are higher in the hierarchy are more important, are considered to affect larger areas, and may take longer to form, even though, as explained, this is a hierarchy of convenience. For instance, delta lobe switching will affect only that lobe, the sequence caused by the switching will be correlatable only over that lobe and will not indicate a basin-wide event. Large sea-level movements, however, will affect the entire delta, the entire basin and all depositional environments: evidence for the event will be widespread. These notional concepts are behind the following descriptions.

Parasequences (in this text) are the lowest building blocks in the sequence stratigraphic hierarchy to be considered. Above them are parasequence-sets, which are formed from nested parasequences. A systems tract, the next entity, is made of parasequence sets (**Figure 17.1**). This is the classic arrangement. However, sequences may be made up of just a single parasequence or even a set of facies. What is identified today as a sequence tends to be rather variable. The classic arrangement is used here by way of example.

Parasequence, parasequence set

To identify a *parasequence* (sedimentary cycle) on the logs, both the succession of facies and their bounding (marine flooding) surfaces should be used. A single parasequence has already been illustrated (**Figure 17.2**). The additional example used here shows three parasequences bounded by coals and flooding surfaces (**Figure 17.19**). The parasequence defining flooding surfaces are seen as high gamma ray, high neutron responses immediately above the coals, although the responses are masked to some extent by the coals themselves (cf. **Figure 17.2**). The individual parasequences are seen as persistent, upwards changes on the logs (or trends in electrosequence parlance, Chapter 16), gamma ray decrease, resistivity increase, neutron decrease and so on (**Figure 17.19**).

In Exxon terminology, these three parasequences

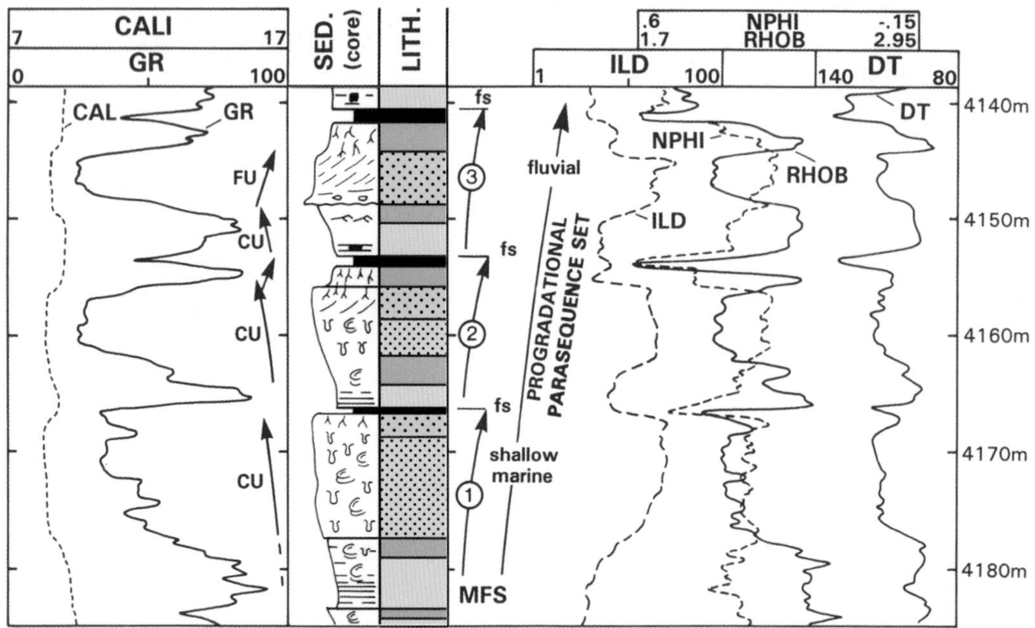

Figure 17.19 Example of a progradational parasequence set. Progressively upwards: the sands become coarser grained; and with higher energy structures; the coals become thicker; and the parasequences become thinner (rate of accommodation less than rate of sedimentation). A maximum flooding event is interpreted at the base of the parasequence set, indicating that these are highstand deposits. fs = flooding surface, MFS = maximum flooding surface, CU = coarsening-up, FU = fining-up.

form a parasequence set. That is, from one parasequence to the next, they show progressively changing characteristics which, in this case, are: they get progressively thinner upwards, the sands get cleaner and more porous (shown by the neutron-density separation), their depositional environment gets shallower, with the fining-up successions getting thicker and both the seat earths and coals getting more important. The environment seems to have been shallowing by steps, each cycle being deposited closer to the shoreline before being covered by the limiting transgression. This is a *prograding parasequence set* (Van Wagoner *et al.* 1990), and the progressive thinning of each set suggests that the rate of progradation was increasing (rate of sediment input constant).

In the classic sequence stratigraphic hierarchy, parasequence sets form systems tracts.

Systems tracts

A systems tract is a *'linkage of contemporaneous depositional systems'* (Posamentier *et al.* 1988), where depositional systems are three dimensional successions of facies. Originally, three systems tracts were recognised: lowstand, transgressive and highstand, although the lowstand is now divided into early and late (forced regressive and normal regressive) systems tracts. A combination of systems tracts forms the sequence (**Figure 17.1**) which is deposited during one major rise and fall of sea-level (Vail *et al.* 1977). The schematic SP, or gamma ray log characteristics of each of the original systems tracts as defined by Exxon, are shown as published (Vail and Wornardt, 1990) (**Figure 17.20**).

A sequence may be made up of all systems tracts or, quite often, just some. For example, a highstand systems tract may be followed by a transgressive systems tract, the lowstand being missing. In the preceding log example (**Figure 17.19**), the prograding parasequence set is bounded at the base by a condensed section, interpreted as a maximum flooding surface, and therefore makes up a highstand systems tract (cf. **Figure 17.20**). This type of highstand parasequence set appears to be the most common, or perhaps easiest to identify, in shallow marine sediments, although such sets should not automatically be attributed to the highstand sea-level phase as similar depositional patterns can develop during sea-level lowering and forced regression (Nummedal *et al.* 1995).

Sequences

Two examples attempt to show the application of a sequence stratigraphic analysis on real log data, rather than dealing in models. The first example is in shallow marine to shelf sediments, the second in deeper water sediments.

In the shallow marine example (**Figure 17.21**), the individual elements in the two selected wells are very distinct: a series of coarsening-up (cleaning-up) parasequences with, at their base, organic-rich condensed sequences overlying thin, burrowed, transgressive deposits. The top of the example section is a well marked, widespread erosional break (sequence boundary *sensu* Exxon); the base is interpreted as an erosional, transgressive surface. The sediments represent some 7–8 Ma.

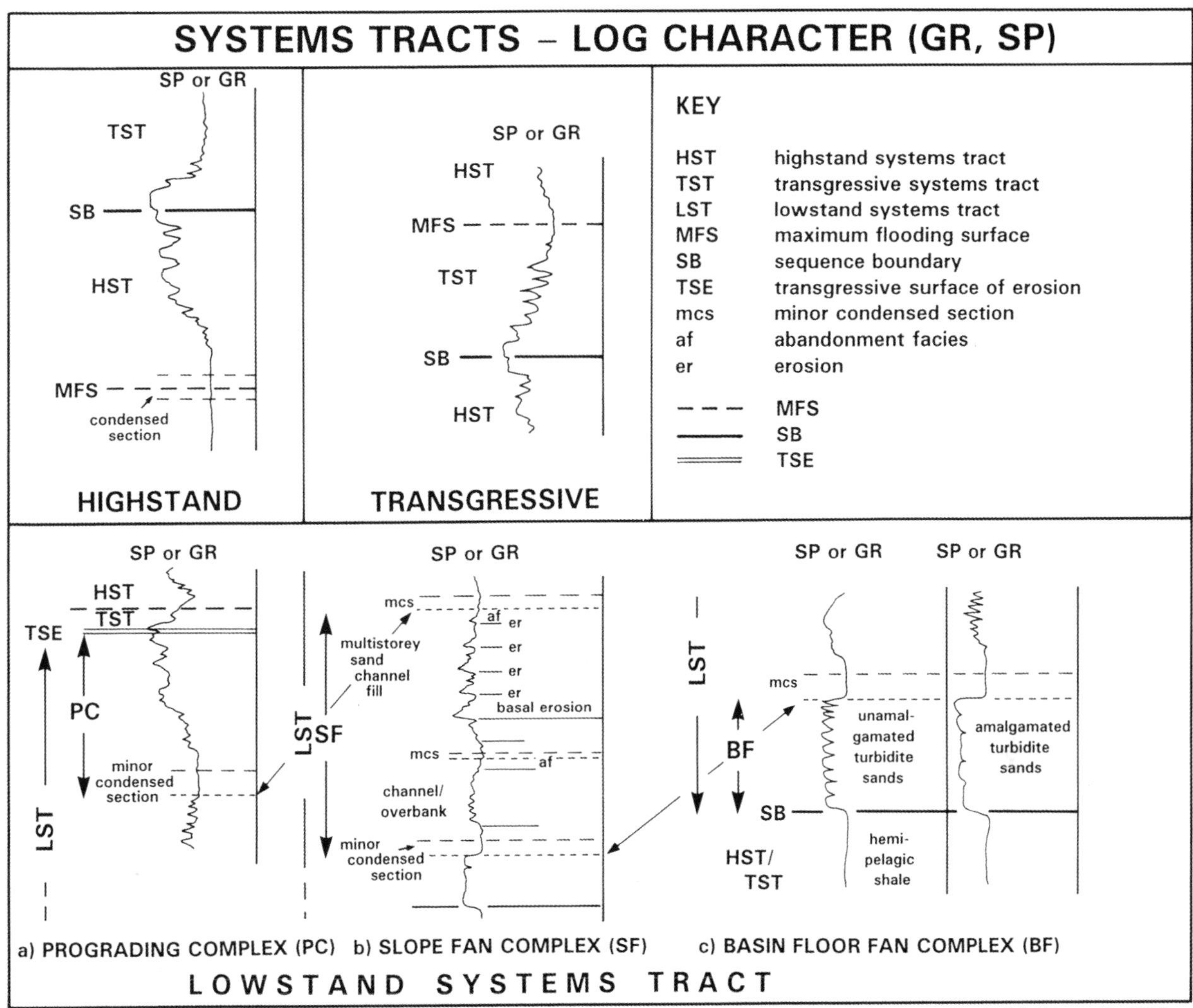

Figure 17.20 Model log patterns of sequence tracts, including deep water deposits (from Vail and Wornardt 1990).

From the study of over 100 wells covering 23,000 km^2 it is known that these parasequences can be correlated, and to some extent, dated. There are obviously changes, but there is a consistent framework made up of flooding surfaces, condensed sequences and closely preceding transgressive deposits. Good sands tend to be very localised. In the two example wells, when the section is broken down using the Exxon approach (**Figure 17.21**, left side), three depositional sequences are interpreted and the marked base of a fourth cuts off the section at the top. Highstand systems tracts dominate, the transgressive tracts are mostly very thin and a lowstand systems tract is only interpreted in sequence 3. The boundary between sequence 1 and 2 is unsatisfactory although the very marked condensed sequence is clear. Besides the highstand systems tracts (which are clearly progradational), the identification of other systems tracts is more dictated by what is required by the model than by a positive identification or a distinctive feature. With the genetic stratigraphic sequence approach (**Figure 17.21**, right side), four genetic stratigraphic, transgressive-regressive sequences are very satisfactorily interpreted. However, the presence of sand in well A and not well B is not well brought out and the status of the surface at the top of the section is not clear.

The second example, of deeper water sands (**Figure 17.22**), is from a Palaeogene shelf edge area in the North Sea for which good quality seismic is available. The two wells are 2.5 km apart. A shale section occurs at both the bottom and at the top of the selected interval. The well logs do not show distinctive depositional patterns (as seen in the previous example) and the principal feature is a thick sand section with more or less prominent, but thin shale intervals. The wells appear reasonably similar and an established lithostratigraphy can be applied to both (**Figure 17.22**, right). However, the line diagram of the seismic shows that the apparent simplicity is false and that the true correlations between the two wells are very complex. The sequence stratigraphic analysis (**Figure 17.22**, left) would not be possible without

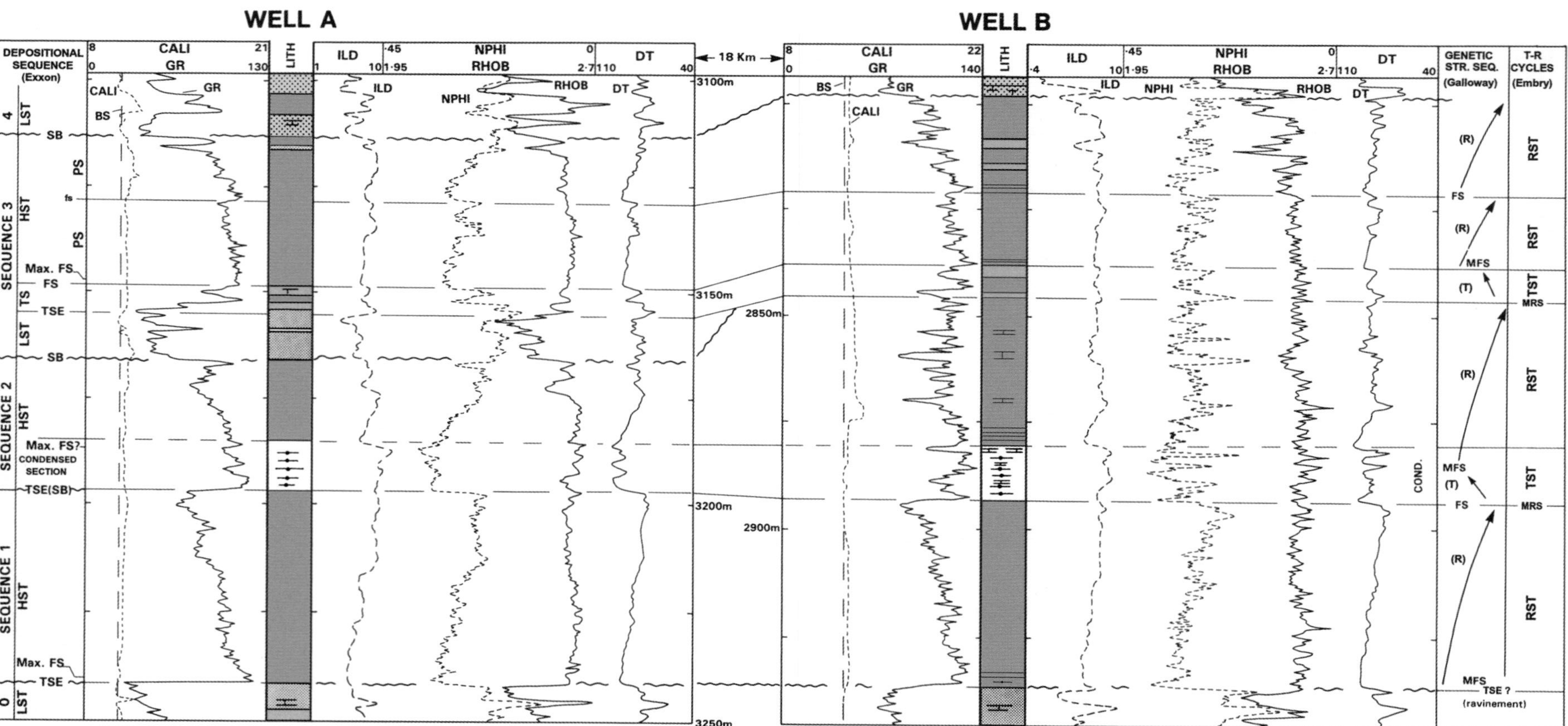

Figure 17.21 Description and correlation using sequence stratigraphic principles in shallow marine sediments. Exxon systems tracts and sequences on the left, Galloway genetic stratigraphic sequences and T-R cycles on the right. *See text* for discussion. Systems tracts:- HST = highstand, TS = transgressive, LST = lowstand, RST = regressive systems tracts. TSE = transgressive surface of erosion: (Max)MFS = (maximum) flooding surface: SB = sequence boundary: MRS = maximum regressive surface: FS flooding surface: PS = parasequence: (R) = regressive: (T) = transgressive.

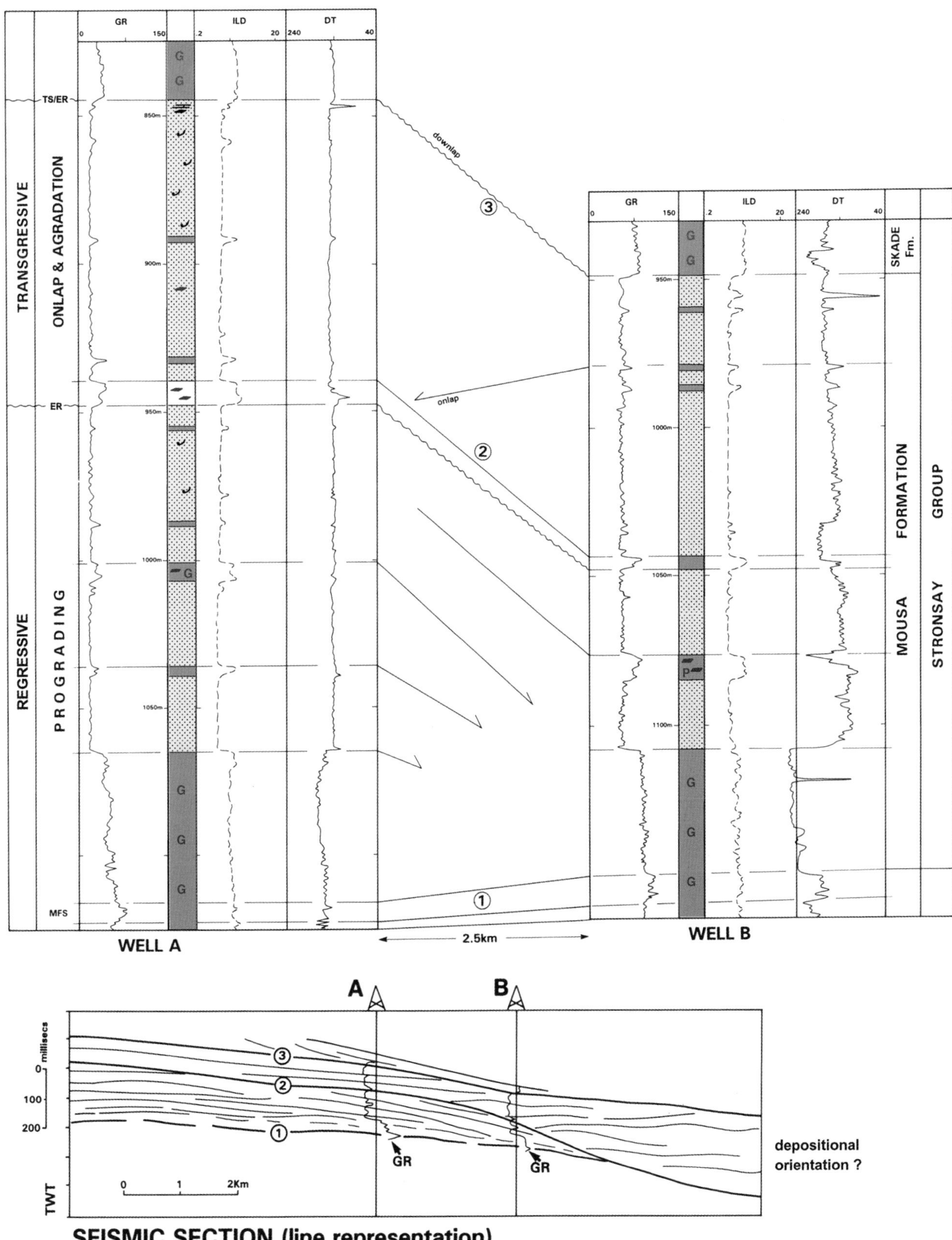

Figure 17.22 Description and correlation using seismic reflectors and sequence stratigraphic principles in deep water turbidite sediments. Without the seismic between the two wells, the correlation indicated would not have been possible. *See text* for discussion. MFS = maximum flooding surface: TS = transgressive surface: ER = erosion. Palaeogene, North Sea.

the seismic, but once in place the complexities can be explained. The sands near the bottom of the section are clearly downlapping on the seismic: they are prograding over a maximum flooding surface (horizon 1) visible on the logs. The sands themselves show internal reflectors on the seismic but no clear cyclicity on the logs; the sands are simply interrupted by shale intervals. The shale interval (horizon 2), correlated between the two wells on seismic evidence, is over a surface showing erosion and so possibly a sequence boundary (Exxon terminology). However, the erosion does not seem to have been subaerial. Above this, the section is markedly transgressive and onlapping, and there is no direct correlation between the wells. In addition, the depositional orientation of this wedge is not known. Finally, another surface showing erosion on the seismic (horizon 3) ends the section and explains the thickness differences in the upper section. The exact nature of this erosion surface is in question.

From this example, it is seen that the lithostratigraphy cannot contend with depositional complexity, that the well logs should not be correlated without the seismic and that tracing key surfaces is a natural result of integrating the logs with the seismic.

Computer techniques in (siliciclastic) sequence stratigraphy

The concepts of sequence stratigraphy are very sophisticated and based on a huge amount of observation and experience. It is inconceivable that such concepts should not make use of the modern technology available for the manipulation of logs. This section describes the senior author's attempts at using interactive computer techniques for the sequence stratigraphic analysis of logs.

The principal routine discussed is the interactive cross-plot. This routine consists of a screen on which a cross-plot is displayed and also the log traces furnishing the cross-plot data. Any two logs may be displayed at any scale over any selected interval. The cross-plot is interactively linked to the log curve display so that groups of points outlined on the cross-plot by a mouse driven rubber band, are immediately identified on the logs; conversely, intervals identified by a mouse defined box on the log curves are highlighted as coloured points on the cross-plot. In other words, points on the cross-plot can be identified on the curves, and intervals on the curves can be identified on the cross-plot. A third log may be added in the Z direction with the same facilities. The use of these capabilities will be illustrated by using real examples.

As was stressed in the work flow (**Figure 17.3**), an important step in sequence stratigrahic analysis is to identify key surfaces. As far as the logs are concerned, key surfaces tend to have extreme, and sometimes anomalous, log responses. This has been described. Condensed sections, for example, have higher than normal gamma ray values, lower than normal densities and so on. Using the interactive cross-plot screen is an effective way to identify these unusual values and to determine their position on the logs. The technique is to explore the few, scattered points on the cross-plot, that is, the outliers that usually surround the points of the main populations of shale, sandstone or limestone. These points may have a banal explanation but, on the other hand, often correspond to important and key surfaces.

The example shows gamma ray values (Y axis) plotted against neutron log values over 55 m of distal, marine shale (**Figure 17.23**). The main shale population is clear from the density of points. When the scattered points outside this main shale area and towards the high gamma ray values are interrogated, they indicate two intervals of high gamma ray (identified in orange on the right of the curve trace column in (**Figure 17.23**), which are interpreted as condensed sections. In addition, when the normal shale responses between the condensed sections are interrogated on the curve traces (green, light blue and dark blue coloured strips to the left of the curve column, **Figure 17.23**), the points highlighted on the cross-plot are in three distinct areas. It appears that there are three different shale types in the 55 m, separated by the condensed sections. The interpretation of this is that the long period of time represented by the condensed sections was sufficient, each time, to change the depositional conditions for the normal shales.

The second example shows an analysis of the neutron and density logs previously used in the electrosequence analysis (**Figure 16.20**) and work flow example (**Figure 17.3**). The small group of points interrogated on the cross-plot with high neutron porosity and low density values, beyond the main shale population, identify the interpreted condensed section and maximum flooding surface at the base of the illustrated interval (**Figure 17.24**). The large area of scattered points interrogated, with high density and low neutron values, identify the carbonate layers near the tops of the minor parasequences, and the few points with low density and low neutron values identify the interpreted transgressive interval at the top of the overall coarsening-up sequence (**Figure 17.3**). All these thin intervals are indicated on the right of the curve column in the appropriate colour and the points interrogated are outlined and labelled on the cross-plot (**Figure 17.24**).

On this same plot, sampling the curve traces through the coarsening-up sequence (intervals to the left of the curve traces) shows the gradual change in lithology from clean shale (interval 1), progressively to silty shales (intervals 2 and 3) and finally to sands (interval 4). This is a very typical form of neutron-density plot (**Figures 12.16–19**). In sequence stratigraphic terms, since the carbonate layers define a series of minor parasequences, this is interpreted as a coarsening-up, prograding, parasequence set. The maximum flooding surface at

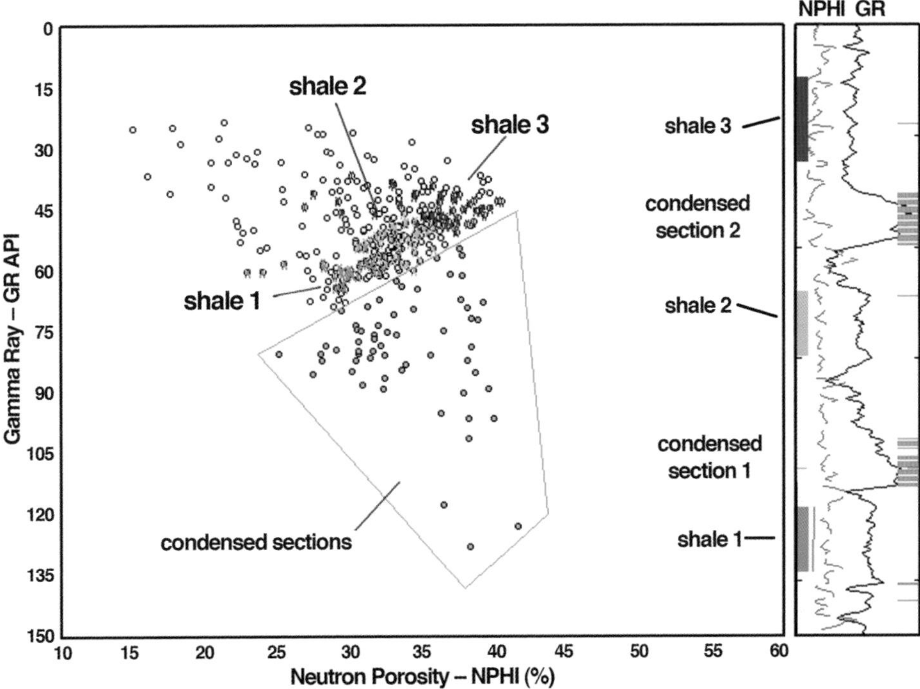

Figure 17.23 Condensed sections and deep water shales explored on an interactive, gamma ray - neutron log cross-plot. The data points from the condensed sections 1 and 2, show anomalous (unusual) log responses and are outlined on the cross-plot by the red box outside the normal shale population. The condensed sections separate three different shale populations: 1 (green), 2 (light blue) and 3 (dark blue). Each shale is seen to have different log responses on the cross-plot, indicating that the condensed sequences separate shales from different electrofacies (TerraStation software routine).

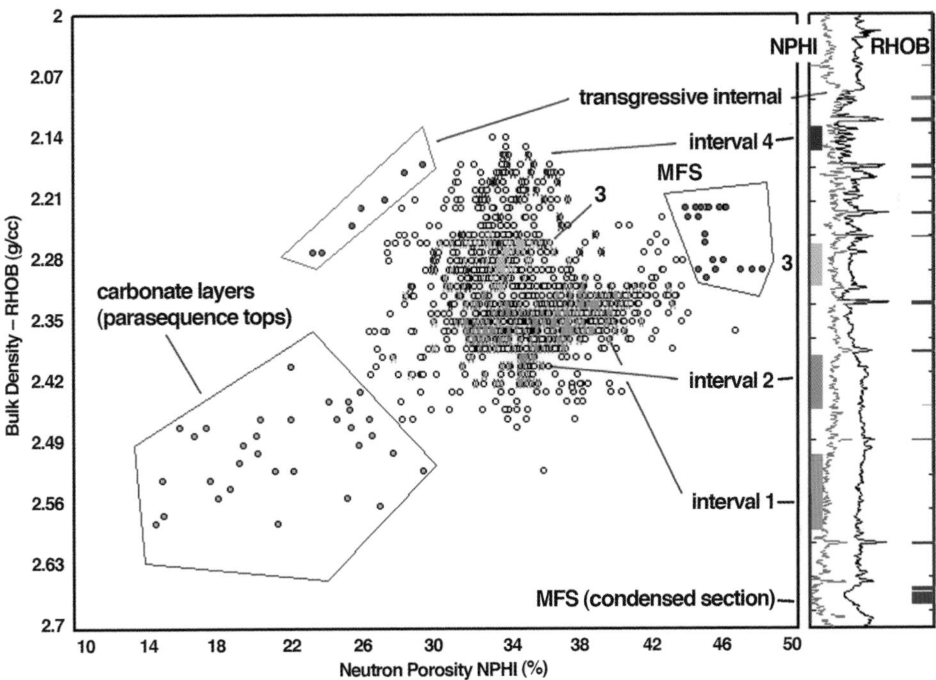

Figure 17.24 The prograding, parasequence set of Figure 17.3 (and Figure16.20) explored on an interactive neutron-density cross-plot. The progradation can be followed on the logs and the cross-plot as the deposits become progressively more sandy through interval 1 (orange), interval 2 (green), interval 3 (light blue) and interval 4 (purple). The transgressive interval shows cleaner sand responses. The calcium carbonate cemented layers, marking parasequence flooding events, are outlined by the box (cross-plot, left) and seen on the right margin of the log plot, in magenta. The condensed section interpreted as a maximum flooding surface is shown by the blue dots on the cross-plot and the blue bar on the log plot (TerraStation software routine).

the base allows it to be interpreted as a highstand systems tract (**Figure 17.3**).

The potential for showing the workings of interactive computer techniques in a book are obviously very limited. But the ability to interrogate and explore logs in this way brings out features that are otherwise missed or not recognised. Any combination of logs may be interrogated and it is common that unforeseen relationships are discovered which help the eventual interpretation. For instance, changes in shale composition can be very difficult to identify on cores, or even in outcrop, but the logs are very sensitive to such changes. The trend from transgression to regression is clearer on the logs than it is in cores (**Figure 17.17**), especially if cross-plots are used as outlined above. But it is probably the ability to investigate key surfaces on the logs which is especially important for sequence stratigraphy. The characteristics which allow these surfaces to be recognised in the rock record, of unusual mineral concentrations or high content of some constituents, are exactly the characteristics that allow these same surfaces to be identified on the logs by their unusual or unique geophysical responses.

In a book it is impossible to describe more.

17.5 Carbonate sequence stratigraphy

The difference between carbonates and siliciclastics

There are two significant properties that make carbonate sequence stratigraphy different from siliciclastic. The first is that carbonate sediments are derived in place (*in-situ*) and not transported in, as are siliciclastics. They are not detrital but come from the so called 'carbonate factory', a name given to the production of carbonate by biotic or abiotic means. Most familiar are tropical reefs which produce abundant carbonate, but only in the photic zone, or water generally less than 60 m (200 ft) deep. Sea-level changes are therefore seen in terms of carbonate production and not sediment supply. However, because production *does* vary with sea-level changes, sequence stratigraphic events do exist in carbonate sediments.

The second difference is that carbonates are affected by chemical dissolution, lithification and diagenesis. Carbonates exposed to rain water, which is slightly acidic, simply dissolve away and deep water carbonates can form lithified surfaces. This creates differences in the significance of carbonate sequence stratigraphic surfaces. So, although sequence stratigraphy can be applied to carbonates, details are different and models must be modified. Some of these are described below.

Carbonate depositional settings

Carbonate environments are influenced by two aspects, the geometry of the carbonate shelf and the type of carbonate factory.

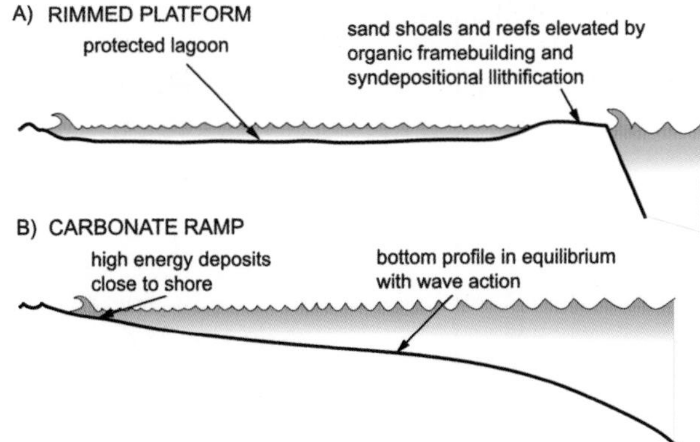

Figure 17.25 The rimmed platform and ramp geometries of typical carbonate depositional environments (modified after Schlager 2005).

Two main geometries are recognised, the rimmed platform and the ramp setting (**Figure 17.25**). Geometrically, rimmed platforms have a flat top, typically covered by a lagoon and tidal flats, with a protecting barrier reef or shoal facing the open ocean and a steep, up to 35° (or more), frontal slope which descends into deep water. The Great Barrier Reef in Australia is an obvious example. The carbonate ramp has a quite different geometry and is a gently sloping depositional surface, which drops gradually into deep water. It more resembles the shelf geometry of siliciclastics. Gharwar, the biggest oil field in the world of Kimmeridgian age, is interpreted as having a ramp setting (Lindsay *et al.* 2006). There are transitions between these two geometrical extremes and, for example, reefs grow up from ramps to form the familiar rimmed platform.

Carbonate factories, the second influence, can be divided into three types: tropical reefs, mud mounds and cool water carbonates (**Figure 17.26**) (Schlager 2005). Volumetrically, tropical reefs are the most abundant, even though production is restricted to the photic zone, the uppermost 60 m (200 ft) or less, of warm tropical waters, today essentially between 30° latitude north and south. Mud mound carbonate production occurs down to 400–500 m (1300–1600 ft) and is not restricted to the photic zone. The fine grained carbonate is precipitated in place to form hard or firm sediment, by biotic or abiotic processes, or a mixture of the two, processes not found in shallow, agitated water. Cool water carbonates are biotically precipitated by heterotrophic (carbon using) organisms and typically consist of a skeletal hash. They too can occur down to 400–500 m (1300–1600 ft) water depths and are geographically widespread, occurring today on the shelves around the British Isles and around Australia and New Zealand. However, they are volumetrically less important than the other factories.

The carbonate factories and the geometrical settings

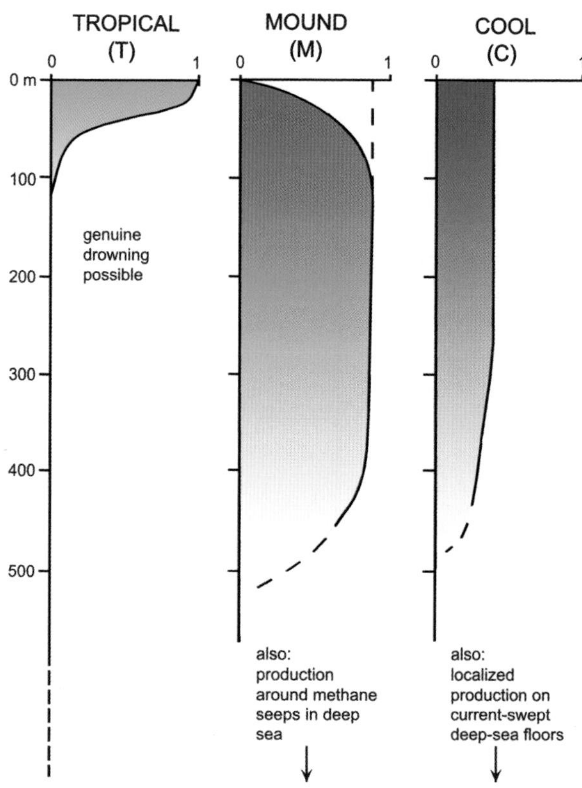

Figure 17.26 Schematic representation of the three carbonate 'factories' (from Schlager 2005).

are not strictly related. Nonetheless, tropical carbonate reefs form rimmed platforms and cool water carbonates form on ramps. Mud mounds will form in deeper water but can build to form platform rims. These relationships tend to form typical facies patterns and, as an example, reefs are associated with protected lagoons over the shelf top and talus and calci-turbidites on the steep slope in front (**Figure 17.27**). Such reefs may be detached from any land since the carbonate sediments are derived *'in situ'* as described. The Great Bahama Bank is the classic example of this type (Harris 2010, Schlager 2005).

Carbonate facies and well logs

To describe carbonate facies, specialists use a whole range of sedimentological, palynological, palaeoecological and lithological information (e.g. Padwellek and Aigner 2003). In the subsurface, all this information is only available from core, which means that carbonate facies studies are essentially core based. Central to these core studies is the recognition of carbonate textures, the Dunham (1962) scheme being the most commonly used (*i.e.* Schlager 2005). Similar facies and texture investigations using well logs are very difficult. The identification of carbonate textures using single trace logs (standard logs) is often unsuccessful because several textures can have the same standard log response (Wang *et al.* 2008). This was noted previously (Chapter 16). In the past, there was no other solution. Now, however, image logs can be used to explore textures in two dimensions and also to identify facies (*i.e.* Collins *et al.* 2006).

The use of image logs, especially high resolution electrical images, in carbonate analysis has grown considerably in recent years and will continue to grow. However, core information to calibrate the images is essential. The example chosen shows high resolution electrical images interpreted in terms of carbonate textures (**Figure 17.28**) (Collins *et al.* 2006 *ibid.*). Despite their detail, the images are difficult to understand in familiar terms, many elements are below image log resolution and require core to be understood. For example, rudstone, a grain supported carbonate that lacks sparite matrix and has more than 10% large grains, creates a typical 'look' to the images despite

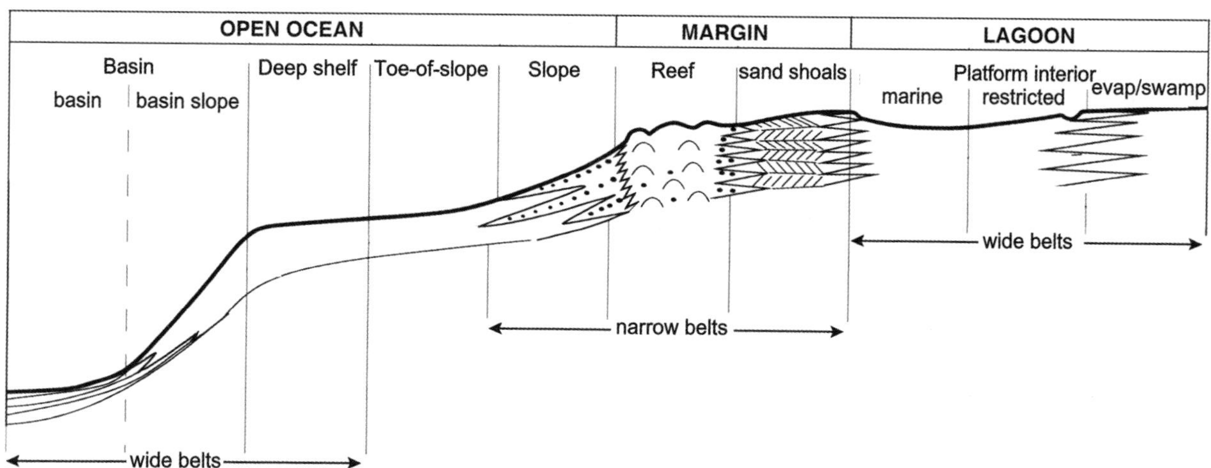

Figure 17.27 Typical carbonate facies as they may be encountered from platform interior, through a reef to deep water (modified after Wilson 1975; Schlager 2005).

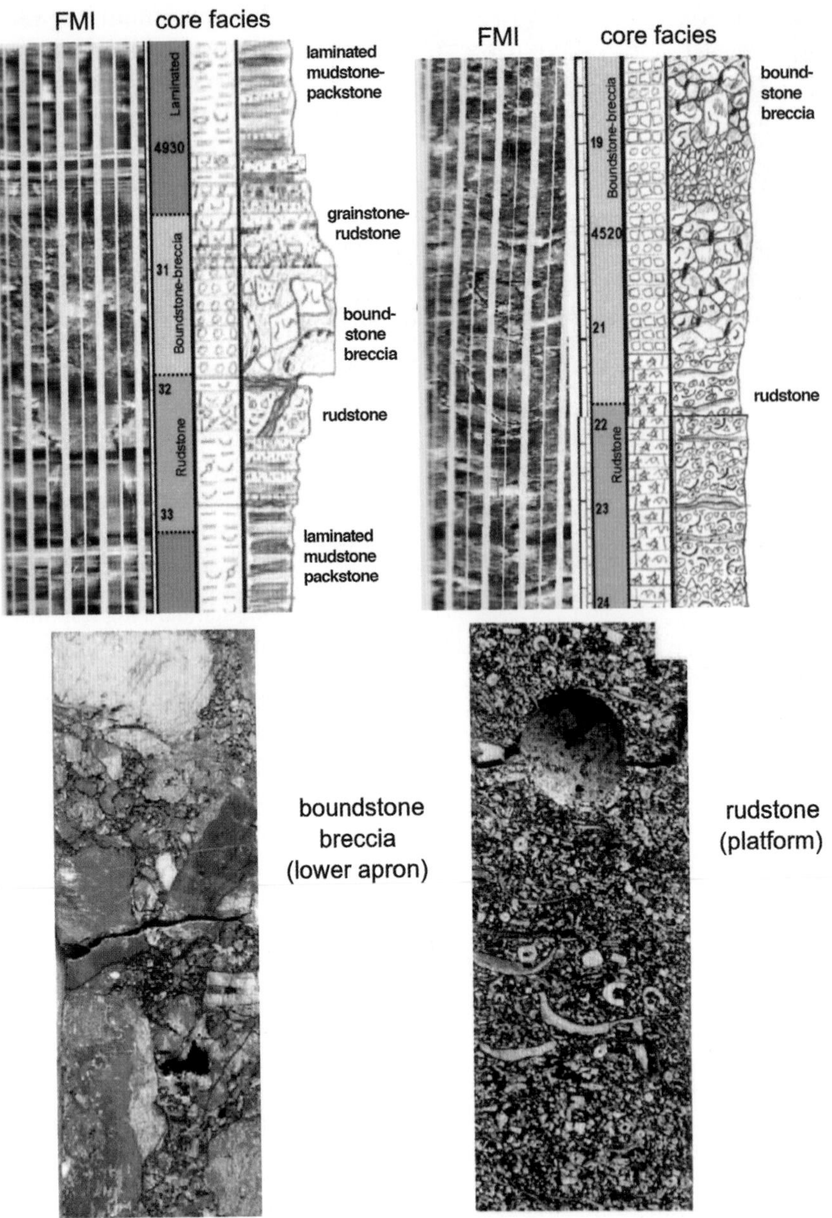

Figure 17.28 Carbonate facies of boundstone breccia (lower apron) and rudstone (platform) as seen on electrical image logs (FMI) and core samples. Carbonate textures are too complex to be characterised by the standard logs but high resolution, wireline electrical images can be distinctive, as in this example (modified after Collins *et al.* 2006). AAPG© (2006) *reprinted by permission of the AAPG whose permission is required for further use.*

the individual elements being largely un-identifiable (**Figure 17.28**). Calibration of this 'image texture' to core allows rock facies to be identified. In other cases, elements are remarkably resolved and allow an immediate diagnosis (**Figure 17.29**). The use of image logs for carbonate facies identification is a developing skill.

Sequence stratigraphic settings

Carbonate surfaces

The dominant surfaces in carbonate successions are exposure surfaces and flooding surfaces: a single surface may record the two events. Physical erosion is less important than in siliciclastics, and the significance of some surfaces may be ambiguous.

Because carbonates are more strongly affected by dissolution than physical erosion (Schlager 2005), this affects how exposure surfaces are expressed. Surfaces which show erosion in siliciclastic sequences will tend to show dissolution, lithification and re-precipitation in carbonates. Dissolution is the chemical reaction by which carbonate dissolves in fresh, meteoric water or deep sea-water undersaturated in calcium carbonate. For example, the subaerial unconformity surface (Exxon sequence boundary) is mainly expressed in

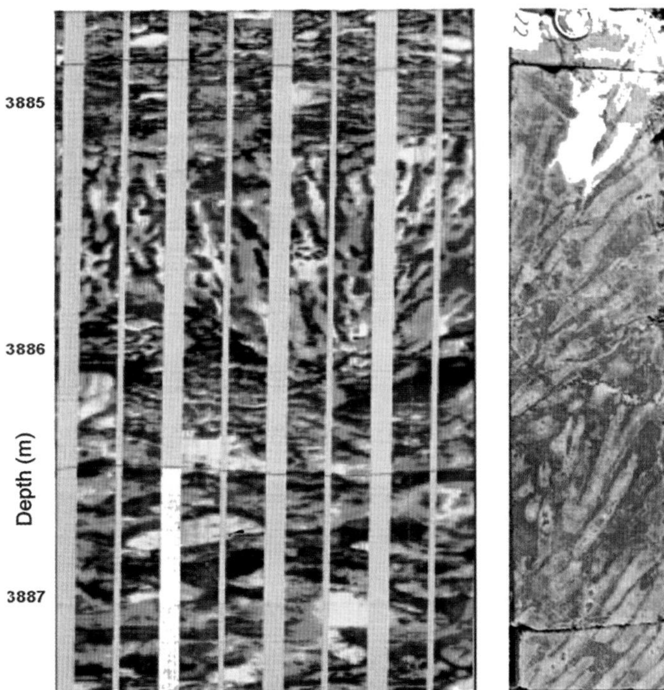

Figure 17.29 A coral in growth position seen in core and shown perfectly on electrical, wireline log images (FMI). The usefulness of such high resolution images in carbonate work is self evident (from Weissenberger *et al.* 2006). AAPG© (2006) *reprinted by permission of the AAPG whose permission is required for further use.*

carbonates as a karst, a surface over which there is dissolution by meteoric water and local re-precipitation. Physical erosion is not so important. As far as well logs are concerned, such textures are probably only recognisable on electrical image logs. Some authors, however, report increased values of uranium associated with exposure surfaces, and this allows them to be identified on the spectral gamma ray log (**Figure 8.28**) (Raddadi *et al.* 2005, Ehrenberg and Svånå 2001). In the deep sea, dissolution may also occur and lead to lithification and formation of a marine hardground. This must not be confused with the effects of subaerial exposure.

Flooding events in carbonates are not expressed in the same way as in siliciclastics. During flooding and transgression, accommodation space for carbonate growth (or precipitation) will simply be created and there will be no erosion, especially if the transgression is over a firm or lithified older surface. The underlying level will simply be covered by a new growth of corals or other sediments (**Figure 17.29**). In fact, flooding may be expressed only as a change from shoaling to deepening facies, so called 'turnaround' (Yose *et al.* 2006, Padwellek and Aigner 2003). Because lithification is important on carbonate platforms, exposure and subsequent drowning may be combined in the same surface and the two events not able to be separated in the sediment record.

Maximum flooding is reported, in mid-Cretaceous carbonates, to be marked by a gamma ray peak associated with an increase in uranium content (Raddadi *et al.* 2005). The origin of the uranium concentration is not certain but may be associated with abundant echinoid fragments found in the flooding interval. It is not certain if this type of occurrence is typical. Other major flooding intervals reported are associated with hardgrounds, or simply with a turnaround from shallowing to deepening parasequences (Yose *et al.* 2006 *op. cit.*). However, in cases where the environmental change accompanying maximum flooding is considerable and rapid, black shales rich in organic matter are found (**Figure 17.30**) (Calner *et al.* 2010).

Some workers have found that surfaces in carbonate sequences are either not present or do not correspond to environmental changes. For example, sequences in the deeper ramp deposits of the Upper Jurassic and S.W. Germany are interpreted to consist of symmetrical deepening and shallowing half cycles (Padwellek and Aigner 2003). These may be driven by Milankovitch influences but there are no distinct surfaces separating the trends: deepening facies simply 'turn around' to shallowing facies through a transition. In another study of slightly older sediments from this same area (S.W. Germany), it was found that sequence turnarounds did not even correspond to apparent sequence stratigraphic boundaries (Ruf *et al.* 2005). The deepening and shallowing half cycles were identified by palynofacies but also by oxygen stable isotope trends, sea-level rise showing warming water, sea-level fall showing cooling water. Trends were more reliable indicators of relative sea level movement than the individual surfaces.

That there is difficulty recognising and classifying carbonate surfaces is illustrated, in addition, by the following example cited by Schlager (2005). A well through a Miocene reef crest in the South China Sea encountered in upwards order: *in situ* coral growth, exposure, subsequent deepening and finally drowning (**Figure 17.31**). The exposure surface is equivalent to the Exxon sequence boundary and is detected in the carbonate facies but has little seismic expression (Erlich *et al.* 1990). The final drowning surface, however, has a large seismic expression and shows apparent geometrical unconformity although on grounds of facies it can be suggested to represent maximum flooding and conformity. The gamma ray log does not respond to these events.

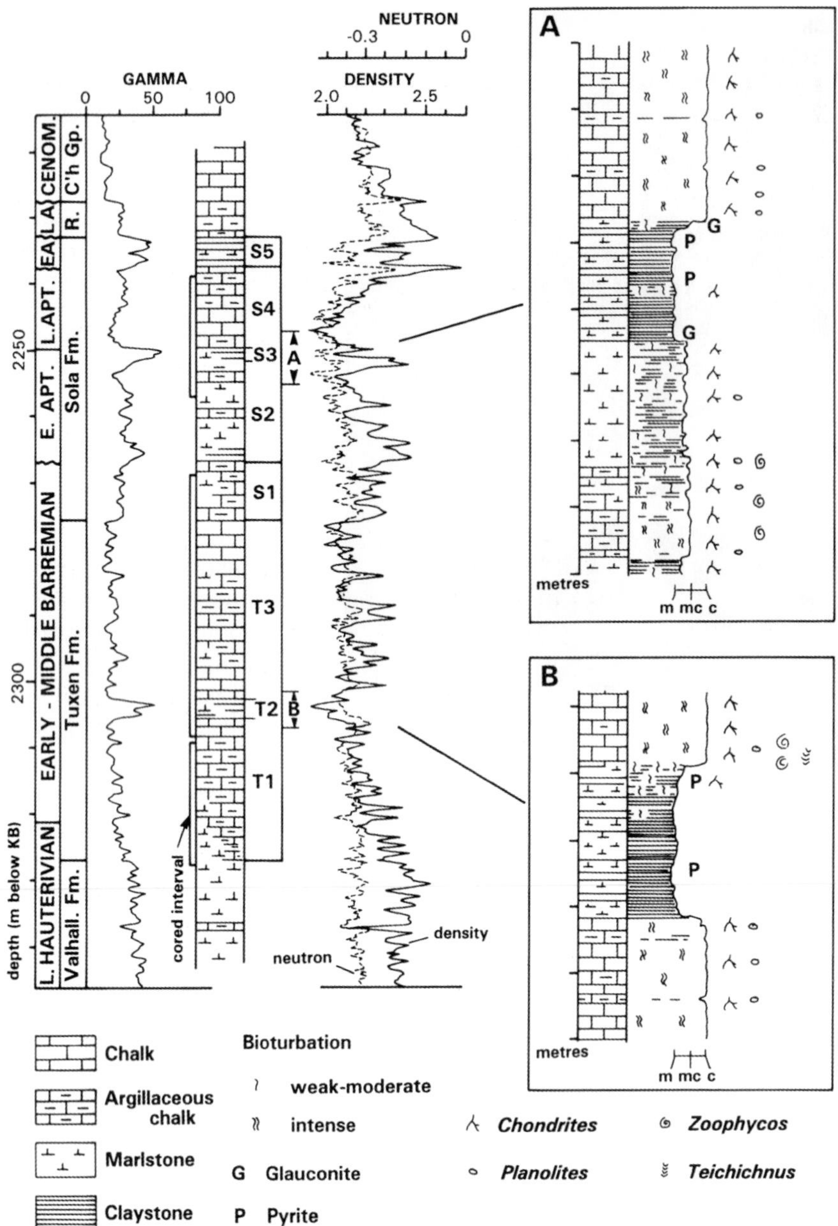

Figure 17.30 Organic rich condensed sequences from a carbonate succession. Lower Cretaceous, Danish North Sea (from Ineson 1993).

Carbonate parasequences

Carbonate parasequences show shoaling, deepening, and oscillating patterns in which neither deepening nor shallowing dominate. Carbonate parasequences are not dominated by shoaling (coarsening-up) sequences as are siliciclastics. In addition, the decrease in mud content from deep to shallow water environments that is typical in siliciclastic parasequences is not a feature of carbonates, and mud content frequently has no depth significance (except in some ramp settings, **Figure 16.21**). For instance, very shallow water lagoonal sediments are largely carbonate mud. In reef environments, where carbonate production is in the photic zone, shallowing-up is expressed by an increase in *in-situ* growth elements, not a decrease in mud (**Figure 17.27**).

The example used to illustrate carbonate, shallowing-up parasequences is from a ramp setting and shows fusilinid, wackestone-packstone (outer ramp) grading to peloidal packstone and wackestone and eventually ooid/peloid, grain dominated packstone (ramp crest) (**Figure 17.32**) (Rupple and Jones 2006). The shallowing trends are marked by an upwards increase in porosity, from low in deeper water peloidal sediments to the highest values in the biogenic, grain dominated sediments deposited in shallow, energetic

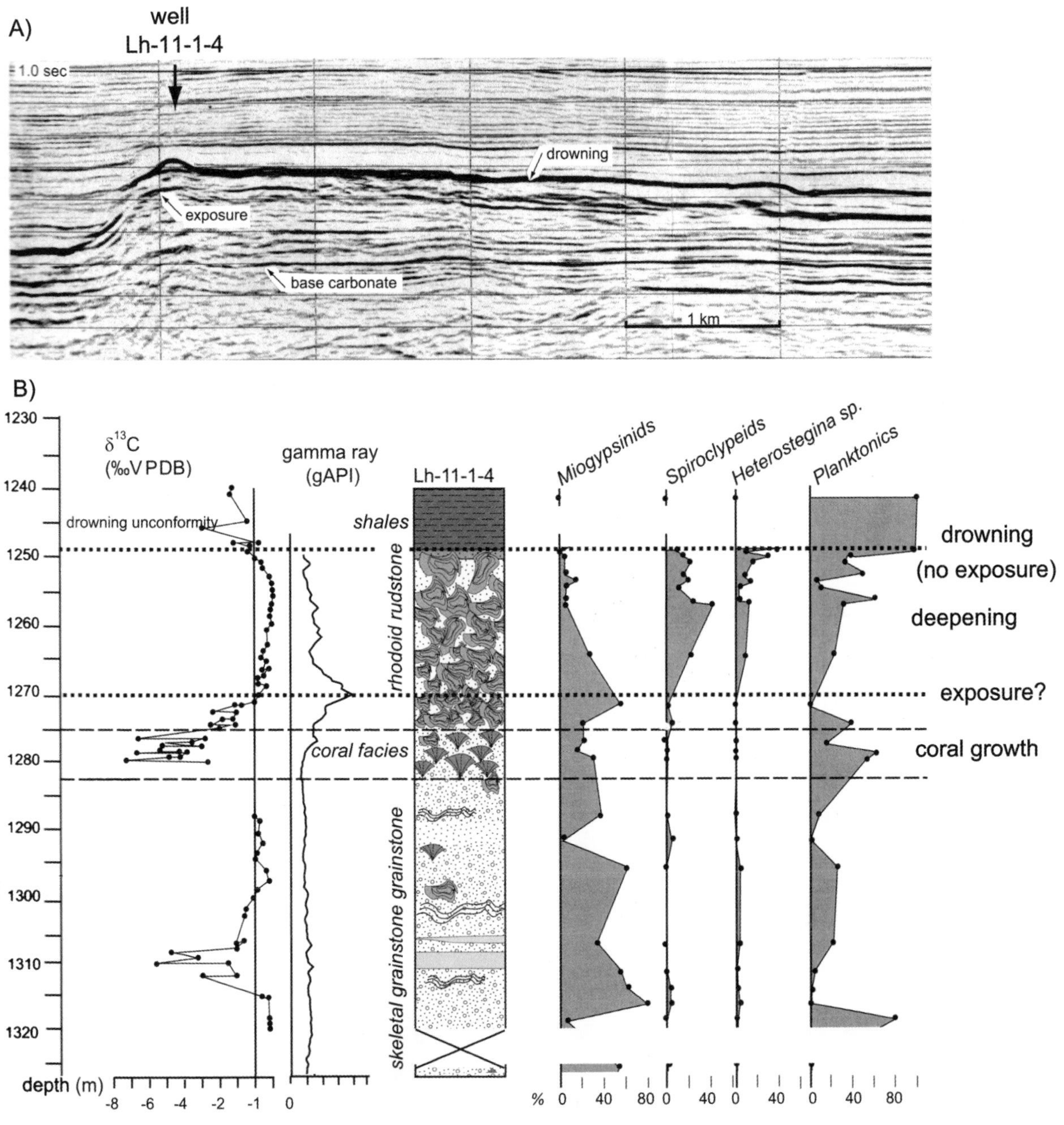

Figure 17.31 Log and seismic example of reef drowning. The eventual drowning of the reef leaves a complex record on the logs. The sequence stratigraphic interpretation of the surfaces and events involved is not as clear as it appears from the seismic (*see* text) (from Schlager 2005 and refs.).

water (Ruppel and Jones 2006 *ibid.*; Strohmenger *et al.* 2006). These facies related porosity trends can be derived from the density-neutron log combination (**Figure 17.32**). The gamma ray log, as is common in carbonates, shows no relationship to facies.

As previously suggested, textures in carbonates are complex and not adequately investigated by single trace logs. This importantly applies to porosity. The example shows a vuggy carbonate beautifully characterised by electrical images (**Figure 17.33**). A single log through such a distribution of voids would provide a similar porosity value for both the vuggy porosity shown and for a high matrix porosity, a quite different texture. This means that in the example above of shallowing-up parasequences, even though the neutron-density logs detect the general trends, the associated texture is not investigated.

Although the common carbonate parasequences show shallowing-up or deepening-up depositional facies related to sea-level movement, because carbonate production is related to light intensity, carbonates are also sensitive to climate change. Some successions,

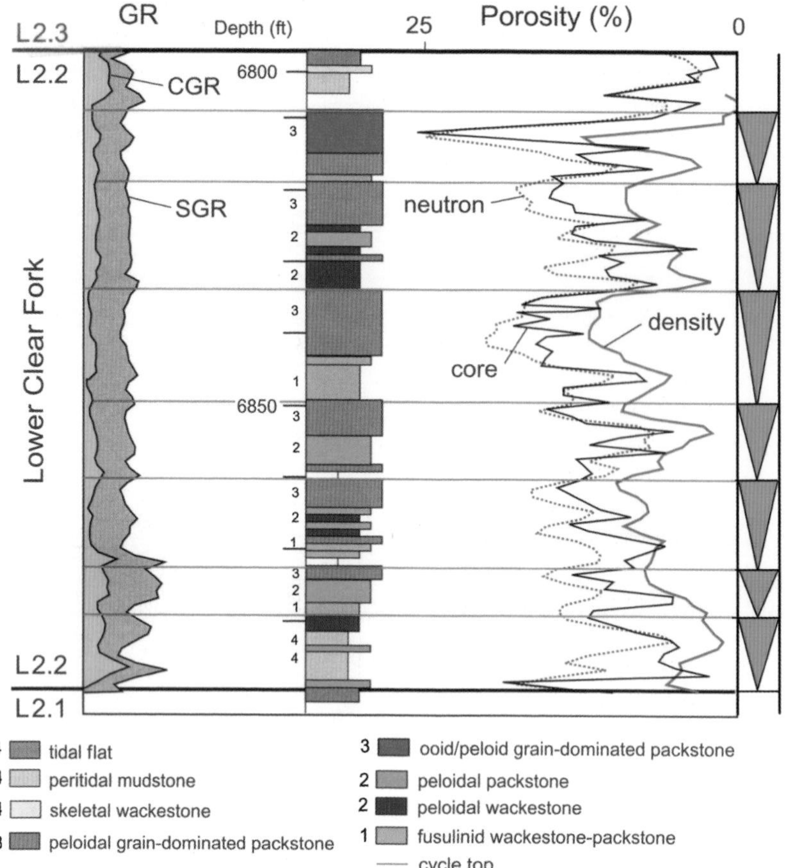

Figure 17.32 Shallowing-up carbonate sequences shown on the porosity logs (density and neutron). Porosity improves as the facies become shallower, as indicated by the core (and log) porosity. The gamma ray log gives no indication of the cyclicity (modified from Ruppel and Jones 2006). AAPG© (2006) *reprinted by permission of the AAPG whose permission is required for further use.*

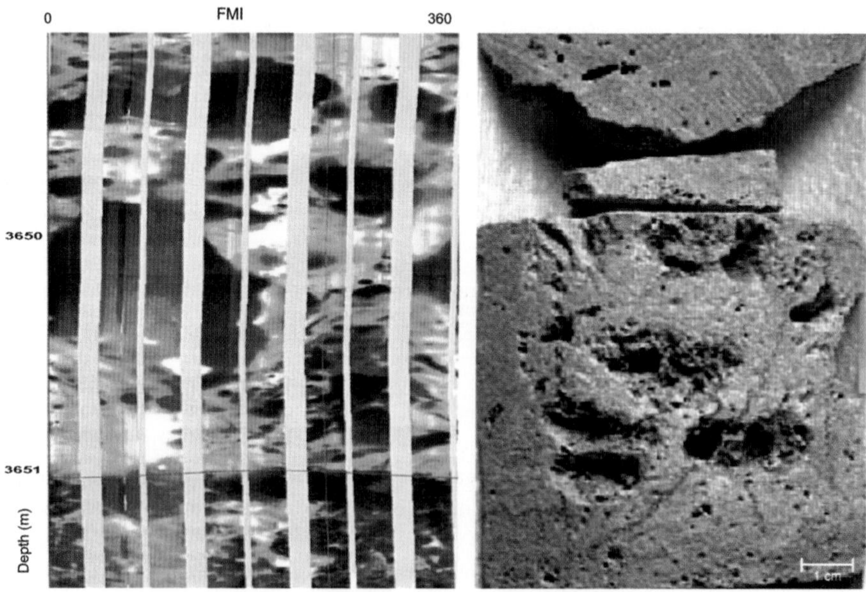

Figure 17.33 Vuggy porosity seen on core and in wireline, electrical images (FMI). Single curve logs cannot characterise this kind of heterogeneous porosity. High resolution electrical images can capture the two dimensions but require special interpretation to be effective (from Weissenberger *et al.* 2006). AAPG© (2006) *reprinted by permission of the AAPG whose permission is required for further use.*

for example, show subtle variations related to Milankovitch frequency rhythms, of solar intensity and orbital shape, which influenced the climatically controlled production of carbonate. This is clearly seen in the oscillating bedding repetitions (mainly couplets of hemipelagic chalk and marl) of the Upper Cretaceous chalk of Europe, which can be correlated over a wide area from Spain to Germany and the UK (Gale 1995).

Carbonate systems tracts

In reef settings, carbonate systems tracts are dominated by highstand and transgressive systems, the lowstand being thin and limited in extent. This is because, when sea-level falls and the reef-top is exposed, no more carbonate is produced and the carbonate factory shuts down. Lowstand deposits consist of only a narrow band of active reefs building on the steep slope of the ancient reef front, there being no wide platform top or lagoon. Slumps are considered to be common in lowstand sediments and facies are dominated by reef and reef front debris.

During transgression and highstand, rising sea-level adds more space and stimulates the carbonate factory, which has its highest rates of production in shallow water. Transgressive and highstand tracts both, therefore, have extensive platform areas (*cf.* **Figure 17.31**). That is, behind the reef front are large, flat, platform tops with lagoons and tidal shoals. During transgression, sea-level rise outstrips growth and the platform is flooded: parasequences backstep. In highstands, however, the rate of growth is equal to or exceeds the rate of sea-level rise: reefs grow vertically upwards and patch reefs can occur in lagoons over the platform. When there is excess carbonate production, it is shed either into the lagoon, but mainly into deeper water on the reef front, so called 'highstand shedding'. The deposits may be calci-tubidites, slumps or storm deposits. There is therefore important sediment accumulation in deep water during carbonate highstand periods, which is the opposite of significant deep water deposition during siliciclastic lowstands.

Comment

This section on carbonate sequence stratigraphy is unsatisfactory from a logging point of view. The inability of single trace logs to detect the complexities of carbonate facies has been emphasised. The use of high resolution electrical image logs has been proposed as a partial remedy to this. In addition, the nuclear resonance imaging log may be used to characterise the pore systems (Chapter 13). Both logs are being applied with some success. However, image logs in carbonates suffer from difficult acquisition conditions and NMR from difficult processing conditions. This will not diminish their use in the future: it will clearly develop. While no satisfactory general methodology for logs in carbonates is proposed, it is hoped that this section has pointed out how and why carbonates differ from siliciclastics and which methods should *not* be applied, especially, of course, unquestioning use of the gamma ray.

17.6 Lithostratigraphy

Type subsurface stratigraphy

It must be remembered that sequence stratigraphy, exciting as it may be, like humans, had humble beginnings. And these beginnings are as important as the present evolutionary state. The simplest use of well logs, and still very important, is in the identification of lithostratigraphic units. Such units allow a well to be divided up into intervals which anybody can identify, regardless of requirements, both in other wells and even at outcrop.

It is good practice to define type lithostratigraphic units. Just as type stratigraphic sections exist at outcrop, so type wells can be designated in the subsurface for particular lithostratigraphic formations. Well logs form the basis for these definitions. The various lithological units for the North Sea, for example, have been defined by the government agencies of the countries concerned (Rhys. 1975; Deegan and Scull, 1977; NAM/RGD, 1980; Vollset and Doré, 1984; Knox and Cordey, 1992). Each lithological unit can now be illustrated in terms of depositional sequences and biostratigraphic events, in addition to the defining well log signatures (**Figure 17.34**).

On a different scale, the stratigraphy of a particular field may be described using a type well and well logs to illustrate each lithostratigraphic interval (e.g. Jamison *et al.* 1980). Names in fields are frequently specific to the operating company. The illustration of the named intervals using well logs enables them to be identified outside the field and by other companies. It avoids annoying name confusion.

The modern North American tendency is to prefer allostratigraphy to lithostratigraphy in defining formal units (NACSN, 1983). Allostratigraphy uses the bounding limits of a sediment interval to define it, contrary to lithostratigraphy which defines what the interval is. In terms of well logs, it is far easier to define the response of the interval itself, even though there are shortcomings, than to define a limiting surface, which can be difficult or impossible to detect.

17.7 Correlation methods

Correlations at outcrop

Before a field is developed, widely spaced exploration wells are correlated in detail over the reservoir interval and predictions made for the infill producer wells about to be drilled. As all geologists know, there are always surprises during the infill phase. Some intervals show unattended continuity, others have unexpected variations. Work at outcrop tends to put a rather sober note on the possibilities for subsurface correlation, at least in some facies.

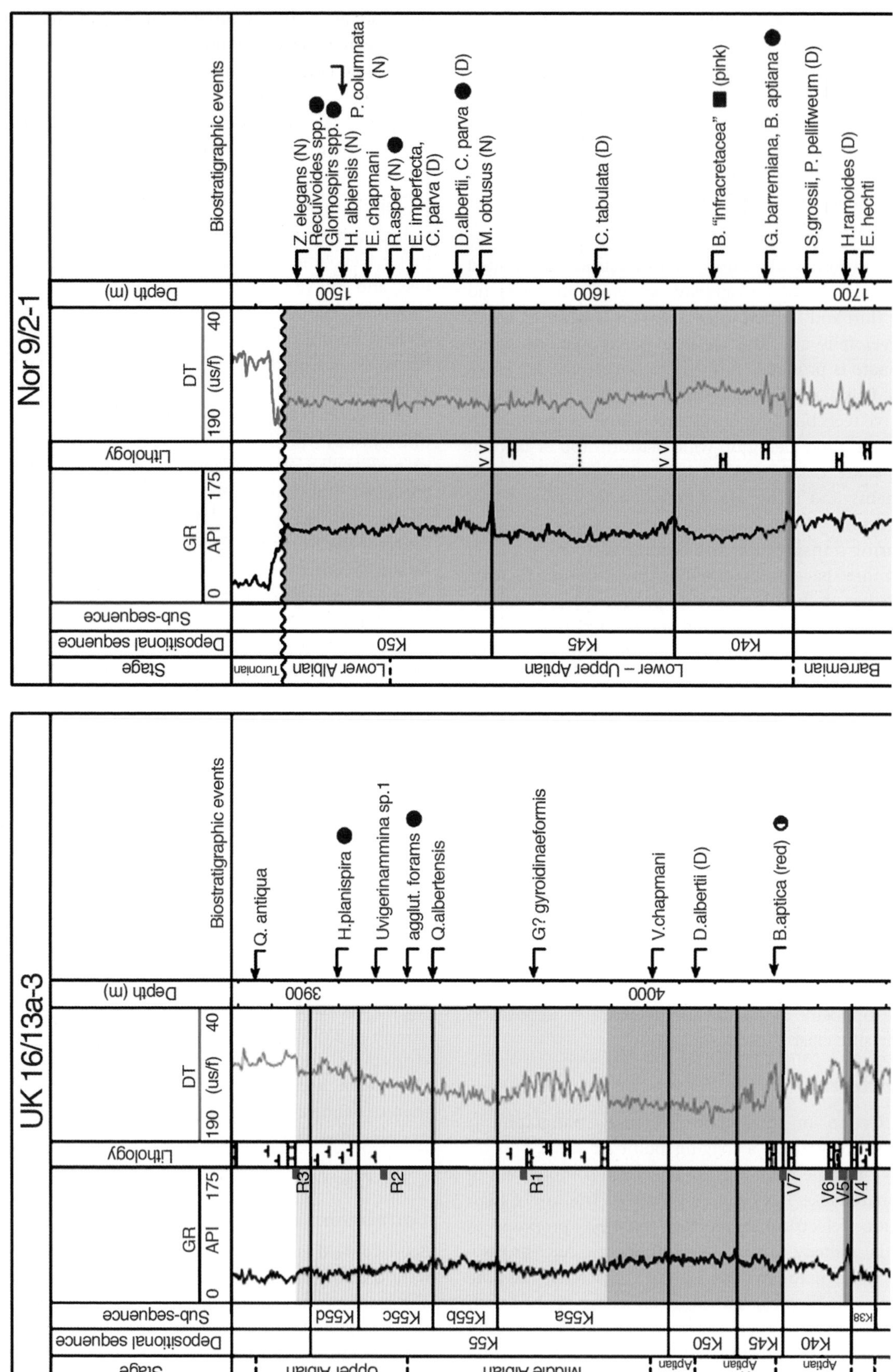

Figure 17.34 Type section of offshore formations (Lower Cretaceous, North Sea) illustrated by well logs (from Evans *et al.* 2003).

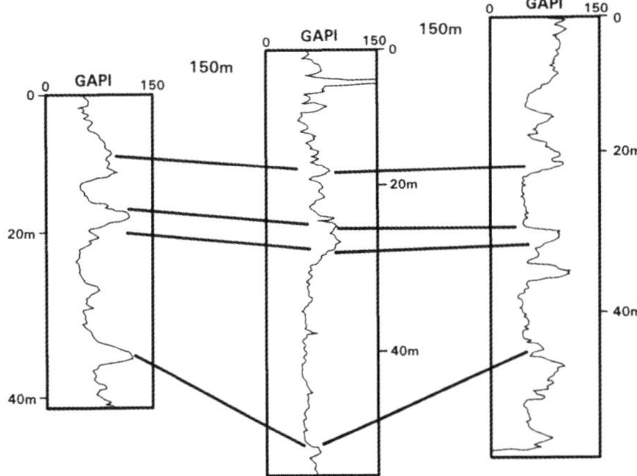

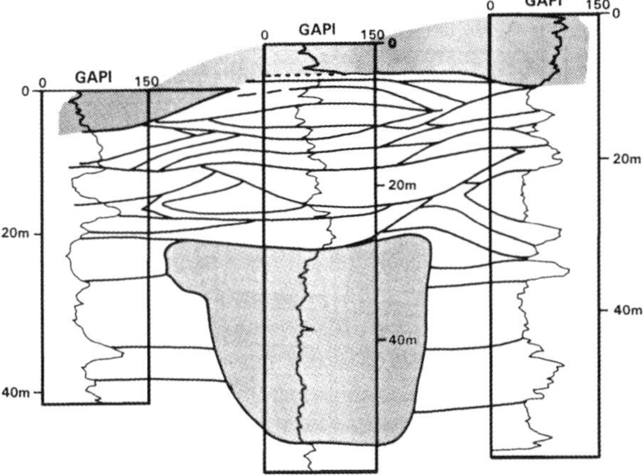

Figure 17.35 The limitations of subsurface correlation illustrated by gamma ray profiles measured in sands and shales along a quarry wall. A. Expected correlations using the gamma ray curves alone. B. The real correlations from following the beds along the quarry wall outcrop (from Slatt *et al.* 1992).

In a very evocative piece of work, a set of gamma ray profiles was logged at intervals along a vertical quarry face using a gamma ray tool lowered from a logging truck (Slatt *et al.* 1992). The correlations suggested by the log profiles were then compared with the actual correlations seen and drawn from the outcrop (**Figure 17.35**). The confidence which would justifiably exist after correlating the logs alone is misplaced, and perhaps explains why development infill wells produce surprises. The logs tend to simplify lithological responses, which in some instances is an advantage, while in others it leads to errors. There is little that can be done about this except to be aware of it.

Marker horizons and time lines

The simplest and most evident form of log correlation is to use log patterns. The pattern may be a distinctive peak, a distinctive shape or a distinctive lithology with unique log responses (this obviously has connotations in sequence stratigraphy). The Lower Cretaceous of the Paris Basin, for example, shows the behaviour of log patterns over a stable, intra-cratonic basin and illustrates traditional correlation (**Figure 17.36**). Today, such correlations are still usual, but associated with detailed biostratigraphy, chemostratigraphy and so on, and an explanation is required as to why these correlations should exist. It is now necessary to know what causes a particular log shape, peak or trough and not just correlate on appearances.

The objective of geological correlation is to reconstruct past depositional surfaces, that is, to identify past time lines. Some deposits are thin compared to the time they take to accumulate and can effectively be used as such time lines. The North Sea (Balder) tuff, previously mentioned as an interval causing a distinctive log shape, is an example (**Figure 16.16**). It is interpreted to have been deposited over perhaps 0.5 Ma and, because material came from the atmosphere, is to be found in deeper water deposits over a very large area. In effect, it is a geological time line and provides excellent correlation over the entire North Sea Basin and contiguous margins. Such ideal horizons are unfortunately rare, but this example does show that when a distinctive log response, or set of responses, can be explained, their correlation can then be understood and used with knowledge, rather than treated simply as just a distinctive shape with an unknown correlation value. Indeed, an important message from sequence stratigraphy is that thin deposits with distinctive log responses can be used as time lines since they are the products of the short lived processes forming key surfaces. The chamosite rich interval of **Figure 17.16** can be correlated over a wide area despite being only a few centimetres thick.

The need to understand log responses is reinforced by the observations in the next section.

False correlations - facies

In sand-shale sequences, correlations often become extremely complex. It is exceedingly easy to correlate two similar-looking sand bodies between two wells, only to find that the fluids they contain are incompatible and that, in reality, they are not related. This frequently happens when facies are stacked or repeated, as is common with sands. In sand-shale sequences, although sand bodies are the reservoirs and therefore important, they should nonetheless *not* form the basis for correlation.

In the example, correlation was based essentially on coals and electrosequences (**Figure 17.37**). From their position and log shape, the sandstone bodies appear to correlate but, in fact, do not, as proved by incompatible fluids. The sands were deposited in channels and the similarities in log shape only indicate similar facies. This is an area of active deltaic deposition with channels forming and being abandoned: individual channel reservoir correlation is extremely complex but the channel facies is frequently repeated.

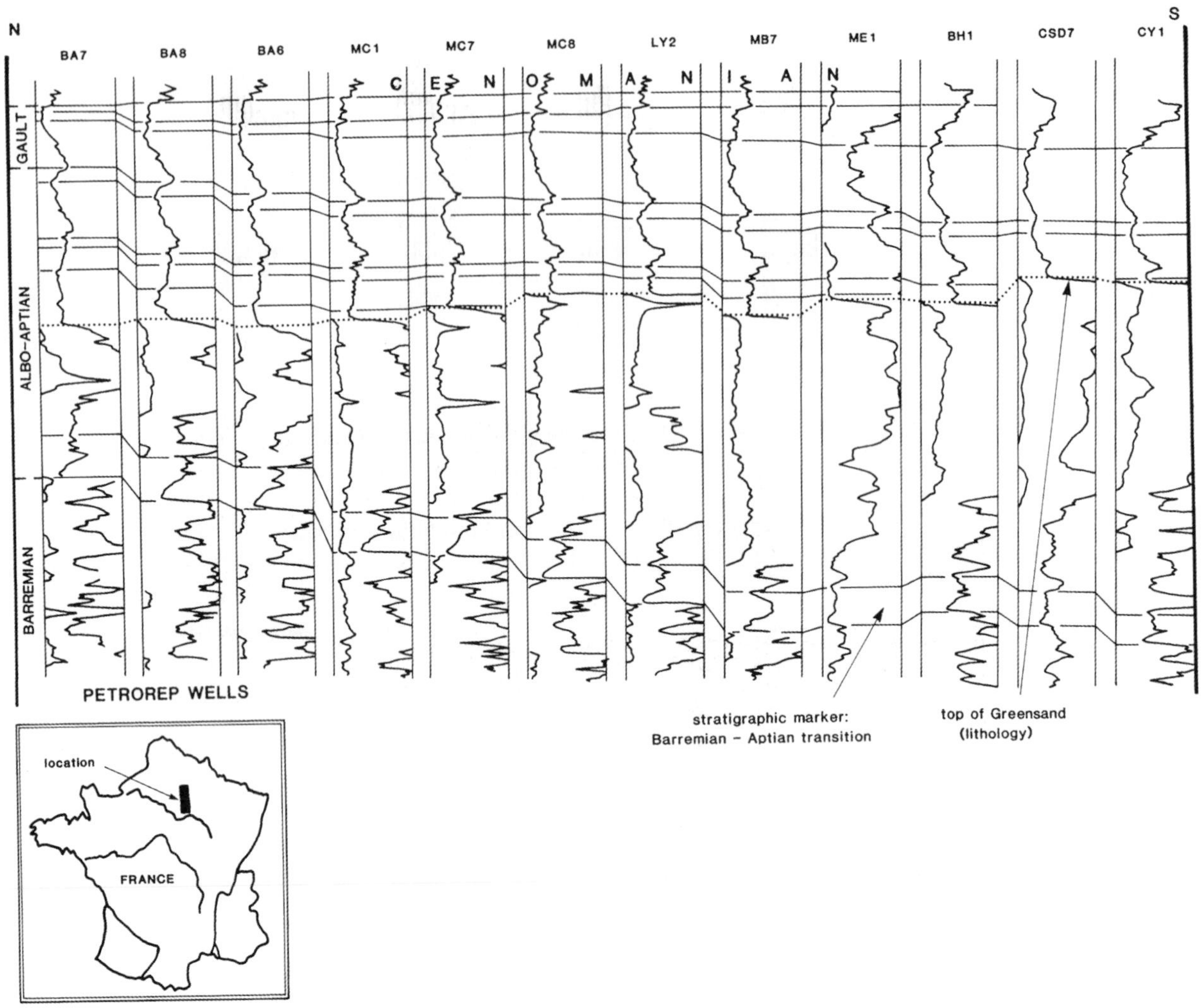

Figure 17.36 Detailed correlation of log markers across the Paris Basin. France. This traditional way of correlating logs is now tied to detailed biostratigraphy: some markers are time transgressive (from Serra 1972).

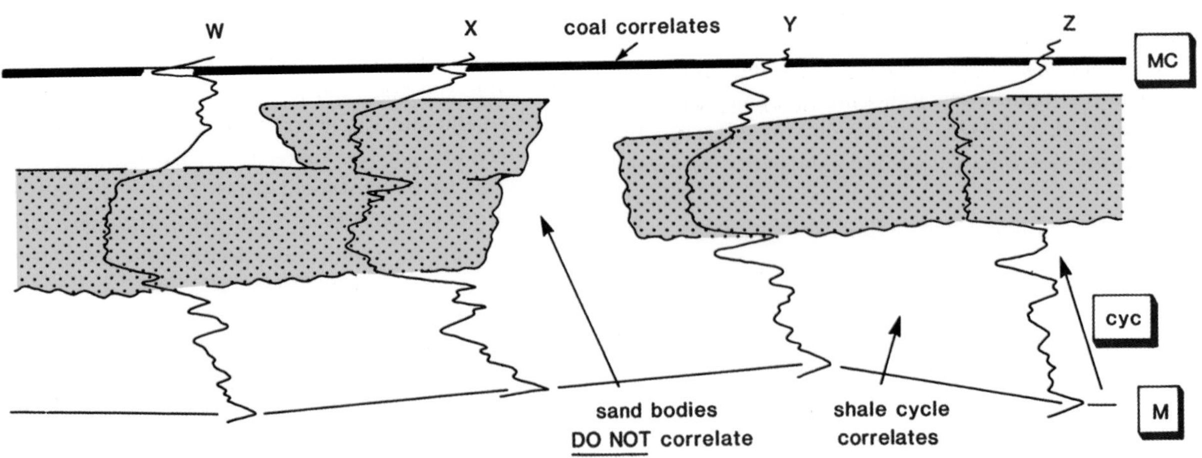

Figure 17.37 Correlation of log shapes in a deltaic complex. From log shapes, the sand-body appears to be continuous, but the shapes only indicate similar facies. Incompatible fluids show that two, separated, sand-bodies exist. Persistent correlations are based on coals and fine-grained facies. MC = marker coal, M = marker, CYC = marker cycle. W to Z is 3.5 km.

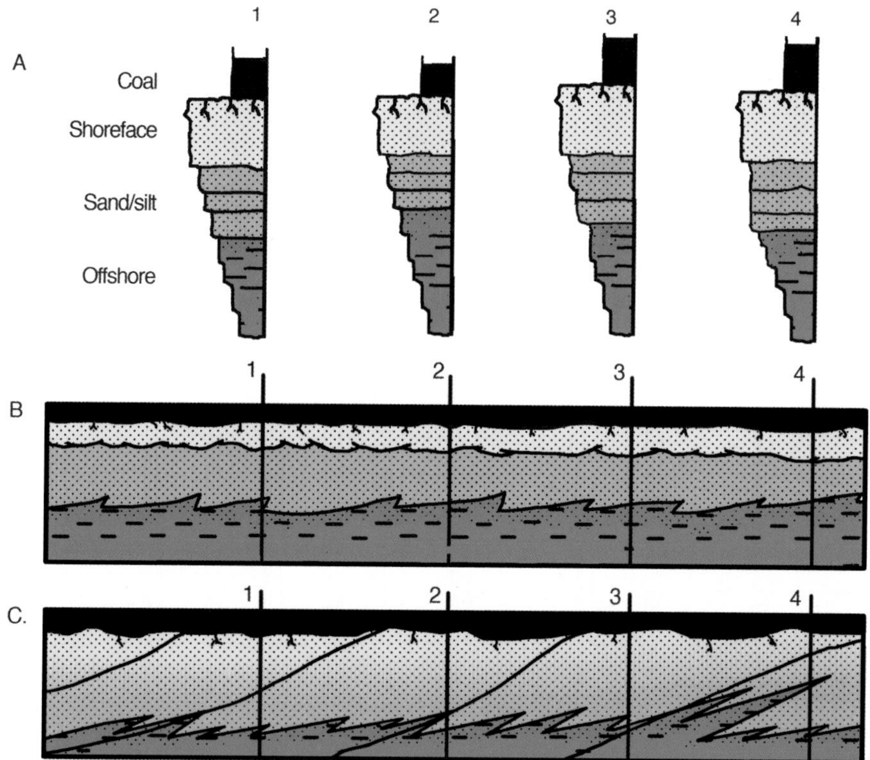

Figure 17.38 Lithostratigraphic correlation as opposed to a correlation that follows time lines. a. Four wells with a coarsening-up succession capped by a coal. b. A lithostratigraphic correlation: it follows the facies. c. Time lines indicate that facies change along time lines, and that a correlation that re-creates the original sediment surface will show facies changes (much modified and re-drawn after Hart and Plint 1993).

Vertical sequences and correlation: depositional topography

The topography of the present day surface of sediment deposition is considered to have been similar in the past. The environments of shelf, slope and basin existed in geological time, as now. The typical coarsening-up sequence is an illustration of this.

Walther's law suggests that a vertically consistent set of facies changes was originally deposited with the same set of facies in horizontal continuity. The vertical succession of sediments was originally distributed horizontally. In a coarsening-up sequence, fine deposits accumulated in the basin, gradually coarser sediments up the slope and the coarsest sediments at the top on the shelf. That is, in any vertical sequence, the deposits at the base are separated in both time and space from the deposits at the top of the sequence. Correlations should reflect these topographic elements.

The schematic diagram (**Figure 17.38**) shows four typical coarsening-up (shallowing-up) parasequences correlated lithostratigraphically, each parasequence resembling the next lithologically. However, when the depositional surfaces are added, effectively time lines, the impossibility of the lithstratigraphic correlation is clear. This is true at any scale, be it a deltaic lobe as above or on a larger scale, as in the next example. The Pennsylvanian to Permian deposits of West Texas were laid down close to the shelf edge (Van Siclen 1958). Correlations over 10 km in these beds, across the palaeo-shelf edge, show the depositional topography as it then was (**Figure 17.39**). The topography is associated with changes in lithology and, in this case, limestones developed on the platform top, reefs on the platform edge and shales in the basin off the shelf slope. Such basin scale topography will be seen as clinoforms on the seismic.

Equally as important as positive depositional topography is erosional topography. Significance in sequence stratigraphy is put on identifying 'valley fills' (**Figure 17.14**). These are valleys cut during a relative sea-level fall and subsequently filled. A modern example is the erosional valley beneath the present day Mississippi which is filled with the present day river deposits (Fisk and McFarlan 1955). In ancient sediments, these deposits can be made evident in well correlations if the correct datum is chosen (**Figure 17.40**).

To show depositional and erosional topography, the choice of datum is obviously critical. In the previous example (**Figure 17.39**), the datum used is near structural but still allows the palaeo-topography to be seen.

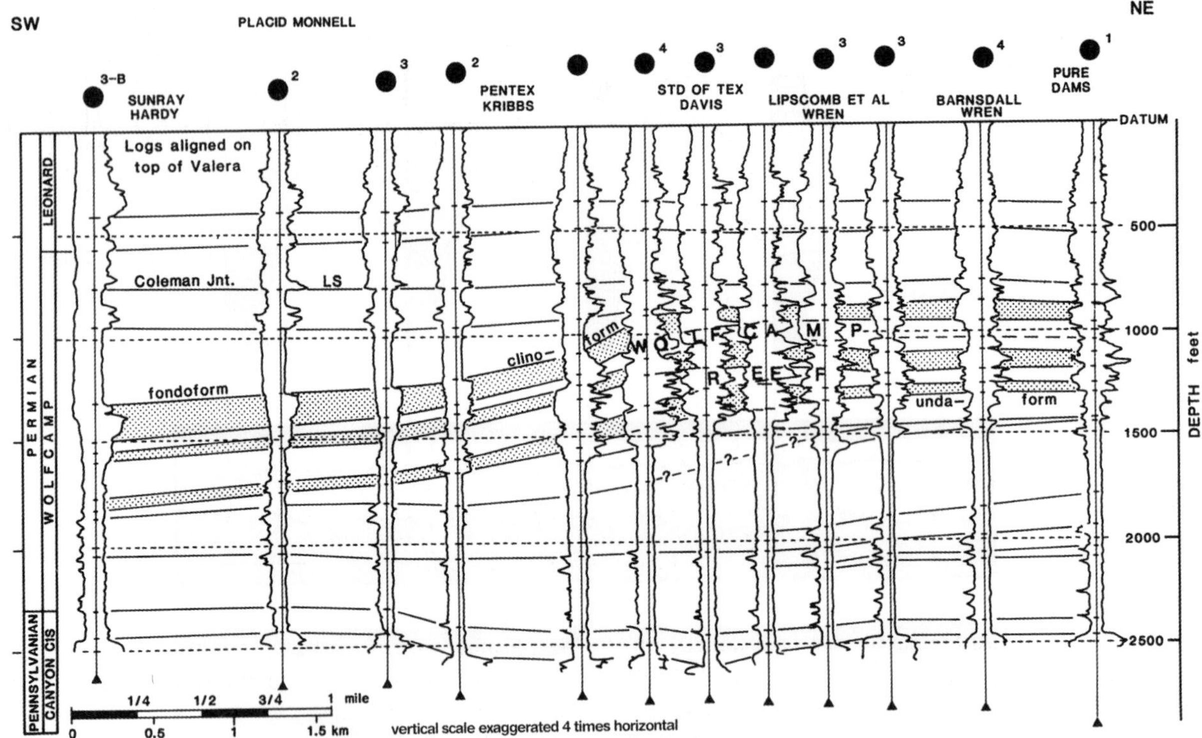

Figure 17.39 Correlation and paleotopography in the Permian of West Texas. Logs: SP to the left, electrical survey to the right (re-drawn from Van Siclen 1958).

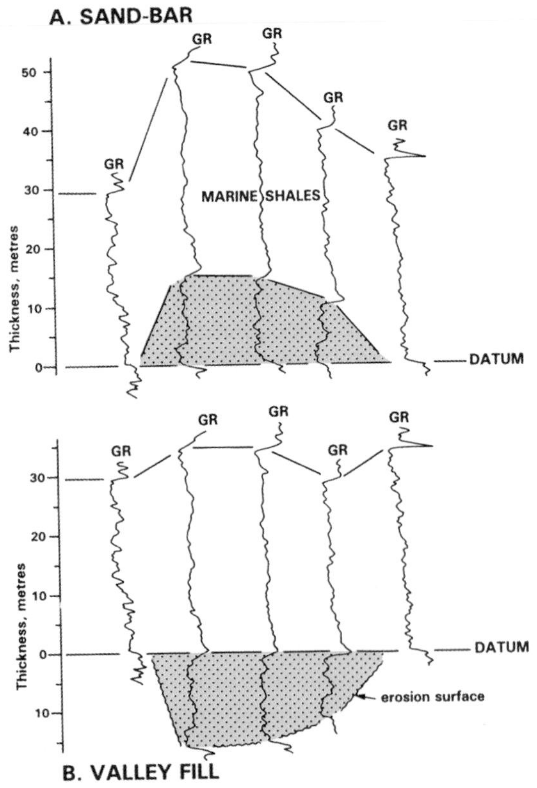

Figure 17.40 The importance of the choice of datum. (A) If the base of the sand is taken as a datum, a sand bar is interpreted (unlikely). (B) If the flooding surface at the top of the sand is taken, valley-fill is interpreted, and the covering shale sequence shows a constant thickness (likely).

This may not always be the case and the chosen datum must correspond to a facies recognised as most likely to have been horizontal at the time of deposition. Coals, for example, are originally flat, but condensed sections and flooding surfaces may not be. The ultimate choice is probably a matter of trial and error.

Correlation and seismic

Why is there a need to say that the seismic should be used in well correlations whenever possible? The geophysicist cannot do his work without using the logs to 'tie' the picked horizons. The same is not true for the geologist. He will not automatically be asked about the seismic control for his correlation: he should be. In fact, log correlation and seismic mapping should be undertaken together: the approach must be iterative. Examining the mapped seismic horizons before completing a log correlation will indicate whether such a correlation is compatible with the mapping or not. The example illustrated previously (**Figure 17.22**) speaks for itself.

Palaeontologically controlled correlations

Palaeontological control is essential in sequence stratigraphic correlation but was not sufficiently stressed above (Section 17.2). This was done deliberately to emphasise the contribution of the logs. But any log study must be integrated with 'event stratigraphy' for reliable correlation (**Figure 17,34**). That is, correlations are based on various biological events, such as blooms or

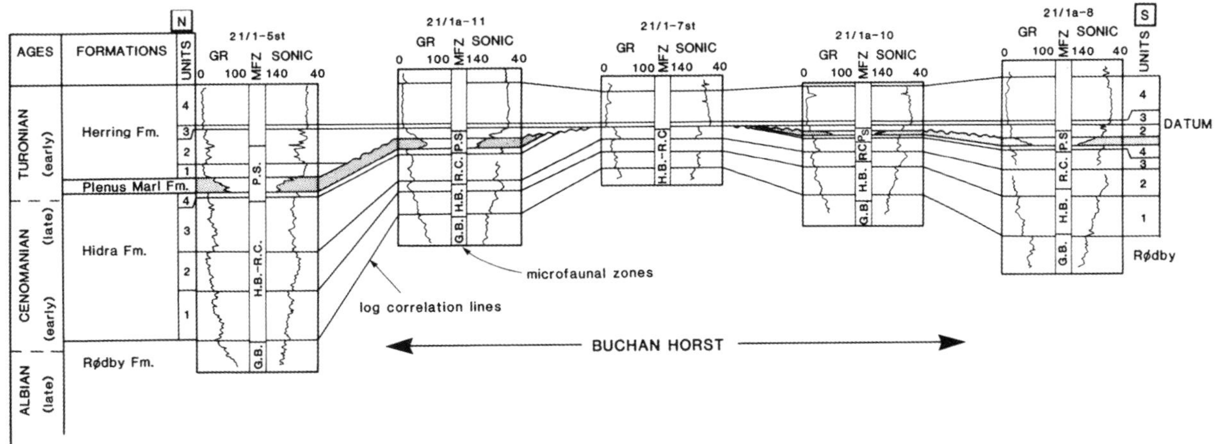

Figure 17.41 Palaeontologically-controlled correlation. The mid-Cretaceous across the Buchan Horst, North Sea. Outside wells are 6 km apart. GR = gamma ray API units. Sonic = Δt microseconds per foot. MFZ = microfaunal zone. P.S. = *Praeglobotruncana stephani* biozone. R.C. = *Rotalipora cushmani* biozone. H.B. = *Hedbergella brittonensis* biozone. G.B. = *Glob igerinelloides bentonensis* biozone (from Burnhill and Ramsay 1981).

extinctions, as well as the traditional appearances and disappearances of species (e.g. Mitchener *et al.* 1992; Martin-Chivelet and Chacón 2007). Some events are considered to be isochronous (as far as the individual basin is concerned) and therefore can be correlated, others are facies controlled. Because of sampling difficulties in the subsurface, biostratigraphic events may not always be identified in a well or be precise. The combined use of event stratigraphy and well logs is therefore essential.

Every specialist considers that his 'discipline' is the most reliable and its results unassailable. The man who has spent his lifetime examining dinoflagellates will argue their value to the denigration of any other information. The man who has spent his lifetime analysing well logs will do the same for the logs! Of course, the essential is to combine information using the strong points of each discipline. Frequently, specialists are unaware of (or unwilling to admit to themselves) the weaknesses in their own speciality.

This is simply to argue that much microbiological information has limitations in accuracy where correlation is concerned. Well logs are, for the greater part, lithostratigraphic records. When the two are combined, there is often a tendency to say that a particular horizon is diachronous because microfauna occur at different levels. This is always a possibility, but distance between wells should be be considered. Wells a few kilometres apart are unlikely to have the same facies with significantly different ages. A careful balance in using the data needs to be achieved.

The example illustrated shows such a balance between log correlation and biostratigraphy nicely achieved (**Figure 17.41**). Middle Cretaceous rocks cover a small pod-like horst (the Buchan Horst) in the central North Sea (Burnhill and Ramsay 1981; Millenium Atlas 2004). The lithostratigraphy shows some continuity but also inexplicable discontinuities. The datings, fine enough for correlation, add sufficient information to explain the discontinuities and to corroborate the continuous log correlations. The combined log and palaeontological correlations show a mid-Cretaceous, early Turonian unconformity over the horst itself with a later Turonian onlap. By correlating the unconformity with a regional Turonian regressive phase, which occurred throughout north-west Europe and North America, the authors show that the erosion was not a result of local movement on the horst, but the result of a global change in sea level (Burnhill and Ramsay 1981 *op. cit.*). The succeeding onlap had a similar cause. Clearly, this sort of reasoning is not possible without mico-palaeontologically dated log correlations.

Computer aided correlation

Considerable effort over the years has been devoted to finding a method to allow logs to be correlated automatically by computer (*see* Doveton 1994 for review). The results have generally not produced helpful tools. Correlation inevitably involves gaps and breaks, changes in thickness and changes in facies. Curve correlation techniques used in dipmeter processing (Chapter 14) are based on the expectation of finding an exactly similar match (Matuszak 1972), and are therefore unsatisfactory for stratigraphic correlation. In this chapter the use of chronostratigraphy, facies change, depositional topography and so on in correlation is described and, without being able to include such concepts, computer correlation will be disregarded, which seems to be the case at present.

A different approach to computer aided correlation is to be more concerned with characterising intervals than actually correlating them, that is, in finding a mathematical method to represent an interval in quantitative terms of lithology, chemostratigraphy, biostratigraphy

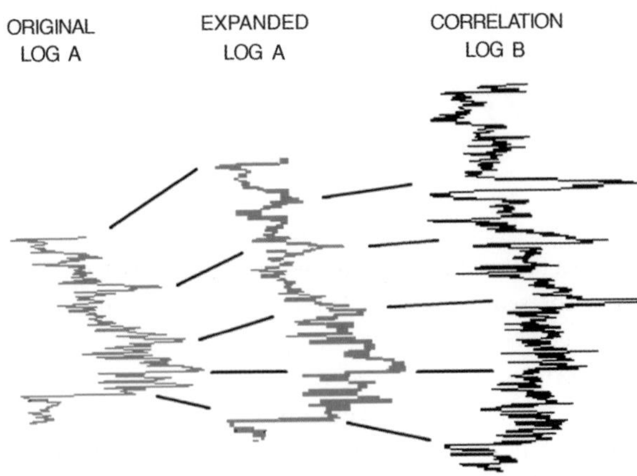

Figure 17.42 Expanding a gamma ray log trace through thin deep marine shale to help correlation. Log A (left red curve) is a thinner section of the interval shown by Log B (black). When Log A is expanded (red curve, centre) the correlation becomes evident.

etc. and then using those quantities to identify similar quantities, which would imply correlation (Bailey and Smith 2010). This is actually more akin to description than correlation but having an objective, quantitative description of an interval is a precursor to correlation.

A second approach to computer use is to create a new format which is more easily correlated. Two routines are common. The first allows a log curve to be stretched or compressed over a certain interval so that differences in accumulation rates on log curves can be eliminated. For instance, if a shale interval is 20 m thick at one location and 100 m thick at another, the routine allows the 20 m of curve to be expanded to 100 m or the 100 m compressed to 20 m. Often log patterns in fine grained deposits are similar despite thickness differences (**Figure 17.42**).

The second routine is to plot standard single curve logs as a colour image, or colour 'bar code', a technique previously discussed in terms of image log processing (**Figure 15.1**). Using such colour presentations, the eye has a greater facility for comparison. The example shows gamma ray logs from eight, closely spaced wells in a producing field, formatted as colour images rather than typical curves (**Figure 17.43**). The eye is able to follow a greater amount of detail than is possible with only the curves. But, of course, careful normalisation and preparation are required, especially with gamma ray logs. The curves themselves may also be added to this format if required, especially as a limit to the colour shading (**Figure 12.8**).

17.8 Conclusion

The subject of sequence stratigraphy dominates this chapter. It is entirely justified. With stratigraphy, sedimentology and the seismic closely linked, big advances have been made in each discipline in separate ways. As far as the logs are concerned, the chapter has tried to show their role as a common database and tool for description, especially the image logs. However, more than just a descriptive tool, the logs form a geological dataset in their own right: they can be applied thus. But this means that advances in log use need to be made, especially in computer techniques which are relevant to all strands of stratigraphy.

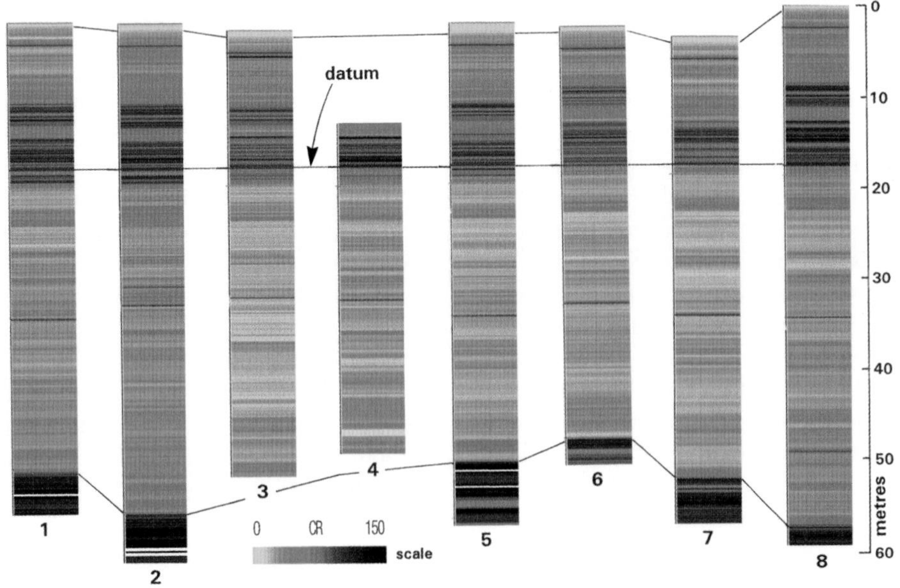

Figure 17.43 Gamma ray logs plotted as colour images allowing a better visual correlation. The gamma ray scale has been normalised and the 8 wells are closely spaced (imaging routine from GeoScene software).

18
CONCLUSIONS

On a bright September afternoon in 2007, a group of mostly older men stood around in an unremarkable field in Alsace, northern France, looking at the grass at their feet. There was nothing to see. But in the minds of all these members of the SAID (Societe pour l'Avancement des Diagraphies), there were reflective thoughts. The piece of grass on which the eyes were focused was where, 80 years before in 1927, Henri Doll, working for Conrad and Marcel Schlumberger, had run the first well log, the first *carottage électrique*. This was Pechelbronn.

It is perhaps symbolic that there is now nothing to see at Pechelbronn, but it was the beginning of today's huge and important well logging industry. What was discovered was simply dissolved into the future. Madame Schlumberger's copper bath tub (now in the Musée de Château de Crèvecœur), in which Conrad carried out his first experiments has become the silicon chip and the software programme. Reflecting on this, it would have been impossible to predict the future from the copper bath, except to say that there would be one!

The lesson of Pechelbronn is that predictions are less useful than having confidence in the present. The future is best left to the astrologers; reality is rooted in the present. So, this book on the geological uses of well logs, ends with an example of just that: logs used for geological ends.

250 metres of standard and electrical image logs from a North Sea well are reproduced in **Figure 18.1,a.** They show the sequence of shales that covers the Palaeocene to Eocene boundary with an age in the region of 55 Ma. The section contains the Palaeocene-Eocene Thermal Maximum (PETM), an event during which ocean water surface temperatures (based on oxygen isotopes) are considered to have suddenly risen by 5°C in the tropics, more than 6° in the Arctic and 4–5°C in ocean bottom waters. The temperature changes are associated with a 30–50% extinction of deep-sea benthic fauna and a 3.5–4.0‰ negative carbon isotope excursion (CIE) in both marine and terrestrial sections. A massive dissociation of methane hydrate (which has the right carbon isotope ratios) has been suggested as a cause, and the volcanic activity during the opening of the North Atlantic as the trigger, although there is no general agreement on either of these.

The PETM has been much researched by the Ocean Drilling Project (ODP) teams because it is considered to show what happens when there is a sudden influx of carbon into the oceans and their sediments, as is the case with the atmosphere at present with anthropogenic carbon dioxide.

According to the ODP work, the PETM began at 55 Ma (54.93–54.98 Ma, the Palaeocene-Eocene boundary) and

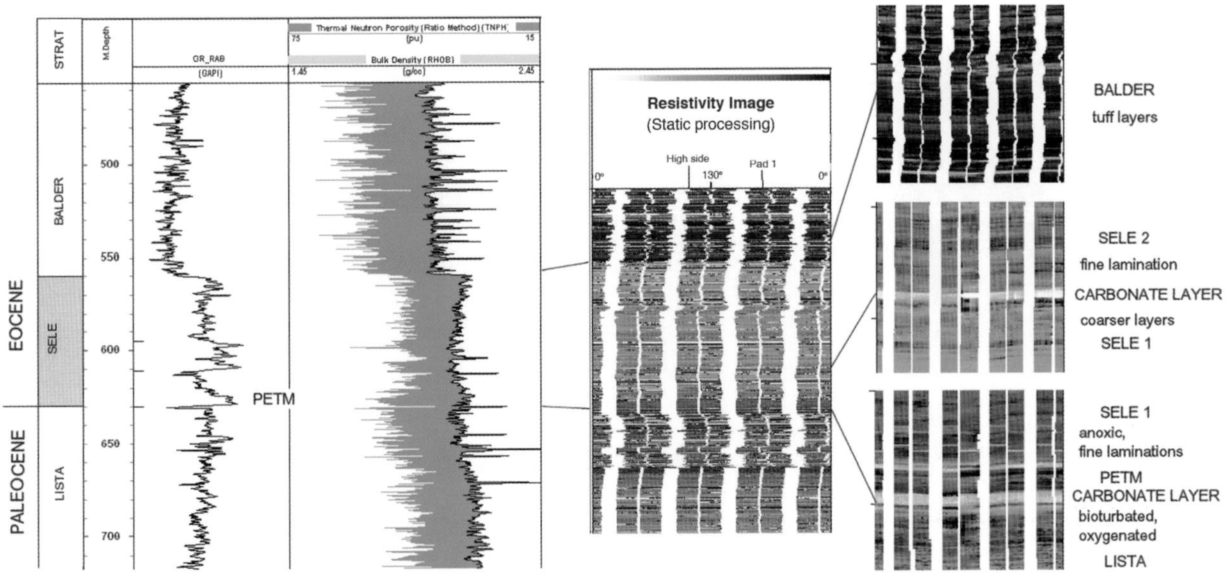

Figure 18.1,a Gamma ray, neutron-density and image logs from the shales across the Palaeocene to Eocene boundary in a North Sea well. The interval contains the Palaeocene Eocene Thermal Maximum (PETM) which is illustrated by the electrical image logs (Schlumberger FMI) to the right of the figure.

lasted for 150–220 ka. The deep-sea calcium carbonate rich oozes sampled by the ODP are normally above the Carbonate Compensation Depth (CCD). The PETM, however, is a 2 m interval, with no calcium carbonate at the base (a dissolution event caused by the CCD rising abruptly) but with levels gradually increasing back to normal at the top (the CCD descending again). It is this 2 m of carbonate poor sediment that represents the initial, rapid rise in temperature and ocean acidification and then progressive recovery some 200 ka later. The event has been found in the Antarctic (ODP site 690), the southern Atlantic (ODP site 208) on Blake Nose (ODP site 1051) and at on-land sites in Italy, North America and elsewhere. It truly is global. And even small, cyclic details seem to correlate between these widely separated sites, the reason being, it is argued, that these small events were caused by climate cycles, the cyclic repetitions being in the Milankovitch precession band (20 ka), some 10 cycles representing the actual event and recovery. Sedimentation rates in the intervals studied varied from 2.0 cm/ka before the event; <1.0 cm/ka during the event; and 3.0 cm/ka during the recovery period. There are indications that the PETM is, in fact, only one (but the largest) of several similar events.

On the figure (**Figure 18.1,a**) the PETM in the example North Sea well is interpreted as beginning at the boundary between the Lista (Palaeocene) and the Sele (Eocene) formations. However, there appear to be two events (marked as Sele 1 and Sele 2 on the figure). The lower event (Sele 1) shows bioturbated shales (Lista) abruptly covered by well laminated shales (Sele 1) with no bioturbation and high gamma ray values (high uranium). There is a 3 cm carbonate layer at the base, followed immediately by the highest gamma ray, which then gradually decreases upwards. These are considered to indicate a change from oxygenated, bioturbated bottom waters, to the anoxic conditions marking the benthic foraminifera extinction event (the PETM), and the decreasing gamma ray as indicating the recovery period. A similar set of changes appear to occur during Sele 2, the top of which is drawn where the gamma ray drops and bioturbation is seen again on the image logs. The overall Sele interval is covered abruptly by the Balder Formation, which has many volcanic ash layers and very distinctive log responses. The three formations of the example section, the Lista, the Sele and the Balder, all show distinct electrofacies (**Figure 18.1,b**).

A spectral analysis has been performed on the gamma ray log curve over the example interval, using a maximum entropy method, with a 40 m window, a 1 m step and performed by CycloLog software (**Figure 18.1,c**). The results show distinct variations in cyclicity between the three formations. The two spectra from the Sele Formation are quite similar, with very marked wavelengths interpreted as 100,000 year, Milankovitch, eccentricity cycles. They are distinctly different from the cycles of the Lista Formation below and the Balder Formation above. The Sele 1 cycles have a peak wavelength of 7 m (the 100 ka eccentricity cycles) and a quite minor wavelength of 2.4 m (40 ka, obliquity cycles?); the Sele 2 has wavelengths of 8.0 m (100 ka) and very minor ones of 2.8 m and 2.1 m; wavelengths in the Lista are 9.0 m (100 ka?) and minor 3.4 m; in the Balder they are 6.5 m, 4.0 m and 2.9 m (**Figure 8.1,c**).

Using this gamma ray spectral analysis and the electrical images, there are two independent means of calculating sedimentation rates and geological time spans for the Sele Formation: using the 100 ka peaks from the

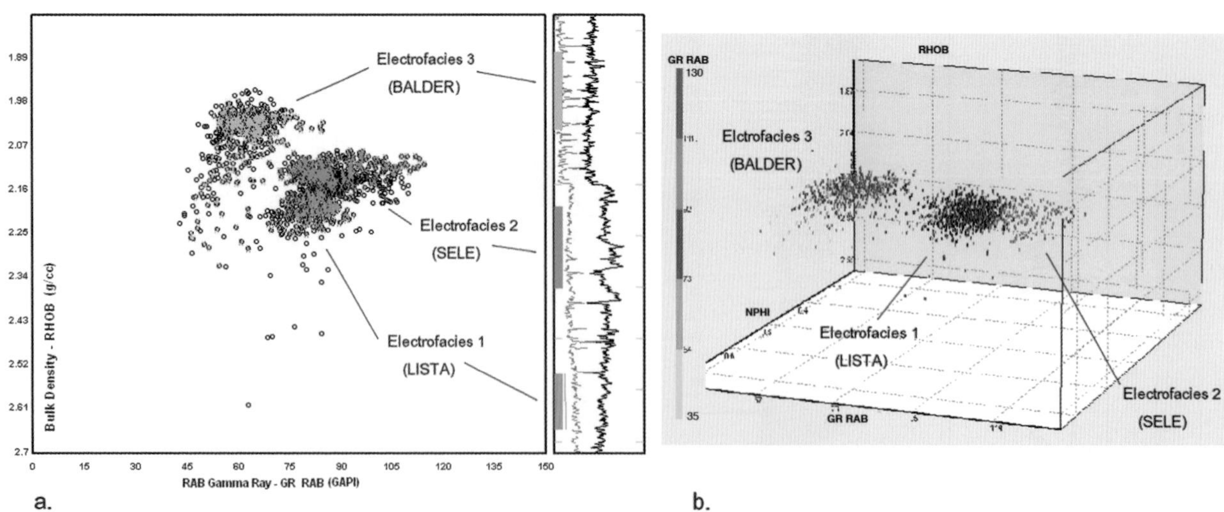

Figure 18.1,b a. An annotated, interactive gamma ray-density cross-plot (TerraSciences routine) and, b. 3-D gamma ray, density, neutron cross-plot (Interactive Petrophysics routine) of the Lista, Sele and Balder Formations. Each formation has a distinct electrofacies on these plots.

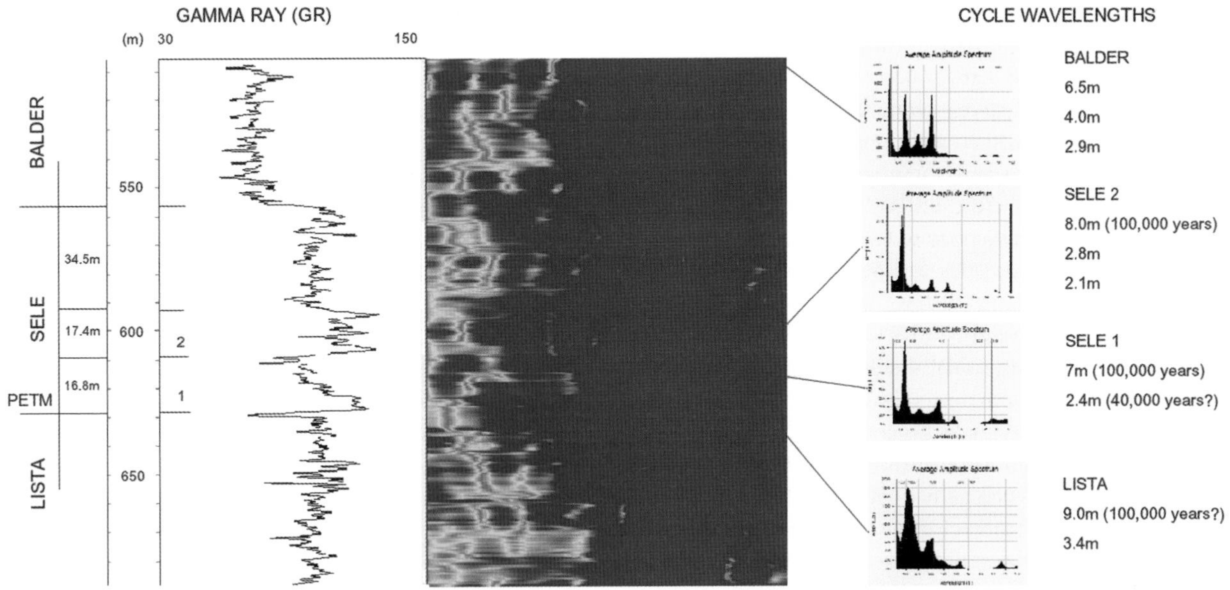

Figure 18.1,c Spectral analysis of the gamma ray log (CycloLog routine), showing two similar spectra from the Sele Formation contrasting with spectra from the Lista and Balder Formations. The peaks in the Sele Formation spectra are interpreted as related to 100,000 year Milankovitch eccentricity cycles.

spectral analysis and using the thickness of laminae seen on the images.

From the spectral analysis, the 100,000 year eccentricity cycles are 7.0 m thick in the Sele 1, meaning that the 16.8 m thick interval will have accumulated in 240,000 years. The equivalent numbers for the Sele 2 are 8.0 m thick cycles, 17.4 m formation thickness and 217,500 years to accumulate. The figures indicate sedimentation rates of 7.0 cm/ka (Sele 1) and 8.0 cm/ka (Sele 2).

On the electrical image log, the average thickness of the thinnest, individual lamina is 2.5 cm (**Figure 18.1,d**). If this represents a 20,000 year precession cycle, the sedimentation rate is approximately 0.125 cm/ka. This does not tally with the rates from the gamma ray

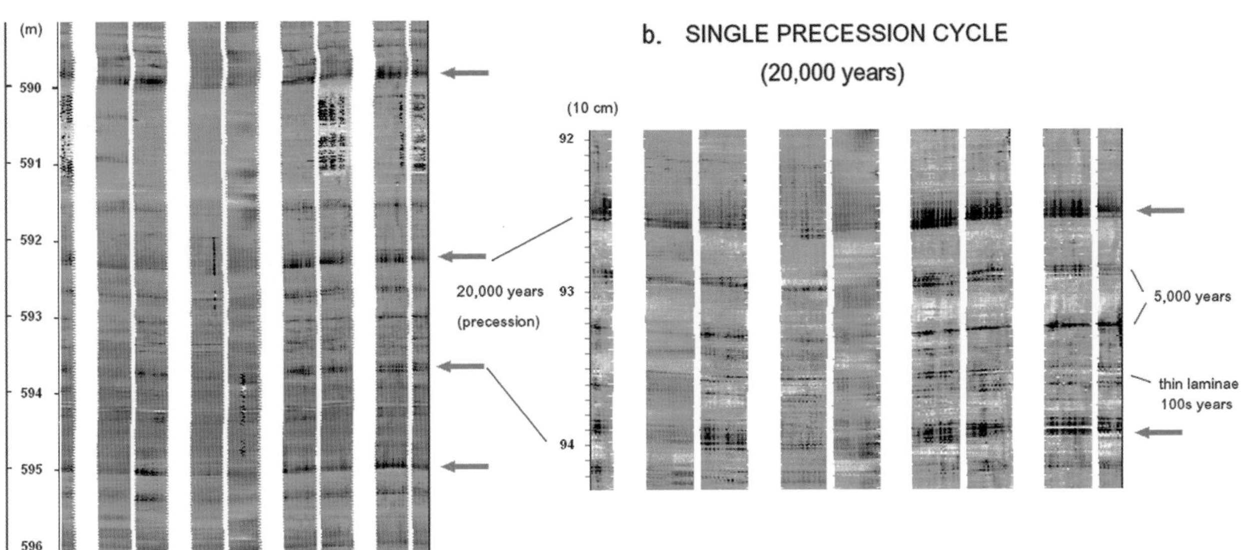

Figure 18.1,d Electrical images (Schlumberger FMI) of precession cycles in the Sele Formation. An individual cycle (20.000 years) is represented by the interval between the red arrows. a. Larger scale section of several cycles. b. A single precessional cycle. The finest laminations represent only hundreds of years.

analysis. However, repetitive bundles of laminae, also recognisable on the images, are between 0.8 m–2.0 m thick (**Figure 18.1,d**). Taking these instead as the 20,000 year signal gives sedimentation rates of between 4.0–10.0 cm/ka, within the range of the gamma ray analysis rates. To see if these were indeed the precession cycles, they were counted. The number, while not exact, is sufficiently accurate to suggest that Sele 1 has between 13 and 15 cycles, and Sele 2 has 15. With these counts, the Sele 1 would have lasted for 280,000 years (14 precessional cycles), and Sele 2 for 300,000 years (15 cycles), not unreasonably dissimilar to the equivalent ages from the gamma ray analysis (240,000 and 217,500 years respectively).

The sedimentation rates from the image counts are between 6.0–7.0 cm/ka and an average from the gamma ray analysis is 7.5 cm/ka. Compared to the deep sea oozes sampled by the ODP (rates of 1–3 cm/ka), these are obviously very high rates, as would be expected from the position of the well in the North Sea. But the surprise is that even with such a very high detrital input, and apparently regardless of oceanic temperatures, Milankovitch cyclicity still influences sedimentation.

Using a rounded average sedimentation rate, from both the image log layer counts and the gamma ray spectral analysis of 7.0 cm/ka, the 68.7 m thickness of the Sele Formation was deposited in approximately 980,000 years. The age of the PETM is 55 Ma (from ODP calculations), which makes the age of the base of the Balder approximately 54.02 Ma, consistent with it just preceding the Atlantic Ocean opening where the first recorded ocean basalt chron is 24 (53 Ma–56.5 Ma).

From this small section it is clear that the global PETM has left a marked signal in the North Sea and that both eccentricity and precession cycles affect the detrital sediments. The finer laminations that permeate the sediments and are visible on the electrical images, spanning only hundreds of years, are not explained. It is not clear if they are cyclic. The responses of the standard logs indicate distinct changes in geophysical (and hence real) sediment properties between each of the Lista, Sele and Balder formations, each forming a distinct electrofacies. The changes will be mineralogical and textural and, at least in the case of the Sele, with a climate influence.

The analysis of this example turns the depth record of the well logs into a record of geological time and associated geological events: a record of local sedimentation but also of globally recognised events. In addition, it shows that the climatic signals found in deep ocean sediments can extend into much shallower environments and that climate can have a cyclical effect even in rapidly deposited sediments.

Clearly, the described observations need independent verification, but it is extraordinary that remote sensing from modern well logs, retrieved from 2–4 km below the surface, can record geological events that took only hundreds of years but also major, global events, in this case those leading up to, and associated with, the opening of the North Atlantic Ocean. The ability of well logs to provide a record of geological events comparable with ocean sediment cores, or even ice cores, needs to be pointed out.

In truth, the grass of Alsace tells us nothing. Pechelbronn is only important as a symbol. More important are the ideas that led to running the first log and which continued to motivate subsequent advances: a motivation still in evidence today. From a geological point of view, technology may have become very sophisticated, but a list of geophysical measurements means nothing if it is not interpreted. A log is just a line: as an outcrop is just a piece of rock. It is only in the informed mind that they become something else.

REFERENCES

Adams, J.A. and Weaver, C.E. (1958) Thorium-uranium ratios as indicators of sedimentary processes: example of concept of geochemical facies, *Bull. Am. Assoc. Petrol. Geol.* **42**(2), 387–430.

Adams, J., Blott, N., Boyeldieu, C., Cheruvier, E., Cull, R., Mobed, R., Haines, P. and Spurlin, J. (1989) Advances in log interpretation in oil-based mud. *Oilfield Review*, **1**, Issue 2, 22–38.

Adams, J., Bourke, L. and Buck, S. (1990) Integrating formation images and cores, with case studies. *Oilfield Review*, **2**, No.1, 52–65

Adams, J., Ayodele, J.K., Bedford, J., Kaars-Sijpesteijn, C.H. and Watts, N.L. (1992) Application of dipmeter data in structural interpretation, Niger Delta. In: *Geological applications of well logs II*, eds. Hurst, A., Griffiths, C.M. and Worthington, P.F. Geol. Soc. London Spec. Pub. **65**, 247–264.

Adeyemo, D., Logan, J.P. and Saha, S., (2005) Enhanced clay characterization and formation evaluation with wireline spectroscopy tool: examples from Nigeria. *SPWLA 46th Ann. Symp. Trans.*, Paper CCC, 1–12.

Adolf, B., Stoller, C., Archer, M., Codazzi, D., el-Halawani, T., Perciot, P., Weller, G., Evans, M., Grant, J., Griffiths, R., Hartman, D., Sirkin, G., Ichiikawa, M., Scott, G., Tribe, I. and White, D. (2005) No more waiting: formation evaluation while drilling. *Oilfield Review*, Autumn 4–21.

Ahr, W., Allen, D., Boyd, A., Bechman, N., Smithson, T., Clerke, E., Gzara, K., Hassall, J., Murty, C., Zubari, H. and Ramamoorthy, R. (2005) Confronting the carbonate conundrum. *Oilfield Review*, Spring, 18–29.

Aigner, T., Schauer, M., Junghans, W. and Reinhardt, L. (1995) Outcrop gamma-ray logging and its applications: examples from the German Triassic. *Sedimentary Geology*, **100**, 47–61.

Akbar, M, Petricola, M., Watfa, M., Badri, M., Charara, M., Boyd, A., Cassel, B., Nurmi, R., Delhomme, J-P., Grace, M., Kenyon, B. and Roestenburg, J. (1995) Classic interpretation problems: evaluating carbonates. *Oilfield Review*, January, 38–57.

Akihisa, K., Tezuka, K., Senoh, O., Uchida, T. (2002) Well log evaluation of gas hydrate saturation in the Miti-Nankai Trough well, offshore South East Japan. *SPWLA 43rd Ann. Symp. Trans.*, Paper BB, 1–14.

Akkurt, R., Vinegar, H., Tutunjian, P. and Guillory, A (1996) NMR logging of natural gas reservoirs. *SPWLA 36th Ann. Symp. Trans.*, Paper N, 1–11.

Alden, M., Arif, F., Billingham, M., Grønnerød, N., Harvey, S., Richards, M. and West, C. (2004) Advancing Downhole Conveyance. *Oilfield Review*, **16**, 3, 30–43.

Afonso de André, C., Mainieri Vieira da Cunha, A., Boonen, P., Valant-Spaight, B., LeFors, S. and Schultz, W. (2004) A comparison of logging-while-drilling and wireline nuclear porosity logs in shales from wells in Brazil. *SPWLA 45th Ann. Symp. Trans.*, Paper D, 1–10.

Al-Khatib, H. and Al-Adani, N. (2009) The reality of borehole fracture propagation into the reservoir formation. *SPWLA 50th Ann. Symp. Trans.*, Paper I, 1–9.

Allaud, L. and Martin, M. (1976) *Schlumberger, histoire d'une technique*. Berger-Levrault, Paris.

Allen, D., Auzerais, F., Dussan, E., Goode, P., Ramakrishnan, T., Schwartz, L., Wilkinson, D., Fordham, E., Hammond, P. and Williams, R.(1991) Invasion Revisited. *Oilfield Review*, **3**, 3, 10–22.

Allen, D., Flaum, C., Ramakrishnan, T., Bedford, J., Castelijns, K., Fairhurst, D., Gubelin, G., Heaton, N., Minh, C., Norville, M., Seim, M., Pritchard, T. and Ramamoorthy, R. (2000) Trends in NMR logging. *Oilfield Review*, Autumn, 2–19.

Allen, D.F. and Jacobsen, S.J. (1987) Resistivity profiling with a multi-frequency induction sonde. *SPWLA 19th Ann. Symp. Trans.*, Paper F, 1–9.

Alm, P.G. (1992) The temperature decay log: a different approach to presenting a temperature survey. In: *Geological applications of well logs II*, eds. Hurst, A., Griffiths, C.M. and Worthington, P.F. Geol. Soc. London Spec. Pub. **65**, 339–348.

Alvarado, R., Damgaard, A., Hansen, P., Raven, M., Heidler, R., Hoshun, R., Kovats, J., Moriss, C., Rose, D. and Wendt, W. (2003) Nuclear magnetic resonance logging while drilling. *Oilfield Review*, Summer, 40–51.

Amer, A., Kilamba, C., Cardoso, E., Rueda, M. and Lopes, A. (2009) An integrated study to understand the effect of anhydrite on wells drilled near fault systems in Pinda formation, offshore Angola. *SPWLA 50th Ann. Symp. Trans.*, Paper H, 1–12.

Anderson, B. and Chew, W.C. (1985) SFL interpretation using high speed synthetic computer generated logs. *SPWLA 26th Ann. Symp. Trans.*, Paper K, 1–17.

Anderson, B., Bonner, S., Lüling, M., and Rosthal, R. (1990) Response of 2 MHz LWD resistivity and wireline induction tools in dipping beds and laminated formations. *SPWLA 31st Ann. Symp. Trans.*, Paper A, 1–25.

Anderson, B, Bonner, S. Lüling, R. and Rosthal, R. (1992) Response of 2MHz LWD resistivity and wireline induction tools in dipping beds and laminated formations. *The Log Analyst*, **33**, No. 5, 461–475.

Anderson, B., Collett, T., Lewis, R. and Dubourg, I. (2005) Using openhole and cased hole resistivity logs to monitor gas hydrate dissociation during thermal test in the Mallik 5L-38 research well, Mackenzie delta, Canada. *SPWLA 46th Ann. Symp. Trans.*, Paper SS, 1–11.

Anderson, B., Druskin, V., Habashy, T., Lee, P., Lüling, R., Barber, T., Grove, G., Lovell, J., Rosthal, R. Tabanou, J., Kennedy, D. and Shen L. (1997) New dimensions in modelling resistivity. *Oilfield Review*, **9**, Issue 1, 40–56.

Andrews, R., Beck, G., Castelijns, K., Chen, A., Fadnes, F., Irvine-Fortescue, J., Williams, S., Hashem, M., Jamaluddin, A., Kurkjian, A., Sass, B., Mullins, O., Rylander, E. and Van Dusen, A. (2001) Quantifying contamination using colour of crude and condensate. *Oilfield Review*, Autumn, 24–43.

Anxionnaz, H., Delfiner, P. and Delhomme, J.P. (1990) Computer-generated core-like descriptions from open-hole logs. *Bull. Am. Assoc. Petrol. Geol.* **74** No. 4, 375–393.

Archie, C.E. (1950) Introduction to petrophysics of reservoir rocks. *Bull. Am. Assoc. Petrol. Geol.* **34**(5), 943–961.

Archie, G. (1942) The electrical resistivity log as an aid in determining some reservoir characteristics. *Trans. AIME*, **146**, 54–62.

Arrayo Franco, J., Mercado Ortiz, M. Gopa, S. De, Renlie, L. and Williams, S. (2006) Sonic investigations in and around the borehole. *Oilfield Review*. Spring, 14–33.

Asquith, G. and Gibson, C. (1982) *Basic well log analysis for geologists*. AAPG Methods in Exploration Series, **216.**

Asquith, G. And Krygowski, D. (2004) *Basic well log analysis, Second edition*. AAPG Methods in Exploration Series, 16, 244p.

Atlas Wireline Services (1992) *Digital Circumferential Borehole Imaging Log (CBIL)*. Tool brochure. Western Atlas International.

Ausbrooks, R., Hurley, N., May, A. and Neese, D. (1999) Pore-size distributions in vuggy carbonates from core images, NMR and capillary pressure. *SPE* **56506**, 1–14.

Ayan, C., Hafez, H., Hurst, S., Kuchuk, F., O'Callaghan, A., Peffer, J., Pop, J. and Zeybek, M (2001) Characterizing permeability with formation testers. *Oilfield Review*, Autumn, 2–23.

Badruzzaman, A. (2004) Nuclear logging technology present and future – an operating company perspective. *SPWLA 45th Ann. Symp. Trans.*, Paper A, 1–14.

Bailey, R. and Smith, D. (2010) Scaling in stratigraphic data series: implications for practical stratigraphy. *First Break*, **28**, No. 1, 57–66.

Baker Atlas (2000) *Reservoir characterisation instrument (RCI)*. Tool brochure, 16p.

Baker Huges INTEQ (2006) *aXcelerate*[sm] *High speed telemetry*. Tool brochure, www.bakerhughes.com/INTEQ

Bakke, K., Gjelberg, J. and Peterson, S. (2007) Compound seismic modelling of the Ainsa II turbidite system, Spain: application to deep-water channel systems offshore Angola. *Marine and Petroleum Geology*, **25**, 1058–1073.

Baldwin, J.L., Bateman, R.M. and Wheatley, C.L. (1990) Application of a neural network to the problem of mineral identification from well logs. *The Log Analyst,* **31** No. 5, 279–293.

Barber, T., Flaum, C., Ellis, D., Jacobson, L. and Smith, M. (1991) Vertical resolution of well logs: recent developments. *Oilfield Review*, **3**, 3, 24–28.

Bargach, S., Falconer, I., Maeso, C., Rasmus, J., Bornemann, T., Plumb, R., Codazzi, D., Hodenfield, K., Ford, G., Hartner, J., Grether, B. and Rohler, H (2000) Real-time LWD: logging for drilling. *Oilfield Review*, Autumn, 58–78

Barriol, Y., Glaser, K., Pop, J., Bartman, B., Corbiel, R., Eriksen, K., Laasted, H., Laidlaw, J., Manin, Y., Morrison, K., Sayers, C., Romero, M. and Volokitin, Y. (2005) The pressures of drilling and production. *Oilfield Review*, Autumn, 22–41

Barton, C.A. and Moos, D. (1988) Analysis of macroscopic fractures in the Cajon Pass scientific drillhole over the interval 1829–2115 meters. *Geophys. Res. Let.* **15**, No. 9, 1013–1016.

Barton, C. and Moos, D. (2010) Geomechanical wellbore imaging: key to managing the asset life cycle. In: *Dipmeter and Borehole Image Log Technology.* Eds: Poppelreiter, M., Garcia-Carballido, C. and Kraaijveld, M. AAPG Memoir, **92**, 81–112.

Barton, C. and Zoback, M. (2002) Wellbore imaging technologies applied to reservoir geomechinics. In: *Geological Application of Well Logs* Eds: Lovell, M. and Parkinson, N. AAPG Methods in Exploration Series, **13**, 229–240.

Barton, C. and Zoback, M. (2002) Discrimination of natural fractures from drilling-induced wellbore failures in wellbore image data – implications for reservoir permeability. *SPE* **78599**, 249–254.

Barton, C., Moos, D. and Tezuka, K. (2009) Geomechanical wellbore imaging: implications for reservoir fracture permeability. *Bull. Am. Assoc .Petrol. Geol.*, **93,** No.11, 1551–1569.

Batzle, M and Wang, Z. (1992) Seismic properties of pore fluids. *Geophysics,* **57**, No. 11, 1396–1408.

Baum, G.R and Vail, P.R. (1988) Sequence stratigraphic concepts applied to Palaeogene outcrops, Gulf Atlantic basins. In: *Sea-level changes: an integrated approach.* Eds. Wilgus, C.K., Hastings, B.S., Kendall, C.G.St.C., Posamentier, H.W., Ross, C.A. and Van Wagoner, J.C. *S.E.P.M Sp. Pub.* **42**, 309–327.

BCCP-Group (1994) The upper Albian of northern Germany: results from the Kirchrode 1/91 borehole, boreal Cretaceous cycles project (BCCP). *Zbl. Geol. Paläont. Teil I,* **H.7/8,** 809–822.

Bean, C., Boonen, P., Deady, R. and Tepper, R. (1998) Important implications from a comparison of LWD and wireline acoustic data from a Gulf of Mexico well. *SPWLA 39th Ann. Symp. Trans.*, Paper S, 1–14.

Belknap, W.B., Dewan, J.T., Kirkpatrick, C.V., Mott, W.E., Pearson, A.J. and Rabson, W.R. (1959) Calibration facility for nuclear logs. *Drill and Prod. Prac. API,* 289–317.

Bell, J.S. (1990) Investigating stress regimes in sedimentary basins using information from oil industry wireline logs and drilling records. In: *Geological applications of wireline logs.*, Eds. Hurst, A., Lovell, M., Morton, A., Geol. Soc. London Spec. Publ. **48,** 305–325.

Bell, J.S. and Gough, D.I. (1979) Northeast-southwest compressive stress in Alberta – evidence from oil wells. *Earth and Planetary Science Letters* **45,** 475–482.

Benfield, M., Ewhro, O., Guo, P., Aoun, W., Oden, E. and Coope, D. (2004) Porosity evaluation in sandstone reservoirs containing light hydrocarbon: an LWD case study from shallow offshore Niger Delta. *SPWLA 45th Ann. Symp. Trans.*, Paper BBB, 1–14.

Bengtson, C.A. (1980) Structural uses of tangent diagrams. *Geology,* **8**, 599–602.

Bengtson, C.A. (1981) Statistical curvature analysis techniques for structural interpretation of dipmeter data. *Bull. Am. Assoc. Petrol. Geol.* **65,** 312-332.

Bengtson, C.A. (1982) Structural and stratigraphic use of dip profiles in petroleum exploration. In: *The deliberate search for the subtle trap.* Bull. Am. Assoc. Petrol. Geol. Memoir **32**, ed. Halbouty, M.T. 31–45.

Benoit, W.R., Sethi, D.K., Fertl, W.H. and Mathews, M. (1980) Geothermal well log analysis at Desert Peak, Nevada. *SPWLA 21st Ann. Symp. Trans.*, Paper AA, 1–41.

Berg, R.R. and Avery, A.H. (1995) Sealing properties of Tertiary growth faults, Texas Gulf Coast. *Bull. Am. Assoc. Petrol. Geol.* **79**, No. 3, 375–393.

Betancourt, S., Davies, T., Kennedy, R., Dong, C., Elshahawi, H., Mullins, O., Nighswander, J. and O'Keefe, M. (2007) Advancing fluid-property measurements. *Oilfield Review*, Autumn, 56–70.

Betancourt, S., Fujisawa, G., Mullin, O., Carnegie, A., Dong, C., Kurkjian, A., Eriksen, K. Haggag, M., Jaramillo, A. and Terabayashi, H. (2003) Analyzing hydrocarbons in the borehole. *Oilfield Review*, Autumn, 54–61.

Bhattacharya, J.P. (1993) The expression and interpretation of marine flooding surfaces and erosional surfaces in core: examples from the Upper Cretaceous Dunvegan Formation, Alberta foreland basin, Canada. In: *Sequence stratigraphy and facies associations,* eds. Posamentier, H.W., Summerhays, C.P., Haq, B.U., Allen, G.P. *IAS Spec. Publ.* **18**, 125–160.

Bhuyan, K and Passey, R. (1994) Clay estimation from GR and neutron-density porosity logs. *SPWLA 35th Ann. Symp. Trans.*, Paper DDD, 1–15.

Bigelow, E.L. (1985) Making more intelligent use of log derived dip information. *The Log Analyst,* **26**, Parts 1–5.

Birchwood, R., Dai, J., Shelander, D., Boswell, R., Collett, T., Cook, A., Dallimore, S., Fujii, K., Fukuhara, M., Kusaka, K., Murray, D. and Saeki, T. (2010) Developments in gas hydrates. *Oilfield Review*, **22**, 1, 18–33.

Bittar, M., Chemali, R., Morys, R., Wilson, J., Hveding, F., Li, S., Knizhnik, S. and Halverson, D (2008) The "depth-of-electrical image", a key parameter in accurate dip computation and geosteering. *SPWLA 49th Ann. Symp. Trans.*, Paper TT, 1–10.

Bjørlykke, K., Dypvik, H. and Finstad, K.G. (1975) The Kimmeridge shale, its composition and radioactivity. *NFP Jurassic Northern N. Sea Symp., Stavanger,* Paper 12, 1–20.

Blackbourn, G.A. (1990) *Cores and Core Logging.* Whittles Publishing, Scotland.

Blackbourn, G.A. (2009) *Cores and Core Logging for Geoscientists. 2nd revised edition.* Whittles Publishing, Scotland.

Blakeman, E.R. (1982) A case study of the effect of shale alteration on sonic transit times. *SPWLA 23rd Ann. Symp. Trans.,* Paper II, 1–14.

Bloch, F., Hansen, W. and Packard, M. (1946) The nuclear induction experiment. *Physical Review.* **70**, 474–485.

Block, L.V., Cheng, C.H. and Duckworth, G.L. (1991) Velocity analysis of multi-receiver full waveform acoustic log data in open and cased holes. *The Log Analyst,* **32**, No. 3, 188–200.

Bonner, S., Burgess, T., Clark, B., Decker, D., Orban, J., Bernhard, P., Luling, M. and White, J. (1993) Measurement at the bit: a new generation of MWD tools. *Oilfield Review*, July, 44–54

Bonner, S., Clark, B., Holenka, J., Voisin, B., Dusang, J., Hansen, R., White, J. and Walsgrove, T. (1992) Logging while drilling: a three year perspective. *Oilfield Review*, July, 4–21.

Bonner, S., Fredette, M., Lovell, J., Montaron, B., Rosthal, R., Tabanou, J., Wu, P., Clark, B., Mills, R. and Williams, R. (1996) Resistivity while drilling – images from the string. *Oilfield Review*, 7, Issue 1, 4–19.

Bonnie, R., Akkurt, R., Al-Waheed, H., Bradford, C., Eyvazzdeh, R., Phillips, E., Aadireddy, P. and Negm, E. (2003) Wireline T_1 logging. *SPE* **84483**, 1–9.

Borkhataria, R., Aigner, T. and Pipping, K. (2006) An unusual, muddy, epeiric carbonate reservoir: The Lower Muschelkalk (Middle Triassic) of the Netherlands. *AAPG Bulletin,* **90**, 1, 61–89.

Bourg, L., Decoster, E., Klein, J. and Gipson, L. (2007) Resistivity logging in horizontal wells in the Orinoco heavy oil belt: laterolog or dielectric propagation LWD tools? *SPWLA 48th Ann. Symp. Trans.*, Paper QQQ, 1–16.

Bourgeois, T., Bramlett, K., Craig, P., Cannon, D., Hodenfield, K., Lovell, J., Harkins, R and Pigram, I. (1998) Pushing the limit of formulation evaluation while drilling. *Oilfield Review,* **10**, 4, 29–39.

Bourke, L.T. (1989) Recognising artefact images on the Formation MicroScanner. *SPWLA 30th Ann. Symp. Trans.,* Paper WW, 1–25.

Bourke, L.T. (1992) Sedimentological borehole image analysis in clastic rocks: a systematic approach to interpretation. In: *Geological applications of wireline logs II.,* eds. Hurst, A., Griffiths, C.M., and Worthington, P.F. Geol. Soc. London Spec. Publ. **65,** 31–42.

Bourke, L.T., Corbin, N., Buck, S.G. and Hudson, G. (1993) Permeability images: a new technique for enhanced reservoir characterisation. In: *Advances in reservoir geology.* Ed. Ashton, M., Geol. Soc. London Spec. Pub. **69,** 219–232.

Boyeldieu, C., Coblentz, A. and Pelissier-Combescure, J. (1984) Formation evaluation in oil base mud wells. *SPWLA 25th Ann., Symp. Trans.,* Paper BB, 1–18.

Bratton, T., Bricout, V., Lam, R., Plona, T., Sinha, B., Tagbor, K., Venkitaraman, A. and Borbas, T. (2004) Rock strength parameters from annular pressure while drilling and dipole sonic dispersion analysis. *SPWLA 45th Ann. Symp. Trans.*, Paper O, 1–14.

Brereton, R. and McCann, D. (1990) A fresh look at predictive equations for compressional wave velocity – porosity. In: *European*

Core Analysis Symposium, 270–298.

Brewer, T., Harvey, P., Barr, S., Haggas, S. and Delius, H. (2005) The interpretation of thermal neutron properties in ocean floor volcanic. In: *Petrophysical properties of crystalline rocks.* Eds: Harvey, P. and Brewer, T. Geol. Soc. London Spec. Publ. **240**, 219–235.

Briceño, M.G. and Peeters, M. (2005) Sloping invasion profiles derived from shallow wireline logs. *Petrophysics,* **46**, No 1, 33–41.

Brie, A., Endo, T., Hoyle, D., Codazzi, D., Esmersoy, C.,Hsu, K., Denoo, S., Mueller, M., Plona, T., Shenoy, R. and Sinha, B. (1998). New directions in sonic logging. *Oilfield Review,* Spring, 40–53.

Bristow, C.S. and Myers, K.J. (1989) Detailed sedimentology and gamma-ray log characteristics of a Namurian delta succession. I: sedimentology and facies analysis. In: *Deltas: sites and traps for fossil fuels.* Eds. Whateley, M.K.G. and Pickering, K.T. Geol. Soc. London Spec. Pub. **41**, 75–80.

Broding, R.A. (1982) Volumetric scan well logging. *The Log Analyst,* **XXIII** (1); 14–19.

Broding, R.A. (1984) Application of the sonic volumetric scan log to cement evaluation. *SPWLA 25th Ann. Symp. Trans.,* Paper JJ, 1–17.

Broggi, G. and Gerdil-Neuillet, F. (1983) Cluster method and log data can determine lithology. *Oil & Gas J.,* July 18, 139–140.

Bücher, C. and Rybach, L. (1996) A simple method to determine heat production from gamma-ray logs. *Marine and Petroleum Geology,* **13**, No. 4, 373–377.

Buckley, D.K. and Oliver, D. (1990) Geophysical logging of water exploration boreholes in the Deccan Trap, Central India. In: *Geological applications of well logs,* eds. Hurst, A., Lovell, M.A. and Morton, A.C. Geol. Soc. London Spec. Publ. **48**, 153–161.

Budding, M.G. and Inglin, H.F. (1981) A reservoir geological model of the Brent Sands in Southern Cormorant. In: *Petroleum Geology of the Continental Shelf of N.W. Europe,* eds. Illing, L.V. and Hobson, G.D., Heyden, London, 326–334.

Bulat, J. and Stoker, S.J. (1987) Uplift determination from internal velocity studies, U.K. southern North Sea. In: *Petroleum Geology of Northwestern Europe,* eds. Brooks, J. and Glennie, K.W., Graham and Trotman, 293–305.

Bunch, A.W.H. and Dromgoole, P.W. (1995) Lithology and fluid prediction from seismic and well data. *Petroleum Geoscience,* **1**, No. 1, 49–57.

Burke, J.A., Campbell, R.L. and Schmidt, A.W. (1969) The lithoporosity cross plot. *SPWLA 10th Ann. Symp. Trans.,* 1–29.

Burnett, T., Koopersmith, C. and Spross, R. (1990) Drill collar effects on MWD epithermal, thermal and capture gamma ray neutron porosity measurements. *SPWLA 31st Ann. Symp. Trans.,* Paper E, 1–20.

Burnhill, T.J. and Ramsay, W.V. (1981) Mid-Cretaceous palaeontology and stratigraphy, central North Sea. In: *Petroleum Geology of the Continental Shelf of N.W. Europe,* eds. Illing, L.V. and Hobson, G.D., Heyden, London, 245–254.

Burst, J.F. (1969) Diagenesis of Gulf coast clayey sediments and its possible relation to petroleum migration. *Bull. Am. Assoc. Petrol Geol.* **53**(1), 73–93.

Bussian, A.E. (1982) A generalised Archie equation, *SPWLA 23rd Ann. Symp. Trans.,* Paper E, 1–12.

Bussian, A.E. (1983) A comparison of shaly sand models. *SPWLA 24th Ann. Symp. Trans.,* Paper E, 1–16.

Butler, J. and Clayton, C.G. (1984) A new philosophy for calibrating oil well logging tools based on neutron transport codes. *SPWLA 25th Ann. Symp. Trans.,* Paper FFF, 1–26.

Calner, M., Lehnert, O. and Joachimski, M. (2010) Carbonate mud mounds, conglomerates, and sea-level history in the Katian (Upper Ordovician) of central Sweden. *Facies,* **56**, 157–172.

Cameron, G.I.F. (1986) Confidence and the identification of foresets in stratigraphic dipmeter surveys. *SPWLA 10th European Form. Eval. Symp.* Paper O, 1–16.

Cameron, G.I.F. (1992) Analysis of dipmeter data for sedimentary orientation. In: *Geological applications of well logs II,* eds. Hurst, A., Griffiths, C.M. and Worthington, P.F. Geol. Soc. London Spec. Pub. **65,** 141–156.

Cameron, G.I.F., Collinson, J.D., Rider, M.H. and Xu, L. (1993). Analogue dipmeter logs through a prograding deltaic sandbody. In: *Advances in reservoir geology.* Ed. Ashton, M. Geol. Soc. London Spec. Pub. **66,** 195–217.

Cant, D.J. (1992) Subsurface facies analysis. In: *Facies models, response to sea-level change,* eds. Walker, R.G. and James, N.P., Geological Soc. Canada, 27–45.

Carpenter, W.W., Best, D. and Evans, M (1997) Applications and interpretation of azimuthally sensitive density measurements acquired while drilling. *SPWLA 38th Ann. Symp. Trans.,* Paper EE, p. 1–12.

Catuneanu, O. (2006) *Principles of sequence stratigraphy.* Elsevier 375p.

Catuneanu, O., Abreu, V., Bhattacharya, J., Blum, M., Dalrymple, R., Eriksson, P., Fielding, C., Fisher, W., Galloway, W., Gibling, M., Giles, K., Holbrook, J., Jordan, R., Kendall, C., Macurda, B., Martinsen, O., Miall, A., Neal, J., Nummedal, D., Pomar, L. Posamentier, H., Pratt, B., Sarg, J., Shanley, K., Steel, R., Strasser, R., Tucker, M. and Winker, C. (2009) Towards a standardization of sequence stratigraphy. *Earth-Science Reviews,* **92**, 1–33.

Catuneanu, O., Bhattacharya, J., Blum, M., Dalrymple, R., Eriksson, P., Fielding, C., Fisher, W., Galloway, W., Gianolla, P., Gibling, M., Giles, K., Holbrook, J., Jordan, R., Kendall, C., Macurda, B., Martinsen, O., Miall, A., Neal, J., Nummedal, D., Posamentier, H., Pratt, B., Shanley, K., Steel, R., Strasser, R. and Tucker, M. (2010) Sequence stratigraphy: a common ground after three decades of development. *First Break,* **28**, No. 1, 41–65.

Chamberlain, A.K. (1984) Surface gamma-ray logs: a correlation tool for frontier areas. *Bull. Am. Assoc. Petrol. Geol.* **68**(8), 1040–1043.

Chang, D., Vinegar, H., Morriss, C. and Straley, S. (1994) Effective porosity, producible fluids and permeability in carbonates from NMR logging. *SPWLA 35th Ann. Symp. Trans.,* Paper A, 1–21.

Chang, D., Vinegar, H., Morriss, C. and Straley, C. (1997) Effective porosity, producible fluid and permeability in carbonates from NMR logging. *The Log Analyst,* **38,** No 2, 60–72.

Chapellier, D. (1992) *Well-logging in hydrogeology.* AA Balkema, Rotterdam, 175p.

Chemali, R., Gianzero, S. and Su, S.M. (1984) The depth of investigation of compressional wave logging for the standard and the long-spacing sonde. *SAID 9th International Formation Evaluation Transactions,* Paper 13, 1–10.

Cheung, P. (1999) Microresistivity and ultrasonic imagers: tool operations and processing principles with reference to commonly encountered artefacts. In: *Borehole imaging: applications and case histories.* Eds. Lovell, M., Williamson, G., and Harvey, P. Geol. Soc. London Spec. Pub. **159**, 45–57.

Cheung, P., Hayman, A., Laronga, R., Cook, G., Flournoy, G., Goetz, P., Marshal, M., Hansen, S., Lamb, M., Bingjian, L., Larsen, M., Orgren, M. and Redden, J. (2001) A clear picture in oil-base muds. *Oilfield Review,* **13**, Issue 4, 2–27.

Cheung, P., Pittman, D., Hayman, R., Laronga, P., Ounadjela, O., Desport, S., Hansen, S., Kear, K., Lamb, M., Borbas, T. and Wendt, B. (2001) Field test results of a new oil-base mud formation imager tool. *SPWLA 42nd Ann. Symp. Trans.,* Paper XX, 1–14.

Chitale, V., Johnson, C., Entzminger, D. and Canter, L. (2010) Application of a modern electrical borehole imager and a new image interpretation technique to evaluate the porosity and permeability in carbonate reservoirs: a case history from the Permian Basin, United States. In: *Dipmeter and Borehole Image Log Technology.* Eds. Poppelreiter, M., Garcia-Carballido, C. and Kraaijveld, M. AAPG Memoir **92**, 295–307.

Chmelik, F.B., Bouma, A.H. and Rezak, R. (1969) Comparison of electrical logs and physical parameters of marine sediment cores. *Gulf Coast Assoc. Geol. Socs. Trans.* **XIX,** 63–70.

Clavier C. (1991) The challenge of logging horizontal wells. *The Log Analyst,* **32**, No.2, 63–84

Clavier, C., Coates, G. and Dumanoir, J. (1977) The theoretical and experimental bases for the 'dual water' model for the interpretation of shaly sands. *52nd Ann. Conf. SPE of AIME,* **118,** SPE paper 6859.

Clennell, M., Dewhurst, D. and Raven, M. (2006) Shale petrophysics: electrical, dielectric and nuclear magnetic resonance studies of shales and clays. *SPWL 47th Ann. Symp. Trans.,* Paper KK, 1–13.

Coats, G., Miller, M., Gillen, M. and Henderson G. (1991) The MRIL in Conoco 33-1: an investigation of a new magnetic resonance imaging log. *SPWL 32nd Ann. Symp. Trans.,* Paper DD, 1–24.

Coats, G., Vinegar, H.J., Tutunjian, P.N. and Gardner, J.S. (1993) Restrictive diffusion from uniform gradient NMR well logging. *SPE* **26472,** 575–590.

Coates, G., Xiao, L. and Prammer, M. (1999) *NMR logging, principles and applications.* Halliburton Energy Services, Houston. 234p.

Cobern, M.E. and Nuckols, E.B. (1985) Application of MWD resistivity relogs to evaluation of formation invasion. *SPWLA 26th Ann. Symp. Trans.,* Paper OO, 1–16.

Cody, R.D. (1971) Adsorption and the reliability of trace elements as environment indicators for shales. *J. Sed. Pet.* **41**(2), 461–471.

Coleman, J.M. and Prior, D.B. (1982) Deltaic environments. In: *Sandstone Depositional Environments,* eds. Scholle, P.A. and Spearing, D., Am Assoc. Petrol. Geol. Mem. **31**, 139–178.

Collett, T. (1998) Well log evaluation of gas hydrate saturation. *SPWLA 38th Ann. Symp. Trans.*, Paper MM, 1–14.

Collett, T., Lewis, R. and Uchida, T. (2000) Growing interest in hydrates. *Oilfield Review*, **12**, No. 2, 42–57.

Collins, J., Kenter, J., Harris, P., Kuanysheva, G., Fischer, D. and Steffen, K. (2006) Facies and reservoir-quality variations in the late Visean to Bashkirian outer platform, rim, and flank of the Tengiz buildup, Precaspian Basin, Kazakhstan. In: *Giant hydrocarbon reservoirs of the world from rocks to reservoir characterization and modeling.* Eds. Harris, P. and Weber, I. AAPG Memoir **88**, 55–95.

Contreras, C., Gamero, H., Drinkwater, N., Geel, G., Luthi, S., Hodgetts, D., Hu, Y., Johannesson, E., Johanesson, M., Mizobe, A., Montaggioni, P., Pestman, P., Ray, S., Shang, R. and Saltmarsh, A. (2003) Investigating clastic reservoir sedimentology. *Oilfield Review*, Spring, 54–76.

Coope, D. (1984) The theory of 2MHz resistivity tool and its application to measurement while drilling. *The Log Analyst,* **25**, No. 3, 35–46.

Coope, D. and Hendricks, E. (1984) Formation evaluation measurements recorded while drilling. *SPWLA 25th Ann. Symp. Trans.*, Paper FF, 1–21.

Cooper, B.S., Coleman, S.H., Barnard, P.C. and Butterworth, J.S. (1975) Paleotemperatures in the northern North Sea basin. In: *Petroleum and the Continental Shelf of N.W. Europe,* ed. Woodland, A.W., Applied Sci. Publ., Barking, 487–492.

Corfield, R.M. and Norris, R.D. (1996) Deep water circulation in the Paleocene ocean. In: *Correlation of the early Paleogene in northwest Europe,* eds. Knox, R.W.O'B., Corfield, R.M. and Dunay, R.E. Geol. Soc. London Spec. Publ. **101,** 443–456.

Cornford, C. (1984) Source rocks and hydrocarbons of the North Sea. In: *Introduction to the Petroleum Geology of the North Sea,* ed. Glennie, K.W., ch. 9, Blackwell, Oxford, 171–204.

Cox, J.W. (1983) Long axis orientation in elongated boreholes and its correlation with rock stress data. *SPWLA 24th Ann. Symp. Trans.,* Paper J, 1–17.

Creaney, S. and Passey, Q.R. (1993) Recurring patterns of Total Organic Carbon and source rock quality within a sequence stratigraphic framework. *Bull. Am. Assoc. Petrol. Geol.* **77** No. 3, 386–401.

Crombie, A., Halford, F., Hashem, M., McNeil, R., Melbourne, G. and Mullins, O. (1998) Innovations in wireline fluid sampling. *Oilfield Review*, Autumn, 26–41.

Cuddy, S. (1997) The application of fuzzy logic to petrophysics. *SPWLA 38th Ann. Symp. Trans.*, Paper S, 1–14.

Cunningham, A.B. and Opstad, E.A. (1992) Use of LWD formation evaluation in the Endicott reservoir North Slope, Alaska, U.S.A. *The Log Analyst*, **33**, No. 5, 439–450.

Cunningham, A.B., Jay, K. and Opstad, E. (1991) Applications of MWD technology in nonconventional wells, Prudhoe Bay, North Slope, Alaska. *The Log Analyst*, **32**, No. 1, 13–23.

Dahlberg, K.E. and Fitz, P.E. (1988) Comparing log-derived and core-derived porosity and mineralogy in thinly bedded reservoirs: an integrated approach. *SPWLA 29th Ann. Symp. Trans.*, Paper W, 1–18.

Darling, H., Patten, D., Young, R.A. and Schwarze, L. (1991) Single-well data integration. *Oilfield Review*, **3**, No. 3, 29–35.

Darling, H., Scott, H. and Toufaily, A. (1997) Applications of an epithermal neutron measurement in formation evaluation. *SPWLA 38th Ann. Symp. Trans.*, Paper NN, 1–12.

Dart, R.D. and Zoback, M.L. (1989) Well-bore breakout-stress analysis within the central and eastern continental United States. *The Log Analyst*, **30,** No. 1, 12–24.

Davatzes, N. and Hickman, S. (2010) Stress, fracture, and fluid-flow analysis using acoustic and electrical image logs in hot fractured granites of the Coso geothermal field, California, U.S.A In: *Dipmeter and Borehole Image Log Technology.* Eds. Poppelreiter, M., Garcia-Carballido, C. and Kraaijveld, M. AAPG Memoir **92**, 259–293.

Davenport, M., Booth, D., Terry, R., Dodds, N. and Rajasingham, R. (2004) The role of formation pressure measurements and samples in understanding the potential of deep water discoveries in offshore Angola. *SPWLA 45th Ann. Symp. Trans.*, Paper M, 1–12.

Davies, D.K. and Ethridge, F.G. (1975) Sandstone composition and depositional environment. *Bull. Am. Assoc. Petrol. Geol.* **59**(2), 239–264.

Davies, S. and Eliott, T. (1996) Spectral gamma ray characterisation of high resolution sequence stratigraphy: examples from Upper Carboniferous fluvio-deltaic systems, County Clare, Ireland. In: *High resolution sequence stratigraphy: innovations and applications,* eds. Howell, J.A. and Aitken, J.F. Geol. Soc. London Spec. Publ. **104,** 25–35.

Davis, J.C. (1986) *Statistics in geology 2nd ed.* John Wiley & Sons, 646p.

De'Ath, N.G. and Schuyleman, S.F. (1981) The geology of the Magnus oil field. In: *Petroleum Geology of the Continental Shelf of N.W. Europe,* eds. Illing, L.V. and Hobson, G.D., Heyden, London, 342–351.

Deegan, C.E. and Scull, B.J. (1977) A proposed standard lithostratigraphic nomenclature for the central and northern North Sea. *Rep. Inst. Geol. Sci. Ldn,* 77/25, and *Bull. Nor. Pet. Dir.* **1**, 35.

Delhomme, J-P. (1992) A quantitative characterisation of formation heterogeneities based on borehole image analysis. *SPWLA 33rd Ann. Symp. Trans.,* Paper T, 1–25.

Delhomme, J-P. and Serra, O. (1984) Dipmeter-derived logs for sedimentological analysis. *SPWLA Trans. 9th European Formation Evaluation Symposium* Paper **50**, 1–15.

DePavia, L., Heaton, N., Ayers, D., Freedman, R., Harris, R., Jorion, B., Kovats, J., Luong, B., Rajan, N., Taherian, R., Walter, K., Willis, D., Scheibal, J. and Garcia, S. (2003) A next-generation wireline NMR logging tool. *SPE* **84482**, 1–7.

Desbrandes, R. (1968) *Théorie et interprétation des diagraphies.* Technip, Paris.

Desbrandes, R. (1982) *Diagraphies dans les sondages.* Technip, Paris, 575p.

Devilliers, M.C. and Werner, P.H., (1990) Example of fault identification using dipmeter data. In: *Geological applications of wireline logs.* Eds. Hurst, A., Lovell, M.A. and Morton, A.C. Geol. Soc. London Spec. Publ. **48**, 287–295.

Dewan, J.T. (1983) *Essentials of Modern Open Hole Log Interpretation,* Pennwell, Tulsa. 361p.

Dickey, P.A. (1969) Increasing concentration of subsurface brines with depth. *Chem. Geol.* **4**, 361–370.

Djafarov, I, Khafizov, S. and Syngaevsky, P. (2004) NMR application in reservoirs with complex lithology: a case study. *Petrophysics,* **45**, No 2, 119–129.

Donald, A. and Bratton, T. (2006) Advancements in acoustic techniques for evaluating open natural fractures. *SPWLA 47th Ann. Symp. Trans.,* Paper QQ, 1–10.

Dong, C., Hegeman, P., Elshahawi, H., Mullins, O., Fujisawa, G. and Kurkjian, A. (2003) Advances in downhole contamination monitoring and GOR measurement of formation fluid samples. *SPWLA 44th Ann. Symp. Trans.*, Paper S, 1–11.

Donovan, W.S. and Hilchie, D.W. (1981) Natural gamma ray emissions in the Muddy J formation in eastern Wyoming. *The Log Analyst* **XXII** (2); 17–22 (re-publication).

Donovan, A.D., Baum, G.R., Blechschmidt, G.L., Loutit, T.S., Pflum, C.E. and Vail, P.R. (1988) Sequence stratigraphic setting of the Cretaceous-Tertiary boundary in Central Alabama. In: *Sea-level changes: an integrated approach,* eds. Wilgus, C.K., Hastings, B.S., Kendall, C.G.St.C., Posamentier, H.W., Ross, C.A. and Van Wagoner, J.C. S.E.P.M .Sp. Pub. **42**, 299–307.

Donselaar, M. and Schmidt, J. (2010) The application of borehole image logs to fluvial facies interpretation. In: *Dipmeter and Borehole Image Log Technology.* Eds: Poppelreiter, M., Garcia-Carballido, C. and Kraaijveld, M. AAPG Memoir **92**, 145–166.

Dorozynski, A. and Oristalgio, M. (2007) *Le sens du courant.* Cherche-Midi, Paris. 327p.

Doveton, J.H. (1986) *Log analysis of subsurface geology: concepts and computer methods.* Wiley and Sons, 273p.

Doveton, J.H. (1991) Lithofacies and geochemical facies profiles from nuclear wireline logs: new subsurface templates for sedimentary modeling. In: *Sedimentary modeling-computer simulations and methods for improved parameter definition.* Eds. Franseen, E.K., Watney, W.L., Kendall, C.J. and Ross, W. *Kansas Geol. Soc. Bull.* **233,** 101–110.

Doveton, J.H. (1994) Geologic log analysis using computer methods *Am. Assoc. Petrol. Geol. Computer applications in geology* **2**, p. 169.

Doveton, J.H. and Prensky, S.E. (1992) Geological application of wireline logs – a synopsis of developments and trends. *The Log Analyst,* **33** No. 3, 286–303.

Dowla, N., Rasmus, J. C., Srivastava, S., Ellis, D and Fulton, C. (2006) Caliper and borehole geometry determination from logging while drilling measurements and images. *SPWLA 47th Ann. Symp. Trans.* Paper YYY, 1–14.

Dresser Atlas (1982) *Well logging and interpretation techniques. The course for home study.* Dresser Atlas Publication.

Dresser Atlas (1983) *Log interpretation charts.* Dresser Atlas Publication.

Dubois, M., Byrnes, A., Bohling, G. and Doveton, J. (2006) Multiscale geologic and petrophysical modelling of the giant Hugoton gas field (Permian), Kansas and Oklahoma, USA. In: *Giant hydrocarbon reservoirs of the world from rocks to reservoir characterization and modeling*. Eds. Harris, P. and Weber, I. AAPG Memoir **88**, 307–353.

Dudley, J.W.II (1993) Quantitative fracture identification with the bore-hole televiewer. *SPWLA 34th Ann. Symp. Trans.*, Paper LL, 1–4.

Duke, W.L., Arnott, R.W.C. and Cheel, R.J. (1991) Shelf sandstones and hummocky cross stratification: new insight on a stormy debate. *Geol.* **19,** 625–628.

Dull, D., Garber, R. and Meddaugh, W. (2006) The sequence stratigraphy of the Maastrictian (Upper Cretaceous) reservoir at Wafra field, Partitioned Neutral Zone, Saudi Arabia and Kuwait: key to reservoir modeling and assessment. In: *Giant Hydrocarbon Reservoirs of the World: from Rocks to Reservoir Characterization and Modelling*, eds. Harris, P. and Weber, J. AAPG Memoir **88,** 247–279.

Dunlap, H.F. and Coats, G.R. (1988) Boron: tracking a trace element. *The Log Analyst*, **29** No. 6, 410–417.

Durrance, E.M. (1986) *Radioactivity* in *geology: Principles and applications.* John Wiley, 441p.

Dyos, C.J. (1987) Inversion of induction log data by method of maximum entropy. *SPWLA 28th Ann. Symp. Trans.*, Paper T, 1–13.

Dypvik, H. and Eriksen, D. Ø. (1983) Natural radioactivity of clastic sediments and the contributions of U, Th and K. *J. Pet. Geol.* **5**(4) 409–416.

Eberli, G.P. and Ginsberg, R.N. (1988) Progradation, NW Great Bahama Bank. In: *Reefs and adjacent areas.*, eds. Geldsetzer, H.H.J., James, N.P. and Tebbutt, G.E. *Canadian Society of Petroleum Geologists, Memoir* 13.

Edmundson, H.N. and Raymer, L.L. (1979) Table of radioactive logging parameters of common minerals. *SPWLA 6th European Symp. Trans., Ldn.*, Paper BB, 1–6.

Edwards, J.M., Ottinger, N.H. and Haskell, R.E. (1967) Nuclear log evaluation of potash deposits. *SPWLA 8th Ann. Symp. Trans.*, Paper L, 1–12.

Ehrenberg, S. N. and Svånå, T. A. (2001) Use of spectral gamma-ray signature to interpret stratigraphic surfaces in carbonate strata: an example from the Finnmark platform (Carboniferous-Permian), Barents Sea. *AAPG Bulletin*, **85**, No 2, 295–308.

Ekstrom, M.P., Dahan, C.A., Chen, M.Y., Lloyd, P.M. and Rossi, D.J. (1987) Formation imaging with microelectrical scanning arrays. *The Log Analyst,* **28,** No. 3, 294–306.

Elkington, P.A. (1995) An introduction to invasion profile imaging. BPB publication.

Ellis, D.V. (1987) *Well-logging for earth scientists.* Elsevier, 532p.

Ellis, D.V. and Singer J. M. (2007) *Well-logging for earth scientists. 2nd Edition,* Springer, 687p.

El-Wazeer, F., Haggag, M. and El-Farouk, O. (1999) Formation evaluation masked by mud invasion. *SPE* **53152,** 1–6.

Emery, D. and Myers, K. (1996) *Sequence Stratigraphy.* Blackwell Science, U.K. 297p.

Enwell, R. E (1998) Nonlinear response of gamma ray logging systems in the Copper Mountain uranium deposits. *The Log Analyst*, **39**, No. 5, 45–53.

Erlich, R., Barrett, S. and Guo, J. (1990) Seismic and geologic characteristics of drowning events on carbonate platforms. *AAPG Bulletin*, **74**, 1523–1537.

Etchecopar, A. and Dubas, M.O. (1992) Methods for geological interpretation of dips. *SPWLA 33rd Ann. Symp. Trans.*, Paper J, 1–21.

Etnyre, L. (1981) Fracture identification in the Panoma Field, Council Grove formation. *The Log Analyst* **XXII** (6); 3–6.

Evans, D, Graham, C., Armour, A. and Bathurst, P. (Eds.) (2003) *The Millennium Atlas: petroleum geology of the central and northern North Sea.* Geological Society London. CD version.

Evans, T.R. (1977) Thermal properties of North Sea rocks. *The Log Analyst* **XVIII** (2); 3–12.

Fan, Y., Deng, S., Zhou, C. and Zhou, F. (2002) Theoretical and experimental studies of membrane potential in shaly sands for improved Rw calculation. *SPWLA 43rd Ann. Symp. Trans.*, Paper AAA, 1–8.

Fang, J.H. and Chen, H.C. (1997) Fuzzy modelling and the prediction of porosity and permeability from the compositional and textural attributes of sandstone. *Journ. Petrol. Geol.* **20**, 185–204.

Fang, J.H., Chen, H.C., Shultz, A.W. and Mahmoud, W. (1992) Computer-aided well log correlation. *Bull. Am. Assoc. Petrol. Geol.* **76** No. 3, 307–317.

Faraguna, J.K., Chace, D.M. and Schmidt, M.G. (1989) An improved televiewer system: image acquisition, analysis and integration. *SPWLA 30th Ann. Symp. Trans.*, Paper UU, 1–11.

Felder, B. and Boyeldieu, C. (1974) The lithodensity log. *SAID 6th European Symposium Transactions,* Paper O, 20.

Fertl,W.H. (ed.)(1976) *Abnormal Formation Pressures Implications to Exploration, Drilling and Production of Oil and Gas Resources.* Elsevier, Amsterdam.

Fertl, W.H. (1977) Shale density studies and their application. In: *Developments in Petroleum Geology I,* ed. Hobson, G.D., Applied Science, Barking, 293–327.

Fertl, W.H. (1979a) Gamma ray spectral data assists in complex formation evaluation *SPWLA 6th European Symp. Trans. Ldn*, Paper Q, 1–32.

Fertl, W.H. (1979b)-1 Occurrence of the neutron absorbing trace element boron, Part I: Boron in rocks. In: *Pulsed Neutron Logging.* SPWLA reprint volume, 274–277.

Fertl, W.H. (1979c)-1 Occurrence of the neutron absorbing trace element boron, Part II: Boron in oil field waters. In: *Pulsed Neutron Logging*. SPWLA reprint volume, 285–288.

Fertl, W.H. (1984) Advances in well logging interpretation. *Oil & Gas J.* April 16th, 85–91.

Fertl, W.H. (1985) Logs help approximate reservoir temperature. *Oil & Gas J.* April 29th, 89–96.

Fertl, W.H. and Rieke, H.H. (1980) Gamma ray spectral evaluation techniques identify fractured shale reservoirs and source rock characteristics. *J. Pet. Tech.* November, 2053–2062.

Fertl, W.H. and Timko, D.J. (1972) How downhole temperature pressures affect drilling. *World Oil,* **7382**(10 parts). June 1972–March 1973.

Fertl, W.H. and Wichmann, P.A. (1977) How to determine static BHT from well data. *World Oil,* January.

Fiet, N. and Gorin, G. (2000) Gamma ray spectrometry as a tool for stratigraphic correlations in the carbonate-dominated, organic rich, pelagic Albian sediment in central Italy. *Ecolog. Geol. Helvetica*, **93**, 175–181.

Finley, R.J and Tyler, N. (1986) Geological characterization of sandstone reservoirs. In: *Reservoir characterisation,* eds. Lake, L.W. and Caroll, H.B. Academic Press, pages 1–38.

Fisher, W.L. (1969) Facies characterization of Gulf Coast basin delta systems, with some Holocene analogues. *Gulf Coast Assoc. Geol. Socs. Trans.* **XIX,** 239–261.

Fisk, H.N. and McFarlan Jr., E. (1955) Late quaternary deltaic deposits of the Mississippi river – local sedimentation and basin tectonics. *Geol. Soc. Am. Spec. Pub. Crust of the Earth,* paper 62, 279.

Flanagan, W.D., Bramblett, R.L., Galford, J.E. Hertzog, R.C., Plasek, R.E. and Olsen, J.R. (1991). A new generation nuclear logging tool. *SPWLA 32nd Ann. Symp. Trans.*, Paper Y, 1–25.

Flaum, C., Galford, J.E. and Hastings, A. (1989) Enhanced vertical resolution processing of dual detector gamma-gamma density logs. *The Log Analyst*, **30**(3), 139–149.

Fletcher, J., Eaton, G. and Greig, R. (2008) The use of magnetic resonance and image logs for reservoir characterisation and geosteering in deepwater west of Shetland. *SPWL 49th Ann. Symp. Trans.*, Paper Z, 1–8.

Fleury, M., Al-Nayadi, K. and Boyd, D. (2005) Water saturation from NMR, resistivity and oil base core in a heterogeneous Middle East carbonate reservoir. *SPWL 46th Ann. Symp. Trans.*, Paper JJJ, 1–16.

Folk, R.L. (1954) The distinction between grain size and mineral composition in sedimentary-rock nomenclature. *Journ. Geol.* **62**, 344–359.

Fons, L. (1969) Geological applications of well logs. *SPWLA 10th Ann. Symp. Trans.* Paper AA, 1–44.

Förster, A. (2001) Analysis of borehole temperature data in the Northeast German Basin: Continuous logs versus bottom hole temperature. *Petroleum Geoscience,* **7**, 241–254.

Freedman, R. and Heaton, N. (2004) Fluid characterization using nuclear magnetic resonance. *Petrophysics,* **45,** No 3, 241–250.

Freedman, R. and Morriss, C. (1995) Processing of data from an NMR logging tool. *SPE* **30560,** 301–316.

Frenkel, M. and Mezzatesta, A. (1998) Minimum and maximum pay estimation using resistivity log data inversion. *SPWLA 39th Ann. Symp. Trans.*, Paper Z, 1–9.

Fricke, S., Madio, D., Adolph, B., Evans, M. and Leveridge, R. (2008) Thermal neutron porosity using pulsed neutron measurements. *SPWLA 49th Ann. Symp. Trans.*, Paper L, 1–8.

Fujisawa, G., Jackson, R., Vannuffelen, S., Terabayashi, T., Yamate, T.,

Dong, C. and O'Keefe, M. (2008) Reservoir fluid characterization with a new-generation downhole fluid analysis tool. *SPWLA 49th Ann. Symp. Trans.* Paper KK, 1–7.

Gale, A. (1995) Cyclostratigraphy and correlation of the Cenomanian stage in Western Europe. In: *Orbital Forcing Timescales and Cyclostratigraphy*. House, M. and Gale, A. Eds., Geol. Soc. London Spec. Pub. **85**, 177–197.

Galloway, W.E. (1968) Depositional systems in the lower Wilcox group, North-Central Gulf Coast basin. *Gulf Coast Assoc. Geol. Socs. Trans.*, **XVIII**, 275–289.

Galloway, W.E. (1989a) Genetic stratigraphic sequences in basin analysis I: architecture and genesis of flooding-surface bounded depositional units. *Bull. Am. Assoc. Petrol Geol.* **73**, 125–142.

Galloway, W.E. (1989b) Genetic stratigraphic sequences in basin analysis II: application to northwest Gulf of Mexico Cenozoic basin. *Bull. Am. Assoc. Petrol. Geol.* **73**, 143–154.

Galloway, W.E. and Hobday, D.K. (1983) *Terrigenous Clastic Depositional Systems. Applications to Petroleum, Coal and Uranium Exploration.* Springer-Verlag, New York.

Gardener, J.S. and Dumanoir, J.L. (1980) Litho-density log interpretation. *SPWLA 21st Ann. Symp. Trans.*, Paper N, 1–23.

Gaymard, R. and Poupon, A. (1968) Response of neutron and formation density logs in hydrocarbon bearing formations. *The Log Analyst* **IX**(5); 3–12.

Gearhart, D.A. and Mathis, G.L. (1987) Development of a spectral litho-density logging tool by use of empirical methods. *The Log Analyst,* **28**, No. 5, 470–487.

Gearhart, Inc. (1983) *Formation Evaluation Data Handbook.* Gearhart Inc. Publication.

Gendron, C.R., Cahill, R.A. and Gilkeson, R.H. (1988) Comparison of spectral gamma ray (SGR) well logging data with instrumental neutron activation analysis (INAA) data for rock types in Northern Illinois. *The Log Analyst,* **29**, No. 5, 345–357.

Genter, A., Castaing, C., Dezayes, C., Tenzer, H., Traineau, H. and Villemin, T. (1997) Comparative analysis of direct (core) and indirect (borehole imaging tools) collection of fracture data in the Hot Dry Rock Soultz reservoir (France). *Journ. Geophys. Res.* **102**, B7, 15,419–15,431.

Georgi, D.T. (1985) Geometrical aspects of borehole televiewer images. *SPWLA 27th Ann. Symp. Trans.*, Paper C, 1–17.

Ghafoori, M., Roostaeian, M. and Sajjadian, V. (2008) Secondary porosity; a key parameter controlling the hydrocarbon production in heterogeneous carbonate reservoirs (case study). *SPWLA 49th Ann. Symp. Trans.*, Paper TTTT, 1–16.

Gilchrist, W. (2008) Compensated neutron log response issues – a tutorial. *SPWLA 49th Ann. Symp. Trans.*, Paper S, 1–11.

Gilreath, J.A. (1966) Electric log characteristics of diapiric shale. In: *Diapirism and Diapirs,* eds. Braunstein, J. and O'Brien, G.D., Am. Assoc. Petrol. Geol. Mem. **8**, 137–144.

Gilreath, J.A., Healy, J.S. and Yelverton, J.N. (1969) Depositional environments defined by dipmeter interpretations. *GCAGS Transactions* **19,** 101–111.

Gingras, M., Pemberton, S. and Saunders, T. (2001) Bathymetry, sediment texture and substrate cohesiveness; their impact on modern *Glossifungites* trace assemblages at Willapa Bay, Washington. *Paleo* **169,** 1–21.

Gladkikh, M., Chen, J. and Chen, S. (2008) Method of determining formation grain size distribution from acoustic velocities and NMR relaxation time spectrum. *SPWLA 49th Ann. Symp. Trans.*, Paper GGG, 1–11.

Goetz, IF., Prins, W.J. and Logar, J.F. (1977) Reservoir delineation by wireline techniques. *6th Ann. Conv. Indonesian Pet. Assoc.*, 1–40.

Goetz, IF., Dupal, L. and Bowler, J. (1979) An investigation into discrepancies between sonic log and seismic check shot velocities. *APEA*, 1–11.

Goldberg, D. and Meltser, A. (2001) High vertical resolution spectral gamma ray logging: a new tool development and field tests. *SPWLA 42nd Ann. Symp. Trans.*, Paper JJ, 1–13.

Goldberg, D and Saito, S. (1998) Detection of gas hydrates using downhole logs. In: *Gas hydrates: relevance to world margin stability and climate change*. Geol. Soc. London Spec. Publ. **137**, Eds. Henriet, J-P. and Mienert, J., 129–132.

Gondouin, M., Tixier, M.P. and Simard, G.L. (1957) An experimental study on the influence of the chemical composition of electrolytes on the SP curve. *Pet. Trans. AIME* **210**, 58–72.

Gonfalini, M. and Anxionnaz, H. (1990) A complete use of structural information from borehole imaging techniques – a case history for a deep carbonate reservoir. SPWLA *31st Ann. Symp. Trans.*, Paper J, 1–25.

Grace, L., Newberry, B. and Harper, J. (1999) Fault visualization from borehole images for sidetrack optimization. In: *Borehole imaging: applications and case histories*. Eds. Lovell, M., Williamson, G. and Harvey, P. Geol. Soc. London Spec. Publ., **159**, 271–281.

Granberry, R.J., Jenkins, R.E. and Bush, D.C. (1968) Grain density values of cores from some Gulf Coast Formations and their importance in formation evaluation. *SPWLA 9th Ann. Symp. Trans.*, Paper N, 1–19.

Gravem, T., Freitag, H-C. and Patterson, D. (2003) North Sea acoustic LWD field test results utilising integrated system approach. *SPWLA 44th Ann. Symp. Trans.*, Paper MM, 1–11.

Graue, E., Helland-Hansen, W., Johnson, J., Lomo, L., Nottvedt, A., Rønning, A. and Steel, R. (1987) Advance and retreat of the Brent Delta system, Norwegian North Sea. In: *Petroleum geology of North West Europe*. eds. Brooks, J. and Glennie, K.W. Proc. 3rd Conf. Pet. Geol. N.W. Europe. 915–938.

Greiss, R-M., Webb, C., White, J., McDonald, B., Flanagan, K., Rodriguez, J. and Scholey, H. (2003) Real-time density and gamma ray images acquired while drilling help to position horizontal wells in a structurally complex North Sea field. *SPWLA 44th Ann. Symp. Trans.*, Paper Z, 1–11.

Griffiths, C.M. (1982) A proposed geologically consistent segmentation and reassignment algorithm for petrophysical borehole logs. In: *Quantitative Stratigraphic Correlation,* eds. Cubitt, J.M. and Reyment, R.A., 287–298.

Griffiths, C.M. and Bakke, S. (1988) Semi-automated well matching using gene-typing algorithms and a numerical lithology derived from wireline logs. *SPWLA 29th Ann. Symp. Trans.*, Paper GG, 1–24.

Griffiths, R., Barber, T. and Faivre, O. (2000) Optimal evaluation of formation resistivities using array induction and array laterolog tools. *SPWLA 41st Ann. Symp. Trans.*, Paper BBB, 1–13.

Guo, P., Gilchrist, W.A., Page, G. and Wills, P. (2002) Interpretation of nuclear logs in formate-based drilling fluids in a North Sea well. *SPWLA 43rd Ann. Symp. Trans.*, Paper BBB, 1–12.

Gupta, R. and Johnson, H. (2002) High resolution facies architecture of heterolithic tidal deposits: an integrated outcrop and electrofacies analysis of a complex reservoir. In: *Geological Application of Well Logs* Eds: Lovell, M. and Parkinson, N. AAPG Methods in Exploration, **13**, 161–184.

Hakvoort, R., Fabris, A., Frenkel, M., Koelman, J. and Loermans, A. (1998) Field measurements and inversion results of the high-definition lateral log. *SPWLA 39th Ann. Symp. Trans.*, Paper C, 1–12.

Haldorsen, J., Johnson, D., Plona, T., Sinha, B., Valero, H-P. and Winkler, K. (2006) Borehole acoustic waves. *Oilfield Review*, Spring, 34–43.

Hall, J., Ponzi ,M., Gonfalini, M. and Maletti, G. (1996) Automatic extraction and characterisation of geological features and textures from borehole images and core photographs. *SPWLA 37th Ann. Symp. Trans.*, Paper CCC, 1–13.

Hallenberg, J. (1973) Interpretation of gamma ray logs. *SPWLA 14th Ann. Symp. Trans.*, Paper G, 1–28.

Hallenburg, J.K. (1978) Use of the spontaneous potential curve in a mineral mapping technique. *SPWLA 19th Ann. Symp. Trans.*, Paper U, 1–12.

Hallenburg, J.K. (1992) Nonhydrocarbon logging. *The Log Analyst,* **33** No. 3, 259–269.

Hansen, T. and Parkinson, D. (1999) Insights from simultaneous acoustic and resistivity imaging. In: *Borehole imaging: applications and case histories*. Eds. Lovell, M., Williamson, G. and Harvey, P. Geol. Soc. London Spec. Pub. **159**, 191–201.

Harker, S.D., McGann, G.J., Bourke, L.T., and Adams, J.T. (1990) Methodology of Formation MicroScanner image interpretation in Claymore and Scappa fields (North Sea). In: *Geological applications of well logs,* eds. Hurst, A., Lovell, M.A. and Morton, A.C. Geol. Soc. London Spec. Pub. **48,** 11–25.

Harris, P. (2010) Delineating and quantifying depositional facies patterns in carbonate reservoirs: insights from modern analogues. *AAPG Bulletin*, **94**, No 1, 61–86.

Hart, B. and Plint, A. (1993) Origin of an erosion surface in shoreface sandstones of the Kakwa member (Upper Cretaceous Cardium formation, Canada): importance for reconstruction of stratal geometry and depositional history. In: *Sequence Stratigraphy and Facies Associations*. Eds. Posamentier, H, Summerhayes, C. Haq, B. and Allen, G.. Int. Assoc. Sedimentologists, Sp. Pub. **18**, 451–467.

Hartmann, D.J. (1975) Effect of bed thickness and pore geometry on log response. *SPWLA 16th Ann. Symp. Trans.*, Paper Y, 1–14.

Hashem, M. and Gustavo, U. (2003) Wireline formation testers: uses beyond pressure and fluid samples – a viable replacement of production tests. *The Log Analyst*, **44**, No. 2, 108–115

Hashem, M. and Ugueto G. (2002) Wireline formation testers: uses beyond pressure and fluid samples – a viable replacement of production tests. *SPWLA 43rd Ann. Symp. Trans.*, Paper XX, 1–14.

Hashem, M., Elshahawi, H. and Ugeto, G. (2004) A decade of formation testing – dos and don'ts and tricks of the trade. *SPWLA 45th Ann. Symp., Trans.* Paper M, 1–9.

Hassan, M. (1973) Radioelements and diagenesis in shale and carbonate sediments. *SAID 2nd Ann. Symp. Trans.*, Paper 8, 1–7.

Hassan, M., Hossin, A. and Combaz, A. (1976) Fundamentals of the differential gamma ray log interpretation technique. *SPWLA 17th Ann. Symp. Trans.*, Paper H, 1–18.

Hawkins, P.J. (1972) Carboniferous sandstone oil reservoirs, East Midlands, England. PhD Thesis, Univ. London (unpublished).

Haynes, F. M., Bergslien, D., Burtz, O. M. and Munkholm, M. S. (2000) Applications of resistivity modeling in reservoir development: examples from Balder field, Norwegian North Sea. *Petrophysics*, **41**, 4, 281–293.

Head, E., Cannon, D., Allen, D. and Colson, L. (1992) Quantitative invasion description. *SPWLA 33rd Ann. Symp. Trans.*, paper B, 1–20.

Helix, R.D.S. (2008) *Reservoir geomechanics for petrophysicists*. SPWLA 49th Ann. Symp. Short course notes, 168p.

Hepp, V., Dumestre, A.C. (1975) Cluster: a method for selecting the most probable dip results from dipmeter surveys, *SPE* **5543**.

Hermanrud, C. and Shen, P.Y. (1989) Virgin rock temperatures from well logs – accuracy analysis for some advanced inversion models. *Marine and Petroleum Geology* **6** No. 4, 360–363.

Hernández, G., Cesares, M., Pérez, R., Barrios, O., Bautista, R., Brewer, R and Torne, J. (2007) "Look ahead" applications of vertical seismic profiles as a litho-structural tool combined with dipole sonic logging: case histories Burgos Basin-Northern Mexico. *SPWLA 48th Ann. Symp. Trans.*, Paper C, 1–13.

Hernandez, M., MacNeill, D., Reeves, M., Kirkwood, A., Lemke, S., Ruszka, J., and Zaeper, R. (2008) High-speed wired drillstring telemetry network delivers increased safety, efficiency, reliability and productivity to the drilling industry. *SPE* **113157**, 1–14.

Herring, E.A. (1973) Estimating abnormal pressures from log data in the North Sea. *Petroleum Engineer,* Nov. *SPE* 4301.

Herron, S and Herron, M. (1996) Quantitative lithology: an application for open and cased hole spectroscopy *SPWLA 37th Ann. Symp. Trans.*, Paper E, 1–14.

Herweijer, J.C., Hocker, C.F.W., Williams, H. and Eastwood, K.M. (1990) The relevance of dip profiles from outcrops as reference for the interpretation of SHDT dip. In: *Geological applications of well logs* eds. Hurst A., Lovell, M.A. and Morton, A.C., Geol. Soc. London Spec. Pub. **48**, 39–43.

Heslop, A. (1974) Gamma-ray log response of shaly sandstones. *SPWLA 15th Ann. Symp. Trans.*, Paper M, 1–11.

Heslop, A. (1975) Porosity in shaly-sands. *SPWLA 16th Ann. Symp Trans.*, Paper F, 1–12.

Hill, A.D. (1990) Temperature logging, Chapter 4. In: *Production logging, theoretical and interpretative elements.* SPE Memoir **14**, 19–36.

Hillis, R.R. (1995) Quantification of Tertiary exhumation in the United Kingdom, southern North Sea using sonic velocity data. *Bull. Am. Assoc. Petrol Geol.*, **79**, No. 1, 130–152.

Hillis, R.R. and Williams, A.F. (1992) Borehole breakouts and stress analysis in the Timor Sea. In: *Geological applications of wireline logs II.*, eds. Hurst, A., Griffiths, C.M., and Worthington, P.F. Geol. Soc. London Spec. Publ. **65**, 157–168.

Hinz, K. and Schepers, R. (1983) SABIS, the digital version of the borehole televiewer. *SPWLA 8th European Symp. Trans., Ldn*, Paper E, 1–20.

Höcker, C.F.W., Eastwood, K.M., Herweijer, J.C. and Adams J.T. (1990) Use of dipmeter data in clastic sedimentological studies. *Bull. Am. Assoc. Petrol. Geol.* **74**, No. 2, 105–118.

Hodson, G.M. (1975) Some aspects of the geology of the middle Jurassic in the northern North Sea with particular reference to electro-physical logs. *NPF Jurassic Northern N. Sea Symp., Stavanger.* Paper 16, 1–39.

Hoffman, L.J.B., Hoogerbrugge, P.J., and Lomas, A.T. (1988) LOGIX: a knowledge based system for petrophysical evaluation. *SPWLA 29th Ann. Symp. Trans.*, Paper R, 1–13.

Honda, H. and Magara, K. (1982) Estimation of irreducible water saturation and effective pore size of mudstones. *J. Pet. Geol,* 4(4), 407–418.

Hood, A., Gutjahr, C.C.M. and Heacock, R.L. (1975) Organic metamorphism and the generation of petroleum. *Bull. Am. Assoc. Petrol. Geol.* **59**, 986–996.

Hornby, B.E. and Luthi, S.M. (1992) An integrated interpretation of fracture apertures computed from electrical borehole scans and reflected Stoneley waves. In: *Geological Applications of Wireline Logs II*. Eds. Hurst, A., Griffiths, C. and Worthington, P. Geol. Soc. London Spec. Pub. **65**, 185–198.

Hornby, B.E., Luthi, S.M. and Plumb, R.A. (1992) Comparison of fracture apertures computed from electrical borehole scans and reflected Stoneley waves: an integrated interpretation. *The Log Analyst*, **33**, No. 1, 50–66.

Hottman, C.E. and Johnson, R.K. (1965) Estimation of formation pressures from log-derived shale properties. *J. Pet. Tech.*, June.

Hsu, K. and Chang, S.K. (1987) Multiple-shot processing of array sonic waveforms. *Geophysics* **52**, No. 10, 1376–1390.

Humphreys, B. and Lott, G.K. (1990) An investigation into nuclear log responses of North Sea Jurassic reservoirs using mineralogical analysis. In: *Geological applications of well logs,* eds. Hurst, A., Lovell, M.A. and Morton, A.C. Geol. Soc. London Spec. Pub. **48**, 223–240.

Hurley, N.F. (1994) Recognition of faults, unconformities and sequence boundaries using cumulative dip plots. *Bull. Am. Assoc. Petrol. Geol.* **78**, No. 8, 1173–1185.

Hürlimann, M., Matteson, A., Massey, J., Allen, D., Fordham, E., Antonsen, F. and Rueslåtten, H. (2003) Application of NMR diffusion editing as chlorite indicator. *Petrophysics,* **45**, No 5, 414–421.

Hursan G., Chen S. and Murphy E. (2005) New NMR two-dimensional inversion of T_1/T_{2app} vs. $T_{2\,app}$ method for gas well petrophysical interpretation. *SPWL 46th Ann. Symp. Trans.*, Paper GGG, 1–7.

Hurst, A. (1990) Natural gamma-ray spectroscopy in hydrocarbon bearing sandstones from the Norwegian continental shelf. In: *Geological applications of well logs*. eds. Hurst, A., Lovell, M. and Morton, A.C. Geol. Soc. London Spec. Pub. **48**, 211–222.

Hurst, A. (1995) Probe permeametry: re-emergence of an old technology. *First Break*, **13** No. 5, 185–192.

Hyndman, R.D. and Ade-Hall, J.M. (1972) Electrical resistivity of basalts from DSDP Leg 26. *Results from Deep Sea Drilling* **XXVI**, ch. 15, 505–508.

Ichara, M.J. and Avbovbo, A.A. (1985) Study identifies Niger Delta log parameter, VSP trends. *Oil & Gas J.* March 4th, 94–101.

Inaba, M., McCormick, D., Mikalsen, T., Nishi, M., Rasmus, J., Rohler, H. and Tribe, Ian (2003) Wellbore imaging goes live. *Oilfield Review,* **15**, 1, 24–37.

Ineson, J.R. (1993) The Lower Cretaceous chalk play in the Danish Central Trough. In: *Petroleum Geology of Northwest Europe* ed. Parker, J.R. Proc. 4th Conf; 175–183.

Ireland, T., Joseph, J., Zimmerman, T., Colley, N., Reignier, P. and Richardson, S. (2005) The MDT tool: a wireline testing breakthrough. *Oilfield Review*, April, 56–65.

Issler, D.R. (1992) A new approach to shale compaction and stratigraphic restoration, Beaufort-Mackenzie Basin and Mackenzie Corridor, Northern Canada. *Bull. Am. Assoc. Petrol. Geol.* **76** No. 8, 1170–1189.

Jackson, M.P.A. and Talbot, C.J. (1986) External shapes, strain rates and dynamics of salt structures. *BGSA*, **97**, 305–323.

Jackson, P.P., Taylor-Smith, D. and Stanford, P.N. (1978) Resistivity porosity particle shape relationships for marine sands. *Geophysics* **43** No. 6, 1250–1268.

Jackson, P.P., Lovell, M.A., Harvey, P.K., Ball, J.K., Williams, C., Ashu, P., Flint, R., Meldrum, P., Reece, G. and Zheng G. (1992) Electrical resistivity core imaging: theoretical and practical experiments as an aid to reservoir characterisation. *SPWLA 33rd Ann. Symp. Trans.*, Paper W, 1–13.

Jacqué, M. and Thouvenin, J. (1975) Lower Tertiary tuffs and volcanic activity in the North Sea. In: *Petroleum and the Continental Shelf of N.W. Europe,* ed. Woodland, A.W., Applied Sci. Publ., Barking, 455–465.

Jamison, H.C., Brockett, L.D. and McIntosh, R.A. (1980) Prudhoe Bay: A 10-year perspective. In: *Giant Oil and Gas Fields of the Decade:* 1968–1978, ed. Halbouty, M.T., Am. Assoc. Petrol. Geol., Mem. **30**, 289–314.

Jan, Y-M. and Harrell, J. (1987) MWD directional-focused gamma ray – a new tool for formation evaluation and drilling control in horizontal wells. *SPWLA 28th Ann. Symp. Trans.*, Paper A, 1–17.

Japsen, P. (2000) Investigation of multi-phase erosion using reconstructed shale trends based on sonic data. Sole Pit axis, North

Sea. *Global and Planetary Change*, **24**, 189–210.

Johnson, W.L. and Linke, W.A. (1978) Some practical applications to improve formation evaluation of sandstones in the Mackenzie Delta. *SPWLA 19th Ann. Symp. Trans.,* Paper C, 1–33.

Joyce, B., Patterson, D., Leggett, J. and Dubinsky, V. (2001) Introduction of a new omni-directional acoustic system for improved real-time LWD sonic logging – tool design and field test results. *SPWLA 42nd Ann. Symp. Trans.*, Paper SS, 1–14.

Kayal, J.R. and Christoffel, D.A. (1989) Coal quality from geophysical logs: Southland Lignite Region, New Zealand, *The Log Analyst*, **30** No. 5, 343–344.

Keith, B.D. and Pittman, E.D. (1983) Bimodal porosity in Oolitic reservoir effect on productivity and log response, Rodessa limestone (lower Cretaceous) East Texas basin. *Bull. Am. Assoc. Petrol. Geol.* **67**(9), 1391–1399.

Kennedy, D., Corley, B., Painchaud, S., Nardi, G. and Hart, E. (2009) Geosteering using deep resistivity images from azimuthal and multiple propagation resistivity. *SPWLA 50th Ann. Symp. Trans.*, Paper ZZ, 1–16.

Kennedy, M.C. (2002) Solutions to some problems in the analysis of well logs in carbonate rocks, Chapter 6. In: *Geological Applications of Well Logs*. Eds: Lovell, M. and Parkinson, N. AAPG Methods in Exploration, **13**, 61-73.

Kennedy, M.C. (2004) Gold fool's: detecting, quantifying and accounting for the effects of pyrite on modern logs. *SPWLA 45th Ann. Symp. Trans.*, Paper WWW, 1–12.

Kenyon, B., Kleinberg, R., Straley, C., Gubelin, G. and Moriss, C. (1995) Nuclear magnetic resonance imaging – technology for the 21st century. *Oilfield Review*, Autumn, 19–33.

Kerzner, M.G. and Frost, E. (1984) Blocking, a new technique for well log interpretation. *J. Pet. Tech.* Feb., 267–275, SPE 11093.

Kessler, C., Varsamis, G., Blanch, J, and Cheng, A. (2004) New development in monopole acoustic logging. *SPWLA 45th Ann. Symp. Trans.*, Paper Z, 1–12.

Keys, W.S. (1979) Borehole geophysics in igneous and metamorphic rocks. *SPWLA 20th Ann. Symp. Trans.,* Paper OO, 1–26.

Kimminau, S. (1994) Traceability-making decisions with uncertain data. *The Log Analyst*, **35**, No. 5, 67–70.

Kirkton, P. (1993) Multi sensor MWD services – current applications and future developments. SPWLA reprint series, *Measurement While Drilling*, 9–32.

Kittridge, M., Braunsdorf, N. and Bryndzia, L. (2008) Seismic petrophysics – integration to enable geologically-sensible rock physics: a Gulf of Mexico demonstration. *SPWLA 49th Ann. Symp. Trans.*, Paper RRR, 1–14.

Kleinberg, R., Straley, C., Kenyon, W., Akkurt, R. and Farooqui, S. (1993) Nuclear magnetic resonance of rocks: T1 vs. T2. *SPE* **26470**, 553–563.

Knecht, L., Ventre, J., Leduc, J-P. and Mathis, B. (2004) Improved formation evaluation in thin beds using petrophysical images. *SPWLA 45th Ann. Symp. Trans.*, Paper PPP, 1–10.

Knott, S.D. (1994) Fault zone thickness versus displacement in the Permo-Triassic sandstones of NW England. *Quart. Journ. Geol. Soc. London* **151**, Pt. 1, 17–26.

Knox, R.W.O'B. (1996) Correlation of the early Paleogene in northwest Europe: an overview. In: *Correlation of the early Paleogene in northwest Europe*, Eds., Knox, R.W.O'B., Corfield, R.M. and Dunay, R.E. Geol. Soc. London Spec. Publ. **101**, 1–11.

Knox, R.W.O'B and Cordey, W.G. (1992) Lithostratigraphic nomenclature of the UK North Sea. *J. Palaeogene of the Central and Northern North Sea*, Eds. Knox, R.W.O'B. and Holloway, S. BGS Publication.

Knox, R.W.O'B. and Morton, A.C. (1983) Stratigraphical distribution of early Palaeogene pyroclastic deposits in the North Sea basin. *Proc. Yorks. Geol. Soc.* **44** Pt. 3, No. 25, 355–363.

Koczy, F.F. (1956) Geochemistry of the radioactive elements in the ocean. *Deep Sea Research* **3**, 93–103.

Koestler, A.G. and Ehrmann W.V. (1991) Description of brittle extensional features in chalk on the crest of a salt ridge (NW Germany). In: *Geometry of normal faults* eds. Roberts, A.M., Yielding, G. and Freeman, B. Geol. Soc. London Spec. Pub. **56**, 113–123.

Kowalchuk, H., Coates, G. and Wells, L. (1974) The evaluation of very shaly formations in Canada using a systematic approach. *SPWLA 15th Ann. Symp. Trans.,* Paper H, 1–21.

Kraaijveld, M. and Epping, W. (2000) Harnessing advanced image analysis technology for quantitative core and borehole image interpretation. *SPWLA 41st Ann. Symp. Trans.*, Paper VV, 1–13.

Krueger, W.C. (1968) Depositional environments of sandstones as interpreted from electrical measurements, an introduction. *Gulf Coasts Assoc. Geol. Soc. Trans.* **XVIII**, 226–241.

Kubala, K., Bastow, M., Thompson, S., Scotchman, I. and Oygard, K. (2003) Geothermal regime, petroleum generation and migration. In: *The Millenium Atlas: petroleum geology of the central and northern North Sea.* Eds: Evans, D., Graham, C., Armour, A. and Bathurst, P. Geol. Soc. London, 289–315.

Kulander, B.R., Dean, S.L. and Ward, B.J.Jr. (1990) Fractured core analysis. *Bull. Am. Assoc. Petrol Geol. Methods in Exploration Series,* **8**, 88p.

Landes, K.K. (1967) Eometamorphism and oil and gas in time and space. *Bull. Am. Soc. Petrol. Geol.* 51(6); 828–841.

Lang, W.H. (1978) The determination of prior depth of burial (uplift and erosion) using interval transit time. *SPWLA 19th Ann. Symp. Trans.,* Paper B, 1–17.

Laubach, S.E., Baumgardner R.W., Monson, E.R., Hunt, E. and Meadoor, K.J. (1988) Fracture detection in low-permeability reservoir sandstone: a comparison of BHTV and FMS to logs and core. *SPE,* Paper 18119, 129–139.

Lavenda, B.H. (1985) Brownian motion. *Scientific American* **252**(2), 56–67.

Lavers, B.A. and Smits, L.J.M. (1977) Recent developments in coal petrophysics. *The Log Analyst* **XVIII** (1); 6–16.

La Vigne, J., Barber, T. and Bratton B. (1997) Strange invasion profiles: what multiarray induction logs can tell us about how oil-based mud affects the invasion process and wellbore stability. *SPWLA 38th Ann. Symp. Trans.*, Paper B, 1–12.

La Vigne, J., Herron, M. and Hertzog, R. (1994) Density-neutron interpretation of shaly sands. *SPWLA 35th Ann. Symp. Trans.*, Paper EEE, 1–16.

Lee, J., Michaels, J., Shammai, M., and Wendt, W. (2003) Precision pressure gradient through disciplined pressure survey. *SPWLA 44th Ann. Symp. Trans.* Paper EE, 1–8

Leslie, H.D. and Mons, F. (1982) Sonic waveform analysis applications. *SPWLA 23rd Ann. Symp. Trans.,* Paper GG, 1–25.

Levorsen, A.I. (1967) *Geology of Petroleum,* 2nd edn., W.H. Freeman & Co., San Francisco.

Lewis, C.R. and Rose, C.C. (1970) A theory relating high temperatures and overpressures. *J. Pet. Tech.,* **22**, 11–16.

Lincecum, T.A.Ma.V., Reinmiller R. and Mattner J. (1993) Natural and induced fracture classification using image analysis. *SPWLA 34th Ann. Symp. Trans.,* Paper J, 1–25.

Lindsay, G., Ong, S., Morris, S. and Lofts, J. (2007) Wellbore stress indicators while drilling: a comparison of induced features from wireline and LWD high resolution electrical images. *SPE/IADC,* **105808**, 1–11.

Linek, M., Jungman, M., Berlage, T., Peching, R. and Clauser, C. (2007) Rock classification based on resistivity patterns in electrical borehole wall images. *J. Geophys Eng,* **4**, 171–183.

Livberg, F. and Mjös, R. (1989) The Cook formation, an offshore sand wedge in the Oseberg area, northern North Sea. In: *Correlation in Hydrocarbon Exploration,* ed. Collinson, J.D., Norwegian Petroleum Soc., 299–312.

Lofts, J. and Bourke, L. (1999) The recognition of artefacts from acoustic and resistivity borehole imaging devices. In: *Borehole imaging: applications and case histories*. Eds. Lovell M., Williamson G., and Harvey P. Geol. Soc. London Spec. Pub. **159**, 59–76.

Lofts, J. and Morris, S. (2010) High-resolution electrical borehole images while drilling. In: *Dipmeter and Borehole Image Log Technology.* Eds: Poppelreiter, M., Garcia-Carballido, C. and Kraaijveld, M. *AAPG* Memoir **92**, 229–252.

Lofts, J. and Page, G. (2002) Defining thin beds and improving net pay with modern logging and core-interpretation techniques. In: *Geological Application of Well Logs* Eds: Lovell, M. and Parkinson, N. AAPG Methods in Exploration **13**, 39–54.

Lofts, J., Evans, M., Pavlovic, M. and Dymmock, S. (2002) A new micro-resistivity imaging device for use in oil-based mud. *SPWLA 45th Ann. Symp. Trans.*, Paper II, 1–14.

Lofts, J., Morris, S., Ritter, R., Chemali, R. and Fulda, C. (2005) High quality electrical borehole images while-drilling provides faster geological-petrophysical interpretation, with increased confidence. *SPWLA 46th Ann. Symp. Trans.*, Paper BB, 1–10.

Lofts, J., Page, G., Wilson, H., Brooks, A., Holehouse, S. and McCalmont, S. (2005) Reconciling depth effectively between wireline and LWD: use, and case histories of a new improved method for handling depth. *SPWLA 46th Ann. Symp. Trans.*, Paper BBB, 1–12.

Lograba, P. J., Hansen, S., Spalberg, M. and Helmy, M. (2010) Borehole image tool design, value of information and tool selection In: *Dipmeter and Borehole Image Log Technology.* Eds: Poppelreiter, M., Garcia-Carballido, C. and Kraaijveld, M. AAPG Memoir **92**, 15–38.

Loutit, T.S., Hardenbol, J., Vail, P.R., Baum, G.R. (1988) Condensed sections: the key to age determination and correlation of continental margin sequences. In: *Sea-level changes: an integrated approach,* eds. Wilgus, C.K., Hastings, B.S., Kendall, C.G.St.C., Posamentier, H.W., Ross, C.A. and Van Wagoner, J.C. S.E.P.M. Sp. Pub. **42**, 183–213.

Lowden, B. (2003) A new method for separating lithologies and estimating thickness-weighted permeability using NMR logs. *SPWL 44th Ann. Symp. Trans.*, Paper FFF, 1–14.

Lubanzadio, M., Goulty, N. and Swarbrick, R. (2006) Dependence of sonic velocity on effective stress in North Sea Mesozoic mudstones. *Marine and Petroleum Geol.*, **23**, 647–653.

Luczaj, A. J. (1998) Regional and stratigraphic distribution of uranium in the Lower Permian Chase group carbonates of southwest Kansas. *The Log Analyst*, **39**, No. 4, 18–26.

Lüning, S. and Kolonic, S. (2003) Uranium spectral gamma-ray response as a proxy for organic richness in black shales: applicability and limitations. *Journ. Petroleum Geology*, **26**, No 2, 153–174.

Lüning, S., Shahin, Y. M., Loydell, D., Al-Rabi, H.T., Masri, A., Tarawneh, B and Kolonic, S. (2005) Anatomy of a world-class source rock: distribution and depositional model of Silurian organic-rich shales in Jordan and implications for hydrocarbon potential. *AAPG Bulletin*, **89**, No 10, 1397–1427.

Luthi, S.M. (1990) Sedimentary structures of elastic rocks identified from electrical borehole images. In: *Geological applications of well logs*, Eds. Hurst A., Lovell, M.A. & Morton, A.C., Geol. Soc London Spec. Pub. **48**, 3–10.

Luthi, S.M. and Souhaité, P. (1990) Fracture apertures from electrical borehole scans. *Geophysics*, **55**, 821–833.

McCall, D.C. and Gardener, J.S. (1982) Litho-density log applications in the Michigan and Illinois basins. *SPWLA 23rd Ann. Symp. Trans.*, paper C, 1–21.

McCalmont, S., Chittick, S., Nurgaliev, R., Russo, J., Deady, R., Market, J., Wilson, J., Sands, P. and Jaunis, E. (2008) Optimal F.E. acquisition in a complex carbonate reservoir: a case study on the Karachaganak Field, Kazakhstan. *SPWLA 49th Ann. Symp. Trans.*, Paper D, 1–8.

McCrossan, R.G. (1961) Resistivity mapping and petrophysical study of Upper Devonian inter-reef calcareous shales of central Alberta, Canada. *Bull. Am. Soc. Petrol. Geol.*, **45**(4), 441–470.

McFadzean, T.B. (1973) Cross-plotting, a neglected technique in log analysis. *SPWLA 14th Ann. Symp. Trans.*, Paper Y, 1–18.

Macgregor, J.R. (1965) Quantitative determination of reservoir pressures from conductivity log. *Bull. Am. Soc. Petrol. Geol.*, **49**(9), 1502–1511.

Maddock, R and Ravnas, R. (2010) Applications of oil-base mud Earth Imager for a high-temperature and high-pressure exploration well. In: *Dipmeter and Borehole Image Log Technology.* Eds: Poppelreiter, M., Garcia-Carballido, C. and Kraaijveld, M. AAPG Memoir **92**, 129–144.

Magara, K. (1968) Compaction and migration of fluids in Miocene mudstones, Nagaoka Plain, Japan. *Bull. Am. Assoc. Petrol. Geol.*, **52**(12), 2466–2501.

Magara, K. (1978) Compaction and fluid migration. *Dev. in Petrol.* Sci., **9.** Elsevier, Amsterdam.

Magara, K. (1980) Comparison of porosity-depth relationships of shale and sandstone. *J. Pet. Geol.*, **3**(2); 175–185.

Malik, M., Salazar, J., Torres-Verdin, C., Wang, G., Lee, H. and Sepehrnoori, K. (2008) Effects of petrophysical properties on array-induction measurements acquired in the presence of oil-base mud-filtrate invasion. *Petrophysics*, **49**, No. 1, 79–92.

Manin, Y., Jacobson, A and Cordera, J. (2005) A new generation of wireline formation tester. *SPWLA 46th Ann. Symp. Trans.* Paper M, 1–7.

Mardon, D., Dodge, S., Thern, H., Chen, S. and Ostroff, G. (2000) Correction of MRIL logs contaminated by borehole signal. *Petrophysics*, July-August, 271–273.

Marett, G. and Kimminan, S. (1990) Logs, charts, and computers: the history of log interpretation modelling. *The Log Analyst*, **31** No. 6, 335–354.

Mari, J.-L., Coppens, F., Gavin, Ph. and Wicquart, E. (1994) *Full waveform acoustic data processing.* Édit. Technip, Paris. 126p.

Market, J. (2007) New broad frequency LWD multipole tool provides high quality compressional and shear data in a wide variety of formations. *SPWLA 48th Ann. Symp. Trans.*, Paper A, 1–14.

Martin, D.W., Spencer, M.C. and Patel, H. (1984) The digital induction – a new approach to improving the response of the induction measurement. *SPWLA 25th Ann. Symp. Trans.*, Paper M, 1–11.

Martin, M. (2004) *Automated lithofacies prediction from well logs.* PhD thesis, University of Edinburgh. 343p.

Martin-Chivelet, J. and Chacón, B. (2007) Event stratigraphy of the upper Cretaceous to lower Eocene hemipelagic sequences of the Prebetic zone (S.E. Spain): record of the onset of tectonic convergence in a passive continental margin. *Sedimentary Geology*, **197**, 141–163.

Mathews, M. (1986). Logging characteristics of methane hydrate. *The Log Analyst*, **27**, No. 3, 26–63.

Mathis, G.L and Gearhart, D. (1989) The vertical resolution of *Pe* and density logs. *The Log Analyst*, **30**, No. 3, 150–161.

Matuszak, D (1972) Stratigraphic correlation of subsurface geologic data by computer. *Mathematical Geology*, **4**, No 4, 331–343.

Maute, R.E. (1992) Electrical logging: state-of-the-art. *The Log Analyst*, **33**, No. 3, 206–227.

Meisner, J., Brooks, A. and Wisniewski, W. (1985) A new measurement-while-drilling gamma ray log calibrator. *SPWLA 46th Ann. Symp. Trans.*, Paper PP, 1–15.

Meister, M., Buysch, A., Pragt, J. and Lee, J. (2004) Lessons learned from formation pressure measurements while drilling. *SPWLA 45th Ann. Symp. Trans.*, Paper S, 1–14.

Meister, M., Pragt J., Buysch, A., Witte, J. Due, G. and Hope, R. (2004) Successful formation pressure testing-while-drilling in Troll field. *InDepth* **10**, 2, 38–49.

Mendoza, A., Preeg, W., Torres-Verdin, C. and Alpak, F. (2007) Monte Carlo modeling of nuclear measurements in vertical and horizontal wells in the presence of mud-filtrate invasion and salt mixing *Petrophysics*, **48**, No. 1, 28–44.

Menger, S. and Prammer, M. (1998) Can NMR porosity replace conventional porosity in formation evaluation? *SPWLA 39th Ann. Symp. Trans.*, Paper RR, 1–9.

Meyer, B.L. and Nederlof, M.H. (1984) Identification of source rocks on wireline logs by density/resistivity and sonic transit time/resistivity crossplots. *Bull. Am. Assoc. Petrol Geol.*, **68**(2), 121–129.

Meyer, C. and Sibbit, A. (1981) GLOBAL: un outil géneral pour l'interprétation des diagraphies. *SAID 7th Ann. European Symp. Trans., Paris,* Comm. 5, 1–27.

Meyer, N., Holehouse, S., Kirkwood, A., Zurcher, D., Chemali, R., Lofts, J. and Page, G. (2005) Improved LWD density images and their handling for thin bed definition and for hole shape visualization. *SPWLA 46th Ann. Symp. Trans.*, Paper Y, 1–11.

Meyer, W. (1995) New two frequency propagation resistivity tools. *SPWLA 36th Ann. Symp. Trans.*, Paper X, 1–13.

Meyer, W., Maher, T. and McLean, D. (1996) New methods improve interpretation of propagation resistivity data *SPWLA 37th Ann. Symp. Trans.*, Paper O, 1–14.

Meyer, W., Thomson, L., Wisler, M. and Wu, J. (1994) A new slimhole multiple propagation resistivity tool. *SPWLA 35th Ann. Symp. Trans.*, Paper NN, 1–21.

Meyer-Gürr, A. (1976) Petroleum engineering. In: *Geology of Petroleum,* 3, ed. Beckman, H., Pitman, London.

Michaels, J., Moody, M. and Shwe, T. (1995) Advances in wireline formation testing. *SPWLA 36th Ann. Symp. Trans.* Paper BBB, 1–11

Michelsen, O. (1989) Revision of the Jurassic lithostratigraphy of the Danish sub-basin. *Geological Survey of Denmark*, series A, **24**, 1–21.

Miesch, E.P. and Albright, J.C. (1967) A study of invasion diameter. *SPWLA 8th Ann. Symp. Trans.*, Paper O, 1–14.

Millward, D., Young, S.R., Beddoe-Stephens, B., Phillips, E.R. and Evans, C. (2002) Gamma-ray, spectral gamma-ray, and neutron-density logs for interpretation of Ordovician volcanic rocks, West Cumbria, England. In: *Geological Applications of Well Logs.* Eds. Lovell, M. and Parkinson, N. AAPG Methods in Exploration Series, No 13, 251–268.

Milner, C.W.D. (1982) Geochemical analyses of sedimentary organic matter and interpretation of maturation and source potential. In: *How to Assess Maturation and Paleotemperatures,* S.E.P.M. Short Course No. 7, 217–252.

Milton, N.J., Bertram, G.T. and Vann, I.R. (1990) Early Paleogene sedimentation and tectonics in the Central North Sea. In: *Tectonic events responsible for Britain's oil and gas reserves.* Geol. Soc. London Spec. Publ. **55,** eds. Hardman, R.F.P. and Brooks, J., 339–351.

Minette, D. (1996) Developments in understanding the physical foundations of formation density and lithology logging. *SPWLA 37th Ann. Symp. Trans.*, Paper JJ, 1–14.

Minh, C., Heaton, N., Ramamoorthy, R., Decoster, E., White, J., Junk, E., Eyvazzadeh, R., Al-Yousef, O., Fiorini, R., Dacion, B. and Lendon, D. (2003) Planning and interpreting NMR fluid-characterisation logs. *SPE* **84478**, 1–12.

Misk, A., Mowat, G., Goetz, J. and Vivet, B. (1977) Effects of hole conditions on log measurements and formation evaluation. *SAID 5th Ann. European Symp. Trans., Paris,* Comm. 22, 1–16.

Mitchener, B.C., Lawrence, D.A., Partington, M.A., Bowman, M.B.J. and Gluyas, J. (1992) Brent Group: sequence stratigraphy and regional implications. In: *Geology of the Brent Group,* eds. Morton, A.C., Haszeldine, R.S., Giles, M.R. and Brown, S., *Geol. Soc. London Spec. Publ.* **61,** 45–80.

Mitchum, R.M. and Van Wagoner, J.C. (1990) High frequency sequences and eustatic cycles in the Gulf of Mexico Basin. In: *11th Ann. Research Conf Gulf Coast Section Soc. Econ. Pal. & Min. Found.* Eds. Armentrout, J.M. and Perkins, R.F., 257–267.

Moline, G.R., Bahr, J.M., Drzewiecki, P.A. and Shepherd, L.D. (1992) Identification and characterisation of pressure seals through the use of wireline logs: a multivariate statistical approach. *The Log Analyst,* **33**, No. 4, 362–372.

Molz, E.B. (2000) Mud velocity corrections for high accuracy standoff/caliper measurements. *SPWLA 41st Ann. Symp. Trans.*, Paper P, 1–14.

Mondol, N., Fawad, M., Jahren, J. and Bjørlykke, K. (2008) Synthetic mudstone compaction trends and their use in pore pressure prediction. *First Break*, **26,** 43–51.

Moody, M., Jones, S. and Leonard, P. (2004) Development and field-testing of a cost effective rotary steerable system. *SPE* **90482**, 1–8.

Moran, J.H. and Attali, G. (1971) Wireline logging operations to 50,000 feet. *8th World Pet. Congress. Trans.*, 149–158.

Moss, B. (1997) The partitioning of petrophysical data: a review. In: *Developments in Petrophysics*. eds. Lovell, M and Harvey, P. Geol. Soc. London, Spec. Publ. **122**, 181–252.

Moss, B., Barson, B., Rakhit, K., Dennis, H. and Swarbrick, R. (2003) Formation pore pressure and formation waters. In: *The Millennium Atlas: petroleum geology of the central and northern North Sea*. Eds. Evans, D., Graham, C., Armour, A. and Bathurst, P. Geol. Soc. London, 317–329.

Mullen, M., Gegg, J., Bonnie, R., Cherry, R. and Riggert, G. (2005) Fluid typing with T1 NMR: incorporating T1 and T2 measurements for improved interpretation in tigh gas sands and unconventional reservoirs. *SPWL 46th Ann. Symp. Trans.*, Paper III, 1–13.

Mullins, O., Beck, G., Cribbs, M., Terabayashi, T. and Kegasawa, K. (2001) Downhole determination of GOR on single-phase fluids by optical spectroscopy. *SPWLA 42nd Ann. Symp. Trans.* Paper M, 1–14.

Murray, D., Kleinberg, R., Sinha, B., Fukuhara, M., Osawa, O., Endo, T. and Namikawa, T. (2005) Formation evaluation of gas hydrate reservoirs. *SPWLA 46th Ann. Symp. Trans.*, Paper SSS, 1–10.

Murray, D., Plona, T. and Valer, H. (2004) Case study of borehole sonic dispersion curve analysis. *SPWLA 45th Ann. Symp. Trans.*, Paper BB, 1–14.

Mwenifumbo, C.J. (1993) Kernel density estimation in the analysis and presentation of borehole geophysical data. *The Log Analyst,* **34**, No. 5, 34–45.

Myers, K.J. (1987) *Onshore-outcrop gamma ray spectrometry as a tool in sedimentological studies*. Unpublished PhD Thesis University London.

Myers, K.J. and Jenkyns, K.F. (1992) Determining total organic carbon contents from well logs: an intercomparison of GST data and a new density log method. In: *Geological applications of wire line logs II,* eds. Hurst, A., Griffiths, C.M., Worthington, P-F. Geol. Soc. London Spec. Publ. **65**, 369–376.

Myers, K.J. and Wignall, P.B. (1987) Understanding Jurassic organic-rich mudrocks – new concepts using gamma ray spectrometry and palaeoecology. In: *Marine and clastic sedimentology: new developments and concepts*. Ed. Leggett, J.K., Graham and Trotman, London.

NACSN (North American Commission on Stratigraphic Nomenclature) (1993) North American stratigraphic code, *Bull. Am. Assoc. Petrol., Geol.* **67**, 841–875.

Nagihara, S. and Smith, M.A. (2008) Regional overview of deep sedimentary thermal gradients of the geopressured zone of Texas-Louisiana continental shelf. *Bull. Am. Assoc. Petrol. Geol.*, **92**, No. 1, 1–14.

Nederlandse Aardolie Maatschappij B.V. and Rijks Geol. Dienst (1980) *Stratigraphic Nomenclature of the Netherlands*. Verlag. K., Ned. Geol. Mijnb. Genoot., p.77.

Neinast, G.S. and Knox, C.C. (1973) Normalization of well log data. *SPWLA 14th Ann. Symp. Trans.* Paper I, 1–9.

Nelson, P.H. and Glenn, W.E. (1975) Influence of bound water on the neutron log in mineralized igneous rocks. *SPWLA 16th Ann. Symp. Trans.*, Paper M, 1–9.

Nelson, R.A. (1987) Fractured reservoirs, turning knowledge into practice. *JPT*, 407–414.

Nelson, R.J. and Mitchell, W.K. (1990) Improved vertical resolution of well logs by resolution matching. *SPWLA 31st Ann. Symp. Trans.*, Paper JJ, 1–25.

Nentwich, E.W. and Yole, R.W. (1982) Sedimentary petrology and stratigraphic analysis of the subsurface Reindeer Formation (Early Tertiary) Mackenzie Delta Beaufort Sea area, Canada. In: *Arctic Geology and Geophysics,* eds. Embry, A.F. and Balkwill, H.R., Canadian Society of Petroleum Geologists, Mem. 8, 5581.

Newberry, B., Grace, L. and Stief, D. (1996) Analysis of carbonate dual porosity systems from borehole electrical images. *SPE* **35158**, 1–7.

Norden, B. and Förster, A. (2006) Thermal conductivity and radiogenic heat production of sedimentary and magmatic rocks in the Northeast German Basin. *Bull. Am. Assoc. Petrol. Geol.*, **90**, No. 6, 939–962.

Nuckols, E., Cobern, M. and Couillard, B (1987) Formation evaluation utilising MWD gamma ray and resistivity measurements with special emphasis on formation invasion. *SPWLA 48th Ann. Symp. Trans.*, Paper U, 1–25.

Nummedal, D. and Swift, D.J.P. (1987) Transgressive stratigraphy at sequence-bounding unconformities: some principles derived from Holocene and Cretaceous examples. In: *Sea level fluctuations and coastal evolution*. Eds. Nummedal, D., Pilkey, O.H. and Howard, J.D. Soc. Econ. Paleontol. Mineral. Spec. Pub. **41**, 241–260.

Nummedal, D., Sanjeev, G., Plint, G.A. and Cole, R.D. (1995) The falling stage systems tract: definition, character and expression in several examples from the Cretaceous of the U.S. western interior. In: *Sedimentary responses to forced regression: recognition, interpretation and reservoir potential.* Geol. Soc. London 7–8 Sept. abstract, 45–46.

Nurmi, R.D. (1984) Geological evaluation of high resolution dipmeter data. *SPWLA 25th Ann. Symp. Trans.*, Paper YY, 1–24.

Nyberg, Ø., Lien, K., Lindberg, P.A. and Smistad, J.K. (1978) Mineral composition, an aid in classical log analysis used in Jurassic sandstones of the northern North Sea. *SPWLA 19th Ann. Symp. Trans.,* Paper M, 1–35.

Oberkircher, J., Steinberger, G. and Robbins, B. (1993) Applications for a multiple depth of investigation MWD resistivity device. *SPWLA 34th Ann. Symp. Trans.*, Paper OO, 1–18.

O'Connor, S.J. and Walker, D. (1993) Palaeocene reservoirs of the Everest trend. In: *Petroleum geology of Northwest Europe*. ed. Parker, J.R., Proc. 4th Conf. Geol. Soc. London, 145–160.

Olesen, J.R. (1990) A new calibration, wellsite verification, and log quality-control system for nuclear tools. *SPWLA 31st Ann. Symp. Trans.,* Paper PP, 1–25.

Onu, C., Buffet, P., Lofts, J. and Morris, S. (2008) Sedimentological characterisation and application of a high-definition while-drilling borehole electrical imager, Brent Group, North Sea. *SPWLA 49th Ann. Symp. Trans.*, Paper VV, 1–14

Owen J.D. (1966) A review of fundamental nuclear physics applied to gamma ray spectral logging. *The Log Analyst*, Sept–Oct, 37–47.

Paillet, F.L. (1991) Acoustic full-waveform logs and fracture permeability. *The Log Analyst,* **32**, No. 3, 256–270.

Paillet, F.L. and Kim, K. (1987) Character and distribution of borehole breakouts and their relationship to in situ stresses in deep Columbia River basalts. *Journ. Geophys. Res.*, **92** No. B7, 6223–6234.

Paillet, F.L., Barton, C., Luthi, S., Rambow, F. and Zemanek, J. (1990) Imaging and its application in well logging – an overview. In: *Borehole imaging,* Eds. Paillet, F.L., Barton, C., Luthi, S., Rambow, F. and Zemanek, J. SPWLA reprint volume, 472p.

Paillet, F.L., Cheng, C.H. and Pennington, W.D. (1992) Acoustic waveform logging – advances in theory and application. *The Log Analyst,* **33** No. 3, 239–258.

Paillet, F.L., Hess, A.E., Cheng, C.H. and Hardin, E. (1987) Characterization of fracture permeability with high-resolution vertical flow measurements during borehole pumping. *Journ. Ground Water,* **25**, No. 1, 28–40.

Paillet, F.L., Keys, W.S. and Hess, A.E. (1985) Effects of lithology on televiewer log quality and fracture interpretation. *SPWLA 27th Ann. Symp. Trans.*, Paper JJ, 1–30.

Paillet, F.L., Novakowski, K. and Lapcevic, P. (1992) Analysis of transient flows in boreholes during pumping in fractured formations. *SPWLA 33rd Ann. Symp. Trans.*, Paper S, 1–22.

Palmer, R., Santos da Silva, A., Al-Hajari, A., Engleman, B., van Zuilekom, T. and Proett, M. (2008) Advances in fluid identification methods using a high resolution densitometer in a Saudi Aramco field. *SPWLA 49th Ann. Symp. Trans.*, Paper MM,1–12.

Parker, J.R. (1977) Deep sea sands. In: *Developments in Petroleum Geology*, 1, ed. Hobson, G.D., Applied Sci. Pub., Barking, 225–242.

Partington, M.A., Mitchener, B.C., Milton, N.J. and Fraser, A.J. (1993a) A genetic stratigraphic sequence stratigraphy for the North Sea late Jurassic and early Cretaceous: stratigraphic distribution and prediction of Kimmeridgian-late Ryazanian reservoirs in the Viking Graben and adjacent areas. In: *Petroleum geology of Northwest Europe*, ed. Parker, J.R. Proc. 4th Conf. Geol. Soc. London, 347–370.

Partington, M.A., Copestake, P., Mitchener, B.C. and Underhill, J.R. (1993b) A biostratigraphic calibration of the North Sea genetic stratigraphic sequences. In: *Petroleum geology of Northwest Europe*, ed. Parker, J.R. Proc. 4th Conf. Geol. Soc. London, 372–386.

Passey, Q., Dahlberg, K., Sullivan, K., Yin, H., Brackett, R., Xiao, Y. and Guzman-Garcia, A. (2006) *Petrophysical evaluation of hydrocarbon pore-thickness in thinly bedded reservoirs*. AAPG Archive Series, 1. 210p.

Passey, Q.R., Creaney, S., Kulla, J.B., Moretti, F.J. and Stroud, J.D. (1990) A practical model for organic richness from porosity and resistivity logs. *Bull. Am. Assoc. Petrol Geol.*, **74** No. 12, 1777–1794.

Pasternack, E.S. and Goodwill, W.P. (1983) Applications of digital borehole televiewer logging. *SPWLA 24th Ann. Symp. Trans.*, Paper X, 1–12.

Patchett, J., Wiley, R. and El Bahr, M. (1993) Modeling the effects of gauconite on some openhole logs from the Lower Senonian in Egypt. *SPWLA 34th Ann. Symp. Trans.*, Paper RR, 1–22.

Patchett, J.G. (1975) An investigation of shale conductivity. *SPWLA 16th Ann. Symp. Trans.*, Paper U, 1–41.

Patchett, J.G. and Coalson, E.B. (1979) The determination of porosity in sandstones and shaly sandstones. Part 1, Quality control. *SPWLA 20th Ann. Symp. Trans.*, Paper QQ, 1–17.

Patchett, J.G. and Coalson, E.B. (1982) The determination of porosity in sandstones and shaly sandstones, Part 2: Effects of complex mineralogy and hydrocarbons. *SPWLA 23rd Ann. Symp. Trans.*, Paper T, 1–50.

Paulissen, W. and Luthi, S. (2010) Integrating magnetostratigraphy, biostratigraphy, cyclostratigraphy and seismic data to obtain a high resolution stratigraphic record: a case study from the Vienna Basin. *First Break*, **28**, No. 1, 67–73.

Pawellek, T. and Aigner, T. (2003) Stratigraphic architecture and gamma ray logs of deeper ramp carbonates (Upper Jurassic, SW Germany). *Sedimentary Geology*, **159**, 203–240.

Payenberg, T. (2002) Paleocurrents from FMS and scribe-oriented core – a comparison. In: *Geological Application of Well Logs* Eds: Lovell, M. and Parkinson, N. AAPG Methods in Exploration, **13**, 185–198.

Pearson, R.A. and Batchelor, AS. (1986) The logging results of viscous simulation in a hot dry rock geothermal well. *SPWLA 10th European Form. Eval. Symp.* Paper U, 1–9.

Pedersen, B. and Constable, M. (2006) Operational procedures and methodology for improving LWD and wireline depth control, Kristin field, Norwegian Sea. *SPWLA 47th Ann. Symp. Trans.*, Paper XXX, 1–14.

Peltonen, C., Marcussen, Ø., Bjørlykke, K. and Jahren, J. (2009) Clay mineral diagenesis and quartz cementation in mudstones: the effects of smectite to illite reaction on rock properties. *Marine and Petroleum Geology*, **26**, No. 6, 887–898

Peraranau, A. and Payne, C. (2006) Time average DTS-porosity relationship. *SPWLA 47th Ann. Symp. Trans.*, Paper WW, 1–4.

Perkins, T., Quirein, J. and Parker, T. (2009) Wireline and LWD borehole image log dip and azimuth uncertainty. *SPWLA 50th Ann. Symp. Trans.*, Paper E, 1–11

Pettijohn, F.J., Potter, P.E. and Siever, R. (1972) *Sand and Sandstone*. Springer-Verlag, New York.

Pezard, P.A. and Anderson, R.N. (1990) In situ measurements of electrical resisitvity, formation anisotropy and tectonic context. *SPWLA 31st Ann. Symp. Trans.*, Paper M., 1–24.

Pezard, P.A., Hiscott, R.N., Lovell, M.A., Collela, A. and Malinverno, A. (1992) Evolution of the Izu-Bonin intraoceanic forearc basin, Western Pacific, from cores and FMS images. In: *Geological applications of wireline logs II.*, eds. Hurst, A., Griffiths, C.M. and Worthington, P.F., Geol. Soc. London Spec. Publ. **65**, 43–69.

Phillips, F.C. (1971) *The use of stereographic projection in structural geology*, 4th edition, Edward Arnold, London, 90p.

Phillips, S. (1987) Dipmeter interpretation of turbidite channel reservoir sandstones, Indian Draw field, New Mexico. In: *Reservoir sedimentology*, eds. Tillman, R.W. and Weber, K.J. S.E.P.M. Sp. Pub. **40**, 113–128.

Pickett, G.R. (1963) Acoustic character logs in the evaluation of sandstone reservoirs. *Journal Petroleum Technology*, **15**, 650–667.

Pied, B. and Poupon, A. (1966) SP base line shifts in Algeria. *SPWLA 7th Ann. Symp. Trans.*, Paper H, 1–12.

Pirson, S.J. (1963) *Handbook of Well Log Analysis*. Prentice Hall, Englewood Cliffs.

Pirson, S.J. (1970) *Geologic Well Log Analysis*. Gulf Publishing, Houston, 370p.

Pistre, V., Kinoshita, T., Endo, T., Schilling, K., Pabon, J., Sinha, B., Plona, T., Ikegami, T. and Johnson, D. (2005) A modular wireline sonic tool for measurement of 3D (azimuthal, radial and axial) formation acoustic properties. *SPWLA 46th Ann. Symp. Trans.*, Paper P, 1–13.

Plint, A.G. (1988) Sharp-based shoreface sequences and 'offshore bars' in the Cardium Formation of Alberta: their relationship to relative changes in sea level. In: *Sea-level changes: an integrated approach*, eds. Wilgus, C.K., Hastings, B.S., Kendall, C.G.St.C., Posamentier, H.W., Ross, C.A. and Van Wagoner, J.C. S.E.P.M. Sp. Pub. **42**, 357–370.

Plona, T., Kane, M., Alford, J., Endo, T., Walsh, J. and Murray D. (2005) Slowness-frequency projection logs: a new method for accurate sonic slowness evaluation. *SPWLA 46th Ann. Symp. Trans.*, Paper T, 1–7.

Plum, R.A. and Hickman, S.H. (1985) Stress-induced borehole elongation – a comparison between the four-arm dipmeter tool and the borehole televiewer in the Auburn geothermal well. *Journ. Geophysical Research*, **90**, No. B7, 5513–5521.

Posamentier, H.W. and Allen, G. (1999) *Siliciclastic sequence stratigraphy – concepts and applications*. S.E.P.M. Concepts in Sedimentology and Paleontology **7**, 210p.

Posamentier, H.W. and James, D.P. (1993) An overview of sequence-stratigraphic concepts: uses and abuses. In: *Sequence stratigraphy and facies associations*, eds. Posamentier, H.W., Summerhays, C.P., Haq, B.U. and Allen, G.P. IAS Spec. Publ. **18**, 3–18.

Posamentier, H.W. and Vail, P.R. (1988) Eustatic controls on clastic deposition II, sequence and systems tracts models. In: *Sea-level changes: an integrated approach*, eds. Wilgus, C.K., Hastings, B.S., Kendall, C.G.St.C., Posamentier, H.W., Ross, C.A. & Van Wagoner, J.C. S.E.P.M. Sp. Pub. **42**, 125–154.

Posamentier, H.W., Allen, G.P., James, D.P. and Tesson, M. (1992) Forced regressions in a sequence stratigraphic framework: concepts, examples and exploration significance. *Bull. Am. Assoc. Petrol. Geol.* **76**, 1687–1709.

Posamentier, H.W., Summerhays, C.P., Haq, B.U. and Allen, G.P. (eds.) (1993) Sequence stratigraphy and facies associations. *Int. Assoc. Sed. Sp. Pub.* **18,** 644p.

Poupon, A., Hoyle, W.R. and Schmidt, A.W. (1970) Log analysis in formations with complex lithologies. *J. Pet. Tech.*, Aug., 995–1005, SPE 2925.

Prammer, M., Bouton, J., Chandler, R. and Drack, E. (1999). Theory and operation of a new, multi-volume, NMR logging system. *SPWLA 40th Ann. Symp. Trans.*, Paper DD, 1–12.

Prammer, M., Bouton, J., Chandler, R., Drack, E. and Miller, M. (1998) A new multiband generation of NMR logging tools. *SPE* **49011**.

Prammer, M., Drack, E., Bouton, J. and Gardner, J. (1996) Measurement of clay-bound water and total porosity by magnetic resonance logging. *The Log Analyst*, November-December, 61–69.

Prammer, M., Goodman, G., Menger, S., Morys, M, Zannoni, S. and Dudley, J. (2000) Field test of an experimental NMR device. *SPWLA 41st Ann. Symp. Trans.*, Paper EEE, 1–19.

Prammer, M., Mardon, D., Coates, G., and Miller, M. (1995) Lithology-independent gas detection by gradient-NMR logging. *SPE* **30562**, 325–336.

Prensky, S. (1992a) Temperature measurements in boreholes – an overview of engineering and scientific applications. *The Log Analyst*, **33** No. 3, 313–333.

Prensky, S. (1992b) Borehole breakouts and in situ rock stress – a review. *The Log Analyst*, **33** No. 3, 304–312.

Proett, M, Waid, M, Heinze, J and Franki, M. (1994) Low permeability interpretation using a new wireline formation tester "tight zone" pressure transient analysis. *SPWLA 35th Ann. Symp. Trans.*, Paper III, 1–25.

Prokoph, A. and Thurow, J. (1995) Sea level controlled preservation of singularities and cyclicity in sedimentary sequences. In: *Predictive high resolution sequence stratigraphy,* NPF conference Stavanger, Norway. (abstract).

Purdy, C.C. (1982) Enhancement of long-spaced sonic transit time data. *SPWLA 23rd Ann. Symp. Trans.*, Paper V, 114.

Quiming, L., Chengbing, L. Maeso, C., Wu, P., Smits, J. Prabawa, H. and Bradfield, J. (2003) Automated interpretation for LWD propagation resistivity tools through integrated model selection. *SPWLA 44th Ann. Symp. Trans.*, Paper UU, 1–14.

Quirein, J.A., Garden, J.S. and Watson, J.T. (1982) Combined natural gamma ray spectral/litho-density measurements applied to complex lithologies. *SPE* **11143**, 1–14.

Quirein, J.A., Kimmanau, S., Lavigne, J., Singer, J. and Wendel, F. (1986) A coherent framework for developing and applying multiple formation evaluation models. *SPWLA 27th Ann. Symp. Trans.*, Paper DD, 1–16.

Quirein, J.A., Smith, H., Chen, D., Perkins, T., Reed, S. and Jacobson, L. (2005) Formation density prediction using pulsed neutron capture tools. *SPWLA 46th Ann. Symp. Trans.*, Paper QQ, 1–10.

Raddadi, M., Vanneau, A., Poupeau, G., Carrio-Schaffhauser, E., Arnaud, H. and Rivera, A. (2005) Interpretation of gamma-ray logs: the distribution of uranium in carbonate platform. *Comptes Rendus Geoscience*, **337**, 1457–1461.

Radtke, R.J., Adolph, R.A., Climent, H., Ortenzi, L. and Wijeyesekera, N. (2003) Improved formation evaluation through image-derived density. *SPWLA 44th Ann. Symp. Trans.*, Paper P, 1–14.

Radtke R. J., Evans M., Rasmus J., Ellis D., Chiaramonte J., Case R., and Stockhausen E. (2006) LWD density response to bed laminations in horizontal and vertical wells. *SPWLA 47th Ann. Symp. Trans.*, Paper ZZ, 1–16.

Raiga-Clemenceau, J. (1988) Taking into account the conductivity contribution of shale laminations when evaluating closely interlaminated sand-shale hydrocarbon-bearing reservoirs. *SPWLA 29th Ann. Symp. Trans.*, Paper DD, 1–14.

Raiga-Clemenceau, J., Martin, J.P. and Nicoletis, S. (1988) The concept of acoustic formation factor for more accurate porosity determination from sonic log data. *The Log Analyst*, **29** No. 1, 54–60.

Ramamoorthy, R., Boyd, A., Neville, T., Seleznev, N., Sun, H., Flaum, C. and Ma, J. (2008) A new workflow for petrophysical and textural evaluation of carbonate reservoirs. *SPWL 49th Ann. Symp. Trans.*, Paper B, 1–15.

Rambow, F.H.K. (1984) The borehole televiewer: some field examples. *SPWLA 25th Ann. Symp. Trans.*, Paper C, 1–22.

Ramsbottom, W.H.C. (1977) Major cycles of transgression and regression (mesotherms) in the Namurian. *Proc. Yorks. Geological Society,* **41**, 261–291.

Ramsey, J.G. (1967) *Folding and fracturing in rocks,* McGraw Hill, New York. 586p.

Ransom, R.C. (1977) Methods based on density and neutron well logging responses to distinguish characteristics of shaly sandstone reservoir rock. *The Log Analyst* **XVIII**(3); 47–63.

Rasmus, J. and Voisin, B. (1990) A framework to estimate pore pressures in real time. *MWD Symposium, LSU,* Baton Rouge 355–376.

Rawson, P.F. and Riley, L.A. (1982) Latest Jurassic early Cretaceous events and the 'Late Cimmerian Unconformity' in North Sea area. *Bull. Am. Soc. Petrol. Geol.* **66**(12), 2628–2648.

Raymer, L.L., Hunt, E.R. and Gardner, J.S. (1980) An improved sonic transit time to porosity transform. *SPWLA 21st Ann. Symp. Trans.,* Paper P, 1–12.

Reiter, M., Mansure, A.J. and Peterson, B.K. (1980) Precision continuous temperature logging and comparison with other types of logs. *Geophysics*, **45**, No. 12, 1857–1868.

Rhodes, D.F. and Mott, W.E. (1966) Quantitative interpretation of gammma-ray spectral logs. *Geophysics*, **31**, 4–10.

Rhys, G.H. (1975) A proposed standard lithostratigraphic nomenclature for the southern North Sea. In: *Petroleum and the Continental Shelf of N.W Europe,* ed. Woodland, A.W., Applied Sci. Pub., Barking. 151–163.

Richards, M. and Bowman, M. (1998) Submarine fans and related depositional systems II: variability in reservoir architecture and wireline log character. *Marine and Petroleum Geology*, **15**, 821–839.

Rider, M.H. (1978) Dipmeter log analysis, an essay. *SPWLA 19th Ann. Symp. Trans.*, paper G, 1–18.

Rider, M.H. (1986) *The geological interpretation of well logs*. Blackie, Glasgow.

Rider, M.H. (1996) *The geological interpretation of well logs. 2nd Edition.* Whittles Publishing, Scotland.

Rider, M.H. (1990) Gamma-ray log shapes used as a facies indicator: critical analysis of an oversimplified methodology. In: *Geological applications of well logs,* eds. Hurst, A., Lovell, M.A. and Morton, A.C. *Geol. Soc. London Spec. Pub.* **48,** 27–38.

Rider, M.H. and Laurier, D. (1979) Sedimentology using a computer treatment of well logs. *SPWLA 6th European Symp. Trans.*, Paper J, 1–12.

Ritter, R., Chemali, R., Lofts, J., Gorek, M., Fulda, C., Morris, S. and Krueger, V. (2004) High resolution visualization of near wellbore geology using while-drilling electrical images. *SPWLA 45th Ann. Symp. Trans.*, Paper PP, 1–13.

Rodney, P., Wisler, M. and Meador, R. (1983) The electromagnetic wave resistivity MWD tool. *SPE* **12167**, 1–14.

Rodriguez, R., Weller, G., Evans, M., Prabawa, H. and Zalan, T. (2009) A new approach for identifying gas reservoirs using multiple LWD density measurements. *SPWLA 50th Ann. Symp. Trans.*, Paper YY, 1–10.

Rose, D., Hansen, P., Damgaard, A. and Raven, M. (2003) A novel approach to real time detection of facies changes in horizontal carbonate wells using LWD NMR. *SPWL 44th Ann. Symp. Trans.*, Paper CCC, 1–11.

Rübel, H.J., Schepers, R. and Schmitz, D. (1986) High resolution televiewer logs from sedimentary formations. *SPWLA 10th European Formation Evaluation Symp.* Paper GG, 1–15.

Rudwick, M.J.L. (1985) *The great Devonian controversy*. University of Chicago Press, 494p.

Ruf, M., Link, E., Pross, J. and Aigner, T. (2005) Integrated sequence stratigraphy: facies, stable isotope and palynofacies analysis in a deeper epicontinental carbonate ramp (Late Jurassic, SW Germany). *Sedimentary Geology*, **175**, 391–414.

Ruppel, S.and Jones, R. (2006) Key role of outcrops and cores in carbonate reservoir characterisation and modelling, Lower Permian Fullerton field, Permian Basin, United States. In: *Giant Hydrocarbon Reservoirs of the World: from Rocks to Reservoir Characterization and Modelling*, eds. Harris, P. and Weber, J. AAPG Memoir **88**, 355–394.

Russel, W.L. (1941) Well logging by radioactivity. *Bull. Am. Soc. Petrol. Geol.* **25**(9), 1768–1788.

Saiha, S. and Visher, C.S. (1968) *Subsurface study of the southern portion of the Bluejacket delta.* Oklahoma Geological Society Guidebook, 33p.

Salazar, J., Torres-Verdin, C., Alpak, F., Habashy, T. and Klein, J. (2006) Estimation of permeability from borehole array induction measurements: application to the petrophysical appraisal of tight gas sands. *Petrophysics*, **47**, No. 6, 527–544.

Salazar, J., Wang, G., Torres-Verdin, C. and Lee, H. (2007). Combined simulation and inversion of SP and resistivity logs for the estimation of connate water resistivity and Archie's cementation exponent. *SPWLA 48th Ann. Symp. Trans.*, Paper H, 1–15.

Salimullah, A.R.M. and Stowe, D.A.V. (1992) Application of FMS images in poorly recovered coring intervals: examples from ODP leg 129. In: *Geological applications of wireline logs II.*, eds. Hurst, A., Griffiths, C.M., and Worthington, P.F., Geol. Soc. London Spec. Publ. **65**, 71–86.

Sallee, J.E. and Wood, B.R. (1984) Use of microresistivity from the dipmeter to improve formation evaluation in thin sands, Northeast Kalimantan, Indonesia. *J. Pet. Tech.*, 10, **36,** 1535–1544.

Sanyal, S.K., Juprasert, S. and Jusbasche, M. (1980) An evaluation of a rhyolite basalt volcanic ash sequence from well logs. *The Log Analyst* **XXI**(1); 3–9.

Sarg, J.F. and Skjold, L.J. (1982) Stratigraphic traps in Paleocene sands in the Balder area, North Sea. In: *The Deliberate Search for the Subtle Trap,* ed. Halbouty, M.T., Am. Assoc. Pet. Geol. Mon. **32**, 197–206.

Sarmiento, R. (1961) Geological factors influencing porosity estimates from velocity logs. *Bull. Am. Soc. Petrol. Geol.*, **45**(5), 633–644.

Schafer, J.N, (1980) A practical method of well evaluation and acreage development for the naturally fractured Austin chalk formation. *The Log Analyst* **XXI**(l); 10–23.

Schenewerk, RA., Sethi, D.K., Fertl, W.H. and Lochmann, M. (1980) Natural gamma ray spectral logging aids granite wash reservoir evaluation. *SPWLA 21st Ann. Symp. Trans.*, Paper BB, 1–23.

Scherer, F.C. (1980) Exploration in East Malaysia of the past decade. In: *Giant Oil Fields of the Decade 1968–1978,* ed. Halbouty, M.T., *Am. Assoc. Pet. Geol. Mem.* **30,** 423–440.

Schlager, W. (2005) *Carbonate sedimentology and sequence stratigraphy.*

S.E.P.M. Concepts in Sedimentology and Paleontology **8**, 200p.

Schlumberger (1970) *Fundamentals of Dipmeter Interpretation.* Schlumberger Publication.

Schlumberger (1972a) *Log Interpretation, I, Principles.* Schlumberger Publication.

Schlumberger (1972b) *The Essentials of Log Interpretation Practice.* Schlumberger Publication.

Schlumberger (1974) *Log Interpretation, II, Applications.* Schlumberger Publication.

Schlumberger (1979) *Log Interpretation Charts. English-Metric.* Schlumberger Publication.

Schlumberger (1982) *Well Evaluation Developments, Continental Europe.* Schlumberger Publication.

Schlumberger (1985) *Log Interpretation Charts.* Schlumberger Publication.

Schlumberger (1986) *Dipmeter interpretation - Fundamentals.* Schlumberger Ltd. U.S.A., 76p.

Schlumberger (1989a) *Log interpretation, principles and applications.* Schlumberger Educational Services.

Schlumberger (1989b) *Log interpretation charts,* 151p.

Schlumberger (1993a). *ARI Azimuthal Resistivity Imager.* Tool Brochure, Schlumberger Wireline and Testing. 24p.

Schlumberger (1993b) *Integrated lithology porosity system: an overview.* 63p.

Schlumberger (1994a) *DSI Dipole Shear Sonic Imager.* Schlumberger Educational Services, 42p.

Schlumberger (1994b) *FMI Fullbore Formation MicroImager.* Schlumberger Educational Services, 42p.

Schlumberger (1995) *Induction Logging Manual.* Online reference book, 119p. www.slb.com

Schlumberger (1997) *Well Evaluation Conference,* Venezuela. 8 Chapters.

Schlumberger (2002) *DSI Dipole Shear Sonic Imager.* Tool Brochure, 33p.

Schlumberger (2005) *Sonic Scanner.* Tool Brochure, 7p. www.slb.com/oilfield

Schmidt, G.W. (1973) Interstitial water composition and geochemistry of deep Gulf Coast shales and sandstones. *Bull. Am. Assoc. Petrol Geol.,* **57**(2), 321–337.

Schmoker, J.W. (1979) Determination of organic content of Appalachian Devonian shales from formation density logs. *Bull. Am. Assoc. Petrol. Geol.,* **63** (9), 1504–1509.

Schmoker, J.W. (1981) Determination of organic-matter content of Appalachian Devonian shales from gamma-ray logs. *Bull. Am. Assoc. Petrol. Geol.,* **65**, 1285–1298.

Schmoker, J.W. and Hester, T.C. (1983) Organic carbon in Bakken formation, United States portion of Williston Basin. *Bull. Am. Assoc. Petrol Geol.,* **67**(12), 2165–2174.

Schroeder, T. (2001) Grappling with LWD resistivity logs. What are R_t and R_{xo}? *SPWLA 42nd Ann. Symp. Trans.,* Paper KK, 1–10.

Schrooten, R., Boratko, E., Singh, H. and Halford, D. (2007) A case study: using wireline pressure measurements to improve reservoir characterization in tight formation gas – Wamsutter Field, Wyoming. *SPE* **109565**, 1–11.

Seiler, D. (1995) Borehole visualization in 3-D. *SPWLA 36th Ann. Symp. Trans.,* Paper UUU, 1–12.

Selley, R.C. (1976) Subsurface environmental analysis of North Sea sediments. *Bull. Am. Assoc. Geol.,* **60**(2), 184–195.

Serra, O. (1972) *Diagraphies et stratigraphie.* Mem. BRGM Fr., No. 77, 775–832.

Serra, O. (1973) Interprétation géologique des diagraphies différées en séries carbonatées. *Bull. Centre Rech. Pau. SNPA* **72**(1), 265–284.

Serra, O. (1974) Interprétation géologique des séries deltaiques à partir des diagraphies différées. Rev. *Assoc.* Fr. Techn. Pet. 227, 9–17.

Serra, O. (1979) Diagraphies différées. Bases de l'interprétation. Tome 1: Acquisition des donées Diagraphiques. *Bull. Centre Rech. Expl.-Prod. Elf Aquitaine,* Mem. **1**, Technip, Paris, 328p.

Serra, O. (1985) *Sedimentary environments from wireline logs.* Schlumberger publications, 211p.

Serra, O. (1989) *Formation MicroScanner Image Interpretation,* Schlumberger Educational Services, 117p.

Serra, O. and Abott, H.T. (1980) The contribution of logging data to sedimentology and stratigraphy. *55th Ann. Conf. Dallas,* 1–19, SP 9270.

Serra, O and Sera, L. (2000) *Diagraphies. Acquisitions et applications.* Editions Serralog, France.

Serra, O. and Sulpice, L. (1975) Sedimentological analysis of sand shale series from well logs. *SPWLA 16th Ann. Symp. Trans.,* Paper W, 1–23.

Serra, O., Baldwin, J. and Quirein, J. (1980) *Theory, interpretation and practical applications of natural gamma ray spectroscopy.* Schlumberger, M. 83214.

Serra, O., Stowe, I. and Motet, D. (1993) True integrated interpretation. *SPWLA 34th Ann. Symp. Trans.,* Paper Z, 1–25.

Shanmugam, G., Bloch, R.B., Mitchell, S.M., Beamish, G.W.J., Hodgkinson, R.J., Damuth, J.E., Straume., T., Syvertsen, S.E. and Shields, K.E. (1995) Basin-floor fans in the North Sea: sequence stratigraphic models vs. sedimentary facies. *Bull. Am. Assoc. Petrol. Geol.,* **79** No. 4, 477–512.

Shaw, H.F. (1980) Clay minerals in sediments and sedimentary rock. In: *Developments in Petroleum Geology 2,* ed. Hobson, G.D., Applied Sci. Pub., Barking, 53–85.

Sherriff, R.E. (1980) *Seismic Stratigraphy.* Int. Human Resources Dev. Corp., Boston.

Sherman, H. and Locke, S. (1975) Depth of investigation of neutron and density sondes for 35 per cent porosity sand. *SPWLA 16th Ann. Symp. Trans.,* Paper Q, 1–14.

Shields, C. and Gahan, M.J. (1974) The dipmeter used to recognise depositional environments. *APEA.,* 181–188.

Siemers, C.T., Tilliman, R.W. and Williamson, C.R. (1981) Deep water clastic sediments: A core workshop. *SEPM Core Workshop 2,* 416p.

Sigal, R. (2002) Coates and SDR permeability: two variations on the same theme. *Petrophysics,* **41**, No 1, 38–46.

Simon-Brygoo, C. (1980) *Analyse qualitative des diagraphies. Essai de méthodes d›interprétation.* These, Univ. Bordeaux, No. 1557 (unpublished).

Sinclair, H. and Cowie, P. (2003) Basin floor topography and scaling of turbidites. *Journal of Geology,* **111**, 277–299.

Sinha, B., Wang, J., Kisra, S., Li, J., Pistre, V., Bratton, T. and Sanders, M. (2008) Estimation of formation stresses using borehole sonic data. *SPWLA 49th Ann. Symp. Trans.,* Paper F, 1–16.

Slatt, R.M. and Davis, R. (2010) Calibrating borehole image and dipmeter logs with outcrops and behind-outcrop cores: case studies and applications to deep-water deposits. In: *Dipmeter and Borehole Image Log Technology.* Eds: Poppelreiter, M., Garcia-Carballido, C. and Kraaijveld, M. AAPG Memoir **92**, 167–194.

Slatt, R.M., Jordan, D.W., D'Agostino, A.E. and Gillespie, R.H. (1992) Outcrop geometry logging to improve understanding of subsurface well log correlation. In: *Geological applications of well logs II,* eds. Hurst, A., Griffiths, C.M. and Worthington, P.F. Geol. Soc. London Spec. Pub. **65**, 3–20.

Sloss, L.L. (1984) Comparative anatomy of cratonic unconformities. In: *Interregional Unconformities and Hydrocarbon Accumulation,* ed. Schlee, J.S., *Am. Assoc. Pet. Geol. Mem.* **36**, 1–36.

Smith, J.W., Thomas, H.E. and Trudell, L.G. (1968) Geologic factors affecting density logs in oil shale. *SPWLA 9th Ann. Symp. Trans.,* Paper P, 1–17.

Smith, M.P. (1990) Enhanced vertical resolution processing of dual-spaced neutron and density tools using standard shop calibration and borehole compensation procedures. *SPWLA 31st Ann. Symp. Trans.,* Paper SS, 1–22.

Smith, M.L., Sondergeld, C.H. and Norris, J.O. (1991) The Amoco Array Sonic Logger. *The Log Analyst,* **32**, No. 3, 201–214.

Smith, T. and Sondergeld, C. (2001) Examination of AVO responses in the eastern deepwater Gulf of Mexico. *Geophysics,* **66**, No. 6, 1864–1876.

Smith, T., Sondergeld, C. and Rai, C. (2003) Gassmann fluid substitutions: a tutorial. *Geophysics,* **68**, No. 2, 430–440.

Smits, J., Benimeli, D., Dubourg, I., Faivre, O., Hoyle, D., Tourillon, V., Trouiller, J-C. and Anderson, B. (1995) High resolution from a new laterolog with azimuthal imaging. *SPE* **30584**, 563–576.

Søllie, F. and Rodgers, G. (1994) Towards better measurements of logging depth. *SPWLA 35th Ann. Symp. Trans.,* Paper D, 1–15.

Sovich, J.P. and Newberry, B. (1993) Quantitative approach to bore hole imaging. *SPWLA 34th Ann. Syrup. Trans.,* Paper FFF, 1–18.

Spears, R., Shray, F., Jacobsen, S., Bowers, M. and Nicosia, W. (2008) Where quicklook petrophysics goes wrong: a case study in a mature South Texas gas field. *SPWLA 49th Ann. Symp. Trans.* Paper PPP, 1–15.

SPWLA (1982) *Shaly sand reprint volume,* S.P.W.L.A. 809p.

Stamm, C, Homann, H., Creden, S., Freitag, H-C., Fulda, C. and Lindsay, G. (2007) Barnett Shale – new LWD sensor technology provides crucial formation evaluation at reduced cost and risk for land operations. *SPWLA 48th Ann. Symp. Trans.,* Paper OO, 1–16.

Standen, E., Nurmi, R., Elwazeer, F. and Ozkanli M. (1993) Quantitative applications of wellbore images to reservoir analysis. *SPWLA 34th Ann. Symp. Trans.*, Paper EEE, 1–15.

Suau, J. and Spurlin, J. (1982) Interpretation of micaceous sandstones in the North Sea. *SPWLA 23rd. Ann. Symp. Trans.* Paper G, 1–32.

Sugiura, J. (2009) Novel mechanical caliper image while drilling and borehole image analysis. *SPWLA 50th Ann. Symp. Trans.*, Paper VV, 1–10.

Sullivan, K.B. and Schepel, K.J. (1995) Borehole image logs: applications in fractured and thinly bedded reservoirs. *SPWLA* 36th *Ann. Symp. Trans.*, Paper T, 1-12.

Taherian, M.R., Habashy, T.M., Schroeder, R.J., Mariani, D.R. and Chen, M.Y. (1992) Laboratory study of the spontaneous potential: Experimental and modelling results. *SPWLA 33rd Ann. Symp. Trans.*, Paper E, 1–25.

Tang, X., Dubinsky, V., Wang, T., Bolshakov, A. and Patterson, D. (2002) Shear-velocity measurement in the logging-while-drilling environment: modelling and field evaluations. *SPWLA 43rd Ann. Symp. Trans.*, Paper RR, 1–14.

Tang, X., Lilly, D. and Petpisit, K. (2007) Analysis of LWD acoustic data validates its accuracy. *SPWLA 48th Ann. Symp. Trans.*, Paper B, 1–12.

Tang, X., Patterson, D., Dubinsky, V., Harrison, C. and Bolshakov, A. (2003) Logging-while-drilling shear and compressional measurements in varying environments. *SPWLA 44th Ann. Symp. Trans.*, Paper II, 1–13.

Taylor, T.J. (1983) Interpretation and application of borehole televiewer surveys. *SPWLA 24th Ann. Symp. Trans.*, Paper QQ, 1–19.

Taylor, T.J. (1991) A method for identifying fault related fracture systems using the borehole televiewer. *SPWLA 32nd Ann. Symp. Trans.*, PaperJJ, 1–19.

Theys, RP. (1991) *Log data acquisition and quality control*. Éditions Technip, Paris, 330p.

Thomas, D.H. (1977) Seismic applications of sonic logs. *SPWLA 5th European Symp. Trans., Paris,* Paper 7, 1–24.

Thomas, E. and Shackleton, N.J. (1996) The Paleocene benthic foraminiferal extinction and stable isotope anomalies. In: *Correlation of the early Paleogene in northwest Europe,* eds., Knox, R.W.O'B., Corfield, R.M. and Dunay, R.E. Geol. Soc. London Spec. Publ. **101,** 401–441.

Thompson, L. (2008) *Atlas of borehole imagery.* AAPG Discovery Series No. 13. 4 CD set.

Threadgold, P. (1971) Some problems and uncertainties in log interpretation. *SPWLA 12th Ann. Symp. Trans.*, Paper W, 1–19.

Tissot, B.P. (1973) Vers l'evaluation quantitative du pétrole formé dans les basins sédimentaires. *Rev. Assoc. Fr. Tech. Pet.* **222**, 27–31.

Tissot, B.P. and Welte, D.H. (1978) *Petroleum Formation and Occurrence: a New Approach to Oil and Gas Exploration.* Springer-Verlag, Berlin.

Tittle, C.W. (1961) Theory of neutron logging. *Geophysics*, **26**(1), 27–39.

Tittman, J. (1986) *Geophysical Well Logging*. Academic Press, 175p.

Tittman, J. and Wahl, J.S. (1965) The physical foundations of formation density logging (gamma-gamma). *Geophysics*, **30**(2), 284–294.

Tixier, M.P. and Alger, R.P. (1967) Log evaluation of non-metallic mineral deposits. *SPWLA 8th Ann. Symp. Trans.*, Paper R, 1–22.

Torres, D., Strickland, R. and Gianzero, M. (1990) A new approach to determining dip and strike using borehole images. *SPWLA 31st Ann. Symp. Trans.*, Paper K, 1–20.

Trouiller, J-C., Delhomme, J-P., Carlin, S. and Anxionnaz, H. (1989) Thin bed reservoir analysis from borehole electrical images. *SPE* **19578**, 61–72,

Truman, R.B., Alger, R.P., Connell, J.G. and Smith, R.L. (1972) Progress report on interpretation of the dual-spacing neutron log (CNL) in the United States. *SPWLA 13th Ann. Symp. Trans.*, Paper U, 1–34.

Underhill, J.A. and Partington, M.A. (1993) Jurassic thermal doming and deflation in the North Sea: implications of the sequence stratigraphic evidence. In: *Petroleum Geology of Northwest Europe,* ed. Parker, J.R. Proc. 4th Conf. 337–346.

Underhill, J.A. and Partington, M.A. (1994) Use of genetic sequence stratigraphy in defining a regional tectonic control on the 'mid-Cimmerian unconformity': implications for North Sea basin development and the global sea-level chart. In: *Siliciclastic sequence stratigraphy.* Eds. Weimer, P. and Posamentier, H.W. AAPG Memoir **58,** 449–484.

Vail, P.R., Mitchum, R.M. and Thomson, S. III, (1977) Seismic stratigraphy and global changes in sea level, part 3: relative changes of sea level from coastal onlap. In: *Seismic Stratigraphy Applications to Hydrocarbon Exploration* ed. Payton, C.E. Bull. Amer. Assoc. Pet. Geol. Mem. **26**, 63–97.

Vail, P.R. and Wornardt, W.W. (1990) Well-log seismic sequence stratigraphy: an integrated tool for the 90s. *G.C.S. SEPM Foundation, 11th Annual Res. Conference, Program and Abstracts,* 379–389.

Van Siclen, De W.C. (1958) Depositional topography examples and theory. *Bull. Am. Assoc. Petrol. Geol.*, **42**(8), 1897–1913.

Van Wagoner, J.C., Mitchum, R.M., Campion, K.M. and Rahmanian, V.D. (1990) *Siliciclastic sequence stratigraphy in well logs, cores and outcrops*. AAPG Methods in exploration series, **7**, 55p.

Venkataramanan, L., Weinheber, P., Mullins, O., Andrews, A. and Gustavson, G. (2006) Pressure gradients and fluid analysis as an aid to determining reservoir compartmentalization. *SPWLA 47th Ann. Symp. Trans.* Paper S,1–11.

Verdur, H., Stinco, L. and Naides, C. (1991) Sedimentological analysis utilising the circumferential borehole acoustic log. *SPWLA 32nd Ann. Symp. Trans.*, Paper II, 1–19.

Vincent, Ph., Gartner, J.E. and Attali, G. (1977) Geodip: an approach to detailed dip determination using correlation by pattern recognition. *SPE* **6823.**

Vollset, J. and Doré, A.G. (1984) A revised Triassic and Jurassic lithostratigraphic nomenclature for the Norwegian North Sea, *NPD Bulletin* **3**, 53p.

Vorren, T.O., Richardsen, G. and Knutsen, S-M. (1991) Cenozoic erosion and sedimentation in the western Barents Sea. *Marine and Petroleum Geology,* **8** No. 3, 317–340.

Waid, C. C. (1987) Effect of tool rotation on the computation of dip. *SPWLA 28th Ann. Symp. Trans.*, Paper Q, 1–22.

Wahl, J.S., Tittman, J., Johnstone, C.W. and Alger, R.P. (1964) The dual spacing formation density log. *J. Pet. Tech.*, December, 1411–1416.

Walker, R.G. (1992) Facies, facies models and modern stratigraphic concepts. In: *Facies models, response to sea level change.* Eds. Walker, R.G. and James, N.P. Geol. Soc. Canada, 1–14.

Walker, T. (1968) A full-wave display of acoustic signal in cased hole. *SPE* **1751**, 811–824.

Wallace, W.E. (1968) Observations on the SP curve in general and offshore problems in particular. *SPWLA 9th Ann. Symp. Trans.*, Paper A, 1–14.

Walsgrove, T.R., Daneshzadeh, M. and Dusang, J.P. (1992) A case study of the interpretational and financial implications of wireline versus measurement while drilling in 'high risk' scenarios. *SPWLA 33rd Ann.* Symp. *Trans.*, Paper G, 1–25.

Walters, E.J. (1968) Statistical study of neutron logs for correlation studies. *SPWLA 9th Ann. Symp. Trans.*, Paper F, 1–15.

Wang, D-L., de Koningh, H. and Coy, G. (2008) Facies identification and prediction based on rock textures from microresistivity images in highly heterogeneous carbonates: a case study from Oman. *SPWLA 49th Ann. Symp. Trans.*, Paper PPPP, 1–14.

Wang, T., Fang, S., Pavlovic, M., Dymmock, S. and Evans, M. (2004) Borehole imaging in nonconductive muds: resolution, depth of investigation and impact of anisotropy. *SPWLA 45th Ann. Symp. Trans.*, Paper NN, 1–14.

Waples, D.W. (1980) Time and temperature in petroleum formation: application of Lopatin's method to petroleum exploration. *Bull. Am. Assoc. Petrol. Geol.*, **64**(6), 916–926.

Waxman, M.H, and Smits, L.J.M. (1968) Electrical conductivities in oil-bearing shaly sand. *Soc. Pet. Eng. J.*, June, 107–122.

Weaver, C.E. and Pollard, L.D. (1973) *The Chemistry of Clay Minerals* (Developments in Sedimentology 15). Elsevier, Amsterdam.

Weger, R., Eberli, G., Baechle, G., Massaferro, J. and Sun, Y-F. (2009) Quantification of pore structure and its effect on sonic velocity and permeability in carbonates. *Am. Assoc. Petrol. Geol. Bulletin.* **93**, No 10, 1297–1317.

Weiland, J., Teff, C. and Donovan, G. (2004) Integrating NMR, rock mechanics, and production evaluation to optimize hydrocarbon production in deepwater GOM. *SPWLA 45th Ann. Symp. Trans.*, Paper VVV, 1–13.

Weissenberger, J., Wierzbicki, R. and Harland, N. (2006) Carbonate sequence stratigraphy and petroleum geology of the Jurassic Deep Panuke field, offshore Nova Scotia, Canada. In: *Giant hydrocarbon reservoirs of the world from rocks to reservoir characterization and modeling.* Eds. Harris, P. and Weber, I. *AAPG* Memoir **88**, 395–431.

Weller, G., Griffiths, R., Stoller, C., Allioli, F., Berheide, M., Evans, M., Labous, L., Dion, D. and Perciot, P. (2005). A new integrated LWD platform brings next-generation formation evaluation services. *SPWLA 46th Ann. Symp. Trans.*, Paper H, 1–15.

Werner, P., Piazza, J-L. and Raiga-Clemenceau, J. (1987) Using dipmeter data for enhanced structural interpretation from the seismic. *SPWLA 28th Ann. Symp. Trans.*, paper II, 1–11.

White, J. (1993) Enhanced reservoir description using induction and laterolog imaging tools. *SPWLA 15th European Evaluation Symp. Stavanger*, Paper B, 1–7.

White, J. (2000) Guidelines for estimating permeability from NMR measurements. *DiaLog*, **8**, No 1, 2–5.

Whittaker, A., Holliday, D.W and Penn I.E. (1985) *Geophysical logs in British stratigraphy*. Geol. Soc. London, Special Report **18,** 1–74.

Wiley, R. (1990) Borehole televiewer revisited. *SPWLA 21st Ann. Trans., Symp.* Paper HH, 1–16.

Wiley, R and Patchett, J.G. (1994) The effects of invasion on density/thermal neutron porosity interpretation. . *SPWLA 35th Ann. Symp. Trans.*, Paper G, 1–14.

Williams, D. (1990) The acoustic log hydrocarbon indicator. *SPWLA 31st Ann. Symp. Trans.*, Paper W, 1–22.

Williams, H. and Soek, H.F. (1993) Predicting reservoir sandbody orientation from dipmeter data: the use of sedimentary dip profiles from outcrop studies. In: *The geological modelling of hydrocarbon reservoirs and outcrop analogues*, eds. Flint, S.S. and Bryant, I.D., IAS special publication 15, 143–156.

Wilson, J. (1975) *Carbonate facies in geologic history*. Springer, New York. 471p.

Winsauer, W.O. and McCardell, W.M. (1953) Ionic double-layer conductivity in reservoir rocks: *Trans AIME,* **198,** 129–134.

Wolff, M. and Pelissier-Combescure, J. (1982) Faciolog-automatic electrofacies determination. *SPWLA 23rd Ann. Symp. Trans.*, Paper FF, 1–23.

Wong, S.A., Startzmann, R.A. and Kuo, T-B. (1989) Enhancing borehole image data on a high-resolution PC. *SPE* **19124,** 37–48.

Worthington, M. (2010) Petrophysical evaluation of gas-hydrate formations. *Petroleum Geoscience*, **16**, 53–66.

Worthington, P. (2000) Recognition and evaluation of low-resistivity. *Petroleum Geoscience,* **6**, 1, 77–92.

Worthington, P. and Costentino, L. (2003) The role of cut-offs in integrated reservoir studies. *SPE* **84387**, 1–16

Wraight, P., Evans, E., Marienbach, E., Rhei-Knudsen, E. and Best, D. (1989) Combination formation density and neutron porosity measurements while drilling. *SPWLA 30th Ann. Symp. Trans.*, Paper B, 1–21.

Wu, J., Torres-Verdin, C., Sepehrnoori, K. and Proett, M. (2005) The influence of water-base mud properties and petrophysical parameters on mudcake growth, filtrate invasion and formation pressure. *Petrophysics,* **46,** No 1, 14–32.

www.feswa.org Formation Evaluation Society of Western Australia.

www-wsm.physik.uni-karlsruhe.de World stress map, Heidelberg Academy of Sciences and Humanities.

Wyllie, M.R.J. (1963) *The Fundamentals of Well Log Interpretation.* 3rd edn., Academic Press, New York.

Wyllie, M.R.J., Gregory, A.R. and Gardener, L.W. (1956) Elastic wave velocities in heterogeneous and porous media. *Geophysics,* **21**(1), 41–70.

Xu, C. (2010) Porosity partitioning and permeability quantification in vuggy carbonates, Permian Basin, West Texas, U.S.A. In: *Dipmeter and Borehole Image Log Technology.* Eds. Poppelreiter, M., Garcia-Carballido, C. and Kraaijveld, M. AAPG Memoir **92**, 309–319.

Xu, H. and Desbrandes, R. (1993) In situ filtrate flowrate measurements with the wireline formation tester. *SPWLA 34th Ann. Symp. Trans.* Paper AAA, 1–14.

Yassir, N.A. and Dusseault, M.B. (1992) Stress trajectory determination in southwestern Ontario from borehole logs. In: *Geological application of wireline logs II.,* eds. Hurst, A., Griffiths, C.M. and Worthington, P-F, Geol. Soc. London Spec. Publ. **65**, 169–178.

Ye, S. and Rabiller, P. (2000) A new tool for electro-facies analysis: multi-resolution graph-based clustering. *SPWLA 41st Ann. Symp. Trans.*, Paper PP, 1–14.

Yose, L., Ruf, A., Strohmenger, C., Schuelke, J., Gombos, A, and Johnson, I. (2006) Thee-dimensional characterization of a heterogeneous carbonate reservoir, Lower Cretaceous, Abu Dhabi (United Arab Emirates). AAPG Memoir 88, *Giant Hydrocarbon Reservoirs of the world, from rocks to reservoir characterization and modeling.* Eds. Harris, P. and Weber, L., 173–212.

Zemanek, J. Caldwell, R.I., Glenn, E.E., Holcomb, S.V., Norton, L.J. and Strauss, A.J.D. (1969) The borehole televiewer – a new logging concept for fracture location and other types of borehole inspection. *JPT,* **21**, 762–774.

Zemanek, J., Glenn, E.E., Norton, L.J. and Caldwell, R.L. (1970) Formation inspection with the borehole televiewer. *Geophysics,* **35,** 254–269.

Zemanek, J., Williams, D.M. and Schmidt, D.P. (1991) Shear-wave logging using multipole sources. *The Log Analyst,* **32**, No. 3, 233–241.

Zittel, R., Beliveau, D., O'Sulliven, T., Mohanty, R. and Miles, J. (2006) Reservoir crude-oil viscosity estimation from wireline NMR measurements – Rajasthan, India. *SPE* **101689**, 1–11.

Zoback, M. (2007) *Reservoir geomechanics*. Cambridge University Press, 464p.

Zoback, M,L., Zoback, M.D., Adams, J., *et al* (1989) Global patterns of tectonic stress. *Nature,* **341**, September 28th, 291–298.

INDEX